History
of
Petroleum Engineering

A

Publication

of the

American Petroleum Institute

Sponsored by the
Executive Committee on Drilling and Production Practice
of the
Institute's Division of Production

Office of the Institute: 1271 Avenue of the Americas, New York, N.Y.
Office of the Division: 300 Corrigan Tower Building, Dallas, Texas

Published 1961

Second Printing, September 1961

Printed in the United States of America
by
Boyd Printing Co., Dallas, Texas

preface

Any volume which undertakes as this one does to deal broadly and intensively with the birth and growth of a profession must accept certain definitions and limitations.

In this case the first and most necessary definition—one which may impress some as arbitrary—is that only the *drilling for and production of* petroleum hydrocarbons is within the compass of petroleum engineering. This exclusion of transportation and refining is admittedly not in complete harmony with usage in these branches of the industry and is ventured with apologies in advance to any engineer who may consider his own field unrightfully excluded.

The converse of the above is also held for these purposes to be true. This is—that *any* engineering applied to the drilling for and production of petroleum hydrocarbons is petroleum engineering. This position is taken with full admission that petroleum engineering is, like mining engineering, neither more nor less than a combination of older and more universal forms of engineering—civil, mechanical, electrical, and chemical. Between the contention at one extreme that petroleum engineering covers all engineering which deals with petroleum, and that at the opposite extreme that there is really no such thing as petroleum engineering, there is latitude for opinion. The position taken here is in the middle ground and it is hoped that it will be generally viewed as a tenable one.

A limitation of some importance is that this work is essentially a history of *American* petroleum engineering. The broader title was chosen in full awareness of and with due respect for the many and considerable contributions to the technology which had their origin in other lands. The geographical limitation was omitted from the title because many of the authors had the material and inclination to make extensive reference to foreign development.

The attribution of credit to individuals and organizations for historic concepts and developments has been a matter for the discretion of the author of each chapter. Each author's assessment of the importance of specific contributions has been conditioned by the sources available to him, by his own perspectives, and, in many cases, by his personal recollection. If any unevenness or omission should be noted it must be remembered that the distinguishing of historical fact within the mass of that which is claimed or that which appears likely is a task which has its thankless aspects.

Ten years have elapsed since this project was authorized by the Executive Committee on Drilling and Production Practice. These years have seen developments in petroleum engineering which rank in importance with the most significant of the period 1920-1950. Since engineer-

v

ing history is being made almost daily, every effort has been made to compress to a minimum the lag between submission of final drafts and publication of the volume. This interval was reduced to a few months; however, it must be taken into account that the significance of some developments of the latter 1950's cannot be confidently assessed for at least a few years to come, thus omission or passing mention of some of these implies no inattention on the part of the authors.

The earliest decision affecting this volume was that editorial policy and content should be controlled by senior professional men who had had either a strong personal influence on the development of the profession or a point of vantage from which to view this development. The group selected for this responsibility was the Editorial Board listed on a preceding page. Each member of this Board has labored cheerfully and patiently at a task that had many frustrations. Each has had the responsibility for the writing of at least part of one chapter. Most have had the responsibility of a full chapter, while three have had total responsibility for two chapters. Although they would say that their efforts were only in partial payment of a debt to the profession of petroleum engineering, it can be said with equal truth that the profession is indebted to each of them, as is the American Petroleum Institute.

The files, reference material, and personal recollections of the members of the Board—a massive source of material in itself—was not adequate for an undertaking as ambitious as this and has been far from being the only source from which material has been acquired. Hundreds of engineers and geologists have been invited to furnish information on specific developments, and dozens of these have responded by extended research and the submission of detailed accounts of those parts of the history which were within their area of specialization and often within their direct personal experience. Each chapter author has acknowledged this major and exceptional assistance in his own manner and to the fullest practical extent. Any contributors not specifically mentioned within a chapter may be nonetheless confident of the gratitude of the Editorial Board. Special mention is due the petroleum equipment and service industry, many representatives of which have gone to great lengths in searching for and sifting information and illustrations.

The Editorial Board expresses appreciation for the continuous support and encouragement accorded this project by the successive Executive Committees on Drilling and Production Practice and for the quality and quantity of the service rendered to the Board by the Division of Production staff, particularly its director, Mr. Wm. H. Strang and its editor, Mrs. Marjorie Kibben. Thanks are also due Mr. Edward L. Estabrook, a pioneer petroleum engineer, who reviewed much of the manuscript and made numerous helpful suggestions on questions of fact and emphasis.

By his efforts much gap and overlap between chapters was eliminated. Overlap has been deliberately provided in some cases in the interests of having each chapter reasonably complete within itself.

This volume is offered without claim or pretense that it is all that should or could be said of the history of petroleum engineering. That which is presented here happens to be that portion which could be chronicled within reasonable time, with voluntary effort, and with only a nominal financial subsidy applicable to research. Regardless of what future efforts may be made in this direction—and it is sincerely hoped that there will be some—it is hoped that this volume will serve for many years to come as a tribute to the character, determination, and intellectual breadth and power of those who have embraced the profession of petroleum engineering. Aspirants for a degree in petroleum engineering will find in these chapters much assurance that their chosen profession has great pride of ancestry and is certain to have an illustrious posterity.

D. V. Carter, Chairman
Editorial Board

Dallas, Texas
May, 1961

contents

Chapter 1

THE ENERGY REVOLUTION

James A. Clark

JAMES ANTHONY CLARK was born in 1907 at Abita Springs, St. Tammany Parish, Louisiana, and was educated in the public schools of Beaumont, Texas, and at Lamar State College of Technology. As an author, oil editor, syndicated columnist, and historian he has been identified with the petroleum industry for over 25 years, winning particular acclaim for *Three Stars for the Colonel* and for co-authorship of *Spindletop.*

Mr. Clark served as lieutenant colonel, United States Army Intelligence, in the South Pacific during World War II. Industrial and professional honors and affiliations include a foundership and secretaryship of the Gulf Coast Historical Association; SPE of AIME, International Oil Scouts Association, Author's Guild, Sigma Delta Chi, National Press Club, and a directorship of the Houston Museum of Natural Science.

One Sunday morning in August more than 100 years ago a water-well driller known as Uncle Billy Smith took a tin dipper from a nail on the wall of the rough clapboarded derrick house, which stood over a strange new kind of well he was boring for Colonel Edwin L. Drake, and withdrew a few ounces of black fluid known as "rock oil" from inches down the casing.

As he did so he knew that Colonel Drake had succeeded in obtaining oil from the first hole ever drilled in the United States for that express purpose. He turned to his son and told him to rush into town and tell Colonel Drake the good news.

That simple act of a simple man of toil who had done his job well gave birth to a new era of progress and enlightenment for mankind, and supplied the impetus necessary to eventually make this country the most powerful and progressive nation the world has ever known, and its individual citizens prosperous beyond even the dreams of their forefathers.

Since that August day in 1859, at a historic spot near Titusville in Pennsylvania on the bank of the Allegheny River, more than 60 billion barrels of petroleum—with a cumulative value of more than $112 billion—has been produced in the United States, in addition to untold amounts of natural gas and gas liquids.

From that small symbolic and prophetic tin dipper of oil has come not only a most dynamic industry, but also a dozen other industries that would have never known the light of day without oil. Chief among these are the automotive and aviation industries which have made every man every other man's neighbor. But these have been only the most obvious beneficiaries of the new age of energy that was presaged by the little tin dipper in the well house of "Drake's Folly" in 1859. A whole new society of people and an entirely new concept of government, education, culture, human relations, and communications have been some of its important by-products.

In short, petroleum has been the natural complement to freedom to further and fulfill the aspirations of the founding fathers of this nation and their descendants, and is available for such service around the earth.

Energy provided by petroleum and applied by the internal-combustion engine (which would have hardly had an excuse to exist without oil) is said "to exceed the total power of all men who ever lived, in a remarkably handy and flexible manner," capable of accomplishing anything from the operation of a toy to the propelling of the greatest ocean liner, providing the thrust for giant jet planes, or the fueling of ballistic missiles.

John Fisher, editor of *Harper's Magazine,* wrote on the occasion of the celebration of the centennial of the Drake well that " . . . it just brought about a revolution in our society more far-reaching than any political upheaval we have ever known . . . (it has) simultaneously changed the geography of a continent . . . touched off a mass migration of a hundred million people . . . shifted occupations of at least half the population . . . sharply raised living standards . . . reshaped moral codes . . . and created a new kind of long-distance warfare capable of carrying annihilation to any acre of the planet." And by the creation of such warfare potentials, it might have ironically assured eventual world peace.

Within months after the Drake well came in, oil had already made a significant contribution toward world history by providing the United States Government with a dollar balance in world trade that prevented an economic collapse and the possible loss of the Civil War. Later American oil was going to every corner of the earth along with the coal-oil lamp, to match cotton as an export product and inaugurate this nation's emergence from a purely agricultural economic status.

In the first decade after Drake, production had moved out of the Allegheny River and its tributary creeks into several other states. It had become an important illuminant and had made possible an acceleration of the machine age through revolutionary lubrication processes. Pioneers of the industry, confronted with problems thrust upon them by the sudden discovery of a new and unexpected and most useful product, had started to cope with those problems. They had learned to transport the oil through pipelines and to refine it into more useful illuminants and lubricants. At Pithole (a boom town that became a ghost town in a year) Samuel Van Syckle built the first pipeline.

In the field they were daily continuing to meet and conquer the challenges of this remarkable new product of nature, most of which involved getting it safely out of the earth and into the hands of people who could put it to use. But a far greater challenge was that of the economic capriciousness of the business. Surpluses and shortages kept the price of oil going up and down like a ball on the end of a rubber string in the hands of a playful boy.

The first man who decided the oil business was one worthy of becoming a staple part of the nation and the world's economic fabric was John D. Rockefeller. Rockefeller, an unknown clerk, formed a partnership with Maurice B. Clark and Samuel Andrews in 1862 to operate a small refinery in Cleveland, Ohio. This business was a success, due largely to the genius of Rockefeller who, 10 years later, formed the Standard Oil Company which was soon to become the world's foremost purchaser of crude oil and shipper of petroleum products. By the 1880's Rockefeller's Standard

Oil Company had become the first important integrated oil company, entering the fields of production, marketing, and transportation.

Rockefeller's dream was to control the supply of oil, terminate the chaos which marked the early years of the business, and stabilize prices. He said these things were necessary if petroleum were to fulfill the promise of becoming an important industry. By 1878 Rockefeller had a dominant position in the refining industry. He left exploration largely to others because of the tremendous risk involved. His cautious and wise policy was to purchase oil where possible and to buy established production only where necessary or advantageous. In 1882 he set up the Standard Oil Trust.

Actions to accomplish the dissolution of this trust were initiated following an adverse decision of the Supreme Court of Ohio in 1892. The court decision did not of itself dissolve the trust, although it was a major factor leading to its voluntary dissolution. After 1892 the means of controlling the Standard Oil interests were reorganized, and within a few years Standard Oil Company (New Jersey) emerged as the parent company and unifying influence. The famous 1911 dissolution decree of the United States Supreme Court required Standard Oil Company (New Jersey) to divest itself of interests in 33 subsidiary companies. It was then, incidentally, that Rockefeller retired after 50 years in the business, to turn his holdings over to his son.

In that 50 years Rockefeller had standardized oil accounting procedures; created a division of labor in specialized fields within the industry; placed emphasis on cost reduction, product quality and standardization, refining efficiency, and elimination of waste. As early as 1890 Rockefeller had also produced the first real system of philanthropy in this nation.

Through the early years of petroleum history, Rockefeller's was by far the most important company to survive the era of wild, merciless, and reckless competition. In the earliest years oil became the most popular of all targets for fraudulent stock trading and reckless gambling. This was to come and go with the years; but by the time some of the most sensational Pennsylvania booms—especially as typified by Pithole—had subjected the public to great hopes to be doused usually with overproduction, the first speculative boom of oil had come to its sad end.

As the pages that follow this introduction will show, little progress was made before the turn of the century in methods of searching for and finding oil. Great strides, however, were being made in its transportation and refining. Marketing progress was the order of each day especially in the field of foreign trade.

The early years of oil also produced what might be called an almost new breed of men. Many of these were daring adventurers who were born poor and saw in this new great field an opportunity to win fame and fortune through the art of being at the right place at the right time with a little cash, some imagination, and more than their share of good fortune.

As the industry progressed many of these early venturers matured into a fraternity of men of new skills, arts, sciences, and technologies. As the earth became more difficult to probe and the location of oil deposits more vexing to find, the weak, the fraudulent and inept were supplanted by the intelligent, industrious, sturdy, daring and dedicated, who were left to carry on the responsibility to the nation and the world created by the finding of oil in the Drake well.

Among those typical of this new kind of industrial adventurer was John Galey, born in Pennsylvania not far from Titusville, almost 19 years to the day before Drake's well came in. The Drake well was barely a month old when he became an oilman. His first significant success came less than a year later when he brought in the renowned Maple Leaf well in Venango County, Pennsylvania. Through the years he had several partners. With one of them, William Hartley, he drilled wells on an island in the middle of the Allegheny. He opened new fields in Butler, Armstrong, and Clarion Counties.

In the 70's Galey developed a number of fields with another team of well-known wildcatters, the McKinney brothers. During the 70's their firm was regarded as the largest in the country, even exceeding in importance the Standard Oil Company. In 1880 Galey became associated with Colonel James M. Guffey and this association brought his greatest achievements, including extensive developments in the McDonald Field of Pennsylvania, the Kile and Fork Fields in West Virginia, and at Neodosha, Kansas. The partnership drilled the first wildcats in Coalinga County, California, discovered Texas' first commercial field at Corsicana, and backed Captain Anthony F. Lucas in the Spindletop venture.

Between the discovery of oil in Pennsylvania in 1859 and the year 1890, the population of the United States almost exactly doubled from 31 million to 62 million. Through these 30 years the industrial revolution was given real meaning through the use of lubrication from rock oil and illumination that permitted study and work far into the evening and in the early morning hours. Educational and social advances were dramatic.

The age of mobility was moving in during the last quarter of the 19th century. Otto built the first successful 4-cycle gasoline engine (1877); Gottlieb Daimler patented the small high-speed internal-combustion engine important in the development of the automobile industry (1887); Diesel patented the internal-combustion engine having autoignition of the fuel (1892); and the Duryea brothers produced what many considered to be America's first gasoline-powered automobile (1893).

Oil was spreading to the vast outlands of America. Beyond the confines of the original oil region around Pennsylvania, discoveries had been made in Texas, California, Oklahoma, Kansas, Wyoming, Indiana, Missouri, Illinois, and Colorado.

Barely a decade after the Drake well, the golden spike had been driven at Promontory marking the completion of the first transcontinental railroad. Ships were carrying oil in makeshift manner to the four corners of the earth. Long crude-oil and product lines had been inaugurated. Before the end of the century the telephone and the incandescent lamp had been accepted; the electric street railway had become a reality; and Marconi had received a patent for his wireless. The era of rapid communication was in its swaddling clothes.

At the close of the 19th century the American oil industry had barely produced its first billion barrels of oil. Many considered the industry a blessing that had come for a stay of 40 years or so but was about on its way out. So true was this that little or no attention was being given the tremendous steps toward the age of mobility that had been made by the inventors. By 1900 there were some 8,000 automobiles in the country, most of them propelled by electricity or coal-generated steam. A handful were gasoline buggies.

Oil as a fuel was being used more or less sparingly, mostly in the new California oil country and in Texas where a railroad was testing it for its potential as a substitute for wood and coal. Yet all recognized that petroleum was not present in sufficient quantities to be useful as a liquid fuel. Even the leaders of the great trust were saying this as one of them had said to Galey when he sought help for his venture in Kansas—"I'll drink every drop of commercial oil you can find west of the Mississippi."

Imagination was dimming. Something was needed, or oil, if it were to be a fuel, would be supplied by foreign sources—if at all. And it was then that a sort of 20th century counterpart of Drake, without the financial backing, was fiddling around with a dream that obsessed him. Pattillo Higgins had read government reports about the anticlinal theory. He had seen oil indications in the oil regions on a visit, and he believed great stores of oil were hidden beneath a little knoll of earth south of his home town of Beaumont in southeast Texas. For a decade he pursued his dream with great hope but scant success. Then he attracted the attention of Captain Anthony F. Lucas, who really had little more claim to being a captain than Drake had to being a colonel. Lucas, who was a trained engineer, tried at what was to become Spindletop and failed. He was looking for salt or sulfur, or—as a last resort—oil. His first effort was a failure. Then with the backing of Guffey and Galey, who had been assured finances for three or four tests by the Mellon brothers of Pittsburgh, Lucas discovered the greatest gusher in history at Spindletop. The supply of oil was considered inexhaustible. Galey proclaimed this the beginning of the liquid-fuel age. And although the supply was far from inexhaustible, it was the beginning of the liquid-fuel age.

Spindletop rekindled the imagination of a nation and especially its oilmen. Another speculative boom followed. Then came a series of new discoveries in salt-dome areas, including the first oil in Louisiana at Jennings. Sour Lake and a half dozen new prolific domes were found in Texas. Such companies as Gulf Oil Corporation and The Texas Company came into existence.

While the Standard Oil Company had fairly well set up efficiency in refining, transportation, and maketing of oil, the fields of drilling and production, in which Standard participated on a much more reduced scale, had not been so well-developed. This was due largely to the reckless competition made necessary by the Rule of Capture, which led to the drilling of unnecessary wells and the rapid deterioration of reservoirs or reservoir energy.

Before the Lucas gusher started spewing 100,000 bbl of oil a day into the air on January 10, 1901, when the 20th century was only 10 days old, the world was still largely dependent upon coal and wood (plus animal dung in many areas) for combustibles. The industrial revolution, which got under way through the use of coal and had been able to maintain its momentum with coal, was geared to what might be called a coal pace. Oil had been able to do little as an illuminant and lubricant to speed that progress. What has been called a fundamental bottleneck had been met in the progress of the industrial revolution. For instance, even as late as 1895 there were only 4 automobiles in this country. Had Spindletop's discovery not made the liquid-fuel age possible, the energy revolution might still be in the future.

Although the internal-combustion engine was to become the chief tool for replacing human and animal power with machine power, sufficient fuel to make that possible was not available before 1901. In 1900, for instance, total horsepower output in the United States was considerably less than 100 billion horsepower hours annually. Of that amount man and beast accounted for two-thirds. Fifty years later, largely through the utilization of liquid-fuel energy, one man working with power-driven mechanical equipment was able to do as much work in 40 hours as 3 men did in 70 hours in 1900. Of course, the central impelling factor in this phenomenal growth was petroleum as a source of energy power. This is the greatest single factor in the difference between living standards in the United States in 1900 and in 1960.

Dr. Allan Nevins has described the period from 1900 to 1930 as the age of accelerated expansion for petroleum, compared with the period between 1859 and 1900 which he described rather colorfully as the shirt-losing period—the era of experimentation.

As the century ended many truly great oil pioneers had developed. They were the men, generally speaking, who would show the way into the liquid-fuel age. Among these was one of the most remarkable men any industry or nation ever produced—Michael Late Benedum. He typi-fied the spirit of the oilman and seemed to be something of a successor—only far more successful financially—to the almost inimitable John Galey. He was born 10 years after the Drake well at Bridgeport, West Virginia, and spent almost 70 of his 90 years in the industry. He started hunting oil on the basis of "creekology," the "vision" of a blind man, and Indian signs. Before he reached petroleum maturity he was among the first to put his faith in modern geophysics. After starting his business career as a flour-mill manager he started in the oil business with Standard Oil Company subsidiaries, but later went out as an independent with Joe Trees.

On the road to earning wide recognition as "the greatest wildcatter of all time and an almost legendary figure in the world of petroleum," Benedum made such discoveries as that of the prolific Caddo Lake Field in Northern Louisiana, Tuxpan in Mexico, the mighty De Mares con-cession in Colombia (which produced almost 20 million barrels of oil annually for 30 years and for which he received $33 million in stock in International Oil Company from his old Standard Oil associates), the remarkable Yates bonanza, and, at the request of Queen Marie, he pio-neered the lush fields of Roumania, including Ploesti. No corner of the earth missed being probed by Mike Benedum who was successful in Kansas, Kentucky, Arkansas, Oklahoma, Texas, and a half dozen other states in this country as well as the Philippines, Canada, Peru, Turkey, Brazil, Colombia, and Roumania.

When he died in 1959 during the centennial year of the oil industry, and only a week or so before the actual anniversary day of the Drake well, it was said of him that he had discovered more oil than any man who ever lived.

Benedum was a symbol of the emerging independent oilman. More successful than most, he was still the pride of many and that included thousands who tried but never made a success in prospecting for oil.

The 20th century was in its infancy in 1902 when Henry Ford or-ganized his Ford Motor Company which would, within 5 years, start turning out the invincible Model T. Only a year after that, in 1903, the Wright brothers made their first successful flight at Kittyhawk when they flew a heavier-than-air, mechanically propelled aircraft (which they would patent in a few years) to embark the world on the air age, as con-firmed by the first transcontinental flight in 1911.

Spindletop came just in time. In 1900 more than 463 million barrels of oil were found. In 1901, including Spindletop, the new discoveries dropped to 169 million barrels, not to reach the 1900 discovery rate again for 10 years. Starting the century with 2.5 billion barrels in reserves, there would not be a decline in accumulated reserves, in spite of an accelerated rate of market demand, for at least the next 60 years.

Yet in the period between 1900 and 1930, which Dr. Nevins described as the expanding years, these were also the wasteful years. Not that waste had not been rampant in the earlier years, it was just that there had never been so much to waste before the Spindletop boom spread the gushing roar of oil to California, Oklahoma, Kansas, West Virginia, and Illinois. And it also was in these years that great discoveries were made in Mexico, Venezuela, and elsewhere in South America.

In this era of expansion and waste another giant of the industry was to write his name indelibly in its annals. He rose to be an influence in behalf of conservation as well as a pioneer in the field of natural gas. His name was Henry L. Doherty, born in Ohio in 1870, also in the infancy of the great energy industry.

Doherty was the first important man to see the stupidity of wanton waste of oil and gas in its true light. Early in his career in the industry he started a one-man campaign to do something about it. His theories and philosophies were brilliant but they met with little acceptance. Even the American Petroleum Institute, during the time he was a member of its directorship, spurned his pleas for greater attention to the conservation of petroleum and the establishment of state and Federal laws, if necessary, to bring about the end of preventable waste. He saw the Rule—or Law—of Capture as the one great road block to effective conservation. He urged the producing states to enact unitization laws. When they refused, he turned to the Federal Government in a personal plea to President Coolidge, who was so impressed that he appointed a Federal Oil Conservation Board in 1924.

It was Doherty's idea that uniform conservation measures to protect irreplaceable natural resources should be effected to assure orderly development of oil and gas fields in the public interest. He evolved a plan which eventually influenced the formation of the Interstate Oil Compact Commission, but only after the great Oklahoma City and East Texas Fields had virtually laid waste the domestic oil industry by saturating the nation with unneeded oil at the very time of its greatest financial depression.

This was not the only (but was the most important) contribution Doherty made to the industry. Others included pioneering in long-line, large-diameter, high-pressure natural-gas transmission lines and building the first natural-gas storage field. He was among the first important leaders to recognize the unlimited possibilities of the science of geology as applied to petroleum. He pioneered in the field of combustion engineering. His investigations gave necessary impetus to research in petrochemicals. He was among the first to advocate oil-burning locomotives and home oil-heating equipment. He did all of this while developing 140 important patents applicable in the gas, cement, chemical, coke, smelting, petroleum, and house-heating industries. And in 1937 he received the award emblematic of the highest distinction in the field of petroleum engineering—the Anthony F. Lucas medal—for "distinguished achievement in improving the technique and practice of finding and producing petroleum."

Sometime before the United States' entry into World War I there was sufficient interest in conservation to cause voluntary prorationing among operators in Oklahoma and Texas. California had already moved in the direction of conservation on a small but significant scale. So, the influence of Doherty was beginning to stir the imagination.

Oil-field waste was not altogether due to greed and carelessness. Its greatest cause was ignorance which included an absence of proper knowledge of coping with production of oil from greater depths at higher pressures. It also included a lack of the necessary tools, equipment, and services. As oil flooded over earthen embankments around wells in Texas, Oklahoma, California, and elsewhere, and gas was flared wantonly and dangerously into the air, the minds of responsible men in the industry began to sober and the words and warnings of Doherty began to take root.

But there was still plenty of oil. In fact, until the Model T brought the automobile count up above 450,000 in 1910, there was far too much oil, and gasoline was a drug on the market to be burned as the waste product it was around most refineries. But Henry Ford changed all of that. Before 1910 most of the 10 percent gasoline cut from a barrel of crude was waste. By 1914 the yield of gasoline from a barrel of crude had doubled and all of it was being sold and used. By the time the first century of oil was to be celebrated, about 45 percent of the yield from a barrel of American oil, and equally that much of the market, was gasoline. By 1916 there were 3,367,889 automobiles in the country and the tin lizzie was no longer a luxury, having been recognized generally as a necessity.

And this development leads to the accomplishment of Dr. William M. Burton, a noted chemist who started his career in the petroleum industry in 1889 assigned to the task of finding out what caused pinholes in oil cans. By 1900 Dr. Burton anticipated that the day would come when demand for gasoline would exceed that for kerosene. To increase the yield of gasoline, Dr. Burton, in 1913, built the first cracking still which would eventually replace the more primitive refining method of straight-line distillation. By his new process he doubled the gasoline yield which

11

is why, by 1916, the gasoline yield was 8.6 gallons to the 42-gallon barrel of crude oil compared with 4.3 gallons in 1904. From that day forward the demand for gasoline has moved upwards, and along with it the yield of gasoline from a barrel of oil.

Oil got the first real test of its mettle in World War I. That was the first time petroleum had been used in warfare since the Romans used it to destroy the fleet of the Saracens about 670 A.D., and later when American Indians sent oil-soaked, flaming arrows into pioneer houses and forts. It was the famous taxicab army which took out from Paris one day in 1918 to meet the Germans that gave oil its most dramatic demonstration of the first world war, although oil-fueled ships had delivered the American army and munitions to France, the first armored tanks were made possible by gasoline and, of course, the first air warfare featured combat on gasoline.

Oil prices, which started climbing during the war years, reached a peak in 1920 at $3.50 a barrel in the wake of rumors that the world was running out of oil. This price incentive produced a rash of exploration activities that resulted in ample oil to start the price on a precipitous slide downward. In 1919 the first successful home fuel-oil burner was developed, providing a better market for "middle of the barrel."

The age of mobility was moving forward with the expanding years of the industry as aviation progressed from Bleriot's flight across the English Channel, through the days of World War I, and down to 1927 when Lindbergh crossed the Atlantic to remove all barriers to the air age. Of course, without oil these things could not have been possible. Oil was contributing to the shrinking of the world and bringing people of all nations closer together while unifying the states and cities of the United States through automotive traffic.

Through these expanding years great progress was being made in the oil-finding sciences and the oil-producing techniques. Men in the field were meeting their challenges as they grew more complex. It was said of that period that practically every idea for the increase of efficiency in the field and in the development of safety came from the roughnecks. But since they had no technical ability they failed to develop their ideas. Finally, when the companies started putting engineers in the field to work with these men, the petroleum engineering profession started to develop.

The discoveries of the Oklahoma City and the great East Texas Fields as the 20's closed brought the oil industry a chaotic crisis matched only by the most devastating economic depression in the history of man. It was at this point that the states got into petroleum regulation on a serious and intelligent basis. Leaders in Texas and Oklahoma, both in the industry and in government, combined their talents to establish oil and gas laws to cope with the threat of unbridled waste. Much of this development echoed the earlier sentiments of Doherty in spirit if not in letter. Before the 30's ended effective conservation in both oil and gas was well in hand. And it was this conservation, in the nick of time, that saved the great oil reservoirs to provide the arsenal of oil with which the free nations again met and conquered tyranny in World War II. This was the first truly great test for oil.

Great pipelines were stretched across the land to meet the demands of the situation. War requirements for 100-octane gasoline, toluene, aviation lubricants, butadiene, synthetic rubber, and other new products, were not only met in the emergency but the way was pointed to further development. When it was all over the Army-Navy board called oil's contribution "without question one of the greatest industrial accomplishments in the history of warfare . . . not a single operation was delayed or impeded because of a lack of petroleum products."

As the oil century passed in parade the industry moved into a new and fascinating, if frustrating, stage. That was the stage of offshore oil. The movement got under way even before the turn of the century when Summerland Field was drilled by whipstocking a hole out under water near Santa Barbara, California, in 1894. Later there were other California fields drilled offshore from land locations. The first wells actually drilled within the boundaries of a body of water were those from platforms in Caddo Lake in northern Louisiana, and at Goose Creek in Texas. The first well in the heavy seas was drilled a short distance offshore in Cameron Parish in 1938. Interest in further overwater development lagged until after the war. The first well ever drilled out of sight of land was a dry hole in 1946 off the Louisiana Coast. The first far offshore well came in as a producer in offshore Louisiana the following year. As the centennial year rolled around, offshore oil was an accomplished fact; but costs, plus a temporary surplus of oil, held operations to a slow pace. Techniques, however, were developing and the men of the industry had acquired know-how in remarkably rapid time.

So, through the years oil has sparked the greatest parade of progress in mankind's history. It seemed to provide the natural energy partner to a hundred significant inventions. In the United States alone by 1959 machines which depend on oil for three quarters of their fuel were doing 99 percent of the work. The cow path has become a superhighway and airlanes criss-cross the skies. The one-horse shay has given way to the station wagon. Petroleum has made possible cheap refrigeration, new fibers, a thousand drugs and chemicals, and plastics to build every conceivable object from beads to boats—all available from the petroleum hydrocarbons.

The explosive forces of the gasoline era created revolutionary changes in agriculture. As the land was depopulated, farm productivity mounted.

Horsepower replaced manpower. The horse gave way to the tractor and the jeep to the point where one 1959 farmer was able to do the work of seven or eight 1900 farmers. Between 1910 and 1959 the farm population dropped from 35 percent to 13 percent and still 800,000 farmers were leaving their land each year. It has been said that a fourth of the remaining eight million farmers could go urban or industrial without loss in farm productivity, largely because of the tools powered by oil. Agriculture uses more petroleum products than any other industry. And the reason is that the drudgery of farm life has been eliminated by oil as productivity is increased by petroleum fertilizers.

In the proper hands petroleum is the world's most magnificent blessing, because it has provided man with an abundance of leisure time. The parents and grandparents of the mid-century generation could afford a vacation only if they were wealthy. Women spent their time sewing, cooking, washing clothes, and doing a hundred chores that petroleum-powered machines do today. At the turn of the century vacations for working men were unheard of. That was a luxury of the idle rich. Yet today's working man can afford to work far fewer hours and have weeks of annual vacations and still produce five times as much as his forefathers. Furthermore, by his productivity he can afford the things that were once meant for the chosen few.

And it is of the petroleum engineers who have been so vital and instrumental in making oil and gas available in abundance that this book is written. They did so with ingenuity, imagination, industry, and perseverance. They are the men who met the challenge of all of the periods of petroleum history. Now, a hundred years after Uncle Billy Smith withdrew that dipper of rock oil from the bore hole of the Drake well, they have earned recognition as the technical and scientific pioneers without whom the world would be almost a century behind in progress, prosperity, and freedom from drudgery.

Chapter 2

CONCEPTS ON OCCURRENCE
OF OIL AND GAS

E. DeGolyer

E. DeGolyer, after receiving an A.B. degree from the University of Oklahoma in 1911, moved rapidly to a pre-eminent position in American geology and geophysics. His early career included service with the United States Geological Survey and the position of chief geologist of the Mexican Eagle Oil Company, wherein he was responsible for the discovery of prolific oil fields on the Golden Lane. He was an organizer and controlling officer of Amerada Petroleum Corporation, and an organizer and senior member of the consulting firm of DeGolyer and MacNaughton.

Academic, professional and industrial honors include an honorary doctorate of science (University of Oklahoma, 1925); the distinguished service award of the Texas Mid-Continent Oil & Gas Association (1939), Anthony F. Lucas medalist (AIME, 1940), and John Fritz medalist (Founder Engineering Societies, 1942) for vision and leadership in development and application of the art of geophysical exploration for petroleum.

Mr. DeGolyer died at his home in Dallas, Texas, in 1956.

A study of oil production in Pennsylvania suggests that the industry had to attain its majority before, out of the welter of misunderstood and neglected observations, outright error, and uncontrolled and mistaken speculations, there began to emerge a rational understanding of the occurrence of oil and gas.

The early oil men were careless to negligent about keeping adequate logs of their wells. In the reports of the second geological survey of Pennsylvania Carll [1] notes that the first systematic collection of well logs was attempted in 1868-1869 by a committee of which he was a member and E. S. Nettleton, C. E., was chairman. Nettleton soon moved away from Pennsylvania and left the material which had been collected with Carll. Carll despaired of securing records adequate for geological study from drillers and employed a special assistant to observe and log six critical wells being drilled near Petrolia in Butler County, then three wells near Edinburgh in Clarion County, and finally one well in the Bradford Field in McKean County. Some idea of the confusion which existed at that time may be had by referring to a statement by Lesley in his letter covering Carll's report: [1] "Not only do practical oil men theorize in spite of themselves (as their drilling along certain compass lines shows in a remarkable manner) but they are as capable of theorizing well and reaching just conclusions as thoroughbred geologists are if they would take the pains, 1. to observe the facts; 2. to exhibit them properly on paper; and 3. to compare together a sufficient number of them, so as to discover their real connection and relationship. No shrewder or more intellectual people exist. No better observers live. If they only believed in scientific methods of research they would need no enlightenment from geologists. But they despise a slow, painstaking, accurate, wide extended systematic investigation."

THE ANTICLINAL THEORY, STRATIGRAPHIC TRAP ACCUMULATION

The Anticlinal Theory of Oil and Gas Accumulation

The anticlinal theory of oil and gas accumulation, which has been of such great service in guiding prospecting for new pools, was suggested early by several distinguished geologists, as indicated following.

a. Henry D. Rogers, formerly head of the Geological Survey of Pennsylvania and at the time Regius Professor of Natural History in the University of Glasgow, on May 2, 1860, only 9 months after the completion of the Drake well, addressed the Philosophical Society of Glasgow [2] on the distribution and probable origin of the petroleum of western Pennsylvania.

---

[1] References are at the end of the chapter.

b. The versatile, but erratic Dr. T. Sterry Hunt, F.R.S., then a member of the Canadian Survey, on February 27, 1861, lectured before the Board of Arts in Montreal[3] on bitumen and mineral oils.

We do not have transcripts of either of the important lectures mentioned but each of the speakers developed his thesis later in a more extended essay, Hunt in 1861[4] and Rogers[5] in 1863.

c. Ebenezer Baldwin Andrews, Professor of Geology in Marietta College and afterward an assistant geologist under Newberry on the Geological Survey of Ohio, described the oil deposits of the Volcano-Burning Springs anticline[6] in 1861.

d. J. P. Lesley, chief of the second geological survey of Pennsylvania, described the occurrence of oil in his little-known essay "Coal Oil" in 1863.[7]

In his Glasgow address, Rogers in 1860[2] is reported to have said "superficially, the gas-and-oil-emitting springs, within the coal-fields, are chiefly found upon the anticlinal flexures of the strata"; and, with regard to the origin of the petroleum and gas, "the presence of these inflammable products in the strata is but one phase of a very widely diffused metamorphism, by subterranean heat, which all the paleozoic formations, the coal measures included, have undergone." He also outlined the carbon-ratio theory which was afterward restated by David White. Rogers said that he regarded the coals as a "sort of very sensitive natural register thermometer, recording the different grades of temperature to which the strata have been exposed"; and the "sandstones", especially certain thick, pale, sandstones of open texture most abundant near the bottom of the lower coal measures "as being adequate reservoir rocks" and noted that "the imperviousness of the argillaceous strata, except where these are fissured as they are apt to be on the anticlinal flexures, serves to hold down the elastic or volatile products, as evidenced by their often sudden and copious effusion when the mud-rocks are perforated, and the more porous grits are entered by the boring tool." Most of this appears to have been speculative reasoning by Rogers for he had not been in Pennsylvania since the completion of the Drake well. He was following the theory of his brilliant brother, William B. Rogers, that the thermal springs of Virginia "issue from the lines of anticlinal axes, or from points very near to such lines", and extending it to include oil and gas seepages. Time has proved that his speculations as to sandstone reservoirs and shale caprock were sound.

In his Montreal address Hunt,[3] who regarded himself as and who was the original proponent of the anticlinal theory, said: "It required, however, a peculiar arrangement of the strata to allow the oil to accumulate and flow out and this will be met with, in the Lecturer's opinion, along lines of folding and disturbance which the geologists have shown to exist in parts of that region." Hunt, in December 1860, had visited the Oil Springs

Pool, Enniskillin Township, County of Lambton, Ontario, the only producing oil field in Canada at that time. He had regarded this field as being on the northern extension of the Cincinnati arch, but on the basis of later information regarding the structure of this area he said that "our knowledge of the structural condition . . . is too limited to enable us to make any very definite assertions regarding the dependence of the gas and oil accumulations on rock structure." Hunt also noted that Sir William Logan[8] in 1846-1848 had shown, many years previously, that the Petroleum Springs of Gaspé were along lines of anticlinal folding. Hunt continued to write for many years on the nature of petroleum occurrence, his best-known paper being that in the *Canadian Naturalist*,[4] reprinted in the *Chemical News* of London and in the *Report of the Smithsonian Institution*, 1862. This paper is notable since it contains the first attempt to explain the theory of anticlinal accumulation. "The oil doubtless rises," says Hunt, "from the Corniferous limestone which we have seen contains petroleum; this being lighter than the water which permeates at the same time the porous strata, rises to the higher portion of the formation, which is the crest of the anticlinal, where the petroleum of a considerable area accumulates and slowly finds its way to the surface through vertical fissures in the overlying Hamilton shales, giving rise to the oil springs of the region."

Hunt continued to write regarding the nature of oil and gas occurrence but he speculated more than he studied, and, in the author's opinion, added little or nothing to his early contributions.

Ebenezer Baldwin Andrews, Professor of Geology at Marietta College, Ohio, and afterward assistant to Newberry on the Ohio Survey, in 1861[6] described the occurrence of oil and gas on the White Oak anticline—the "West Virginia Oil Break." This paper is notable as being the first description of anticlinal occurrence of oil, and likewise because of its failure to recognize the trap function of the anticline. Andrews was a pronounced fissurite and the anticline to him suggested only a locus for fissures.

Lesley, Pennsylvania State Geologist in 1863, gave some adherence to the anticlinal theory.[7] "In some parts of the western coal-field," he says, "the dip is as high as five degrees and the basins from five to ten miles. Sharp flexures make local dips of thirty degrees or more, and a central sub-anticlinal is sure to subdivide the basins. In the secondary basins thus formed the wells are more perfectly artesian as to the salt water; but it is upon the sub-dividing anticlinals that the gas and oil collect. In such regions it is asserted that all the blowing and many of the spouting wells are ranged along the summits of such anticlinals."

Hanns Höfer, geologist and professor in the Mining Academy of Lobsan, Austria, visited the United States with the commission sent by his country to the Centennial in Philadelphia. He was the author of the commission's report on the oil fields of North America.[9] Höfer, who long after[10] regarded himself as "vater der anticlinal theorie", after reciting that "in Canada, Ohio, West Virginia, beyond doubt, the chief quantity of oil is accumulated on the crest of anticlines" and arguing for his assumption that Pennsylvania oil may also be anticlinal, concludes: "Thus, the anticlines are the safest indications for prospecting; since one found that the gently folded anticlines carry oil in excellent quantities whereas in the sharper anticlines of the same formation in the Alleghany mountains, only scattered traces have been found."

All was not clear sailing for the anticlinal theory, however. In the first publication of the *Pennsylvania Second Geological Survey Report* on oil and gas, Henry E. Wrigley[11] foreshadowed a description of the prevailing stratigraphic-trap type of structure. "There is therefore, within reach of the drill, no continuous bed of oil bearing sand rock but a series of scattered disc-shaped deposits . . . These separate and detached beds of third sand rock are lens-shaped, being thin at the edges as before stated." He had previously defined "a producing spot as one overlying a bed of conglomerate from three to seventy-five feet in thickness, the thickest part of the rock giving the best well, and this thickness being generally found in the center of the area, the rock tapering off at the edges." Höfer[9] follows Wrigley, whom he quotes.

J. P. Lesley, after his early pronouncement for the anticlinal theory in 1863[7] reneged with great vigor in 1865.[12] "There are no anticlinal axes in the Pennsylvania oil regions of the Beaver Creek River, nor in the East Kentucky oil region of the Sandy and Licking waters. The only well defined anticlinal among oil fields is a mere upsqueeze crossing the Ohio River near Marietta."

He referred to the theory again in 1880[13] as "now a deservedly forgotten superstition." The truth of the matter is that the oil and gas of the Appalachian geosyncline occurs chiefly in stratigraphic traps. There are more recent expert opinions on this subject. Fancher in 1934[14] noted: "It is definitely established that accumulation within this area has been controlled only to a limited extent by structure in the majority of cases and largely by local sand conditions." Cathcart[15] in 1934 noted that: "When oil and gas fields of western Pennsylvania are plotted on a map showing structure contours very little relationship between the occurrence of oil and gas and structural highs is apparent." Even of Bradford, anticlinal in structure but with variations of as much as 400 ft in elevation of the pool limit, Fettke in 1937[16] said: "The outlines of the pool conform as closely to structure as sand conditions permit." Of the fields located by White in accordance with his theory, only the Grapeville gas field is anticlinal; the others are stratigraphic traps.

The most practical study of the "West Virginia Oil Break" and one of the most practical and fruitful presentations of the anticlinal theory was made by F. W. Minshall, superintendent of an oil company at Marietta, Ohio, in 1864, a refiner at Parkersburg, West Virginia, from 1869 to 1876, an able observer and self-taught geologist of much ability. He determined well elevations by barometer and undertook in 1878 a careful profile of the axis with cross sections at Horseneck, White Oak, and Burning Springs. He found that the fold was undulating, forming domes and saddles; that the productive oil and gas wells were on the domes; and that the dry holes were too far down the flanks of the fold or in the saddles between domes. Minshall presented the results of his study in an article in the *State Journal* of Parkersburg, West Virginia. Peckham[17] in his *Petroleum Production Technology and Uses of Petroleum and its Products*, Vol. X, Washington, 1884, quotes from the Minshall article and publishes sections furnished by him. Peckham concludes: "Taken as a whole the rocks form inverted basins with flat bottoms and sloping sides. In these inverted basins nature for thousands of years has been collecting gases as the chemist collects them in inverted bottles over his pneumatic cistern . . . The undulations of the rock shown by this profile, taken in connection with the known laws of hydrostatic pressure, satisfactorily account for the failures and show that part of the anticlinal is filled with accumulations of waters, and also what part must contain the accumulation of oil and gas."

Dr. Israel C. White shortly thereafter—in 1885—announced his rediscovery of the anticlinal theory.[18] White's conclusions were based upon his examination in June 1883 of the geological structure of the areas surrounding the great gas wells of the Appalachian region and, as expressed at that time to J. J. Vandergrift of the Forest Oil Company for whom the work as done, he found that: "The rock disturbance caused by anticlinal waves was the main and important factor in the occurrence of both petroleum and natural gas." During the two years which elapsed before the publication of this conclusion, White claims to have located "the important gas and oil field near Washington, Pennsylvania; also the Grapeville gas field along the great arch of the same name in Westmoreland; and the Belleveron (*sic*) field on the Monongahela River and during the same period or later the Taylortown field of Washington and the Mannington field, West Virginia."

White acknowledged freely the priority of Hunt, Andrews, and Höfer in the discovery of the anticlinal theory but states that its rediscovery was based upon his own field studies and without knowledge that the others "had many years previously discerned and published practically the same conclusions." He credits William A. Erseman of Allegheny, Pennsylvania, an oil operator of many years' experience, with suggesting he had noticed that the principal gas fields then known in western Pennsylvania were situated close to where anticlinal axes were drawn on geological maps and with the inference that, therefore, there must be some connection between the gas wells and the anticlines.

While the geologists spread their speculations in print, operating men in the region put forward and followed for a while certain theories of their own. The Drake well had been drilled on Watson's Flat in the valley of Oil Creek. For several years after the completion of this well the drilling of wells was confined almost exclusively to the flat valleys of the principal streams. The impression prevailed that there was some connection, some parallelism, between the streams on the surface and "oil veins" beneath. Finally it was proved by drilling that the occurrence of oil-bearing territory was regardless of any and all topographical features of the surface (Carll, 1875, p. 10).[19]

The "Belt-line" Theory

The "belt" or "belt-line" theory grew out of the early recognition by Pennsylvania operators that almost every oil field was much longer than it was broad and that the longest dimension generally followed the same direction—the magical North 22½ deg East.

The birth of this theory must have been very early and its parentage unknown. As early as 1865, we find Lesley declaring against it. "There are no 'belts of oil' as some imagine, distinguishable upon the surface," he said; and continued: "The belts of wells have been caused by the fact that they are sunk in valleys, and that they have clustered along certain outcrops in order to avoid the need of going down to inconvenient depths." "All straight-edge locations of wells upon a map are mere charlatanry," he warned.

Notwithstanding this early evidence, the development of the theory is all but universally credited to Cyrus D. Angell, probably because of his spectacular success in applying it. Angell entered the oil business in 1867. In a sketch of his life, probably autobiographical, it is said that during the first three years of his experience he "became interested in observations and geological investigations which led to development of the 'Belt theory'; establishing the fact that the second and third oil producing sand rocks extended in belt lines from northeast to southwest, on an angle of 22½° with a regular and continuous dip of the rocks to the southwest" and that he outlined the theory in 1870.

Peckham's account[17] is that Angell had "observed in the 'upper country' " that a narrow belt extending across from Scrubgrass, on the Allegheny River, to Petroleum Center, on Oil Creek, included many of the best wells in that region of Pennsylvania. In the 'lower country' he projected a similar belt, lying in a direction nearly parallel with the first, and extending from Saint Petersburg, in Clarion County, Pennsylvania, through Parker's Landing to Bear Creek, in Butler County. Angell obtained a number of leases and his selection was most successful.

"The results have shown that the oil rock lies in belts or in long and narrow areas, having a general northeast and southwest extension, often not more than 30 rods in width, but several miles in length; that the sand rock is thickest and most productive along the axis of the belt, thinning out toward its borders, the upper surface being level and the under surface curved upward from the center; that the present configuration of the surface has no relation to the form, extent, or direction of the 'belt'. These facts established, and their successful application abundantly demonstrated by the remarkable success attending Angell's operations, have given a certain degree of accuracy to the development of oil territory that it never possessed before. On the other hand, they have led to very exaggerated views, some enthusiasts affirming their belief that the line of north 16° east, upon which Angell achieved his first success, governed the direction and extent of territory containing oil from Canada to Tennessee.

"During the early years of this decade, when Angell's efforts and sagacity were being rewarded in the lower country with success in a most substantial form, other operators struck out from the 'upper country' of Oil Creek in a general northeast direction, some on a line north 16° east, others north 22½° east, and others on still other lines, often traced over the forest-covered hills of that region with a compass, and located their wells in the expectation of finding other sand-bars of the ancient sea from which the oil would rush to the surface. They finally reached the town of Bradford, in McKean County, a locality which some thought could never produce oil."

The belt-line theory had some considerable validity and is still in use in the oil fields today under different names. The men of the second Pennsylvania geological survey—Lesley, Ashburner, Chance and Carll—considered the belts to be depositional, i.e., porous streaks or old shore lines. The adherents of the structural theory—Edward Orton, for example—considered that the belts, insofar as they were valid, were structural. We now know that the men of the Pennsylvania survey were right, but for many years such technical niceties were of no concern to the practical operator and today we use the terms "trend" or "trend line" in exactly the same sense that "belt" and "belt line" were used by the Pennsylvanians.

During the reign of the theory of fissured reservoirs, less technical writers, starting with Andrews' vertical fissure, extended and elaborated it. The Rev. S. J. M. Eaton in 1866[20] postulated a cavern reservoir with veins extending from the reservoir to the point where they were intersected by the drill, and the resulting wells produced gas, oil, or water according to the position of the intake and of the vein in the reservoir.

Cone and Johns in 1870[21] also held to the theory of crevice reservoirs as did J. T. Henry in 1873.[22]

There is much in the early literature which can be interpreted as a description of stratigraphic traps, but it seems to me that one of the clearest expressions of the fundamentals was that made by Carl D. Smith in 1914[23] in his description of Glenn Pool. Smith considered "that in this area geologic structure controls, to a large extent, the accumulations of oil and gas." A careful reading of his paper, however, suggests that about all he insisted upon were dipping beds and the gravitational stratification of oil, gas, and water. He concludes: "But reservoirs are produced as effectively by a combination of monoclinal dip and lack of porosity or absence of sand as by anticlinal structure."

The anticlinal theory had the decided advantage that, in addition to being practically and theoretically as sound as the stratigraphic-trap theory, it afforded useful clues to the prospector in his search for new pools, a value not possessed by the stratigraphic-trap type of pool. And so the anticlinal theory survived and was verified by the development of the early pools of California and the Gulf Costal region in the early 1900's; by the development of the Illinois fields somewhat later; by the development of the Cushing Pool, Oklahoma, in 1913 and 1914; by the discovery in 1914 and 1915 of the famous Augusta and Eldorado Fields of Kansas, as well as by scores of fields which followed.

RESERVOIR ROCK

The "Fissure" Controversy

A theory, largely current during the first 20 years of the industry, was that rocks had to be fissured in order to provide reservoir space. This bit of oil-country folklore probably originated with the first well. Uncle Billy Smith, who drilled the Drake well, reported when the hole had reached a depth of 69 ft, the tools dropped 6 in. into a crevice or fissure and oil began to come into the hole. This belief was widely held. Wrigley[11] says: "The oil of the Drake well was found not in a sand rock but in a crevice."

One may doubt whether Uncle Billy actually saw the tools drop, but finding a fissure soon became an essential. On this point, Carll[1] says: "It was the popular belief that a fissure must be struck in the oil sand or a well would be a failure." Entertaining this idea, the driller, upon reaching the sand, was constantly on the alert to find a crevice; and if he happened to get a good well, he always remembered that at a certain spot the drill dropped, and his judgment of the distance it fell would now, of course, be influenced somewhat by the production of the well. As a consequence, crevices have been reported all the way from 1 in. to 3 ft. in depth. It was not to be wondered at, perhaps, that the driller did find crevices, when the geologist told him they ought to be there and his employer considered them essential to a paying well. Neither was it surprising that those who had never seen an oil well should freely accept the opinions of those who were supposed to understand the subject thoroughly.

"The crevice furor finally became so great that an instrument was devised and patented called a 'crevice searcher'. It was lowered into a well by means of poles like sucker rods, and designed to indicate how many, where located, were the crevices in the oil sands. The cylindrical body of the searcher, which was about two feet long, nearly filled the bore hole. In lowering it, whenever a crevice was reached a little finger about an inch long (which was kept pressed out against the wall of the well by a spring) snapped out into the opening and checked the downward movement. Then by raising the rods until the finger struck the top of the crevice, its exact measurement could be obtained. When this was done and the depth recorded, the finger was drawn back by a cord running along the rods to the well mouth, thus unlocking the instrument from the crevice and allowing it to be lowered until another one was found." (Carll 1880, 245-246.[1])

Carll's complaint about geologists was well justified. "Fissures are filled with oil, gas, and salt water," said Lesley,[7] "and different wells strike them at different depths. The oil-bearing sand rocks seem charged from top to bottom with gas and blow off from every fissure as it is passed through by the augur."

Andrews[6] elaborated and sustained the theory of fissured reservoirs. He even published a theoretical cross section of a highly dipping fissure with water, oil, and gas gravitationally stratified. He considered that "the oil is accumulated in the fissures of the rocks, and that these fissures are more or less vertical there is abundant proof." He continued: "In the broken rocks as found along the central line of a great uplift, we meet with the largest quantity of oil", and classified the rocks of western Virginia and southeastern Ohio as "those which are almost entirely horizontal, those which have a dip of fifteen to forty feet to the mile, and those which are broken and dislocated by an uplift." The horizontal rocks contain few fissures and are not productive of oil. The dipping rocks contain "as a result of uplifting forces, many fissures" and produce oil. It was, however, "in regions where the strata have been most disturbed and where the fissures are most numerous that the most oil is found"; and he concluded, "it would appear to be a law, that the quantity of oil is in a direct ratio to the amount of fissures."

The theory of fissured reservoirs died, but slowly. Höfer,[9] as late as 1877, considered fissures important and thought that their best source was anticlinal folding. With the more careful keeping of well logs it finally faded away. Carll (1880, p. 246[1]) says that: "Since the introduction of the plan of drilling wells dry, that is through large casing which prevents the surface water from entering the hole, this device (the crevice searcher) has gone into disrepute", and crevices are not so much talked about.

As late as 1880 Carll (*op. cit.*) admits that: "In the oil rocks it seems quite probable that in some localities and under certain conditions, fissures do exist", and notes more generally that: "Some oil producers stoutly maintain that a flowing well of one, two or three thousand barrels per day cannot be obtained unless a crevice is struck; that a sandrock, however porous it may be, cannot afford a sufficient channel for so large a quantity of fluid to come into a well". The gusher wells and wells too closely spaced and showing interference in production doubtless served to confirm the general belief in fissures. In addition to questioning the existence of crevices, Carll first showed quantitatively that there was a high degree of probability that a sand could yield oil fast enough to account for even the greatest gushers.

Other Early Ideas on Oil and Gas Accumulation

Notwithstanding that Rogers'[2] recognition in 1860 of sandstone as being adequate reservoir rock and the argillaceous strata as the cap rocks, and Winchell's[24] acceptance of sandstone as an adequate reservoir in the same year, it was the knowledge gained by more exact study of the wells that finally overthrew the fissure theory.

In considering the nature of reservoir rock, we note that the ingenious Carll (1880, p. 272, *op. cit.*) had all but discovered interstitial water when he noted that when oil sands were being deposited "the interspaces between sand and pebbles, which now contain oil, must have been filled with salt water, for they could not go down unoccupied." He did not pursue the thought, however, and another 50 years elapsed before its discovery.

It is a pity that the able Carll did not pursue his thinking further and demonstrate that his stratigraphic traps performed a trap function in the accumulation of oil and gas but little different and quite as effective as that performed by traps of structural origin.

OIL-POOL ENERGIES

Development of the Dissolved-gas Theory of Oil Expulsion

The earliest wells drilled in northwestern Pennsylvania were pumpers, and it may be presumed that they differed too little from ordinary water wells in their functioning to excite much speculative comment. By mid-May 1861, some 20 months after the completion of the Drake well, 135 wells had been drilled in the Regions. Only two of these had been flowing wells—the Hequembourg, completed August 1860 on the bank of the Allegheny River opposite the town of Tideoute, and the ill-fated Little

Merrick which came in on Oil Creek, flowing 3,000 bbl daily and caught fire, a disaster in which 19 lives were lost.

In May 1861, the "Fountain Well" on the David McElhenny farm, Oil Creek, came in flowing 300 bbl daily, a production which it sustained for 15 months. It was the first of the Third Sand flowing wells, and it was followed by a series of spectacular gushers during the remainder of 1861, throughout 1862, and until the late summer of 1863. Most striking of these wells were Phillips No. 2, Tarr farm, completed October 1861, and the Noble & Delamater well, Farrell farm, completed January 1863—each flowing an initial production of 4,000 bbl daily. The Noble & Delamater well produced more than a million and a half barrels of oil during its life-time and netted its owners some 5 million dollars. This well suffered interference from the nearby Caldwell well which, in consequence, was bought for $145,000 and plugged. Phillips No. 2 also suffered interference from the Woodward well, drilled but 4 rods distant. Water from the Woodward flooded the Phillips and presently neither well would produce unless they were pumped simultaneously. Finally the owners of the Phillips bought the Woodward lease for a half million dollars and plugged the well.

These flowing wells with their great production of gas and oil caused men to think about the energies which made such production possible. The first reference found is in Lesley's little-known essay on "Coal Oil"[7] published in 1863. "Whence comes this gas, if not by subterranean distillation?" said he; and continues: "It is impossible to postulate the gas first and the oil afterwards, for that order would require the generation of pressure sufficient afterwards, and the oil would be in the condition of a mechanically explosible fluid, as it is in the case of coal-mine fire damp. Whence then comes the oil and how has it collected in reservoirs? It is easy after these questions have been answered to describe the mechanical pro-pulsion of the oil to the surface, partly by gravity and partly by the pres-sure of the gas it has itself generated through natural fissures producing natural oil springs, or through artificial augur holes." It must be admitted that these conclusions do not seem as clear to the reader as they may have seemed to their author.

Lesley persevered, however, and in a private report in 1865[25] came up with the gas concept, a theory which has served us well.

The gas concept is, essentially, that oil in its original undisturbed state underground always contains gas in solution. Rarely the amount of such gas may be as low as 20 cu ft per bbl, but, generally, it amounts to 300 to 800 cu ft per bbl. The importance of this condition is that the oil-gas solution, being of lower viscosity than the oil alone, moves or is moved more easily through the reservoir rock, and that one of the prime moving agents is the expansion of the dissolved gas under reduced pressures. This effect alone is great enough in certain fields to cause wells to flow over long periods of time.

In this private report, Lesley, after noting the importance of the hydrostatic pressure of bottom water says: "And to this is added the force which the gases, chemically disengaged from the petroleum, press upon both rock and water to escape. In the sand rocks and gravel-beds, no doubt, all three elements—salt water, oil and gas—remain mechanically combined. But in the same ramifying caves of limestone, and in the quasi-fissures which penetrate the sandrocks, they are separated by specific gravity into three places, the gas occupying the upper, the oil in the middle, and water the bottom of each cavity." The recognition that much gas occurs in solution in the oil was advanced doctrine for that day. Indeed, this is the first foreshadowing of the gas concept that this author has found. Lesley's great error, however, was to regard salt water as intersoluble with oil and gas. He never did recede from this error, since at the very end of his professional life he still held that "it is impossible, therefore, that any arrangement of water, oil and gas can occur in the deep oil-rocks, such as occurs in a bottle", and that under certain conditions "the water, oil and gas, at great depths, if they could exist at all, would remain practically mixed like the carbonic acid gas in a soda fountain."

Robert Briggs, a broadly educated engineer, in early 1865 visited the Venango County, Pennsylvania, oil region and on June 16, 1865, in a stated meeting of the American Philosophical Society in Philadelphia,[26] "made a verbal communication of his views respecting the nature of the force by which petroleum is brought to the surface, regarding it as an intimate mechanical mixture of the gases, into which the petroleum spontaneously decomposes with the petroleum fluid, like that which exists between carbonic acid and water in a soda fountain." This appears to have been the first clear statement of the gas concept. Lesley and Briggs were friends and, it may be, had discussed the subject between themselves, since each of them appeals to the famous soda-water analogy which has continued to be used time and again in the discussion of the nature of the oil-gas solution.

John F. Carll, oil expert to the second Pennsylvania geological survey under Lesley, gives the best of the early descriptions of the nature of the oil-gas solution and of the function of the gas in the production of the oil. He states:[1] "Oil and gas in their normal condition appear to lie in the sand rock not as distinct bodies occupying separate portions of the rock, but as one substance, the gas being as thoroughly incorporated with the oil as gas is with water in a bottle of soda water. Drawing oil from the rock may be compared to drawing beer from the barrel. The barrel is placed in the cellar and a bar pump inserted. At first the liquor flows freely through the tube without using the pump, but presently the gas weakens and the pump is called into requisition; and finally, the gas pressure in the barrel becomes so weak that a vent hole must be made to admit atmospheric pressure before the barrel can be completely emptied even by the pump."

It has been suggested elsewhere in this chapter that these early statements apparently did not receive widespread recognition, because theorizing with regard to oil and gas occurrence was then something of a monopoly of the geologists, who were entranced by the sweet reasonableness of the gravitational stratification of oil, gas, and water upon which they leaned heavily to support their anticlinal theory. Briggs was an engineer and Carll, though he was described by Orton as "our leading production authority", was regarded by I. C. White as "an old county surveyor with no imagination and unable to generalize on the data he collected." Actually, Carll seems to have been, on this subject at least, a very able generalizer and is well entitled to be regarded as the father of petroleum engineering.

This early recognition of the functional importance of gas seems to have received no further attention for many years from either scientists, technologists, or practical men concerned with the oil industry. The gas concept had to wait until the period of 1913 to 1916 to be rediscovered, and until somewhat later to be properly evaluated and used.

One notable expression in this long period of neglect of the gas concept is in the statement made by Dr. C. Willard Hayes[27] in 1903. "After his study of Spindletop and such other fields as had been found in the Gulf Coast area by that time, Dr. C. Willard Hayes expressed himself with regard to the importance of flowing energy with clearness unusual for that time: 'In addition to the expansive force of the gas there is also probably some hydrostatic pressure in this field, but its influence in producing the phenomena of a gusher must be relatively insignificant. . . . If the pressure producing the gushing in an oil pool is due chiefly to the expansive force of gas, it follows that this force will expel only a part of the oil, and the remainder will necessarily be won by pumping or by supplying the place of the natural gas by compressed air. It is evident, therefore, that the gas should never be allowed to escape freely from an oil pool, for, aside from the waste of a valuable fuel, the force needed to expel the oil is at the same time being lost.' "

The United States Bureau of Mines was organized in 1910, and the earliest effort of its Petroleum Division was a survey of waste in the oil fields. These studies resulted in findings of underground waste resulting from inadequate casing and cementing procedure and the consequent loss of oil and gas through premature flooding, as well as the more evident surface wastes, the magnitude of which had inspired the investigation.

It was L. G. Huntley[28] who seems first to have rediscovered the gas concept. In a notable paper which comes very close to our present understanding with regard to underground physical waste he says: "The decline of gas pressure in the pool through the exhaustion of the lighter hydrocarbons acts in a variety of ways to cause the decline of wells. In the first place, the reduction of the specific gravity of the oil remaining in the rock indirectly affects the production. . . . The practice of allowing the free escape of vapors, instead of endeavoring to make each cubic foot of gas in expanding perform its quota of work in the expulsion of liquid petroleum, is a direct cause of the decline of flowing wells. It is almost as direct a factor in the decline of pumping wells, as the intrastrata gas pressure is the means of keeping up the continuous movement of the fluid toward the well when the well is pumped."

In 1916, J. O. Lewis[29] was joint author of a paper in which the only recognized wastes of petroleum were those caused by premature flooding of sands and by migration and dissipation into other sands. But, by the following year,[30] he had come apparently to a full recognition of the function of solution gas, regarding it as "an especially important factor in the recovery of oil from the formations in which it is found." He noted that: "When a well is drilled through the impervious strata, capping an oil sand, the pressure is released at that point and an avenue of escape for the oil and gas is afforded. The gas absorbed in the oil immediately expands and flows toward the hole, moving oil with it. . . . There can be no doubt that the predominant expulsive force is the energy stored in the compressed gas absorbed in or associated with the oil. . . . The proportion of oil recovered from an oil sand may be said to represent a balance of the energy originally stored in the oil sand, with the waste of energy and the opposition to the expulsion of the oil. This might be termed the 'energy of expulsion' and will depend not only on the natural conditions, but also upon the manner in which the producer operates his wells. . . . As it is the energy contained in the compressed and absorbed gas rather than the oil that is exhausted, it is but logical to judge the efficiency of a producing method largely by the relative quantities of gas produced with each barrel of oil. If by a change in method the producer lessens the proportion of gas with each barrel of oil, he should increase the total recovery of oil correspondingly, even if the rate of production is temporarily reduced somewhat."

The classic paper in our understanding of the importance of solution gas is that by C. E. Beecher and I. P. Parkhurst[31] reporting the results of experiments carried on at the instigation and under the direction of Henry L. Doherty. These experiments were of such vital importance to our understanding of underground oil occurrence that they may be said to mark a turning point in the art of oil production. The experiments, apparently carried out in 1924, gave a quantitative basis for our understanding of the solubility of gas in oil and the viscosity-reducing effect of such gas. Among their conclusions Beecher and Parkhurst stated that: "At a pressure of five hundred pounds and a temperature of 70° F., it was found that a natural gas such as is associated with the oil would reduce the viscosity about fifty per cent when a given crude was saturated with the gas. . . . A

30

large percentage of oil which present production methods fail to remove from the sand is held by capillarity. As the gas dissolved in the oil escapes, the surface tension is increased and, likewise, the capillary force which is a measure of the surface tension. If this increase in surface tension could be prevented during the process of extracting oil from the sands, a greater volume of oil should be recovered."

Upon the insistence of Doherty, and largely as a result of these experiments, the American Petroleum Institute in 1927 appointed its Gas Conservation Committee which appointed a technical subcommittee. It in turn appointed regional subcommittees which met at Ponca City, Oklahoma, October 17, 18, and 19 and reviewed the whole matter of the nature of the occurrence of gas in oil. With the completion of the work of these committees and the submission of a report by H. C. Miller,[32] it may be said that oilmen had come practically to the present understanding of the nature of the oil-gas solution in the reservoir.

Early Concepts Concerning Water Drives

Another natural force important as a source of energy in oil production is water drive. It was probably recognized early and is the force referred to by early writers as hydrostatic. Orton in 1888[33] refers to it as a theory which "appeals to water pressure in the oil and gas-rock, as the course of the flow of both these substances" and notes by way of explanation that "everyone is acquainted with the phenomena and explanation of artesian wells." He regards it as a natural water flood, since he concludes: "With the exhaustion of a gas field or an oil field, these substances are followed up and replaced by salt water."

Out of this commonly held concept came water flooding as a technique for oil recovery—first the natural floods recognized by Carll, and afterward the artificial floods.

It is fortunate for our nation and our industry that some understanding of oil-field energies had been developed before the 1930's when the flood of oil resulting chiefly from the discovery of the mammoth East Texas Pool had become so great that it could no longer be marketed nor stored. Conservation was invoked as a sanction for proration, and properly so. Wells were put on restricted instead of open flow or, under certain conditions, entirely closed. For the first time in the history of the industry the petroleum engineer was able to study the effect of various rates of flow on gas and pressure conservation. New indices of the effectiveness of reservoir management, such as bottom-hole pressures and gas-oil ratios, were developed. The result has been continuous and substantial improvement in our knowledge of the nature and functioning of those energies which make possible a proper production of oil and gas.

REFERENCES

[1]Carll, John F: The Geology of the Oil Regions of Warren, Venango, Clarion and Butler Counties, *Pennsylvania 2nd Geol. Survey Report,* **III**, xxiv, 482, and atlas (1880).

[2]Rogers, H. D: On the Distribution and Probable Origin of the Petroleum or Rock Oil of West Pennsylvania, New York and Ohio, *Proc. Philos. Soc. Glasgow,* **4**, 355 (1860).

[3]Hunt, T. Sterry: Bitumen and Mineral Oils, *Montreal Gazette,* March 1 (1861). Board of Arts Lecture.

[4]Hunt, T. Sterry: Notes on the History of Petroleum or Rock Oil, *Canadian Naturalist and Geologist,* **VI [4]** 241, August (1860).

[5]Rogers, H. D: Coal and Petroleum, *Good Words,* 374, London, May (1863). Reprint, without identification of author, *Harper's New Monthly Magazine,* **27**, 259 (1863). Identified by J. V. Howell.

[6]Andrews, E. B: Rock Oil, Its Geological Relations and Distribution, *Am. Jour. Sci.,* **32 [21]** 85 (1891)

[7]Lesley, J. P: Coal Oil, *37th Cong., 3rd Sess., H. Doc. 78, Report of the Commissioner of Agriculture for the Year 1862,* 429, Washington (1863).

[8]Logan, William E: *Canadian Geol. Survey, Report of Progress,* 1844, 1846.

[9]Hofer, Prof. Hanns: Die Petroleum-Industrie Nord Amerikas. Nericht uber die Weltanstellung in Philadelphia, 1876, *Henaus-geben von de Oesterreichischen Commission,* **VIII**, 166, Wien (1877).

[10]Hofer, Prof. Hanns: On the Development of the Anticlinal Theory, *Econ. Geology,* **5**, 492 (1910).

[11]Wrigley, Henry E: Special Report on the Petroleum of Pennsylvania, *Pennsylvania 2nd Geol. Survey Report, Philadelphia* (1875).

[12]Lesley, J. P: Discussion at Meeting, Dec. 1, 1865, *Proc. Am. Philos. Soc.,* **10**, 190 (1865).

[13]Lesley, J. P: Annual Report of the State Geologist, *Pennsylvania 2nd Geol. Survey Report* (1880).

[14]Fancher, G. H: Oil and Gas Development in Pennsylvania, *Trans. Am. Inst. Mining Met. Engrs. (Petroleum Development and Technology)* **107**, 278 (1934).

[15]Cathcart, S. H: Geologic Structure in the Plateaus Region of Northern Penna. and its Relation to the Occurrence of Gas in the Oriskany Sand, *Pennsylvania Topog. and Geol. Survey Bull.* 108, March (1934).

[16]Fettke, C. R: Geology and Oil Resources of the Bradford Field, Pennsylvania and New York, *Pennsylvania Topog. and Geol. Survey Bull.,* 116 (1937).

[17]Peckham, S. F: Production, Technology, and Uses of Petroleum and its Products, *Tenth Census of the United States,* **X,** vi and 301, Washington (1884).

[18]White, I. C: The Geology of Natural Gas, *Science,* **5 [2]** 521, June 26 (1885).

[19]Carll, J. F: Report of Progress in the Venango Oil District, *Pennsylvania 2nd Geol. Survey Report,* **1**, 1 (1875).

[20]Eaton, Rev. S. J. M: *Petroleum: A History of the Oil Region of Venango County, Pennsylvania. It Resources, Mode of Development, and Value; Embracing a Discussion of Ancient Oil Operations; with a Map, and Illustrations of Oil Scenes and Boring Implements,* 299, J. P. Skelly & Co., Philadelphia, 1866.

[21]Cone, Andrew, and Johns, Walter R: *Petrolia: A Brief History of the Pennsylvania Petroleum Region,* New York, 1870.

[22]Henry, J. T: *The Early and Later History of Petroleum,* Philadelphia, 1873.

[23]Smith, Carl D: Glenn Pool, Oklahoma, *U. S. Geol. Survey Bull. 541,* 34, Washington (1914).

[24]Winchell, A: First Biennial Report of the Progress of the Geological Survey of Michigan, Embracing Observations on the Geology, Zoology and Botany of the Lower Peninsula. Made to the Governor, December 31, 1860. By Authority, 339, Lansing (1861).

[25]Lesley, J. P: Geological Report on the Brady's Bend Iron and Coal Company's Lane in Armstrong County, Pennsylvania, Wrappers, 20 pp., 2 maps, 1 plate section, 1 fig. (1865).

[26]Briggs, R: On the Solution of Gas in Oil, *Proc. Am. Philos. Soc.,* **10,** 136 (1865).

[27]Hayes, C. W: Oil Fields of the Texas-Louisiana Coastal Plain, *U. S. Geol. Survey Bull. 213,* 350, Washington (1903).

[28]Huntley, L. G: Possible Causes of the Decline of Oil Wells and Suggested Methods of Prolonging Yield, *U. S. Bur. Mines Tech. Paper 51* (1913).

[29]Lewis, James O. and McMurray, William F: Underground Wastes in Oil and Gas Fields and Methods of Prevention, *U. S. Bur. Mines Tech. Paper 130,* Washington (1916).

[30]Lewis, James O: Methods for Increasing the Recovery from Oil Sands, *U. S. Bur. Mines Bull. 148,* Washington (1917).

[31]Beecher, C. E., and Parkhurst, I. P: Effect of Dissolved Gases upon the Viscosity and Surface Tension of Crude Oil, 51, *Petroleum Development and Technology in 1926,* American Institute of Mining and Metallurgical Engineers, New York, 1927.

[32]Miller, H. C: *Function of Natural Gas in the Production of Oil,* American Petroleum Institute, New York, 1929.

[33]Orton, Edward: Report of the Geological Survey of Ohio, *Econ. Geology,* **VI,** Columbus, Ohio (1888).

BIBLIOGRAPHY

Campbell, Marius R: Historical Review of Theories Advanced by American Geologists to Account for the Origin and Accumulation of Oil, *Econ. Geology,* **6 [II]** 363 (1911).

Hunt, T. Sterry: Petroleum: Its Geological Relations Considered with Especial Reference to its Occurrence in Gaspe; Being a Report Addressed to the Hon. Commissioner of Crown Lands, Quebec (1865).

Lesley, J. P: The Geology of the Pittsburg Region, *Trans. Am. Inst. Min. Engrs.,* **XIV,** 654 (1886).

Malcolm Wyatt: The Oil and Gas Fields of Ontario and Quebec, *Canada Dept. of Mines Geol. Survey, Mem. 81, Geol. Series 67,* Ottawa (1915).

Andrews, E. B: Petroleum in its Geological Relations, *Am. Jour. Sci.,* **42 [2]** 33 (1866).

Chapter 3

SOURCES OF MEN

C. A. WARNER

CHARLES A. WARNER was born in Jefferson, New York, in 1894. After receiving an A.B. degree from Cornell University, he was employed in 1917 as a field geologist for Empire Gas & Fuel Company. After four years of service in the Mid-Continent area he joined Houston Oil Company of Texas as Mid-Continent district manager. He was transferred in 1932 to Houston and assigned additional duties including company-wide supervision of land and leasing activities and petroleum engineering. He was elected a director in 1941; vice-president in 1944; and secretary in 1952, continuing in these capacities until liquidation of the company in 1956. He then established consulting offices in Houston.

Mr. Warner's professional affiliations include API, AAPG, AIME, and Texas Mid-Continent Oil & Gas Association. He is a trustee of the Texas Gulf Coast Historical Association and the author of the books, *Field Mapping for the Oil Geologist* (1921); *Texas Oil and Gas Since 1543* (1939), and many historical and technical articles.

The sources of men currently entering the oil industry as petroleum engineers are primarily the schools or departments of petroleum engineering at various universities and colleges. Other sources include schools or departments of geology and of chemical, civil, electrical, mechanical, or mining engineering, and men with practical experience but without a collegiate degree.

Antedating the birth of the oil industry, however—which in the United States, is generally recognized as having taken place in 1859— were the innumerable men with varying degrees of skill and education who contributed directly or indirectly to basic engineering principles that later became integral parts of the petroleum industry and are embodied in petroleum engineering as it is practiced today. These earliest engineers include the prehistoric men who first dug holes with bare hands in search of water; the Chinese who utilized the spring pole for drilling, and devised a method of cementing and pipelines of bamboo hundreds of years before the Christian era; the inhabitants around the Caspian Sea and the early Romans who collected oil from the surface of the water or from man-made pits and made use of it as an illuminant and as a medicine; the early builders of pyramids, coliseums, aqueducts, etc.; and the primitive men who first sank shafts near oil seeps in the Titusville area of Pennsylvania, the Oil Springs area of Texas, and elsewhere. Also included among such pioneer engineers should be Archimedes, who knew the principles of the hydrometer; Leonardo da Vinci, who is credited with inventing threaded pipe (ceramic); David and Joseph Ruffner, who utilized the spring-pole method of the Chinese in drilling wells for salt brine in West Virginia about 1806, and to whom should go credit for use of the packer; William Morris, who received a patent in 1831 for a design of drilling jars; the French engineer, Fauvelle, who employed a water-flushed set of tools for drilling in 1845; and the many other engineers who contributed in so many ways to advance present-day petroleum engineering. Little is known today of the sources of knowledge and information available to these early practical engineers, many of whom had no technical training.

The experience and the training of the men who, beginning with the Drake well in 1859, contributed in one way or another to the advancement of engineering in drilling for and production of oil and gas was oftentimes far removed from what would today be classed as engineering training, but these men completed the work they undertook and were true engineers in the broad sense of the word. As reported in *The Oil and Gas Journal* (August 23, 1936), Col. Edwin

L. Drake had a district school education, had worked as a salesman, as a railroad express agent, and as a railroad conductor; and his driller, "Uncle Billy" Smith, was a blacksmith from Tarentum, Pa. These men, utilizing the earlier known principles of percussion drilling, which they supplemented and augmented by innovations of their own, successfully completed the discovery well of the American oil industry. Among the other pioneer engineers were T. F. Rowland, who was granted a patent in May 1869, for an offshore drilling rig; Alanson Ashford Sumner, who suggested the feasibility of piping oil from western Pennsylvania across the Allegheny Mountains to the Atlantic Coast; and the Baker brothers, operating a rotary device for drilling water wells in the Dakota Territory in the early 1880's. It is also interesting to note that a French civil engineer, Leschot, used a power-driven rotary drill with a diamond-studded bit in 1860; that a patent for the bottom-hole control bean was granted to John D. Rockefeller before 1890; and that a philosopher, Robert Briggs, described the coexistence of oil and gas in the reservoir to a meeting of the American Philosophical Society in 1865.

The early application of the principles of mining engineering in the production of oil soon after the completion of the Drake well is described by Dr. L. C. Uren, on p. 39 of *Bull. 118,* Division of Mines, California, 1940, where he states: "An interesting development of the early '60's in Ventura County, was the driving of a number of tunnels for oil drainage. With portals in the ravine below the precipitous slopes of Sulphur Mountain, these tunnels, though less than a thousand feet long, were so situated that they penetrated oil sands well below the surface. For many years they continued to produce small quantities of oil. Drainage of oil through mine openings had previously been practiced in a primitive way in other parts of the world, but the Sulphur Mountain tunnels are of interest as the first successful enterprise of the kind in the Western Hemisphere, and there have been few since."

John F. Carll (who could well be termed "the father of petroleum engineering") was a self-taught civil engineer and geologist, but he was one of the first to describe in written form the problems involved in assembling accurate drilling data. He also performed crude experiments in capillary action, pointed out possible benefits of water flooding, and outlined various other phases and aspects of what are today fundamentals in petroleum engineering.

Arthur John Phinney, a geologist, describing "The Natural Gas Fields of Indiana" in the 11th Annual Report of the United States Geological Survey, 1891, states: "These substances, however, arrange themselves in the order of their specific gravities. The water being heaviest seeks the lowest point; the petroleum takes its position above the water, while the gas, being lightest of all, seeks the highest point attainable." On p. 657, Phinney states: "The relation between rock texture and flow is proved by the behavior of the wells."

Other evidence of early engineering thinking about drilling practices is found on p. 102, Part 6, of the 19th Annual Report of the U.S.G.S., 1897-98, where it is stated, concerning the Corsicana, Texas, field: "Some of the wells have been put down by a rotary drill. The bit, with projecting wings, is secured to the end of the tubing, and water is pumped through it, escaping out of the sides of the bit and washing the loosened material on the outside of the tubing to the surface. This is a rapid and cheap method of sinking wells and is generally successful, unless solid rock or boulders are encountered, but it is objectionable owing to the heavy water pressure put on the oil sand in drilling it."

The blowing out of the Lucas gusher at Spindletop in 1901 was an historic petroleum engineering problem; and Capt. Anthony F. Lucas, an engineer who had been educated in Austria—previously employed as a mining engineer in Louisiana, and then engaged in drilling his second test well in search of oil at the "Big Hill"—was equal to the emergency. It was under his direct supervision that the well was brought under control. The manner in which this was accomplished was described by him in detail at a meeting of the American Institute of Mining and Metallurgical Engineers at Richmond, Virginia, in February 1901 *(Trans.* **XXXI***)*.

During the first decade of the present century, geologists working with the United States Geological Survey evidenced a concept of engineering in connection with the production of oil wells in advance of the general knowledge of the times. In *Bull. 213: Contributions to Economic Geology,* 1902, C. W. Hayes stated: ". . . the gas should never be allowed to escape freely from an oil pool, for, aside from the waste of a valuable fuel, the force needed to expel the oil is at the same time being lost." In *Bull. 321: Geology and Oil Resources of the Summerland District, Santa Barbara County, California,* 1907, Ralph Arnold discussed costs of drilling and producing, the treating of oil, etc. In *Bull. 357: Preliminary Report on the Coalinga Oil District, Fresno and Kings Counties, California,* 1908, by Ralph Arnold and Robert Anderson, it was pointed out that: "In order to avoid the dangers incident to faulty drilling and handling of wells, the operators should meet and exchange information about the underground geology." Such men were the advance guard of the legions later to be known as petroleum engineers.

Evidence of the adaptation of other types of engineering to the production and movement of petroleum was furnished in 1905, when Gulf Oil Corporation ". . . directed George S. Davison, an expert in water problems with no previous oil experience, to design and construct a pipe line from the newly discovered Glenn Pool, in Oklahoma, to Port Arthur, Texas." (Gulf Oil Corporation memo.)

The first foundations of petroleum engineering as a distinct profession were laid in California. E. T. Dumble, chief geologist for the Southern Pacific Railroad Company, was also president of the Kern Trading and Oil Company, the California division of which was under the direction of F. M. Anderson, a graduate from Willamette in Oregon in 1889, with M. E. Lombardi—a mining engineer—the head of the drilling division, and "Cy" McLaughlin—a geologist—directing oil operations. In the spring of 1907, Anderson employed five graduates of the department of geology and mining at Stanford University and assigned them to various oil fields for the purpose of collecting well information and doing area geology. Shortly afterward, in 1908, the Associated Oil Company, in California, organized a geological department under the direction of W. R. Hamilton, a graduate of Stanford University. He was followed by W. A. Williams, also a graduate of Stanford University, who was later to become the first chief petroleum technologist for the Petroleum and Natural Gas Division of the Bureau of Mines. Paul Paine and Ben Lindsly, graduates of Massachusetts Institute of Technology, worked as geologists for the Honolulu Oil Company at North Midway and at Buena Vista Hills, California, and used peg models to depict certain underground conditions.

It was in the second decade of the century, however, that petroleum engineering began to be a recognized profession and the sources of its men to come more clearly into focus. As this period opened, men technically trained in various universities were employed in many oil fields, chiefly in California. These men, although generally classed as geologists, frequently found themselves devoting as much as 80 percent or more of their time to problems of an engineering nature. They included such civil engineers, mining engineers, geologists, etc. as R. D. Bush, E. G. Gaylord, R. P. McLaughlin, R. B. Moran, Chester Naramore, E. B. Latham, R. S. Haseltine, F. B. Tough, and others, their ranks increasing from year to year as such men as Col. George C. Burrell, E. W. Dean, E. DeGolyer, E. L. Estabrook, John Lovejoy, A. W. Peake, and John Suman entered the oil industry as newly graduated geologists or engineers or transferred to the industry from other occupations. Most of these men, although classed as "resident geologists," "exploitation geologists," or "resident engineers" were acting as petroleum engineers.

The United States Geological Survey had, for many years, reported on production of oil and gas and problems of the industry, but in 1910 the United States Bureau of Mines was organized to take over the work for all mining operations. J. A. Holmes, the first director, charted the course of the new Bureau and was instrumental in advancing engineering studies in the petroleum industry. Much consideration was given at first to such problems as gas wastage, and the early publications show that serious thought and study were devoted to safety measures and prevention of waste. It was not long, however, before detailed studies were being made of cementing procedures, casing seats, and other problems dealing with water intrusion; and in 1913 engineers of the Bureau were assigned to the Cushing, Oklahoma, field at the height of the boom there to study drilling problems.

By the middle of this decade, a few of the leaders of the oil industry began to realize the worth of the trained technician in oil-field operations, and the American Institute of Mining and Metallurgical Engineers created an Oil and Gas Committee where papers of importance to the industry could be presented and discussed. The Petroleum and Natural Gas Division of the Bureau of Mines was beginning to prove its value to companies and to individual operators; the California Legislature set up the Division of Oil and Gas within the State Mining Bureau; various institutions of higher learning began to offer courses which developed into petroleum engineering; and some companies began to train men for specialized engineering positions.

The Oil and Gas Committee of the American Institute of Mining Engineers was created in 1913 with Capt. Anthony F. Lucas as its first chairman, and listed such distinguished members as Ralph Arnold, David T. Day, Frederick G. Clapp, Edwin T. Dumble, John R. Edwards, R. S. Haseltine, Phillip W. Henry, Walter O. Snelling, William L. Watts, H. A. Wheeler, and W. A. Williams. This was the first open forum where papers dealing with geological and engineering phases of the oil industry could be presented for open discussion, and through it we can trace the growth of petroleum engineering and sources of its engineers. The following AIME papers of this period are of particular significance:

Vol. LI (1915) :   "The Role and Fate of Connate Water in Oil and Gas Sands," Roswell H. Johnson, Professor, Oil and Gas Production, University of Pittsburgh.

"Comparative Costs of Rotary and Standard Drilling," M. L. Requa.

Vol. LII (1915) : "The Cost of Maintaining Production in California Oil Fields", M. E. Lombardi, Superintendent of Construction and Development, Kern Trading and Oil Company.

"Protecting California Oil Fields from Infiltration Water", R. P. McLaughlin, State Oil and Gas Supervisor.

Vol. LIV (1916) : "The Control of Petroleum and Natural Gas Wells," Alfred G. Heggem, M. E., Tulsa, Okla., *Petroleum Engineer*. (*Note*: This is the first time the designation of "Petroleum Engineer" is affixed to the name of an author.)

In Vol. LVI (1916-17) W. R. Hamilton, A.B., is listed as a Petroleum and Mining Engineer, William H. Kobbe as Petroleum Engineer, and Dorsey Hager as a Petroleum Geologist and Engineer. In Vol. LVII (1917) Carl H. Beal is listed as a Petroleum Technologist, and V. R. Garfias is listed as Assistant Professor, Petroleum Engineering, Stanford University. The dividing line between a petroleum geologist and a petroleum engineer, or a mining engineer and a petroleum engineer was difficult to determine at the time of World War I.

The Petroleum and Natural Gas Division of the Bureau of Mines, officially recognized as a unit on July 1, 1914, with W. A. Williams as chief petroleum technologist, was to prove a most outstanding source of petroleum engineers in the early days of the profession. The influence exerted by these early engineers is well-expressed by H. C. Fowler in *Bureau of Mines Information Circular No. 6737, 1933*, where he states: "During the first years of the Petroleum Division of the Bureau of Mines there were few petroleum technologists in the employ of the oil companies, and, in addition to their basic studies, engineers of the Bureau were called upon to render all manner of service to the companies, frequently taking direct charge of the work, with the consent of the operators, in an effort to bring about corrective measures or improved methods."

Another source of petroleum engineers—and a most important one in the early days of the profession—was the Division of Oil and Gas in the State Mining Bureau of California. This division, a pioneer in the regulation of field operations by a state agency, was set up by the passage of legislation in 1915, and its regulations concerning the exclusion of water in oil wells became the accepted standards for oil-field practice everywhere. The events leading up to the passage of California's conservation law, which did so much to accelerate the use of engineering in production practice by the oil industry, are therefore of interest and of importance historically.

Mention has been made of the fact that as early as 1907 and 1908 the Kern Trading and Oil Company and the Associated Oil Company began to employ geologists in connection with their operations. These men, accustomed to the detailed practices of engineering, began the collection of data relative to underground conditions and their relationship to the behavior and production of oil, gas, and water and to the general behavior of producing wells. Through the assembly and correlation of such data it was gradually recognized by them that encroaching waters and expanding gas had a part in the mechanism of oil production, and that control of these factors might have something to do with more efficient and more complete extraction. Other operators became cognizant of underground losses resulting from failure to exclude water in oil-bearing formations, and a group of operators in Coalinga Field, where water troubles were particularly bad, banded together in an informal association and employed an engineer (M. J. Kirwan) to advise them concerning problems of shutting off water. A large majority of the oil-field operators at that time did not employ any technical help and consequently had no one competent to work out subsurface correlations and to solve water problems.

Realizing that concerted action might be a benefit to all, some efforts were made in California to obtain a law authorizing the formation of districts similar to irrigation districts, which would have been empowered to regulate certain activities in oil-field operations in each district. That this movement failed to obtain general support is said to have been due to the fact that small operators feared the domination of large companies. At about the same time, a comprehensive study of the oil industry in the state was made by the California State Mining Bureau which had followed developments of the industry within the state and had issued several reports covering different fields. These activities, together with the realization that beneficial results were accruing to those companies employing geologists and engineers, and the belief by many that the utilization of sound engineering practices by all would be of benefit to the entire industry culminated in the passage of an act in 1915 intended to control oil-field operations. Men engaged in the industry in California at the time advise that Roy P. McLaughlin, chief of the Petroleum Department of the State Mining Bureau was the "spark plug of the movement" that led to the passage of the law. This act provided for the appointment of a state oil and gas supervisor and a number of deputies, each of whom should be either a geologist or an engineer, and conferred ". . . authority to supervise the drilling, operation, and maintenance and abandonment of petroleum or gas wells in the State of California so as to prevent, as far as possible, damage to underground petroleum and gas deposits from the infiltration of water . . . and the loss of petroleum and natural gas." The entire cost of administration of this act was assessed against the oil companies so there was no opposition to it from a tax standpoint.

R. P. McLaughlin became the first oil and gas supervisor under the new law and he immediately filled the posts of deputy supervisors with qualified engineers and insisted that they require the oil companies to meet the requirements of the Bureau. As expressed by McLaughlin, "That . . . the State Mining Bureau Law, as it was generally called, did actually prove workable and was made to serve its purpose is due in large part to the good fortune of the supervisor in being able to find available several competent and enthusiastic young engineers who went into the field as deputies. They were stationed directly at the scenes of operation of the oil fields and had authority to make final decisions . . ." Under the terms of the new law, operators were required to file intentions to drill, logs of wells, production data, etc., and to receive approval of all major drilling and abandonment operations. It was therefore incumbent upon the operators to collect and correlate information pertaining to field operations. This work could best be done by trained technicians, and the early idea of some of the "practical oil men" that ". . . a petroleum engineer was a geologist who had seen an oil derrick . . ." gave way gradually to the realization that engineering methods actually paid profits in dollars and cents.

After 1917 more men with geological and engineering training were employed by California operators, and many young engineers, upon returning from military service, found that an entirely new and expanding field of employment had been opened up during their absence. Those early field engineers, together with such early deputy supervisors as J. B. Case, R. E. Collom, M. J. Kirwan, R. B. Moran, Chester Naramore, and others, pioneered in furnishing trained engineers to the petroleum industry and to the Bureau of Mines. The importance of the training given oil-field engineers employed by the California State Mining Bureau is well exemplified by the fact that by 1920 the Bureau was finding it difficult to locate new men to replace the trained engineers hired from it by the various oil companies. The thoroughness of the training of its engineers and a complete history of its early petroleum engineering work, together with subsequent operations, are well set forth in the publications of the Division which have been continuous since 1915.

While the earliest members of the new profession of petroleum engineering were generally geologists or mining engineers, the teaching of courses in the geology of oil, in oil and gas law, and in similar subjects, together with the increasing demand for men trained specifically for engineering in the petroleum industry, combined in the development and adoption of curricula leading to a degree in petroleum engineering.

Concurrently with the establishment in 1910 of the Bureau of Mines, which has been such a bulwark of petroleum engineering, was the offering that year by the University of Pittsburgh of three courses in oil and gas and three courses in oil and gas law. These courses, the first to be offered dealing directly with the oil and gas industry, were the forerunners of others to follow. In the 10 years which followed, and prior to 1920, other universities and colleges were to offer courses intended to assist those interested in oil development, but only two—the University of Pittsburgh and the University of California—established Departments of Petroleum Engineering or adopted a full undergraduate curriculum in that branch of engineering.*

Subsequent to the early courses at the University of Pittsburgh, M.M. Valerius requested a course in petroleum geology at the Missouri School of Mines, which had no such course at that time. Complying with his request, however, V. H. McNutt, a young geology instructor, was assigned to instruct Valerius. The following year, the school offered elective courses in petroleum geology, and in 1914 it added a course in petroleum-production methods.

"Oil and gas geology" was given as a new course at the University of Pittsburgh by Roswell H. Johnson in 1912. E. B. Durham gave a course in petroleum technology at the University of California in 1913 and the first courses in a new 4-year curriculum in petroleum engineering were given there by L. C. Uren in 1915. In 1914, V. R. Garfias was lecturing on courses in "Technology of Petroleum" at Stanford University. In 1916, the University of West Virginia offered a course in oil and gas engineering; the Colorado School of Mines offered a course in petroleum geology; Oklahoma A. & M. College offered a course in petroleum technology, with C. K. Francis as instructor; and a short course of lectures dealing with petroleum geology and oil production, refining, and marketing was announced by Kendall College (predecessor to the University of Tulsa); and in 1918 a course in petroleum chemistry was added at Colorado School of Mines. Indication of the reasons for interest in these new courses is found in the following excerpt from the *Twenty-Sixth Annual Catalogue*, 1916-1917, of Oklahoma A. & M. College relative to the course to be given in petroleum technology: "This is a special course the purpose of which is to train men for positions in the petroleum industry. There is a great demand for young men properly prepared, so that those who complete the work have no difficulty in securing positions at good salaries. It is advisable that those who propose to elect this course should have previous work in chemistry and physics, and if possible should have had the first courses in surveying, drawing and the elements of mechanical engineering."

It was at the University of Pittsburgh, however, that the first degrees in petroleum engineering were conferred, and the following summary of the origin of the department there and the transition from courses dealing with the fundamentals in petroleum engineering to courses identified as petroleum engineering, is based on information by H. G. Botset, the present head of the department, by Geo. M. Bevier and E. H. Sloan who graduated just prior to the inauguration of the

---

*The information which follows with respect to the development of education in petroleum engineering has been secured from a questionnaire forwarded to some 20-odd universities and colleges as supplemented by personal communications and by data previously published in *Transactions* of the AIME, *The Oil and Gas Journal, World Oil (Oil Weekly), The Petroleum Engineer,* and *Finding and Producing Oil* (API, 1939).

degree of Petroleum Engineer, and by F. Arthur Johnson, the first American to receive such degree.

According to Botset, "The School of Mines at the University was granting the Geological engineering degree in 1910. During this year, three courses in petroleum and natural gas were taught by the Mining Engineering School. These courses covered the origin, distribution and exploitation of petroleum. Three courses in oil and gas law were also offered that year. At this time, Dr. M. E. Wadsworth was professor of Mining Geology and presumably taught these courses. In 1910 a course was taught by H. B. Meller in drilling and well survey. There was also a graduate program of research in petroleum and natural gas in the year 1910. In 1912 Roswell Johnson was listed as Assistant Professor of Oil and Gas Mining. In this year there was established an oil and gas laboratory in which the students studied the effect of capillarity and hydraulics on oil accumulation. There was also a seminar in oil and gas which covered current developments in that area. In 1912 we find listed the first course specifically in the production of oil and gas. It was a four-credit course running two semesters and covering drilling, leasing, pumping, shooting, storage, and transportation. In this year there was also offered a five-credit course in the examination of oil and gas properties. In the 1912-13 bulletin, Oil and Gas was listed as a separate division in the School of Mines, and 5 separate courses in this field were offered. It appears to be the equivalent of today's petroleum option in Mining Engineering, carrying a separate curriculum during the junior and senior years."

In the 1914-1915 bulletin, petroleum engineering was listed as a separate department granting the degree of Petroleum Engineer, and 12 courses were offered in the field of oil and gas, with Roswell H. Johnson, full professor of oil and gas, head of the department, and with L. G. Hunt-ley, E.M., listed as a lecturer on foreign oil fields. The purpose of the petroleum engineering course was aptly stated in the following quotation from the University of Pittsburgh School of Mines *Bulletin,* 1914:

"The courses in oil and gas are planned to equip men to (a) determine the relative chances of success in finding oil and gas by drilling at different points; (b) methods by which wells are most efficiently spaced, drilled and operated; (c) methods by which the business of oil and gas production is transacted. So much of the oil and gas industry is carried on by crude and ineffcient methods that a technical training in these lines greatly increases the efficiency of the worker as compared with the usual training by imitation alone. The practice in the summers is an important part of the work. In the first and second summers the student ordinarily works on an oil lease; in the third he will work as a geologic aid on the

Federal or a State Survey, or again in prospective or developed properties.

"There are two courses—one leading to specialization in prospecting, the geological option, and the other leading to specialization in operation. The second may be modified further by those specializing in the business aspects of the oil industry. Students desiring to specialize in petroleum refining, will find courses outlined under Chemical Engineering."

As expressed by Botset, "It would appear that the men who established this petroleum engineering curriculum were well in advance of their time, as is indicated by their attention in laboratory work to capillary forces as a factor in reservoir performance."

Prior to the organization of the department, courses dealing with oil and gas geology or petroleum geology, according to Bevier, ". . . consisted of studies of the various geological formations and different types of structures, geology field trips, estimation of oil and gas reserves and a study of the different types of drilling equipment and production methods." Such courses, given by Prof. Johnson, enabled one, as expressed by Sloan, ". . . to hire out as a Petroleum Geologist to the oil companies who were using geology at that time."

The first petroleum engineering degree was granted in 1915, and the graduating class of that year included 8 students from the School of Mines, 4 of whom were enrolled in the oil and gas course and could select the degree of petroleum engineer should they so desire. The 4 were: "Chun Young Chan, Canton, China . . . Frederick Arthur Johnson, New Castle, Pa. . . . Baerin Y Long, Szechin, China" and "George W. Meyers, Lancaster, Pa." "After discussion of the relative merits of a Petroleum Engineer or Engineer of Mines degree George W. Meyers decided to accept the degree of Engineer of Mines on the basis of its world wide honorable acceptance. The remaining three decided to cast our lot with the then unknown." With respect to the education of a petroleum engineer, and his early experiences, the following additional excerpts from a communication from F. A. Johnson are of interest:

". . . during an interview relative my first job in the oil industry . . . a Standard Oil official inquired—What is a petroleum engineer? . . .

"The foundation of the petroleum engineer then as today constituted the basic studies. Recalling my personal experience these included all engineering mathematics, analytical mechanics, mechanics of materials, graphic statics and graphics, chemistry, qualitative and quantitative analysis, mining methods and metallurgy, structural and historical geology, economic geology, a thorough course in mineralogy, petrology and invertebrate paleontology and the languages . . .

"The road of the petroleum engineer like that of the geologist was not easy in the early days when both, practicing in the same field of geology, endeavored to convince the hard headed oil operator that he was a useful asset in his business. . . .

"Probably the first turning point to a somewhat general acceptance of the petroleum engineer in the oil industry arrived in the early part of the year 1919 when the United States Treasury Department under the direction of Dr. Ralph Arnold called together men of the industry to formulate methods for the determination of an oil and gas tax structure, (involving consideration for discovery) . . . He demonstrated the usefulness of his curves to officials and operators and thus helped the oil industry and himself at the same time . . . Today the petroleum engineer takes his place in the oil and gas industry from the standpoint of merit . . .

"The three degrees in petroleum engineering were granted by the University of Pittsburgh at commencement exercises June 16, 1915."

Information relative to certain other schools of higher learning important as sources of petroleum engineers is summarized following.

University of California, Berkeley, Calif.

The first classes of petroleum engineering type taught there were in 1913, and the first 4-year complete undergraduate course in petroleum engineering was offered there in 1915 "as a curriculum in the College of Mining," its purpose being "to prepare engineers for the oil industry."

The first head of this "division" was L. C. Uren, a graduate of the College of Mining, University of California, who had previously been engaged in both teaching and industry practice.

The "division" specialized in "Petroleum Production Engineering (embracing all engineering operations in oil-field exploitation)." It participates in research work covering "all problems encountered in any phase of oil-field exploitation."

Degrees offered by the division are B.S., M.S., M.Eng., P.E., and Ph.D.

Colorado School of Mines, Golden, Colo.

The Petroleum Engineering Department started "as a course in petroleum geology in 1916 and in petroleum chemistry in 1918." The Department was organized in 1922 because "Dr. V. C. Alderson, President, was very much interested in the oil industry." "Max Ball, who became a trustee to the School in 1923, strongly supported Dr. Alderson in his efforts to establish courses in petroleum technology."

The first head of the department W. H. Kirby, formerly engaged in industry as ". . . a pipe line builder."

The department was organized to instruct in all branches of petroleum engineering, including refining. It participates in research work with respect to general production problems.

Degrees offered by the department are P.E. and M.S.

University of Houston, Houston, Texas

The first classes in petroleum engineering taught there were in 1945.

The department was organized in 1947 when "The first department chairman, by means of correspondence, visits, and personal conversation with educational and industry personnel, laid out the curriculum." It was organized "to better meet the demand of industry."

The first head of the department was C. V. Kirkpatrick, a graduate in petroleum production engineering at Texas A. and M., and who had previously been engaged in industry practice.

The department placed early emphasis on reservoir development and control. It participates in research work with respect to problems dealing with reservoirs, electric logging, and gas lift.

Degrees offered by the department are B.S. and M.S.

University of Kansas, Lawrence, Kans.

The first classes in petroleum engineering taught there were in 1937, when the department was organized with a full 4-year course. It was organized "to meet requirements set out by the State Board of Regents."

The first head of the department was Eugene A. Stephenson, a graduate of Adrian College and of the University of Chicago. He had previously been engaged both in teaching and in industry practice.

The department placed early emphasis on "Primary Reservoir Engineering." It participates in research work with respect to problems dealing with reservoir engineering and secondary recovery.

Degrees offered by the department are B.S., M.S., and Ph.D.

Louisiana State University, Baton Rouge, La.

The first classes of petroleum engineering type taught there were through the Geology Department, in 1924.

49

The Petroleum Engineering Department was organized by Dr. Henry V. Howe in 1927 "to teach courses in Petroleum Engineering."

The first and present head of the department was B. C. Craft, a graduate of Stanford University in mining engineering, and previously engaged in industry practice.

The department placed early emphasis on drilling and production methods. It participates in research work with respect to reservoir engineering and oil-field exploitation.

Degrees offered by the department are B.S. and M.S.

Missouri School of Mines and Metallurgy, Rolla, Mo.

The first class of petroleum engineering type there was taught in 1912 as a course in petroleum geology.

The department was organized in 1922 when "many of our graduates in Mining and Geology were entering the Petroleum industry. These students were asking for instruction in Petroleum, and courses were organized . . . to meet demands of industry."

The first head of the department was C. R. Forbes, a graduate of Michigan College of Mines and previously engaged both in teaching and industry practice.

"The department offers curricula in both Petroleum Engineering and Petroleum Engineering with a Geology option. The latter is a geological engineering curriculum with emphasis on petroleum. The department participates in research dealing with production and reservoir problems including secondary recovery."

Degrees offered by the department are B.S., M.S., and Ph.D

New Mexico Institute of Mining and Technology, Socorro, N.M.

The first classes in petroleum engineering were taught there in 1935.

The department was organized in 1935 as an outgrowth of petroleum geology and in order to meet student demand.

The first head of the department was G. T. Harley, a graduate of the New Mexico School of Mines and previously engaged in teaching.

The department did not place emphasis on any particular branch of petroleum engineering, and it does not participate in research work.

It offers the degree of B.S. in P.E.

The Ohio State University, Columbus, Ohio

"Professor E. V. O'Rourke started teaching petroleum courses in 1926, and gradually expanded his offerings." In 1950, the Department of Mines Engineering was changed to Department of Mining and Petroleum Engineering, and the previous option in petroleum engineering was changed to a full curriculum.

The first head of the present Petroleum Engineering Department was Tell Ertl, a graduate of the University of Washington and of Columbia University. He had previously been engaged both in teaching and in industry practice.

The department covers all branches of petroleum engineering, and it participates in research work with respect to problems relating to reservoir engineering, Ohio production, and drilling.

Degrees offered by the department are Bachelor of Petroleum Engineering, Bachelor of Mining Engineering, and M.Sc.

University of Oklahoma, Norman, Okla.

Classes in petroleum engineering were first taught there in 1924, when the department was organized to meet "a desire among oil companies for something in addition to Geologists."

The first head of the department was H. C. George, a mining engineer with degrees from Pennsylvania State and the University of Pittsburgh and previously engaged in industry practice, including work with the U. S. Bureau of Mines.

The department did not specialize in any particular branch but covered drilling, production, and refining. It participates in research work on problems relating to production, secondary recovery, flow of fluids and reservoir mechanics.

Degrees offered by the department are B.S. and M.S.

University of Southern California, Los Angeles, Calif.

Classes of a petroleum engineering type were first taught in 1926 in the Geological Department.

The Petroleum Engineering Department was organized in 1929 "to fill the need of developing engineers for handling technical problems in petroleum production."

The first head of the department was John Franklin Dodge, a graduate of the University of California and of the University of Southern California. He had previously been engaged in both teaching and industry.

The department was organized to include all phases of petroleum engineering; and it participates in research work relating to problems in relative permeability, drilling fluids, completion practice, and oil recovery.

Degrees offered are B.E., M.E., and Ph.D.

Stanford University, Stanford, Calif.

The first designated "petroleum technology" courses given were by V. R. Garfias in 1914, and consisted of a series of lectures covering, among other things, reservoir behavior as controlled by geological conditions.

The Petroleum Engineering Division was established as a curriculum about 1921 in the Department of Mining Engineering and the School of Mineral Sciences, and is now a division of the School of Mineral Sciences. The head of the Mining Engineering Department in 1921 was Theodore J. Hoover, a graduate of Stanford University and previously engaged in industry practice. The first head of the petroleum engineering curriculum was Frederick G. Tickell, a graduate of the University of California and previously engaged in industry practice.

The division was intended to include all branches or phases of petroleumn engineering, and it participates in research work with respect to problems in reservoir engineering.

Degrees offered by the School of Mineral Sciences are M.S., E.M., and Ph.D.

Agricultural and Mechanical College of Texas, College Station, Texas

Classes in petroleum engineering were first taught there in 1929, following the organization of the department to meet the need of engineers technically trained for the petroleum industry.

The first head of the department was J. B. Joyce, a graduate of the college, who had previously been engaged in industry practice, particularly in refining.

The department was originally called the Department of Petroleum Production Engineering, and was intended to include all branches of such engineering. It engages in research work dealing with problems in production.

Degrees offered by the department are B.S., M.S., B.P.E., and Ph.D.

Texas College of Arts and Industry, Kingsville, Texas

This school specialized in natural-gas engineering, which was first taught there following the organization of the Petroleum and Natural Gas Engineering Section in 1936.

The section was organized so that ". . . specialized engineers, trained primarily in natural-gas operations, would be available as the industry developed."

The first professor of the Petroleum and Natural Gas Section was Frank H. Dotterweich, a graduate of Johns Hopkins University, and previously engaged in industry practice.

The section specializes in natural-gas engineering and engages in research relating thereto.

Degrees offered by the department are B.S. and M.S. (Petroleum and Natural Gas Engineering).

Texas Technological College, Lubbock, Texas

The first classes in petroleum engineering taught there were in 1939.

The Department of Petroleum Engineering was organized in 1948 at the request of industry and of students of the college.

The first head of the department was W. L. Ducker, a graduate of the University of Oklahoma and previously engaged in industry practice. The department specialized at first in production and natural-gas options. It participates in research work dealing with various drilling and production problems.

Degrees offered by the department are B.S. and M.S., and B.A.

The University of Texas, Austin, Texas

The first classes in petroleum engineering were taught in 1928, and were given by Dr. E. H. Sellards of the Bureau of Economic Geology and by Dr. E. P. Schoch of the Department of Chemistry.

The Petroleum Engineering Department was formed in 1930, following the adoption in 1929 of a formal curriculum which included graduate as well as undergraduate work.

The first chairman of the department was F. B. Plummer, a graduate of Dartmouth, who had received additional training as a graduate student in chemistry and geology at the University of Chicago, and who had formerly been engaged both in industry practice and in teaching.

The department was organized to include all phases of petroleum engineering. It participates in research work covering problems dealing with primary and secondary recovery, drilling, salt-water disposal, reservoir engineering, and applied chemistry.

Degrees offered by the department are B.S. in P.E., M.S. in P.E., and Ph.D.

The University of Tulsa, Tulsa, Okla.

The first classes of a petroleum engineering type taught at Kendall College, the predecessor school, consisted of a short course of lectures dealing with petroleum geology, oil production, etc., announced in December 1916.

The Petroleum Engineering Department was organized in September 1928 ". . . because of general interest in the petroleum industry in Tulsa and the Mid-Continent area."

The first head of the department was R. C. Beckstrom, a graduate of the University of Nebraska and of the University of Oklahoma. He had previously been engaged both in teaching and in industry practice.

The department was started as an undergraduate course and did not specialize at first, although it concentrated on production. It participates in research work in problems dealing with all phases of production.

Degrees offered by the department are B.S. in P.E., M.P.E., and M.S. in P.E.

West Virginia University, Morgantown, W. Va.

The first classes of the petroleum engineering type taught were in 1915, and in 1916 courses were given in oil and gas engineering. The Petroleum Engineering Department started as an oil and gas option in mining engineering, and was organized in 1926 as a petroleum engineering option "to meet the demand for petroleum engineers by the oil and gas industry in the State of West Virginia."

The first head of the department was C. E. Lawall, a graduate of Lehigh University. He had previously been engaged both in teaching and in industry practice.

The department specialized at first in discovery, production, and transportation. It participates in research work with respect to production and gas-measurement problems.

Degrees offered by the department are B.S.E.M. (petroleum engineering option) and M.S.E.M. (petroleum engineering option).

Other institutions of higher learning in which petroleum engineering is taught include:

Montana School of Mines, which has a petroleum option in mining engineering.

*Oklahoma A. and M.,** where a course in petroleum engineering is an option in mining engineering.

Pennsylvania State College,† where petroleum engineering is represented by a division of the School of Mineral Industries.

University of Alabama, where a petroleum engineering curriculum was first announced in 1941 as a division of the College of Engineering.

University of Illinois, where petroleum engineering is recognized as a phase of mechanical engineering, and some specialized courses in petroleum geology are offered in the Department of Geology.

University of Minnesota, where petroleum engineering courses are a part of the Department of Mining and Petroleum Engineering.

University of North Dakota, which has a petroleum branch in the School of Engineering.

---

*Designated *Oklahoma State University* in 1958.
†Designated *Pennsylvania State University* in 1954.

Among the first to inaugurate a program of training men for specialized engineering positions was Henry L. Doherty, under whose direction the Doherty Training School was organized and operated out of the Empire Gas & Fuel Company offices at Bartlesville, Okla., beginning in the summer of 1916. The purpose of this training school was "... to train graduates from the various technical and engineering schools in the United States, through employment as Junior Engineers in the Doherty Training School, in the oil and gas business as operated by the Empire companies throughout the Mid-Continent fields." In connection with the Doherty Training School it was pointed out that the type of educated and trained men needed are:

"1. Men who when trained can help to protect our investments by proper construction and operation, by courteous and straightforward dealing with investors, customers, the public, state and municipal authorities, regulatory bodies and fellow employees.

"2. Men who can aid in the development and extension of our markets through rendering the best of service and through the most economical utilization of resources.

"3. Men who can help solve problems, technical and human, and can meet situations as they develop.

"We naturally choose graduates in mechanical, electrical, civil and chemical engineering as well as graduates from geological courses as being best suited to our training work as they will have to deal with men and affairs, meeting, pleasing and convincing these with whom they deal. Men are desired who are sound mentally, morally, and physically and who will develop through the exercise of initiative, tact and cooperation as engineers, leaders and executives; men who think straight and act promptly, effectively and justly; men who can quickly familiarize themselves with all the factors of a situation and then form sound judgement and who have the ability to express these judgments so as to convince others."

The petroleum engineer of today is a result of the need, which became very apparent early in this century, for men capable of devising and putting into practice in the oil industry more efficient methods of exploration and production than had previously been used. It was in this period, when serious thought was being given to technical problems of petroleum production by everyone concerned with the industry, that *Oil Production Methods* was written by Paul Paine and Ben Stroud in 1913; *Principles of Oil and Gas Production* was written by Roswell Johnson and L. G. Huntley in 1916; *Petroleum Production Methods* was written by John Suman, and *Deep Well Drilling* by Walter Jeffery, in 1921; and the first designated petroleum engineering textbook, *Petroleum Production Engineering*, was written by L. C. Uren in 1924.

Of equal importance, however, in assisting the petroleum-engineer-to-be were various publications of the United States Bureau of Mines, including such classics as *The Decline and Ultimate Production of Oil Wells, with Notes on the Valuation of Oil Properties*, by C. H. Beal in 1919; *Underground Conditions in Oil Fields*, by A. W. Ambrose in 1921; and *Function of Natural Gas in the Production of Oil*, published by the American Petroleum Institute in 1929.

The half dozen American institutions of higher learning offering degrees in engineering a century ago have increased more than 25-fold, and the 150-odd such institutions today are graduating some 20,000 professional engineers annually, many of whom are to be found in one phase or another of the petroleum industry. Even with this tremendous upsurge in engineering education, however, it should be borne in mind that many valuable additions to the technology of petroleum engineering have come from the driller, the roughneck, the roustabout, operators in machine shops, blacksmiths, and others. Not only the universities and highly developed research organizations, but every group of oil-field workmen must be classed as actual or potential sources of petroleum engineers.

Evidence of the varying sources of college-trained petroleum engineers today is furnished by statistics from one large oil-producing company. This company reports that of 95 production engineers employed by it and having Bachelor degrees—17 being supervisory and 78 non-supervisory employees—5 of the supervisory and 32 of the non-supervisory engineers are petroleum engineers; 4 supervisory and 14 non-supervisory are mechanical engineers; and the remaining 8 supervisory and 32 non-supervisory engineers represent chemical, civil, electrical, and other branches of engineering. The group of 95 represents students from 38 schools or colleges.

A list of early petroleum engineers, including men who practiced such engineering or completed their studies in the period after the discovery of the Drake well and prior to 1920 is given in Table 1.

Table 1
Early Petroleum Engineers
(1860-1920)

Name	School or University	Degrees	Year	Degree In, or Major Interest
Adams, H. H.	Bucknell	B.S.	1907	
Albertson, N. M.	Chicago	B.S.	1913	Geology and Mining
		E.M.	1914	
Ambrose, A. W.	Leland Stanford	A.B.	1914	Geology
		E.M.	1920	
Ames, Elmer R.	Leland Stanford	A.B.; C.E.	1917	
Anderson, F. M.	Willamette (Oregon)	A.B.	1889	Geology
	California	M.S.	1897	
Anderson, H. H.	California	M.E.	1914	Engineering
Arnold, Ralph	Leland Stanford	A.B.	1889	Geology
		A.M.	1900	
		Ph.D.	1902	

56

Table 1 (Cont'd)

Name	School or University	Degrees	Year	Degree In, or Major Interest
Baden, Martin W.	Southwestern College	A.B.		
Baker, R. C.	....			
Ball, Max W.	Colorado School of Mines	E.M.	1906	Geology and Mining
Barkis, Bruce	California	E.M.	1916	Mining Engineering
Barnes, Roy M.	California	B.S.	1917	Geology
Beal, Carl H.	Leland Stanford	A.B.	1912	Geology
		A.M.	1915	
Beall, K. E.	Purdue	B.S.	1919	Electrical Engineering
Beecher, C. E.	Leland Stanford	B.S.	1913	Civil Engineering
		Engr.	1914	
Bell, A. H.	California School of Mechanical Arts	....	1909	
Bennett, E. O.	Leland Stanford	A.B.	1916	Engineering
		M.E.	1919	
Bevier, George M.	Pittsburgh	B.S.	1914	Geology-Petroleum
Biddison, P. McD.	Kansas State Agricultural College	B.S.	1904	Electrical Engineering
Blatchley, R. S.	Indiana	A.B.	1908	Chemistry and Geology
Borden, G. S.	California	B.S.	1918	
Bossler, R. B.	Pittsburgh	B.S.	1918	PETROLEUM ENGINEERING
Bowie, C. P.	California	B.S.	1904	Engineering
Brantly, J. E.	Alabama	B.S.	1911	
		E.M.	1912	
Briggs, Robert M.	?	?		
Brunel, L. J.	California	B.S.	1916	
Bryan, Barnabas	Leland Stanford	B.S.	1909	
Burling, Lancaster D.	Wisconsin	B.S.	1905	Engineering
Burrell, George	Ohio State	....	1904	Chemical Engineering
Burrell, Logan	?	?		
Bush, R. D.	California	....	1909	Civil Engineering and Geology
Campbell, E. P.	Leland Stanford	C.E.	1911	Engineering
Carll, John F.	....			
Cattell, R. A.	California	B.S.	1912	Civil Engineering
Cavins, O. A.	California	E.M.	1915	Mining Engineering
Chan, C. Y.	Pittsburgh	B.S.	1915	PETROLEUM ENGINEERING
Christie, L. G.	California	B.S.	1920	PETROLEUM ENGINEERING
Clapp, Frederick G.	Massachusetts Institute of Technology	B.S.	1901	Geology
Collom, R. E.	Leland Stanford	A.B.	1906	Geology and Mining
Comins, D.	Royal Military Academy (England)	....	1915	
Corless, George	Michigan	A.B.	1911	Geology and Engineering
		A.M.	1912	
Coste, Eugene	?	?		
Cottrell, F. G.	California	B.S.	**1896**	
Cox, Thomas M.	....			
Cowell, T. R.	Pittsburgh	B.S.	1919	PETROLEUM ENGINEERING
Crandall, Roderic	Leland Stanford	A.B.	1906	
		A.M.	1907	
Cutler, W. W.	Princeton	B.S.	1906	
	Columbia	E.M.	1909	Mining
Daly, Marcel R.	Paris (France)	?	1878	Engineering and Geology
Davis, Herbert R.	Stevens Institute of Technology	M.E.	1898	Engineering
Davis, Ralph E.	Wisconsin	B.S.	1906	Geology
Davison, George S.	Rensselaer Polytechnic Institute	C.E.	1878	Engineering
Day, David T.	Johns Hopkins	A.B.	1881	Chemistry
		Ph.D.	1884	
Dean, E. W.	Clark; Yale	A.B.	1908	Chemical Engineering
		A.M.	1912	
		Ph.D.	1914	
Decius, L. C.	Leland Stanford	A.B.	1913	Geology and Mining

Table 1 (Cont'd)

Name	School or University	Degrees	Year	Degree In, or Major Interest
DeGolyer, E. L.	Oklahoma	A.B.	1911	Geology
Dievendorf, H. M.	Leland Stanford	A.M.	1917	Geology and Mining
Dodge, John Franklin	California	B.S.	1912	Mining and Geology
Dow, D. B.	Nebraska	B.S.	1917	Chemical Engineering
Duce, J. Terry	Colorado	A.B.	1915	Geology
Dumble, E. T.	Washington and Lee	B.S.	1874	Geology
Dunn, I. L.				
Easton, H. D.	Pennsylvania State; Kentucky	B.S.; E.M.	1905	Mining
Elliott, J. E.	Leland Stanford	A.B.	1911	Geology and Mining
Estabrook, E. L.	Pittsburgh	E.M.	1911	Mining
Ferguson, R. N.	Leland Stanford	A.B.	1907	Geology and Mining
Finley, D. D.	Kansas	?	1914	Engineering
Finney, W. R.	Leland Stanford	A.B.; M.E.	1913	Engineering
Fohs, F. Julius	Columbia	----------	1909	
Forker, W. M.	California	----------	1912	
Foster, A. W.	Pittsburgh	B.S.	1920	PETROLEUM ENGINEERING
Foster, Dean E.	Wisconsin	B.S.	1906	
Fowler, H. C.	Leland Stanford	A.B.; C.E.	1915	Engineering
Garfias, V. R.	Leland Stanford	A.B.	1907	
		A.M.	1912	
		M.E.	1914	
Garrett, L. P.	Texas	----------	1903	Geology
Gaylord, E. G.	California	B.S.	1911	Mining Engineering
Geis, W. H.	California	B.S.	1915	Mining Engineering
George, H. C.	Pennsylvania State	B.S.	1904	Mining and Engineering
	Pittsburgh	E.M.	1906	
Gester, G. C.	California	B.S.	1909	Mining and Geology
Goodrich, H. B.	Harvard	A.B.	1892	Geology
Grinsfelder, S.	California	B.S.	1920	PETROLEUM ENGINEERING
Hager, Dorsey	Washington	?	1909	Geology
	Columbia	?	1910	
Hamaker, R. G.	Leland Stanford	A.B.	1916	Civil Engineering
Hamilton, Fletcher	California	B.S.	1904	Engineering
Hamilton, W. R.	Leland Stanford	A.B.	1904	Engineering
Haseltine, R. S.	California	A.B.	1903	Mining Engineering
Hayes, C. W.	Oberlin; Johns Hopkins	Ph.D.		Chemistry and Geology
Heald, K. C.	Colorado College	B.S.	1912	Mining Engineering
Heggem, A. G.	Cornell	M.E.	1897	Engineering
Henley, A. S.	Leland Stanford	?	1904	Geology and Mining
Hennen, R. V.	West Virginia	A.B.	1900	Engineering
		C.E.	1901	Engineering
Henry, Phillip W.	Rensselaer Polytechnic Institute	C.E.	1887	Engineering
Henson, G. B.	Kansas	A.B.		
Herald, Frank A.	Oklahoma	A.B.	1910	Geology
Herold, Stanley C.	Leland Stanford	A.B.	1909	
Hill, C. C.	Pittsburgh	B.S.	1918	PETROLEUM ENGINEERING
Hill, Frank		----------		
Hill, H. B.	Ohio State	?	1907	Mining
Hill, H. H.	Wyoming	A.B.	1911	Chemistry
	Washington	A.M.	1913	
Hoefer, Philip von	?	?		
Holmes, B. M.	?	?		
Hook, J. S.	Leland Stanford	A.B.	1910	Geology
		A.M.	1913	
Hopper, W. E.	Cornell	A.B.	1908	Geology
		A.M.	1910	
Howe, Henry V.	Oregon	A.B.	1916	History and Geology
		Ph.D.	1922	
Howell, J. E.	Alabama Polytechnic Institute	B.S.	1919	Electrical Engineering

Table 1 (Cont'd)

Name	School or University	Degrees	Year	Degree In, or Major Interest
Hubbard, William E.	Wisconsin	A.B.	1915	
		E.M.	1917	
Huntley, L. G.	Carnegie Institute of Technology	B.S.	1908	Geology
Jeffrey, Walter	?	?		
Jensen, Joseph	Utah	B.S.	1908	Mining and Engineering
Johnson, Frederick A.	Pittsburgh	B.S.	1915	PETROLEUM ENGINEERING
Johnson, Roswell H.	Chicago	B.S.	1900	Zoology
	Wisconsin	M.S.	1903	
Keeler, C. M.	Chicago	B.S.	1912	
Kelly, R. B.	Alabama Polytechnic Institute	B.S.	1919	Engineering
Kirby, W. H.	?	?		Engineering
Kirwan, M. J.	Lawrence; Wisconsin	?		
Knapp, Arthur	Cornell	M.E.	1907	Engineering
Knappen, R. S.	Ohio Wesleyan	B.S.	1913	Geology
Kobbe, William H.	Yale	?	1904	Engineering
Latham, E. B.	?	?		Mining Engineering
Lewis, J. O.	Leland Stanford	A.B.	1917	Engineering
Lindsly, Ben E.	Massachusetts Institute of Technology	B.S.	1905	Engineering
Lombardi, M. E.	California	E.M.	1911	Mining Engineering
Long, Carl T.	California	B.S.	1920	PETROLEUM ENGINEERING
Longyear, R. D.	Williams	A.B.	1914	
	Wisconsin	A.M.	1915	
Lovejoy, John M.	Columbia School of Mines	E.M.	1911	Mining Engineering
Lucas, A. F.	Polytechnic Institute (Gratz, Austria)	?	?	Engineering
	Naval Academy Fiume and Pola, Austria)	?	1878	
Lynton, E. D.	Missouri School of Mines	B.S.	1912	
Manning, Van H.	Mississippi	?	1880	Engineering
	Pittsburgh	E.D.	1919	
McLaughlin, Cyrus	?	?		Geology
McLaughlin, R. P.	Leland Stanford	A.B.	1902	Engineering
McMaster, Robert N.	Southern California	B.S.	1916	
McMurray, W. F.				
McNutt, V. H.	Missouri School of Mines	B.S.	1910	Geology and Engineering
		A.M.	1911	
		E.M.	1914	
Melcher, A. F.	Central College (Missouri)	B.S.	1907	Geology
		M.S.	1909	
Menke, J. H.	Leland Stanford	A.B.	1910	Geology
Miller, H. C.	Michigan College of Mines	E.M.	1911	Mining Engineering
Millikan, C. V.	Oklahoma A. & M.	B.S.	1917	Geology and Engineering
	Pittsburgh	M.S.	1920	
Mills, R. Van A.	Columbia	E.M.	1906	Mining Engineering
Moody, Graham B.	California	B.S.	1912	Chemistry, Geology, Paleontology
Moran, R. B.	Leland Stanford	A.B.	1907	Geology and Mining
Mundt, William C.	Michigan	B.S.	1904	
Naramore, Chester	Leland Stanford	A.B.	1903	Geology and Mining
Nolan, E. D.	Leland Stanford	A.B.	1917	Geology
Nowels, K. B.	Colorado College	B.S.	1917	Geology
Oberfell, G. C.	Miami	A.B.	1910	Chemistry
O'Neill, F. E.	California	B.S.	1918	Engineering
Oliphant, F. A.	?	?		
Orcutt, W. W.	Leland Stanford	A.B.; C.E.	1895	Geology and Civil Engineering
Padgett, Fred W.	Pittsburgh	B.S.	1912	Engineering
		M.S.	1913	
Paine, Paul	Massachusetts Institute of Technology	B.S.	1904	

Table 1 (Cont'd)

Name	School or University	Degrees	Year	Degree In, or Major Interest
Panyity, L. S.	Pittsburgh	B.S.	1915	Engineering
Peake, A. W.	Leland Stanford	A.B.	1912	Mining and Geology
Pemberton, J. R.	Leland Stanford	A.B.	1909	Geology and Mining
Pepperberg, L. J.	Nebraska	A.B.	1905	Geology
Perkins, A. A.		------------		
Phinney, A. J.	?	?		
Plummer, F. B.	Dartmouth	B.S.	1909	Geology
Pollard, J. A.		------------		
Porter, Hollis P.	Tulane	. --------	1893-94	
Power, Harry H.	Washington State	B.S.	1919	Chemical Engineering
Prior, Frank O.	Leland Stanford	A.B.	1918	Engineering
Rae, Colin C.	California	B.S.	1912	
Reger, David	West Virginia	B.S.	1909	Civil Engineering
Rehm, F. E.	Leland Stanford	A.B.	1916	
Requa, M. L.	?	?		
Rife, Byron	Purdue	B.S.; M.E.	1916	
Rittman, Walter F.	Ohio Northern	C.E.	1905	
	Swarthmore	A.B.	1908	Chemistry
Roark, Louis	Oklahoma	A.B.	1912	Geology
Robinson, B. F.	Pittsburgh	B.S.	1919	PETROLEUM ENGINEERING
Rubel, A. C.	Arizona	B.S.	1917	
Russell, Joseph	Texas	E.E.	1914	Electrical Engineering
Saunders, W. L.	Pennsylvania	B.S.	1876	
Schoch, E. P.	Texas	C.E.	1891	Chemistry
		A.M.	1896	
Schwarzenbeck, F. X.	Leland Stanford	A.B.	1918	Geology
Sclater, K. C.	California	B.S.		
Scott, W. W.	Leland Stanford	A.B.	1916	Geology
Sedgwick, A. E.	Southern California	B.S.	1916	Geology and Engineering
		M.S.	1918	
Severson, S. B.	Wisconsin	B.S.	1907	
Shannon, P. F.	Kentucky	B.S.	1907	Civil Engineering
Scharpenberg, C. C.	?	?		
Shaw, S. F.	Columbia	E.M.	1903	Mining
Sinsheimer, Warren	California	----------	1907	
Sloan, E. H.	Pittsburgh	B.S.	1914	Geology-Petroleum
Smith, Erwin W.	Texas A. & M.	C.E.	1910	
Snelling, Walter O.	George Washington	B.S.	1904	Chemistry
Somers, R. E.	Harvard	A.B.	1908	Geology
		A.M.	1910	
	Cornell	Ph.D.	1915	
Soyster, M. H.	California	A.B.	1916	
Stephenson, Eugene A.	Adrian College	B.S.	1905	Geology and General
	Chicago	Ph.D.	1917	Science
Stewart, Lyman	?	?		
Stoner, R. C.	California	B.S.	1912	Natural Sciences
Stroud, Ben K.	California	A.B.	1904	
Suman, John R.	California	B.S.	1912	Mining Engineering
Sutton, Chase E.	California	B.S.	1918	Engineering
Swigart, T. E.	Leland Stanford	A.B.	1917	
Taff, Joseph A.	Texas	B.S.	1894	Geology
Templeton, R. R.	Leland Stanford	A.B.	1915	Geology
Tickell, F. G.	California	B.S.	1912	Mining Engineering
		E.M.	1927	
Tough, F. B.	Columbia	E.M.	1910	Mining Engineering
Trimble, T. L.	Pittsburgh	B.S.	1919	PETROLEUM ENGINEERING
Udden, J. A.	Augusta College	A.M.	1889	
Umpleby, J. B.	Washington; Chicago	A.B.	1908	
		M.S.	1909	
		Ph.D.	1910	
Upham, H. R.	Pittsburgh	B.S.	1919	PETROLEUM ENGINEERING

Table 1 (Cont'd)

Name	School or University	Degrees	Year	Degree In, or Major Interest
Uren, L. C.	California	B.S.	1911	
Valerius, M. M.	Missouri School of Mines	....	1913	
Van der Linden, B. H.	Delft (Holland)	A.M.	1906	
Vaughn, W. H.		....		
Vedder, Dwight G.	California	B.S.	1915	Engineering
Wagy, E. W.	California	B.S.	1909	Mining Engineering
Warner, C. A.	Cornell	A.B.	1917	Geology
Watson, Charles D.	Kansas	?	1915	Engineering
Watts, William L.	?	?		
Weaver, Paul	Columbia	A.B.	1908	Geology
Wheeler, H. A.	Columbia	E.M.	1880	Mining Engineering
Wiggins, John H.	Leland Stanford	A.B.; C.E.	1911	Engineering
Wilhelm, V.	Leland Stanford	A.B.	1907	Geology and Mining
Williams, W. A.	Leland Stanford	A.B.	1903	Geology and Mining
Wrather, W. E.	Chicago	Ph.B.	1907	Geology
Wright, A. P.	Pittsburgh	E.M.	1913	Engineering
Wyer, S. S.	Ohio State	M.E.	1903	Engineering

ACKNOWLEDGMENT

Much of the data reflected herein are available from more than one source and accordingly individual references are made only in the case of a direct quotation from a publication or communication. Among the publications which were consulted freely were those of the United States Bureau of Mines, the United States Geological Survey, the American Institute of Mining and Metallurgical Engineers and its Petroleum Division, the American Association of Petroleum Geologists, the American Petroleum Institute, *The Oil and Gas Journal, World Oil, The Petroleum Engineer, Who's Who in Engineering, Who's Who in America,* the California Division of Mines, and geological surveys of various states—including Illinois, Oklahoma, Pennsylvania, and Texas—and of alumni associations of colleges and universities.

In addition to the members of the Editorial Board, *History of Petroleum Engineering,* special thanks for valuable suggestions and information are given to K. F. Anderson, Ralph Arnold, Clark F. Barb, Carroll M. Beeson, George M. Bevier, H. G. Botset, R. A. Cattell, W. F. Cloud, George Corless, Benjamin C. Craft, Frank A. Dotterweich, W. L. Ducker, J. E. Elliott, Tell Ertl, E. L. Estabrook, George Fancher, E. G. Gaylord, V. R. Garfias, J. M. Halliwell, R. K. Heston, H. B. Hill, Frederick A. Johnson, C. V. Kirkpatrick, R. W. Laird, R. P. McLaughlin, V. B. Monnett, Chester Naramore, H. H. Power, J. Paul Roston, A. C. Rubel, Joe H. Russell, K. C. Sclater, E. H. Sloan, Eugene A. Stephenson, A. B. Stevens, L. B. Taylor, F. G. Tickell, L. C. Uren, A. W. Walker, Paul Weaver, and C. L. Wilson.

Thanks are also expressed to the secretaries of alumni associations and technical societies, to the Federal Records Center, and to the many others who have assisted in the preparation of this material.

Chapter 4

EVOLUTION BY COMPANIES

John R. Suman

JOHN ROBERT SUMAN, born in Daleville, Indiana in 1890, was educated at the Universities of Southern California and California and received a B. S. degree from the latter in 1912. His first postgraduation employment was with Rio Bravo Oil Company, of which he became chief engineer before moving, in 1917, to the Roxana Petroleum Corporation. He rejoined Rio Bravo in 1919 and became its vice president and general manager in 1925.

In 1927 Mr. Suman became associated with Humble Oil & Refining Company as a director, assuming its vice presidency for production in 1933. In 1945 he was elected vice president and a director of Standard Oil Company (New Jersey) and served as such until corporate retirement in 1955, opening then a consulting office in Houston, Texas.

His academic, professional and industrial honors are many and major. Those of the American Petroleum Institute include a directorship (1947-55); an honorary directorship (1955 to date); chairmanship of its Division of Development and Production Engineering (1928-29), and chairmanship of its Central Committee on Standardization of Oil-field Equipment (1947-55). AIME honors include receipt of the Lucas Medal (1943), "... for distinguished achievement in improving the technique and practice of producing petroleum". He was a director of American Standards Association (1948-50) and is a member of AAPG and Institute of Petroleum.

A Tau Beta Pi, Mr. Suman was awarded an honorary doctorate of engineering by South Dakota School of Mines. He is the author of numerous technical papers and of *Petroleum Production Methods*, which has been a standard reference work for many years.

64

INTRODUCTION

The beginnings of petroleum engineering in the oil industry of the United States came from the work of many men, who as lease operators or workmen sought to find easier and better ways of carrying on their business of drilling wells and producing oil, and it was more than 40 years after Colonel Drake's discovery well was drilled that the corporate operating organizations in the oil fields began to employ engineers and geologists to do some of the jobs now included in petroleum engineering.

The evolution of petroleum engineering among the operating companies had its beginnings in California soon after 1900. In a number of the oil fields of that state the amount of water being produced with the oil was increasing rapidly and threatened to flood the oil sands. Much of the water was fresh and was believed to be entering the productive formations through wells that had been improperly completed or abandoned without adequate plugging. Many individuals among the geologists, operators, and engineering consultants in California were studying the problem during the early 1900's; but the first American oil-field operating corporation known to have made an organized effort to obtain correct subsurface information on its properties in order to set casing more uniformly and to obtain better water shut-offs, was the Kern Trading and Oil Company, a subsidiary of the Southern Pacific Railroad Company, which had been organized in 1902 to develop the railroad company's land-grant acreage in the California oil fields. Prof. E. T. Dumble, Chief Geologist of the Southern Pacific Railroad, was president of Kern Trading and Oil Company; and F. M. Anderson (University of Oregon, 1889, and Ph.D. Stanford, 1895), was the manager in California. Mining Engineer M. E. Lombardi was head of the drilling division, and Cyrus McLaughlin directed the oil-producing operations. In the spring of 1907, Anderson hired five graduates of the Department of Geology and Mining of Stanford University and stationed them in the oil fields in which Kern Trading and Oil Company operated, as "resident geologists" to do surface and subsurface geology, and particularly to follow the drilling of the new wells and correlate them with the old wells in order to locate the sources and points of entry of the invading fresh water and to find casing points

---

Chapter prepared with assistance of Edward L. Estabrook, and with reports from many oil companies on the history of petroleum engineering in their organizations.

likely to protect the oil sands from further surface-water intrusion. Among the men hired by Kern Trading and Oil Company as resident geologists during the period 1907 to 1911, the following are known: R. D. Bush, E. G. Gaylord, E. B. Latham, R. B. Moran, and F. B. Tough. Others hired later were O. A. Cavins, R. N. Ferguson, G. C. Gester, J. H. Menke, and R. C. Stoner. Several of these men were graduates in Mining Engineering, and after a few years as resident geologists they began to call themselves petroleum engineers.

In Texas, the Southern Pacific Railroad Company organized the Rio Bravo Oil Company to develop its oil properties, and in 1912 John R. Suman, a newly graduated engineer, was hired to do areal and economic geology along the railroad line. After a year or two, Suman moved into Rio Bravo's oil work and became a pioneer in petroleum engineering on the Gulf Coast.

The idea of using special geological and engineering personnel in the oil fields to study subsurface conditions took hold rapidly in California. The water-intrusion situation was serious and the leaders of the industry quickly recognized the value of this new approach to the problem. Associations of operators were formed and geologists and engineers hired to work on subsurface problems, either for individual companies or for the associations. When cooperative efforts to control water intrusion were nullified by the refusal of some lease operators to participate, indignation was widespread in business and petroleum circles; and, in 1915, the Legislature of the State of California acted to make it obligatory upon all operators of petroleum properties to comply with the rules established for setting casing to shut off upper water from oil and gas reservoirs. The Division of Oil and Gas Operations of the California State Mining Bureau was established "for the purpose of supervising oil-field operations, with special reference to the matter of shutting off water in the oil fields and conserving the state's oil and gas resources." The expense of the division was assessed against the oil operators of the state.

The California Oil and Gas Division was organized with R. P. McLaughlin as the first supervisor and R. E. Collom, M. J. Kirwan, R. B. Moran, and Chester Naramore as deputy supervisors. The rules established by the division required that, before any well in California could be drilled into a prospective oil or gas reservoir, casing must be set and cemented and, after a prescribed interval, be tested in the presence of a representative of the division to prove that all upper waters were definitely excluded. Failure to obtain results which the Oil and Gas Division would approve could lead to long and expensive delays. In this situation self-interest soon compelled every operator to employ or consult with competent subsurface advisors on the selection of casing points and on cementing practices, and the subsurface phases of petroleum engineering very soon became an established part of California petroleum technology.

While the use of resident geologists in the oil fields of California was the first step in the development of the subsurface phase of petroleum engineering, it also brought about the beginning of that intimate association of engineers with oil-field operations which is the real foundation of present-day petroleum engineering. The field superintendents to whom these "resident geologists" made their daily reports soon found that a young engineer trained to collect facts and report them in intelligible form was a useful man to have around the lease, and many of the boys found themselves being kept so busy with operating matters that they could hardly find time to attend to their geologic work. Chester Naramore tells of preparing tables of collapsing pressures, weights per foot of casing, etc., in Coalinga Field in 1911 and of working with practical operators like R. C. Baker and Al Guiberson to design and obtain stronger casing, drilling and tubing collars, steel derricks, quicker-setting cement, etc. which were needed to handle the increasing depth to which oil wells were continually being drilled.

The first oil company to organize its subsurface geologists and field engineers into a working group which reported to the operating officials, rather than to the chief geologist, appears to have been the Shell Company of California. B. H. Van der Linden, a geologist with some years of oil-field experience with the Shell Company in the Dutch East Indies, set up the Shell producing organization in California in 1913 and hired J. E. (Brick) Elliot as chief geologist, and E. D. (Dan) Nolan as development geologist. Among the young engineers and geologists who joined the Shell organization in California from 1914 to 1917 were A. W. (Pete) Ambrose, W. W. (Dago) Scott, R. R. (Rick) Templeton, F. E. (Fat) Rehm, and T. E. (Ted) Swigart. In 1916, Van der Linden established his production geologists as a separate group called "exploitation engineers." With Van der Linden in charge and W. C. McDuffie as general superintendent, the Shell Company in California became a leader in developing the techniques of petroleum engineering.

The use of engineers in oil-field operations in California grew rapidly after the California Division of Oil and Gas Operations was established, but for several years there was no general agreement on the title to be applied to such men. There were exploitation engineers, petroleum production engineers, drilling engineers, production engineers, and a few petroleum engineers. Among the early users of the title "petroleum en-

gineer" were W. R. Hamilton of California, whose assistance is acknowl-
edged by J. O. Lewis in the introduction to his Bulletin No. 148 of the
U. S. Bureau of Mines in 1917 entitled "Methods of Increasing the
Recovery of Oil Sands"; Alfred G. Heggem of Tulsa, Okla.; and Wm.
H. Kobble, "petroleum engineer" for the Pierce Oil Company of St.
Louis. The first use of the term "petroleum engineer" by a large oil
company appears to have been in 1920 when E. W. Wagy was appointed
petroleum engineer of Standard Oil Co. of California. Then, in 1921,
General Petroleum began applying that title to the head-office engineers
who supervised the work of "resident geologists." By 1925, the use of the
titles "petroleum engineer," and "petroleum production engineer" was
widespread among the oil-field operators of the world.

TECHNICAL PUBLICATIONS BY OIL-COMPANY EMPLOYEES

One phase of the "evolution by companies" of petroleum engineering during the period 1914 to 1927 can be traced in the transactions of
the technical societies before which the problems of the growing science
were brought up for discussion. For the purposes of this chapter the
scientific papers prepared and presented at the meetings by the employees
of the operating petroleum companies are of special interest. Papers
written by oil-company employees not only reflected the status of
petroleum-engineering thinking within that company organization, but
the number of companies which supplied contributors indicated the
extent to which petroleum engineering was being adopted by the industry. For convenience, the authors and the papers contributed, have been
grouped in six categories as follows:

		No. of Papers
1.	Employees of operating petroleum companies	82
2.	Engineers from U. S. Bureau of Mines	22
3.	Members of other federal and state organizations	20
4.	Faculty or students of colleges and universities	17
5.	Employees of supply and service companies	32
6.	Consultants to the petroleum industry	34
	Total	207

Table 1 lists the 207 papers by year of publication, and by societies
where presented. Many short articles appearing in the *AIME Transactions*
have been omitted from the tabulation, as have unsigned reports and discussion material.

The American Institute of Mining and Metallurgical Engineers
(AIME) since 1914, the American Association of Petroleum Geologists
(AAPG) since 1916, and the American Petroleum Institute (API) since

1919, have been the leading national societies interested in petroleum operation and development. Of the papers listed, 131 were presented before the AIME, 45 before the API, and 31 before the AAPG.

The business affiliations of the authors of these published articles are not always stated in the transactions of the societies and, in a few cases, company employees may erroneously have been listed as consultants or vice versa. The authors listed as employees of operating companies (Col. 1, Table 1) include petroleum engineers, geologists, executives, chemists, pipeliners, field operating men, gas-plant operators, and electrical engineers. Only about 10 percent of the authors described themselves as "petroleum engineers". In 1917 to 1924, inclusive, only 2 out of 22 oil-company employee authors used the title "petroleum engineer"; but after 1925, when the industry generally had adopted that title, an increasing number of authors are so listed. The rate at which petroleum engineering developed within the organizations of the operating companies during the period is clearly indicated in Col. 2 of Table 1. Commencing with one technical paper in 1915, the output of oil-company employee authors rose slowly for 10 years; and then after 1923 increased rapidly, until in 1927 they accounted for 18 out of 31 technical papers listed.

During the years from 1915 to 1923, the contributions to petroleum engineering literature by oil-company employees came from only 11 companies; whereas in the 4 years from 1924 to 1927, inclusive, contributions by employees came from 24 companies.

This upsurge of technical reporting by oil-company employees was significant not only of the considerable increase in the number of company men engaged in petroleum engineering work, but also of the widespread interest and support being given to it by the managements of the producing oil companies. Permission to publish technical material derived from company operations was but a small part of the management's contribution. Back of the whole effort there were oil-company managers keenly interested in the new techniques and confident that the exchange of ideas and information at the meetings of the technical societies would be of real value in developing both men and methods of work within their companies.

Consultants and independent students of the petroleum industry were the earliest contributors to the literature of petroleum engineering, and they continued throughout the period of this tabulation to present from 1 to 5 papers per year. The technicians of the U. S. Bureau of Mines and of other federal and state organizations, excluding all of their official publications, presented a total of 42 papers. From educational institutions the increased number of contributions after 1925 reflected the greater number at which education in petroleum engineering was being given. Publications in the transactions of the API from representatives of the supply and service companies were largely concerned with the API standardization program.

In Table 2 there are listed in chronological order the names of the oil companies whose employees contributed the 82 technical papers tabulated in Col. 2 of Table 1. The associations before which the papers were presented are identified by their respective initials. Some of the company names listed have disappeared through corporate mergers or have been superseded by new corporations.

The four companies whose employees were most active in the publication of technical papers during the years 1915 to 1927, inclusive, were the Marland group operating in Oklahoma, Texas, and California (now Continental Oil Co.) with 9 contributions, Union Oil Co. of California with 9, Midwest Refining Co. of Wyoming (later Stanolind Oil and Gas Co. and now Pan American Petroleum Corp.) with 8, and Amerada Petroleum Corporation of Oklahoma with 7 contributions; and together they accounted for 33 out of the total 82 papers listed. A second group of 11 companies produced another 36 papers—5 by Shell; 4 each by Gulf, Empire (Cities Service), Phillips, and the Tidewater Associated group; 3 each by Rio Bravo, Standard of California, and Texas; and 2 each by Humble, Sun, and General Petroleum. The remaining 13 papers were presented by employees of 13 other companies. Authors from California prepared 25 papers; 47 came from Texas, Gulf Coast, and Mid-Continent; and 10 from other parts of the United States. The employee authors represented 28 different operating oil companies or corporate groups with subsidiary operating companies.

Table 1

Technical Articles on Subjects Pertaining to Petroleum Engineering Published by AIME, AAPG, and API from 1914 to 1927, Inclusive, Tabulated by the Business or Professional Connections of the Authors

1	2	3	4	5	6	7	8
	Employees of Operating Petroleum Companies	Engineers from Bureau of Mines	Members of Other Federal or State Organiza- tions	From Colleges and Univer- sities	From Supply and Service Companies	Con- sultants to Petroleum Industry	Total
a. By Years							
1914	—	—	—	—	—	3	3
1915	1	—	1	1	1	1	5
1916	1	—	—	—	—	4	5
1917	3	—	1	—	—	—	4
1918	—	1	1	—	—	2	4
1919	3	3	1	—	—	1	8
1920	1	3	4	—	—	5	13
1921	1	—	2	—	—	3	6
1922	4	2	2	1	5	2	16
1923	1	3	2	—	2	3	11
1924	10	1	1	1	1	—	14
1925	17	3	2	6	12	2	42
1926	22	3	2	5	8	5	45
1927	18	3	1	3	3	3	31
Total	82	22	20	17	32	34	207
b. By Societies Where Presented							
AIME	48	16	11	12	14	30	131
API	24	2	—	3	16	—	45
AAPG	10	4	9	2	2	4	31
Total	82	22	20	17	32	34	207

Table 2

List, by Years, of the Oil Companies Whose Employees Contributed
Technical Papers Pertaining to Petroleum Engineering, to AIME,
AAPG, and API from 1914 to 1927, Inclusive, in Order
of Time of Presentation

Year	Where Published	Name of Company
1915	AIME	Kern Trading and Oil Company
1916	AAPG	Empire Gas and Fuel Company
1917	AIME	Pierce Oil Corporation
	AAPG	Gulf Production Co.
	AIME	Producers Oil Company
1919	AIME	Empire Gas and Fuel Company (2 papers)
	AIME	Ohio Fuel Supply Company
1920	AIME	Marland Refining Company
1921	AAPG	Amerada Petroleum Corporation
1922	AAPG	Amerada Petroleum Corporation
	AIME	Midwest Refining Company
	API	The Texas Company
	API	Sun Oil Company
1923	AIME	Amerada Petroleum Corporation
1924	API	Hope Natural Gas Company
	API	Standard Oil Company of California
	AAPG	Associated Oil Company
	API	General Petroleum Corporation
	API	Union Oil Company of California
	AAPG	Union Oil Company of California
	AAPG	Phillips Petroleum Company
	AAPG	Atlantic Oil Producing Company
	AAPG	Pacific Oil Company (Standard Oil Co. of California)
	AIME	Amerada Petroleum Corporation
1925	AIME	Sun Oil Company
	AIME	Midwest Refining Company (3 papers)
	AAPG	Rio Bravo Oil Company
	AIME	Rio Bravo Oil Company
	API	The Texas Company
	API	Phillips Petroleum Company (2 papers)
	API	General Petroleum Corporation
	API	Humble Oil & Refining Company

Table 2 (Cont'd)

Year	Where Published	Name of Company
	AIME	Tidal Oil Company
	AIME	Amerada Petroleum Corporation
	AIME	California Petroleum Corporation
	AIME	Miley Oil Company
	AIME	Standard Pipe Line Company
	AIME	Pan American Western Petroleum Company
1926	AIME	Tidal Oil Company
	API	Tidal Oil Company
	AIME	Gulf Production Company
	AIME	Skelly Oil Corporation
	AIME	Phillips Petroleum Company
	AIME	Standard Oil Company of California
	AIME	Midwest Refining Company
1926	AIME	Roxana Petroleum Corporation (Shell)
	AIME	Pure Oil Company
	AIME	Humble Oil & Refining Company
	AIME	Amerada Petroleum Corporation
	AIME	Chanslor-Canfield Midway Oil Company
	AIME	Empire Gas and Fuel Company
	AIME	Marland Oil Company of Texas (2 papers)
	API	Union Oil Company of California (2 papers)
	API	Gypsy Oil Company (2 papers)
	API	Shell Company of California
	API	Rio Bravo Oil Company
	API	The Texas Company
1927	AIME	Midwest Refining Company (2 papers)
	API	Midwest Refining Company
	AIME	Roxana Petroleum Company (Shell)
	AIME	Union Oil Company (4 papers)
	API	Union Oil Company
	AIME	Amerada Petroleum Corporation
	AIME	Marland Oil Company of California (2 papers)
	API	Marland Oil Company
	AIME	Marland Oil Company of Texas (3 papers)
	API	Shell Company of California (2 papers)

About one half of the 80 papers written by oil-company employees were specifically concerned with drilling and production and the remainder covered standardization, corrosion, and other aspects of oil- and gas-production problems. Not all of the technical ideas presented in these papers are valid in the light of our present knowledge. The authors were pioneers in many of the present techniques of petroleum engineering and, in some cases, dealt with subjects in which the basic facts were not fully developed or understood. Notwithstanding such deficiencies in the theoretical background, these early papers contained much constructive thinking and played an important part in the rapid advance in technical competence which distinguished the petroleum producing industry during the 20's.

The years 1914-1927, covered by Tables 1 and 2, were important in the evolution of petroleum engineering as a technical profession. In 1914 there were very few men in the United States who called themselves "petroleum engineers", and by 1927 there were dozens of them and many of the larger oil operators had recruited sizable engineering staffs and appointed chief petroleum engineers. In some companies petroleum engineering started as a separate department reporting direct to the general manager, in others it was a part of the Production Division, and in a few cases was attached to the Geological Department; but by 1927 there was no longer any doubt that petroleum engineering was paying its way in the oil business. Some indication of its progress since 1927 may be gained from the fact that the membership of the Petroleum Branch of the AIME now exceeds 13,000, as compared to the few hundred members who were interested in petroleum matters in 1927.

EVOLUTION BY COMPANIES

The chronological summaries of petroleum-engineering history given in the following pages have been compiled from the abundant material furnished by various oil companies and from the 1947-48 correspondence of D. V. Carter during his first efforts to obtain material for this volume. The names of early workers in petroleum engineering have been given whenever available. The material is arranged in alphabetical order by companies, as follows:

*Name changed to Pan American Petroleum Corp., 1957.

Amerada Petroleum Corporation

1919—Amerada organized, with technical men in management.

1922—Brought first torsion balance to U. S. A.
Hired C. V. Millikan as a geologist.

1923—Made studies at Brock Field (Okla.) on effects of back pressure on gas-oil ratio.[1]

1924—Made tests of gas-oil ratio in flush-producing wells.[2]

1925—Transferred C. V. Millikan to producing department.

1926—Made study of gas-oil ratios as related to the decline of oil production.[3]

1928—Made first bottom-hole pressure measurements.
Ran deviation tests on drilling holes.
Determined that controlled drilling rates permitted reduction in hole deviation.

1929—Developed self-contained recording bottom-hole pressure gage.[4]

1930—Used vibrating mud screen (Hobbs Field, New Mexico).

1934—Commenced using recording pressure gage in all drill-stem tests.[5]

1935-36—Established policy of using temperature surveys in all wells to determine height of cement behind oil string.[6]

1939—Developed equipment for electric logging simultaneously with drilling.[7]

1957—Geophysical Research Corp., a subsidiary of Amerada, completed development of a surface recording subsurface pressure gage.

From the beginning, Amerada has consistently investigated new equipment, methods, and procedures; and has contributed both technically and practically to the advancement of producing and drilling practices.

References

[1]Lovejoy, J. M: Effect of Back Pressures on Wells in Brock Field, *Trans. Am. Inst. Mining Met. Engrs.*, **70**, 1173 (1923-24).

[2]Millikan, C. V: Use of Gas Meters for Determination of Pay Strata in Oil Sands, *Petroleum Development and Technology*, **71**, 183 (1925).

[3]Millikan, C. V: Gas-Oil Ratios as Related to Decline of Oil Production, *Petroleum Development and Technology in 1926*, 155, American Institute of Mining and Metallurgical Engineers, Inc., New York, 1927.

[4]Millikan, C. V. and Sidwell, C. V: Bottom-Hole Pressures in Oil Wells, *Trans. Am. Inst. Mining Met. Engrs. (Petroleum Development and Technology)* 194 (1931).

[5]Christie, R. S: Use of Recording Pressure Gages in Drill-Stem Tests, *API Drilling and Production Practice*, 8 (1936).

[6]Millikan, C. V: Temperature Surveys in Oil Wells, *Trans. Am. Inst. Mining Met. Engrs. (Petroleum Development and Technology)* **142**, 15 (1941) (reprint, p. 77).

[7]Hawthorne and Owen: Mechanical Practicability of Electrical Logging While Drilling, *Petroleum Engr.* (1940).

4. EVOLUTION BY COMPANIES

The Atlantic Refining Company

1920—Atlantic Oil Producing Company employed Walter Meier as first engineer. He was assigned to survey land and to design lease equipment.

1924—Edgar Kraus presented a paper before AAPG on "Logging Wells Drilled by Rotary Method."[1]

1926-29—There was engineering interest in production by use of gas lift and in lease use of gas. H. M. Staggs and W. W. Scott worked on development of gas-lift valves. Tapered tubing was used in a well in west Texas. A paraffin knife was developed. Built a gasoline plant at Pampa and participated in a compressor plant at Seminole for gas lift. Made proration studies in Seminole and Wink.

1929—H. M. Staggs was appointed general superintendent and chief petroleum engineer.

1930—A gas-injection project was conducted in the Shipley Field in Ward County, Texas, to increase recovery and to prolong the flowing life of the wells.

1931—A liquid-level control valve and an intermitter valve were developed for use in gas lift.

1929-33—Studies of well behavior and flow characteristics of wells were begun. GOR tests were made in McElroy, east Texas and Oklahoma. Studies of well-completion techniques to shut off gas were made.

1933—Reservoir engineering was established as a unit of engineering effort.

1934—Petroleum engineering laboratory established under J. D. Collett, Jr., to determine rock permeability and porosity.

1937—The Atlantic Oil Producing Company merged with and became the crude-oil production department of The Atlantic Refining Company.

1937-42—Studies continued in the areas of production practices and equipment, reservoir characteristics, well completions, and proration.

1942—Production research division of research and development department was established in Dallas with L. P. Whorton in charge. First problems were associated with reservoir fluid-flow characteristics.

1944—The petroleum engineering section was established as a unit of the production department with B. E. Moir as chief petroleum engineer. Within the section, separate groups were established for reservoir engineering, chemical engineering, mechanical engineering and production engineering. The functions of the petroleum engineering laboratory which had been formed in 1934 were in-

77

cluded in the chemical engineering group, the responsibilities of which were enlarged to include the evaluation of various types of materials used in operations, the study of operating problems which required a chemical approach, and additional measurements of reservoir rock which were called for by new developments in reservoir engineering.

1945—A dual-intermitter gas-lift installation was made in Louisiana.

1946—The chemical engineering group developed a new porosimeter, known as the Kaye-Freeman porosimeter.

Radioactive tracers were used in salt water to check a primary cement job and locate zone of injection.

1947—Standard designs for selection of combination casing strings were developed and issued.

1948—Constructed building to house the chemical engineering group of the petroleum engineering section and the Atlantic research staff working on crude-oil production problems. The responsibility of the chemical engineering group was broadened to include studies of corrosion and PVT studies.

Atlantic participated in a gas-cycling—pressure-maintenance project in the McKamie Field in Arkansas.

A program of training was instituted for engineering graduates entering the domestic crude-oil department.

Plastic-coated tubing was installed in certain wells in Arkansas to combat corrosive environment.

Investigation made to determine the cost of corrosion in producing operations.

Standard installation methods and drawings for tank-battery equipment installations were developed and adopted.

1949—A high-pressure gas-injection program was begun in the Block 31 Field in Texas as a result of miscibility studies by the research department. Gas was injected at a pressure high enough to cause miscible displacement of oil.

1949—The following were developed by the chemical engineering group: a graphical system for the identification of oil-field brines using chemical analyses, a soluble plug for the removal of paraffin from flow lines, and the use of an electrolytic model in the studies of secondary recovery.

1950—Methods and procedures to be used in designing rod-pump installations were developed, and a manual was written.

1951—Submersible tank-battery barges were installed in Mustang Island in Corpus Christi Bay.

A field-wide unitized glycol-injection low-temperature separation facility was installed near Corpus Christi, Texas.

Criteria for testing production packers and test equipment to evaluate the performance of packers in the shop rather than in the field were developed. Packer-performance test facilities were built and used as a part of the laboratory facilities.

V. E. Stepp was appointed chief petroleum engineer.

1952—An installation of automatic lease flow control equipment was made in East Texas.

1953—Training courses were devised and conducted by engineers to teach the field personnel the basic principles of hydraulic pumping operations.

The mechanical engineering and production engineering groups of the petroleum engineering section were combined to form the production engineering group.

1954—Atlantic established a regional-manager type of production organization with a decentralization of activities which included the petroleum engineering activities. Petroleum engineering components were placed in the regions, some of which were already in the field under the older organization. Staff components were retained in the central office under the jurisdiction of the chief petroleum engineer having the same components of groups, composed of reservoir, production, and chemical engineering.

Reference

[1]Kraus, Edgar: Logging Wells Drilled by Rotary Method, *Am. Assoc. Petroleum Geologists Bull.*, **8**, 641 (1924).

British-American Oil Producing Company

1935-36—W. K. Whiteford joined British-American in fall of 1935 and a field engineering staff was set up in Oklahoma City Field under J. F. Crawford as district petroleum engineer.

1937-39—Petroleum engineering department established in Tulsa office under John A. McCutchin as chief engineer. Oklahoma City staff included M. Chenault, M. F. Owens, and Pat McDonald.

1940-42—Company pioneered in tidelands development and discovered offshore oil field near Sabine Pass, Texas. J. J. Arps and R. C. Graham joined British-American as district engineers.

1943-48— J. J. Arps promoted to chief engineer with headquarters in Tulsa. O. I. Torkelsen became district engineer for California, and H. R. Wyckoff for Wyoming. Arps wrote paper on decline-curve analysis.[1]

1949-51—G. M. Stearns became chief engineer in 1949, and a separate department in production research and economics was established under J. J. Arps.

Training program for young engineers instituted.

Electric well logging school at various operating centers conducted under Dr. R. G. Hamilton. Special slide rule—the "Arps-Hamilton Loganalyzer"—designed for use in quantitative electrical log work.

1952-53—Facilities installed for injection of 20,000 bbl per day of water into Tensleep sand at Steamboat Butte Field (Wyo.) to restore and maintain reservoir pressure. Project described by E. W. Rogers in "Pressure Maintenance by Water Injection at the Steamboat Butte Field".[2]

1954-56—Established separate gas and gasoline department under D. W. Conaway. Arps published two papers on estimation of reserves.[3,4]

References

[1]Arps, J. J: Analysis of Decline Curves, *Trans. Am. Inst. Mining Met. Engrs. (Petroleum Development and Technology)* **160,** 228 (1936) (reprint, p. 451).

[2]Rogers, E. W: Pressure Maintenance by Water Injection at Steamboat Butte Field, *Petroleum Engr.*, B-78, Oct. (1953).

[3]Arps, J. J. and Roberts, T. G: The Effect of the Relative Permeability Ratio, the Oil Gravity, and the Solution Gas-Oil Ratio on the Primary Recovery from a Depletion-type Reservoir, *Trans. Am. Inst. Mining Met. Engrs. (Petroleum Development and Technology)* **204,** 120 (1955).

[4]Arps, J. J: Estimation of Primary Oil Reserves, *J. Petr. Tech.*, **VIII [8]** 182, Aug. (1956); also *Trans. Am. Inst. Mining Met. Engrs. (Petroleum Development and Technology)* 182 (1956).

Cities Service Oil Company, Successor to Empire Gas & Fuel Company

1916—Established training course for engineers in Empire Gas and Fuel Company in Bartlesville, Okla. A. W. McCoy wrote paper, "Some Effects of Capillarity on Oil Accumulation."[1]
H. R. Shidel published paper on "Cement Plugging For Exclusion of Bottom-Hole Water in Augusta Field, Kansas."[2]

1919—A. W. McCoy, with H. R. Shidel and E. A. Trager published paper on "Investigations Concerning Oil-Water Emulsion."[3]

1917-23—Engineering work carried out at El Dorado Field (Kans.) included electrification of oil-well pumping, dehydration of oil, combating underground corrosion, plugging off water, improvements in all types of oil-field equipment, especially pumping and drilling.
The first chemical treatment in oil wells for corrosion is believed to have been done at El Dorado Field (Kans.) by J. C. Walker. Evaporation losses were serious and company constructed gastight wooden tanks.
Floyd C. Brown was engineer in charge.
R. D. Bush from California State Oil and Gas Division was hired to direct bottom-hole plugging at El Dorado.

1924—C. E. Beecher was directed by Henry L. Doherty to make a study of the physical characteristics of crude oil in underground reservoirs and of the function of natural gas in oil production. Beecher and Ivan Parkhurst found that large volumes of gas would dissolve in crude oil under reservoir pressures and gave to the crude a reduced viscosity and surface tension.[4] This new knowledge that natural gas had important functions in oil production, in addition to being a source of energy, greatly stimulated interest in the conservation of natural gas.

1925—C. E. Beecher was appointed chief petroleum engineer. Early problems included secondary recovery of crude by air and gas drives, gas lift, equipment studies, treatment of emulsions, corrosion problems, unit operations, etc. Parkhurst and Beecher designed and operated equipment for taking dynamometer cards for pumping wells. Use of this tool reduced electric-power requirements.

1926—Large air-injection project was started in the El Dorado Field in 1926 by construction of a plant to serve 4,985 productive acres of a shallow sand at about 700 ft. It continued in operation for 27 years, until 1954. Water flooding is now being successfully applied to the same sand.

The Seminole and Oklahoma City Fields brought problems of straight-hole drilling, control of wells producing sand, production methods for proration, gas lift, deep-well pumping, bottom-hole pressures, drilling and completion practices, cementing casing, etc.

M. J. Kirwan and J. R. Hatfield were active in this work.

1954—Currently all lines of petroleum engineering are being followed, especially reservoir engineering.

References

[1]McCoy, A. W: Some Effects of Capillarity on Oil Accumulation, *Am. Assoc. Petroleum Geologists Bull.*, **1**, 140 (1916).

[2]McCoy, A. W; Shidel, H. R; and Trager, E. A: Investigations Concerning Oil-Water Emulsion, *Trans. Am. Inst. Mining Met. Engrs.*, **LXI**, 430 (1919).

[3]Shidel, H. R: Cement Plugging for Exclusion of Bottom-Hole Water in Augusta Field, Kansas, *Trans. Am. Inst. Mining Met. Engrs.*, **LXI**, 595 (1919).

[4]Beecher, C. E. and Parkhurst, I. P: Effect of Dissolved Gas upon the Viscosity and Surface Tension of Crude Oil, *Petroleum Development and Technology in 1926*, 51, American Institute of Mining and Metallurgical Engineers, Inc., New York, 1927.

Continental Oil Company, Including the Marland Oil Company (Which Was Merged With Continental in 1929)

Marland had engineers doing petroleum engineering work in the early 1920's, among whom were: A. H. Bell, E. O. Bennett,

B. B. Boatright, E. P. Campbell, R. W. Christie, E. V. Foran, E. H. Griswold, N. O. Miller, R. Van A. Mills, G. L. Nye, W. A. Oberlin, C. H. Pishny, K. C. Sclater, W. Shutts, B. R. Stephenson, H. Vance, W. V. Vietti, J. E. Warren, E. W. Webb, W. J. Wilkins.

1925—Appointed "chief production engineers" as follows: E. O. Bennett for Marland Oil Company of Texas; K. C. Sclater for Marland Oil Company of Oklahoma; and A. H. Bell for Marland Oil Company of California.

1926—Bennett and Sclater presented a paper before the AIME reporting use of bottom-hole pressure bomb.[1]

1927—Vietti and Oberlin presented paper before AIME on paraffin problems in handling Texas Panhandle crude oil.[2]
N. O. Miller devised methods of balancing a fluid column in bore hole to overbalance the pressure in gas well in order to use cable tools for drilling in the pay section without loss of gas.
Marland Oil Co. and Roeser and Pendleton, Inc. developed large-scale pressure-maintenance gas-injection program in Cook Pool, Shackleford County, Texas, from which it is estimated that 70 percent of original oil has been recovered.
Injected gas at 1,500 psi in Bixby sand at Seal Beach (Calif.)

1928—Sclater and Stephenson presented paper at AIME describing use of bottom-hole device to secure sample of oil under reservoir conditions.[3] Also described a bottom-hole temperature and pressure bomb for obtaining true gas-oil ratio at reservoir conditions. Griswold and Wilkins presented paper on "Pressure Control of Oil Wells" showing that conservation of gas energy results in increased recovery of oil from a reservoir.[4]
Participated in drilling Group No. 1 Oil Corporation Well 1-B in west Texas, then deepest well in the world and deepest oil producer.

1929—E. H. Griswold reported on use of acid bottle in crooked-hole surveys and drew attention to distortion of subsurface data by crooked holes.[5]

1925-30—Major problems worked on by production engineers:
1. Unitization.
2. Gas-oil control.
3. Gas lift.
4. Efficient operation of wells.
5. Measurement of original pressures, temperatures, and gas-oil ratios in reservoirs.

6. Deviation of bore holes.
7. Deep-well drilling.
8. Paraffin control.
9. Gas injection.

1931-35—Reduced petroleum engineering activity during depression. Work done in drilling problems, selection of casing points and depth of pay penetration, low gas-oil ratios and control of water encroachment.

Developed further the technique of "drilling in" under pressure using oil as circulating medium.

1936-40—Petroleum engineering organization expanded.

Studied reservoir data, planned development drilling, and worked on proration problems.

Exploitation engineers took responsibility for selection of casing points, depth of pay penetration, etc.

1936—Commenced gas injection in Tepetate Field (La.) at 3,700 psi, project combining field stabilization of crude and gasoline recovery plant.

E. O. Bennett played leading part in Tepetate project; and, in recognition of work in field of gas injection, received Hanlon award of the NGAA in 1942.

In the middle 1930's, R. Van A. Mills did early work on drilling through heaving shales using silicate mud and continuous circulation.

Started two-phase pipeline transporting both crude oil and high-pressure gas in a single line.

1938—Continental well KCLA2 Wasco Field (Calif.) set new world record for depth—15,004 ft.

1941-45—Engineering staff depleted by war. Worked on reservoir studies, proration matters, and spacing problems.

1943—R. W. French in charge of petroleum engineering.

1946-50—Engineering staff expanded; production research group set up; reservoir studies. Developed pressure maintenance project at Walden, Colo., on carbon dioxide reservoir containing 6 percent hydrocarbons. Difficulties included very severe corrosion.

1946—Engineering training program adopted.

1947—Meyer H. Dubrow became chief petroleum engineer.

Water flooding commenced in limestone formation in nearly depleted Garber Pool (Kans.).

Limestone water-injection pressure-maintenance project started in Todd Field, Crockett County, Texas.

Separate production research group set up in development and research department.

1951-54—At the end of this period, the petroleum engineering organization included approximately 150 engineers, including trainees, divided into six groups, viz., reservoir, proration, civil, mechanical, natural-gas, and electrical engineers, supplemented by the production research laboratory staff of 60 working on: *a,* electric logging; *b,* reservoir mechanics; *c,* well completion and well stimulation; *d,* corrosion and allied chemical work; *e,* core analyses and core research; *f,* metallurgic problems.

The petroleum engineering group is a part of the production department staff at each level. Only the reservoir section is centralized in the headquarters group.

The petroleum engineers and those in the petroleum engineering organization are responsible for:

1. Well spacing.
2. Well-completion techniques.
3. Proration and conservation measures relating to producing oil and gas wells.
4. Reservoir-performance studies.
5. Calculation of oil and gas reserves.
6. Economics of developing oil and gas fields.
7. Unitization matters.
8. Overall planning of development programs.
9. Well-stimulation methods and planning of various other remedial measures to control gas and water, and increase ultimate oil recovery.
10. Economics studies, design and operation of secondary-recovery projects and pressure-maintenance projects involving gas or water injection, and gas cycling.

1955—Engineering organization modified by integrating all engineers into a single group headed by a chief engineer. This enables the engineers to be responsible for other than a specialized engineering function and permits them to receive broader experience and training for advancement to supervisory engineering or managerial positions.

References

[1]Bennett, E. O. and Sclater, K. C: Some New Aspects of the Gas Lift, *Petroleum Development and Technology in 1926,* 115, American Institute of Mining and Metallurgical Engineers, Inc., New York, 1927.
[2]Vietti, W. V. and Oberlin, W. A.: Problems Encountered in Handling Panhandle Crude, *Petroleum Development and Technology in 1927,* 269, American Institute of Mining and Metallurgical Engineers, Inc., New York, 1928.

[3]Sclater, K. C. and Stephenson, B. R: Measurement of Original Pressure, Temperature, and Gas-Oil Ratio in Oil Sands, *Petroleum Development and Technology in 1926*, 119, American Institute of Mining and Metallurgical Engineers, Inc., New York, 1927.

[4]Griswold, E. H. and Wilkins, W. J: Pressure Control of Oil Wells, *Trans. Am. Inst. Mining Met. Engrs. (Petroleum Development and Technology)* 104 (1928).

[5]Griswold, E. H: Acid Bottle Method of Subsurface Well Survey and its Application, *Trans Am. Inst. Mining Met. Engrs. (Petroleum Development and Technology)* 41 (1929).

Gulf Oil Corporation

1917—Dr. F. M. Siebert established research department at Houston, studying emulsions, corrosion, and muds.

H. E. Minor took "rotary basket cores." Core studies began then. Paul Paine, from California, installed air-lift plant at El Dorado, Kans.

1921—Joe H. Russell appointed chief production engineer and organized the first production engineering department for Gulf.

1923—Drilled 4,000-ft rotary holes at Tonkawa, Okla.

1924—H. P. Porter appointed chief production engineer for Tulsa (Okla.) Division. Natural-gasoline production was transferred from refining department to production department. Stanley H. Gill assigned solely to corrosion problems.

1925—Chas. H. Prater assigned solely to emulsion treating.

J. T. Richards demonstrated importance of subsurface correlation by rotary samples at Tonkawa, Okla.

1923-25—Hild semi-automatic electric drive for drilling rigs was developed by Westinghouse Co. and used by Gulf in Texas Coastal fields.

1926—J. H. Russell, Assistant Superintendent of Production, wrote paper on "Improved Drilling and Production Methods in the Gulf Coast Field."[1]

R. L. Wright of Gypsy Oil Co. spoke on "Present Oil Well Cementing Practice" before API in Dec. 1926.

First secondary-recovery operation. Injected air into wells in Kansas, Oklahoma, and Louisiana.

Financed development of time bomb for well shooting.

1927—Established Gulf Research and Development Company under Dr. Paul D. Foote as research department for entire corporation.

First district petroleum engineer appointed.

Bottom-hole temperature survey made.

Dr. B. B. Wescott recommended use of high-manganese sucker rods.

1928—Oscar Hatcher developed screen for catching rotary samples. Drilled 40 wells in Seminole with rotary equipment.

W. F. Rogers coated undersides of tank decks with aluminum foil to prevent corrosion.[2]

Abandoned air injection into oil reservoirs and substituted natural gas.

Research laboratory initiated studies on permeability and capillary phenomena.

R. S. Knappen suggested use of hydrofluoric acid for crooked-hole surveys.

100 wells surveyed. Offered premium to drilling contractors for holes with less than 10 percent deviation (reduced to 5 percent in 1930).

1929—R. L. Wright succeeded Hollis Porter as chief production engineer of Tulsa Division.

Stanley H. Gill wrapped pipe with greased felt and copper foil to prevent corrosion from without.

1929—Tubing run under pressure in West Texas.

Began controlled disposal of salt water by use of ponds.

First "production-control" unit set up.

Ran bottom-hole samples.

Employed J. Van Henst as mud engineer.

Formal program of core studies instituted.

Employed C. and M. Schlumberger on three-months trial to run electric log surveys in Seminole (Okla.), Kansas, and Texas Gulf Coast.

1930—Established system of reports on all well troubles, with copy to research department and with inspection and analysis of equipment failures.

Bottom-hole pressure bombs were run in flowing and in closed-in wells.

Used oil as drilling fluid in coring salt.

1925-30—Gulf engineers experimented with intermittent gas lift controlled by clock mechanisms.

1931—H. H. Power was chief production engineer at Tulsa 1931-36.

Ran submerged hydraulic pump at Fruitvale, Calif.

Screens and casing perforations were back-washed.

1932—First Gulf well in Oklahoma acidized using inhibitor.[3]

Established use of electrical analogs in study of interference between wells, etc.

1933—Developed theory of corrosion fatigue of sucker rods.[4]

First used salt-water disposal wells.

Hydrofluoric acid used in California in effort to remove silt behind pipe perforations.

1934—E. N. Kemler developed well-weighing dynamometer.[5]

Paul G. Exline designed Gulf-type bottom-hole pressure bomb to secure more precise data.[6]

1935—Chemical water-shutoff methods developed by H. T. Kennedy were successfully used in Oklahoma.[7]

Used gun for perforating casing.

1936—Gulf's first water-flood project started at Bird Creek (Okla.).

Formed drilling and reconditioning unit in engineering department.

Formed separate unit to estimate reserves and compare with production statistics.

K. B. Barnes equipped Gulf's first core laboratory at Tulsa.

1937—Commenced use of cathodic protection against corrosion.

Patented successful formation tester. Did a squeeze-cement job. Muskat published *The Flow of Homogeneous Fluids through Porous Media.*[8]

First formal engineering conference at Pittsburgh research laboratory. Gulf petroleum engineering work was organized on a division basis and the research laboratory was the point of coordination.

1938—Research laboratory built sonic fluid-level indicator for use in pumping wells.

1936-38—Gulf developed many instruments for securing subsurface information.

1930-38—Cementing operations were studied. Wrote new specifications for oil-well cement. Investigated contamination. Studied drilling muds. Experimented with scratchers and centralizers.

1939—P. G. Exline and H. J. EnDean described a rolling-ball viscosimeter which measured oil-well fluids under conditions existing in the reservoir.[9]

1940—Used diamond bits in oil-well drilling.

1941—L. C. Case proposed injection of polyphosphates into annular space of oil wells to prevent formation of scale.

Production research coordinating committee formed.

1942—Successful chemical treatment of oil well to prevent internal corrosion of tubing and casing. First treatment was with sodium hydroxide.

1943—A. J. Teplitz showed that cement frequently channelled through the drilling mud and failed to protect sands as expected.[10]

1945—Developed automatic controls on pumping wells to shut off without presence of pumper.

Muskat published basic differential equations combining material balance principles and relative-permeability characteristics of reservoirs.[11]

At Paloma (Calif.) used oil-base mud to prevent intrusion of water into producing oil sands.

1946—Jet casing perforation introduced—patents issued to Muskat, Parker, Kehl.

1947—Developed flow meter to determine volume of fluid entering a well below any point.[12]

Developed X-ray method of determining oil or water saturations of cores.[13]

1948—Developed formulas for making quantitative determination of salinity and saturation of interstitial water, and for estimation of porosity from electric well logs.[14,15,16]

1950—Pressure packed gravel in well at Sour Lake (Texas).

1951—Patented diesel-oil—bentonite squeeze process for correction of lost circulation in rotary wells.

References

[1]Russell, J. H: Improved Drilling and Production Methods in the Gulf Coast Field, *Petroleum Development and Technology in 1926,* 248, American Institute of Mining and Metallurgical Engineers, Inc., New York, 1927.

[2]Subcommittee on Production Corrosion: Corrosion of Production Equipment, *Proc. Am. Pet. Inst., Sect. IV (Prod. Bul. 206)* 153 (1930).

[3]Chapman, M. E: Some of the Theoretical and Practical Aspects of the Acid Treatment of Limestone Wells, *Oil Gas J.,* 10, Oct. 12 (1933).

[4]Wescott, Blaine B. and Bowers, C. Norman: Corrosion Fatigue and Sucker Rod Failures, *Proc. Am. Pet. Inst., Sect. IV (Prod. Bul. 212)* 29 (1933).

[5]Kemler, E. N: New Type of Dynamometer for Study of Pumping Problems, *Trans. Am. Inst. Mining Met. Engrs. (Petroleum Development and Technology)* **114,** 69 (1935).

[6]Exline, Paul G: A Precision Gage for Subsurface Pressure Measurements, *API Drilling and Production Practice,* 116 (1936).

[7]Kennedy, H. T: Chemical Methods for Shutting Off Water in Oil and Gas Wells, *Trans. Am. Inst. Mining Met. Engrs. (Petroleum Development and Technology),* **118,** 177 (1936).

[8]Muskat, Morris: *The Flow of Homogeneous Fluids through Porous Media,* McGraw-Hill Book Co., Inc., New York, 1937.

[9]Exline, Paul G. and EnDean, H. J: Viscosity Determination of Subsurface Samples of Crude Oil, *API Drilling and Production Practice,* 659 (1939).

[10]Teplitz, A. J. and Hassebroek, W. E: An Investigation of Oil-Well Cementing, *API Drilling and Production Practice,* 76 (1946).

[11]Muskat, Morris: *J. Applied Physics,* **16,** 147 (1945).

[12]Morgan, F; Reed, D. W; and Gray, L. L; Meter for Measuring Distribution of Gas Flow in Well Bores, *Trans. Am. Inst. Mining Met. Engrs. (Petroleum Development and Technology)* **174,** 253 (1948).

[13]Boyer, R. L; Morgan, F; and Muskat, M: A New Method for Measurement of Oil Saturation in Cores, *Trans. Am. Inst. Mining Met. Engrs. (Petroleum Development and Technology)* **170,** 115 (1947).

[14]Wyllie, M. R. J: Quantitative Analysis of Electrochemical Component of the SP Curve, *Trans. Am. Inst. Mining Met. Engrs. (Petroleum Development and Technology)* **186**, 17 (1949).

[15]Wyllie, M. R. J. and Rose, W. D: Some Theoretical Considerations Related to Quantitative Evaluation of Physical Characteristics of Reservoir Rocks from Electrical Log Data, *Trans. Am. Inst. Mining Met. Engrs. (Petroleum Development and Technology)* **189**, 105 (1950).

[16]Morgan, F; Wyllie, M. R. J; and Fulton, P. F: New Technique for Measurement of Formation Factors and Resistivity Indices of Porous Media, *Trans. Am. Inst. Mining Met. Engrs. (Petroleum Development and Technology)* **192**, 371 (1951).

Honolulu Oil Corporation

1909—First geological engineer was Paul Paine. Used peg models for study of subsurface structure.

1915—Paul Paine appointed field superintendent.

1926—Started gas injection in Buena Vista Hills.

1934—Started slow-motion pumping in Buena Vista Hills.

1940—Installed hydraulic power oil tubing lifters for dewaxing tubing in hydraulic pumping systems in Slaughter Field (West Texas).

Houston Oil Company of Texas

1920-25—A. S. Henley and C. A. Warner, geologists, advised on well completions, sand penetration, etc.

1924—Warner and W. B. Duncan adopted practice of completing wells at Cromwell Field (Okla.), above oil-water contact to reduce volume of water to be handled.

1930—Repressuring started in North Cole Bruni area of Texas with F. Y. Hutchison in charge.

1932—C. A. Warner, as petroleum engineer, represented the company in proration hearings in Texas.

1946—Established group of "petroleum engineers" under W. C. Dinger, chief petroleum engineer.
Petroleum engineering covers:
1. Subsurface.
2. Producing.
3. Natural gas.
4. Corrosion.
5. Equipment for testing.
6. Reservoir behavior.
7. Reserve estimates.
8. Salt-water disposal.
9. Proration and efficient conservation practices.

1956—Assets acquired by The Atlantic Refining Co.

Lion Oil Company

1934—First employed petroleum engineering at El Dorado (Kans.) for well-testing and pumping operations.

1938—Petroleum engineering section established under J. E. Howell. Studied well completions, remedial work, reservoirs, analysis of equipment and materials, well testing, and evaluations.

1945-49—Separate section of petroleum engineering set up to study reservoirs, reserves, and to make evaluations.
Emphasis on MER's, pressure maintenance, secondary recovery, unitization, and well-completion practices.

1949-54—Started petroleum engineering training program.
Special preparations made for hearings before regulatory bodies. Studies for proper selection of materials and equipment.

1956—Assets acquired by Monsanto Chemical Co.

Ohio Oil Company

1924—Commenced gas injection in old fields of Illinois under supervision of J. C. Askam.

1927—Commenced air injection in Trenton lime in Ohio.
Water injection and acid treatments were also used.

1930—Haynesville Field unitized.
Millard H. Flood hired as petroleum engineer and coordinator for Haynesville project.

1932—Subsidiary, Mid-Kansas Oil and Gas Company, formed petroleum engineering department under supervision of Frank R. Clark, chief geologist, with Lyndon L. Foley as chief engineer.
J. D. Wheeler hired as district petroleum engineer, for East Texas, and R. R. Kyner, for West Texas district.
Kyner became company's engineering representative on Yates Pool Engineering Committee.

1936—Company had five petroleum engineers at work.

1941—Instituted a company-wide petroleum engineering department with J. D. Wheeler chief petroleum engineer.
Personnel of the petroleum engineering department (all engineers) increased from 2 in 1930 to 151 in 1954.

1948—Engineer training program instituted.

1954—Research department, separate from the petroleum engineering department, started.
The trend of petroleum engineering work of the Ohio Oil Company has evolved to include the following:
  1. Increased oil recovery through air, gas, and water injection.
  2. Proration.

3. Gas conservation.
4. Producing methods.
5. Bottom-hole pressure and gas-oil ratio measurements.
6. Gasoline-extraction plants.
7. Unitization.
8. Subsurface well problems.
9. Electrical logging.
10. Reservoir engineering.
11. Water flooding.
12. Water disposal.
13. Cycling and model studies.
14. Estimation of oil and gas reserves and evaluation of oil and gas properties.

Phillips Petroleum Company

1924—J. M. Sands gave description of Burbank Oil Field, Osage County, Okla.[1]

1925—Employed E. G. Guidinger to establish petroleum engineering section in the production department, but he became occupied with special assignments such as gas-repressuring projects and air-lift projects and did not organize the production engineering group until 1928. Started gas repressuring in Pershing Pool (Osage County, Okla.).

1926—Started gas repressuring in North Burbank (Osage).
Started air injection in Bartlesville sand properties north of Bartlesville (Okla.).
Constructed and operated an air-lift plant at Smackover, Ark.
F. E. Rice discussed "Present and Future Methods of Manufacturing Natural Gasoline" before API at Annual Meeting.[3]
Geo. P. Bunn spoke before AIME in New York on "Advances in Natural-Gasoline Manufacturing Methods."

1927—Installed submerged electrical centrifugal pump (Reda) on Haupt lease, eastern Kansas.

1928—Guidinger organized a production engineering group in the production department and they worked on gas lift, well completions, and production-equipment problems in Seminole (Okla.), Oklahoma City, and the Texas Panhandle.

1932—D. R. Knowlton became chief engineer of the production department. An engineer training program was started with 10 men in Oklahoma fields and 3 in Texas. The training required a 2-year period.
The production department engineers occupied themselves with:

1. Engineering pertaining to subsurface well problems—shut-offs, completion depths, formations, bottom-hole plugging; and, in the Texas Panhandle, they determined the casing point on development wells.
2. Producing methods in tubing, chokes, control of gas-oil ratios, and selection and design of artificial-lift systems.
3. Oil handling from well to pipeline—gas traps, field tankage, oil treating, and gravity conservation.
4. Drilling and production equipment—rig fronts, pumping units, christmas trees, sucker rods, screens, and tools and special devices for intermittent gas lift.
5. Equipment for testing—bottom-hole pressure gages, samplers, and crooked-hole surveys.
6. Reservoir behavior—core analyses, electric logs, porosity and permeability, and fluid mechanisms.
7. Increased oil recovery—injection of water or gas, producing rates, well spacing, and acid treatments.
8. Salt-water disposal.
9. Economics of oil and gas production.
10. Proration, conservation controls, and unit operation.

1934—K. H. Hachmuth and Don L. Katz physically determined the equilibrium constants for Oklahoma City crude oil and did additional work with material-balance data.[3]

1935—Unitized 2,760 acres in the South Burbank Field (Okla.) and initiated pressure maintenance by gas injection.
Production research group was set up in the research department and work was commenced on basic information pertaining to reservoir engineering.

1936—Organized reservoir engineering group, active in proration, conservation, unitization, and secondary recovery.

1937—An improved bottom-hole sampler, using tapered plug valves, a new valve mechanism, and a spring-driven timing mechanism for opening valves at proper depth, was designed and used successfully.
Developed Coody's Bluff area for water flooding.

1938—An economic evaluation of multi-stage field separators, using experimental K constants, was carried out by K. H. Hachmuth and D. L. Katz.
Phillips pioneered in the development and use of the hot-wire hydrocarbon mud analyzer for detecting gas zones.
Smackover, Arkansas—replaced old rig fronts and single-cylinder gas engines with twin-crank pumping units and electric motors.

1939—Western Kansas—productivity indices were used for establishing well potentials and allowables in lieu of physical potentials which were previously used. Physical potentials on large fluid volume wells had resulted in the tearing up of sucker rods and surface equipment and excessive costs.

Prepared and issued a Production Engineering Manual which set forth the method and procedure to be used in designing artificial-lift systems, casing strings, pipelines, and camp utilities. Sections on gas lift, gas compression, and corrosion were added at later dates.

1941—Shuler Unit was formed and gas repressuring initiated.

Installed liquefied petroleum gas (LPG) fuel systems on company well-servicing units.

1942—Started water flooding in Greenwood County, Kansas.

Applied infra-red and ultra-violet absorption spectrometry to the routine analysis of the C_4 hydrocarbons.

1943—Recognized carbon dioxide as a prevalent corrosive agent in oil and gas wells.

1944—Reported a correlation between the partial pressure of carbon dioxide with the severity of corrosion in gas-condensate wells.

1945—Studied the influence of the metalographic structure on corrosion of equipment in oil and gas wells.

1946—Sodium carboxymethylcellulose (Driscose*) was developed and introduced to the industry for treatment of drilling mud, particularly to obtain low water loss and stability.

1947—Medrano Unit was formed and gas repressuring initiated.

West Edmond (Okla.) Unit was formed and gas repressuring initiated.

Successful diamond coring of the Ellenberger formation, at 9,500 to 10,000 ft, was carried out with 99 percent core recovery at the Phillips' Alma No. 7 Well, TXL Field, Ector County, Texas.

Introduced the idea of industry-wide cooperative research program on the drilling of wells. As a result, Drilling Research, Inc., was organized July 19, 1948.

Recognized importance of ductility in performance of tubular goods for high-pressure wells, and in 1954 proposed a ductility test that so far has shown a significant correlation with field performance.

Installed remote air controls on clutch and brake of company well-servicing units.

1948—Made installation of 9-percent nickel tubing in corrosive gas-condensate wells to minimize corrosion of tubing.

1949—North Burbank (Okla.) Unit was formed and water flooding initiated.

---

*Registered trade mark.

1950—Continuous-flow gas lift—reported a correlation that permitted calculation of the performance of continuous-flow gas lift and determination of the most efficient operating pressure and point of injection.

1951—High-pressure gas injection was initiated at the San Roque Field in Venezuela, involving reinjection of separator gas at 3,000 psig.

1952—Procedure for realizing the higher gas-lift efficiencies predicted by the 1950 correlation was worked out. This consisted essentially of using a small string of tubing to conduct the injected gas from the surface to the point of injection in the hole and thus eliminate the surging that resulted through injection of gas down the annulus.

Developed hydraulic-power-driven tubing tongs, and automatic controls for the hydraulic power pump.

Initiated industry-wide cooperative research program on sucker-rod pumping with the result that Sucker Rod Pumping Research, Inc. was organized January 18, 1954.

Conducted successful test to determine the practicability of using a centrifuge to separate heavy materials from drilling mud.

Developed a very light-weight cement slurry.

Diacel* cement slurries, with densities as low as 10.8 lb per gal and longer thickening times (better pumpability), were developed for deep-well cementing. The new cement replaced conventional slurries with minimum densities of 12.5 lb per gal.

1953—Started a program for evaluation of aerated-mud rotary drilling. Made the first installation of 9-percent chromium tubing to minimize corrosion in high-pressure condensate wells.

1954—Large-scale field evaluations of bactericides and other water additives were performed at the Phillips-operated Burbank Water Flood Unit.

Expanded the use of prefabricated, pre-stressed portable concrete bases to apply to all sizes of pumping units.

1955—A comprehensive field evaluation of the use of the hydraulic cyclone for drilling-mud treatment was conducted on a series of deep-well projects. Durable cyclones of tungsten carbide were developed and proved to be superior for sand removal, and virtually competitive for barite recovery, to existing centrifuge equipment.

1956—Lease automatic custody-transfer system installed at North Burbank Unit Battery #95.

1957—Lease automatic custody transfer, automatic well testing, and automatic well control installed on Ranch "C" lease in Texas, as

*Registered trade mark.

a completely automatic oil-producing facility to handle and deliver oil to the pipeline unattended.

1958—A field application of LPG flooding to a watered-out reservoir was started in the Burkett Field, Greenwood County, Kansas. Phillips No. 1-EE University Well, Pecos County, Texas, was drilled to more than 24,357 ft, the world's deepest hole.

The production department is organized into production districts with roughly a 50- to 100-mile radius. They are staffed with a superintendent and assistant superintendent—the latter supervise district staff engineers carrying on field production engineering work of all types. In the division offices, there are one or two reservoir engineers and a general staff engineer. The main concentration of petroleum production and reservoir engineer specialists is at Bartlesville, Okla.

References

[1]Sands, J. M: *Am. Assoc. of Petroleum Geologists Bull.,* **[8]** 584 (1924).

[2]Rice, F. E: Present and Future Methods of Manufacturing Natural Gasoline, *API Bulletin* **VII, [27]** 241, April 12 (1926).

[3]Katz, D. L. and Hachmuth, K. H: Vaporization Equilibrium Constants in a Crude Oil-Natural Gas System, *Ind. and Eng. Chem.,* **29,** 1072, Sept. (1937).

Plymouth Oil Company

1937-38—H. M. Lievzey established petroleum engineering department, with W. L. Parker as assistant engineer.

1938-39—Set up production records, started bottom-hole surveys, studied gas lift, control of gas-oil ratio (GOR), and stop-cocking.

1940-44—During the war petroleum engineering department greatly reduced, and outside consultants used where necessary.

Started gas injection in two principal sands of Plymouth Field and began small water-flooding project in same field.

1945-50—With return of engineers from war, conservation studies resumed. Built two gasoline plants which were operated by the petroleum engineering department.

Pure Oil Company

1925—H. C. O. Clarke organized production engineering department of The Pure Oil Company on an equal basis with existing geological, mechanical engineering, and operating departments. Production engineering department first located at Mexia, Texas, where Clarke was assisted by R. B. Kelly, division engineer, and H. H. Allen, staff engineer. Later, W. W. Scott was located at Tulsa as production engineer for Kansas, Oklahoma, and Arkansas.

Later in 1925, the headquarters of the production engineering department was moved to the general offices of the company.

H. J. Lowe became assistant production engineer in the general offices at Columbus, Ohio, and then at Chicago, Illinois.

Later, R. H. Carr became chief production engineer.

1926—H. C. O. Clarke and H. J. Lowe presented papers at AIME entitled "Increasing Recovery and Its Economic Effects."[1]

1925-30—Production engineers worked on improving and developing production techniques, shutting off water in producing wells, and conditioning wells for reworking.

1930—Increased attention given to mechanical phases of drilling and producing. "Drilling-mud group" formed to study drilling and mud problems.

Developed commercial use of hydrochloric acid for acidizing limestone formations.

Sucker rods, insert-type pumps, tubing protectors, etc. investigated.

Unitized the Van Field (Texas) and after 25 years (1955) the discovery well was still flowing.

1938—Pure and Superior Oil Companies drilled first well in open waters of Gulf of Mexico and, on March 17, 1938, discovered the Creole Field (oil) off the coast of Louisiana.

Did work in water flooding.

1945-54—Production engineering department was expanded to include chemical, mechanical, civil, and electrical engineers, all of whom work closely with the research and development laboratories.

References

[1]Clarke, H. C. O. and Lowe, H. J: Increasing Recovery and Its Economic Effects, *Petroleum Development and Technology in 1926*, 241, American Institute of Mining and Metallurgical Engineers, Inc., New York, 1927.

Rio Bravo Oil Company

1919—John R. Suman became Assistant to the General Manager of Rio Bravo, Dr. E. T. Dumble.

1922-23—Dr. Dumble introduced micropalaentology as a means of identifying oil - producing formations in Gulf Coast oil fields. Engineering group divided into three sections, viz., producing, construction, and surveying.

Production engineering section worked principally on drilling and production practices and equipment.

1924—Instituted a program of field testing of new equipment with complete operating records under the supervision of producing engineers.

1925—Experimented with adjustable chokes to control flowing production.

John R. Suman presented a paper at AIME on "The Sanding of Oil Wells"[1] and at AAPG on "The Saratoga Oil Field, Hardin County, Texas."[2]

1926—John R. Suman made report to API on "Proper Installation and Care of Oil-field Boilers."[3]

1926—Electrified central pumping powers.

1926-27—Adopted "stellite" facing on drilling bits.

1927—Electrified unit pumping installations.

Used air lift at Pierce Junction oil field (Texas).

Tested kick-off valves.

1920-35—Early use of subsurface directional surveys and directional drilling because operations were conducted on narrow railway rights of way and around piercement-type salt domes.

Made early use of bentonite-cement mix for drilling through cavernous porosity at Barbers' Hill oil field (Texas).

1934—Used phosphate as mud additive in Pierce Junction oil field (Texas).

References

[1]Suman, John R: The Sanding of Oil Wells, *Petroleum Development and Technology in 1925*, 196, American Institute of Mining and Metallurgical Engineers, Inc., New York, 1926.

[2]Suman, John R: The Saratoga Oil Field, *Am. Assoc. Petroleum Geologist Bull.*, **9**, 263 (1925).

[3]Suman, John R: Proper Installation and Care of Oil-Field Boilers, *Am. Pet. Inst. Bulletin*, **VIII [6]** 31, Jan. 31 (1927).

Seaboard Oil Company (formerly Milham Exploration Company)

1927—N. A. Rousselot and D. E. Curry, petroleum engineers, supervised drilling the discovery well in the Kettleman Hills Field (Calif.). Weighting material was used in the mud stream.

1930—Seaboard, the largest individual interest in the Kettleman North Dome Association in California, through KNDA initiated the extensive use of electric logging.

1938—Seaboard and Tide Water Associated Oil Company jointly built a gas-recycling plant at Cayuga Field (Texas).

1943—Established a petroleum engineering department under the production department with Jack Hayes as chief petroleum engineer.

1945—Seaboard and Tide Water Associated Oil Company put in operation the pressure-maintenance program by high-pressure (4,000 psi) water injection in the New Hope Field (Texas).

1949—Organized a training program for petroleum engineers.

1953—Organized a separate natural-gas and gas-utilization department.

Petroleum engineering embraces:

    a. Production problems.

    b. Proration practices.

    c. Reservoir-performance studies.

    d. Conservation practices.

    e. Reservoir estimates.

    f. Salt-water disposal.

    g. Corrosion.

    h. Equipment testing.

Shell Oil Company
(Including Predecessor and Subsidiary Companies)

1913-17—B. H. van der Linden set up a producing organization in California in 1913 and combined geologists and field engineers into a working group. Among the engineers and geologists who joined the organization from 1914 to 1917 were J. E. Elliott, E. D. Nolan, A. W. Ambrose, W. W. Scott, R. R. Templeton, F. E. Rehm, and T. E. Swigart.

1915—Wells were drilled in the Coalinga Field (Calif.) using the rotary method.

1917—At the Coalinga East Side Field with the permission of the California State Oil and Gas Supervisor, R. P. McLaughlin, a well was drilled to the oil sand, with no intermediate casing, the water sands being sealed off with mud. This resulted in the saving of one or more strings of pipe.

1918-19—W. A. J. M. van der Gracht introduced the core barrel to company operations in the Mid-Continent. Coring was started in shallow exploration wells at Santa Fe Springs and later in the Coalinga Field (Calif.) with the Holland core drill (also called the Koster drill).

1919—A petroleum engineering section was established under G. S. Rollins as area engineer, with offices in St. Louis. R. B. Roark and L. Roark, geologists, were transferred to petroleum engineering section as resident field engineers at the Yale and Healdton Fields (Okla.).

1921—Studies on the use of foraminifera for correlation purposes were started in California. However, the results were not put to practical use until about 1924 when G. E. Miller devised workable methods of correlation.

1922—H. H. Anderson wrote a company report on drilling muds mixed from 24 typical California clays describing the chemical characteristics of the muds and the effects of alkalines and salines on the mixtures. The mechanics of the penetration of the mud-laden fluid into the sandy formations and the plastering effects of mud on the walls of the hole were also described.

1923—Barite was added to mud as a weighting material to control gas while drilling with cable tools in the Ventura Field (Calif.).

1924—Production engineering activities were initiated and gas-lift operations were started at Tonkawa, Braman, and the Seminole Fields (Okla.) under the supervision of R. W. Bond.

T. E. Swigart was employed as chief production engineer in California and initiated projects in gas lifting, gas storage in the Dominguez Field (in cooperation with Union Oil Co. of California) and the control of flowing wells in an effort to lower gas-oil ratios and conserve gas energy in the reservoir.

An oil-well water-locating device was developed and was named after one of its inventors, Dr. F. W. Huber. Oil-well water was successfully located by electrical means in wells in the Long Beach Field (Calif.).

1926—R. W. Bond and W. H. Collins, both petroleum engineers, initiated one of the early gas-drive projects in the Mid-Continent area on the Zollers lease in the Key West Field (Okla.).

1927—Deflection surveys, utilizing the hydroflouric acid bottle method, were initiated by W. H. Morrison and soon were run on a routine basis on most company wells drilled in the Mid-Continent area.

Inaugurated a training program for engineering personnel. The training schedule called for up to two years practical experience in the field prior to going to work as an engineer.

1928—Shell Development Company was organized to do basic hydrocarbon research. Later, in 1945, all research for the exploration and production departments was concentrated in Houston under the direction of Dr. H. Gershinowitz.

1929—The Schlumberger electric-logging device was introduced into California on an experimental basis. At that time, only one electric property, the specific resistance, was measured.

1930—Petroleum engineering section expanded to include a group specializing in production geology under the supervision of B. van der Schilden. This group standardized the preparation of detailed maps, cross sections, and isopachs of oil fields.

1931—G. Moir was transferred to California where he modernized the petroleum engineering section. Subsequently, petroleum engineers in Shell were known as exploitation engineers.

1932—The Schlumberger electric log, now measuring both spontaneous potential (SP) and specific resistance, was pioneered by the Royal Dutch Shell group in Venezuela and shortly afterward brought to the United States and routine use commenced.

99

1933—The value of acidization of limestone was recognized and used on a company well in the Greenwich Field (Kans.).

Dr. O. Wilhelm was transferred to California where he introduced many of the present-day methods used by the company's production geologists. Later, in Houston, he was responsible for the organization of a modern production geology section for which he initiated a training program.

1934—Used bottom-hole pressure recorder below a drill-stem tester in Shell-Wilbert No. 8 in the White Castle Field (La.).

Shell reservoir engineering had its early beginnings within the Mid-Continent area during this year. C. H. Keplinger prepared several company reports dealing with core-analysis techniques and with the use of bottom-hole pressure measurements in determining open-flow well potentials. Later, in 1935, A. F. Van Everdingen was transferred to Houston where he was instrumental in organizing and expanding reservoir engineering activities.

1934-36—R. C. McCurdy was assigned to the study of electric logging as a result of which he proposed a wider spacing of the electrodes by means of which data were obtained for the lateral investigation curve.

1935—Many refinements in exploitation engineering procedures were started under the supervision of H. Bloemgarten and A. J. Galloway.

1936—A contribution to the evaluation of oil properties was the concept of "Average Annual Percent Profit" which was advanced by A. F. Van Everdingen and S. F. Bowlby in a company report. The concept was brought to industry attention by J. J. Arps in his paper "Profitability Analysis of Proposed Capital Expenditures for Development Drilling and Appraisal of Producing Properties".[1]

P. E. Lehr and H. T. Wyatt patented the "Depthograph" method of locating fluid levels in oil wells.

Work in the development of a bottom-hole instrument for recording the subsurface action of oil-well plunger pumps was carried out by W. E. Gilbert.[2]

1936-37—J. F. Redmond initiated the use of the extraction gravimetric method of determining the fluid content of cores and later installed the company's first core-analysis laboratory in Tulsa.

1937—A water flood was initiated for the Xenia-Rockford Field (Kans.).

1938—An oil-base drilling fluid was tested in two wells in the Round Mountain Field (Calif.). Pioneer work on oil-base mud was done by R. D. Dawson and P. H. Huisman.

1941—G. E. Archie reported the basic relations between porosity, resistivity, and fluid content, and presented methods for using these
relations in electric-log interpretations.[3]
L. J. Klinkenberg prepared a paper on "The Permeability of Porous
Media to Liquids and Gases".[4]

1942—During this period significant contributions were made by G. L.
Hassler, E. Brunner, and T. J. Deahl toward an understanding of
the role of capillarity in the production of oil.[5]

1945—J. F. Redmond and M. A. Westbrook reported a method of obtaining porosities of consolidated formations from drill cuttings.[6]

1948—Installed equipment for the automatic custody transfer of crude
oil in the Antelope Field (Texas).
Initiated a training program in Houston for engineers and geologists. This training was professional in nature as contrasted to
the practical training given to engineers.
W. R. Purcell presented a paper on capillary pressures. This paper
discussed the use of mercury-injection procedures for determining
pore-size distribution of capillaries available for conducting fluid
and provided a method for obtaining relative-permeability and
saturation data.[7]

1949—G. E. Archie presented a paper on the petrophysics of reservoir
rocks.[8]
A. F. Van Everdingen and W. Hurst wrote a paper on the application of the Laplace transformation to flow problems in reservoirs.[9]

1951—Completed the field-wide unitization of the Elk City Field and
formulated plans for a cycling project. The successful unitization
of this field is considered notable because of the complexity of
ownership and the diverse reservoir content (gas, gas condensate,
and oil).
C. H. Fay and M. Prats presented a paper before the Third World
Petroleum Congress on the application of numerical methods in
determining the optimum operating procedures for gas-cycling
and flooding operations.[10]

1952—Used data-processing and electronic-computer methods to solve
engineering problems.
A. F. Van Everdingen wrote a paper on the skin effect and its influence on the productive capacity of the well.[11]
M. K. Hubbert wrote a paper discussing the entrapment of petroleum under hydrodynamic conditions.[12]

1956—C. S. Matthews and H. C. Lefkovits presented a paper having to
do with the gravity-drainage performance of depletion-type reservoirs in the stripper stage.[13]

M. K. Hubbert and D. G. Willis presented a paper discussing the mechanics of hydraulic fracturing of underground reservoirs.[14]

1957—T. M. Doscher and L. Weber investigated the use of the membrane filter as a means of determining the quality of water for subsurface injection.[15]

References

[1]Arps, J. J: Profitability of Capital Expenditures for Development Drilling and Appraisal of Producing Properties, *AIME J. Petr. Tech.*, 13, July (1958).

[2]Gilbert, W. E: An Oil-Well Pump Dynagraph, *API Drilling and Production Practice*, 94 (1936).

[3]Archie, G. E: The Electrical Resistivity Log as an Aid in Determining Some Reservoir Characteristics, *Trans. Am. Inst. Mining Met. Engrs. (Petroleum Development and Technology)*, **146**, 54 (1942).

[4]Klinkenberg, L. J: The Permeability of Porous Media to Liquids and Gases, *API Drilling and Production Practice*, 200 (1941).

[5]Hassler, G. L; Brunner, E; and Deahl, T. J: The Role of Capillarity in Oil Production, *Trans. Am. Inst. Mining Met. Engrs. (Petroleum Development and Technology)*, **155**, 155 (1944).

[6]Redmond, J. F. and Westbrook, M. A: A New Technique for Determining the Porosity of Drill Cuttings, *Trans. Am. Inst. Mining Met. Engrs. (Petroleum Development and Technology)*, **165**, 219 (1946).

[7]Purcell, W. R: Capillary Pressures—Their Measurement Using Mercury and the Calculation of Permeability Therefrom, *Trans. Am. Inst. Mining Met. Engrs. (Petroleum Development and Technology)*, **186**, 39 (1949).

[8]Archie, G. E: Introduction to Petrophysics of Reservoir Rocks, *Am. Assoc. Petroleum Geologists Bull.*, **34** [5] 943, May (1950).

[9]Van Everdingen, A. F. and Hurst, W: The Application of the Laplace Transformation to Flow Problems in Reservoirs, *Trans. Am. Inst. Mining Met. Engrs. (Petroleum Development and Technology)*, **186**, 305 (1949).

[10]Fay, C. H. and Prats, M: The Application of Numerical Methods to Cycling and Flooding Problems, *Proc. Third World Pet. Congress, Section II*, 555 (1951).

[11]Van Everdingen, A. F: The Skin Effect and Its Influence on the Productive Capacity of a Well, *Trans. Am. Inst. Mining Met. Engrs. (Petroleum Development and Technology)*, **198**, 171 (1953).

[12]Hubbert, M. K: Entrapment of Petroleum Under Hydrodynamic Conditions, *Am. Assoc. Petroleum Geologists Bull.*, **37** [8] 1954, August (1953).

[13]Matthews, C. S. and Lefkovits, H. C: Gravity Drainage Performance of Depletion-type Reservoirs in the Stripper Stage, *Trans. Am. Inst. Mining Met. Engrs. (Petroleum Development and Technology)*, **207**, 265 (1956).

[14]Hubbert, M. K. and Willis, D. G: Mechanics of Hydraulic Fracturing, *Trans. Am. Inst. Mining Met. Engrs. (Petroleum Development and Technology)*, **210**, 153 (1957).

[15]Doscher, T. M. and Weber, L: The Use of the Membrane Filter in Determining Quality of Water for Subsurface Injection, *API Drilling and Production Practice*, 169 (1957).

Sinclair Oil & Gas Company, Including Prairie Oil and Gas Company

1926—Subsurface studies, salt-water disposal, and gas-lift methods of production were initiated by Raymond M. Carr in the Garber Field of Oklahoma. Air repressuring was started in Nowata County, Oklahoma. Injected gas in the cooperative repressuring program in the Burbank Field (Okla.).

1927—Gas-lift operations in the Seminole Field (Okla.), were expanded by Lloyd Holsapple. During the next few years, petroleum engineering principles were applied to gas-lift operations, oil treating, pumping equipment, and crooked holes. Gas repressuring was started in Butler and Greenwood Counties, Kansas.

1928—Gas repressuring was expanded in Greenwood County, Kansas, by Donald W. Bennett.

1931—Bottom-hole pressure tests were run in the East Texas Field.

1932—The merger with the Prairie Oil and Gas Company added C. C. Carlisle and F. H. Rhees to engineering staff. Started intensive gas-repressuring project in Nowata County, Oklahoma. J. H. Rankin contributed engineering analyses of repressuring in north-central Texas

1935—Large-scale vapor recovery systems were installed in the East Texas Field.

1936—H. H. Elliston was placed in charge of engineering for the subsurface disposal of produced salt water.

1941—Successful field-wide pressure-maintenance operations started with gas injection in Wertz Field (Wyo.).

Present—Sinclair Oil & Gas Company petroleum engineering work now covers nearly all phases of reservoir-performance study, control, and improvement. These include the conventional techniques of observation including electrical and radioactive logging, core analysis, bottom-hole pressures, and gas-oil ratios. From this information, conclusions are reached concerning producing methods, reserves, unitization, proration, water flooding, water disposal, etc. There is a chief engineer and an assistant chief together with various civil, mechanical, and reservoir engineers located in the general offices at Tulsa, Oklahoma, on the staff of the vice-president, production department.

Since the decentralization into operating divisions in the latter part of 1954, division engineers have been located at each division headquarters. These division engineers have a staff sufficient to perform necessary production engineering in that particular area. Research work in petroleum engineering is done separately by Sinclair Research Laboratories, Inc. Natural-gas and gasoline extraction are also handled by a separate gas and gas-products department.

Socony-Mobil and its Autonomous Affiliates General Petroleum and Magnolia Petroleum

Socony-Mobil Oil Company, Inc.

1944—John C. Case, Vice-President, established the petroleum engineer-

ing section of the producing department at the New York headquarters with C. A. Moon as chief petroleum engineer. Early
problems included:

   a. Formation of petroleum engineering groups for foreign
      operations.
   b. Analysis and advice on oil-field development.
   c. Preparation of production forecasts, and the review of
      reserves.
   d. Formation of a production research group.

1945—Reservoir data was accumulated and studies commenced.

1946—Production research was inaugurated at the field research laboratories in Dallas, with activities to include research in well-bore
mechanics and reservoir mechanics.

Water flooding in New York State was studied.

1947—An oil-field equipment specialist was employed and equipment
and tools received added attention.

Studies of producing methods, MER determination, and control
of GOR were undertaken.

Promoted bottom-hole sampling and PVT analyses by affiliates.

1948—Well-logging specialist employed.

Training course for petroleum engineers established.

1949—Additional petroleum engineering groups for foreign subsidiaries
were formed.

1950-54—With expanded foreign operations, studies of the petroleum
engineering groups became more extensive. The following were
investigated:

   a. Equipment testing.
   b. New well-logging tools and methods. Development of more
      logging specialists.
   c. Economic evaluations of various field development pro-
      grams including gas injection, water flooding, and unitiza-
      tion of oil and gas properties.
   d. Coordination of the reserve estimation effort.
   e. Producing department budget.

The group was enlarged by adding additional specialists in drilling, production, and reservoir engineering. The staff engaged in
production research at the field research laboratories was gradually
increased to about 120 men.

General Petroleum Corporation

1912—Began using "resident geologists" in California oil fields.

1912-21—Resident geologists spent increasing amounts of work time
on oil-field development instead of geology.

1921—Applied term "petroleum engineer" to head-office men who supervised "resident geologists."

1923—Organized engineering test group in engineering department which, in 1924, became "production engineering and equipment" section.

Designed sucker-rod dynamometers.

1924—J. A. Zublin gave a paper at API on "Pumping Deep Wells in California."[1]

1928—Changed title of "resident geologists" to "petroleum engineers."

1948-54—Engineering in the production department divided into two sections, viz., production engineering and equipment, and petroleum engineering.

Production engineering and equipment section functions are:
   a. Production research and laboratory.
   b. Production engineering.
   c. Drilling engineering.
   d. Materials engineering.
   e. Equipment engineering.
   f. Equipment records.
   g. Vapor recovery.

Petroleum engineering section functions are:
   a. Subsurface well problems.
   b. Planning lease development and well spacing.
   c. Scouting.
   d. Reservoir studies in collaboration with production engineering section.
   e. Methods of increasing oil recovery from reservoirs.
   f. Unit operations.
   g. Oil and gas reserves and estimates.
   h. Evaluations.

References

[1]Zublin, John A: Pumping Deep Wells in California, *Proc. Am. Pet. Inst.*, 55 (1924).

Magnolia Petroleum Company

1931—D. V. Carter employed as petroleum engineer but acted in capacity of chief petroleum engineer until August 1, 1934. Early engineering activities included the solution of production problems, design of equipment, acquisition of reservoir performance data and physical properties, and evaluation of all departmental proposals including oil and gas property purchases.

1934—Petroleum engineering department organized within the producing department on August 1, 1934 with D. V. Carter as chief petroleum engineer. The department was established as a line organization with personnel working with, but not for, producing department supervisors at field level. Department was assigned the responsibility of advising management on application of sound petroleum engineering principles to all phases of Magnolia's drilling and producing operations.

1935—All produced gas from a group of producing wells in the O'Hern Field, Webb and Duval Counties, Texas, was injected into a key well at an injection pressure of approximately 900 psi.[1]

1936—Prepared first annual reserve estimate with analyses on every field in Magnolia's operating territory. Work was actually started in 1935 but first report not completed until 1936. This report was and is being prepared by young engineers, under the supervision of experienced engineers, in the field. This experience has aided the young engineers in acquiring a better knowledge of reservoir performance and competitive operations.

1937—Started gas-injection operations in the Bull Bayou Field, Louisiana.

1941—Petroleum engineering department graduate engineering personnel had increased to 25 at the start of World War II. Activities that were initiated in the early days and continue to be important petroleum engineering functions are:
  a. Data measurements and recording.
  b. Equipment studies.
  c. Studies of production problems.
  d. Drilling and completion studies.
  e. Routine laboratory tests, including fluid behavior and core analyses.
  f. Reservoir-behavior analyses.
  g. Unitization.
  h. Proration.
  i. Reserve estimates.
  j. Economic evaluations.

1942—Magnolia's first water-flood project designed and started by petroleum engineering department. This, the West Burkburnett Field, Wichita County, Texas, was an outstandingly successful water flood. Since 1942 the department has been active in the initiation and control of the company's fluid-injection operations. By the end of 1954, Magnolia was participating in 109 secondary-recovery and pressure-maintenance projects, of which 77 were operated by the company.
Established a central petroleum engineering laboratory in Dallas to replace two field laboratories located at Kermit and the West Ranch Field, Texas. This laboratory was modernized and placed

in a new building in early 1956 and handles routine and special core analyses and routine fluid-behavior analyses.

1944—D. V. Carter presented paper on estimating petroleum reserves to the Association Research Committee Conference, sponsored by the American Association of Petroleum Geologists, in Dallas, Texas, March 21, 1944.[2]

1945—The petroleum engineering department was expanded to include a new position of assistant chief petroleum engineer (first filled by Dan C. Williams), and a division petroleum engineer position in each of the west Texas, Shreveport, and Gulf Coast divisions.

Initiated training program for beginning engineers who are placed in the field under the producing department for approximately six months of training as roustabouts and roughnecks before being assigned to the engineering department as junior petroleum engineers.

New position of petroleum engineer assistant was created at district level to be filled by other than graduate petroleum engineers, but personnel with oil-field producing experience, to record and gather routine field tests and other information. This procedure permitted more efficient utilization of engineering manpower and has provided a better background for the assistants, many of whom later transfer into supervisory positions of the producing department.

1946—D. V. Carter wrote paper on utilization of engineering committees.[3] E. C. Patton, Jr. wrote paper on evaluation of pressure maintenance by gas injection for which he was awarded the 1948 Raymond Memorial Award of the AIME.[4]

1947—C. H. Hudson promoted to assistant chief petroleum engineer, replacing Dan C. Williams (resigned).

1949—Began water injection into the Morein sand, Mamou Field, Evangeline Parish, Louisiana, using high water-injection pressures (over 2,500 psig) in a deep reservoir (approximately 11,500 ft subsurface). The oil had a high shrinkage factor and maintenance of reservoir pressure has substantially increased recovery.

1954—By the end of 1954 the graduate petroleum engineering personnel had increased to 160 and there were also a number of young engineers in the training program. By October 1958, the number of petroleum engineers had increased to 220, with 386 total employees in the department.

1955—Separate drilling engineering section was established in the home office with new positions of drilling engineers and supervisors in the field. In addition, mud technician positions were established and filled with qualified craftsmen, not necessarily men with college degrees. These engineers function in same capacity as others in the department in that they work with, but not for, supervisors of the producing department and drilling tools.

The petroleum engineering department is a line organization with authority vested in the department. The department is a complete unit within itself with authority to employ, promote, and train its personnel. The organization is comprised of a central control and administrative office located in Dallas, Texas, with offices in each producing division and district. The Dallas staff is divided into six sections headed by a section chief under the chief and assistant chief petroleum engineers as follows:

a. Reserves and evaluation.
b. Secondary recovery.
c. Proration and legal.
d. Production and equipment.
e. Drilling.
f. Reservoir engineering.

In addition, a specialist is employed under the direct supervision of the chief and assistant chief petroleum engineers to study chemical and corrosion matters, and also coordinates research and technical service matters with the field research laboratory.

In addition to the four papers listed in the references following, the petroleum engineers of the Magnolia Petroleum Company published 32 technical papers during the period 1947-1958, inclusive.

For several years Magnolia has provided a fellowship program for employees. Under this program four petroleum engineers returned to college to obtain advanced degrees. The theses prepared by these men are listed following.[5,6,7,8]

References and Bibliography

[1]Magnolia's New Type Repressuring Plant Sustains Reservoir Energy, *Oil Gas J.*, **34** [**17**] 38, Sept. 12 (1935).

[2]Carter, D. V: Applications of Reserve Estimates of Hydrocarbon Fluids (Crude Oil, Gas, and Condensate), *Am. Assoc. Petroleum Geologists Bull.*, **28** [**5**] 630, May (1944).

[3]Carter, D. V: Petroleum Engineering Committees, Their Present Activities and Their Potentialities, *Oil Gas J.*, **44** [**46**] 92, Mar. 23 (1946). Also *Oil Weekly* (in 2 parts): Part 1, **121** [**4**] 55, Mar. 25 (1946); Part 2: **121** [**5**] 24, April 1, (1946). Also *Petroleum Engr.* (in 2 parts; title, "Organization and Functioning of Oil-field Engineering Committees"): Part 1, **17** [**11**] 88, July (1946); Part 2, **17** [**12**] 74, Aug. (1946).

[4]Patton E. C., Jr: Evaluation of Pressure Maintenance by Internal Gas Injection in Volumetrically Controlled Reservoirs, *Trans. Am. Inst. Mining Met. Engrs. (Petroleum Development and Technology)*, **170**, 112 (1947).

[5]Coleman, Dwayne M: The Recovery of Oil from Carbonate Reservoirs by Fluid Injection. Submitted to the Graduate School of A & M College of Texas, August 1954.

[6]Schmalz, J. P: A Statistical Study of Core Analysis Data. Submitted to the Graduate Faculty of the University of Oklahoma, 1950.

[7]Van Meter, O. E: An Investigation of the Correlation of Core Analysis Data with Original Core Saturations in the Kelly-Snyder Field, Scurry County, Texas. A thesis submitted to the Graduate School of A & M College of Texas, June 1952.

[8]Young, Gerald S: A Study of K_g/K_o Values from Reservoir Performance. Submitted to the Graduate School of A & M College of Texas, August 1957.

Crego, William O. and Henagan, James M: Report on the Mamou Field Pressure Maintenance Project, *AIME J. Petr. Tech.*, **3**, Oct. (1951); *Trans. Am. Inst. Mining Met. Engrs. (Petroleum Development and Technology)* **192**, 263 (1951).

Holland, H. K., Jr: West Burkburnett Field Water-Flood Project Will be Largest Pattern Project in North Texas, *Oil Gas J.*, **47**, 88, April 28 (1949); *The Petroleum Engr.*, **21**, B-12 *(Ref. Annual)* (1949).

Marrs, Doyle: Miscible Drive Field Application: Parks Field, *AIME J. Petr. Tech.*, **10**, 20, May (1958).

Whitney, J. W. W: West Burkburnett Water Flood, *Oil Gas J.*, **53** [33] 93, Dec. 20 (1954).

Standard Oil Company of California and Predecessor Companies — Pacific Coast Oil Company, The Kern Trading and Oil Company, and Pacific Oil Company

Pacific Coast Oil Company

Organized in 1879. Purchased by Standard Oil Co. (N. J.) in 1900 and transferred its properties to Standard Oil Company of California when organized in 1906.

The Kern Trading and Oil Company

Organized in 1903 by Southern Pacific Railroad Company. Properties transferred to Pacific Oil Company in 1921.

1907—Located "resident geologists" in oil fields. Studied subsurface conditions with cross sections.

1911—J. A. Taff became "geologist in charge."

1915—E. G. Gaylord appointed head "development geologist."

Pacific Oil Company

Merged with Standard Oil Company of California in 1926.

1921—J. A. Taff appointed chief geologist.

1924—E. G. Gaylord and J. A. Taff prepared a paper on "Geological Organization of an Oil Company."[1]

Standard Oil Company of California

1908—Purchased three rotary outfits at Beaumont, Texas; and in August started rotary drilling at Midway, Coalinga, and King City oil fields (Calif.).

Organized geological department under Dr. E. A. Starke, geologist and chemist.

1909—As contribution to efforts to exclude water from oil-producing strata, Standard posted on its derricks description of formations encountered in drilling each well.

1920—E. W. Wagy appointed petroleum engineer in December 1920.

1923—Wagy succeeded by E. J. Young with title "chief petroleum engineer".

1926—When Pacific Oil Company lands acquired, E. G. Gaylord became chief petroleum engineer for Standard Oil Co. of California.

1924—Organized "production engineering" section in production department.

E. J. Young developed "water witch". (Huber of the Shell Company also developed a water witch in 1924.)

1926—F. D. Bly gave paper at AIME on "Corrosion of Underground Pipe Lines."[2]

1927—Gaylord helped inspire API Research Project 37, covering analysis of petroleum fractions under wide range of pressure and temperature.

1929—G. V. D. Marx developed spring-actuated depth recorder.

1931—Joined with Kettleman West Dome Association in unitization of Kettleman Hills Field (Calif.).

1932—July 1, 1932, J. H. Menke appointed assistant chief petroleum engineer.

1934—Established joint research laboratory at Kettleman Hills with North Dome Association, which was burned out in 1936.

1936—Production technology laboratory started at La Habra (Calif.) under direction of E. G. Gaylord and J. E. Gosline.

1939—Established an engineer's training course.

1943—Participated in gas-injection project at Elk Hills (Calif.).

1944—Commenced injection of gas at West Coyote (Calif.).

Commenced water injection at Greeley Field (Calif.).

1946—Production technology laboratory became part of California Research Corporation.

1947—E. G. Gaylord took charge of oil-field research division of California Research Corporation, and W. A. Eardley succeeded as chief petroleum engineer.

1948—Participated in gas injection at Kettleman Hills (Calif.).

1951—A. F. Turman named chief petroleum engineer.

1953—Petroleum engineering division grew from 45 engineers in 1932 to 180 at end of 1953.

Members of Standard Oil Co. of California engineering staff have published 90 papers since 1925, 19 of which were in the AIME transactions, 36 in API publications, and 35 in other publications. December 1, 1953: Consolidation of engineering activities in producing department made. A. F. Turman appointed chief en-

gineer; C. W. Dawson appointed associate chief engineer; and
J. T. Crooker appointed assistant chief engineer.

References

[1]Gaylord, E. G. and Taff, J. A: Geological Organization of an Oil Company, *Am. Assoc. Petroleum Geologists Bulletin*, **8**, 651 (1924).

[2]Bly, E. P: Corrosion of Underground Pipe Lines, *Petroleum Development and Technology in 1926*, 501, American Institute of Mining and Metallurgical Engineers, Inc., New York, 1927.

Standard Oil Company (Indiana) and Subsidiaries — Midwest Refining Company and Stanolind Oil and Gas Company

Midwest Refining Company

1914—A. W. (Al) Peake hired from California to be field superintendent at Big Muddy Field (Wyo.).

1916—Built natural-gasoline plant at Salt Creek Field (Wyo.); Al Peake
and W. R. (Cap) Finney in charge.

1920—Appointed E. L. (Ned) Estabrook petroleum production engineer.

Early problems were subsurface control, building up production
statistics, proration of Salt Creek Field, bottom-hole pressures,
bottom-hole water analyses, remedial work on old wells, and control of gas-oil ratios by choking and back pressure.

1921—Pipeline proration of Salt Creek Field instituted by Midwest
Refining Company on March 1, 1921, and continued until
December 1, 1923.

1922—E. L. Estabrook gave paper at AIME on "Production Problems in
the Grass Creek Oil Field."

1925—Salt Creek Field (Wyo.) was completely electrified; F. O. Prior,
electrical engineer.

Fred E. Wood appointed petroleum engineer.

Contributions to early petroleum engineering literature by employees
of Midwest Refining Company:

Estabrook, E. L: Production Problems in the Grass Creek Oil Field, *Trans. Am. Inst. Mining Met. Engrs.*, **68**, 1130 (1932).

Estabrook, E. L. and Rader, Clarence M: History of Production of Salt Creek Oil Field, Wyo., *Petroleum Development and Technology in 1925*, 199, American Institute of Mining and Metallurgical Engineers, Inc., New York, 1926.

Young, H. W. and Estabrook, E. L: Waters of the Salt Creek Field, Wyoming, *Petroleum Development and Technology in 1925*, 255, American Institute of Mining and Metallurgical Engineers, Inc., New York, 1926.

Holmes, J. A: Shutting-in of the Rangely Gas Well, *Petroleum Development and Technology in 1925*, 179, American Institute of Mining and Metallurgical Engineers, Inc., New York, 1926.

Wood, F. E; Young, H. W; and Buell, A. W: Handling Congealing Oils and Paraffin in Salt Creek Field, Wyoming, *Petroleum Development and Technology in 1927*, 262, American Institute of Mining and Metallurgical Engineers, Inc., New York, 1928.

Finney, W. R. and Young, H. W: Scale and Corrosion Problems in Gasoline Plants, *Petroleum Development and Technology in 1926*, 536, American Institute of Mining and Metallurgical Engineers, Inc., New York, 1927.

Peake, A. W. and Prior, F. O: Use of Electricity for Oil-Field Operations in Wyoming, *Petroleum Development and Technology in 1927*, 194, American Institute of Mining and Metallurgical Engineers, Inc., New York, 1928.

Stanolind Oil and Gas Company

1931—Stanolind organized.

Set up petroleum engineering section with George S. Bays as chief petroleum engineer.

Subsequent heads of petroleum engineering section were M. C. Hoffman, John R. Evans, L. E. Elkins, Whitney M. Elias, and Lewis Finch, Jr., present incumbent.

Began general reservoir-behavior studies—took bottom-hole pressures.

1932—Started acidizing oil formations in Kansas, Oklahoma, and Louisiana.

Tested cores to determine suitability to acid treatment.

Started production laboratory work on cores.

Planned control of water advances in East Texas Field using bottom-hole chokes. Used very large water withdrawals as oil-scavenging technique in Hendricks Pool (Texas).

1933—Used fractional analysis of oil-field gases.

Began development of well completions from the bottom up.

1935—Made bottom-hole sample collections.

Started research on oil-well cementing.

1936—Set up proration group in the petroleum engineering section to handle technical proration problems.

1936-38—Used small models for testing oil recovery by various production methods.

Studied oil-field brine disposal.

Did laboratory research on drilling-mud problems.

Designated an engineer in each division office to handle conservation problems.

1939—Organized unit operation of the Salt Creek Field (Wyo.).

Experimented with injection of inert gases at Salt Creek Field.

Studied control of water coning in limestone reservoirs.

1940—Made studies of vertical permeability in depleted oil reservoirs.

1941—Completed Stanolind's first cycling plant. Assigned engineers to high-pressure compression plants to furnish technical assistance to operating personnel.

Made electrolytic-model studies to evaluate well spacing and withdrawal rates on cycling projects, and studied optimum trap pressures applicable.

1943—Producing department laboratory set up as independent research unit.

1945—Set up special group in petroleum engineering section to handle unitization matters. Stanolind has participated in 54 unitized projects, of which it operates 15.

Initiated water-injection project at West Hackberry Field (La.) at depth below 10,000 ft.

1946—Pioneered gas injection in limestone reservoir at Cedar Lake Field. General office of petroleum engineering section divided into reservoir unit and operating unit.

As of 1954, some 60 engineers worked in the reservoir unit and 200 in operations unit.

1945-49—Four natural-gasoline plants, ranging in capacity from 12,000 Mcf per day to 190,000 Mcf per day, were completed and construction was started on three other plants.

Built gas-sweetening and sulfur-recovery plants.

1953—Constructed new gasoline plant and enlarged three others. Installed two sulfur-recovery units, two isobutane separating facilities, and one installation for production of ethane concentrate.

Standard Oil Company (N.J.) — The Carter Oil Company, A Subsidiary; Humble Oil & Refining Company, An Autonomous Affiliate

Standard Oil Company (N.J.)

1924—H. C. Cooper of Hope Natural Gas Co. gave paper before API on "Deep Drilling."[1]

1928—Established production research and engineering department in Standard Oil Development Company, with H. H. (Harry) Hill in charge, as coordinating center for technical activities of Jersey's producing affiliates in the United States and abroad.

1936—Arrangements with affiliates were formalized by contracts providing for purchase by Standard Oil Development Company of research results from affiliates' laboratories.

Later, the petroleum engineering activities were transferred to the producing coordination department of Standard Oil Co. (N. J.), while coordination of production research remained with the Standard Oil Development Company.

1943—Standard Oil Company (N. J.) issued "Joint Progress Report on Reservoir Efficiency and Well Spacing" by the Committees on

Reservoir Development and Operation of the Standard Oil Company (New Jersey) Affiliated Companies and of the Humble Oil & Refining Company. The report was distributed gratis to libraries, educational institutions, oil companies, service companies and individuals. Approximately 6,000 copies of the report were distributed from the time it was issued in 1943 to January 1955.

References

[1]Cooper, H. C: Deep Drilling, *API Bulletin,* **V [75]** 61, Dec. 31 (1924).

The Carter Oil Company

1917—C. D. Watson headed first Carter engineering group.
Began to use rotary drill in Oklahoma.

1918—Air repressuring started near El Dorado, Kansas.
Manufactured tubular-steel drilling derrick.
Built an absorption gasoline plant.

1919—C. D. Watson appointed chief engineer and chief scout.

1923—Used oil and gas separators at Cromwell Field (Okla.).

1924—Made special hard-surfaced drilling bits.

1925—Used calcium chloride to accelerate setting of cement.
Established Tulsa service laboratory.

1926—Production engineering division established in engineering department.
Engaged S. F. Shaw to direct gas-lift work.
Gas repressuring started at Burbank Field (Okla.).

1927—Gas-lift production averaged about 35,000 bbl per day for year.
Gas repressuring started at Cromwell Field (Okla.).
Manufactured a "collar buster" tool for recovery of casing.
Used twin-crank oil-pumping unit.

1929—Took bottom-hole pressures.
Weighed well by counterbalancing. Low-temperature gas analyses made at Tulsa laboratory.

1926-30—Ivan S. Salnikov, Paul Lambright, Tip Moroney, George Shaner, and M. L. (Mike) Haider joined Carter production engineering division.

1931—Used back-pressure tests to determine open-flow potentials of gas wells.
Started water flooding at Nowata Field (Okla.).

1932—F. W. Floyd appointed chief petroleum engineer.

1933—Organized training program for young engineers.
Began acid treatment of oil wells.

1934—Initiated South Burbank Field (Okla.) pressure-maintenance project.

114

1935—M. L. (Mike) Haider appointed chief petroleum engineer.
  Used pressure drilling at Fitts Field (Okla.).
1936—Began organization of reservoir engineering group.
  Used temperature survey to locate top of cement.
1937—Used time-switch electric pumping.
  Started research laboratory with L. R. Hodell in charge. (By 1954 the research laboratory had total personnel of 225.)
1938—Initiated "Sunflower" pressure-maintenance project at Loudon Field (Ill.).
1939—Successfully ran string of welded casing.
  Built a successful pressure core barrel.
  Cooperated with service companies in development of multi-zone completions with shootable windows and J-tool windows.
1940—Started drilling deeper with acid.
  Used Calgon injection to combat gypsum.
1942—Constructed electric oil-pool analyzer.
  Began using casing centralizer and wall scratchers.
  Worked with service companies on experiments with pozzolan cements.
1943—Began underground storage of LPG.
1944—Used plastic in plug-back jobs.
1945—Insulated flow lines from casing strings to combat corrosion.
1950—Started reservoir engineering school—six-week course—classes of plus or minus 25 men.

Humble Oil & Refining Company

1920-37—Engineering division of producing department participated in API standardization studies and worked on maintenance records of equipment, electrified pumping, gas handling and accounting, repressuring, and air- and gas-lift problems.
  Refinery department started production research on emulsion-breaking chemicals, design of natural-gasoline plants, and field evaporation losses.
  W. S. Farish, president, was leader in advocating more efficient regulation of crude-oil production in Texas.
1926—H. L. Edwards, chief production engineer, gave a paper at AIME entitled "Improved Drilling and Production Methods in North and Central Texas."[1]
1927—John R. Suman became head of Humble's producing department.
  Placed production or gas engineers in field divisions, and established a specialized petroleum production engineering service at Houston.

1928—Petroleum engineering division organized with W. W. (Dago) Scott as chief petroleum engineer.

1929—Production research division organized with Dr. H. D. Wilde in charge.

Student engineering training program instituted.

Repressuring with gas had been started about 1926; and in 1929, 16 projects were under way, including Sugarland Field (Texas), a pressure-maintenance project, and Olney Field (Texas), a depleted reservoir restored to production.

Started publication of monthly engineering report.

Divided petroleum engineering division into electrical, gas, chemical, engineering, and petroleum engineering sections.

1929-30—Company engineers had recognized "that the effect of dissolved gas in oil, permeability, porosity, gas-oil ratios, and bottomhole pressure could be resolved into predictions of reservoir condition and recovery of oil." This early approach to reservoir analysis was presented before the AIME in 1929.[2]

1926-30—Participated in the Yates Field (Texas) voluntary production agreement with John R. Suman as Chairman of the Yates Pool Advisory Committee (1930).

1931-35—Use of caustic soda and tannic acid to reduce viscosity of drilling muds was started in 1930, as were studies on control of gel strength of mud, weighted oil muds, and high-pH muds.

In 1934, field tests were made with sodium hexameta-phosphate as mud-viscosity agent.

Sodium silicate muds were tested in 1935.

The need for cements with longer setting time was demonstrated.

In marine engineering, Humble built a submersible-type barge rig for use in the marshes.

Humble research engineers studied proration and well-spacing procedures and recommended the abandonment of taking openflow potentials of wells and the inclusion of an acreage factor in allocating production in prorated oil pools.

1931—Produced first company-designed subsurface-pressure gage.

1932—Produced company-designed subsurface-oil sampler.

Issued specifications on drilling-mud materials.

Unitized rotary drawworks was fabricated and steel derrick and engine substructure bases were put in service with important reductions in moving time of drilling rigs.

Humble scientists published a technical paper suggesting that oil recovery from a reservoir was independent of well spacing.[3]

1933—Built an expansion gas porosimeter.

1934—Bottom-hole pressure gages were first used to: *1.* Measure formation flowing and shut-in pressure in connection with drill-stem tests. *2.* Measure pressure loss in drill pipe while circulating drilling fluid. (Due to characteristics of drilling mud, conventional friction factors for pressure loss did not apply.) *3.* Measure reduction in hydrostatic pressure of the mud column when withdrawing drill pipe from the hole. (This was ascertained to be the cause of blowouts from normal-pressure formations being drilled with mud of adequate weight.)

John R. Suman questioned the Cutler close-spacing theory and suggested that wider spacing might give more oil recovery because of reduced reservoir-energy dissipation.[4]

Humble engineers completed development of the volumetric balance equation upon which studies had commenced in the late 1920's.[5,6,7]

Presence of connate water in oil sands studied.

1935—Commenced field work in low-temperature separation equipment for natural gas.

1936—Production practices section set up in the petroleum engineering division.

Casing and tubing sizes reduced, and the cost of casing strings in deep wells further reduced by designing casing strings to withstand increasing stresses with depth.

Research division constructed scale models of reservoirs.

Surface-active chemicals were studied.

1937—Research on behavior of light hydrocarbons in reservoirs.

Studies were made on: *a,* the best method of determining from cores the amount of connate water in a reservoir; *b,* the recovery efficiency of the water-drive mechanism; *c,* various phases of reservoir mechanics.

Recording subsurface temperature gage was built.

1938—High voltage (880 volts) installed in several oil fields.

Drilling practice section established in the petroleum engineering division.

1939—Recording subsurface temperature gage used to find casing leaks.

Aluminum electric cable used with important reductions in cost of installation.

1940—Published company manual, *The Principles of Reservoir Behavior.*

Developed new type of flow treater.

Petroleum engineering division began reviewing all requests for well workovers.

1936-40—In 1936 obtained from manufacturers a cement suitable for deep-well use.

Commenced slim-hole drilling program with $6\frac{1}{8}$-in. hole from surface casing to total depth.

In 1938 commenced practice of using cement or lime with alkaline tannate mud to control viscosity.

Rotary drilling bits were under continual study as to design, materials, and nozzle shapes and sizes. In 1937, this work was extended to consider the effects of the weight on the bit, the rates of circulation, and speed of rotation.

Bottom-hole pressure surveys covered 25 oil and gas fields in 1937, and increased to 115 fields in 1939.

Experiments were conducted with small tubing as a means of prolonging flowing life of oil wells.

During the last half of the 1930's, procedures were developed for determination of connate water, calculation of oil and gas equilibria at separator conditions, analysis of abnormal pressures in the Gulf Coast (from which came the familiar 0.465 pressure gradient used in that area), 2- and 3-phase flow in unconsolidated sands, the dissolved-gas-drive procedure, MER, displacement calculations for water-drive and gas-cap-drive reservoirs, capillary behavior, measurement of viscosity of oil under reservoir conditions, and the unsteady-state radial-flow equation for water drive.

1941-45—Exhaust-steam stack blowers used in 1942 and a water-treating system devised which prolonged the life of oil-field boilers from 5 years to 15 years. Experiments showed that use of 5-in. OD drill pipe reduced hydraulic-horsepower requirements for circulation of the drilling fluid compared to $4\frac{1}{2}$-in. drill pipe. Rotary scratchers for use in oil-well cementing, and cement modified with bentonite were introduced.

In 1944 started school of reservoir engineering which, in 10 years, was attended by 203 Humble employees.

1946-50—Detailed studies were commenced in 1946 of factors affecting drilling speed and recommendations which included high nozzle fluid velocities when drilling with drag bits were presented to API in 1948.[8] A study of rock-bit drilling was presented in 1950.[9] The results of these studies were reduced mathematically to curves as a method for the selection of bits with optimum nozzle sizes for maximum penetration rates.

Casing perforations were studied and led to development of more powerful perforators, as well as one as small as $1\frac{3}{4}$-in. OD. Perforation was facilitated by development of cement containing bentonite and calcium lignosulfonate with low tensile strength and not subject to shattering.

In 1949 Humble issued a 1,100-page manual on reservoir engineering for the guidance of its field personnel.

Electric analyzer secured for use in reservoir studies.

Sand-production problems were studied; and, by 1949, small gravel was being placed in wells to exclude fine sand.

Offshore operations were resumed.

1951-54—In 1952 equipment was put in use to do cementing and perforating in wells without use of drilling rig. By 1953, techniques had been developed which made it possible to remove sand from a well without using a drilling rig and to perform a complete workover job without killing the well. Unitization of field reservoirs began to expand rapidly, and a permanent "unitization" organization was set up.

In 1952, work was intensified on improving methods of measuring and testing crude oil and on making tank batteries more automatic in operation.

Much engineering effort devoted to problems of offshore installations.

Medium-sized digital computer obtained in 1952 for use of research and engineering personnel. A second machine obtained in 1953.

1954—Reservoir engineering laboratory started at Houston research center.

References

[1]Edwards, Harry L: Improved Drilling and Production Methods in North and Central Texas, *Petroleum Development and Technology in 1926,* 255, American Institute of Mining and Metallurgical Engineers, Inc., New York, 1927.

[2]Coleman, Stewart; Wilde, H. D., Jr; and Moore, Thomas W: Quantitative Effect of Gas-Oil Ratios on Decline of Average Rock Pressure, *Trans. Am. Inst. Mining Met. Engrs. (Petroleum Development and Technology),* 174 (1930).

[3]Wilde, H. D., Jr. and Moore, T. V: Hydrodynamics of Reservoir Drainage and Its Relation to Well Spacing, *Proc. Am. Pet. Inst., Sect. IV (Prod. Bul. 210)* 83 (1932).

[4]Suman, John R: The Well Spacing Problem—Low Well Density Increases Ultimate Recovery, *API Drilling and Production Practice,* 158 (1934).

[5]Moore, T. V; Schilthuis, R. J; and Hurst, William: Determination of Permeability from Field Data, *Proc. Am. Pet. Inst., Sect. IV (Prod. Bul. 211)* 4 (1933); also *Oil Weekly,* 19, May 22 (1933), and *Oil Gas J.,* **32 [1]** 58 (1933).

[6]Hurst, William: Unsteady Flow of Fluids in Oil Reservoirs, *Physics,* **5,** 20, Jan. (1934).

[7]Schilthuis, Ralph J. and Hurst, William: Variations in Pressure in the East Texas Field, *Trans. Am. Inst. Mining Met. Engrs. (Petroleum Development and Technology)* **114,** 164 (1935); also *Oil Gas J.,* **33,** 22, **34,** 12.

[8]Nolley, J. P; Cannon, G. E; and Ragland, Douglas: The Relation of Nozzle Fluid

Velocity to Rate of Penetration with Drag-type Rotary Bits, *API Drilling and Production Practice*, 22 (1948).

[9]Bielstein, W. J. and Cannon, G. E: Factors Affecting the Rate of Penetration of Rock Bits, *API Drilling and Production Practice*, 61 (1950).

Standard Oil Company of Ohio—Producing Subsidiary, Sohio Petroleum Co.

1940—Company acquired first oil- and gas-producing property.

1941-46—Production department was organized with six engineers for property appraisal, estimation of reserves, and for some field engineering.

1946—Engineering work started on unitization, cycling projects, gasoline plants, etc. Technical service laboratory organized for core analysis, subsurface-fluid sample analysis, etc.

1947—Engineering department organized under R. W. French. Additional experienced engineers hired and engineering training program started. West Edmond Hunton Lime Unit formed as first unit under Oklahoma statute with Sohio as operator.

1951-52—Large-scale interference test conducted in the Spraberry Field of west Texas to determine effect of well spacing on recovery efficiency.

1953—Company organization changed to division-manager type. Engineering organization modified to place engineers in headquarters, divisions, and districts. Activities include study of drilling program, well completions, operating methods and costs, secondary recovery, reserves, proration matters. About 60 engineers, as such, employed in the production department.

Sun Oil Company

1924—F. H. Lahee wrote paper on "Comparative Study of Well Logs on the Mexia Type of Structure."[1]

1928—Geological department made studies of crooked holes and well cores.[2]

1931—Petroleum engineering section of geological department organized for studies of reservoir problems in East Texas Field, using bottom-hole pressure gage. Work done by engineers D. M. Collingsworth and A. S. Rhea.

1934—Petroleum engineering section of geological department expanded to other operating areas, in cooperation with the producing department.
Studied conservation of gas and reservoir energy, producing rates, and reservoir flood control, artificial lift, storage losses, recovery estimates, etc.

1947—Dallas petroleum engineering group of the geological department transferred to division operating department with A. S. Rhea as division chief petroleum engineer. Each district office has a district petroleum engineer.

Group of senior engineers under F. G. Prutzman, Assistant Chief Petroleum Engineer, forms headquarters staff at Dallas.

1948—Production and petroleum engineering departments were integrated into the operating department with A. S. Rhea serving as chief petroleum engineer and assistant production superintendent.

Petroleum engineering divided into two sections: *a*, reservoir studies and secondary recovery; and *b*, drilling and producing operations.

1954—The arrangement and division of operations in the company somewhat as follows:

a. Subsurface well problems—geological phases handled by geologists and completion practices by petroleum engineers.

b. Producing methods handled by petroleum engineers.

c. Oil handling—chokes, gas traps, field tankage, evaporation, water, oil heading, corrosion, etc. Company practice followed general industry practice.

d. Drilling and producing equipment—in the past had been a minor problem of the engineers, but now receiving more intensive study.

e. Handling and use of natural gas—handle to obtain greatest volume stabilized salable crude.

f. Equipment for testing—logs and their interpretation handled by the geologists; subsurface sampling by the engineers; crooked-hole problems handled by service companies.

g. Reservoir behavior—all phases under petroleum engineering except core work.

h. Increased oil recovery—separate organization on secondary recovery set up in 1947.

i. Unit operations—unit operations not a function of the petroleum engineering department. Recommendations on unitization from geological and engineering groups are submitted to management. Operations of units handled by operating department.

References

[1]Lahee, F. H: Comparative Study of Well Logs on the Mexia Type of Structure, *Trans. Am. Inst. Mining Met. Engrs. (Petroleum Development and Technology)* **71,** 1329 (1925).

[2]Lahee, F. H: Problem of Crooked Holes, *American Assoc. Petroleum Geologists Bull.*, **13**, 1119 (1927).

Sunray Mid-Continent Oil Company, Including Barnsdall Oil Co.

Merged with Barnsdall Oil Company in 1950 and with Mid-Continent Oil Company in 1955.

Early 1930's—engineers used on property evaluation, plant design, and research.

Late 1930's—organized an engineering section of the production department with Jack H. Abernathy in charge. Activities included studies of producing methods, design and selection of producing equipment, cost analyses and economics of production, subsurface well problems, salt-water disposal, natural-gas processing, reservoir behavior, proration and conservation, unit operations, pressure maintenance, and secondary recovery.

1937—Developed logging trailers for drilling wells—work under direction of John T. Hayward.

1943—Commenced injecting water into producing formation of Midway Field (Ark.). Project instituted early in life of field to maintain pressure and increase ultimate recovery—very successful. W. L. Horner largely responsible.

1945—At Newhall Potrero Field (Calif.) after October 1945, all produced gas returned to formation for pressure maintenance. Engineers R. E. Foss and Oran A. Graybeal largely responsible.

1946—Started water- and gas-injection program in West Tepatate Field (La.)—under direction of H. F. Beardmore and W. L. Horner—which was a pressure-maintenance project combining water and gas injection and completely unitized oil operation.
Benton Field (La.) unitized and field shut in until complete cycling facilities installed. W. L. Horner and H. W. Manley largely responsible.

1947—Designed and developed submersible drilling barge for operation in deep unprotected waters. John T. Hayward largely responsible. Started production service laboratory, headed by Dr. Charles W. Ziemer.

1954—J. H. Douma named manager of engineering division of production department. Functions include: reservoir studies, development and production engineering, reserves and evaluations, unitization and proration, mechanical and civil engineering.
Almost one third of total daily oil production obtained from pressure-maintenance and secondary-recovery projects.

1955—Evaluation department established with Dr. Charles W. Ziemer as manager.

The Texas Company

1916—T. B. Hoffer and Ross Catlett worked on production department engineering problems.

1919—J. R. Thomas employed as engineer—worked on correlation and construction well log cross sections.

1920-25—Engineers worked on current drilling and producing problems. Gas-oil ratios were obtained; peg models were constructed; analyses of subsurface waters were made; and the use of dyes to trace underground water was studied.

1922—A. B. Steen gave a paper at API on "Standardization in the Oil Industry from the Engineer's Point of View."[1]

1923—C. B. Williams hired as petroleum engineer to work on balancing of central-power pumping installations, etc. Initiated secondary recovery.

1925—Organized separate group of engineers as petroleum engineering department on a division basis, but with no chief petroleum engineer.

W. V. Vietti was first petroleum engineer with South Texas Division. No company-wide petroleum engineering organization until 1942. Started geophysical laboratory.

1926—E. J. Nicklos as National Vice-Chairman of API Committee on Standardization of Rotary Drilling Equipment, read a paper before the API entitled "Recommended Practice for Care of Rotary-Drilling Equipment."[2]

1926-30—Studied economics of drilling and production. Experimented with tapered tubing. Gas drives were started in various oil fields. Some work done on MER's. Reserve and valuation sections of petroleum engineers were organized in some divisions. Petroleum engineering duties were performed by W. V. Vietti, F. L. Davis, G. I. McBride, H. Strader, D. K. Wasson, H. W. Mills and R. L. Keyes.

1931-35—Rapid expansion of petroleum engineering department from 15 to 61 men. Petroleum engineering work was extended to include drilling mud, cementing, potential tests, emulsion treating, and gas lift. Bottom-hole pressure surveys were made, equipment standardization studied, and reservoir engineering started.

1933—Encouraged electric logging in all company operations.
Studied well spacing and salt-water disposal problems.

Started a water-flood project and began work on unitization problems.

Encouraged studies of reservoir behavior.

1936-40—Increased activity in all phases of petroleum engineering. Work on gas drives and water flooding expanded. Corrosion studies started.

1941—Geophysical and production research laboratory moved to Bellaire—33 employees.

1942—W. V. Vietti became first chief petroleum engineer.

1947—Research laboratory reorganized as research division of the producing department.

Production research includes experimental studies on phase equilibria, fluid dynamics, corrosion, drilling fluids, clay chemistry, electric-log interpretation, and secondary-recovery processes.

1941-54—Petroleum engineering continued to expand rapidly, particularly in reservoir engineering and secondary recovery.

From 12 engineers in 1929, the department has increased to over 300 in 1954.

References

[1]Steen, A. B: Standardization in the Oil Industry from the Engineer's Point of View, *API Bulletin*, **III** [62] 63 (1922) (Third Annual Meeting).

[2]Nicklos, E. J: Recommended Practice for Care of Rotary-Drilling Equipment, *API Bulletin*, **VIII** [6] 56 (1926) (Seventh Annual Meeting).

Texas Gulf Producing Company, Including Its Predecessor, the Humphreys Corporation, and Acquired Properties from Snowden-McSweeney, Ohio Fuel Supply Company, and Fohs Oil Company

Early 1930's—Humphreys Corporation engineering was in charge of S. A. Judson.

1941—Humphreys acquired by Texas Gulf Producing Company.

1944—Acquired Snowden-McSweeney properties.

1945—O. K. Holman appointed chief engineer.

1946—Acquired properties Ohio Fuel Supply Company and Fohs Oil Company. No engineers available from these companies.

1947—Two engineers working on reserve and reservoir problems.

1949-50—Production engineers assigned to production department reporting to area superintendents.

1954—Seven engineers in production department—the chief engineer, a production engineer, and an exploitation engineer at Houston; three production engineers in West Texas-New Mexico Division, and one production engineer in Louisiana Division.

1. A superintendent or production engineer is responsible for drilling and production operations, equipment specifications, factual well records, production and regulatory reports.

2. An exploitation engineer is responsible for proration problems, reservoir control, logging and coring procedures and interpretation, evaluation, and reserves.

Tidewater Associated Oil Company and Predecessors

Amalgamated Oil Company

1907—Fred B. Henderson, manager of Amalgamated, used graphic log strips.

1917—Joseph Jenson appointed head geologist. Duties included supervision of resident geologists who did petroleum engineering work.

1923—Properties transferred to Associated Oil Company.

Associated Oil Company

1907—Geological Department organized under W. R. Hamilton. Staff included R. P. McLaughlin, Robert Moran, Billy Williams, Roy M. Ferguson, and W. L. Walker.

Billy Williams became chief geologist in 1911 and brought Walker back to California. Roy M. Ferguson specialized in work for Amalgamated Oil Company in southern California.

McLaughlin worked for Associated Oil Company in San Joaquin from 1908 to 1913.

1913—Geological Department was discontinued in 1913, but in 1915 geological and resident engineers came under the supervision of J. A. Taff, geologist of the Southern Pacific Company at the time the Southern Pacific Company owned control of Associated Oil Company.

1920—Introduced practice of cementing shoe of surface conductor strings.

1924—Joseph Jensen and Glenn D. Robertson published paper on "New Development Problems and Their Solution in the Southern California Oil Fields."[1]

Tidewater Oil Company

1925—A. A. Beard and R. A. Bonnell of Tidal Oil Company wrote paper on "Cleaning Oil Wells by Compressed Air."[2]

1926—A. A. Beard gave paper at API entitled "Restoring Pressure with Air, Gas and Water."[3]

1926—J. E. Roth of Tidal Oil Company presented paper to AIME on "The Application of Pressure to the Elliott Pool, Nowata County, Oklahoma."[4]

Tidewater Associated Oil Company

1927—Joseph Jensen appointed head field geologist with supervision of all petroleum engineers.

1929—Joseph Jensen made chief petroleum engineer and head of petroleum engineering department, which then handled all work pertaining to drilling. Shortly thereafter the petroleum engineering department was extended to include petroleum production engineering.

1936—Tidewater Associated became the operating organization.

Associated Oil Company and Tidewater Associated Oil Company

Established records for deepest rotary wells in the world as follows:

Well	Field	Date	Depth, Ft
Butterworth #1	Santa Fe Springs	Nov. 12, 1921	4,683
Clarke #2	Santa Fe Springs	June 6, 1929	8,165
Lloyd #57	Ventura Avenue	April 28, 1931	8,823
Lloyd #83	Ventura Avenue	July 12, 1932	9,710
Lloyd #131	Ventura Avenue	Aug. 3, 1935	9,846
McGonigle	Ventura Avenue	Jan. 17, 1937	10,569

Lloyd #83 had the largest ultimate production of any well completed in California history, and was brought in under complete control at the time of completion without loss of any oil. The tubing of this well was $4\frac{3}{4}$-in. flow string, which was used in well from time of completion until September 1952. By the end of 1954, the well had produced 4,668,697 bbl, with an average gas-oil ratio of 1,715 Mcf per bbl.

References

[1] Jensen, J. and Robertson, Glenn D: New Development Problems and Their Solution in the Southern California Oil Fields, *Am. Assoc. Petroleum Geologists Bull.*, **8,** 135 (1924).

[2] Beard, A. A. and Bonnell, k. A: Cleaning Oil Wells with Compressed Air, *Petroleum Development and Technology in 1925*, 170, American Institute of Mining and Metallurgical Engineers, Inc., New York, 1926.

[3] Beard, A. A: Restoring Pressure with Air, Gas, and Water, *API Bulletin*, **VIII [6]** 62 (1926) (Seventh Annual Meeting).

[4] Roth, J. E: The Application of Pressure to the Elliot Pool, *Petroleum Development and Technology in 1926*, 195, American Institute of Mining and Metallurgical Engineers, Inc., New York, 1927.

Union Oil Company of California

1887-91—Operated tunnels into oil sands at Sulphur Mountain (Calif.)

1903—Frank Hill used cement in oil wells to shut off water, Lompoc (Calif.).

1911—Used gas lift at Cat Canyon (Calif.).

1918—R. W. Phelps hired as field (resident) geologist.

1921—R. R. (Ric) Templeton employed as chief subsurface geologist.

1922—Templeton made chief petroleum engineer.

1924—R. R. Templeton and C. R. McCollum described the Santa Fe Springs Field before the AAPG.[1]

1925-29—Union had petroleum engineers in three districts who reported to the district superintendent.

1927—A. C. Rubel addressed the API on "The Advent and Relation of the Production and Development Engineer to the Industry."[2]

1928—At the AIME meeting in February 1928, F. W. Hertel and H. H. Dievendorff described "Deep-well Drilling Technique"[3]; and F. W. Lake and H. A. Brett gave a paper entitled "Sucker-rod Strains and Stresses."[4]

1929—A. C. Rubel appointed chief petroleum engineer (February), and since then the district petroleum engineers have reported to the chief petroleum engineer instead of to district superintendents. Rubel became assistant manager of operations (September), and Edmund Jusson, Jr. appointed chief petroleum engineer.

1936-55—W. S. Eggleston was chief petroleum engineer.

1955 to date—Chas. F. Bowden has been chief petroleum engineer.
Petroleum engineering department has authority and responsibility to perform these functions:
  a. Petroleum engineering or development engineering.
  b. Production or reservoir engineering.
  c. Geological or subsurface engineering.
  d. Valuation engineering—reserve estimates.
  e. Economic engineering.
  f. Training of engineers and field supervisors.
The engineers are part of the operating personnel rather than advisors and have authority to plan and supervise development and production functions such as:
  a. Location of wells.
  b. Well spacing.
  c. Rate of development.
  d. Well depths.
  e. Casing points (they actually measure the casing in and supervise the cement job).
  f. Coring (they determine when, where, and how much coring is to be done).
  g. Well-completion practice (choice of screen sizes, etc.).
  h. How the well will be completed and at what rates produced.

i. All remedial work is directly under the supervision of petroleum engineers.

References and Bibliography

[1]Templeton, R. R. and McCollum, C. R: *Am. Assoc. Petroleum Geologists Bull.*, **8,** 178 (1924).

[2]Rubel, A. C: The Advent and Relation of the Development and Production Engineers of the Industry, *API Bulletin*, **IX [7]** 306 (1927) (Eighth Annual Meeting).

[3]Hertel, F. W. and Dievendorff, H. H: Deep-Well Drilling Technique, *Petroleum Development and Technology in 1927*, 350, American Institute of Mining and Metallurgical Engineers, Inc., New York, 1928.

[4]Lake, F. W. and Brett, H. A: Sucker-rod Strains and Stresses, *Petroleum Development and Technology in 1927*, 337, American Institute of Mining and Metallurgical Engineers, Inc., New York, 1928.

Hill, F. F: Cementing Deep Wells, *API Bulletin*, **V [75]** 65 (1924) (Fifth Annual Meeting).

Hill, F. F: Lifting Oil With Gas, *API Bulletin*, **VIII [6]** 67 (1926) (Seventh Annual Meeting).

Gibbs, R. D. and Taylor, C. C: Handling Recirculated Gas, *Petroleum Development and Technology in 1927*, 49, American Institute of Mining and Metallurgical Engineers, Inc., New York, 1928.

Lake, F. W: Relation of the Air-Gas Lift to Gas-Oil Ratios and Effect on Ultimate Production, *Petroleum Development and Technology in 1927*, 173, American Institute of Mining and Metallurgical Engineers, Inc., New York, 1928.

Union Producing Company

1936—Production engineering organized as separate department on company basis, and separate engineering group set up in the Shreveport District. Prior to this time, several engineers had been employed in drilling and production operations.

1936-38—Worked on drilling and production operations and studied conservation practices during the development of the Rodessa Field.

1939-41—Conducted engineering studies as to the feasibility and economics of gas cycling in the Agua Dulce, Cotton Valley, North Houston, and Katy gas fields, which were among the first fields in which this type of operation was practiced. Represented the company on the various operating committees connected with unitization and cycling programs. Engineers were assigned to those cycling projects operated by Union. Production engineering departments were organized in the Houston, Beeville, and Jackson Districts, concentrating on drilling and production operations. Initiated laboratory studies of condensate producing wells to determine phase behavior at various pressures and temperatures.

1942-45—Engineers prepared all applications and represented the company before Federal agencies to obtain approval for the drilling of wells and for the procurement of steel requirements. Initiated the company's first secondary oil-recovery operation in the Pettus Field. Engineers were assigned to represent the company at hearings pertaining to oil and gas conservation before state regulatory bodies and this has become a major function of the department.

1946-50—With increased personnel, a planned program of testing and obtaining data and information on oil and gas fields and on individual oil and gas wells in these fields was enlarged. Unitization, both field-wide and for individual wells, had increased and engineers were used to assist in the formation of these units and to represent the company on operating committees. Burnell-North Pettus and Benton cycling projects were put into operation.

1951-56—Emphasis on reservoir-performance studies of the various oil and gas reservoirs to increase ultimate recovery of oil and gas resulted in initiation of gas-injection and water-flooding operations in the Kent Bayou and Tinsley oil fields. Engineers have taken an increasing part in the preparation and analysis of the budgets, as well as evaluation studies. Engineers have been assigned to the study of gas-storage projects as well as the reworking operations on wells in gas-storage projects. Gas-availability studies have been a function of the engineering departments. Training obtained in drilling and production operations has resulted in the placement of a number of engineers in positions of responsibility in the drilling and production department.

Significant Dates in Evolution of Petroleum Engineering

From the preceding summaries, the significant dates in the evolution of petroleum engineers as a separate group of employees have been tabulated. Some of the early dates represent the real beginnings of petroleum engineering work, but in most cases they mark an organizational change where the men who had been doing petroleum engineering work for the company were set up as a separate group under the title of petroleum engineers. Some of the larger companies had been using petroleum engineers either through consulting firms or as employees for 20 years and more before finally organizing a petroleum engineering department. Others never have set up a separate department, and their petroleum engineers are members of the engineering or producing staffs.

1907—Kern Trading and Oil Co. hired resident geologists.
Associated Oil Company organized geological department and started subsurface work.

1908—Chanslor-Canfield Oil Co. of California began using resident geologists.

1909—Honolulu Oil Co. hired a geological engineer.

1912—General Petroleum Corp. hired resident geologists.

1914—Universal Consolidated Oil Co. was using resident geologists.

1916—Shell Oil Co. of California combined engineers and geologists in "working group."

1919—Shell Oil Co. established petroleum engineering section in St. Louis, Mo.

1920—Standard Oil Co. of California appointed a petroleum engineer.
Standard Oil Co. (Ind.)—Midwest appointed a petroleum production engineer.

1921—Gulf Oil Corp. appointed a chief production engineer.
General Petroleum Corp. applied title "petroleum engineer" to supervisor of resident geologists.

1922—Union Oil Co. of California appointed a chief petroleum engineer.

1923—Rio Bravo Oil Co. organized production engineering section.
The Texas Co. hired first petroleum engineer.

1925—Continental Oil Co. (Marland) appointed three regional chief production engineers.
Cities Service Oil Co. appointed a chief petroleum engineer.
The Pure Oil Co. organized production engineering department.

1926—The Carter Oil Co. set up production engineering division in engineering department.

1927—Gulf Oil Corp. appointed a district petroleum engineer.

1928—Phillips Petroleum Co. organized a production engineering group in production department.
General Petroleum Corp. changed title of resident geologists to petroleum engineers.
Humble Oil & Refining Co.—petroleum engineering division organized.
Standard Oil Co. (N. J.) established coordinating group for production engineering and research of all affiliates.

1929—The Atlantic Refining Co. appointed chief petroleum engineer in production department.
Tidewater Associated Oil Co. appointed a chief petroleum engineer.

1931—Magnolia Petroleum Co. hired a petroleum engineer.
  Stanolind Oil and Gas Co. set up a petroleum engineering section.
  Sun Oil Co. organized petroleum engineering section in geological
  department.
1932—The Ohio Oil Co. organized petroleum engineering department
  in a subsidiary company.
  The Carter Oil Co. appointed a chief petroleum engineer.
1934—Magnolia Petroleum Co. organized a petroleum engineering department in production division.
1936—Union Producing Co. organized production engineering as a
  separate department.
1937—Plymouth Oil Co. organized petroleum engineering department.
1938—Lion Oil Co. set up a petroleum engineering section.
  British-American Oil Producing Co. organized a petroleum engineering department.
1939—Sunray Oil Corp. organized engineering section in production
  department.
1941—The Ohio Oil Co. instituted company-wide petroleum engineering
  department.
1942—The Texas Co. organized company-wide petroleum engineering
  department.
1943—Seaboard Oil Co. of Delaware established a petroleum engineering
  department.
1944—Socony Mobil Oil Co., Inc. established petroleum engineering
  section in production department, New York.
1945—Texas Gulf Producing Co. appointed chief engineer in production
  department.
1946—Houston Oil Co. of Texas appointed chief petroleum engineer.
1947—Standard Oil Co. (Ohio) organized petroleum engineering department.

The work of the petroleum engineers has broadened through the year since 1907 from the subsurface studies of the "resident geologists," to the operation and direction of every phase of oil- and gas-producing operations. From a handful of young mining engineers and geologists trying to find casing seats and cementing methods that would shut off the upper waters of the California oil fields, the petroleum engineers are now numbered in the thousands and have contributed substantially to making petroleum production a highly technical and soundly engineered enterprise. Guided by industry-supported research, the recurring problems of deep drilling have been met; producing methods have been improved; and ways have been found to increase very materially the amounts of crude oil which can profitably be extracted from the reservoirs. Equipment and materials have been studied and, with the cooperation of the manufacturers and the leadership of the API, the industry can now obtain supplies from manufacturers in any of the leading industrial countries of the world which will be of uniform and approved quality and design. Through its publications, the API has made available to everyone the details of its material specifications and full instructions for the care and safe usage of API standard equipment. The oil-producing companies can look back with satisfaction upon their technical accomplishments during the past 50 years and their exploration and research staffs and petroleum engineers share in that pride.

book two
drilling and completing wells

Chapter 5

PERCUSSION-DRILLING SYSTEM

J. E. Brantly

John Edward Brantly was born in Macon, Georgia in 1892 and received B.S. (1911) and E.M. (1912) degrees from the University of Alabama. He instructed in geology at his alma mater from 1911 to 1914, becoming then assistant state geologist of Alabama until military service in 1917. Upon discharge in 1918 he became a member of the consulting geological firm of Hill, Brantly and McFarland. From 1921 until 1928 he was chief foreign geologist for The Atlantic Refining Company.

In 1928 Mr. Brantly organized Drilling & Exploration Company and served as president of that international drilling contracting firm until retirement in 1952. Following retirement he served a year as assistant deputy administrator of the Petroleum Administration for Defense.

Academic, professional and industrial honors include Sigma Xi and Tau Beta Pi. He was an organizer of the American Association of Oilwell Drilling Contractors and served two terms as president of that association. In 1957 he received the Anthony F. Lucas medal of AIME. Mr. Brantly is the author of *Rotary Drilling Handbook* and has been a prominent contributor to technical literature on geology and oil-well drilling. He is the holder of numerous patents on drilling equipment.

134

᠂᠊᠂ 5 ᠂᠊᠂

INTRODUCTION

This chapter and the following one have to do with ways and means of creating holes in the crust of the earth for the purpose of moving therefrom liquids or fluids, with particular reference to petroleum in its various crude forms, including gas. In order that a reasonably complete study may be made it will be desirable to start back of the beginnings of civilization, when prehistoric man scraped out or created depressions in dry stream beds in search of the ever-necessary water, and look through the records of the centuries at the various ways and means men have devised for the digging of holes, including both major and minor changes and improvements in tools and practices down to the most modern methods and equipment.

An effort has been made to present a reasonably broad and comprehensive record of the history of drilling or boring holes or wells. Detailed discussions will be presented of those tools, machines, and practices that have been of primary and basic importance in arriving at the present developments in mechanical equipment and its efficient use. Because of their value as descriptive matter and illustration of operations, liberal use has been made of photographs and sketches.

Beginning a few hundred years before Christ, there is increasing mention in ancient writings of the digging of wells for water, brine, and oil, with some very sketchy discussions or descriptions of the tools and methods used. Beginning some time after the commencement of the Christian Era and extending to about 1800 A. D., very little was recorded about well digging although such work doubtless continued at an increasing rate and with gradually improving tools and methods.

From 1800 to 1859 there is a considerable amount of information available concerning many wells, particularly in America, as our expanding population pushed into new areas where the subsoil had to be penetrated to provide needed supplies of potable water and brine for the manufacture of salt. In Europe, and especially in France, there are records of many water wells bored during this period.

For many centuries prior to 1859, holes had been dug for the express purpose of producing crude petroleum in its various forms; and wells that were drilled or bored, or even dug with pick and shovel, in search of water or brine had produced petroleum or gas as by-products. Reports of the accidental production of petroleum appears in the history of the early wells of China and was noted in many of the wells that were drilled for brine in the Appalachian Mountain region.

Fig. 1—Three Methods of Digging Holes in 1800
(Courtesy Philadelphia Academy of Fine Arts)
(Description on p. 176)

5. PERCUSSION-DRILLING SYSTEM

The first well that is recognized as having been bored or drilled in America for the express purpose of producing "rock oil" was the Drake well, completed on or about August 27, 1859 at a depth of 69½ ft. This discovery and the publicity given it resulted in the first American oil boom; and during the next few years many other wells were drilled in Pennsylvania, New York, West Virginia, and Kentucky in search of petroleum in commercial quantity, particularly in those localities where its presence had been indicated or proved earlier in wells drilled for brine.

The first percussion boring tools of which we have records were developed in China, and centuries later there began to be records of their use in Europe and America; but whether the idea had spread from China or was independently developed in the West there is no record. So simple a procedure might well have come into use independently in many centers of recent civilization. With the completion of the Drake oil well, the development and improvement of percussion-drilling equipment were very rapid for a few decades and then went through a period of relatively few changes except in machine design and weight, until the rotary system of drilling came into prominence with the completion of the Spindletop well near Beaumont, Texas, in 1901. The percussion-drilling system had been used almost exclusively up to the 19th century, although rotary-drilling tools had been known to the ancient Egyptians.

The modern hydraulic rotary system had been developing in America during two decades preceding 1900 for the drilling of water wells and shallow oil wells in areas where the percussion method could not be used satisfactorily. Rotating hydraulic diamond-drilling machines and bits were invented in 1863, and had been in use in America since 1872.

The improvements in rotary-drilling equipment after the Spindletop discovery in 1901 and up to the year 1915 were relatively modest; but from 1915 to 1927 there were substantial changes in the machinery, without much progress in drilling practice. Cable-tool percussion equipment was also being increased in weight and power for deeper drilling, but without much change in tools or practices. The percussion drill was still an important tool in the petroleum industry.

Since about 1927 the development and improvement in rotary equipment and drilling practices have been revolutionary, and the petroleum industry now has available fine machinery designed and built in many sizes and types for use in drilling wells from a few hundred to 25,000 ft in depth; and its drilling practices are based upon sound engineering and scientific principles. Percussion drilling, during this period, has declined very rapidly to a relatively minor role in oil-well drilling.

Time Periods

The history of the art of sinking wells into the crust of the earth in search of water, brine, and gas may be divided into time periods somewhat as given following.

1. Peoples of prehistoric cultures dug holes and wells by hand, without the use of tools other than those found in natural form; and the same procedures can be observed in present-day Paleolothic cultures.

2. From prehistoric times to about 600 B. C. was the period of hand-dug wells using crudely manufactured tools of the bar, pick-and-shovel type, with skins or baskets for removing waste, and rope of leather or natural fibers. With the invention of the wheel by the Sumerians some 4000 B. C., windlasses and pulleys doubtless came into use.

3. The period from about 600 B. C. to 1800 A. D. was made notable by the work of the Chinese of the Chou Dynasty in drilling brine wells with percussion tools, and by deep hand-dug holes in Japan, Burma, Europe, and probably Africa. It seems quite reasonable to assume that the Greeks and Romans, with their broad technical knowledge and mechanical skill, practiced the art of water-well digging and possibly drilling, although the contemporary writers recorded little data on such activities. By 1500 A. D. the Chinese seem to have developed the art of drilling "deep" wells, possibly to as much as 2,000 ft.

4. From 1800 to 1859, in both America and Europe, there was rapid improvement in drilling equipment and operating methods—so much so that by the end of the 1850's many wells had been drilled to depths of around 2,000 ft; and some of the European water wells of the period were as large as 2 ft in diameter at depths in excess of 1,500 ft.

5. Succeeding the completion of the Drake well in 1859 and continuing to about 1880, the percussion well-drilling industry made great advances in mechanical equipment and technical skill. Drilling machines and standard rigs were developed into types, forms, and principles of operation that have carried down to modern times without basic changes except in small details of machinery and in the sources of power.

6. From about 1880 to 1930 the development of standard drilling rigs and tools was completed, but relatively few additions were made to the tools except those used on the derrick floors for handling pipe. Many portable and semi-portable machines were likewise developed, built, and used.

7. Beginning in 1930 or thereabouts, the need for faster drilling, rig portability, and greater overall efficiency brought about the development of the one-package internal-combustion-engine-driven cable-tool drilling machine of modern manufacture. These machines were not basic-

ally new, for many of similar type had been built directly after the turn of the century. However, the older rigs did not have the depth capacity or the portability of the modern machines because of the lack, at that time, of suitable steels and of a power plant of reasonable size and weight.

In 1901 came the first important oil well to be completed with rotary tools—the Spindletop gusher—and although cable tools continued to drill the great majority of all wells for some years to come, rotary equipment soon replaced percussion tools in the areas of younger and softer formations. By 1920 rotary rigs were drilling practically all wells in such areas as the Coastal Plains and had begun to make inroads on all cable-tool rigs in the softer areas of Oklahoma, Kansas, and North Texas. The first rotary reached these areas about 1914 or 1915.

With the perfection of the rolling-cutter rock bits for rotary drilling in the late 1920's, cable tools commenced to lose ground rapidly in all of the oil-producing areas. By 1950 practically all of the oil wells of the United States and of the world at large were being drilled by rotary rigs, except in a few regions such as the oil fields of the northeastern Paleozoics of the United States, parts of the Permian Basin in Texas, and a few minor areas abroad.

Classification of Well Drilling

The tabulation following classifies and subdivides the art of well drilling by methods and types of equipment.

Methods of Drilling	Types of Equipment
Percussion	
Cable Tools, wet	Chinese spring board
	Spring-pole
	Jerk-line
	Spudder
	Standard rig (walking beam)
	Machines
	Spudder
	Walking-beam
Solid-rod Tools, wet	Canadian
	Galician
	Free-fall
Circulation	
Hollow-rod Tools	Fauvelle
	Fauck "rapid"
	American
Through Casing	Cable tool
	Rod tool

Methods of Drilling	Types of Equipment
Rotary	
Dry or wet	Cutters and tube, coring
	Augers
Hydraulic, circulating	
Core drill with	Diamond set bits
	Chilled shot
	Toothed cutter
	Hard inserts
	Rolling cutters
	Drag cutters
Full-hole cutting with	Drag bits
	Fishtail
	Multiple blade
	Rolling cutter bits
	Hard insert (diamond bits)
	Subsurface hydraulic turbine with
	one of above bits
Combination	
Rotary, hydraulic with	Various tools and bits
Percussion, wet or hydraulic	
with	Various tools and bits
Rotary-Percussion	
Hydraulic, circulating	Rotating tools with
	Vibration elements
	Electric
	Hydraulic
	Mechanical
	Jarring elements
	Cams
	Springs
	Hydraulic
Others	Burning, fusing, or calcining
	Flame
	Electric arc
	Explosives
	Projectiles
	Shaped charges
	Solution
	Solvents

In addition to the various applications of the precussion- and rotary-drilling systems as actually used, experimental work has been done on other new basic principles of making holes in the earth such as by electrical vibration or hammer drive applied with a constant force and by explosions with conventional or shaped charges, or with projectiles.

Some of the several possible methods for drilling wells listed in the last section of the foregoing tabulation, such as rock fusion, are in actual commercial use on shallow holes used in mining and surface quarrying. However, up to the present time, for various reasons none of these several experimental methods has found successful application in the drilling or forming of deep holes for the production of oil or gas.

It would seem reasonable to assume that one or more of these or other different basic principles of drilling will be successfully applied to oil wells at some time in the future. Improvements and further development of present conventional drilling systems will, without question, increase very materially the efficiency of oil-well drilling. The subsurface hydraulic turbine was first invented and patented by George Westinghouse in 1889; and has since been worked on by many experimenters including, in recent years and at the present time, both the Russians and the French. C. C. Scharpenberg (Standard Oil Co. of California) also experimented with the tool in the 1920's.

Since the completion of the Drake well, drilling tools have increased vastly in number, type, efficiency, and capacity. The rather sketchy, sparse, and sometimes uncertain information concerning the details of the equipment and practices used in drilling this first oil well and earlier brine wells has been expanded into an almost limitless amount of fine technical data, and complete and detailed information on present-day equipment and oil-well drilling. The relatively few rigs in existence in the 1860's drilled a few hundred shallow wells. In 1959, less than 100 years later some 6,000 rigs, both cable-tool and rotary, completed more than 50,000 wells with an average depth of about 4,200 ft.

Research studies preliminary to writing this story of drilling equipment and drilling practices disclosed that positive data and detailed information range from little or nothing to very meager, in the early days, to an amount in modern times far in excess of that which can be used.

Most of the available data prior to 1859 have been incorporated in this article and an attempt has been made to give the broad historical picture of drilling and drilling tools with the development of the most important items in drilling rigs from their earliest conception, or the first model, to the units presently in use. Little space will be given to modern tools of either the cable-tool or rotary systems inasmuch as they are hardly a part of history as yet and the literature concerning them is abundant.

PREHISTORIC AND ANCIENT

During earliest times men lived in or under natural shelters of various kinds, such as rock ledges, caves, hollow trees, dense forests, or even bushes and shrubs. Some of the first manual labor performed by *Homo sapiens* and his man-like predecessors was doubtless the digging of holes in the ground near his shelters in search of food and water. Indeed, this method of obtaining food and water or, expressed differently, this *reason* for digging holes into the earth had been handed down to him by the animals of the plains and the forests, so it might be said that the earliest digging was pursued through instinct rather than reason.

As the ability to reason and experience were gained, man doubtless used such aids as broken sticks or sharp bones found in the forest or on the plains; and with further development of his power to reason, coupled with experience, he doubtless shaped hand tools of wood, bone, or stone. His next step was the development of greatly advanced tools in combinations of poles with bone or shaped stones attached to one end. With such equipment, gradually improved, man became capable of digging holes to any reasonable depth even as they are being dug today, here and everywhere, with pick and shovel and rope and bucket.

The earliest records available concerning wells have to do with Asia Minor or the region of the earliest Biblical stories. This was dry country and the requirement for water was urgent. It followed naturally that the digging of water wells developed in the wide arid and semi-arid areas through Persia and Asia Minor as the population spread into the inter-stream areas.

At the present time throughout these regions, water for household purposes and for irrigation is obtained from single hand-dug wells—quite similar to those of our own country—or from a system of connected wells known as "kanats." These kanats compose a system of wells and connect-

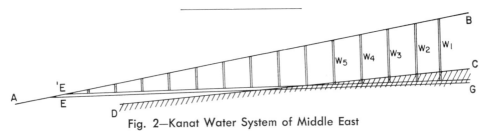

Fig. 2—Kanat Water System of Middle East

The line AB shows the natural surface of the land and CD the level of the subsoil water. E-G shows the *qanat* or tunnel (4 ft. 2 inches high and 28 inches wide. W1, W2 W3 are wells, 30 inches diameter and 20 to 150 yards apart, which are required firstly for removing the spoil when (a) the *qanat* is being constructed and (b) periodic cleaning is being effected, and secondly for ventilation. They are made up to E, the beginning of the *haranj*.

The following is a vocabulary of some of the common terms used in *qanat* construction:

W1.   *Madar chah* (mother well).
    The section of *qanat* in water-bearing strata is known as *ab deh* (water-giving).
    The work in the dry strata is called *khushki-kar* (dry work).

'E.   When the bed of the *qanat* comes within 2½ to 1½ metres from the natural surface the tunnel ceases and gives way to an open channel known as *haranj* until its water spills into a sump or irrigation ditches.

Pushteh.   Section of a *qanat* between two wells.

Moghani.   Qanat or quanat builders. Col. E. Noel (see p. 450).

ing tunnels dug along the talus slopes at the foot of a mountain system (Fig 2). A hole is dug near the mountain until a satisfactory water sand or water gravel is encountered. Two or three hundred feet, more or less, down the slope a second well is dug. At similar distances further down the incline a third hole is dug, and so on until the flat valley at the foot of the slope has been reached. These wells vary in depth from the maximum at the mountain to the minimum or zero at the valley end of the line of holes. A tunnel is then dug connecting the kanats in such a manner that the water encountered near the mountain will flow gently downhill through the tunnel, past the bottom of each well, and out into the ditches or reservoir on the plain or valley at the lower end. The earth removed from the holes and the tunnel is piled around the top of the wells.

Some of these systems are thought to have been producing water for thousands of years. In at least one system the deepest hole is said to be in excess of 1,000 ft from surface to bottom.

The 15th verse of the 26th chapter of Genesis reads as follows:
"For all the wells which his father's servants had digged in the days of Abraham his father, the Philistines had stopped them, and filled them with earth."

The 18th verse of the same chapter says:
"Isaac digged again the wells of water, which they had digged in the days of Abraham his father; for the Philistines had stopped them . . ."

The 19th verse states that:
"Isaac's servants digged in the valley and found there a well of springing water." (Artesian?)

It seems quite possible that the 15th and the 18th verses refer to a system of kanats, while the 19th verse refers to a single well in the valley at the foot of the talus slope. These single wells were used for irrigation as well as for household use by the rather laborious lifting of water from the well onto the land. Both hand and animal power were and are still used in the operation.

This 26th chapter of Genesis, in particular, and other chapters of the Bible give references to wells dug for both oil and water. Exodus, 17th chapter, 6th verse states " . . . and thou shalt smite the rock and there shall come water out of it, that the people may drink . . . "

There are many recorded uses of pitch or tar or "slime", both in the Bible and in the writings of the earliest historians. For example, the ark of Noah was "pitched within and without"; and it is recorded that Moses' basket was made waterproof with the same substance. It is doubtless true that much of this asphaltic material was obtained from seepages, but it is also probable that wells were dug by hand on the seepages to increase the available supply. Sennacherib of Assyria is reported to have had such a well dug on the upper Tigris River, probably near the great Kirkuk oil field. The well was said to have been sunk to 37 ft and to have been curbed with blocks of "alabaster". Fig. 3 shows an idealized sketch of such a well. With the many oil and gas seepages—small and large—scattered through Asia Minor, it is likely that there were many other hand-dug wells and that the asphalt and oil recovered therefrom were used for various purposes such as heat and light and mortar. Oil and asphalt are known to have been used extensively by the Babylonians.

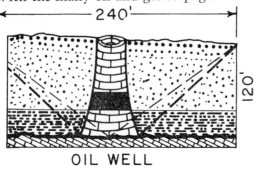

OIL WELL

Fig. 3—Idealized Sketch of Ancient Hand-dug Well in Asia Minor

Herodotus (circa 450 B. C.) described an oil seepage at Zacynthus and recorded that a well dug near Ardericca produced asphalt, salt (water), and oil. These materials were recovered from the well by the use of a "swipe" made of half a goat's skin on the end of the pole, rope, or leather thong. These early wells were doubtless dug with shaped tools and later with bronze and then iron tools. Windlasses and iron tools came into use some centuries B. C.

So far as is known all of the wells or holes dug for water or oil in Asia Minor or the Middle East in B. C. centuries were holes dug manually with hand tools. The depths to which they were dug are not often recorded.

Strabo, Dioscordies, and Pliny (circa 50 A. D.) record the use of oil in torches for illumination both in Agriegentun (Sicily) and Rome about the time of Nero. Plutarch (66 A. D.) mentions petroleum found near what is now the Kirkuk oil field in Northern Iraq.

EASTERN HEMISPHERE — ASIA

China

The earliest record of drilled or bored wells in China goes back to the Chou Dynasty (1122 to 256 B.C.). About 600 B. C. Confucious writes of wells apparently a few hundred feet deep in the region between Chungking and the border of Tibet. If the Chinese were capable of drilling wells to depths of several hundred feet in 600 B. C., they must have been occupied over many centuries prior to this time in developing the art to its then state of perfection. These wells were dug for brine from which salt was precipitated for domestic and other uses in a vast area of inland China.

To reconstruct what may have been the course of events leading up to the digging of such wells, it may be assumed that there were salt-water or brine seepages in some parts of the district. To obtain brine in larger quantities, holes or wells were dug by hand into the seepages or near them. As sands became exhausted of brine new holes or wells were needed,

Fig. 4—Chinese Rig

or the old ones needed to be deepened. Digging by hand became increasingly laborious and difficult. New tools and methods were necessary and the ingenuity of an intelligent and cultured people was brought into play. It is doubtful that the resulting Chinese drilling tools were really "invented"; they probably evolved and were developed and improved over centuries of time, long before the beginning of the Christian era; and with only minor modifications, insofar as known, are being used at the present time for the same purpose in the same country by descendants of the same people. Marco Polo mentions the Chinese well drilling in the stories of his travels in the 12th Century.

It was recorded that many of these early wells produced natural gas which was used for lighting and heating in the vicinity of the holes. There were no metal pipelines through which gas could be moved very far from the mouth of the well that produced it, but short bamboo lines were devised for both brine and gas.

In 1944 M. T. Archer of The National Supply Company, an engineer of great experience in the drilling-equipment industry, journeyed to China and while there made a trip into the country northwest of Chungking in which these brine wells were being drilled. Following is his description of the area and the drilling operation.

"Drilling in Tzu-Liu-Ching, China

"In Southwestern China, near the Tibetan Plateau, is a region where some sixty million Chinese live and prosper. It is 1,500 miles from the nearest seaport and 1,000 miles from the nearest railroad. In spite of their isolation the Chinese here have evolved practices in the salt industry and particularly in methods of well drilling and production which are strikingly like those employed elsewhere in the world. Hand labor conditions and scarcity of good lumber and steel have resulted in some methods different from our own.

" . . . Exactly when the first well was drilled here is shrouded in the mists of antiquity. Probably it was over 2,000 years ago. Local tradition has it that the field had not assumed importance before the Han Dynasty, and perhaps no well was flowing at the time Caesar made his excursion into Gaul. . . ." (See Fig. 4.)

"Other salt-producing districts in this province are known which are said to be of even greater age. Nevertheless, Tzu-Liu-Ching can claim as an unchallenged record the drilling of wells over 2,000 feet deep at least 200 years before Drake spudded in. There were shallow wells here at the time of Christ.

"The first salt was undoubtedly obtained from salt springs. At present it comes from the strong brine located at depth. The field is some fifteen miles in length and about two miles wide; the ground is hilly with irregular drainage. The wells are scattered irregularly without regard to topography. The structure is a typical anticline.

"As the shallow wells became exhausted they were deepened to lower producing sands. New brines, and later gas, were found and exhausted. Prospecting was carried still deeper until stage by stage the field reached its present condition. Today most of the salt water comes from a producing sand lying 3,000 to 3,100 feet below the surface, near the axis of the anticline, while the gas is found in horizons 200 to 800 feet deeper. The deepest well in the field is 4,305 feet and still drilling.

"Coinciding with the gradual deepening of the wells came the evolution in drilling methods. While many tools and methods are still primitive, the Chinese nevertheless have shown remarkable ingenuity in adapting the material at hand, as well as in the application of many mechanical expedients. They are drilling 4,000 foot holes in about four years at a cost of $17,000.

Fig. 5 (left)—Base of Chinese Derrick Legs

Fig. 6 (below) — Chinese Drilling
Method
(After Coldre)

"Chinese Derricks

"The Chinese derrick is wholly different from the American or European rig. A drilling rig, 50 to 70 feet high, consisting of two main shear legs and two bracing legs, is first erected. The shear legs are about 34 feet apart at the base, while the bracing legs are somewhat closer together, so that the ground plan is not a square but a diamond. The legs are made up of several small-diameter peeled pine and cedar poles, eight to ten inches in diameter. These are bound together every two feet with strong bamboo rope made taut with cedar wedges. The main legs are often three feet in diameter at the base." (See Fig. 5.)

"The two taller shear legs on the long diagonal are about four feet apart at the top, and carry the crown block. One of the bracing legs on the shorter diagonal reaches to a horizontal girt ten feet below the crown pulley and the other bracing comes to a second girt about twenty feet below the first. There are no true braces in any parts of the Chinese rigs; they don't seem to have known this art.

"This rig is used for bailing while drilling is in progress. After the well is completed and the bailing of salt water is begun as a production method, the rig is usually heightened to a total of 120 to 160 feet, by the erection of two high shear legs placed on the diagonals of the parallelogram outside the original legs and braced with six additional bracing legs. Each corner of the final rig is formed of three legs, one outside the other, with the outermost about 48 feet apart. When completed, the whole affair looks like a 'Chinese puzzle' more than a modern derrick.

"A spool is supported about 20 feet above the well and the diameter is just enough to allow a line from the bull wheel to pass over and drop freely into the hole. Three feet from the hole and four feet apart are two uprights which carry a trip beam. In drilling, two platforms are built, one on each side of the trip beam (walking beam). Three to five coolies step from one platform onto the beam, forcing it down and lifting the bit on the other end of the lever, and then step across to the other platform, leaving the beam fly upwards. Twenty to forty strokes per minute are averaged day and night." (See Fig. 6.)

"In drilling, the line is attached to a primitive notched stick, used as a substitute for a temper screw. The free end is doubled over and pushed down the hole to keep it out of the way. At the top of the trip pole is a swivel which is tied to a piece of soft rope, which is given a half hitch around the temper screw. To let out the screw the driller takes up slack and changes his hitch to a higher notch on the stick.

"In pulling out, the free end of the line is run over the spool and attached to the circumference of the bull wheel, 15 to 20 feet in diameter, with a vertical axis, which is located in the hoisting shed about 100 feet away from the rig. Two to six water buffaloes are hitched to the circumference of the wheel, and as the animals walk slowly around a circular

148

tread they wind up the line. It takes about twenty minutes to pull up 3,000 feet of line. When lowering the tools, the wheel is controlled by a bamboo friction brake.

"The horizontal bull wheel is a carry-over from the more ancient times. Throughout history primitive peoples have recorded the use of such bull wheels for raising loads. In fact, that is where the title comes from. Our modern practice has merely turned the axis of this wheel to a horizontal position and operated it by power instead of by the bulls.

"The drilling line is formed of pliable strips of bamboo 40 feet in length, and inch and a half to two inches in width, and three-sixteenths of an inch in thickness. The strips are notched and bound together with strong hemp cord protected by a rawhide covering. One strip is used to depths of about 1,500 feet, two are used for the upper half of the line for depths between 1,500 and 2,500 feet, and a third is attached to the upper part for greater depths. Bamboo rope, which is much used in the field for other purposes, is not used for drilling on account of its stretch. The Chinese driller is unable to use an elastic line and for this reason cannot employ steel rope.

"The native-made bits and stems are grooved pieces weighing about 300 pounds. Sharpening is poor in large bits on account of poor heating methods, but is often excellent in the bits under eight inches.

"The collar and stem are about $3\frac{1}{2}$ inches in diameter with gently sloping shoulders. The blade is very short with shallow water courses and cutting edge concaved or slightly cut out at center. Another type of bit has a shank which is twisted around like a corkscrew through 360 degrees. The spiral edge of the shank is notched into cutting teeth, which are thought to help in rounding out the hole on the upstroke of the drill. Two steel guides are often attached to the upper part of the stem. Several small transverse cleats are welded on the guide and act as reamers in rounding out the hole.

"The stem ends in a slightly expanded head. A sheath made of four flat strips of bamboo is securely bound to the stem and head by hemp cord. At the other end of the sheath is a piece of 2-inch pipe 10 inches long, in which slides the square end of a bar of iron weighing about 75 pounds, which may be called the sinker bar. The sinker bar has about 6 inches play in the sheath. On the upstroke a square head on the end of the bar strikes the bottom of the sheath and thus produces the same effect as our present-day drilling jars.

"To change bits a halfhitch is taken around the stem below the jars. The hemp binding is cut with a knife. The jars are swung back to a hook on the sampson posts. The bits and stem are then lifted from the hole by the screw. Another bit and stem is run into the hole and attached to the jars and sinker bar by tying up the bamboo sheath with hemp-cord." (See Fig. 7.)

149

Fig. 7—Chinese Rig Changing Bits

"Many forms of fishing tools have been devised. Most are spears, grabs, or sockets. A combined spear and bamboo socket is much used in fishing for small articles. It is quite evident, therefore, that the ancient forms of fishing tools used by the Chinese are, if anything, a forerunner of our present-day cable-tool fishing devices." (See Fig. 76 and 77, p. 229.)

"When starting a well a hollow wood or stone conductor is put around the hole for the first eighteen feet. When drilling starts an $18\frac{1}{2}$-inch bit is usually used for the first 120 to 250 feet of hole. Heavy, neatly turned and pointed wooden casing is set to this depth to shut off surface water. The inside diameter of the casing is 8 to 10 inches. The remainder of the hole is carried on down with an 8-inch or smaller bit. Below the first 250 feet casing is rarely used. The deepest wells have more than 4,000 feet of open hole.

"Apparently the holes stand up very well without casing (though in some wells casing is used). Caves are encountered in certain beds during drilling but are taken care of by a crude method of cementing. Lime, water, and wood oil are mixed and lowered to the bottom of the hole in a bailer and dumped. Five to fifteen bailers are run in and left to harden fifteen or thirty days. The hole is then drilled out again. The cement partially penetrates the cracks in the rock adjacent to the hole and to a certain extent prevents further caving. Another method is to dump several bailers of dry lime on the bottom, mix it with water by means of the drill, leave it in the hole for twelve hours and then resume drilling.

"Detailed well logs are kept by the Chinese drillers, somewhat in the nature of our present-day logs. They are of interest in showing the progress made by the drillers through the various formations, and in

150

giving information regarding the time lost on fishing jobs, etc. We will not attempt to translate the whole log, but make a few mentions of certain items. For instance, the data reads this way: the 7th Moon, 22—meaning the seventh moon, twenty-second day. Following are a few samples:

"7th Moon, 22nd Day—142-ft depth, drilled 3 ft, today.
Drilled in surface hole.
Character of rock, red sandstone.
"Later, an entry near the end of the record reads:
10th Moon, 14th Day—2,682 ft. Amount drilled—2 ft.
Drilling in 4-inch hole. Gray Limestone. Caving from a green marl at 2,641 ft. Broke the line. Fishing to the 11th Moon, 25th Day. Cemented and let set until the 12th Moon, 18th Day. Continued drilling.

"Drilling is not unduly slow considering the crude methods in use and the character of the rocks. The best estimate that can be obtained shows that four feet of hole a day can be made for the first 2,400 feet. Below this level the character of the rock changes and progress is slower. Drilling speeds and cost are approximately as follows:

Depth	Time to Drill	Total Cost
1,200'	10 months	$3,500.00
2,400'	2 years	7,750.00
3,000'	2 years 8 Ms.	10,500.00
3,500'	3 years 6 Ms.	14,000.00
4,000'	4 years 4 Ms.	17,500.00

"Cost of the first 1,200 feet is high on account of including the cost of preparatory work, setting casing, etc.

"The rigs cost about $2,000.00 to $3,000.00, according to their height. Equipment, including houses, rigs, tools, casing and lines, costs about $7,500.00. Wages in the field run about 11 to 22 cents a day and board (rice, parched corn, and once in a while a little pork). A bonus is paid when the monthly drilling average exceeds a fixed figure. The crew consists of eleven men a shift; twelve hours on and twelve hours off. Natural gas is found in several horizons but at the present time most of the production is between 3,250 and 3,400 feet and again between 3,800 and 3,900 feet.

"The most prolific salt water sands are at 3,100 feet and when a well is drilled deeper it is for the purpose of securing gas alone. Gas is used in evaporating the salt water from the brine wells and to some extent for domestic purposes but it is not employed as a fuel under steam boilers. The flow is never strong and issues at little pressure. The best well in the field came in about the year 1900 and yields approximately 400,000 cubic feet a day at the present time.

"The remarkable thing about the whole field is the manner in which

151

the Chinese have adapted bamboo in various forms to their work. It is used for drilling lines. It is also used for making the bailing lines which handle the bailers to depths of over 3,000 feet. Pieces of large diameter are used as pipe line. Joints and girths are little used in the rigs and are seldom nailed; they are bound together with bamboo rope tightened with wedges. Except in the drilling bits there is no iron on these Chinese rigs.

"The only improvement over a period of many years is the introduction of steam hoisting engines which are used in bailing. This caused the construction of higher rigs to enable lifting bailers of greater length and capacity. In the last five years, to increase the capacity of the bailers, wells 7 and 8 inches in diameter have been drilled instead of the old-fashioned 4- or 5-inch holes.

"Primitive as the many applications at the Tzu-Liu-Ching Field appear, they do seem to fit the conditions that exist and produce results satisfactory to the natives."

Japan

The Japanese have been familiar with the use of petroleum for illumination and other purposes for many centuries and appear to have been first to either drill or dig deep wells for the express purpose of producing oil. B. S. Lyman, in his "Reports on the Geology of Japan" published in 1877, states that wells were dug by hand some 600 to 900 ft in depth for the purpose of producing oil. The earliest date when such wells were sunk is not definitely known, although 600 A.D. is given as the approximate time. The actual digging was carried on by two men—one being in the hole digging while the other was on the surface running a bellows to pump air to the bottom of the hole to his companion worker. After about 3 hours they changed places. The dirt was hauled up by several men on the surface, but the tools and methods used are not stated. The wells were about $3\frac{1}{2}$ ft square and were timbered from top to bottom to prevent caving.

The digging of holes in the earth to such depths, and especially with petroleum gas present, was no mean accomplishment for the times—nor would it be a simple operation even today. This is further evidence of the considerable mechanical ability of the old cultures or societies.

Burma

In 1765 Major Michael Symes of the British Army, while ambassador to Burma, visited the oil fields of that country and reported on them in the journal of the British Embassy. Some 40 years prior to this the Dutchman, Herman Moernaave, likewise visited the oil fields of Burma as did the Rev. J. N. Cushing in 1881. Major Symes reports that at the time of his visit some 500 wells had been dug by hand into the oil sands supplying Burma and parts of India with their production. Rev. Cushing states that the wells were some 5 ft square and were curbed with split boards as the wells were sunk. The well diggers worked periods of 2 to 20 min; and when one man was overcome by gas from the diggings, he was replaced by another. The

Fig. 8—Burmese Hand-dug Well

Fig. 9—Hoisting Cuttings or Driller on
Burmese Oil Well

(Burmah Petroleum Co. Sketches)

circulation of fresh air into the wells, as was the case in Japan, is not recorded by the visitors to Burma. Moernaave's comments are lost.

These operations date back some hundreds of years; and, with the addition of oxygen helmets and other modern safety devices and tools, are carried on in the same manner today.

Fig. 8 shows a Burmese hand-dug well, dug in the ancient manner except for the head piece. Fig. 9 illustrates an ancient method of hoisting that has been used in quite recent times. Modern drilled wells are shown in the background.

EASTERN HEMISPHERE — EUROPE

Russia

In the 13th century Marco Polo made his journeys eastward across Asia Minor and into China. He passed Baku en route and saw the fire temples, or the "Eternal Fires of Surakhani," of the followers of Zoroaster, the great Persian philosopher who founded the religion of the fire worshippers of the Parsees. These fires of seepage gas in what are now the Baku oil fields, are supposed to have burned from ancient times until the drilling of the oil wells in modern times which decreased the pressure in the reservoir and shut off the flow of gas to the surface. There are no records of wells being drilled at Baku in the early centuries, but in 1723 Peter the Great granted concessions on the area to private individuals who dug wells by hand and produced some oil. Development of the field commenced in earnest about 1872. Oil from this area had been used by the Persians for many centuries before the Russian acquisition. From Baku, Marco Polo continued his journey into China where he wrote of the drilling of the brine wells in Western China.

In the Kouban District in the Russian Caucasus, the Russian Colonel Novosiltsoff drilled the first well at Peklo near the Black Sea to a depth of 182 ft. It produced 250 bbl of oil daily. There seems to be no record of the tools or methods used, but possibly this was the original introduction of percussion-drilling tools into that region of Southern Russia.

153

Mr. Dwyer of the United States consular service, in a letter written August 10, 1880, stated that in the Baku oil field on the shore of the Caspian Sea there were 136 wells at the end of the year 1860, 220 wells in 1862, 415 wells in 1872. All of these were dug by hand. He further states that the first well was drilled in Baku in 1871. In 1874 there were 50 wells; in 1876, 101 wells; and in 1879, 301 wells had been drilled in the district.

France

In 1498 oil sands in the Pechelbronn area in Alsace were discovered and the work of producing oil was begun. Shafts were sunk and tunnels and galleries cut from which the oil flowed and accumulated in sumps, whence it was moved to the surface, probably in pails. These workings have been in operation periodically since their discovery and were worked extensively in World War I and particularly during World War II. The first oil well was dug in 1745 by M. de la Sablonniere. During the years 1745 to 1785 several were sunk to depths varying from 10 to 25 meters. From 1785 to 1849 the following wells were drilled (or dug).*

Name of Well and Year Drilled	Depth, Meters
Pluton — 1785	35
Antoine — 1788	35
Catherine — 1794	31
Andre Achille — 1802	34
Marie Louise — 1810	50
August I — 1822	50
Adele — 1833	33½
August II — 1837	54½
Gluck Auf — 1838	40
Madeline — 1839	72
Salome — 1841	62
Joseph — 1849	57

All of these wells were dug for oil and all were prior to the Drake well of 1859. The method of drilling or digging is not given. It seems probable that the wells subsequent to 1795, when a 330-meter water well was drilled near St. Nicholas d'Abremont, were dug with percussion tools borne by rod.

A considerable impetus to the art of drilling deep wells in France was furnished in 1818 when the government appropriated funds to drill to depths of 2,000 ft in search of artesian water for the city of Paris. French engineers devised wrought-iron drilling tools suspended on jointed wooden poles, and the poles and tools were raised and dropped by a windlass activated by manual or other power. Manpower was used until a depth of 150 meters was reached, from which point the power of 3 horses was applied

*Letters from M. Rene Navarre, President of the Institut Francais du Petrole.

through a winch and gear mechanism to depth of 1,116 ft. At this point a rotary method of drilling is said to have been developed. The power of 6 horses was applied until the well was completed at a depth of 1,780 ft. The work of drilling to this great depth required 10 years. There are no detailed descriptions known of the tools and equipment used in these operations. The use of a rotary method of drilling, as indicated in the records, is most surprising and may be questionable.

Beginning with the operations of the late 1700's and continuing on down through the 19th century, French well-diggers and engineers designed, developed, and manufactured a great variety of drilling tools, as evidenced by the catalogs published in the middle and latter part of the 19th century, which will be discussed later.

A pamphlet published in 1855, entitled *Applied Geologic Treatise of Deposits and Development of Useful Minerals*, by M. Amédée Burat, professor of geology in the Central School of Arts and Manufacturing, carries the illustration shown as Fig. 10 herein. This sketch indicates considerable advancement in the art of well drilling by the middle of the 19th century. The walking beam is manually operated and a second beam carries a weight to balance the weight of the rods. The driller is operating the feed-off device apparently somewhat like a temper screw.

Another publication of 1861 is entitled *Guide Du Sondeur on Traité Théorique et Practique des Sondages (Driller's Guide or Treatise on Theory and Practice of Drilling)*, by MM. Degousee and Ch. Laurent. It contains brief reviews of well drilling in China, England, and Germany. It also discusses the Fauvelle system (see p. 288) and describes the drilling methods of France. The rig of Fig. 10 seems to have been developed in 1853 and to have drilled many of the deep wells of the 1850's and later.

Thus it is quite apparent that Europe, and especially France, was well advanced in the technique of well drilling by the percussion method in the mid-1800's.

A few of the many water wells drilled in France prior to 1860, listed for the author by M. Rene Navarre, President of the French Institute of Petroleum are:

Paris Grenelle

Corner Rue Bouchut and Rue Valentin Hauy: Drilled from 1833 to 1841—depth, 540 meters.

Seine Inferieure

Le Havre: Drilled 1792—depth, 82 meters or 269 ft.

Drilled 1830—depth, 203 meters or 676 ft.

Elheur: Drilled in 1834—depth, 149 meters or 489 ft.

Lillers: In this village there are several old water wells, one of which was dug on the grounds of the ancient convent of Chartreaux in the year 1126 and is still in use. The wells in Lillers were

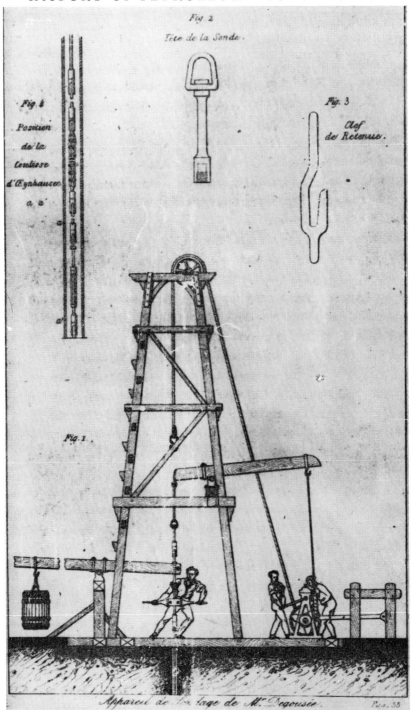

Fig. 10—French Rig of 1853 or Earlier (M. Degousee)

carried to depths between 10 and 40 meters. These wells were very probably dug by hand.

St. Nicholas d'Abremont: Drilled 1795—depth, 330 meters or 1,092 ft.

Sooteville-les-Rouen: Drilled 1849 to 1852—depth, 317 meters or 1,036 ft.

Seine

Drancy Pres Les Bourget: Drilled 1753—depth, 80 meters or 262 ft.

Epinay (by the Marquise de Grollier): Drilled 1827—depth, 56 meters or 184 ft.

Suresne: Drilled 1827—depth, 167 meters or 548 ft.

These last three wells were cited by Hericart de Thury in *Consideration Geologiques et Physiques sur la cause du Jaillissement des Eaux des Puits Fores*, Firmin Didot, Paris, 1829.

Several other wells were drilled in the provinces of Aisne, Ardennes, Cher, Cote d'Or, Eure, Indre-et-Loire, Maine-et-Loire, and Yonne prior to the year 1860. These wells varied in depth from 100 meters to 304 meters. A well of this latter depth was drilled in Laon in Aisne in 1830.

It is quite evident from this considerable list of wells, to which doubtless many others could be added, that the French had developed the tools and art of drilling deep wells as early as 1795 when a hole 333 meters or 1,092 ft was drilled, which was a remarkable feat at that early date. This well antedates by some 25 years any wells of comparable depth drilled in the United States.

These water wells of France were of diameters varying from a few inches to more than 2 ft, according to various references. For example, a well at Passy near Paris was started on September 15, 1855, and had reached a depth of 1,732 ft by March 1857. This well was later deepened to 1,922 ft and had a diameter of 2 ft 4 in. at the bottom. Other wells of comparable diameter and depth were bored in the Paris Basin to supply water to the City of Paris.

In 1845 M. Fauvelle, a French engineer, drilled a well near Perpignan, France, with hollow-rod tools through which water was circulated to remove the cuttings. The depth of the well was 560 ft. Drilling was started July 1, 1845, and finished July 23—a time period of approximately 22 days which was a very creditable performance for that period. Some have given Fauvelle credit for having established the basic principles of fluid-circulating rotary drilling. It appears, however, that his tools were not operated with a rotary motion but with the reciprocating vertical motion of rod tools. Fauvelle's contribution to the drilling industry was the use of circulating fluid to remove cuttings, but not the use of a rotary motion.

Bavaria

At Kissingen in Bavaria, a well was completed in 1850, to a depth of 1,878 ft, that flowed salt water to a height of 58 ft above the well head.

The activating force was carbon dioxide entering the hole at a point about 200 ft above bottom.

Austria

In 1859 Professor August Beer of the faculty of the School of Mines at Pribram, Austria, published a volume entitled *Erdbohrkunde,* in which he discussed various drilling methods of the day, including the possibility of using a rotary motion for earth boring.

England

Many water wells were drilled in England but their depths were quite shallow owing to the existence in the London area of good water sands within 100 or 200 ft of the surface. No records have been found of English drilling equipment of these early years, but the Beart patent of 1844, discussed in Chapter 6 herein, indicates considerable knowledge of that method of drilling.

We have little specific data on wells drilled in Austria, Germany, and Great Britain in the early years of well drilling, but the completion in 1850 of the Kessingen well mentioned previously indicates that the art was as well advanced in those countries as in France or America.

Thus, before the drilling of the Drake well the art of deep-well drilling had been well-developed in Europe; and the hole diameter on the Continent tended to be much greater than any reported in the United States.

Galician Oil Fields

The oil fields of Galicia had been worked by means of hand-dug pits since 1506 until the advent of Canadian pole drilling tools in the 1860's. After many changes and modifications, the Canadian pole tools came to be known as "Galician pole tools."

Other Regions

The presence of petroleum has been known from ancient times in many regions of the world and oil was doubtless produced or gathered and used in most of them. Some of these were Sumatra, Borneo, Iran, Iraq, and various countries of the Middle East and Europe. Many of these areas of seepage now have developed commercial production. No records of early operations in these countries have been found.

WESTERN HEMISPHERE

During the year 1510 Columbus shipped samples of asphalt from Trinidad to Spain; and in the latter part of the same century Sir Walter Raleigh sent similar samples to England. Asphalt from these seepages had been used for many generations by the Carib Indians in caulking their dugout canoes, and the early European explorers and merchants soon adopted the practice in caulking their ships. The Trinidad asphalt lake spreads over many acres, and the solid asphalt can be broken out with picks and loaded by hand for transportation. Asphalt oozing up from below refills the excavations. No wells are necessary.

In 1625 a paraffinic petroleum residue called "manjack" was exported from the island of Barbados in the West Indies to England. This material was recovered from seepages of light oil in the northern part of the island called "Scotland". The drilling of oil wells on both Trinidad and Barbados came at a much later time.

United States

The early American colonist learned the use of oil for medicinal purposes from the Indians. Oil seepages were present in western New York State, western Pennsylvania, and western Virginia. One in particular occurred in a gravel pit near Titusville, Pennsylvania. The most notable of the Virginian seepages were the gas vents or "burning springs" near Charlestown, West Virginia, which were visited by General Washington in 1775 and included in lands given him by the State of Virginia for his military services.

As the early Scotch-Irish, Germans, and French Hugenots moved westward in the latter part of the 18th century they became familiar with many of the oil seepages and the associated salt licks. Their visits to the salt licks were for two purposes—one for game that visited the licks to obtain salt and the other to procure salt for their own use. Although their primary interest was in salt they also became familiar with petroleum and used it principally for medicinal purposes, as well as a lubricant and fuel.

As the population increased, the need for salt likewise increased. It was first obtained by processing brine from seepages and by dissolving salt from the saturated soil. When such sources became inadequate to meet the demand, pits or hand-dug wells were sunk on or near the salt springs.

Ruffner Brothers Well

In 1806 the Ruffner brothers, David and Joseph, farmers who had moved in from farther east and had also engaged in the business of recovering salt from the salt springs, conceived the idea of boring a well to intercept the formation from which the brine was derived in order that they might obtain a liquid of higher salt concentration and in larger quantities. They selected a site near a salt spring on the edge of the flat land along the Great Kanawha River near Charleston, West Virginia. Their first problem was to sink a curb through the unconsolidated materials until they encountered a good source of brine, or to bed rock. To act as a curb to support the walls of the hole they selected a sycamore "gum" about 4 ft in diameter and hollow. The inside diameter of the gum is given as 4 ft. Similar logs are still in use as "bee gums", from which the name is derived. They may have wall thicknesses of the order of $1\frac{1}{2}$ to 2 in., thus allowing a working space with a diameter in excess of $3\frac{1}{2}$ ft in a 4-ft gum. Apparently the Ruffners had some idea as to the depth to bed rock, probably obtained by probing with a sharp-pointed pole, for it is related that they had some 16 or 17 ft to penetrate down to bed rock. For their casing, they cut their gum of the proper length, held it erect by braces, and erected a platform on top with sufficient space for two men to work. Then, with a man inside with pick and shovel and two men on top operating a bucket made of half a whiskey barrel, they carried their casing down to the hard formation which lay below the soft river-terrace material.

It was found that salt water of considerable strength or concentration came into the hole from the bed rock but in too small a quantity. The brothers then decided to continue boring into the earth by drilling with a bit of the type used in quarry work. They obtained a pole some 20 ft in length—probably of hemlock—supported it in the middle with a forked stick, and anchored the heavy end to the ground in such a position that the small end was directly over the center of the hole. To the small end they attached a long iron drill with a 2½-in. steel chisel bit. This tool was fastened to the spring pole by several wraps of a rope attached to the end of the iron drill rod. Another short rope with loops on each end was next attached to the free end of the spring pole and used by two men to pull the pole down, allowing the bit to strike bottom. Then, with the foot weight lifted, the springing of the pole jerked the bit from bottom thus giving a reciprocating percussion motion to the tool (Fig. 11). "Kicking down the well" was the slang description of drilling with spring pole and rope stirrups or foot treadles.

The boring was continued until January 1808, about a year and a half of work, at which time a considerable flow of salt water was encountered that satisfied the requirements of the undertaking. Thus was developed the spring-pole method, using solid rods, of drilling salt wells, that was to be the principal method used for the succeeding 50 years.

When they began to produce the brine from their bore, the Ruffners found that water solutions and fresh waters from above were contaminating their strong solution; and they had to find some method of shutting off the upper fluids in order that only their strong bottom-hole fluid might

Fig. 11—Spring Poles of Ruffner Brothers Type

160

enter the bore. At this time they had no metal and were forced to use the only material available, which was wood. Because their bore had been drilled with a 2½-in. tool, they needed a sapling 2½ in. in outside diameter. This was simple to obtain, but the problem of boring out a hole offered difficulties which at that time they could not overcome. Finally they split the sapling down the middle thus having 2 half-round lengths of 40 ft each. These were whittled out in their centers so that when placed together they formed a hollow tube which was then tightly wrapped with twine from one end to the other. To further assure a shutoff of the undesirable liquid from above, the lower end of the tube carried a "bag of wrapping" which, when inserted into the hole and pressed into place, is reported to have given a perfect shutoff so that undiluted brine flowed from the formation on bottom up the tube and into the gum casing from which it was recovered with an ordinary well sweep and bucket.

Dr. J. P. Hale, early West Virginia historian, stated, "Thus was bored and tubed, rigged, and worked, the first rock-bored salt well west of the Alleghenys if not in the United States. The wonder is not that it required 18 months or more to prepare, bore, and complete this well for use, but rather that it was accomplished at all under the circumstances."

Dr. Paul H. Price, State Geologist of West Virginia, makes the following statement in the article from which the foregoing account of the Ruffner brothers well was taken:* "The successful boring of the Ruffner well and the resulting spread of the salt industry has never received the attention it deserves nor the recognition it should have as laying the foundation of the future great American industry in petroleum. In nearly all of these salt wells petroleum made its appearance and was a source of considerable annoyance. Nevertheless the occurrence of petroleum was thus marked as waiting only for the impetus of economic demand to direct man's attention from salt to oil. Of even greater importance to the future oil industry was the development of the fundamental principles of the mechanics and the equipment of deep-well drilling—the boring tools that were the result of the ingenuity and resourcefulness of the Ruffner brothers."

The spring pole was used until well past the 1860's and the solid rods became the Canadian pole-drilling system in the early 1860's and later the Galician system, both of which are still in use. In addition, as far as is known, the Ruffner brothers used the first tubing with an open-hole packer to shut off the fluids above the bottom of the hole. In developing this practical method of drilling wells, which resulted in a considerable increase in brine production throughout the Allegheny Mountains with oil and gas occurring in a considerable number of the wells, the Ruffner brothers would seem to be deserving of more recognition than they have received for their services in the establishment and growth of the American petroleum industry.

---

*Am. Assoc. Petroleum Geologists Bull., April (1947).

Brine Wells of 1808 to 1859

Following the Ruffner brothers completion of their first brine well, many additional wells were drilled in the Kanawaha Valley for the manufacture of salt. Some of these wells produced substantial quantities of oil which was considered to be undesirable and a detriment to the salt operation, and was allowed to flow into the river, thus originating the name of "Old Greasy" by which the Kanawha was known for many years. From West Virginia, the drilling operations spread rapidly into adjoining states and particularly into Kentucky. Zadock Cramer's *Navigator,* published in 1812 in Pittsburgh, states that a Mr. Colquohoun, owner of Big Bone Lick, bored a well 150 ft deep in 1810 and "would go deeper if necessary". Other wells were drilled to depths of 200 ft to 400 ft in Cumberland County, Lewis County, and Perry County. A still deeper well was drilled near Manchester on Goose Creek in Clay County.

During this time, about 1814, one of the first—if not *the* first—oil wells to attract widespread attention was drilled for salt water on Rennix Springs near Burkesville, Cumberland County, Kentucky. The well was about 475 ft deep. Oil was struck and the well came in with oil flowing into the Cumberland River and covering it completely for miles downstream. The oil on the surface of the river became ignited. This was the famous "American Well".

At about the same time a well making oil with considerable gas was drilled by Samuel White about 4 miles above Greensburg, Kentucky, on the Green River. No attempt was made to develop the area for oil and gas until some years later. As was usual, the original well had been drilled for salt water.

From West Virginia and western Pennsylvania, salt-well operations spread westward into Ohio where many wells were drilled. Several of these were not successful brine wells because of the presence of oil and gas. These records indicate that many oil and gas wells had been drilled in the Alleghenys some 25 to 30 years before the Drake Well. Although these operations were not intended to develop oil and gas, they nevertheless proved its presence over a vast area; and its exploitation began very soon after the Drake well came in and showed that there was a market for crude oil for the production of kerosene.

Potable water was a requirement in many sections of the East and the newly settled country between the Alleghenys and the Mississippi River; and many wells were drilled in these areas and southward into Alabama prior to the year 1860. One of the most famous of these was the Belcher Sugar Refinery well in St. Louis which was commenced in 1849 and completed in 1854 at a depth of 2,193 ft. In 1858 a well was completed at Louisville, Kentucky, at a depth of 2,086 ft after a drilling time of some 16 months. This was indeed a splendid accomplishment at that early date.

During these same years artesian wells were drilled in lower Illinois and along the coastal plain of Alabama and on the south Atlantic seaboard.

The literature of the period gives little technical information on the rigs themselves, but something can be learned from the following description taken from the patent on drilling jars granted William Morris on September 4, 1841 (see also p. 240).

"Tools

"The auger used on Kanawha for years past is constructed as follows— two poles made out of solid oak timber or other substantial wood, sixteen feet long, made smooth and round, and about two inches in diameter, are united by two plates of iron, convex on the outward side, and concave on the inner side, so as to fit the poles. The ends of the poles are first rabbeted together and plates about thirty inches in length are laid on opposite sides of the poles, at the place where the poles are united, when five rivets passing through each plate and the poles so united, are well clenched, the center rivet passing through the rabbet in the poles of aforesaid. Care should be taken when uniting the poles to keep the whole of it perfectly straight. Plates of half the length of those described as aforesaid are welded on the opposite sides of a square bar of iron about six inches long, and one inch, or one and a quarter inch square. These latter plates so welded are slipped over one end of the pole, the pole being shaped so as to be easily driven between the plates. These plates are in like manner confined to the poles by rivets passing through the plates and pole, and well clenched. A preparation of the same kind is put upon the other end of the pole. On the bars on which plates are welded as aforesaid screws are made, the one a male, the other a female screw, and one of the size to receive the other. Then poles may be continued to any given depth, each being about thirty-three feet long, and screwed the one upon the other. Immediately below the male screw, a shoulder is made on each side of the square bar, by which the pole or poles when suspended, may be caught in an iron clamp, and held until another is screwed on in letting down the auger, and unscrewed in taking it up. At the lower end of the auger a square or round iron bar of about one and one-quarter inch in diameter and varying from eighteen to twenty-five feet in length, is used to give weight to the auger, and is called the sinker. At the upper end of the sinker a male screw is formed, on which the poles aforesaid are screwed. At the lower end of the sinker a female screw is formed. To complete the auger, a bit or boring chisel is necessary, with a male screw at the upper end, onto which the sinker is screwed. The bit is generally from twelve to fifteen inches long, about one and a quarter inches thick, and for three or four inches from the bottom upward, of the width that the perforation in the rock or earth

163

is desired to be made. The lower end of the bit, and that part of it, with which the boring is done is made of steel and brought to an edge with the hammer at an angle of about forty-five degrees, from each side, so as to make the edge in the middle of the bit and cut across the entire diameter as well as the center of the hole to be bored. This edge is also of a convex form keeping the center of the hole boring deeper than the sides. In letting the auger down the bit is first put in the clamp onto which the sinker is screwed. They are let down until the upper end of the sinker only is exposed, which is caught in the clamp and held until the first pole is screwed on, and then let down, and so on from pole to pole until the bit reaches the bottom. The pole thus screwed together is raised, from one foot to eighteen inches and permitted to drop suddenly on the bottom and in rapid succession, until the bit is dulled, or the sides so worn by friction as to diminish the size of the hole, so much as to require it to be resharpened by the hammer, and drawn out again to the width of the hole to be bored. In letting down a fresh bit, it is often necessary to ream out the bottom of the hole where the former bit had been much worn by friction. It often happens with the most careful hands, in letting down the auger, that it gets loose, and drops to the bottom, and if the former one had been much worn, the fresh bit, drawn to the full width fastens very tight, and often occasions much delay and expense to extricate it.

"From the construction of this auger it is manifest that every part of it must participate in the jar which succeeds every fall of it, in boring, and that consequently a heavy sinker, increasing the jar, cannot be used without serious injury to the wooden poles and it is equally manifest that the progress in boring mainly depends upon the weight of the sinker. To give weight to the sinker and thereby expedite the boring without injury to the poles, and to extricate the bit when fastened by falling as aforesaid, or sand settling around it or other obstruction below the upper end of the sinker were great desiderati in boring Artesian wells, and is that which I claim to have accomplished in my improvement aforesaid."

The only description that has been found of the actual operation of a drilling rig prior to 1860 is an account by Capt. John Pope, later General Pope, of a well drilled for water by the United States Army in the Pecos Valley of Texas. A digest of his rather voluminous letters together with verbatim quotations from some are given following.

John Pope, then Brevet Captain, Topographical Engineers, was instructed by the War Draft on January 5, 1855, to test the practicability of procuring water by artesian wells in the arid plains of Texas in the area between the headwaters of the Colorado River of Texas and the Pecos River, and not far south of the Texas-New Mexico boundary. Capt. Pope recommended 4 wells at intervals of 25 miles, with expected depths of about 600 ft. His estimate of cost was:

Tools, rods, augers, chisels, derrick	
irons, etc., for boring 700 ft.	$ 1,250
Travelling forge and equipment	500
Wooden tubes for 700 ft.	250
Pay and subsistence for men for 8 months	8,016
Cost of wagons and mules for transporting	
provisions and tools	9,500
	$ 19,516
For each additional well	5,472
Total cost of 4 wells	$ 35,932
From which deduct sale of mules, wagons,	
and boring instruments	7,400
Final cost	$ 28,532

The point selected for the first trial was upon the Llano Estacado near latitude 32 deg, about 15 miles east of the Pecos, at the mouth of Delaware Creek, where water for the use of the party could be conveniently obtained from the river. The party arrived at this point in the latter part of May 1855, and started the boring operation about the first of June. Water was reached at a depth of 360 ft. The water was pure and clear and rose 70 ft in the well and remained that height, the level of Delaware Creek. The unexpected softness of the formation made it necessary to use all of the 500 ft of tubing which had been brought with the party. About the middle of September, at a depth of 640 ft, a second supply of water was encountered in a sandstone. Water from this horizon rose rapidly 390 ft. It was still rising when caving in of the marly clay below the tubing filled in the well to a height of 70 ft above bottom and effectively bridged off the water sand. An attempt was made to remove the cavings with mud sand pumps, but after continuous labor of 12 days and nights without making any impression, this cleanout job was discontinued. The well continued to cave; and without additional pipe, it could not be completed.

While Capt. Pope was waiting for additional casing he and his party took up the second phase of his assignment—that of ascertaining the practicability of drilling artesian and other wells upon the route explored between the Rio Grande of New Mexico and the Gila River of Arizona. The point selected was 10 miles from Fort Fillmore, on the high plain west of the Rio Grande. The operations were begun about the first of November 1855, and continued until February 15, 1856, at which time a depth of 293 ft had been bored through a porphyritic detrital deposit, slightly united by calcareous cement, with occasional beds of tenacious yellow and red clay. The boring, which was very difficult, had not passed through this formation when the party returned to the Pecos to meet the new supply of tubing which was expected about the first of April.

The party of Capt. Pope arrived on the Pecos the second time about the last of March 1856, and resumed the boring for an artesian well about 5 miles east of where the work had been carried on the previous year. Beginning to bore on April 5, 1856, the depth of 245 ft was reached by the 16th. Here water was encountered, which rose 25 ft in the well, and remained at the same level to which the first water met with in the preceding year had risen. The new supply of tubing was now needed, but it had not arrived. The tubing was prepared in Philadelphia and, after inspection by Capt. Humphreys, left there on January 20, 1856. It consisted of 1,200 ft of wrought-iron tubes, 3-in. internal diameter, with a thickness a little exceeding 3/16 in., cut in lengths of 9 ft, with screw joints. As a precaution, 400 ft of 1¼-in. wrought-iron pipe in lengths of 9 ft, with screw joints—such as used for boring rods—were sent with the tubing, as they would doubtless be of use for other purposes, if not wanted or not suitable for boring rods. The pipe arrived at Capt. Pope's camp on the Pecos on April 29, 1856.

With the tubes, a depth of 450 ft was soon attained. Then the third piece of tube from the bottom gave away, spreading outside of and partly enveloping the piece below, and rendering it impracticable to continue the well further. As much of the tubing as could be got out was withdrawn and the work again started at the surface on May 20, 1856. At the depth of 676 ft, the lower stream was met with, the water rising to within 110 ft of the surface.

On July 20, a depth of 809 ft was attained. The 1,200 ft of boring rods (wooden) that had been taken originally with the party had been reduced by breakage to 860 ft. The hope was expressed that, with the use of ash tent poles of the party and command (the country not affording supplies of suitable wood), the depth of 1,000 ft would be attained by the close of August, if water was not sooner reached. This anticipation, however, was not realized. At the depth of 830 ft, after passing through strata of clays, marls, and soft sandstones, the boring entered hard sandstone. On August 26, 1856, Capt. Pope reported that the work had been brought to a close at the depth of 861 ft, as his boring rods had been exhausted and all the boring material in his possession consumed.*

The following letter from Capt. Pope to Capt. Humphreys gives probably the first and best description of the principal parts of the drilling equipment and difficulties of such drilling operations prepared up to that time by an experienced engineer. It is for such reasons that the reports and letters of Captain Pope on the operation on the Pecos River are included in the history.

Camp on Pecos River, May 1, 1858

SIR: I submit the following report of operations in the prosecution of the experiment of sinking an artesian well on the "Llano Estacado."

---

*Report of Capt. Humphreys to Secretary of War, Jefferson Davis, dated Nov. 29, 1856.

The boring is done by means of oak poles, 1¾ inches in diameter, in 16 feet sections joined in twos by heavy iron straps. Each boring rod is therefore 32 feet long with a male screw at one end and a female screw at the other, both having very strong and heavy threads. The drill has a straight edge of 3½ inches, and is attached to an iron rod 30 feet long and 1¼ inch in diameter. To the upper end of this rod (or sinker) is attached a pair of iron slips (jars), having a play of 16 inches and to these are screwed on the wooden poles, up to the surface. The upper end of the poles is attached by a movable chain to a spring beam worked by steam, and (boring at the usual speed) the drill falls fifty-five times in a minute. The borings are pumped out by a sand pump of copper, nine feet long, which works with a rope passing around a drum attached to the steam engine. The hole is pumped out on an average once in 2½ hours of boring.

The difficulties we have encountered have resulted from the peculiar soft and crumbling strata of variegated marls and clays, which are of an uncommon thickness, not, I believe, to be found elsewhere within the range of geological examination. It has been necessary in this case to line the well with tubing from the surface, and as combining strength and lightness, wrought iron tubing 3/10th of an inch was brought out with the expedition.

The first difficulty met with was in sinking the tubing to a depth of 81 feet lower than it was left last year (810 feet). Although with the under cutting drills it was easy to enlarge the bore below the tube so as to admit the latter to pass down freely, yet the friction along the sides resulting from the crumbling and falling of loose slightly coherent strata around it, was so great that it required driving so heavily as it would bear to force it down. Next the iron sinker broke off in the middle and before anything could be put down to withdraw it the well caved in for sixty feet above it and completely covered it. Six weeks were passed in clearing the well and getting out the broken sinker. Next the water used in the engine, in consequence of large quantities of lime and sand held in suspension soon coated the flues of the boiler with a very hard scale and caused them to leak badly. It was therefore necessary to take down the engine and reflue the boiler entirely, inserting manheads for cleaning. Very shortly after we again resumed boring we passed into alternating thin strata of blue slate and flint limestone, the most difficult strata we have yet encountered. Water pours in at several places in the well in considerable streams, and very soon washes away the slate, which is soft but leaves the sharp jagged edges of the hard limestone fully exposed; in a very little while the wooden rods working through these strata would be cut in two; iron rods were substituted, but they were soon bent so badly, by coming into violent contact with the sharp limestone, as to be useless; I therefore was obligated either to diminish the bore by inserting smaller tubing, or sink the large tubing to the bottom. The exceeding difficulty of the last plan induced me to prefer the former, and the hole was lined with three-inch copper tubing from the lower to the upper thin layer of limestone. Unfortunately, very soon after effecting this, the iron slips broke immediately beneath the bottom of the copper tube, and so spread apart that they could not be withdrawn through the tube; it was therefore necessary first to take out the tube—a work of difficulty. It was all gotten out except nine feet of the lower part, which pulled off, and had to be bored and speared up. The boring up and pumping out of the copper tube was completed yesterday, and the head of the broken slips is now exposed so that they can be withdrawn.

Since our arrival at this camp we have been thus embarrassed by difficulties and breakages, altogether due to a most peculiar, difficult, and uncommon formation of great and hitherto unknown thickness. The strata are so distinctively marked that they can be easily recognized in their outcrop between the Pecos River and Guadalupe Mountains; and we have reached the stratum of slate exposed plainly at the head of Delaware Creek, about forty feet above the issue of the powerful fresh and mineral springs which form the sources of that stream.

The winter here has also greatly incommoded us from inadequate protection of the men from unusually inclement weather for this region, and there were many days during the severe northers, incident to this country, in which it was impossible to work. The spring is now fairly open, and I trust we shall soon be able to finish this work, as I am altogether certain that the water is but a little way below us.

I am, sir, respectfully, your obedient servant.

JOHN POPE
Captain Top'l Engineers

Capt. A. A. Humphreys, Corps Top'l Engineers
Washington, D. C., in charge of Occie Expl's and Surveys

On June 4, 1858, Capt. Pope reports that boring operations were resumed after the recovery of a broken sinker bar and bit. During the early half of June their efforts to force down the $3\frac{1}{2}$-in. iron tubing (casing) were not entirely successful. The spring-type under-reamer was used to enlarge the bore to $4\frac{1}{2}$ in. for a depth of 78 ft below the bottom of the tube. The tube was then driven 12 ft further, when the threads on 3 couplings or joints and the lower part of the tube were so badly crushed as to render it impracticable to drive it further. The tubing (or casing) could not be withdrawn for the same reason and it became necessary to run the smaller-diameter copper tube inside the $3\frac{1}{2}$-in. iron tube. Certainly this operation was "running out of hole" very rapidly.

On June 30, 1858, Capt. Pope addressed a letter to Capt. Humphreys in which he stated that he had in his organization the most experienced and capable drilling superintendent to be found in the West, together with a full crew of drillers and mechanics who had been employed all of their lives in well-digging and who, together with the superintendent, Mr. Brown, had drilled the deep well at the Belcher Sugar Refinery in St. Louis, mentioned previously.

On July 27, 1858, Capt. Pope wrote to Capt. Humphreys as follows:

Camp on Pecos River, July 27, 1858

SIR. I regret to be obliged to report that the operation at this place has not advanced in the least since the date of my last report, and that in my judgement and in conformity also with the opinion of Mr. Brown, the superintendent and principal mechanic of the artesian well boring, it will be impracticable without largely increased facilities and consequent expenditures to prosecute the work further. The difficulties resulting from extreme singularity and extent of geological structure, together with the extremely injurious action of the Pecos River water upon iron machinery I have already explained to the department.

The boiler of the steam engine has been completely devoured by the acids of the water so that iron nuts half an inch thick crumble in the hands like clay. The plungers of the supply pump and steam chest are completely honeycombed, and every part of the engine accessible to the water has been more or less injured by it. It has been necessary to procure a new boiler in view of any future work, and I have therefore, sent three wagons to Indianola to bring one up. I endeavored after the complete destruction of the boiler to carry on the work by hand, but after a depth of nine hundred feet, boring by hand even under favorable circumstances is nearly impracticable. In the present case it is wholly so.

On August 22, 1858, Capt. Pope addressed a letter to Capt. Humphreys in part as follows:

SIR: I have the honor to report that since the date of my last report, the work of boring has been completely arrested, as with men it is impossible to handle an auger of 1050 feet. I am waiting the return of the wagons sent to Indianola, Texas, for a new boiler, but I have to say that I do not consider it practicable to carry these borings to greater depth with any means within reach of the appropriation. It will in my judgment be a waste of time and money further to prosecute the work under present circumstances. I therefore recommend that the party be moved to some other of the points designated in my instructions, where the chance of success will be far better.

* * * *

The first effect of such a geological structure is the necessity of

169

tubing any well to be bored from the very surface, and forcing or trying to force the tube to follow the auger closely. This I found is easy enough to do, as I had come prepared for such obstacles and had plenty of wrought iron tubing and spring or undercutting drills. With the latter we were able, without the least difficulty, to enlarge the bore, below the tube, to any size necessary; but we had not progressed more than six hundred feet with the work, until the friction along the sides of the tube, from top to bottom, resulting from the falling in around of the loose, crumbling strata, absolutely prevented it from moving down, although the bore below was a full inch and a half greater in diameter than the outside of the tubing. I then commenced to drive, and succeeded, by using great care, in getting it down two hundred feet further. Beyond that depth, the friction became so great, that the force necessary to overcome it crushed the wrought iron tube, and stripped off the screw threads at the joints.

It was impossible to carry the boring below the tube, as the crumbling strata of marls and soft sandstones commenced at once to fall in, when unsupported, and filled up the well faster than it could be pumped out. I had, however, anticipated this difficulty, and had brought out tubing of different diameters; and as soon as I found that the large tube could be drawn no further, a smaller one was pressed down inside, and the diameter of the well reduced.

For a while this obviated the difficulty, but after one hundred and fifty feet the small tube could no longer be forced down, and the strata still continued soft, and fell in constantly.

By these means and with the severest labor I ever saw, both night and day, exposed on this bleak plain with little protection to an inclement winter, we succeeded in reaching a depth of 1050 feet; no change whatever has occurred in the strata; they are as soft and crumbling at the bottom of the well as at the top, and it is impossible to say how much longer they will continue so.

The first account known of the running and "carrying" of casing and underreaming is contained in Capt. Pope's letters. Similar practices had doubtless been followed by the same crew that had drilled the St. Louis Belcher well and others. The underreamer was evidently not a new tool.

Drake Well

The *Dartmouth Alumni Magazine* for April 1951 carries a story on the developments leading to the drilling of the Drake well, with quotations from several publications and articles on the subject. In substance it states that four Dartmouth graduates, viz., Dr. Francis Beattie Brewer, class of 1843, George Henry Bissell, class of 1845, Dr. Dixi Crosby, medical class of 1820, and Albert Harrison Crosby, class of 1848, were responsible for the original arrangements which led to the drilling of the well by Col. Drake. According to the story, Dr. Brewer, after practicing medicine for several years in the New England states, moved to Titusville, Pa. in 1851, and became associated with a lumbering firm of which his father was a senior partner. Dr. Brewer, shortly after his arrival, became interested in an oil seepage on the company's property on Oil Creek. After an examination of the area Dr. Brewer convinced the members of the lumber firm that they should attempt to develop the oil resources of the area, which he believed could be made into a profitable venture. As a result the lumber company obtained the first lease in the history of the petroleum industry in the United States, on property owned by J. O. Angier of Titusville. In the fall of 1853 Dr. Brewer took samples of the oil to Dartmouth where it was examined by Dr. Crosby of the Medical School and Prof. Hubbard of the Department of Chemistry. These men pronounced it "valuable indeed".

Dr. Brewer left the bottle of petroleum with Dr. Crosby and a few weeks later it was seen by George H. Bissell who was intrigued by it. The resulting conversations between Crosby and Bissell are credited with being the beginning of the petroleum industry of the country.

After further discussions of the project and the acquisition of property, including the Hibbard farm near Titusville, the Certificate of Incorporation of the Pennsylvania Rock Oil Company of New York was filed in Albany on December 30, 1854, giving $250,000 as capital stock. After various vicissitudes and the organization of the Pennsylvania Rock Oil Company of Connecticut, so little progress had been made other than in financing that J. M. Townsend and other majority stockholders organized the Seneca Oil Company in March 1858 and took over the Hibbard lease. Realizing that someone must find means for bringing petroleum to the surface of the ground, Col. E. L. Drake was sent to Titusville in 1858 as the general agent for the Seneca Oil Company, to attempt to drill for and produce oil in larger quantities. George Bissell is given credit for first conceiving of the idea of boring for oil.

It should be borne in mind that many oil wells had been drilled in western Pennsylvania, West Virginia, Kentucky, and Ohio during the 40 years prior to the completion of the Drake well in 1859. Most of these wells had been drilled in search of brine for the production of salt, but oil was produced from some of them and was used commercially. It is quite possible that within the later years wells were drilled solely for the production of oil or gas. In fact, the records indicate that such a well had been drilled some years previously in the Tarentum area of western Pennsylvania. Despite these facts, of which there are ample records, it is nevertheless true that the Drake well was very definitely drilled for the sole purpose of producing oil; and with its successful completion and the publicity given it, and with the additional fact that the value of petroleum

171

was just then being recognized, it can properly be given the credit for marking the beginning of the petroleum industry as presently known.

Upon his arrival in Titusville, Col. Drake investigated means and methods of boring a hole and was brought into contact with William Smith who became known later in the oil fraternity as "Uncle Billy Smith". Uncle Billy was a blacksmith and knew of the methods used in the working of iron and in the drilling of wells. Because of this knowledge, he and his nephew were engaged by Col. Drake to make the tools, assemble and construct the drilling apparatus, and drill the wells.

The following paragraphs on the tools and operation of the Drake well were prepared by Ferd J. Spang:

"At that time the only malleable metal known to be economically usable in considerable quantity was wrought iron which was produced by the puddling of molten cast iron pigs until it became free of carbon and thus became fibrous, forgeable, and weldable. Its primary source of supply was Sweden, although this process was in a state of development in America and it is known that some limited supply of wrought iron of smaller sizes was available in the Pittsburgh District at that time.

"Crucible cast steel was produced, in very limited quantities, by mixing melted portions of wrought iron and small cast pigs to the total desired mass chemical composition in a crucible, after which it was cast into small ingots and forged into bars which were used to make edged tools such as razors and knives, and was face welded to the body portion of hand tools to provide the cutting edges of axes, mattocks, picks and other similar devices.

"Little was known in a practical way concerning threaded portions of metal devices other than bolts and nuts which were scarce and difficult to obtain. It was common practice to attach one apparatus to another by means of keys and wedges or by riveting or fire welding them together. For these reasons it is probable that the tool with which the Drake well was drilled consisted of an iron bar (for weight), the upper end of which was forged into an eye on to which the rope or cable was tied or spliced and the lower end spread or built up by side welding iron lugs to it to form a head which was sheath welded or capped with a layer of crucible steel to provide it with a cutting edge or bit head.

"The structure of the hoisting rig and the housing of the machinery for the drilling operation was such that sufficient room was provided for the laying down of a full length drilling tool in order to heat, resharpen, and harden its head or cutting edge. There is nothing of record that would indicate the prior use of the separate tool units which later came into use.

"The drilling portion or bit end of the one piece tool was flat and of a width equivalent to the internal diameter of the well bore. This head, sheathed with steel, was sharpened somewhat like a chisel, and, obviously, such a tool could only drill a hole which would sooner or later lose its roundness and become flat. Consequently, it was necessary to have a second reamer type of drilling tool which had a flat end. Such a tool was sheath welded with a relatively flat steel face. The sharpened tool was used to drill ahead until the bore hole lost a fully round shape, after which the tool was withdrawn and the hole filled with rock to a point above the irregular shaped portion; the flat tool was then used to re-drill the hole, thus reaming it and forming it to proper roundness.

"Each of these tools frequently became fast in the hole and this posed a great problem to the operator. The only method of loosening it was to use another round bar, attached to a similar rope, to strike the first bar and cause it to be knocked or shaken loose. It is not known if drilling jars were used on this well though they had been developed some twenty years earlier and patented in 1841 by Wm. Morris.

"The method of reciprocating the drilling cable in the drilling of the Drake well is not definitely known; however, it is known that the power was supplied by a steam boat type engine and boiler of probably five or six horsepower. This power was conveyed by a belt to a large pulley mounted on a jack shaft. The one end of the shaft was fitted with a crank and a pin (later known to be the bandwheel, the crank, and the wrist pin). It is thought by some that a walking beam was used to actuate the tools, with one end fixed to a post, the other to the jack shaft crank, the tools hanging in the middle. Others think a jerk line was used.

"No means of using this mechanical power to withdraw the drilling tool from the well bore was provided; however, a pair of double wooden wheels were mounted on a wooden shaft with its axis at right angles to the bandwheel shaft. Each of these double wheels were fitted with crosswise wooden strips to form ladders which were used as moveable treadles upon which the driller and tool dresser could tread and thus supply weight to turn the shaft and withdraw the cable and tool from the well bore . . . The descent of the tools was likewise controlled by the use of these treadles.

"The type of bailer or sand pump used for the removal of the drilling fluid from the well bore is not definitely known; however, a method subsequently followed consisted of a tube into which had been fitted a clapper type leather valve with a hitch or bail at the upper end. This tube or bailer must have been run by hand as no provision for any kind of a reel for spooling the hoisting line was available at that time. The bailer was emptied of its mud fluid by tipping

173

it endwise after it had been withdrawn from the hole.

"The method of operation consisted of driving a surface pipe or conductor through the soft alluvial fill of glacial origin, found in that valley, until the pipe had reached bed rock. This alluvial fill extended in depth to the neighborhood of twenty feet and was of such a type of formation as to contain surface water. The surface pipe was used to shut out this water and to prevent the caving in of the well. The surface pipe was driven by hand, using a wooden maul, and followed the hole as it was drilled or bailed to bed rock.

"When the Drake well was drilled in to the depth of sixty-nine feet on August 27, 1859, there was then no evidence of oil and operators became greatly discouraged that petroleum had not been discovered. For this reason the well was shut down, but during the time it stood, perhaps several days at the most, it was observed that the hole had partly filled with petroleum, and, consequently, the word was heralded throughout the area that the Drake well had really become a successful venture."

The following description of Titusville in 1865 appeared in *Rig and Reel* in July 1920:

"*Titusville*, situated in Crawford County, Penna. at the head of Oil Creek, had only 150 inhabitants in 1857. In one year it increased to 350. Lumber was worth from five to ten dollars per thousand feet for the best qualities. The number of buildings were about 35 of all kinds. The importation of merchandise about one hundred tons per annum. The trade was local, and everything was done upon the long credit system, and nothing exported but lumber. In 1865, the population is estimated at from 5,000 to 6,000. Lumber is worth from $25 to $50 per thousand, and the supply inadequate to the demand. The number of buildings are now over one thousand. The importation of merchandise, etc., during the year 1863, over the Oil Creek Railroad was 70,000 tons, and the exports of oil alone equal to 750,000 barrels. It is estimated that the exports from Titusville will amount this year to over $18,000,000, and the imports will largely exceed those of last year; at least the local trade has kept even pace with the improvements in the way of buildings. There are now in progress several fine stone and brick buildings which give the place a substantial appearance. In 1858, town lots could have been purchased from $30 to $40 each. In 1864, lots were selling from $1200 to $1800 each and sought after.

"The Watson Flat is a tract of flat land situated in the bend and on both sides of Oil Creek, adjoining and below Titusville. This flat land was at one time greatly in favor but after the large flowing wells were discovered below the Shaeffer Farm, less attention was given to lands above. Recently, however, the Watson Flat has been brought into notice again, and several flowing wells have been opened, and now hundreds of derricks spot its surface. This extensive tract of rich bottom-land, being in close proximity to Titusville and the depot of the Oil Creek Railroad, will no doubt be found more attractive than the territory farther down the creek. It is said that the quality of oil found here is very superior; and it is generally believed that when wells are sunk to the depth of 1200 feet, the largest flowing wells will be found."

With the completion of the Drake well, the oil industry was under way and soon hundreds of wells had been drilled in western Pennsylvania, New York, West Virginia, and on westward into Ohio. It was in these areas that the basic principle of the cable-tool drilling system, as now known, were developed and perfected. By 1875 or 1880, with a few exceptions, all of the basic items of the rig had been brought into use.

Cable tools were sent to Texas to drill the Nacogdoches oil field in the 1860's and to California in the 1870's. About 1890 cable tools were moved into Oklahoma and with them practically all of the oil fields in that state and North Texas, up to about 1920, were found and developed. Cable tools drilled all of the wells in California in the latter part of the 19th century and until about 1908, when rotary equipment was introduced from the Texas Gulf Coast.

Even as late as 1920 there was still a question in the minds of many experienced oil-field operators whether or not rotary tools would ever displace cable tools. However, no sooner had this opinion been publicly expressed by a number of prominent oil men of the period than the rotary began its rapid and presently complete ascendancy over cable tools. By about 1930 rotaries had entirely replaced cable tools, except in the eastern oil fields and in parts of Oklahoma, North Texas, the Permian Basin, and shallow areas in the Rocky Mountains. With the perfection of rotary equipment and of roller-cutting rock bits, standard cable-tool drilling rigs and cable-tool percussion-drilling machines disappeared almost entirely from the oil fields except in the eastern states where they still predominate.

Canada

A well drilled near Petrolia, Ontario, Canada, in 1857 was completed as a flowing oil well. Its original objective was water. In Tait's *The Wild-catters* (p. 3, 4, 5), it is related that J. H. Williams, in 1858, set up a small refinery on Black Creek, in southwestern Ontario, to refine seepage oil. He later dug wells by hand into the seepages. To increase his supply of crude, he drilled and completed a well in August 1859 at about the same time the Drake well was completed.

Peru

During the year 1867 the first two wells in the Zorritos Fields in northwestern Peru were drilled. The first of these was completed at a depth of 146 ft as a 60-bbl oil well. The second was completed shortly thereafter

175

as a 10-bbl well at 220 ft. These wells initiated the oil industry in Peru and were doubtless drilled with tools shipped in from western Pennsylvania.

New Zealand

J. D. Henry, *Oil Fields of New Zealand*, 1911, records that the first well on the islands was dug and drilled by Messrs. Carter, Smith, Scott, and Ross under the operating title, Carter & Co. The location was near the shore end of the breakwater of Monturoa, westerly along the beach from New Plymouth and in what is presently known as the New Plymouth or Egmont Oil Field. After reaching a depth of about 60 ft by hand-dug shaft on March 17, 1866, it was decided to continue the search for oil by boring with percussion-type tools then in common use in both Europe and America. The spring-pole method of drilling was first used under a tripod and later under a 4-legged derrick. The hole was drilled to a total depth of 300 ft without production. This first well was known as the Alpha well and the derrick bore a placard "to oil or London". The second well in this area was drilled by the Peoples Petroleum Company some 500 yards from the Alpha well and was known as the Beta well. A spring pole operating under a tripod was used to drill a 4-in. hole to 516 ft. This tripod bore the placard "to oil or Edinburgh". Neither objective was reached.

During the 1870's wells were drilled on North Island on and near seepages in the Bisborne area. On top of Waitangi Hill the writer found in October of 1954 a Farrar & Trefts engine, patented in 1872 and manufactured about the same time. There was other equipment of comparable vintage, including a locomotive-type boiler, a portable boiler with engine mounted on it, and bits and stems of a probably later day. No record was found of the type of equipment used, but Henry states that the spring pole went out of use in about 1866. It is assumed, therefore, that a walking-beam type of rig or machine was used.

PERCUSSION-TOOL DRILLING MACHINES AND RIG LAYOUTS

The first drilling machine ever used was doubtless the windlass placed directly over the hole being dug and operated by one or more men. Fig. 1. is a reproduction of a painting by Charles Wilson Peale signed and dated in 1806, which pictures the digging and earth-handling equipment of that time, including the windlass, and a chain bucket pump and excavator. The painting also shows a 5-legged braced derrick and other items of equipment used in the excavation. This painting has no direct bearing on the drilling of oil wells, but it does show two methods of removing diggings from a well or hole in the ground that have been in existence for centuries; and for that reason, it has seemed fitting to reproduce this great work of early American art near the beginning of this chapter (see p. 136).

The earliest percussion-drilling machines of which we have knowledge are those of the early Chinese which had reached a point of considerable development at the time of Confucius at about 600 B. C., and without doubt their beginning antedated that year by a considerable period.

According to Techlenburg *(op. cit.)* the Chinese also used the spring-pole method of drilling as shown in Fig. 68, p. 219.

One type of early American spring pole operated by one or more men with foot stirrups is illustrated in Fig. 12.*

Fig. 12—Early Spring-pole Drilling Rig

Another type of spring pole in which the teeter board is used rather than the foot stirrups is shown in Fig. 67 (p. 219). It is interesting to note that rods are being used in this operation, supported by a chain over the spring pole, as was done in the early Canadian pole-tool system. The heavy end of the pole is not shown in this sketch.

Another type of spring pole shown by Techlenburg and used in Belgium in 1828 is shown in Fig. 66 (p. 219). Still another spring-pole machine somewhat more highly perfected and using a teeter board for power and temper screw and clamps for supporting the tools at the end of the drilling line, is shown with tripod in Fig. 43. This illustration is taken from W. H. MacGarvey who was intimately connected with the establishment of the petroleum industry in Canada, and was one of the founders of the Galician-Carpathian Petroleum Corp. MacGarvey did perhaps more than any one single individual to develop the Canadian and Galician methods of drilling. The first great Canadian gusher, the celebrated Shaw well near Petrolia, Ontario, was drilled with a spring-pole rig.

Unfortunately there seem to be no reliable descriptions of percussion-drilling rigs between 1810 and 1860 including those which drilled the Belcher well at St. Louis, the Pecos Valley well in West Texas,† or even the Drake well at Titusville. Ferd J. Spang (see p. 172) thinks it quite possible that Drake may have used a chain line from the crank on the steam engine to the drilling line. Another description shows a walking beam hinged to a post at one end and attached through a pitman to the crank of the engine at the other end, with the drilling tools hanging from the center of the walking beam. There can be no doubt but that a steam engine was the source of power for drilling the Drake well, but the tools may have been handled in and out of the hole by foot treadles on the bull wheel.

Baroid News Bulletin, March-April (1954).
†See p. 164-170 for tools and practices.

Illustrations of the Drake rig show a housed-in, 4-legged derrick (see Fig. 49, p. 207).

After the Drake well was completed, a publication of D. Appleton & Co., New York, entitled *Petroleum—Its History and Development*, describes the drilling rigs and engines then in use. To quote:

"Engines used are of every conceivable type, portable, stationary, upright and oscillating. Portable and stationary are the kinds now in general use. These are from 8 to 30 horsepower, principally the former.

"Derricks 11′ to 12′ square at base, 30′ in height, converging to 2½ feet at top with girth and brace. Derricks are now (1869) built of sawed lumber or boards, 2″ thick and from 6″ to 8″ wide, the two edges being spiked together, forming a half square on each corner of the foundation, which is 14′ to 16′ square and in some localities more. The derrick is now put up in sections, being braced transversely as it goes up, in order to secure the strength necessary, until it

Fig. 13—Rig of the 1860's

reaches the proper height, which for deep wells is about 56′ . . . and at the top it forms a square of from 2′ to 3′. (Fig. 13 shows a rig of the 1860's.)

"The bull wheel . . . is a shaft of timber 6′ to 8′ long and 6″ to 8″ in diameter, the ends of the shaft are banded with iron and a journal of inch-iron driven into each end for it to revolve upon.

"Sampson post is of hewed timber, 12″ to 15″ square and usually 18′ in height, erected on heavy timber, framed, crossing each other, bedded firmly in the ground with a mortise to receive the tenon on bottom of post; also, a brace on each side reaching nearly to the top of the post. On the top of this are the irons fitted to receive the working beam, which is balanced on the top of the Sampson post, admitting the working motion required in drilling and pumping. The working beam is a stick of timber, from 20 to 26 feet long, 8 to 10 inches square at each end, 8 by 14 to 16 inches in the middle with iron attachments in the center fitting to a similar one on the Sampson post. To the end over the well is an iron joint for attaching the temper screw when drilling and sucker rods when pumping. On the other

Fig. 14—The Shamburg Petroleum Company's Wells on the Atkinson Farm near Oil Creek, 1860

end of the working beam is an iron joint for attaching the pitman bar, which connects the same with the crank, or band wheel shaft.

"The band wheel is usually about 6' in diameter with a 6-inch face ... The engine is usually placed from 8 to 12 feet distant from the band wheel and connected by rubber or other belting. The belting in general use is 6 inches in width.

"The sand pump now in use is a cylinder of wrought iron, 6 to 8 feet in length ... to which a half inch rope is attached passing over a pulley suspended in the derrick some 20 feet above the floor and back

Fig. 15—The Myers Wells on Cherry-tree Run, 1870

Fig. 16 (above)—Portable Drilling
Machine of 1878

Fig. 17 (right)—Early Spudder, 1892

to the sand pump reel attached to the jack frame . . . This shaft is propelled by means of a friction pulley, controlled by the driver on the derrick by rope attachment."

At first wood was the only material used for derricks. As greater strength was required for deeper drilling, heavier and heavier timbers and lumber were used. Finally in 1892 the first steel derrick, 72 ft in height, was constructed and made available to the industry to satisfy the demand for still greater strength and more efficient construction. Fig. 14 and 15 are photographs of typical wells in 1860 and 1870.

In 1875 Robert Magee Downie, founder of the Keystone Driller Co., is said to have conceived the idea of a portable drilling machine. It was built about 1878 in Butler County, Pa. and drilled its first well shortly thereafter. The spring pole was still used but motion to the pole was applied by a steam engine. The boiler, engine, and hoisting reels were all unitized on one frame and mounted on wheels. Three poles, joined at the top, formed the derrick. The new machine proved capable of drilling a well 6 in. in diameter at a rate of 40 ft to 50 ft per day. By 1880 the spring pole gave way to a walking beam mounted in the assembly. Fig. 16 shows one of the last spring-pole machines. By 1888 the machine became self-propelled, with power supplied by its own engine. Many self-propelled unitized machines have been built since 1888 to drill both water and oil wells.

The walking beam and temper screw were generally used to impart drilling motion and for gradually lowering the tools during the drilling operations. In 1892 a new approach was developed by M. R. Downie for imparting motion to the tools. The new method eliminated the need for the temper screw entirely. Downie's development of the spudder was the first radical departure from the conventional manner of drilling with cable tools. Spudding had long been used in starting a new hole, but only until the top of the tools was deep enough to safely attach the temper screw. Downie's method permitted and used the spudding principle to drill to any desired depth. At about that time the mast was first integrated into the machine, and not built or erected separately. One of the early spudders is illustrated in Fig. 17.

Spudding differs from the conventional walking-beam method in that the drilling line is not gripped by a clamp and the clamp attached through the temper screw to the beam that raises and lowers the tools to impart the drilling motion. Instead, the drilling line is carried over a pulley just above the main drilling reel and then in a horizontal plane to another pulley, called the "spudding pulley," which is attached to a beam that hinges at the back of the machine. The forward end of the beam holding the spudding sheave is attached to a pitman that raises and lowers the spudding sheave. The drilling line goes under the spudding sheave, then vertically to another sheave at the top of the mast, and from there into the hole being drilled. Drilling motion is obtained by the up-and-down travel of the spudding sheave on the drilling line. This new principle had many advantages, but was not widely used for deep wells until the late 1920's and the early 1930's, when it really came into general acceptance. The spudder motion is in general use today, for any depth of cable-tool drilling.

In 1896 C. S. Wright of Quaker City, Ohio, designed and built another type of drilling machine. His design was inspired by the need for

Fig. 18—National Rig about 1900

181

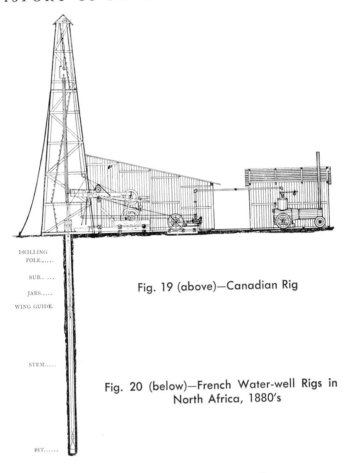

DRILLING POLE.....

SUB....

JARS.....

WING GUIDE.

STEM.....

BIT......

Fig. 19 (above)—Canadian Rig

Fig. 20 (below)—French Water-well Rigs in
North Africa, 1880's

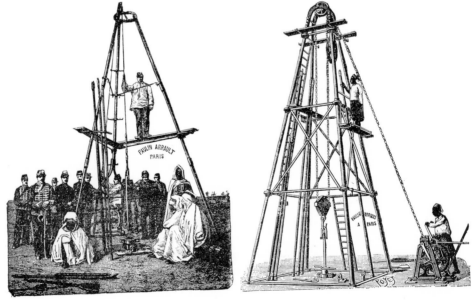

reducing the labor required for building the conventional standard rig. The machine was not portable but was integrated into units that could be easily assembled. It used an A-type mast instead of the more cumbersome standard derrick. The original machine is shown in Fig. 17. Later improvements evolved into the machine shown in Fig. 18. Wright's patents, ideas, and designs were taken over finally by The National Supply Co. which built and sold the famous and popular National machines. Some of the principal features of the National were the A-type mast, the location of the sand reel, bull wheel, and calf wheel between the mast and the engine, and the use of friction wheels brought in contact with one another to transfer power from the band-wheel shaft to the other reels. The walking beam was suspended between the legs of the mast and a temper screw attached to the end of the beam.

A Canadian drilling outfit for drilling with wooden poles is shown in Fig. 19. This illustration shows a rig of about 1890 including a portable locomotive-type boiler, steam engine together with the band wheel, pitman, samson post, and walking beam. The illustration likewise shows the manner of feed of the Canadian-type rig with a chain having two wraps around the rounded projection from the top of the walking beam, with the lower end attached to the drill rods and the other end passing lengthwise along the walking beam to a drum with ratchet on top of the walking beam directly over the samson post. This is the type rig which was sent to the Galician fields and developed further there. The string of tools is also shown. The two rigs illustrated in Fig. 20* are shown digging water wells in northern Africa in the late 1880's and show two more of the various types of rigs built to drill with the same hole tools. Fig. 80-84 are taken from the same publication and show the tools used by these rigs in drilling water wells to 600 or 700 ft in depth.

Some of the important patents on drilling machines are as follows:

L. Disbrow, patent of 1830, shows the earliest drilling machine (Fig. 44) of a mechanical type of which we have record. The tools employed with this rig and included in the patent application are shown in Fig. 78, p. 229.

John Y. Smith received Patent No. 47,868, on May 23, 1865, for a rather complicated steam-operated mechanical drilling rig with a vertical steam cylinder placed directly over the bore which, through rather complicated devices, operates the tools. It seems unlikely that this equipment was ever successfully used, but at least it shows the trend of thought at that time.

Walter Hyde received Patent No. 46,673 dated March 7, 1865, on a portable drilling machine. The drilling line passes from the top of the string of tools over the crown sheave at the top of the mast downward around a small sheave near the floor, then upward to a drum around which

---

*Paulin Arrault: *Bulletin Paris Exposition,* 10 (1889).

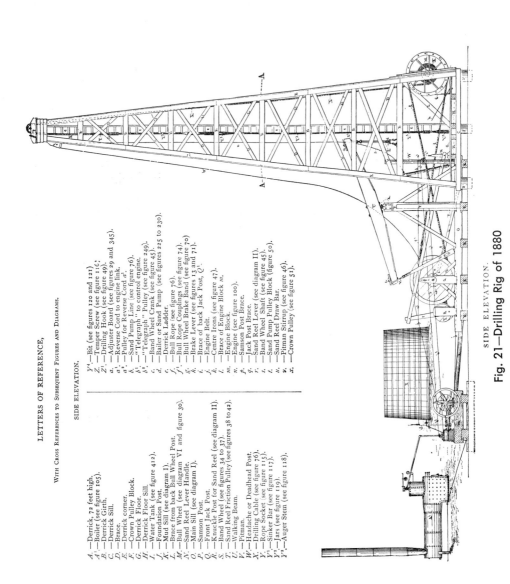

LETTERS OF REFERENCE,

WITH CROSS REFERENCES TO SUBSEQUENT FIGURES AND DIAGRAMS.

SIDE ELEVATION.

A. —Derrick, 72 feet high.
A¹. —Boiler (see figure 105).
B. —Derrick Girth.
C. —Derrick Sill.
D. —Brace.
E. —Derrick corner.
F. —Crown Pulley Block.
G. —Derrick Floor.
H. —Derrick Floor Sill.
I. —Water Tank (see figure 412).
J. —Foundation Post.
K. —Mud Sill (see diagram I).
L. —Brace from back Bull Wheel Post.
M. —Bull Wheel (see diagram VI and figure 30).
N. —Sand Reel Lever Handle.
O. —Main Sill (see diagram I).
P. —Samson Post.
Q. —Front Jack Post.
R. —Knuckle Post for Sand Reel (see diagram II).
S. —Band Wheel (see figures 34 to 37).
T. —Sand Reel Friction Pulley (see figures 38 to 42).
U. —Walking Beam.
V. —Pitman.
W. —Headache or Deadhead Post.
X. —Drilling Cable (see figure 76).
Y. —Rope Socket (see figure 115).
Y¹. —Sinker Bar (see figure 117).
Y². —Jars (see figure 119).
Y³. —Auger Stem (see figure 118).

Y⁴. —Bit (see figures 120 and 121).
Z. —Temper Screw (see figure 116).
Z¹. —Drilling Hook (see figure 49).
a¹. —Adjuster Board (see figures 29 and 345).
a². —Reverse Cord to engine link.
b. —Pulley for Reverse Cord d².
b¹. —Sand Pump Line (see figure 76).
b². —"Telegraph" to control engine.
c. —"Telegraph" Pulley (see figure 249).
c¹. —Band Wheel Crank (see figure 45).
d. —Bailer or Sand Pump (see figures 225 to 230).
e. —Derrick Ladder.
f. —Bull Rope (see figure 76).
f¹. —Bull Rope Couplings (see figure 74).
g. —Bull Wheel Brake Band (see figure 70).
i. —Brake Lever (see figures 13 and 71).
i¹. —Brace of back Jack Post, Q¹.
j. —Engine Belt.
k. —Centre Irons (see figure 47).
l. —Brace of Engine Block m.
m. —Engine Block.
n. —Engine (see figure 100).
p. —Samson Post Brace.
q. —Jack Post Brace.
r. —Sand Reel Lever (see diagram II).
s. —Band Wheel Shaft (see figure 45).
t. —Sand Pump Pulley Block (see figure 50).
u. —Sand Reel Draw Bar.
x. —Pitman Stirrup (see figure 46).
x¹. —Crown Pulley (see figure 51).

SIDE ELEVATION.

Fig. 21—Drilling Rig of 1880

the line spooled. This drum has a rachet and pawl to permit feeding off. The pulley below the drum is fixed to a hinged frame which is given an up-and-down motion by two beams on a driven wheel. This apparatus was apparently designed for shallow drilling and it gives what may be the earliest suggestion of spudder-type motion to the drilling tools.

L. Rust on May 9, 1882 was granted two patents, No. 257,766 and 257,767, on a chain-and-gear driven integrated drilling machine in which the motion to the tools was provided by a spudder-type mechanism. J. G. Martin on March 18, 1884, received Patent No. 295,413 on a walking-beam type drilling machine mounted on wheels. A steam engine occupied the center of the frame. The band wheel was belt-driven from the crank-shaft of the engine, while the bull wheel and sand reel were gear-driven. The mast was hinged and pulled back onto a post on the back end of the machine. This machine should have operated satisfactorily for shallow drilling.

H. S. and C. E. Glenn received Patent No. 472,619 on April 12, 1892, on a wheel-mounted drilling rig containing a vertical boiler and a vertical engine. One end of the walking beam was fixed while the pitman gave the drilling motion and was about four fifths of the distance along the walking beam toward the drilling-tool end. This machine was self-propelled by sprockets and chain on each of the rear wheels. It is doubtful that this outfit was ever extensively used, although the sketch indicates that with good construction it would have been entirely practicable for relatively shallow drilling.

Patent No. 466,970, P. Wompler, Patent No. 566,383, J. J. Dues, and Patent No. 523,787 and Patent No. 698,033, G. D. Loomis (1902) all show mounted portable drilling machines of more or less practicability and are of value historically in that they indicate the trend of the times and the very considerable efforts that were being expended to develop practical and rugged machines.

These early patents on drilling machines using chain, gearing, and drums, rather than ropes and bull wheels, are of further importance in that they are the forerunners of the most modern machines of today.

Fig. 21 shows a complete standard cable-tool drilling rig of the early 1880's. The equipment shown includes a locomotive-type boiler of probably 20 to 30 hp, with 100 lb working pressure; single-cylinder, "single-barrel" or "mail-pouch" slide-valve engine, 12 to 15 hp; and a sand reel operated by friction from the back side of the band wheel—the band wheel with crank, the pitman, the walking beam, the samson post, the head-ache post, the engine throttle with telegraph cord, the bull ropes in position, and the bull wheel. The sand line is shown passing over a pulley below the water table on the bull-wheel side of the derrick, while the string of drilling tools is hanging on the manila drilling line, having been withdrawn from the hole. The drilling string consists of the rope socket, sinker bar,

Fig. 22 (above)—Floor of a Cable-tool Rig, 1890

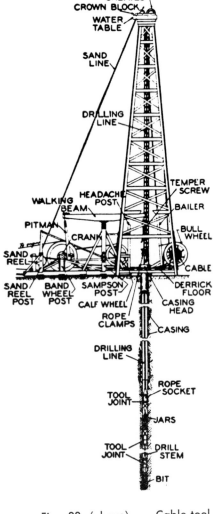

Fig. 23 (above) — Cable-tool Drilling Rig

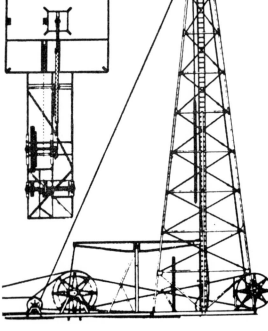

Fig. 24 (left)—Early Steel Drilling Rig, 1892

jars, auger stem, and bit. The temper screw and clamps are hanging from the walking beam, while the bailer is standing in one corner of the derrick. The derrick appears to be 68 ft high built of 2 x 6's and 2 x 8's with nails or spikes. It has a single crown sheave. This illustration, including the water tank, shows a complete cable-tool rig of the day with the exception of the forge and anvil and accessory tools and equipment.

Fig. 22 shows the floor of a cable-tool rig of the early 1890's. Fig. 23 illustrates a cable-tool drilling rig with parts, and Fig. 24 is a line sketch of an early steel drilling rig (about 1892).

Fig. 25 shows a California-type drilling rig handling casing. The calf wheel—formerly called the extra bull wheel—which first came into general use in California circa 1900, is shown in position handling the casing with blocks suspended below the crown sheave and at the floor, and with elevators attached to the casing. The calf wheel and bull wheel appear to have been operated with manila rope, and the sand reel was controlled by a line that passed over a pulley at the crown of the derrick rather than below the water table. This is the earliest illustration of this type rig, although there were probably others in use in the latter part of the 19th century. In a California-type rig, about 1915, the suspended crown block for handling casing had been replaced by a fixed crown block. With this exception the rig appears to be entirely similar to that of 10 years before.

The Knupp rig was patented by Jacob C. Knupp and James G. Green of Warren, Pa. on March 14, 1905, Patent No. 784,571. The special feature of this semi-portable rig was the design of the mast, which had two legs spread at the bottom to the outside of the working floor with cross pieces between the legs and two legs placed in front and back. It is reported that only a few of these rigs were placed in service (about 1905) because of weaknesses in the mast. It is interesting, however, in that the type of mast construction was quite similar to that of the present day.

Fig. 26 shows a Parkersburg rig with string of tools, in use about 1905. Fig. 27 shows the famous old Star portable drilling machine with folding mast. This rig was in operation about 1900 or a little later. Fig. 28 shows a combination Columbia Drilling Machine of about 1904, equipped to handle either cable- or rotary-drilling tools.

During the early part of the century many skid-mounted and wheel-mounted drilling rigs were built. They were designed primarily for shallow drilling and, as the search for oil and gas went deeper, the standard cable-tool rig was used almost exclusively. A few machines, such as the Star drilling rig and the Ft. Worth Spudder, survived into the 1930's and 1940's and some are in use at the present time, although most of them have either been modernized and improved, or have been replaced by the steel machines of modern types.

In summary—cable-tool drilling rigs were developed originally as non-portable knock-down equipment that was re-erected at each location.

CALIFORNIA RIG

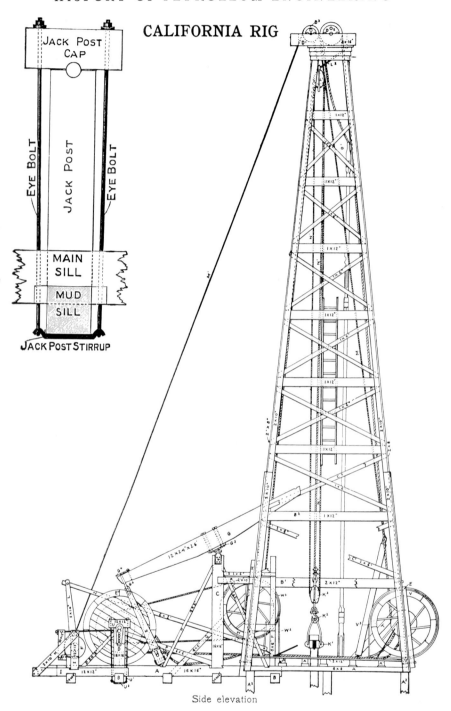

Side elevation

Fig. 25—California Drilling Rig, Circa 1900

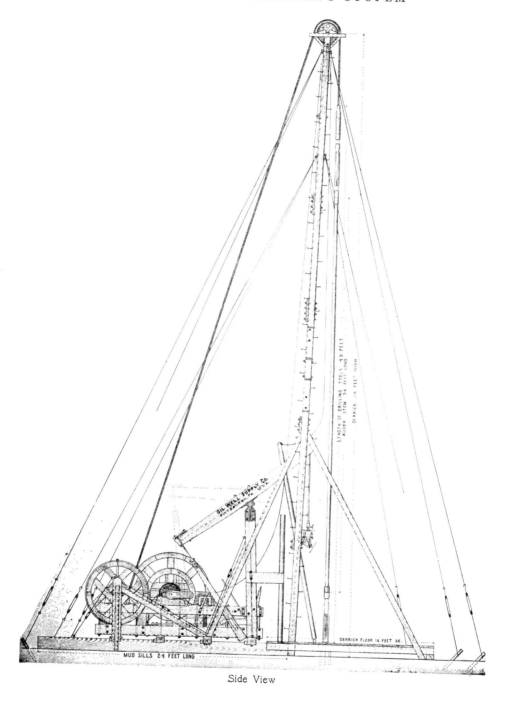

Side View

Fig. 26—Parkersburg Drilling Rig, 1905

Fig. 27 (above)—Star Drilling
Rig, 1905

Fig. 28 (right) — Columbia
Combination Rig, 1905
All-steel drilling traction machine with rotary attachment
and slush pump.

As early as the 1860's shortly after the Drake well, many portable and semi-portable machines were designed and built. There are few records concerning the use of these machines and it seems probable that the great majority of oil wells other than the very shallow ones were drilled with what had come to be known as "standard cable-tool rigs", and the less-rugged portable equipment was relegated to water-well drilling and a few very shallow oil developments. Only in recent years have the portable cable-tool drilling machines re-established themselves.

One of the difficulties in construction of a satisfactory portable rig of the early years of the industry—in fact until quite recently—was caused by the weight and disadvantages inherent in the type power plants used.

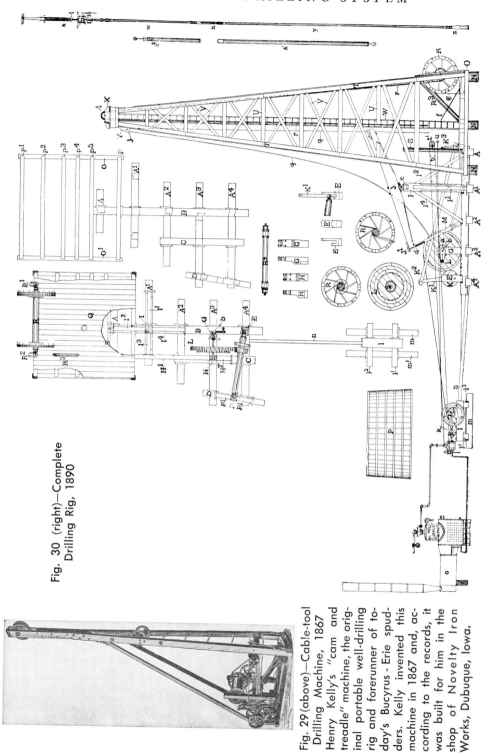

Fig. 30 (right)—Complete
Drilling Rig, 1890

Fig. 29 (above)—Cable-tool Drilling Machine, 1867 Henry Kelly's "cam and treadle" machine, the original portable well-drilling rig and forerunner of today's Bucyrus - Erie spudders. Kelly invented this machine in 1867 and, according to the records, it was built for him in the shop of Novelty Iron Works, Dubuque, Iowa.

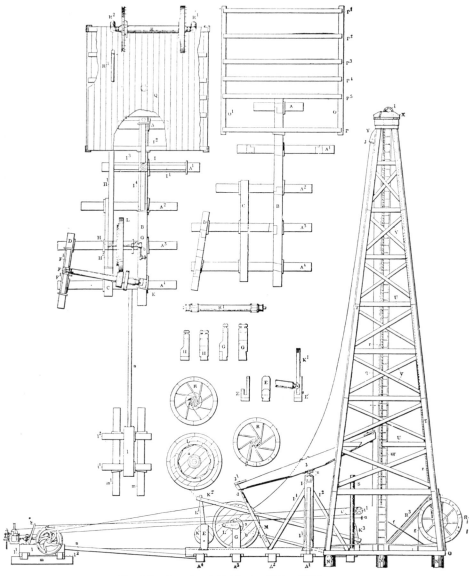

Fig. 31—Standard Cable-tool Rig, 1905

A boiler of a reasonable horsepower capacity was quite heavy and required mountings of its own. The motion of the reciprocating steam engine resulted in considerable vibration, which necessitated a foundation free of the drilling rig itself. With the development and perfection of internal-combustion engines and the improvement in design and materials of chain and sprockets and gears, the drilling machines of today became possible and practicable.

Fig. 34 (above)—Fort Worth Spudder, 1934

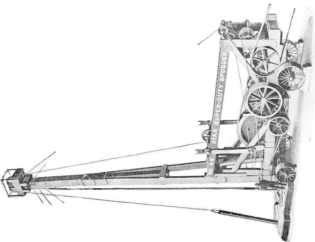

Fig. 33 (above)—Star Spudder, 1935

Fig. 35 (left) — Spudder of 1920's
One of the first all-steel cable-tool drills.

Fig. 32 (above)—All-steel Drilling Rig, 1922 — Tubular Derrick

193

Fig. 36 (above)—Machine of 1937
One of the first rigs in the Illinois oil fields
in 1938 — actually a water-well drill, it
was adapted for shallow oil-well drilling
and prompted development of the 24-L
spudder and larger rigs designed specifically for petroleum recovery. (Bucyrus-
Erie Company Photo)

Fig. 38 (above)—Modern Cable-tool
Drilling Machine

Fig. 39 (above)—Drilling In, Oklahoma,
Circa 1910

Fig. 37 (above)—Machine of 1937
(Ideco Photo)

194

Fig. 40 (left) — Pulling Out the Bailer, Oklahoma, Circa 1910

Fig. 41 (right)—No. 2 National Drilling Machine, Oklahoma, Circa 1910

Because of the similarity of these machines with other types of equipment, such as cranes, steam shovels, drag-line excavators, etc., the manufacture of portable drilling machines has been taken over largely by manufacturers other than the builders of the original machines and of the rotary and other oil-field equipment of today. Fig. 29 through 41 illustrate various cable-tool drilling machines and rigs of the period 1867 through 1937.

SYSTEMS OF PERCUSSION DRILLING

A classification of percussion-drilling systems has been given previously in this chapter. Most of these have been discussed, but the basic principles and major parts of each system or type of equipment follow together with references to preceding discussions.

Chinese Drilling System

The Chinese system of percussion drilling, which may have been the earliest developed other than the digging of wells by hand, used manpower for the actuation of the drilling tools through the use of spring boards. A drilling line constructed from strips of the outer part of bamboo was attached to the tools, passed over a roller at the top of the derrick, then under a wheel or pulley at the ground level, and thence around a large-diameter fabricated bull wheel powered by one or more oxen. The derrick was com-

195

posed of poles lashed together with two principal legs with braces. Bamboo was used for bailers and for casing the hole. Chinese tools are further discussed on p. 144-152 and 228.

Spring Pole

The spring-pole system of drilling is illustrated and discussed on p. 218-220. This system used wooden (ash) rods first and later manila cable hung from the small end of a springy pole, such as hemlock. The butt end of the pole was held to the ground and the middle point was supported some 4 to 6 ft off the ground.

Motion was imparted to the drilling tools by using manpower, horsepower, or finally the steam engine to pull the flexible end of the pole downward, permitting the bit to strike bottom, and then allowing the spring of the pole to lift the tools into position for the next sroke. The same type tools could be used for either the cable or pole systems.

Jerk Line

The jerk line was merely another method of imparting the proper motion to the tools. Motion was developed by passing a line over the crank on the band-wheel shaft and then to a pulley or other device on the drilling line. This system was and is used on standard cable-tool rigs and rigs of other types for spudding in the well and attaining sufficient depth to bury the string of tools and permit attachment of the temper screw.

Spudder

The spudder-type rig imparts the motion to the drilling line by passing the drilling line through a pulley attached to a working arm that moves in the required reciprocating motion. Drilling tools used are of the standard cable-tool type.

Standard Rig

The standard cable-tool rig consists of a source of power, usually a single-cylinder steam engine, and a band wheel with a crank attached by means of which the walking beam is actuated. The tools are suspended from the walking beam, which is supported by the samson post in the center. The tools and casing are handled with bull wheels and calf wheel. The drilling and fishing tools are those used in the usual cable-tool rig (see p. 236-240).

Portable Machines

Portable machines impart drilling motion to the tools through the use of a jerk line, spudder attachment, or a walking beam.

SOLID-ROD TOOLS

Ruffner or Rod-tool System

This system of drilling, used by the French prior to 1800, was possibly developed by the Ruffner brothers from drills used in quarrying and without knowledge of the French operations (see p. 154 and 159). The records show that rods were used in the Ruffner well and others of that per-

iod, in the Belcher well at St. Louis in the early 1850's, and in the Pecos
Valley well drilled by Capt. Pope of the army in the late 1850's (see p.
164-170). It appears that a fiber drilling line was used in the Drake well.
Canadian

The pole-tool system of drilling moved to Canada, probably in the
1850's but at least as early as the beginning of the oil industry in Ontario in
the 1860's, and was developed and perfected into what came to be known
as the "Canadian system." Canadian tools were later moved to Galicia and
further developed into the "Galician system" (see p. 177).
Free-fall

This system of drilling is known as the free-fall or Russian free-fall
because of the type of jars used. The Russians used solid rods and, in consequence, it is placed under that classification of percussion drilling. Free-
fall jars, however, were developed and used on pole or cable-tool systems in Western Europe particularly in France (see p. 235, Fig. 3 on
Fig. 84). The motion was imparted to the rods in the Canadian and Russian systems by the use of the walking beam. Free-fall jars are discussed
on the following page.
Hollow Rods

Hollow rods were used in the Fauck rapid system of drilling. The
drilling motion was imparted to the rods by a cam-actuated device giving
a stroke of not more than 6 or 7 in. at the rate of 70 to 80 strokes per min.
Water or fluid was circulated down through the hollow rods and up the
bore. This system was used in Europe and was said to be quite effective in
some areas, particularly under German operation. The circulation of fluid
through hollow rods or tubes was developed by Fauvelle (see p. 157 and
288).

Hollow rods or pipe through which fluid is circulated are likewise
used in drilling water wells in some parts of America, especially Florida.
On these light rigs the drilling motion is imparted by passing a line attached
to the top of the rods over a crown sheave and around a cathead. The driller
works the cathead line while his assistant rotates the rods or bit a little more
than one half around and then back again.
Casing Circulation

This system is said to have been developed in California in the early
1900's in order to permit the use of cable tools in soft formations. Drilling
was done with an under-reamer through casing, hanging in the hole on
casing blocks and elevators, in such a manner that the pipe could be lowered
as hole was made. Mud-laden fluid was circulated down the casing and up
outside by the use of the usual mud pump (see Chapter 6). Either cable
or rod could be used with this system. In California cable was used exclusively. The method was superseded by the hydraulic rotary system.
Russian Drilling Methods (From **Rig and Reel,** *(Parkersburg) Oct.-Nov. 1923)*

"Modern drilling methods represented by both rotary and cable tools gradually found their way into the Russian oil fields of Baku, Grozny, Cheleken and Emba (1923). But the vast majority of wells have been put down by Russian percussion drilling or pole tool systems.

"It involves the use of iron rods $1\frac{3}{4}$ inches in diameter as the medium on which drilling tools are suspended. The chisel-shaped bit is screwed into an underreamer while a pair of cutters is placed in the special cavities on the sides of the underreamer so that underreaming and drilling are effected simultaneously.

"Above the underreamer is a drill stem, a rectangular iron bar 6 inches by 25 feet, with two four-piece sets of guide wings for maintenance of concentrical and vertical position of the tools. The guide wings always travel up and down in the casing which is lowered every 18 feet, or so, of drilling. The drill stem is sometimes made heavier by addition of a sinker bar.

"The drilling tools are generally connected onto the line of rods by a special appliance known as a 'free-fall.' This is a device that operates at the end of the upward movement of the beam on which the line of rods is suspended by means of a temper screw. This sudden release of the tools and their consequent 'free-fall' to the bottom of the well furnishes the drilling force that crushes formations. This fall does not exceed a distance of some six feet.

"The size of the wells is enormous, 44 inches is the initial diameter. The bit, cutters, underreamers, elevators, tongs and other tools are correspondingly huge and not easily handled.

"The casing used is of the riveted type. It is made up of sheet iron pipe, $\frac{1}{4}$ inch thick, with a collar riveted on the outside of each joint. Each joint must be riveted to the next as the casing goes down into the well. Often, stands of four joints are riveted together on the outside of the derrick, and when these stands are lowered into the well, a long stick carries rivets into the holes of the lower joint and collar. After all rivets are in place an expanding back-up is inserted before the rivets are hammered upon the outside by a crew of twelve roughnecks on the derrick floor.

"Successive strings of casing decrease in size by two inches. Oil strings of 22, 20, 18 inches are common. The wells are generally bailed and not pumped.

"The derricks are usually 80 feet high, constructed with four large round trees, one at each corner. They are then completely boarded in. The crown block has six sheaves. Power for drilling is, in the majority of cases, supplied by 90 horsepower electric motors. In other cases a steam engine is used.

"The drilling machine is a huge outfit, quite cumbersome, with two steel pitmans, one at each side of the triangular framed wooden beam whose vertex is directly above the well. It has two drums, one serving as sand reel, and the other as calf wheel or bull wheel, as the case may be in the process of drilling. The hoisting line for handling rods is two inches in diameter, and the casing lines are $1\frac{1}{4}$ inches. Sand lines vary from $\frac{5}{8}$ inch to $1\frac{1}{4}$ inches, depending on the size of the bailer as well as the depth of the well. The rotary movement of the tools is accomplished through turning of the temper screw connections by hand.

"The drilling is slow. Every now and then the casing has to be worked up and down to prevent its freezing. It takes from two to three years to drill a well 2800 feet deep, and a considerable outlay of money is involved for power, casing and cement. Labor, however, is rather cheap. The best drillers are satisfied with the equivalent of $50 per month, while roughnecks are content to get along on $15.

"Russian cementing methods are crude but are practiced on an enormous scale. Quite often, intermediate casing, having been cut off at the casing shoes, is pulled out and space thus generated is filled with cement. Thousands of barrels of cement are poured into the well. In fact, a Russian well is a gigantic cement skyscraper buried underground. And considering the amount of iron and cement lowered into the ground it is not surprising that years are necessary to complete a well by this method.

"As it is impossible to pour in the required quantity of cement all at once, 60 barrel portions are let down, one at a time, and after the hardening of each portion, other batches follow.

"The inside of the casing lowered last is artificially 'plugged-up' with sand and gravel to prevent a possible collapse of the casing. When the cementing work is entirely completed the artificial plug is drilled through again. Cases of cementing work and 'cleaning the plug' that last for seven to eight months are quite common.

"Of the special tools used by Russians, one should first mention the perforator which is lowered into the well on the sand line and operated by a system of pulleys and telegraph cord. This device cuts discs out of the casing. These discs are retained on the machine and give a definite proof of the work done, as well as the number of perforated holes. Collar holes, for instance, give two discs.

"Another valuable machine is the apparatus for detecting the deviation of the drilled well from the vertical. It works quite satisfactorily within 400 feet and prevents the well from going 'crooked' at the start. The importance of this in the case of bailed wells can be readily appreciated.

"Then there is a substantial collection of fishing tools. In fact, a large number of them. Especially serviceable are the so-called fishing rods. They are 3 ½ inches in diameter, solid round iron, and so connected with each other by means of a sliding sleeve that they can be safely rotated to the right or to the left without danger of unscrewing.

"Hydraulic jacks are used extensively on fishing jobs. Unscrewing of lost tools is effected by means of a powerful worm-gear winder, operated either by hand or by the engine.

"Quite unique are the casing swedges. They are large rollers, adjustable in size, mounted on a powerful frame and operated on fishing rods. With these swedges large casings, 24″ - 36″ in diameter, are gradually brought back to original shape even after a serious collapse.

"The most ancient method of drilling wells by hand is not uncommon in the Baku fields even today. It is still employed by the Tartar natives. The wells dug by this method are naturally shallow, some 300 feet in depth.

"A digger working at the bottom of the shaft has a helper on the surface who hoists the 'drillings' on a small winch and ventilates the well by a fan and canvas tube. Signals between the man in the well and the man on the surface are exchanged by means of a rope.

"Sometimes an inrush of gas suffocates the driller. Not so long ago police regulations were very severe with regard to accidents in drilling operations. Employers, fearing the responsibilities of fatal accidents would bribe the helper, hire a new driller and give him instructions to side-track the body of his dead predecessor. This would be done in a side grave in the well and the new man would proceed with his task.

"Well shafts that were thus 'enriched' by the body of a fellow worker were superstitiously considered by the natives as being lucky in oil production.

"Ancient methods still mingle with modern in Russian oil fields today (1923)."

Derricks

Undoubtedly the first method of removing material dug from a well, by means other than throwing out or carrying out manually, was by the use of a skin or a container of some character attached to a vine, thong, or a rope. In shallow holes and with light loads the container with its burden was doubtless hauled out hand over hand by one or two workmen standing at the mouth of the bore. When the load became too heavy to handle in this manner, the well may have been placed beneath the limb of a tree with the line thrown over the limb with one man on the fall-line side and one or more men on the tight-line side hauling up on the load. Next in order the

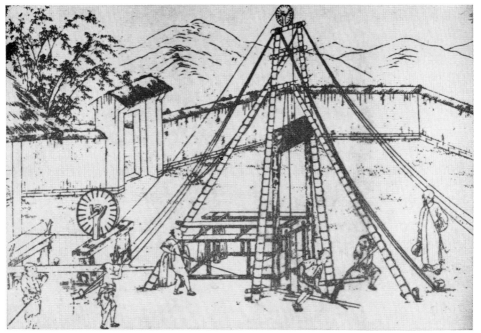

Fig. 42—Chinese Derrick

tripod seems to have been the simplest structure to invent, but it could be used only with considerable difficulty prior to the invention of the pulley or a substitute. Therefore, it may be assumed that the windlass in some form preceded the tripod, if we assume that the pulley followed the windlass. Under this assumption the first structure to support the load being withdrawn from the hole was that which supported the windlass or log on which the thong or line was wound.

Succeeding the invention of the pulley in some form, the tripod, mast, or 4-legged structure would have been the logical developments. The first description we have of a structure that might be called a derrick is of that used in the drilling of the brine wells in China. It is not known just how far back this type of equipment was used, but according to the records available, at least several hundred years. It is assumed that the Chinese equipment in use today with relatively minor modifications is the same as that utilized in the time of Confucious 600 years B.C. Certainly if wells were drilled to several hundred feet in depth at that early date, the beginning of the industry and the development of equipment must have been begun sometime—possibly centuries—prior to that date. The Chinese derrick of recent times is shown in *National Geographic Magazine*, p. 332, August-September 1944. A sketch of what is supposed to be an older Chinese rig, including the derrick, is shown in Fig. 9, p. 225, Vol. LIV *Transactions of the American Institute of Mining and Metallurgical*

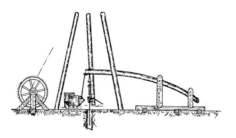

Fig. 43 (above) — Tripod over Spring Pole Temper Screw and Teeter Board (MacGarvey)

L. Disbrow.
App's. for Boring in Earth.
Nº
NO 57   REISSUED OCT. 20,1843

Fig. 44 (right)—Four-legged Derrick, Circa 1825

Engineers (1916), taken from an article by Louis Coldre in the December 1914 issue of *Western Engineering,* San Francisco.

This Chinese derrick consisted of a leaning A-frame with the top surmounted by a pulley directly over the bore. This leaning A-frame was supported by one or two legs leaning into it from opposite sides of the bore. The legs themselves were composed of several trees or poles a few inches in diameter lashed together with rope made of bamboo. The lashings were tightened by the use of wedges. No girts or braces seem to have been used (see Fig. 42 and Fig. 5, p. 147).

The tripod seems to have been the first derrick structure used in more modern times and was probably employed, together with a single pulley, in many much-earlier operations than those of which we have record. Probably a tripod was used by the Ruffner brothers over the spring pole with which they drilled their first well, completed January 15, 1808. There are many records of the use of the tripod into the 1860's, when the spring pole was being supplanted by other means for imparting motion to the tools in the hole (Fig. 43).

The tripod consisted of three stout poles of sufficient length lashed together at the small end and spread at the bottom end over the bore. A single pulley was hung from the lashings at the top.

The exact date of the advent of the 4-legged derrick is not definitely known, but L. Disbrow, in a patent issued March 24, 1825 and another issued November 1, 1830, shows 4-legged derricks over a drilling operation.

Fig. 44 shows a reissue of the Disbrow patent of March 24, 1825.

The Thom system of drilling, employed in England and in some of the shallow oil fields of the East Indies, used the tripod at least as late as 1911. The Thom system used a variation of the head frame used in digging mine shafts.* Tripods were used in connection with small diamond drills until relatively recent times and are doubtless still so employed.

Following the drilling boom of the 1860's a number of drilling machines were developed which used generally single-pole masts or braced or guyed ladder-type masts for the relatively shallow wells drilled with this equipment. Derricks with 4 legs composed of squared timbers with girts and braces were used in the 1860's, both in the eastern oil fields and in Canada. They likewise are shown in Patent No. 47,868 issued May 23, 1865 to John Y. Smith, in Patent No. 48,006 issued May 30, 1865 to D. H. Wiswell and George W. Shaw, and in Patent No. 52,642 issued February 13, 1866 to S. H. Goucher.

Patent No. 130,706 was issued August 20, 1872 to Samuel S. Fertig. This patent covers a wooden derrick more or less of the present-day type with legs built of 2 x 6's or 2 x 8's put together principally with bolts rather than nails.

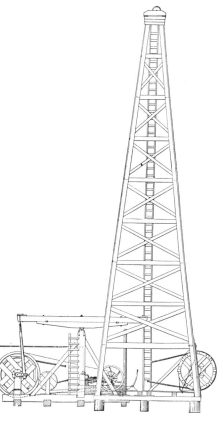

Derricks with square timber legs and using wooden girts with iron rods with turnbuckles for bracing were in use in California as late as 1920. A derrick of this type stood over an abandoned well at the foot of Pyramid Hill near Devils Den in the San Joaquin Valley in California at least as late as 1940. Few, if any, derricks of the type were in actual use in that state as late as 1930. Because derricks were usually left over the wells in producing fields for cleanout and remedial work, there was little if any economy in the use of any type of wooden derrick other than those made entirely of lumber and timbers and put together with nails. At least since 1910, and probably since the earliest built, the great majority of wooden derricks were so constructed. Those used over dry holes were frequently, if not usually, dismantled and the usable lumber utilized in other derricks.

Derricks of this type were used much more generally than steel, at

Fig. 45—Wooden Derrick of Type First Built, Circa 1870

*Woodworth, R. B: The Evolution of Drilling Rigs, *Trans Am. Inst. Mining Egrs.*, **LIV**, 216 (1916).

least into the late 1920's. One of the last great oil fields in which practically all of the towers were built of wood was the Signal Hill Field in California. In the 1920's the use of steel commenced to replace wood very rapidly, and by the early 1930's relatively few wooden derricks were built. There are doubtless still a few in use in isolated areas where lumber is relatively cheap and old tools are used.

The old-time drillers, both cable-tool and rotary, felt that the wooden derricks gave better motion to the tools in cable-tool drilling; and the driller felt safer in pulling on pipe under the wooden derrick than under steel because he was of the opinion that the wooden structure gave earlier warning of a too-heavy pull than did the steel derrick.

These early wooden derricks (Fig. 45) were usually built 10 ft to the first girt and 7 ft between succeeding girts up to the water table. That means the derricks were usually built in heights of 10 ft plus multiples of 7 ft plus the height of the water table. This design carries through in the most recent wooden derricks and likewise in practically all steel derricks; although in the late part of the last century and the early part of this century, steel derricks with girts 14 ft apart were constructed.

Masts (see p. 193) were used very extensively in the latter part of the last century and in the early part of the 20th century. They then disappeared almost completely except for shallow work in a few of the standard cable-tool rigs which ordinarily used an 84-ft wooden or steel derrick. Beginning with 1940 portable cable-tool drilling machines with masts again put in their appearance. This equipment was, of course, vastly improved over the early rigs and was capable of drilling to the then-usual depth of cable-tool holes. At the present time, because of its portability, ease of transportation, and simplicity in erection, still more-improved drilling machines with masts have come into very general use in cable-tool areas while the standard rig once used for all important operations has practically disappeared (p. 185 and 192).

One of the most important developments in oil-well drilling equipment was the steel derrick. The

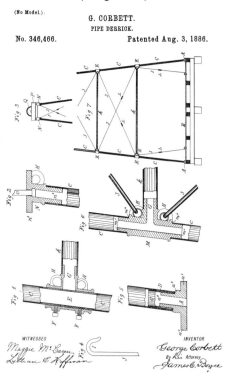

(No Model.)

G. CORBETT.
PIPE DERRICK.

No. 346,466.   Patented Aug. 3, 1886.

WITNESSES   INVENTOR
Maggie McLaren   George Corbett
Lillian C Hoffman   By ___ Attorney
                           James C. Boyce

Fig. 46—Sketch — Steel Derrick, Corbett Patent, 1886

first reference to it was in Patent No. 210,007 granted in 1878 to Jesse Burton. A more complete description is given in a patent granted to George Corbett of Bradford, Pa. in 1886 (Fig. 46).

The development of the pipe derrick as a large commercial enterprise was the result of the successful use of the forged-steel clamp patented in the first instance by T. A. Neill, field superintendent for the South Penn Oil Co. In 1908 it occurred to Neill that a steel derrick suitable for pumping and cleaning wells could be successfully fabricated of second-hand pipe. He constructed a small wooden model indicating his idea of a clamp for the purposes of joining two pieces of pipe together without a thread, and at the same

Fig. 47—Original Lee C. Moore Tubular Derrick, 1908

time reinforcing the joint. This model was turned over to Lee C. Moore of Lee C. Moore & Co., Inc., and the first 80-ft derrick was built in Mannington, W. Va., with clamps made of cast steel for joining the leg sections together. This first derrick demonstrated not only that pipe derricks would prove a success for cleaning purposes but also for heavy work as well, and Neill proceeded to cover his invention by letters patent (No. 933,386) dated September 7, 1909. Rights of exclusive manufacture passed to Lee C. Moore & Co., Inc., with reservation of a shop license to the South Penn Oil Co. for the construction of derricks for its own uses. Fig. 47 shows the first Lee C. Moore tubular derrick. Fig. 48 shows an early steel derrick; and Fig. 49 shows the Drake well and a standard cable-tool rig, circa 1892, with wooden derrick.

Power

Percussion drilling or, as it is usually expressed, cable-tool drilling, has always required power for two purposes—for lowering the tools to the bottom of the hole and withdrawing them, and for handling casing or tubing in the well; and to give the drilling motion to the tools.

On the brine wells of China (p. 144-152), manpower on a spring board was used to impart drilling motion to the tools. The hoisting of the tools and handling of casing or tubes was done by ox power through the medium of the "bull wheel" which, on the Chinese rigs, had a vertical axis. Spring-pole drilling in America used manpower to impart the proper drilling motion, and for withdrawing and lowering the tools.

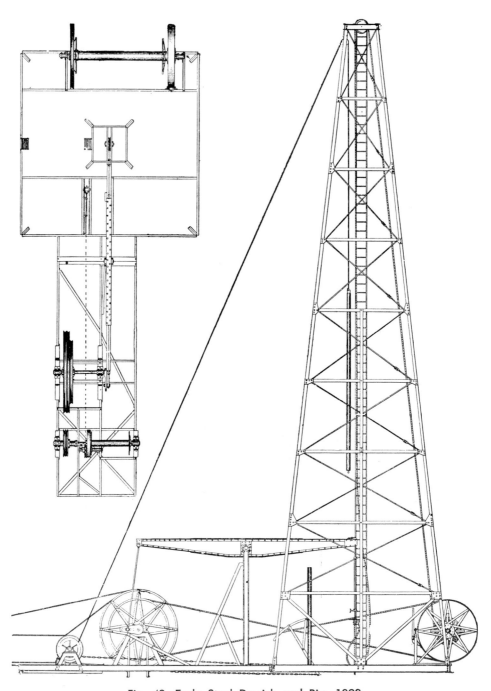

Fig. 48—Early Steel Derrick and Rig, 1892

The First Oil Well.

Drilled by Col. Drake in 1859, near Titusville, Pa.

Fig. 49—Drake Well and Wooden Derrick of 1892

Methods varied from hand-over-hand hoisting, through hand-powered windlasses or drums, to foot-powered bull wheels and probably steam-powered drums and bull wheels. In later developments the drilling motion was imparted by steam power through a walking beam or through other means, while hoisting was still accomplished by bull wheels with foot rungs around the periphery of double flanges on either side. This type rig was used at least into the 1860's when steam-powered bull wheels were developed.

CABLE-TOOL DRILLING POWER PLANTS

Animal Power

The Drake well marked neither the end of the use of manpower or animal power in well drilling nor the initial use of steam power. At least 5 years before the Drake well, steam power had been used in drilling a 2,200-ft water well at the Belcher Sugar Refinery in St. Louis. For many years after the birth of the oil industry, shallow holes were "kicked down" by the spring-pole method, and there is also evidence that horsepower was used in some cases. Fig. 50b shows a "horse power" from an 1892 Oil Well Supply Co.* catalog, on the same page with a steam drilling engine (Fig. 50a), with the notation: "Horse powers are made to be worked by from 2 to 8 horses." In 1861 the Agnew well at Walnut Bend, Pa. was drilled with horse power. The Oil Well catalogs of 1884 and 1892 show several models of the machine. Fig. 50c shows hoisting with horse power in the early 1900's.

Drake's Power Plant

Because Drake's well symbolizes the beginnings of the petroleum industry, it is particularly interesting to establish the type of machinery he used. Unfortunately, little was written on this subject and the history is somewhat confusing, the engine and boiler being attributed both to W. M. Faber & Company, Pittsburgh, and to Erie City Iron Works, Erie.

Perhaps the most authoritative information comes from the papers collected by Giddens as curator of Drake Well Memorial Park. Among these is a 1909 interview with Samuel B. Smith (son of the driller) who worked on the well: ". . . Samuel B. Smith says he is positive the engine was not a Faber, at least he has never been able to find a Faber engine in any way resembling it. To the best of his recollection it was an Erie engine, although he says he cannot prove this. One detail he does remember and that is that it had a regular iron frame and not a wooden frame like the Faber engines of the period. He says it was an engine with a short stroke, from 12 to 18 inches. The boiler was a stationary boiler and was built into a solid brick and stone wall. The boiler had only a single flue and Samuel B. Smith says the remarkable thing about it is that he has never been able to find another single-flue boiler of this particular type.

*In 1952, this company became an operating division of United States Steel Corp., and is now "Oil Well Supply Division, United States Steel Corp."

Fig. 50a (upper left)—Steam Engine, 1890

Fig. 50b (lower left)—Horse Power, 1890-1900

Fig. 50c (upper right)—Hoisting with Horse Power, Circa 1900

Fig. 51 (lower right)—Faber Long John Engine, Circa 1860

INNIS DUPLEX DRILLING ENGINE.

FOR DRILLING VERY DEEP WELLS.

(This Engine was used to drill the two deepest wells that have been drilled, viz., 4,500 and 4,650 feet.)

HORSE POWER.

HORSE POWERS ARE MADE TO BE WORKED BY FROM 2 TO 8 HORSES.

Yet it was not of course constructed for the express purpose of using it in conjunction with drilling oil wells. It merely happened to have some unique features not found in the ordinary boilers of those times."

Giddens also quotes a 1909 interview with Harrison Locke, a young man living near the well, who later entered the drilling-tool business:

"As I remember it the boiler was a stationary boiler of the tubular variety—perhaps 20 H.P. I cannot tell where that boiler was made, but I am positive that the engine was an Erie engine. I was familiar enough with the different kinds of engines even at that time, so that I am sure that I could not be mistaken as to whether an engine was an Erie engine or not. The boiler exploded—went all to pieces—at the time of the first oil well fire in the fall of 1859. The engine was badly damaged in the same fire, but was afterwards overhauled and made to do considerable service."

Giddens quotes from Drake's letter of August 16, 1858: ". . . I have contracted for an engine to be ready for boring by the first of September. The engine will cost $500.00 in Erie, which is about $100.00 less than the same or one like it would cost at the East . . ."

In a 1940 publication, Erie City Iron Works states: "Somehow, between hurry-up orders for engines, boilers and railroad cars, the Erie City Iron Works had found time to sandwich in a rush job for a Crawford County dreamer who needed a boiler and a drilling rig. The dreamer was Colonel E. L. Drake, and the use he made of the equipment was to drill the first oil well in the history of the world . . ."*

On the other hand, the great number of times that the name of W. M. Faber & Company is mentioned in connection with the Drake well lends credence to its claims. The following description and Fig. 51 are taken from an *Oil and Gas Journal* story written on the occasion of the Diamond Jubilee of the Petroleum industry in 1934:

"Mr. Drake started this work in 1858 and hoped to have drilling under way by September of that year. He ordered an engine and boiler from W. M. Faber & Co. of Pittsburgh, Pa., and the outfit cost about $2,000 f. o. b. factory. The engine was known as the 'Long John.'

"The boiler was of the one-flue stationary type, the flue being near the bottom of the 30-inch diameter by 12 or 14-foot long shell. This shell was erected in a stone setting. Wood was used for fuel. The rating on this boiler was about 10 horsepower, but the working pressure is not reported.

"The engine was set at the side of the boiler and the steam from

*P. W. Bishop, Head Curator, Dept. of Arts and Manufactures, Smithsonian Institution, who has done much research work on the subject, is of the opinion that the engine was built in Erie by Liddell & Co., now Erie City Iron Works. (Letter from Mr. Bishop to the writer.)

the boiler delivered direct into the engine cylinder. This engine was rated at 6 horsepower and was of the same type as used on steamboats on the Monongahela, Allegheny and Ohio Rivers in the fifties. To reverse the engine the eccentric rod was disconnected from the lower end of the rocker arm, which was provided with a pin for the purpose, and by means of a lever at the upper end on the rocker arm the valves were manually operated to admit steam at proper intervals to run the engine in the reverse direction. A bell was hung in the engine room, attached to a cord running to the derrick, and signals were agreed upon for operating the engine, that is, for running it fast or slow, or stopping.

"A heavy flywheel was provided with this engine and at the end of the flywheel shaft a crank was attached. On the steamboat this crank imparted motion to the beam driving the paddle wheels. At the Drake well the pitman between this crank and the end of the working beam gave the beam what was called a 'grasshopper' motion. The 'working beam' as it was then called extended through the derrick to a vertical upright pole set outside of the rig and to this post one end of the working beam was attached . . ."

Crum has the following to say about the use of the Faber engine on the Drake well: "The boiler and engine used were of Pittsburgh manufacture, made by W. M. Faber & Co., and colloquially known as 'Long John.' It was an improvement over the 'spring pole' but no oil well workers of today could be induced to toy with it."

Fig. 52 is a reconstructed assembly of the Drake rig, showing the relation of the engine to the pitman and also how the walking beam was originally pivoted at the end rather than in the middle. Obviously this was a first step from the old spring pole.

It is significant that Drake's bull wheels were not driven by the engine but rather were tramped by the driller and his helper, using the rungs in the circumferences of the two wheels. A wooden ratchet operating on these same rungs served as a brake. Fig. 53 illustrates the bull wheel of or immediately following the Drake well.

Samuel B. Smith had this to say about the manual operation of the bull wheels: "I cannot tell you why my father did not use the engine. The question as to why he did not do it that way has never occurred to me until I was asked why. That he did overlook it, I am sure. I ought to know because I helped to drive that particular pipe by hauling up that battering ram with that windlass myself. And pretty hard work it was too."

Evolution of the Standard Rig

It is difficult to determine just when the so-called standard cable-tool rig evolved, but from early photographs it is evident that within less than 10 years after the drilling of the Drake well the cable-tool rig as we know it today was in use, including the center-pivoted walking beam, the band

211

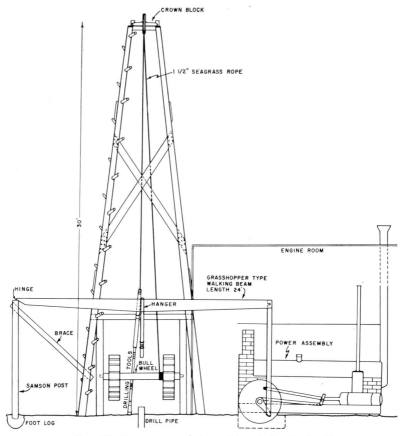

Fig. 52—Reconstructed Assembly of the Drake Rig

wheel, rope-driven bull wheels, and with the engine moved well back from the hole. There is even some evidence that bull ropes were in use much before Drake's time. Evidently cost and expediency had a lot to do with the design of the early cable-tool rigs.

In time came the friction sand reel, the rope-driven calf wheel, then chain-driven reels. The chain-driven sand reel was introduced by Parkersburg Rig and Reel Company in 1920.

Engines of 1860-1900

Obviously the early drilling engines were not designed for this particular purpose, but were those designed for such applications as river boats and saw mills. Crum says:

"It was several years, however, before engines and boilers were designed especially for the severe strain of drilling and handling oil wells. This was done by the late C. M. Farrar of Buffalo, who designed first a boiler, and then an engine, both made famous by Samuel G. Bayne, now President of the Seaboard National Bank in New York,

Fig. 53—Bull Wheel, Circa 1860
Note foot treadles and ratchet brake.

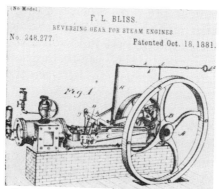

Fig. 55—Typical Ajax Drilling Engine
of 1881

Fig. 54—Engine of Wood and Mann
Portable Rig

Fig. 56—Farrar & Trefts "Old Style"
Rotary Valve Engine

but for many years the general agent for boilers, engines, tubing, casing and other oil well supplies, the foundation of the present National Supply Company. The Wood & Mann portable outfit, in which the small engine was mounted upon the boiler (Fig. 54), was the popular type of the shallow territory adjacent to Oil Creek. These manufacturers are believed to have made the first eccentric link reverse engine used in the oil country, but they did not keep pace with the demand for heavier machinery."

By the 1870's and the early 1880's several manufacturers were making engines specifically designed for drilling. Among these are the following names, together with the approximate date of their first drilling-engine manufacture: Ajax Iron Works of Corry (1878); Bovaird & Seyfang of Bradford (1890); Farrar & Trefts of Buffalo (1872); Oil Well Supply Company of Oil City (early 1880's); Struthers-Wells of Titusville; and Titusville Iron Works (1875-1880).

These early engines were of single-cylinder horizontal design ranging in size from an 8-in. bore by 12-in. stroke rated at 12 hp, to a 12 x 12 engine rated at 30 hp. These ratings were probably based on steam pressures of less than 100 lb and on engine speeds of 100 to 150 rpm.

Fig. 55, from U.S. Patent No. 428,277 of 1881, shows the typical drilling engine of that time. This engine had an unbalanced D-slide valve with the double eccentric link motion which Stephenson had adopted for his locomotive more than 40 years before. This Bliss (Ajax Iron Works) patent, covering the use of a rigid reversing control to the derrick floor, was considered revolutionary at the time and infringement suits created much interest. It is interesting to note that the testimony in this litigation indicated that piston valves had been used in the oil fields even before this time, although they did not again appear in the drilling industry until the 1920's. They were discarded in favor of the D-slide valve which apparently was better able to not only withstand the corrosive oil-field waters but also was able to relieve excessive cylinder pressures when a slug of water would be carried over from the boiler into the cylinder. However, this D-slide valve involved considerable friction so that the link would not always drop by gravity when it had been raised by the rope connection commonly used, and which, together with chain connections between the bell-crank and the links, is shown in Fig. 58.

Fig. 56 shows a Farrar & Trefts rotary valve engine from a 1901 catalog. This cut was labeled "old style." Fig. 57 shows the Farrar & Trefts "Daisy" D-slide valve engine which superseded the engine of Fig. 56.

Another curiosity among early drilling engines is the Innis duplex or twin drilling engine (Fig. 58) from an 1892 Oil Well catalog. Apparently it never found wide favor, although a notation reads as follows: "For drilling very deep wells. This engine was used to drill the two deepest wells that had been drilled, viz., 4500 and 4650 feet." Apparently 2-cylinder drilling engines did not again come into common use until they were adopted for rotary drilling about 1918. Undoubtedly there was no need for the complications of a two-cylinder engine for cable-tool drilling, particularly since heavy flywheels were needed to maintain the drilling motion. In the rebirth of the twin-cylinder drilling engine for rotary-drilling applications, rapid reversing was essential, so the flywheels were eliminated and two cylinders were necessary to prevent stalling on dead center.

Fig. 57 (above)—Farrar & Trefts Improved "Daisy" Engine with D-slide Valve, 1872
Fig. 58 (right)—Innis Two-cylinder Drilling Engine

5. PERCUSSION-DRILLING SYSTEM

Boilers of 1860-1900

Apparently the Drake well used a stationary-type boiler in a masonry setting, a construction which was to be little used in the oil field except in such areas as parts of California where a single stationary boiler installation served to drill several wells.

The locomotive-type boiler with a self-contained firebox became practically standard for cable-tool drilling, being made by many manufacturers. Fig. 59 from an 1892 Oil Well catalog describes these boilers in sizes from 15 to 40 hp.

Apparently a few portable combination boilers and engines were used for shallow drilling. Fig. 60 is from the Oil Well 1892 catalog. This construction was not widely used because of its limited capacity and the fire hazard occasioned by the proximity of the boiler to the rig.

Cable-tool Steam Engines after 1900

Except for size, comparatively few changes have been made in cable-tool steam drilling engines up to the present time. The Stephenson link motion and the D-slide valve construction have remained standard, although between 1910 and 1920 balancing plates were added to this valve.

In the middle 1920's these engines were semi-enclosed, the crosshead and crank pins being lubricated by splash, while the main bearings and valve gear remained as before. Throughout the years removable flywheel rings were used to secure the correct drilling motion at various depths.

Engines in sizes of 13 x 14 and 14 x 14 were developed around 1915. Sixteen by sixteen single-cylinder cable-tool engines were cataloged at various times throughout this period, but there is little record of this size ever having been used except perhaps in some South American fields.

The last general cataloging of cable-tool drilling engines was from 1930 to 1940. At this time single-cylinder semi-enclosed D-slide valve engines were available in sizes from 10 x 12 rated at 20 hp, to 14 x 14 rated at 50 hp. These were used with boilers rated at 150 lb working pressure. Fig. 61 is an Ajax semi-enclosed engine, typical of the last models of cable-tool steam engines.

Jeffery in 1921 gave the following list of drilling specifications and equipment which probably remained valid so long as steam was used, and it is indicative of the relation of size to service.

Depth, Feet	Engine Size, Inches	Boiler Horsepower	Engine Horsepower
1,800	10½ x 12	23	25
2,500	11 x 12	25	25
3,000	11½ x 12	28	30
4,000	12 x 12 or 14 x 14	30 or 50	50
5,000	14 x 14	50	50
7,500	14 x 14 or 2-12 x 12	50 or 60	2-30

Cable-tool Boilers after 1900

Few changes were made in cable-tool boilers after 1900. At the time the use of steam for cable-tool drilling declined, they were much like the early boilers of Fig. 59 except they were then built in sizes as large as 60 hp and for working pressures of from 125 to 150 lb. Inasmuch as rotary-drilling boilers simply continued the design in larger sizes and higher pressures, it is difficult to determine where cable-tool boilers left off and rotary boilers began. Later developments in boilers will be shown in Chapter 6.

Gas was used to power steam drilling engines and engines built for the purpose of pumping wells with standard

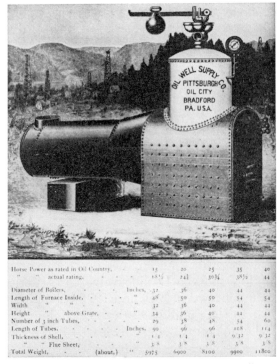

Horse Power as rated in Oil Country,			15	20	25	35	40
" " actual rating,			18½	24½	30¾	38½	44
Diameter of Boilers,	Inches,	32	36	40	44	44
Length of Furnace Inside,	"	48	50	50	54	54
Width " "	"	32	36	40	44	44
Height " above Grate,	"	34	36	40	44	44
Number of 3 inch Tubes,	"	29	38	48	54	60
Length of Tubes.	Inches,	90	96	96	108	114
Thickness of Shell,	"	1.4	1.4	1.4	9.32	9.32
" " Flue Sheet,	"	3.8	3.8	3.8	3.8	3.8
Total Weight,	(about,)	"	5975	6900	8100	9900	11800

Fig. 59—Typical Early Locomotive-type Drilling Boiler

rig fronts, soon after the Drake well was completed. It was also used at times for drilling. The gas was not ignited.

Internal-combustion Engines for Cable-tool Drilling

Joseph Reid's Patent No. 685,641, issued in 1901 (Fig. 62) clearly describes the application of a single-cylinder horizontal gas engine and a reversing clutch to drilling service. Multicylinder vertical gas engines

Fig. 60 — Combination Boiler and Engine

Fig. 61—Typical Single-cylinder Drilling Engine of the 1930's

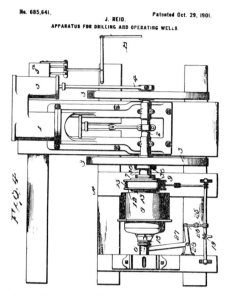

No. 685,641.
J. REID.
APPARATUS FOR DRILLING AND OPERATING WELLS.
Patented Oct. 29, 1901.

Fig. 62 — Reid Patented Gas Drilling Engine

Fig. 63—Clark Drilling Engine

Fig. 64—Young Drilling Engine

also came into use. In 1918 Clark Engine Company built a 4-cylinder 8 1/2 x 11 gas engine which was mounted on wheels as shown in Fig. 63.

Young Engine Company, also in 1918, started adapting higher-speed multicylinder engines to cable-tool drilling, using a right-angle drive as shown in Fig. 64. These engines have been made up to 1954 in increasingly larger sizes, the present line ranging from a 120-hp 4-cylinder engine to a 275-hp 8-cylinder engine. (Internal-combustion engines should not be directly compared with steam engines on a horsepower basis because of the different operating characteristics.)

By 1954 steam had practically vanished from cable-tool drilling and most of the work is now being done with portable rigs with self-contained internal-combustion engines. Separate engines are used only on some of the older types of machines or for very deep cable-tool drilling using standard rigs. These internal-combustion engines include not only spark-ignited engines running interchangeably on gasoline, gas, or butane, but also diesel engines.

Cable-tool Drilling with Electricity

No great amount of cable-tool drilling has ever been done with electricity, but from time to time it has been found advantageous to use a-c motors where transmission lines were convenient. Inasmuch as it was comparatively easy to use standard a-c wound rotor motors, it is difficult to pinpoint the inception of this practice.

General Electric records the building of a special multispeed double-induction motor for cable-tool drilling as early as 1910. By 1912 conventional a-c motors were used.

By 1920 a reasonable number of applications had been made. Some of these used 50-hp and 75-hp single-speed motors, while others used 15/35 hp to 35/75 hp double-rated motors, the lower rating being at 600 rpm and the higher at 1,200 rpm. Many of these installations used twin motors, and gear reducers as well as belt countershafts were used. The use of electricity was largely discontinued during the 1930's in favor of internal-combustion engine power.

Cable-tool Transmission Elements

Plain-laid Manila rope for driving the bull wheels and either leather or canvas belt for driving the band wheels were the earliest power transmission elements.

Flat belts have been standard for engine-to-band-wheel drives throughout the history of the standard rig. Likewise bull ropes, in sizes from 2- to 3-in. and either single or double, and in exceptional cases triple, have been used to drive the standard-rig bull wheels.

Sand reels were friction-driven until the 1920's, after which time roller chain came into general use. The chain had been developed for rotary rigs. Calf wheels, originally rope-driven, were ultimately converted to 1030 (No. 3 API) oil-field roller chain. With the changeover to unitized portable drilling rigs and machines, oil-field chains, short-pitch American standard chains, and V-belts are used.

Methods of Imparting Motion to Tools

The first machine used for imparting the drilling motion to percussion tools was doubtless the spring board used on the ancient Chinese drilling rigs. This device was placed on a center fulcrum somewhat in the manner of a seesaw. One end extended through a loop attached to the poles or line supporting the drilling tools, while the other end was free. The drilling motion was imparted by one or more men jumping from a platform to the free end of the board, thus lifting the tools from bottom; thence jumping back to the platform assisted by the spring of the board, at the same time allowing the tools to **fall to the** bottom in the drilling motion. A close inspection of the sketch on p. 147 will disclose this device. This method of drilling is still in general use, or was at the time of M. T. Archer's visit to China in 1944 (see p. 148).

The next device of which there is record is the spring pole of the type employed by the Ruffner brothers on the well completed by them January 1808. Fig. 65 illustrates a spring pole of the period. Fig. 66, 67, and 68 illustrate variations of the spring-pole method of drilling used in Belgium, America, and China.

Fig. 65 (left)—Spring Pole Type used to drill the Ruffner Brothers and many later wells.

Fig. 66 (right)—Spring-pole Drilling Machine Used by Jobard at Brussels in 1828

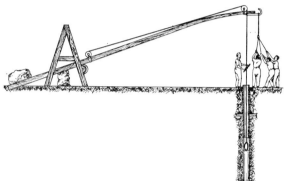

Fig. 67 (left) — A Spring - Pole Drilling Machine of the Early 1800's
The "teeter - board" method of actuating the tools. The anchored end of the pole (at right) is not shown.

Fig. 68 (right)—Chinese Spring Pole

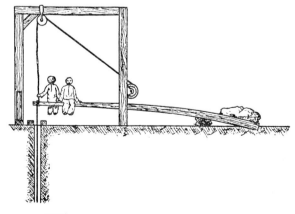

The spring pole was used extensively in the drilling of brine wells in western Virginia and adjacent regions prior to 1860 and in drilling water wells in various parts of the country. It was likewise used in 1828 (see Fig. 66) and, according to Techlenburg (*Handbuck der Tieffohrkunde*, Vol. IV, Plate II), went out of general use in the oil fields of Europe in the middle 1860's. According to Henry *(op. cit.)* the spring pole was replaced by other types of equipment in New Zealand in 1866. It is probable that Europe saw a general disappearance of the spring pole about the same time, as stated by Techlenberg.

The advent or invention of the walking beam is not positively recorded. The first definite record seems to be of the French machine built in 1853 (see p. 156). On the Pecos River in 1858 Capt. John Pope used a "spring beam" (see p. 167) which was actuated by a steam engine. He does not describe the mechanics of this operation, but it would be relatively simple to impart the spring-pole drilling motion with a steam engine. On the other hand he could have used a less-than-rigid beam balanced in the middle and operated with the motion of a walking beam with a spring component.

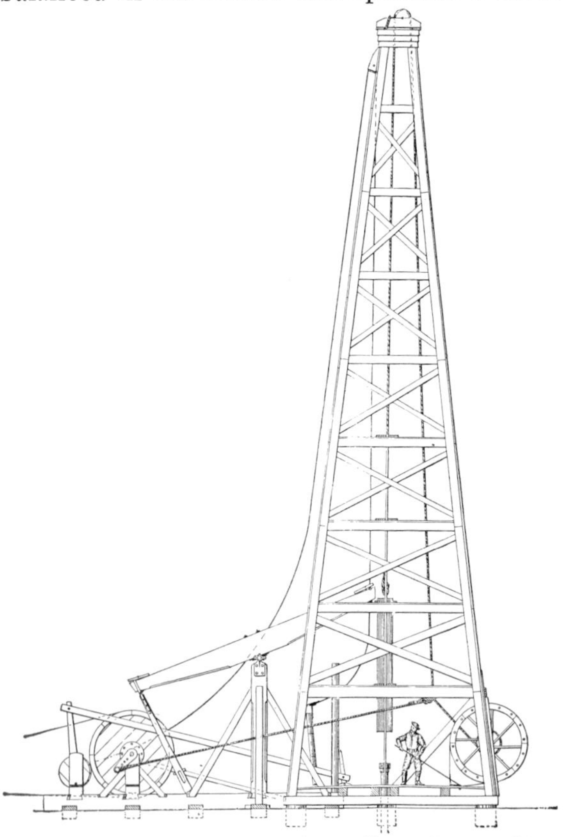

There is no good description extant of the equipment used in drilling the Drake well. Spang assumes that the steam engine used in drilling the well imparted a jerk-line motion to the tools, whereas others believe a walking beam with the tools hanging from the center was employed. On the other hand, still others believe the walking beam of later type was used. Fig. 69 illustrates a cable-tool rig with walking beam, circa 1880.

Fig. 70 shows a type of jerk-line motion on a heavy rig. It will be noted that this motion is quite different from the usual jerk-line spudding motion.

It has been recorded that the engine used on the Drake well was of the

Fig. 69—Cable-tool Rig with Walking Beam, Circa 1880

steamboat type that included a long walking beam which had a motion entirely similar to the later-day walking beam of cable-tool drilling rigs. It was a short step to apply the walking-beam motion to the drilling rig to give the required motion to the tools. The walking beam was in general use by 1884 and appears in the Oil Well catalog of that year.

During the latter part of the 19th century and on into the early part of the 20th century both drilling machines and standard rigs were in general use. Some of the portable machines used walking beams as did the National, the Corbett, and the Parkersburg.

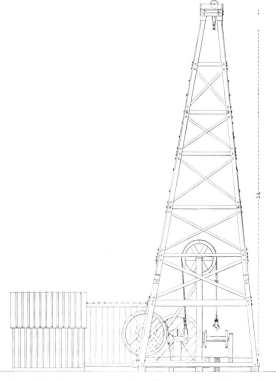

Fig. 70—Type of Jerk-line Motion on a Heavy Rig

In the early 1900's, as the depth of wells increased, the spudder and jerk-line type motions went out of use almost entirely except on very light machines. Beginning in the late 1920's and early 1930's drilling machines of the spudder type came back into use and are now generally used in all types of operations including the deepest. Drilling machines are discussed herein beginning on p. 180.

Hoisting

As with many other items on the cable-tool rig, the earliest records of hoisting equipment are from the Chinese brine wells. Early sketches show a drum or bull wheel with vertical axis being powered by oxen, (see Fig. 7, p. 150). The next records of such hoisting equipment go back to the middle 19th century. No records have been found describing or showing the type of hoisting equipment used on the Ruffner brothers' well or other wells of that period. With the increase in depth of the wells drilled immediately following 1808, there must have been developed some type of drum or bull wheel used for the purpose of handling the tools in and out of the well and for handling casing. Capt. Pope, in his descriptions of the Pecos Valley well drilled between 1855 and 1858 (see p. 164) does not describe his hoisting mechanism nor state how it was pow-

221

ered. He did use a steam engine, however, and it is quite possible that this engine was the source of power for hoisting.

As shown on p. 212, Fig. 52, the hoisting mechanism or bull wheel of the time of the Drake well was man-powered by foot rungs on either side of or across the two flanges of the wheel.

The first application of steam power to the bull wheel is not definitely known but it was probably not used on the Drake well, because it seems to be a matter of record that foot treadles were provided in that rig, which enabled the driller and tool dresser to hoist and lower the tools.

The Oil Well catalog of 1884 shows and describes standard cable-tool rigs quite similar to those in use about 1920. That is, the engine powered the band wheel which, through the rope groove and bull rope, drove the bull wheel. The sand reel was driven by a friction pulley working against the band wheel between the sides of the driving belt. Similar rigs have been in use on isolated jobs in quite recent times and it is quite possible that rigs of this type are still in service. Rope-driven bull wheels are still common on the latest standard cable-tool rigs.

With the advent of drilling machines in the late 1870's and early 1880's, the bull wheel became more nearly a hoisting drum and was first driven by friction pulleys and later by means of chains. In the early part of the century chain, gears, and friction drives for the bull wheels or hoisting drums were in common use. With the reintroduction of cable-tool drilling machines in the 1930's, chain drives were used almost exclusively throughout the rig.

Bull wheels in the early years of their use were built entirely of wood, including the journals and bearings, except that they were put together with metal nails, pins, and bolts. About 1880, or somewhat prior to that time, the wooden journals were cut off and replaced by cast-iron ends or gudgeons of considerably smaller diameter than the round timber that composed the bull-wheel shaft (Fig. 71).

Iron sand reels were apparently first constructed in the early 1880's or in the 1870's (Fig. 72).

The extra bull wheel had the rope pulley and the brake band about one third of the way in from the right-hand end of the shaft; the early bull wheels had the rope pulley on one end of the shaft and the band wheel on the other. Another design included two band wheels with one or two tug pulleys on one of them.

The extra bull wheel was developed into the calf wheel and was so named in the early 1900's. In fact, about 1906, it was still called the "extra bull wheel" as well as the "calf wheel." California operators of 1900 to 1902 are credited with the development of the calf wheel as finally used.

The eight spokes of the early standard bull wheel under both the tug rim and band wheel were fastened to octagonal sections of the wooden bull-wheel shafts just in from the journals. About 1910 there was some consideration given to the building of bull wheels and calf wheels of part steel or all steel. On November 20, 1909, C. W. Seeley and C. S. Ross of Hollywood, California, filed patent application for a bull wheel having a tubular steel shaft to which was attached 8 stubbed cast-iron or steel spokes to which wooden spokes were bolted. This patent was issued January 10, 1911, as Patent No. 981,128, and about that time this type construction came into use.

On November 16, 1910, R. B. Woodworth of Pittsburgh, Pennsylvania, filed

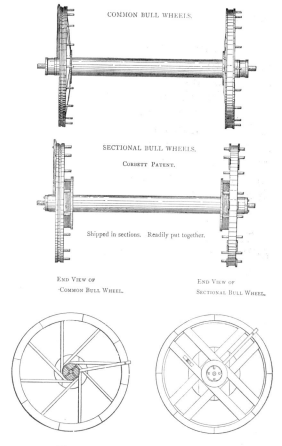

Fig. 71—Bull Wheels of 1880

application and received Patent No. 1,020,069 on March 12, 1912, on a bull wheel that was all steel except that the working surfaces of the band wheel and of the tug pulley were built of wood. About the same time, another patent application was filed on an all-steel bull wheel having structural differences from the other. This patent was issued as **No.** 1,090,184 on March 17, 1914.

Following the issuance of these patents, steel bull wheels came into use about 1915 or possibly a little earlier, but this type of construction did not supplant the wooden wheels, except for the shaft, until the advent of the all-steel cable-tool drilling machines of the mid-1930's. In the 1920's all-steel wheels were built that eliminated the use of wood in the tug pulleys and band wheels. The usual bull wheel of the 1920's was all steel with the exception of the wood cants on the working surface of the brake wheel. This initiated the use of lining in the steel brake bands. Until about 1920 sand reels quite generally had friction drive which, of course, did not require the use of a clutch. About 1920 chain-driven sand reels with clutches came into use, and some calf wheels likewise had chain drives. Modern cable-tool drilling machines use hoisting drums more nearly related to the rotary-rig hoisting and sand-reel drums.

DRILLING STRING

The earliest cable-tool drilling string of which there is knowledge was that used by the Chinese in drilling brine wells to which several references have been previously made. These tools consisted of a drilling cable built of strips of the outer part of bamboo poles attached to complete bamboo poles on bottom which carried the bit or digging tools on the lower extremity.

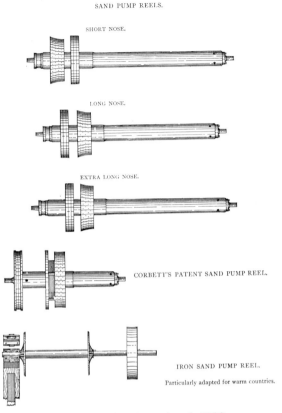

SAND PUMP REELS.

SHORT NOSE.

LONG NOSE.

EXTRA LONG NOSE.

CORBETT'S PATENT SAND PUMP REEL.

IRON SAND PUMP REEL.

Particularly adapted for warm countries.

Fig. 72—Sand Reels of 1880

Rods

The next drilling string of which we have a positive description is the type used by the Ruffner brothers in drilling on the Kanawha River in the early part of the century and as described in the William Morris patent on drilling jars, granted in 1841. A few paragraphs are quoted on p. 163 and 164.

The early wells of the pre-Drake period, including the Belcher well drilled to about 2,000 ft in St. Louis in the 1850's (see p. 162) and the Pecos Valley well drilled by Capt. Pope of the army engineers during the same period (p. 164), used rods, probably of the type described by Morris. Drill rods were taken to Canada during the 1850's where they were used in what became known as the Canadian pole-tool system of drilling. This was later developed into the Galician system in the Galician oil fields of Europe. The early rods were of wood, usually ash or hickory, whereas the later rods, used particularly in the Russian oil fields, were made of iron or steel. The original joints connecting the rods were of sleeve-and-pin types to be followed by screwed joints.

Beginning with Fauvelle in 1845 (p. 288, Chapter 6, rotary drilling, and p. 157), hollow tubes were substituted for solid iron rods on some rigs. Water was circulated through the rods to remove the cuttings. This system was further developed by Fauck in what became known as the Fauck rapid system, briefly described on p. 197. Hollow rods are likewise used for drilling water wells in the United States and particularly in Florida where $3/4$-in. or 1-in. standard pipe is generally used. With continuous circulation and removal of cuttings, it is only necessary to withdraw the rods to change bits.

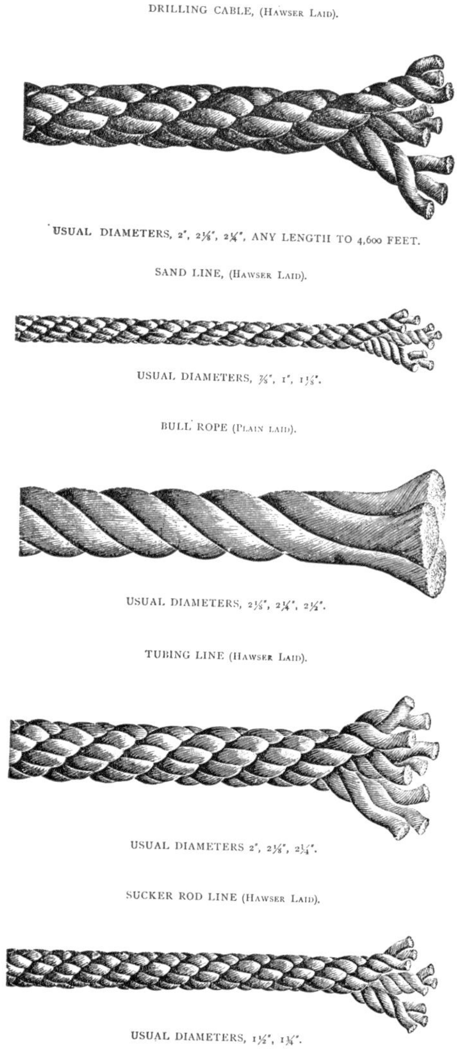

Cables

It is not definitely known just when cable first came into use in the drilling of wells, but it was probably during the first 50 years of the century; although it appears that at least up to the time of the Drake well the most of the rigs used rod tools. Sometime succeeding the completion of the Drake well, pole tools went out of general use in the United States and were followed by hemp or manila drilling cable. The drilling line, known as the drilling cable, as it was developed by about 1880 was usually hawser-laid and varied from 2 to $2\frac{1}{4}$ in. in diameter. The sand line was of similar type but small in size varying from $7/8$ in. to $1\frac{1}{8}$ in. in diameter. The bull ropes, or those which drove the bull wheel from the band wheel, were plain or soft-laid in sizes from $2\frac{1}{8}$ to $2\frac{1}{2}$ in. Fig. 73 illustrates the several varieties of rope used in wells during the middle of the last half of the 19th century.

With the increase in depth of wells, the manila line ceased to be a satisfactory tool. The sand line was first replaced by steel in the late

DRILLING CABLE, (Hawser Laid).

USUAL DIAMETERS, 2", $2\frac{1}{8}$", $2\frac{1}{4}$", ANY LENGTH TO 4,600 FEET.

SAND LINE, (Hawser Laid).

USUAL DIAMETERS, $7/8$", 1", $1\frac{1}{8}$".

BULL ROPE (Plain Laid).

USUAL DIAMETERS, $2\frac{1}{8}$", $2\frac{1}{4}$", $2\frac{1}{2}$".

TUBING LINE (Hawser Laid).

USUAL DIAMETERS 2", $2\frac{1}{8}$", $2\frac{1}{4}$".

SUCKER ROD LINE (Hawser Laid).

USUAL DIAMETERS, $1\frac{1}{2}$", $1\frac{3}{4}$".

Fig. 73 — Oil-well Drilling Cable or Rope Used in 1890

1890's or the early 1900's, with the use of steel drilling lines coming a few years later.

The Yellow Strand, a publication of Broderick and Bascom Rope Company, for August 1908 states: "Both wire and manila rope are used for well drilling . . . but manila rope is generally used until sand, water, or gas is struck. . . . Manila rope gives the drill a peculiar twist when striking a blow that greatly increases its penetrating power."

The Oil Well catalog for 1907 shows both steel sand line and drilling line (Fig. 74).

The steel sand line seems to have replaced the manila line in practically all oil fields about 1900 or even a little earlier. The steel drilling line first came into frequent use in the Mid-Continent and California fields around 1905 and in the Eastern fields somewhat later. A manila line "cracker" some 200 ft in length was necessary to give the required back-and-forth rotary motion to the tools. A "stiff" socket was then used.

With the development of the swivel socket about 1915 (earliest seen is in the Oil Well catalog of 1916), the required motion could be given the tools without the use of a "cracker." In the 1920's the swivel socket with full wire line came into general use in the Western fields and some years later in the Eastern areas. In 1930 full-length wire lines and swivel sockets were used almost exclusively in the former area; in the latter, manila line was used on shallow wells and wire lines with manila crackers on deep wells, both with stiff sockets.

During the 1930's the full wire drilling line with swivel sockets came into universal use except on a few shallow and isolated rigs in the Eastern fields.

Steel drilling lines of the present day are built of alloy steels in a variety of types and sizes. Sand lines are usually ⅝ in. in outside diameter and are composed of 6 segments of 7 wires each. Drilling lines may be plow steel or a stronger alloy, and are commonly 6 x 19 in structure and ¾-in. to 1⅛-in. diameter.

Because of the excessive weight of drilling lines in deep wells, much thought has been given in years past to tapered lines.

In *The Yellow Strand,* Vol. 10, dated October 1909, the offer is made to build tapered drilling lines composed of three sections having different diameters. The wires of different diameters connecting one section to another were to be joined by electric welding. The same publication for 1915 states that a tapered drilling line had been manufactured and shipped in February of the preceding year. The shipping reel contained 9,000 ft of tapered drilling cable composed of an upper section

5. PERCUSSION-DRILLING SYSTEM

SAND LINE

Made from special cast steel wire of a high tensile strength, combined with toughness and extra wearing qualities. Each wire is carefully tested to insure uniformity and durability.

Sand lines, all sizes; are composed of 6 strands of 7 wires each, or 42 wires in all, laid around a hemp center.

Size - - - - - - - - - - - - - - - - - - inches	$\frac{3}{8}$	$\frac{7}{16}$	$\frac{1}{2}$	$\frac{9}{16}$	$\frac{5}{8}$
Weight, per foot - - - - - - - - - - - - - - lbs.	.22	.30	.39	.50	.62
Breaking strain in tons of 2,000 pounds - - - -	4.8	6.6	8.4	10	13
Proper working loads in tons of 2,000 pounds- - - -	1	$1\frac{1}{3}$	$1\frac{3}{4}$	$2\frac{1}{4}$	$2\frac{1}{2}$
Per foot - - - - - - - - - - - - - - - - - -	$0 05\frac{1}{2}$	$06\frac{1}{2}$	$07\frac{1}{2}$	09	11

TUBING AND CASING LINES

Are composed of 6 strands of 19 wires each, or 114 wires in all, laid around a hemp center. These are more pliable than the ropes used for sand line purposes.

Size - - - - - - - - - - - - - - - - inches	$\frac{5}{8}$	$\frac{3}{4}$	$\frac{7}{8}$	1	$1\frac{1}{8}$	$1\frac{1}{4}$
Breaking strain in tons of 2,000 pounds - - -	13.6	19.4	26.	34.	42.	50.
Proper working loads in tons of 2,000 pounds -	$2\frac{3}{4}$	$3\frac{3}{4}$	$5\frac{1}{4}$	$6\frac{3}{4}$	$8\frac{1}{2}$	10
Approximate weight, per foot - - - - - lbs.	.62	.89	1.20	1.58	2.00	2.50
Per foot - - - - - - - - - - - - - - -	$0 14	18	23	30	38	46

WIRE SUCKER ROD LINE, LEFT TWIST

Size - inches	$\frac{3}{8}$	$\frac{1}{2}$
Made of 6 strands of 19 wires each, crucible cast steel, per foot - - -	$0 09\frac{1}{2}$	11
Made of 6 strands of 25 wires each, crucible steel, patent flattened strand, per foot -	- - -	$14\frac{1}{2}$

LESCHEN'S PATENT FLATTENED STRAND DRILLING ROPE

Size - - - - - - - - inches	$\frac{3}{8}$	$\frac{1}{2}$	$\frac{5}{8}$	$\frac{3}{4}$	$\frac{7}{8}$	1	$1\frac{1}{8}$	$1\frac{1}{4}$
Approximate weight, per foot, lbs.	.25	.40	.68	.93	1.20	1.64	2.00	2.40
Per foot - - - - - - - - -	$0 07	10	14	$20\frac{1}{2}$	$27\frac{1}{2}$	35	45	54
Hawser laid drilling cables for cleaning out wells - - - -	- - -	- - -	- - -	$19\frac{1}{2}$	$26\frac{1}{2}$	34	- - -	- - -

Fig. 74—Wire Rope of 1906

---

of 3,000 ft of 1⅛-in. line, 3,000 ft of 1-in. line, and 3,000 ft of ⅞-in. line—all joined together in one length so as to make a continuous rope. This line was used to drill a well in excess of 7,000 ft deep.

In 1942 R. B. Anderson of Columbian Carbon Company became interested in tapered line and had the following to say in a letter dated May 4, 1953: "The tapered drilling line is not a new development and I cannot claim to be originating anything new. I had become interested in the use of tapered drilling lines in 1942. The first lines we bought were tapered in a conventional manner of short distances in the neighborhood of 75 feet. These lines wore out at the tapered point very quickly. We therefore started working with the wire rope people endeavoring to have them increase the length of the tapered section. In 1944 and 1945 we had them increase the tapers to 500 feet in length. In late 1945 we finally had one wire rope company make up a line that was continuously tapered from the point where tapering first started to practically the end of the line. This type of line did eliminate the rapid wear that sometimes occurred near point of taper and gave us a line that had the maximum strength with the least weight possible when suspended in a hole and used in cable tool drilling. This development of securing a continuous taper has made the tapered line the success that it has proved to be. There have been several wells drilled with tapered lines to depths of 10,000 feet and more. Recently the Peoples Natural Gas Company, I believe, drilled a well with cable tools to a depth of approximately 12,000 feet with a tapered drilling line." The American Petroleum Institute Committee on Standardization of Wire Rope drew up specifications for tapered drilling lines in the year 1951.

As already related, drilling rods were first used on percussion-drilling rigs in America on the Ruffner well beginning in 1806. They went out of service in this country apparently during the 1860's, although it is possible that scattered rigs still used this tool. In Canada, however, drill rods continued to be used until quite recent times, as was also the case in a number of the European fields and in Russia, where they are still said to be in use. Hollow drill rods with fluid circulation are still used in this country and in Europe.

Drilling Bits

The first cable-tool or rod-tool drilling bits of which there are records were those used by the Chinese in brine-well drilling many hundred years ago. Although they were, in detail, quite different from the tools of today both in design and in weight, they are nevertheless quite similar in basic principle to the tools used in the early days of the cable-tool water-well drilling industry both in Europe and America. Fig. 75, 76, and 77 illustrate Chinese drilling and fishing tools.

The earliest American bits seem to have been diamond-pointed at the cutting end resulting largely, no doubt, from the fact that little weight was used above the bit. The next development appears to have been a flat, relatively thin bit with a more or less straight cutting edge.

228

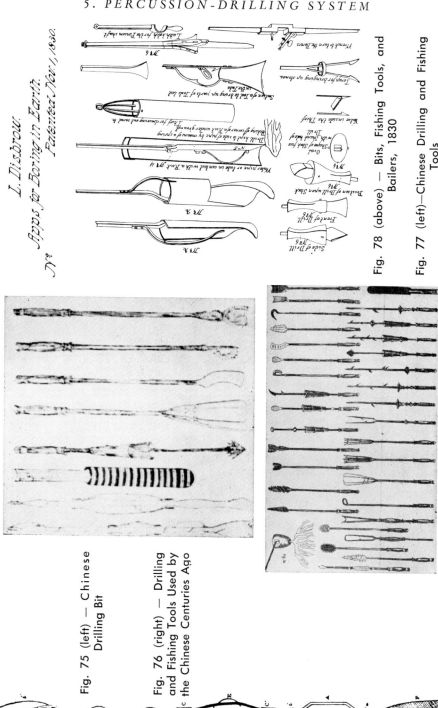

Fig. 78 (above) — Bits, Fishing Tools, and Bailers, 1830

Fig. 77 (left)—Chinese Drilling and Fishing Tools

Fig. 75 (left) — Chinese Drilling Bit

Fig. 76 (right) — Drilling and Fishing Tools Used by the Chinese Centuries Ago

Fig. 79 — Well-drilling Tools
of about 1865
(Acme Fishing Tool Co. Photo)

Indicia:

(1-2)   Drilling Bits,

(3)   Drilling Jars,

(4)   Rope Socket,

(5-6-7) Wrenches,

(8)   Temper Screw,

(9)   Sinker (Straight Pins),

(10)   Comb. Jar-Sinker,

(11)   Stem.

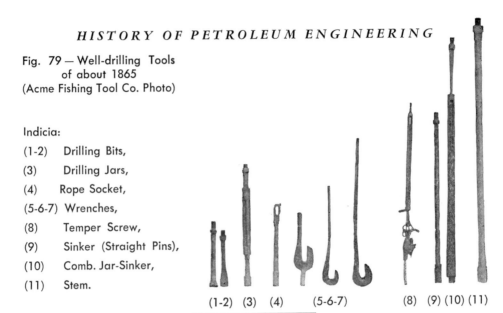

(1-2) (3)   (4)   (5-6-7)   (8) (9) (10) (11)

Digging bits of this type are used at the present time in digging holes by hand in earth or in stone.

Tools and equipment used in drilling the Ruffner brothers' well are mentioned briefly on p. 159 and 160. Three types of bits, together with fishing tools and bailers used in drilling operations of 1830, are shown in Fig. 78. Fig. 79 shows tools of circa 1865.

The best records of early American and European tools are those shown in a few old catalogs still in existence. A catalog published in 1890 by Paulin Arrault of Paris, manufacturer of drilling equipment, shows a number of plates of drilling tools and drilling equipment used in France and its colonies in the 1880's and probably earlier. Several of these plates are reproduced herein. Fig. 80 (Plate 2) shows bits and reamers of types and sizes considerably different and larger than those used in this country. Fig. 81 (Plate 3) shows sand pumps, bits, reamers, and what appear to be coring tools. Fig. 82 (Plate 4) shows sand pumps and bailers, most of which have cutting tools or at least tools on the bottom. Fig. 83 (Plate 12) shows cable-tool core bits, while Fig. 84 (Plate 15) shows strings of tools including a temper screw, drill rods, a girt, free-fall jars, and stems and bits.

The larger tools are apparently designed for large-diameter water wells of which many were drilled in the Paris Basin as early as the 1850's (see p. 154), whereas the small tools are built for small-bore deep-hole work. These plates, together with the descriptions of the tools in the catalog, indicate a well-drilling industry, principally for water, that was considerably advanced in France in the 1880's. The very large variety of tools displayed on the plates of this catalog is more extensive than used in America at the same time.

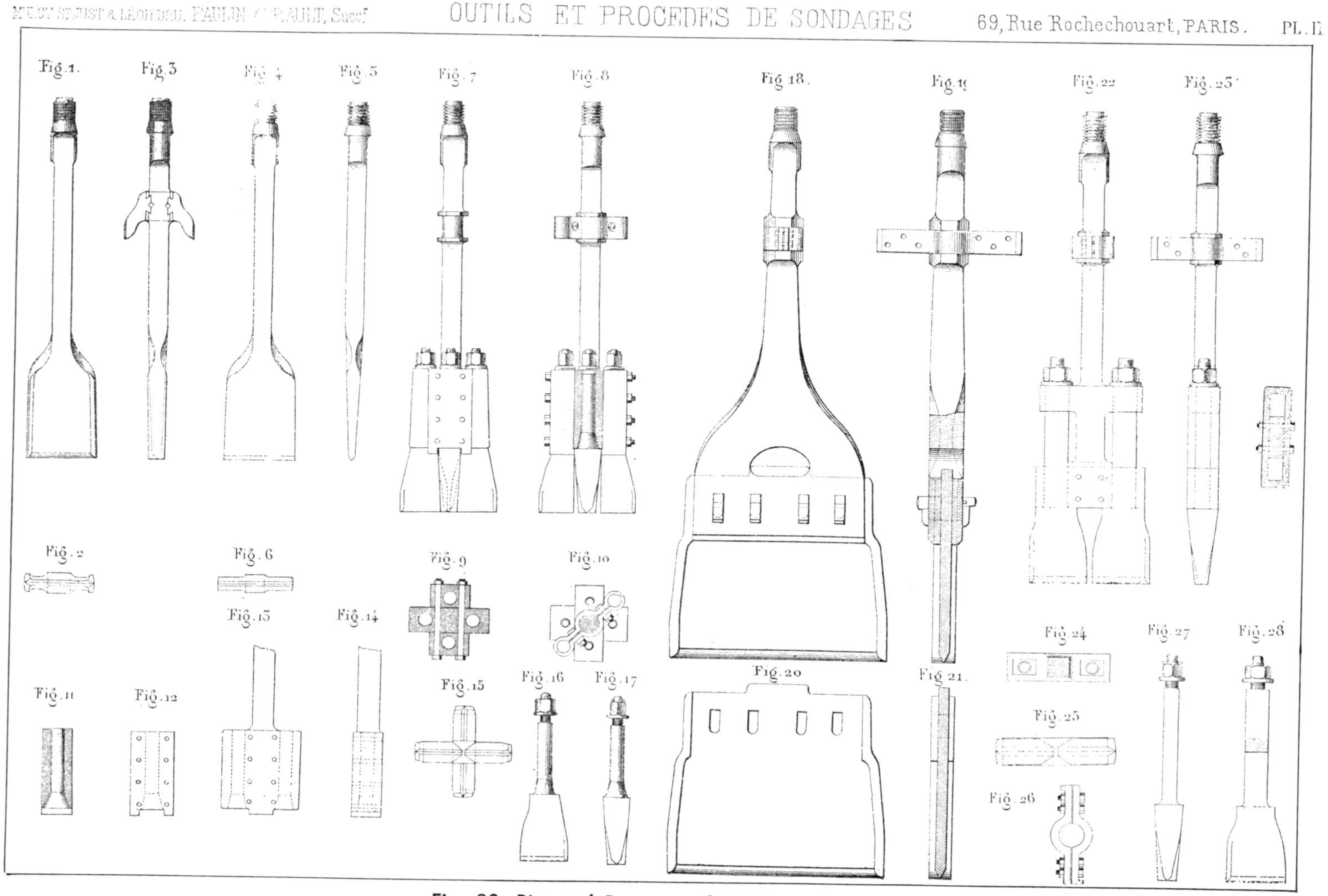

Fig. 80—Bits and Reamers of 1880's — French

OUTILS ET PROCEDES DE SONDAGES. 89.Rue Rochechouart, PARIS. Pl. III.

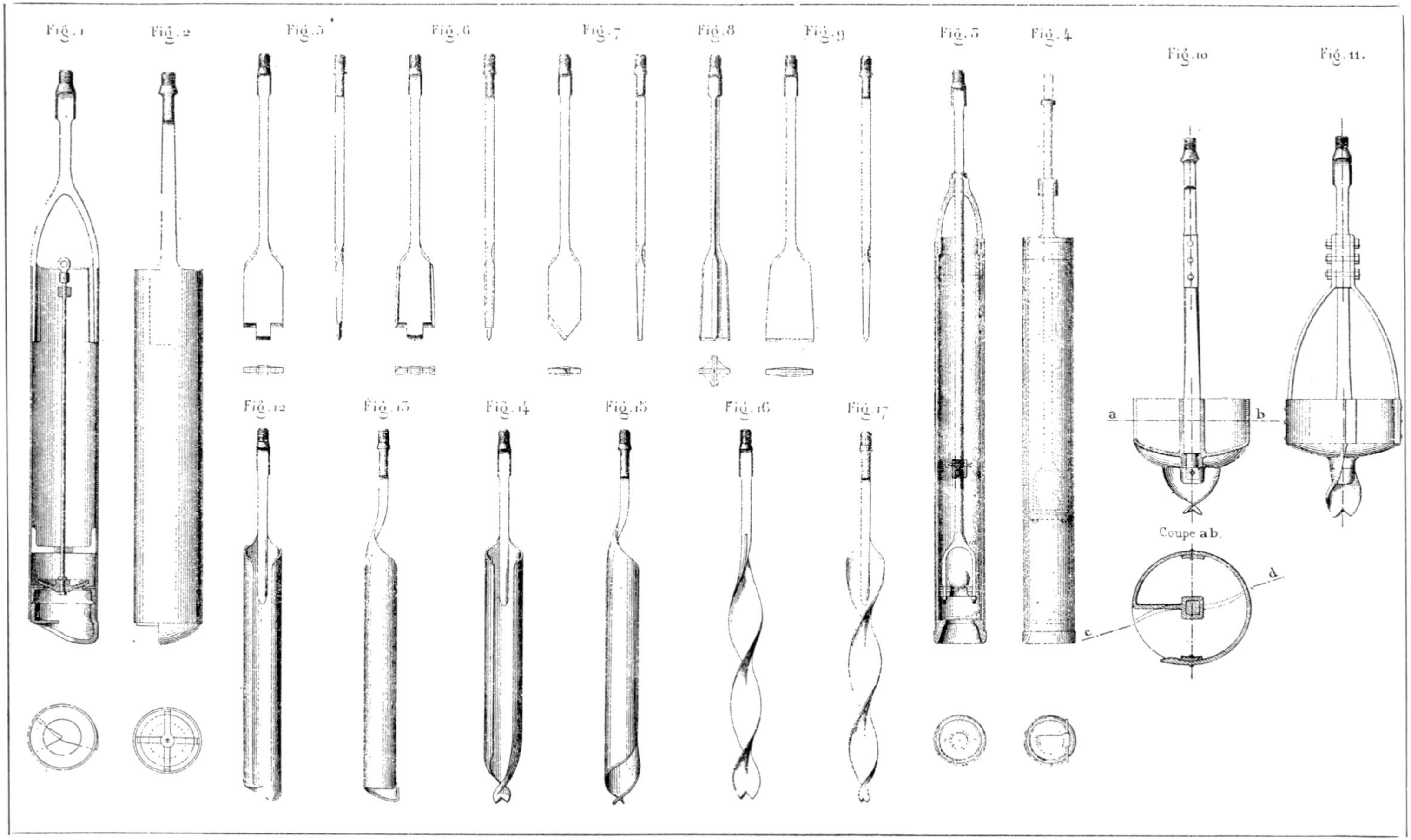

MULOT St JUST & LÉON DRU. PAULIN ARRAULT, Sucr.

Fig. 81—Sand Pumps, Bits, Reamers, Coring Tools — French

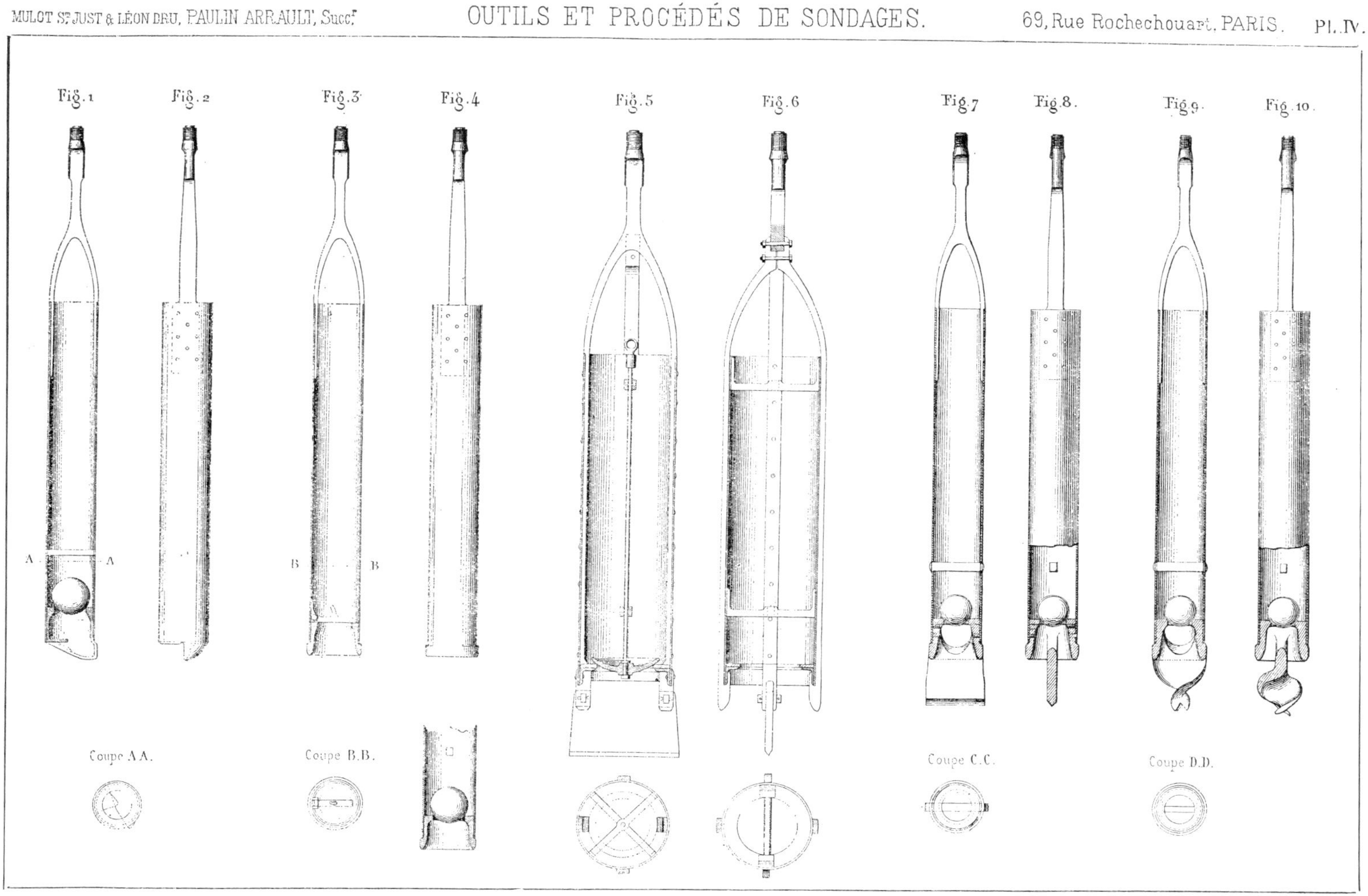
MULOT St JUST & LÉON DRU, PAULIN ARRAULT, Succr
OUTILS ET PROCÉDÉS DE SONDAGES.
69, Rue Rochechouart. PARIS.
Pl. IV.
Fig. 1
Fig. 2
Fig. 3
Fig. 4
Fig. 5
Fig. 6
Fig. 7
Fig. 8.
Fig. 9.
Fig. 10.
A
A
B
B
Coupe A.A.
Coupe B.B.
Coupe C.C.
Coupe D.D.

Fig. 82—Sand Pumps and Bailers — French

OUTILS ET PROCEDES DE SONDAGES

M. T & M. E JUST & LÉONIDRU, PAULIN ARRAULT, Succ.ʳ

69, Rue Rochechouart, PARIS.

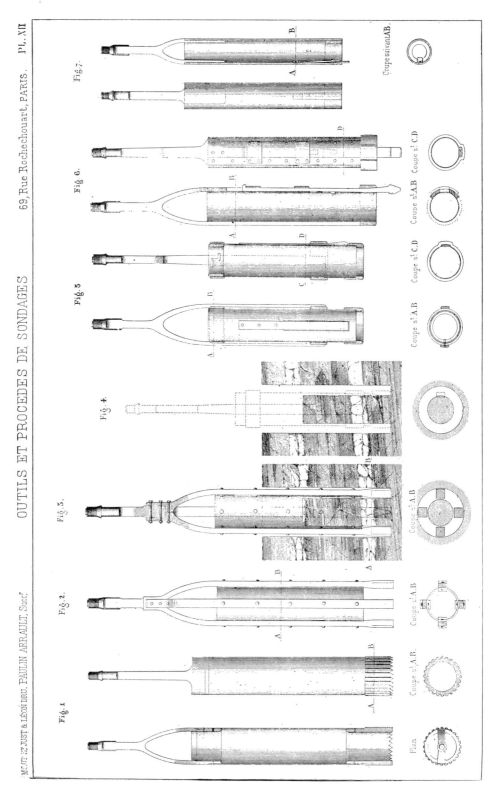

Fig. 1.
Fig. 2.
Fig. 3.
Fig. 4.
Fig. 5
Fig. 6.
Fig. 7.

Fig. 83—Cable-tool Core Bits — French

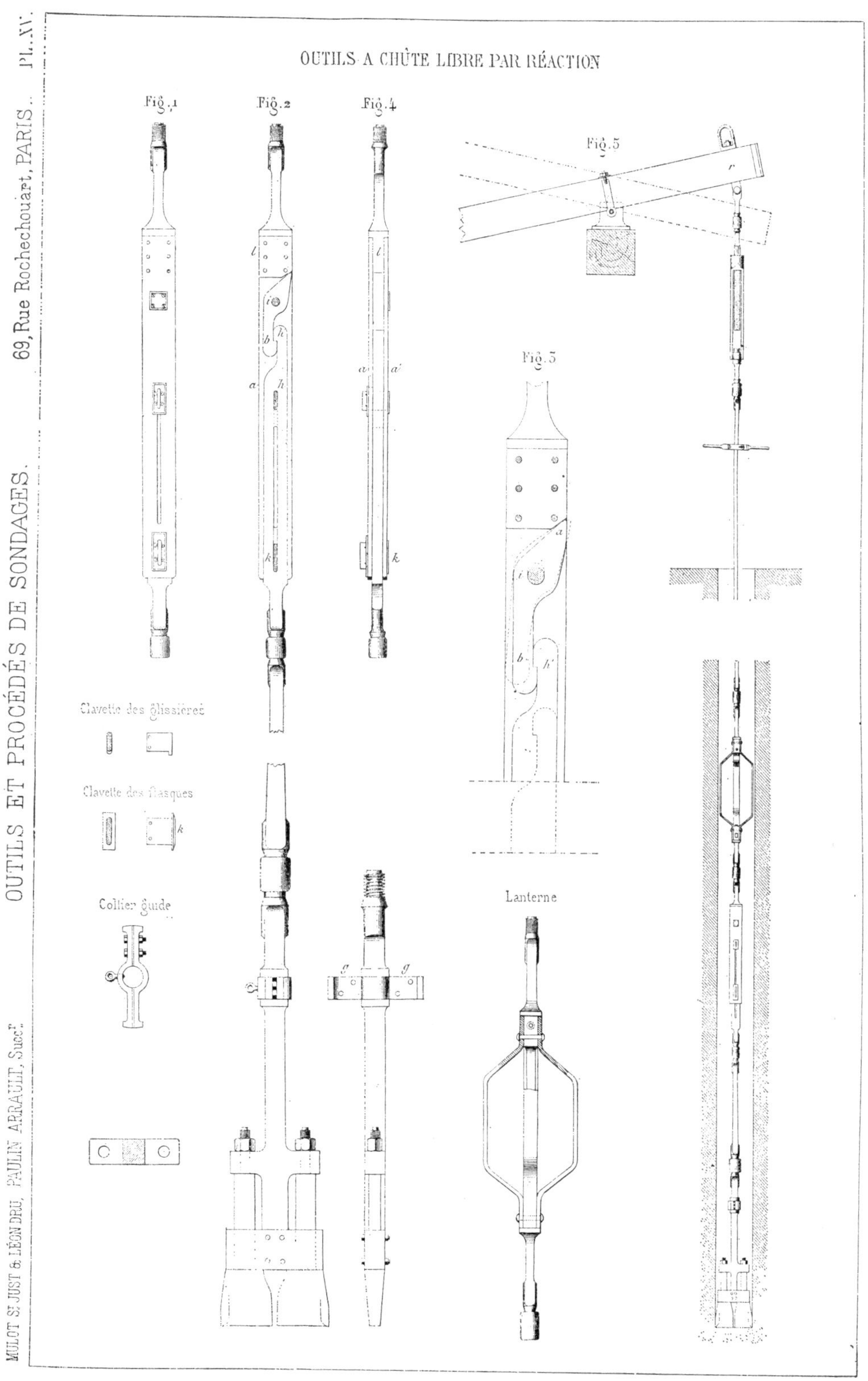

Fig. 84—Strings of French Tools — Temper Screw, Drill Rods, Girt, Free-fall Jars, Stems, and Bits

235

Fig. 85 shows bits and other tools of 1865. Cable-tool drilling operations during the latter part of the 19th century and on into the present time used one type of bit for practically all actual drilling. Fig. 86 shows cable-tool bits with straight pins and boxes, circa 1880.

Flat bits (Fig. 87) preceded the heavy-bodied fluted bits of Fig. 86, and star bits with three or four wings were sometimes used. Reamers had either rounded bits or were star-shaped (Fig. 88). Fig. 89 illustrates ordinary bits of 1935, Fig. 90 a variety of bits and other tools of 1955, and Fig. 91 a cable-tool core barrel of modern design.

It will be noted that there is little change in design of cable-tool bits used in the American oil fields within the past 75 years. New types have been tried and discarded and a few special tools added to the string. There has been great and constant improvement in the steels used, however, including the use of hard alloys on the face of the bits. This practice commenced in the late 1920's with the introduction of the chrome-nickel

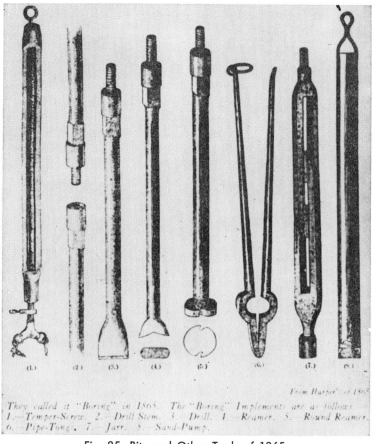

From Harper's of 1865.
They called it "Boring" in 1865. The "Boring" Implements are as follows:
1.—Temper-Screw. 2.—Drill Stem. 3.—Drill. 4.—Reamer. 5.—Round Reamer.
6.—Pipe-Tong. 7.—Jarr. 8.—Sand-Pump.

Fig. 85—Bits and Other Tools of 1865

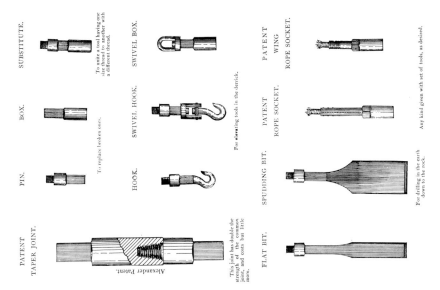

Fig. 87—Bits and Other Tools, Circa 1880
Note first taper thread.

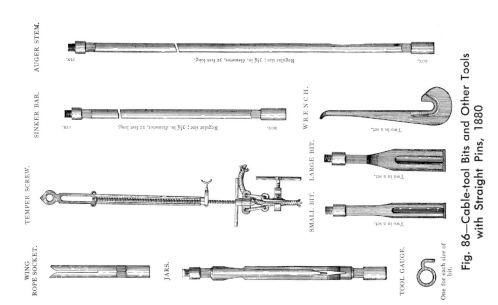

Fig. 86—Cable-tool Bits and Other Tools
with Straight Pins, 1880

and tungsten carbide alloys. Dressing cable-tool bits with hard alloy offered a slightly different problem from rotary bits. The manner of dressing bits likewise changed from derrick-floor forges, anvils, and sledge hammers to shop forges and power hammers and electric welding.

Fishing Tools

Fishing tools of the early years of the oil industry were not considerably different from those of today except that they lacked the refinement and complication of some of the present-day tools. They included the horn socket with adjustable bowl to take hold of any loose tools in the well. There were long friction sockets with a straight barrel to take

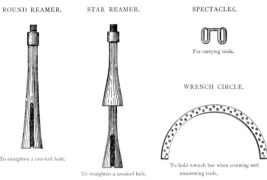

ROUND REAMER.   STAR REAMER.   SPECTACLES.

For carrying tools.

WRENCH CIRCLE.

To straighten a crooked hole.

To straighten a crooked hole.   To hold wrench bar when screwing and unscrewing tools.

STAR BITS.

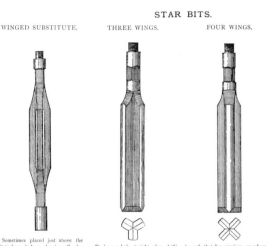

WINGED SUBSTITUTE.   THREE WINGS.   FOUR WINGS.

Sometimes placed just above the bit to keep it from glancing off, also above the round reamer to keep it to its place.

To keep a hole straight when drilling in rock that has crevices, or where the strata are inclined. The bits being long and nearly the full size of the hole are not liable to glance.

Fig. 88 (above)—Star Drilling Bits and Other Tools, Circa 1880

Fig. 89 (left)—Cable-tool Bits of 1935

Fig. 90 (below) — Variety of Bits and Other Tools, 1955

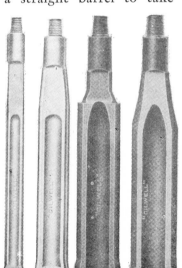

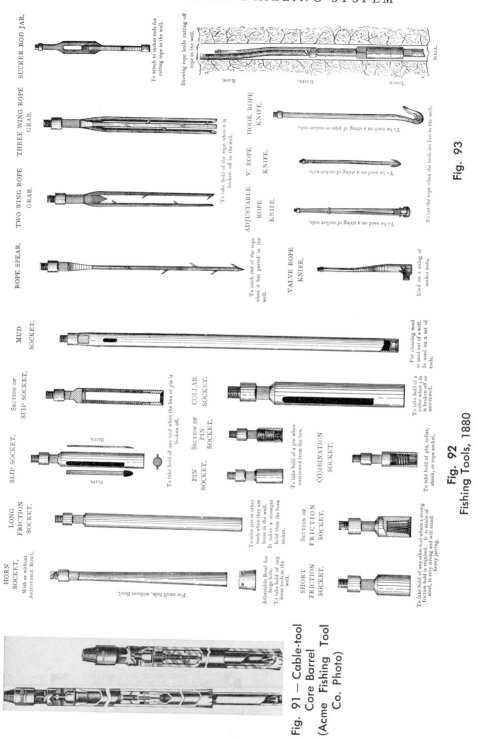

SUCKER ROD JAR.
To attach to sucker rods for cutting rope in the well.

Showing rope knife cutting off rope in the well.

ROPE. KNIFE. TOOLS. WELL.

THREE WING ROPE GRAB.

TWO WING ROPE GRAB.

To take hold of the rope when it is broken off in the well.

ROPE SPEAR.

To catch end of the rope when it has parted in the well.

HOOK ROPE KNIFE.
To be used on a string of pipe or sucker rods.

ADJUSTABLE V. ROPE KNIFE.
To be used on a string of sucker rods.

ROPE KNIFE.
To be used on a string of sucker rods.
To cut the rope when the tools are fast in the well.

VALVE ROPE KNIFE.
Used on a string of sucker rods.

Fig. 93

MUD SOCKET.
For cleaning mud or sand out of a well. Is used on a set of tools.

SECTION OF SLIP SOCKET.

SLIP SOCKET.
SLIPS. SLIPS.
To take hold of any tool when the box or pin is broken off.

COLLAR SOCKET.
To take hold of a collar when it is broken off or unscrewed.

SECTION OF PIN SOCKET.

PIN SOCKET.
To take hold of a pin when unscrewed from the box.

COMBINATION SOCKET.
To take hold of pin, collar, shank, or rope socket.

LONG FRICTION SOCKET.
To size jars or other tools when they are loose in the well. It takes a stronger hold than the horn socket.

HORN SOCKET,
With or without Adjustable Bowl.
Adjustable Bowl for large hole.
To take hold of any loose tools in the well.
For small hole, without Bowl.

SECTION OF FRICTION SOCKET.

SHORT FRICTION SOCKET.

To take hold of any other tool where a strong friction hold is required. It is made of steel, is very strong and will stand heavy jarring.

Fig. 92
Fishing Tools, 1880

Fig. 91 — Cable-tool Core Barrel (Acme Fishing Tool Co. Photo)

friction hold on tools that could be stripped over. There were slip sockets, pin sockets, collar sockets, rope spears, two- and three-wing rope grabs, mouse traps with a flapper valve in the bottom for recovering small objects, grabs for taking hold of any loose tools that they could, latch jacks for recovering bailers, spuds of various types and sizes, hooks, casing spears, casing splitters, casing cutters, and a host of special tools for special jobs. Fig. 92 and 93 show a few of these tools to indicate the similarity with present-day equipment. Fig. 94, 95, and 96 show fishing tools of the 1950's.

Chinese, French, and early American tools are shown on some of the illustrations with bits (Fig. 75 to 85).

Jars

In the early days of rod-tool and cable-tool drilling, it was found that on a dead pull it was sometimes difficult to pick up the bit from the bottom of the hole, especially in soft and cavey formations. In order to overcome this difficulty, William Morris, in the late 1830's, placed two or three links of heavy chain between the lines and the drill stem. He then adjusted the motion through the length of the line hanging on the spring pole so that when the bit hit bottom the upper link would continue for a few inches into the hole before beginning the upward stroke. With the upward stroke the upper link would hit the upper part of the lower link thus resulting in a jar that would lift the tools from the bottom of the hole more readily then did a steady pull. This was the origin of jars — one of the most important tools on a cable-tool rig and without which the drilling operations that have been conducted with these tools would have been extremely slow and difficult.

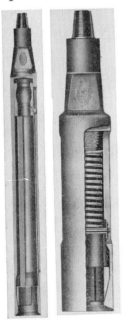

These early jars were made of wrought iron, wore very rapidly, and freqently broke — with the hard service to which they were subjected. To reduce wear and consequent breakage, the inner faces of the two links were

| Fig. 94 | Fig. 95 | Fig. 96 |

Modern Fishing Tools

welded over or sheathed with a layer of hard steel such as is used in the bit of an ax. There was still the problem, however, of keeping the links in alignment. This was solved in part by welding girts along the sides of the links to keep them in vertical position and to prevent the top half from falling over to a horizontal position in the bore.

It is recorded in the literature that William Morris, who is credited with having had the original idea for cable-tool jars, did not patent his invention and received little or no money from it. Insofar as remuneration is concerned this statement may be perfectly true, but it is not correct insofar as his having received a patent is concerned.

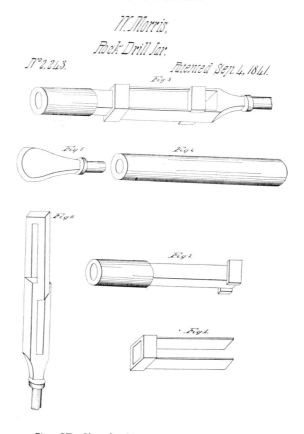

Fig. 97—Sketch—Morris Patent, 1841—Rock Drill Jar

On September 4, 1841, William Morris of Kanawha County, Virginia (now West Virginia) received Letters Patent No. 2,243 covering the first jars designed and built purposely for use in a pole-tool drilling string. The preamble of his specifications reads as follows:

"Be it known that I, William Morris, of the County of Kanawha and State of Virginia, having invented a new and useful improvement upon the auger for boring artesian wells; and, as a necessary preliminary to the description of said improvement, I will first describe the auger to which the improvement has been applied by me.

"That auger is the one which has been in common use on the Kanawha River for many years in boring for salt water, and is believed to be the cheapest and best now in use in the United States. But my improvement can be applied advantageously to any other auger used in boring wells of small caliber."

Fig. 97 is a reproduction of the sketch from the Morris patent. In addition to several views of the jars, it includes figures showing the

241

threaded connections of both a sinker bar and bit in use at the time. The patent letter also gives what is probably the best description of the assembly of the drilling string below the temper screw up to that time (see p. 163).

(see p. 163).

On June 16, 1868, Patent No. 78,958 was issued to John C. Bryan, assignee of Edward Guillod, inventor, covering "new and useful improvements in the construction of drilling jars for oil wells." The following describes not only the improvement but the operation of the jars as well.

"Drilling-jars for deep Artesian or oil wells, were previous to the date of this invention, usually made of wrought iron alone, and in rare instances entirely of steel, the shape and form being substantially similar to that shown in the drawings. When made wholly of wrought iron the heads and inner faces of the links became battered and upset or worn, so that they frequently became locked together and inoperative while in the well, and could only be removed by lowering and attaching another set of tools and jars, which in turn were equally liable to the same defect. If made wholly of steel, the jars are too costly and not infrequently break from a lack of sufficient tensile strength in the link-bars, as well as in the shank and pin. The strain and wear on such jars are very great, since they are required to lift or jerk at each stroke of the drill a set of tools weighing from 500 to 1000 pounds at an average rate of 30 to 40 blows per minute, and when, as sometimes happens, a set of tools becomes fast in the well it becomes necessary to jar them constantly for days and sometimes weeks before they are loosened, and in such case the success or failure of the attempt to remove the tools depends mainly upon the strength and durability of the jars, as the breaking or cracking of a jar-link in the well frequently necessitates the abandonment of the well.

"The nature of this invention consists in so combining iron and steel in the manufacture of drilling jars as to secure the necessary tensile strength in the parts subjected to great longitudinal strain and the hardness of steel in the parts which give and receive the blow and which are subject to great frictional wear, and such end is secured by welding into the wrought iron jar a steel head-piece to receive the blow, and by making of steel the inner faces of the link-bars where the frictional wear is greatest."

Since the 1860's the basic design of jars has not been changed; but there have been considerable improvements, and the metal of the jars is of the best obtainable for the purpose. Fig. 86 shows an 1880 set of drilling tools including a set of jars. Fig. 98 shows a modern set. It will be noted that the principal difference between the two tools is in the threaded connections at the top which, in the older jar, is a straight thread and in the modern tool a tapered thread.

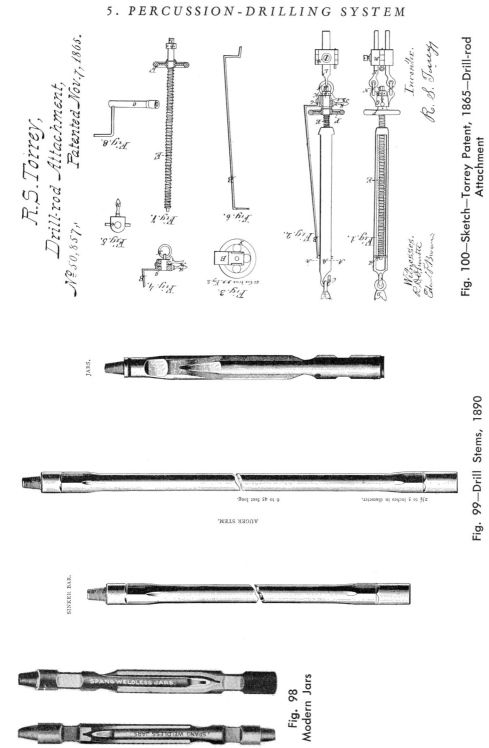

Fig. 100—Sketch—Torrey Patent, 1865—Drill-rod Attachment

Fig. 99—Drill Stems, 1890

Fig. 98
Modern Jars

In the early part of the last half of the 19th century, succeeding the introduction of oil-well drilling tools into Europe, a different type of jars was developed generally called "free-fall" jars. (See Fig. 84, Plate XV, Arrault, Fig. 1, 2, 3, and 4.) Tools of this type are so designed that, as the string of tools reaches the upper limit of the stroke after retrieving the tools from bottom, a latch built into the jars is released permitting the lower section with the bit to fall freely to the bottom of the hole. This is immediately followed by the downstroke of the drilling string. Upon reaching the bottom of the stroke, the latch engages the companion shoulder in the lower section of the jars to which the bit is attached and this part, with the bit and sinker bar if any, is retrieved and falls again upon reaching the upper limit of the retrieving stroke. This is the system used in the early drilling operations and possibly even at the present time in the great Baku Field on the shores of the Caspian Sea in Russia (see p. 153 and 197).

Stems

It is not known what means the Chinese used to add weight to the bit, but probably the bit itself with a long shank of bamboo. When rods came into use with the Ruffner brothers in 1806—and probably earlier in Europe—the weight of the rods themselves served the purpose.

Morris, in his patent papers, states that a heavy solid rod was used below the wooden rods in the 1830's. Whether rods or cable were used, considerable weight has always been required above the bit. With the introduction of jars additional weight was needed above the jars to render them effective on the retrieving stroke.

By 1884 iron "auger" stems 3½ in. in diameter and 32 ft long were in use. A "sinker bar", also about 3½ in. in diameter by 12 ft long, was used above the jars. Fig. 99 illustrates drill stems, circa 1890.

Stems of today are practically the same as those of earlier years except in size, length, and quality of steel.

Fig. 86 illustrates, with other tools, an auger stem and sinker bar of 1880. Note the straight threads.

Feed

There is no record of the method by which the early Chinese cable-tool drillers fed out line as the bit made hole, but possibly it was by the same notched-stick arrangement which was observed by M. T. Archer in 1944 (see p. 148). In France something resembling a "temper screw" may have been in use before 1853 (see p. 156).

In America the early method of feeding off more line as the bit made hole was by raising the line either by taking several wraps of the line around the spring pole and holding it by friction with one end snubbed or weighted in such a manner that it would feed off automatically or could be fed off as the bit made hole. Where rods were used on the spring pole, they were hung into the links of a chain passed around the pole. As the bit drilled off, the chain was let out a link, and so on, until there was sufficient space to insert another length of rod. On the Canadian-type pole rig the feed was accomplished by means of a small drum on the end of the walking beam, over which the line or chain supporting the rods was passed (see Fig. 19, p. 182). Subsequent to the completion of the Drake well in 1859, a temper screw was developed in the United States (see Fig. 85). On November 7, 1865, Patent No. 50,857 was issued to R. S. Torrey of Bangor, Maine, for "new and useful improvements in temper bar and screw for drilling purposes" (Fig. 100).

When manila rope is used as the drilling line in cable-tool drilling, it is necessary to use the temper screw. However, with the advent of the steel line it became common practice in some areas and with many drillers to slip the line through the clamps rather than to feed off with the temper screw.

Where the jerk-line or spudder-type motion was used, beginning in the 1860's or even earlier, the drilling line was carried on a drum or bull wheel from which it was spooled off as the bit drilled ahead. This is the common method of feeding off the line used on the drilling machines of the present time.

Clamps

For use between the temper screw and drilling line, some device was necessary to hold the line and support the weight of the tools while drilling. When the temper screw was fed out its length, this device had to be such that the line could be moved to a new hold while the temper screw was being run up for a new stroke. The answer to this was the line clamps developed apparently in the early 1860's and shown in Fig. 100, taken from the R. S. Torrey patent. This patent has to do with "improvements" in the operation of the temper screw or temper bar and has no new claims insofar as the clamps are concerned. It is apparent then that these clamps were developed prior to the date of the patent. On Aug. 12, 1873, W. H. Downing received patent papers covering improvements on rope clamps. On drilling machines of modern types clamps are not required, except those using walking-beam motion.

Rope Sockets

The first rope sockets were built for the purpose of fastening the rope to the drilling tools below. Prior to this time the rope was threaded into an eye in the top of the stem and tied to hold the tools. The knot thus formed wore rapidly against the walls of the hole, resulting in frequent loss of the tools. These rope sockets were made in two parts, the upper of which was bored with a bell shape to the hole in the lower end. To assemble the rope in the socket, the cable

245

was threaded through the upper half of the socket separated into its several strands, each of which was wrapped with soft line to increase its size so that when the two halves of the socket were made up together the enlarged end of the cable could not be pulled through the bore of the upper half. This was the basic design of the original stiff rope socket and has not been changed materially.

With the development of the wire lines a socket of similar type was used, but so built that the end of wire cable could be enlarged by inserting a core

Fig. 101 — Modern Swivel Rope Sockets

and wrapping it or by babbiting. The stiff sockets were not entirely satisfactory for wire-line drilling because the tools did not rotate satisfactorily. This resulted in the building of the swivel socket designed somewhat similarly to the stiff socket except that the wire line was threaded through and then babbitted into a cylinder which fits freely into a proper recess, forming a swivel joint. This joint permits the line and bit to rotate with respect to each other. This type socket is in general use today. It was first developed in the early part of the 20th century.

Fig. 86 illustrates one type of stiff rope socket of 1884, and Fig. 101 a modern swivel socket.

Taper Joints

The early oil-well tools used straight threads in the joints. The changeover from straight-thread joints to taper-thread joints was made between 1884 and 1892, with the taper joint having been developed under the Alexander patent somewhat prior to 1884 (see Fig. 87 to 99).

An illustration of the Alexander patent taper joint is shown in Fig. 87. All other illustrations in the Oil Well catalog of 1884 show straight-thread joints.

On the other hand, the Oil Well catalog of 1892 shows taper joints on all drilling tools, including the same illustration of the Alexander patent taper joint. The invention and development of this joint was one of the important mileposts in the drilling industry. The rotary tool joint was developed from it by Whittier in 1908-1912 (see p. 330 in Chapter 6).

The French tools shown, taken from a catalog dated 1890, do not indicate the use of taper joints. On the other hand the R. Brochot catalog, undated but published apparently about the turn of the century, indicates the use of taper joints. Modern taper joints are entirely similar to those of 1890.

By the year 1900 probably 30 to 40 taper joints of different designs and in numerous sizes were in use. A few years later the Ireland and Hughes joint was introduced in the Oil City area and became the most prominent in use. Its accuracy, however, was dependent upon copies produced by various manufacturers made in an unkempt manner and this led to many discrepancies which were costly and bothersome to operators in various areas. It was from troubles of this kind that the need for the standardization of cable-tool joints became evident and this work was begun by the Division of Production of the American Petroleum Institute in the early part of the 1920's.

Jacks

The tightening and separating of the original small screwed tool joints did not involve any great problem. They were fitted with straight pins and boxes and could ordinarily be tightened and loosened with any small wrench of a grappling type. However, when the size was increased, the problems of tightening them together and breaking them apart became more involved. This brought about the forging of either a square or a flat into each of the two elements at some distance away from the threaded portions and the use of a solid forged wrench (see Fig. 103), built to fit snugly the square or flat of the tools. The force necessary to make up or break out the joints was first supplied by the use of a fulcrum bar to which two chains were attached. The ends of these two chains could be fastened to the ends of the two wrenches by means of hooking the chain links into either a tongue or claw formed on the end of each wrench. Thus the chain links could be adjusted to bridge any gap which occurred between the wrench ends as a result of varying shoulder positions. The fulcrum bar was attached to the chains by two clevises which, in turn, were fastened to the fulcrum bar at some short distance from each other, giving a leverage action in the movement of the bar. This method of tightening joints is still practiced in some oil-field operations and is used quite extensively in the water-well drilling industry. It did not, however, completely solve the problem.

The next effort to obtain tighter set to the tool joint was by the use of a pinch bar wrench and plate. This plate was comprised of a flat strip of iron perforated with two staggered rows of pinch-bar holes. The end of the plate was fitted with a hook to which one wrench end was engaged. The plate was several feet in length. The pinch bar had a point which would engage the perforated holes, and had a crescent-shaped forged saddle about 4 or 5 in. above the point into which the end of the second wrench was engaged. The pinch bar acted as a fulcrum by the engagement of the point of the bar with the perforation of the

Fig. 102—Wrench Circle

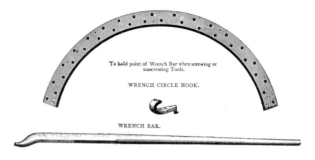

To hold point of Wrench Bar when screwing or unscrewing Tools.

WRENCH CIRCLE HOOK.

WRENCH BAR.

plate, the wrench end with the saddle, and the operating end being moved by the force of the workman to tighten and to loosen the joints (see Fig. 102).

Later came the adoption for well work of the mechanical jack, used by the railroad workers for raising and lowering rails as the ballast was filled below the ties. This jack was fitted with pawls, much the same as the automatically reciprocating jacks in general use at the present time. At that time the pawls had to be moved from one notch to another by hand. This type of jack was adapted to the tightening and loosening of well tool joints by operating it horizontally upon a notched track. One end of this track was fitted with a hook receptacle to engage one wrench end, and the face of the jack body was used to exert the pressure against the opposite wrench. Inasmuch as this bar was straight, it became necessary to adjust the track back and forth as the gap between the two wrench ends changed. This led to the adoption of a

BARRETT'S PATENT OIL WELL JACK FOR TIGHTENING AND LOOSENING JOINTS.

SECTIONAL VIEW.

PARTS.

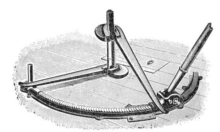

In this Jack there is an improved reversing appliance, by which the spring levers are dispensed with. The carriage can be moved on or off the rack. by holding the handle at the position shown in cut when set for reversing.

A.—Base.
B.—Socket Lever.
C.—Shield.
D.—Spring.
F.—Lowering Block.
G.—Eccentric.
H.—Socket Side Plates.
J.—Two inch Wrench Pin.
L.—Long Pawl.
M.—Short Pawl.
N.—Rack.
P.—Bushing.
Q.—Fulcrum Pin.

SCREWS FOR ABOVE.

D.—Spring Screw.
E.—Lifting Screw.
F.—Low Block Screw.
G.—Eccentric Screw.
L.—Long Pawl Screw.
M.—Short Pawl Screw.

Fig. 103—Circle Jack, 1892

circular track slightly longer than one quarter of the circumference of the part of the wrench moved, which became the automatic circle jack (Fig. 103).

These changes took place within the 30 years following the drilling of the Drake well. The size of the jack and track has been increased and improved steels are used, but the original design is closely followed at the present time. It is possible that the future may provide improved tools for the tightening and loosening of joints, including means of more accurately determining the degree of their tightness. One such concept has proved to be generally acceptable where it has been tried.

Elevators

No records appear as to the method of handling casing and tubing in the early years of the well-drilling industry. It is probable that slings around the pipe were used for shallow wells. For still longer strings, pipe clamps were bolted around the tube below the collar, with wings on either side to engage a rope sling. With the coming of deeper wells and more wells, this method of handling casing was too awkward and time-consuming for general use. This necessitated the invention and development of elevators. The records on these developments are not complete; but by 1880 or shortly thereafter, the Fisher and Fair patent elevators were highly developed tools and were in use. Spiders and slips had not yet been developed, so two elevators were needed. In fact, the use of two elevators was quite common practice on cable-tool rigs until as late as 1920, although spiders and slips or rings and wedges had come into use about 1890 but were used largely for pulling casing with hydraulic jacks and not for running pipe (Fig. 104).

Fig. 105 illustrates a Fisher patent elevator, circa 1880, and Fig. 106 a Fair patent elevator of about 1890. Later elevators are discussed and illustrated in Chapter 6.

Casing Tongs and Wrenches

The earliest water-well casing seems to have been put together by riveted collars and possibly by insert joints. As threaded casing was developed, circa 1825, tools for making up the pipe were likewise necessary. The first of these were probably ordinary manila rope or chain slings slightly longer than the circumference of the pipe. The sling was passed around the pipe with one end passed between the lines at the turn-around of the other end. A pole was then passed through the free end, which had been doubled back on itself, and used as a lever. The pull on the pole tightened the sling, developing sufficient friction to permit the make-up of the pipe. This tool is occasionally used today and probably will continue to be used as long as one joint of pipe is screwed into another. A rope attached to a sharpened steel grip and with a loop and pole in the free end was likewise used (Fig. 107).

249

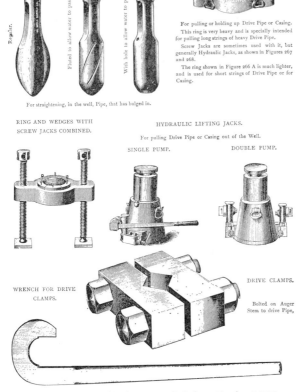

PIPE SWEDGES.

RING AND WEDGES.

Regular.

Fluted to allow water to pass.

With hole to allow water to pass.

For straightening, in the well, Pipe, that has bulged in.

For pulling or holding up Drive Pipe or Casing. This ring is very heavy and is specially intended for pulling long strings of heavy Drive Pipe.

Screw Jacks are sometimes used with it, but generally Hydraulic Jacks, as shown in Figures 267 and 268.

The ring shown in Figure 266 A is much lighter, and is used for short strings of Drive Pipe or for Casing.

RING AND WEDGES WITH SCREW JACKS COMBINED.

HYDRAULIC LIFTING JACKS.

For pulling Drive Pipe or Casing out of the Well.

SINGLE PUMP.

DOUBLE PUMP.

WRENCH FOR DRIVE CLAMPS.

DRIVE CLAMPS.

Bolted on Auger Stem to drive Pipe,

Fig. 104—Rings, Wedges, and Other Tools, 1890

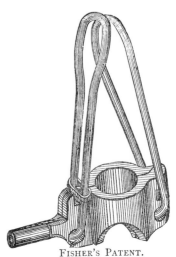

FISHER'S PATENT.

Fig. 105—Fisher Elevator

FAIR'S PATENT.

Fig. 106—Fair Elevator

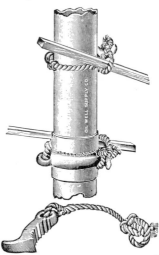

Fig. 107 — Casing Grip and Rope

Where considerable strings of pipe were to be run such tools as these caused considerable delay and the drillers soon borrowed an idea from the pipe fitters and developed their tools into larger sizes for use on well casing. The chain tong without a toothed bearing surface on the pipe may have been the first of these, to be followed by the same tool with teeth that would dig into the metal of the pipe and prevent slippage. The casing tongs of about 1880 were apparently developed from the old blacksmith tongs by cutting off one-half of the working finger to a short length and bending the other half to reach somewhat more than half way around the circumference of the pipe. The ends of the short finger and the long finger were shaped to dig into the pipe upon engagement, as shown in Fig. 108. Also illustrated are early chain tongs that had been developed some years before 1890.

Lay's patent tong inserted a key of hard steel into the short finger to engage the pipe more securely and to prevent wear. However, these two-handled tongs were quite awkward and probably remained in service on casing only until chain tongs were developed to take their place.

The Crumbie patent tongs were developed about this time, and were

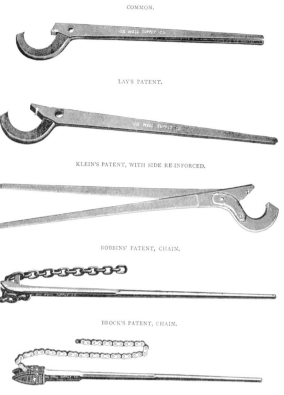

COMMON.

LAY'S PATENT.

KLEIN'S PATENT, WITH SIDE RE-INFORCED.

ROBBINS' PATENT, CHAIN.

BROCK'S PATENT, CHAIN.

Fig. 108—Casing Tools

not too different from tubing tongs and casing tongs of the present day. By 1890 the two-handled casing tongs described were still in use, but chain tongs had been developed to practically the same types and designs that are in common use today in cable-tool drilling.

With the coming of the rotary-drilling industry and much more frequent use of casing or drill-pipe tongs for going in and coming out of the hole, more highly perfected tools were necessary. They were developed into large sizes and used on casing as well as on drill pipe. These tools are discussed and illustrated on p. 354 and 355 of the chapter on rotary drilling.

Casing and Tubing

In the drilling of wells generally it is now and doubtless always has been necessary to use some means for supporting the walls of the hole to prevent caving, except where hard formations begin at the surface and continue to bottom. The various means employed have included cribbing made of stone, round timbers, hewn timbers or planking, burned or fired clay, and tubes or round sections made of fired clay, cement or concrete, bamboo, hollow logs, bored logs, split poles with the centers of each grooved and the two halves then placed together and wrapped, fabricated wood and very thin iron or copper sheeting, copper tubes, wrought-iron tubes or pipe, cast-iron pipe, and alloy-steel pipe of various analyses of modern manufacture.

In the simpler hand-dug or shallow bored wells of the past and present, most of these various materials were and still are used as a single wall-supporting medium or "casing." In more complicated and deeper percussion-tool borings, two or more alloy-steel "casing strings" are used for the sole purpose of supporting the walls of the hole to prevent caving, both while drilling and after the hole or well is completed. Each succeeding "string" is, of necessity, of smaller outside diameter than the inside diameter of the preceding one. As the bore proceeds, the size of the drilling tools is correspondingly reduced to sizes that will pass through the last tube inserted in the bore. In hard-rock areas the formations may permit open-hole drilling except for the surface pipe, unless excessive amounts of water are encountered.

The second purpose for which hollow tubes were originally placed in the bore was to prevent contamination of the fluid to be produced by fluids of overlying strata. This has doubtless been common practice since earliest times, especially when the fluid to be produced was other than potable or irrigation water. It was always necessary to get a shutoff or something approximating a shutoff of the fluids above the bottom of the tube or casing to prevent contamination of the fluid for the recovery of which the well was drilled.

These are the basic principles of which there are, of course, many and various complications and ramifications in modern oil- and gas-well drilling. The use of casing has reached a very high point of perfection in rotary drilling. In cable-tool wells the conditions and practices have been more or less the same for many years.

The third purpose for which hollow tubes, pipe, or tubing was inserted into the well was as the orifice through which the fluid sought could be produced, either by natural flow or pumping. This production string was at first the final casing run and packed off, but later smaller tubing was hung inside the larger pipe or casing.

Ancient

There are few or no data on the manner in which the wells of Biblical times were cased or curbed, but it is reasonable to assume that those dug in unconsolidated materials of valleys used something to support the walls of the wells, either pole cribbing or masonry. The kanats (or qanats) dug in the talus slopes at the foot of mountains and hills (see p. 142) probably did not need curbing in most cases since the nature of the material composing the slopes was such that the walls would stand. This was aided by the fact that the walls were always dry. The writer has seen many in the high valleys of Iran and not one was

curbed. Some were 200 ft or more
deep.

On the other hand a shallow well
in Southern Turkey, in the village
in which Abraham was said to have
spent some time, was walled with
flat limestone flags of the area for
a depth of about 25 ft. The well
was said to have been dug before
the birth of Abraham (1900 B. C.)
and to have been used continuously
since that time — which at least
makes an interesting story!

For at least the past several hundred years the Chinese seem to have
used bamboo to case the holes drilled
for brine production (Fig. 109).

Fig. 109 — Chinese Making Bamboo Casing

It seems probable that the same type casing was used from the beginning of well drilling in China, although other materials such as clay pipe
could have been utilized. It is improbable that wells a few hundred feet
deep and producing brine could have avoided caving without casing of
some type. Also the brines would have been contaminated. Most Chinese
wells are said to carry no casing below 400 ft to 500 ft in depth, however.

The Japanese, about 600 A.D. and later (see p. 152), dug oil wells
by hand to depths of 600 to 900 ft and curbed the wells from top to
bottom with timbers.

The wells dug in Burma, possibly some centuries later, were curbed
or cased and split boards, as related on p. 152-153.

1806-1859

Although there is conclusive evidence of the drilling of wells prior
to 1806, the operation of the Ruffner brothers in 1806-1808 is the
earliest—other than those mentioned—on which data have been found.
The Ruffners sank a hollow sycamore log or "bee gum" some 4 ft in
inside diameter through the river-bottom silts and gravel to bed rock
at 17 ft. After getting a water shutoff around the bottom of the
"gum" curbing or surface conductor casing, they drilled a 45-ft hole
below the bottom of the gum to satisfactory brine production. To
eliminate contamination with weaker brines and fresh water from above,
they cased or tubed the bore with a 2½-in. pole that had been split,
grooved in each half, placed together again, and then wrapped tightly
with twine and inserted in the bore, which had been drilled with a 2½-in.
bit.

253

This hollowed pole, with a "bag of wrappings" for a packer on the lower end, served as both the water shutoff string and the production or eduction tubing. The well flowed into the gum from which it was bailed with a "sweep" or "swipe".

Many brine wells were dug in the Alleghany Mountains during the next 50 years before the Drake well was commenced, but the records are quite incomplete insofar as the equipment and mechanics of the operations are concerned.

During the 1850's several deep wells were drilled including the Belcher Sugar Refinery well in St. Louis, drilled to 2,193 ft, and the Dupont well of Louisville drilled to 2,086 ft. The literature on these wells does not mention casing but it seems certain that casing of some type was used to support the walls at least in the upper part of the bores, even though both wells were in hard-rock country. Wooden tubes may have been used at the surface, with copper or wrought iron in the longer strings.

The story of the wells drilled by the U. S. Army in the Pecos Valley, Texas, in the late 1850's under the direction of Capt. John Pope has been told at some length on p. 164 to 170.

Capt. Pope discussed the difficulties of "carrying" $3\frac{1}{2}$-in. iron tubing (the second string) from a depth of 810 ft to 971 ft with the use of a spring-type underreamer. The hole was drilled to a total depth of 1,050 ft, where it had to be abandoned because the casing could not be carried or driven below 971 ft and the hole was caving badly at 1,050 ft. Capt. Pope also mentions the use of copper tubing as a 3-in. "liner."

During this period, wells were being drilled in the Paris Basin and in Bavaria to depths approaching 2,000 ft. No mention of casing has been found in the literature, but some of these wells were commenced with diameters of 6 ft and finished with diameters of 2 ft. Many of these wells were artesian and, unless the walls of the holes were very hard throughout, some casing must have been needed. A few years later (1880) catalogs listed and carried illustrations of small- and large-size pipe.

Drive pipe is mentioned with some frequency in connection with the operations between the Ruffner well of 1806-1808 and the Drake well of 1859. In the latter, pipe was driven to the hard rock at about 20 ft below the surface where a shutoff was obtained. The hole was then carried to $69\frac{1}{2}$ ft where production was encountered. Apparently the well was completed without further casing although some may have been run later. The formations below the drive pipe were hard.

During the 1860's and 1870's many patents relating to "tubing" and "tubing wells" were applied for and granted. It is doubtful, however, that there were many if any disclosures of a new art original with those to whom the patents were granted. There were variations from common practices set forth in many of the patents, but the basic principles of casing or tubing wells commenced at least with the Ruffner brothers and was a well-known art and common practice by the time of the Drake well. The use of "seed-bag" type packers to get water shutoff was likewise used by the Ruffners and other early operators.

That casing was used in many, if not most, of the deeper wells is a logical conclusion, since it is doubtful that they could have been drilled and produced otherwise.

It seems probable that water and brine wells were pumped through unpacked tubing hung in the larger casing as well as through the casing itself. The use of plunger pumps in small pipe was not an unknown art at that time.

1860-1884

The literature prior to 1884 contains relatively little technical information on pipe used as casing and tubing, so it is necessary to make some surmises as to what must have been done. One difficulty is that in the literature of the period what is now called "casing" was, until some time after the completion of the Drake well—probably about 1870, referred to by its generic name of "tubes" or "tubing."

During these early years the final string of pipe was run to bottom or to the depth required and "packed off" with a seed bag or other packer to prevent contamination of the oil and its escape outside the pipe. The seed-bag packer consisted of a skin or cloth bag tied around and near the bottom of the lowest joint in the string—partly filled with flax seed, grain, or beans—tied at the top and then lowered into the hole on the length of casing. The seed would eventually swell and usually "get a shutoff." At other times the pipe was merely set on a shoulder or in hard shale with the same result.

One of the great and valuable developments or "inventions" in the oil-producing industry was the pumping and flowing of wells through "tubing" as it is now known. The invention or development of this method or basic principle is hidden in the mysteries of the 1860's and 1870's along with many other developments.

Brine wells and water wells of the early years were doubtless pumped through small tubing inside the larger tubing (or casing), as well as directly in or through small-size tubing (or casing) set on or near bottom. Doubtless later oil wells were at times pumped in the same manner. With the annulus between the two strings closed or packed off, some of these wells probably flowed through the tubing. As a result of this practice, and to allow more working space in the annulus, the size of the last or water-shutoff string—the "oil string" in the Mid-Continent or "water string" in California—was increased and an un-

255

packed string of smaller pipe or tubing was run and hung inside as the eduction or production string, as a matter of common practice.

Patent No. 50,919, issued to M. J. Dickerson and Jacob Struber on Nov. 14, 1865, was for the "application and use of a distinct packing tube around or to which the seed bag is attached and made of larger diameter than the eduction tube and through which the eduction tube passes, so that the eduction tube may be inserted, removed, raised or lowered without disturbing the seed bag or unpacking the well."

Thus the "eduction tubing," which was the casing as now known, was enlarged and a smaller unpacked string inserted as the production pipe, or tubing as we now know it.

There are many other patents of similar nature. The basic patents were declared void by the courts in that they did not describe a new method of producing oil or a new system of fixing or placing tubes in a well. The art had been known and practiced more than 50 years before the patents of the mid-1860's. The beginning of the use of eduction or production tubing may have been about this time but it appears that Dickerson and Struber thought they had invented the use of a larger-size casing that was packed off. It is quite possible that they were among the first to recognize the value of oil-well tubing as it is now known and used.

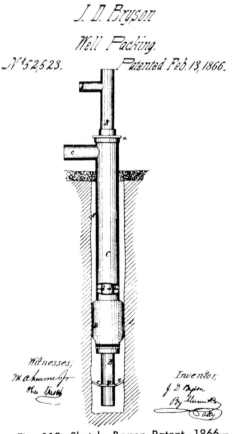

Fig. 110—Sketch—Bryson Patent, 1866— Well Packing

Although the use of a separate outside casing to shut off upper water was without question one of the great developments of oil-well producing, it is doubtful that it properly could be called an "invention." Fig. 110 reproduces the sketch from the Bryson patent of 1866.

John F. Carll in the *Pennsylvania 2nd Geological Survey Report*, Vol. I (1880), discusses briefly the tools, equipment, and methods of drilling oil wells in the first 20 years of the industry in Pennsylvania. Included is a description of the drilling practices employed on a presumably average well in each of the years 1861,

1868, and 1878. Of particular interest are his references to the manner of casing and tubing the wells.

The well of 1861 set fabricated wooden conductor pipe through the upper weathered zone to "bed rock." Inside this surface conductor pipe a 4-in. hole was drilled "wet" into the oil sand. A string of "tubing" with a seed-bag packer was then run to the top of the oil sand, after which the well was tested for a water shutoff by bailing. If there was no shutoff, the tubing with packer was pulled and rerun until a shutoff was obtained. The well was then put on production. The packer was the usual leather "boot-leg" tied at the bottom near and around the lower end of the tubing, filled with flax seed, tied at the top of the packer, and lowered into the well. This "tubing" served as the casing as now known and was likewise the pipe through which the oil was produced.

The well of 1868 used either wooden conductor pipe or wrought-iron drive pipe carried through the weathered zone to bed rock. A 5½-in. "wet" hole was then drilled into or through the oil sand. A string of 3¼-in. "casing" was next run with a seed bag or patented packer of the day, and a shutoff attempted on top of the oil sand. Thereupon, 2-in. "tubing" was run inside the casing without a packer and used as the eduction tubing in the present-day manner.

The typical well of 1878 drove 8-in. wrought-iron pipe, with a steel shoe, through an 8-in. hole to bedrock. A 7⅞-in. hole was then drilled inside the surface drive pipe through the water-bearing sands. At this point the hole was reduced gradually to 5½ in., leaving a sloping or beveled shoulder. A string of 5½-in. casing with a thick bottom collar or shoe was run and seated on the shoulder.

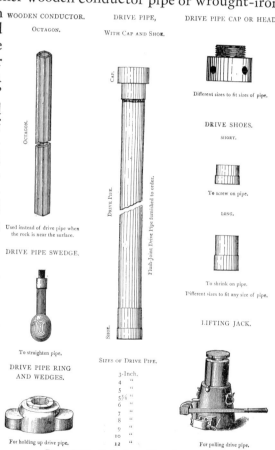

Fig. 111—Tubular Goods and Tools
(From *Oil Well Supply Co. Catalog*, 1884)

With a bevel on the shoe to fit the shoulder, the pipe was rotated for a tight fit and tested for a water shutoff. The contractor was required to get a shutoff on this string before he could carry the hole ahead and into the oil sand. Tubing was then run, with or without working barrel with an anchor below, and the well put on production by flowing or pumping.

Although the old seed bag, a ball of tough clay, or other material were also used to assist in getting a shutoff, the method of setting the pipe on a shoulder served quite generally until the practice of cementing was developed. This came about around 1903-1910 in California and a few years later in the Mid-Continent. (See the chapter in this *History* on cementing.)

Thus the use of eduction tubing inside a string of packed-off tubing seems to have been quite common practice in the Pennsylvania oil fields in the mid-1860's. In view of the fact that the early brine wells (beginning with Ruffner) had also used a string of packed-off tubing (casing) to prevent contamination of the brine by upper weaker fluids and that this practice was common in 1861, it would appear that the "invention" or new development concerned the smaller unpacked tubing inside the larger packed-off tubing. The smaller tubing thus could be moved or pulled to clean out the well without disturbing the casing seat and admitting contaminating fluids. Some wells would flow through this small tubing but not through the larger casing string. This in itself was one of the great and valuable developments in the industry. Casing sizes were doubtless increased as a matter of convenience in the mechanical operations and to avoid "running out of hole."

Thus, the use of tubing or casing in wells seems to have developed over the early years of the drilling industry in America after a rather advanced beginning by the Ruffner brothers. It seems to have been a well-known art at the time of the Drake well. That the art was equally or further advanced in Europe, is evidenced by the records of the wells drilled (see p. 154-157).

The Oil Well catalog published in October 1884 shows wooden conductor pipe, drive pipe, and regular and inserted-joint (wrought-iron) casing. Sizes listed range from 2-in. ID to 10-in. ID (Fig. 111 and 112). Tubing is likewise shown and listed in sizes ranging from 1-in. ID to 12-in. ID (Fig.

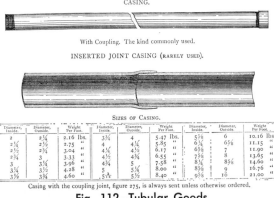

CASING.

With Coupling. The kind commonly used.

INSERTED JOINT CASING (RARELY USED).

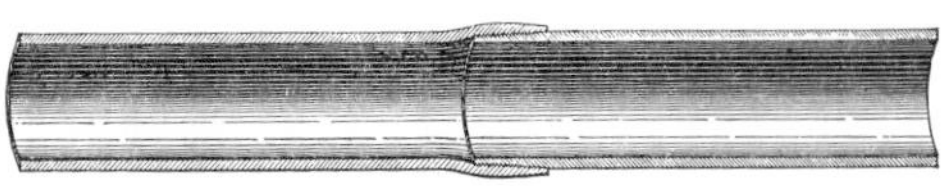

SIZES OF CASING.

Diameter, Inside.	Diameter, Outside.	Weight Per Foot.	Diameter, Inside.	Diameter, Outside.	Weight Per Foot.	Diameter, Inside.	Diameter, Outside.	Weight Per Foot.
2	2¼	2.16 lbs.	3¾	4	5.47 lbs.	5⅝	6	10.16 lbs.
2¼	2½	2.75 "	4	4¼	5.85 "	6¼	6⅝	11.15 "
2½	2¾	3.04 "	4¼	4½	6.17 "	6⅝	7	11.90 "
2¾	3	3.33 "	4½	4¾	6.55 "	7⅝	8	13.65 "
3	3¼	3.96 "	4¾	5	7.58 "	8¼	8⅝	14.60 "
3¼	3½	4.28 "	5	5¼	8.00 "	8⅝	9	16.76 "
3½	3¾	4.60 "	5 3/16	5½	8.40 "	9⅝	10	21.00 "

Casing with the coupling joint, figure 275, is always sent unless otherwise ordered.

Fig. 112—Tubular Goods

113). These sizes are placed below "tubing" called "flush-joint tubing or drive pipe," so it seems probable that these sizes are for drive pipe or flush-joint casing rather than e-duction tubing. The scale of the sketches suggests that the "tubing" is of the smaller dimensions.

Post-1880

The Oil Well catalog for 1892 illustrates c a s i n g, d r i v e pipe, flush-joint "pipe," inserted-joint "cas-ing," and flush-joint "cas-ing," all of almost modern design except the thread forms. Casing sizes listed range from 2-in. to 15½-in. ID, or 2¼-in. to 16-in. OD

COUPLING.   WITH SLEEVE COUPLING.

The sleeve protects the threads and binds on the tubing, making a stronger joint. It guides the tubing into the coupling and prevents "cross-threading."

COMMON COUPLING.   TUBING WITH COMMON COUPLING.

FLUSH-JOINT TUBING OR DRIVE PIPE.

The ends of the tube are turned out and a thread cut on—no couplings used—flush outside. Furnished only to order.
SIZES OF TUBING MADE: 1, 1¼, 1½, 2, 2½, 3, 3½, 4, 5, 6, 7, 8, 9, 10, 12-inch.

Fig. 113—Casing and Tubing, 1884

(note both are listed). Threads are 14 to the inch in sizes 7⅝-in. OD and 11½ to the inch up to 16-in. OD. Both threads are listed from 5¼-in. OD to 7⅞-in. OD.

Tubing is listed in sizes from 1-in. to 6-in. ID. Threads per inch are 11½ up to 3½-in. ID, 10 per inch on 4-in., and 8 per inch on 6-in.

There appears to have been little change in the specifications of oil-country tubular goods at least until the early 1900's when both butt-welded and lap-welded pipe are listed. Other specifications and sizes seem to have been the same.

What later came to be known as "short-coupling" casing was used exclusively until about 1912 when "long couplings" were made and came into use in California (see p. 329).

By 1916 some 8-thread casing was being manufactured in a few of the larger sizes, but 14-thread up to 7¼-in. and 11½-thread from 5-in. to 15½-in. in most sizes and weights were usual. The exception was in "California casing" which had 10 threads to the inch and "long coup-lings" on all weights and sizes. At this time cable-tool holes used by far the greater part of the casing manufactured. Note couplings in Fig. 113.

Seamless oil-field tubular goods came on the market about 1920. Since that time great improvements have been made in steel, joints, and precision of manufacture, which are all recorded in detail in API speci-fications. One of the great improvements was the change from **V** threads to round threads in the mid-1930's, brought about largely by California engineers.

In 1926 API casing specifications were published. At that time "Boston" oil-well casing was manufactured. This was light-weight pipe in 2-in. to 15½-in. sizes with 8 to 14 threads per inch in various sizes that had been in use for many years. Lap-welded and seamless Diamond BX and Diamond B8 (10 and 8 threads per inch) were also standard items of manufacture.

API casing specifications eliminated a few sizes and added others, up to 24½-in. OD. Casing in sizes from 4¾-in. to 8⅝-in. had 10 threads per inch, whereas larger sizes had 8 threads per inch. All were **V** threads on ¾-in. taper. Designation of casing was changed to the outside diameter sizes. Special casings, such as inserted-joint and flush-joint, were also available.

At about this time—the mid-1920's—it became apparent that rotary tools would dominate the oil fields, so casing was built largely with rotary holes in mind although the new pipe was equally serviceable in cable-tool wells. This encroachment of rotary rigs on cable-tool territory was brought about largely by improvements in the rolling-cutter rock bits—which improvements included better bearings and the use of mud-laden fluid as the lubricant instead of the awkward lubricators—improved tooth forms, better steels, and hard-facing alloys for the teeth. The new tooth forms and tungsten carbide really made the difference.

Modern casing and tubing are manufactured in many grades with tensile strength up to 110,000 psi (1958). There are several joint designs promoted by various manufacturers, as well as those included in API specifications.

DRILLING PRACTICES

The drilling practices in percussion drilling, whether cable or rod tools are used, are the same in major basic principles in all areas and have been from the beginning, with deviations to meet the conditions or requirements of the formations encountered, type of oil, or methods of production. These practices likewise include considerable variation in hole sizes and in casing run—again due to the nature of the formations, the nature of the materials to be produced, or the tubular goods available.

In general most early shallow holes in America were small. The Pecos Valley well, for example, of which we have the best record, used 3½-in. OD casing which required the drilling of a hole 4 or 5 in. in diameter. Early Chinese brine wells that were cased used bamboo casing and were generally some several inches in diameter. In the hard-rock country of the Alleghanies, after getting through the soft surface material, holes varying in diameter from 3 to 8 in. are drilled in which 2½-in. to 6⅝-in. casing is set. French wells (water) were frequently much larger.

On the other hand in soft formations where considerable difficulty may be encountered with caving, the starting hole may be as large as 30 in. in diameter and the finishing hole as small as 6 or 8 in., with many intermediate hole sizes and casing sizes. In the early days of California, when cable tools were generally used, it was likewise necessary to begin with large holes, possibly 20 in. or more in diameter, drill as far as possible, and carry the pipe until it froze. The hole was then reduced in size to that of the inside diameter of the frozen pipe, carried down until caving commenced—at which time another string was inserted and carried on down until it froze, and so on until the top of the oil sand was reached. Then the water string was run and cemented or set on a shoulder and the well drilled in. Following the completion of the well or immediately after the water string was run, the larger strings of casing were recovered, if possible, to be used again. It was to avoid the necessity of using an excessive number of strings of pipe that the casing circulating system was developed.

In 1917 the Union Oil Co. of California successfully used the reverse method of circulation in drilling in the Coalinga, Midway, and other fields. This is described by M. Van Couvering in *Summary of Operations, California Oil Fields*, Aug. 1920, as follows:

"The principal feature of the equipment is a special packing head which permits circulation of mud-laden fluid at all times except when passing a collar of the 8¼" casing through the packing head. This head consists of a packing bowl containing rope packing, resting on a shoulder of the bowl, and a spider with a downward extension which compresses the packing. The 8¼" casing rests on slips which in turn, rest on the spider mentioned above. In addition, the spider is held down by a pair of anchor bolts which are attached, at their lower end, to a clamp on a 10" collar. This collar also serves as a coupling between the 10" casing and the packing bowl, which rests upon it. When it is desired to move the 8¼" casing, it is only necessary to remove the slips, when the packing head will be held in place by the anchor bolts.

"The upper portion of the 10" casing consists of a short nipple, into the side of which is welded a section of 4" pipe. When the work has been completed the 10" nipple can be removed and used at other wells.

"The fluid is pumped into the 10" casing through the 4" pipe mentioned above. The packing head prevents its exit at the surface between the 10" and 8¼" casings, so it is forced downward between these casings and muds the formations exposed below the shoe of the 10" casing. When the shoe of the 8¼" casing is reached, that portion of the fluid which did not pass into the formations passes upward, inside the 8¼" casing, to the surface, where it overflows and is caught in a concrete basin below the floor. The dimensions of this basin are 10' x 10' x 4' deep."

To eliminate the necessity for using several strings in drilling a well, because of soft formations, methods of circulating casing were being developed and perfected to a considerable extent at the time of the movement of the first rotary drilling tools from Texas to California in 1908. The cable-tool drilling system and cable-tool equipment in California were then more highly developed and more rugged than rotary equipment and, where the formations were favorable, could drill holes more rapidly and more economically than could the rotary tools. On the other hand where the formations were soft and would not stand in open hole, the cable-tool system was at considerable disadvantage and casing circulation was used. With the advent of the rotary and the improvement and strengthening of that equipment, use of the cable-tool system in California was quickly displaced—as it had been in the soft formation country in the Mid-Continent; and the further development of hydraulic percussion drilling ended. It is interesting to speculate on what might have developed in cable-tool drilling had the hydraulic rotary system not been introduced and perfected. Certainly American ingenuity would not have failed to find a way to get the holes down to the oil sands.

In addition to the usefulness of mud-laden fluid in supporting the walls of the hole in cable-tool drilling, it was also useful in controlling high pressures that might be encountered. In the early part of the century many wells blew out and were lost or cratered as the result of drilling into high-pressure gas in Oklahoma and the Gulf Coast. Also when drilling through a gas horizon to a deeper zone, it became necessary to set a string of pipe to case off the gas or to drill on through to the lower zone with the gas escaping at the casing head, thus causing a serious fire hazard and other disadvantages.

In 1912 and 1913, A. G. Heggem and J. A. Pollard of the Bureau of Mines studied these problems in Oklahoma and recommended the use of mud-laden fluid in drilling cable-tool holes, both to control the high-pressure fluids encountered and to prevent caving in drilling through soft formations. Discussion of their studies and recommendations were published in *Technical Papers 66* and *68*, *Petroleum Technology 14* and *15*, respectively, Bureau of Mines, 1914. The greatest difficulty encountered was in prevailing upon the operators to drill with a hole full of fluid because of their fear that the fluid would kill the well or mud off such producing horizons as might be encountered.

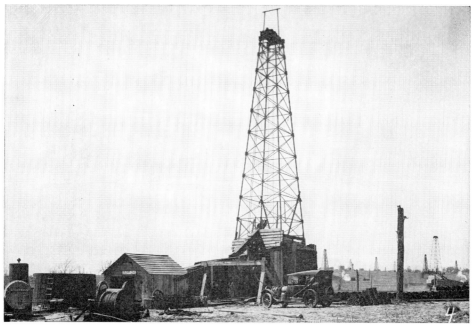

Fig. 114—Depew Oklahoma Field, 1923

Fig. 115—Church and Fields Pool, Crane County, Texas, about 1930

It was necessary to practically guarantee to the operators that no damage would be done by the mud-laden fluid before it was tried in 1913.

The first well for demonstration was offered by Henry N. Greis of Tulsa, Oklahoma, located in the S ½ SE ¼, Sec. 8, T. 17N. R. 7E. The hole was first drilled to a depth of 1,700 ft where gas was encountered which, upon reaching the surface, was ignited from the fire of the forge on the derrick floor, destroying the rig. The derrick was rebuilt and the hole continued to 2,140 ft with the gas escaping. It was then filled with mud which brought the gas under control, and the well was deepened to 2,157 ft which was 10 ft into the Wheeler sand where it was completed as a 22-MMcf well. Apparently no damage had been done insofar as the mud-laden fluid was concerned.

As late as the 1930's many wells were drilled with combination tools in Oklahoma and West Texas. Casing was set on top of the hard formation, usually through the Permian, with rotary equipment and hole continued to the top of the producing horizon with cable tools. The oil string (water string) was then run and cemented and the well drilled in with tools.

In cable-tool drilling, casing sizes varied from 30 in. or more on down in the Baku Field, about 20 in. to 7 in. in California, from 12 or 14 in. to 6⅝ in. in the Mid-Continent, and from 10¾ to 5½ in. in the Appalachian fields. The earlier wells—drilled before the perfection of heavy cable-tool strings—used casing of much smaller sizes, generally 4¾ in. or less.

Fig. 114 shows the Depew Field in Oklahoma with both steel and wooden derricks, 1923. During this period the rotary was gradually replacing cable tools in the Mid-Continent. Fig. 115 shows one of the last areas in Texas where cable tools are still used (photo about 1930).

CONCLUSION

Percussion systems of drilling have enjoyed very long and very useful periods of service; but since the advent of rotary rigs about 1895, they have lost ground constantly to the hydraulic rotary system of drilling in percentage of wells drilled. Actually there may be as many cable-tool rigs in operation today as in their heyday, but most of their work is in shallow water-well drilling.

The first loss of areas to the rotary came in water-well drilling in the Great Plains from the Dakotas to Texas, and then in the oil fields near Corsicana, Texas, during the last 5 years of the 19th century. Next the Gulf Coast and other areas of soft formations, in which it was extremely difficult if not impossible to drill deep cable-tool holes, adopted the rotary system. California followed in 1908, when the rotary was first successfully used in that state.

In the middle and late 1920's with the vast improvement in rotary bits and rotary equipment generally, cable tools commenced to lose ground to the rotary in areas that had previously been exclusively cable-tool territory—such as Oklahoma, North Texas, Kansas, the Rocky Mountain fields, and in the Middle West.

By 1940 cable-tool rigs were almost entirely confined to those areas where the formations were sufficiently hard to permit drilling without carrying pipe. These areas included the Eastern oil fields, parts of the Permian Basin, and a few places in the Mid-Continent and Rocky Mountain areas.

The changeover was delayed in many areas by the use of combination rigs, i.e., where the rotary would drill one part of the hole and cable tools the other. The rotary may set surface pipe or an intermediate string, with the tools finishing the hole; or the tools may set a surface string through upper hard formations, with the rotary finishing up. This is still common practice in parts of the Permian Basin.

The future of cable-tool drilling seems to depend more upon future developments in rotary, or some entirely new methods of drilling than upon the cable tools themselves. Although certainly improvements can and will be made in cable tools and practices, still the basic principles of operation with their time-consuming features must remain more or less the same.

At the present time the cable-tool rig can drill in certain types of formation that are peculiarly suited to the method, at less cost per foot or well than can the present rotary system. Until there are radical improvements in the rotary tools and equipment, this division of drilling areas will doubtless continue. New methods of making holes in the crust of the earth for the purpose of producing oil or gas could affect both present systems to the extent of eliminating them from use. Such a new method does not appear to be in the offing at this time.

Modern cable-tool drilling methods and practices are little different from those of 20, 40, or 60 years ago. Tools are practically identical in design. However, the steels in use and the methods of dressing bits have improved greatly, while the self-contained drilling machines bear little resemblance to the old standard drilling rigs and spudders. Fig. 116 through 119 show modern cable-tool drilling equipment.

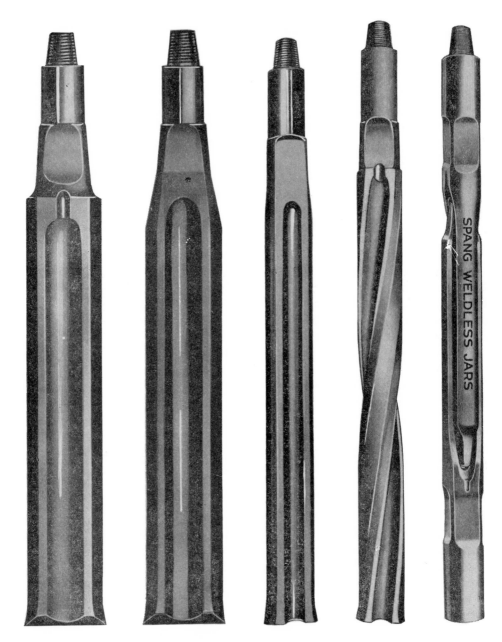

Fig. 116—Four Cable-tool Bits and a Set of Jars of 1960
(Courtesy Spang and Company)

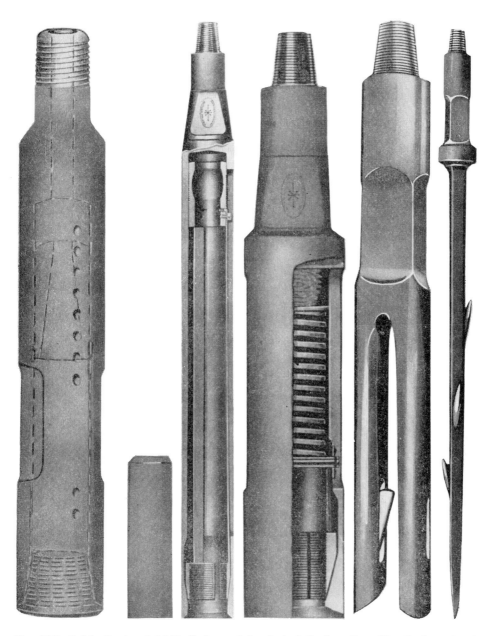

Fig. 117—Cable Tools of 1960 (Left to right: Swivel Socket, Two Slip Sockets, Latch
Jack, Rope Spear)
(Courtesy Spang and Company)

Fig. 118—Cable-tool Drilling Machines, Shallow Drilling in Kentucky, 1959
(Courtesy Bucyrus-Erie Company)

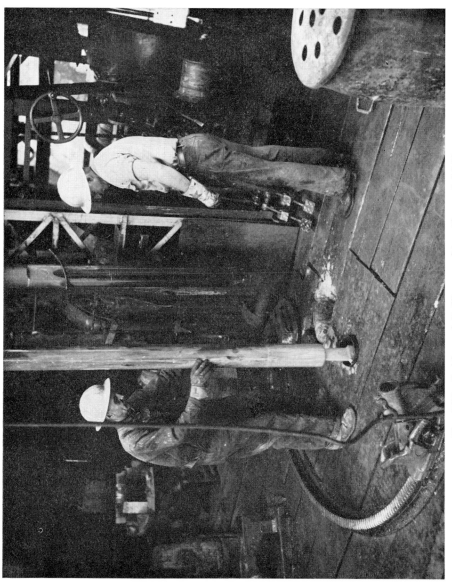

Fig. 119—Cable-tool Drilling-machine Floor of 1959
(Note forge and anvil for dressing bits.)
(Courtesy Bucyrus-Erie Company)

Chapter 6

HYDRAULIC ROTARY-DRILLING SYSTEM

With Addendum on Pneumatic Rotary Drilling

J. E. Brantly

Mr. Brantly's photograph and biography appear
on page 134.

⌭ 6 ⌭

INTRODUCTION

Methods of drilling or boring holes in the earth by the percussion method were developed and came into prominent use long before the rotary system of drilling, as we now know it, was invented. The story of digging holes into the crust of the earth, in any manner for any purpose prior to 1900, is related at the beginning of Chapter 5, Percussion-drilling System. This chapter will be confined to methods related to the rotary system, and particularly to the hydraulic rotary system, of drilling or boring holes in the earth. Pneumatic rotary drilling is covered in an addendum which begins on p. 438.

The invention and development of rotary-drilling equipment and rotary-drilling practices has been marked by several stages of varying activity, and it seems desirable to divide the story into those approximate periods of development and progress. It is doubtful that any two authors would arrive at precisely the same subdivisions, and the present writer could quite logically develop divisions different from those that will be presented. However, after having done the research work from the literature available to him and having completed the historical records of the various items of equipment and drilling practices, it seems that the subdivisions used herein divide the life span of the art of drilling with rotating tools into very definite time intervals of accomplishment and major change. Time intervals that have been selected are *1*, Pre-historic-1844; *2*, 1844-1900; *3*, 1900-1915; *4*, 1915-1928; *5*, 1928-1934; *6*, 1934-1940; *7*, 1940-1960 (this interval divided into the periods 1940-1946 and 1946-1960).

Most unfortunately the literature on rotary oil-well drilling for the first 20 years of its important activity in the petroleum industry is quite limited, nor is it very abundant for the following 10 or more years, or until the very early 1930's. From that time on to the present the printed records have grown greatly in volume, accuracy, and value. Yet the most important basic inventions and developments, insofar as equipment and tools are concerned, all occurred during or prior to the year 1934. Since 1934 progress in rotary drilling has been largely a matter of improvement of machinery, tools, accessories, and operating practices.

The scarcity of literature in the early years is accounted for by the fact that few engineers or others who were interested in technical writing concerned themselves with the mechanical processes of drilling oil wells. There are a few outstanding exceptions among oil-field and industry engineers, equipment engineers, and writers; and our authentic sources of information are the writings of these few men, the memory of others, a very few books, the patent files, and a few periodicals and catalogs.

The discussion of the first time interval, from pre-historic times to the first record of a rotary-drilling outfit that is known to have circulated fluid for the purpose of removing the cuttings from the bore, will be largely conjectural. Few records of any kind have been found of rotary-drilling machines or tools of any type for boring holes in the earth prior to 1844, although such equipment probably existed and was used. From about 1865 when the rotary diamond-drilling machine was first used, to the drilling of the Lucas Spindletop well in 1900, the second time interval was a period of ideas, invention, and development. The number of modern items of equipment, and of parts of the rotary rig, that were anticipated in descriptions and patents during this interval is truly amazing. Many tools in use today and important parts of the rotary-drilling rig were either described or actually built and used during the second half of the 19th century. The year 1900 or the drilling of the Lucas Spindletop well is selected as the end of this period because, with the completion of that vastly important oil well on January 10, 1901, rotary-drilling equipment and practices were definitely established as practical means and methods for drilling oil and gas wells in the formations of the Gulf Coast areas. Several hundred shallow oil wells had been drilled with rotary tools prior to that time and doubtless a much greater number of water wells. To the operators and drillers of the late 1800's must go the credit for having developed the equipment with which such a well as the Lucas gusher was to be drilled and cased.

During the years from 1900-1915 (time interval 3), the struggle to introduce rotary-drilling equipment into the oil industry was intensive but did not always meet with success, except in areas of soft formations such as the Gulf Coast. During the latter years of this period fewer than 10 percent of the oil wells completed in the United States were drilled with rotary tools; and even on many of those wells, the rotary was only used to set the casing above the oil sand, after which the well was completed with cable tools. There was little change in the machinery during this 15-year interval, although quite naturally much basic experience was gained, and drilling and completion practices were greatly improved. This was the foundation period for future advances in procedures and machinery, and especially for the development of several highly important modern tools, some of which had been invented prior to 1900.

The 4th time interval runs approximately from 1915 to 1928. During these 12 to 14 years rotary-drilling equipment was established very definitely as an important method of drilling oil wells and as the only method that could be used satisfactorily in areas where the formations were soft. It was a period of considerable improvement in drilling equipment and drilling practices. The old equipment of the pre-1915 era was either abandoned or improved. New and somewhat heavier and better machinery was manufactured for practically all purposes; and there was considerable development of auxiliary equipment and tools, with at least a beginning on studies of the various technical aspects of drilling practices. Probably the most important advances of the period were the development of mud pumps of larger capacity and the beginning of vast improvement in bits.

The 5th time interval, from 1928 to 1934, was marked by the discovery and development of great oil fields especially in central Oklahoma, in Texas, and in California. In the Oklahoma oil fields, including the relatively deep Seminole area and the Oklahoma City Pool, the drilling was highly competitive and there were insistent demands for equipment that could drill holes and complete wells in minimum lengths of time. This resulted in the development of heavy and powerful drilling equipment comparable, or in fact equal in these regards, to all but the very heaviest rigs of the present day. The urge for more speed and faster well completions brought on the difficulties of crooked holes and drill-pipe failures, and accentuated other problems such as inadequate drilling fluid, low bit footage, the length of time required to rig up, lack of drilling-control instruments, etc., the solution of which required engineering studies and brought the petroleum engineers into all phases of the drilling operations and finally into the selection of the practices to be used in the drilling of oil wells. Heavy equipment and fast drilling were developed during the early part of the period; the latter part was devoted to the perfection of the equipment and to establishing sound drilling practices.

The 6th interval of time includes the year 1934 and goes through the year 1940, or to the beginning of World War II. During the first 4 years of this period, 1934-1937, the rate of penetration with rotary drills increased more rapidly than during any similar period before or since. Engineering studies of drilling procedures, and of the results obtained with the heavy equipment that had been put into service during the preceding few years, were put to use and basic new principles were developed. During this 4-year period, rate of penetration about reached the optimum for the drilling equipment, tools, and practices of the day with the then-experience of the engineers and the rig personnel. During the last 2 years of this interval, the rate of increase in the efficiency of the rotary-drilling operation seems to have been somewhat reduced. The use of steam, which had until then been almost the only source of power, began to decline and the internal-combustion engine began to develop as the most important prime mover.

The war years are included within the last time interval, 1940-1960. During these years the engineers, manufacturing plants, and the metals that had played an all-important part in the increase of the efficiency of rotary-drilling operations were largely diverted to the manufacture of implements of war. The personnel employed in the oil fields moved in large numbers either into the military service or into war industries. In consequence there was, at first, an actual decline in average drilling efficiency and in rate of penetration; although by the end of the period, prewar standards had been regained, and the final and modern era of rotary-drilling operations began in 1946. With the end of the war, instead of a decrease in the demand for petroleum products, there was a great increase throughout the world. Many new oil wells and oil fields were required to meet this rapidly growing consumption. Practically all of the equipment then in use was of prewar manufacture and either obsolete or worn out, and there was a great demand on the manufacturers for new and better tools. Fortunately, the pent-up ideas and plans of the equipment engineers and drilling engineers were adequate to cope with the situation. Many new designs were introduced, and the vast improvements incorporated in modern drilling rigs were begun and have continued to develop to the present day. With the ever-increasing need for deeper and cheaper drilling these and even greater advances will, without question, continue into the future. As great improvement has been shown in drilling practices and methods as in the equipment itself. Portable rigs received special attention, and by 1950 the steam rig had largely been replaced by "power" rigs.

The history of the rotary-drilling industry, machinery, equipment, tools, and drilling practices could be written in almost any length and detail that might be desired. There are practical limits, however, within which the story for its present purposes must be confined. The writer and editor must select those items which appear to be historically the most important and of the greatest interest to the reader. It may be expected that the future will continue to bring vastly improved machinery, tools, and drilling practices into use, many of which will bear little relation and similarity to those in use today. The story of the old and the obsolete should be set down as a matter of historical record, and will be done in another publication in much greater detail than is permissible in this *History*.

TIME PERIODS IN ROTARY DRILLING

Pre-1844 A.D.

The method of boring or drilling holes by rotating a tool of some description in the object in which a hole is desired, long antedates any historical records of which we have knowledge. Just as certainly, the first method of all for digging a hole in the ground was by the use of paws—then hands—and later with sticks or other suitable digging objects or tools. A brief discussion of probable and actual methods such as these is given in the early part of the preceding chapter on percussion drilling.

Prehistoric

It appears to be probable, based on the complication of the process, that the boring or drilling of holes with a rotary motion came sometime later than simple digging and was first used only to perforate bone or shells or to drill holes in wood. This would have seemed to primitive man to be a difficult operation compared to digging or scratching out a hole in a creek bed in search of water, or in the earth in search of roots or other food; and it must have been developed under a considerably higher culture. Making fire by rotating a stick on a piece of wood using the palms or with a bow is a prehistoric art that is still practiced by some primitive people whose mechanical ability has advanced little beyond this point.

Ancient Egyptian Stone Boring

The first known record of the practical use of holes bored in the earth by the rotary method are the holes and half holes in rock resulting from drilling in stone quarries as early as the construction of the pyramids some 3,000 years B.C. Egyptian workmen and artisans likewise bored holes in the making of utensils and ornamental objects. Specimens of these cores may be seen in several museums that house relics of ancient Egyptian culture.

There probably were at least two methods then used for drilling rotary holes in rock. Most likely the first was by rotating a solid rod in the stone to be worked and thus wearing a hole to the desired depth. As experience in the art progressed quartz sand or some variety of a still harder mineral, together with water, were probably used in the bore between the tools and the stone as an abrasive medium. The drillers of that day apparently realized that they were cutting a greater area of stone than was necessary, and thereupon an inventive mind devised an improved tool consisting of a tube of some satisfactory material that was rotated at the desired point in the stone, with granulated mineral as an abrasive. With the development of a kerf or groove in which the tube could work and be held in position, the matter of drilling to the required depth was a question of time and labor; and there seems to have been, in those days, an adequate supply of both of these commodities. Relics of the resulting cores have been found in ancient Egyptian works.

According to Dr. Alexander Bawawy, holes were drilled in quartzite, diorite, porphyry, quartz or rock crystal, and obsidian in diameters from 0.007 in. to 28 in. Bore holes as deep as 20 ft have been found. The use of tubular or core drills in the boring process, with some hard material such as corundum or diamond as the cutting medium, is indicated by helical grooves both on cores recovered and on the walls of core holes. The bores were used in quarry work, in cutting lines for hieroglyphs, making vases, hollowing out granite sarcophagi, and in the building or sculpture of statues. A tool for excavating the inside of vases consisted of sharp-edged flint that would go through the neck of the object to be excavated, attached to a forked stick as the rotating handle. Augers and bow drills were used for boring soft wood and stone.

The Egyptian collection of the Metropolitan Museum of Art in New York contains two drill cores, one of basalt and the other of obsidian, which date from the XXth to the XXIInd Dynasties, and there are many cores in the Egyptian Room of the British Museum in London.

The drilling of a 20-ft core hole through hard rock possibly as early as 3000 B.C. was an amazing accomplishment and indicates the intelligence and advanced skill of the early Egyptians.

Leonardo

The earliest known drawing of a plan for a rotating machine for boring holes in the earth is a machine invented, described, and sketched by the great artist, architect, and engineer, Leonardo da Vinci (1452-1519). Fig. 1 shows his sketch and description of a small machine and auger. Fig. 2 shows a sketch of a larger machine and includes a 4-legged derrick which supports the drill screws and rods and which serves as a guide to the drill stem. They seem to be sketches with no scale given and the sizes must be assumed. The smaller machine was probably designed to be operated by men standing on the ground. The machine in Fig. 2, which appears to have ladder rungs between the legs of the derrick, must have been considerably larger.

Photostatic copies of these sketches and descriptions* were submitted to members of the faculty of the University of Pennsylvania,† who very kindly deciphered the backward penmanship and translated the rather old Italian. The descriptions of the machines are incomplete but, with the help of the sketches, the manner of operation can be determined. In the smaller sketch, Fig. 1, there are two horizontal arms for rotating the working parts of the device. The lower and longer arm is attached to a cylinder that can be rotated in a proper bearing but which moves neither up nor down. There is doubtless a short and heavy helical thread on the inside.

The shorter and upper handlebar is attached to the drill stem itself with the auger bit on bottom. This auger stem apparently has an outside helical screw or thread which meshes with the inside helical thread of the short cylinder attached to the longer arm.

When boring, the longer handlebar was fixed so that it could not rotate. The upper arms were then rotated manually, thus threading the screw on the auger stem through the screw in the cylinder attached to the longer arms or bar resulting in the auger being rotated or "screwed" into the ground. When the full stroke of the screw thread had been reached the upper handlebar was fixed in place and the lower bar rotated in the same direction. The bit or auger thus was lifted from the bore without being rotated, bringing the cuttings with it. The direction of rotation was from right to left, or counter-clockwise, as was Leonardo's writing.

To say the least, this is a very ingenious device, and had it been invented or sketched by any other than Leonardo, the conclusion might be reached that it was similar to tools in common use—and of course it may

---

*Submitted by the Italian Ing. Mario Messeranti.
†Through Dr. Karl G. Miller of the University of Pennsylvania.

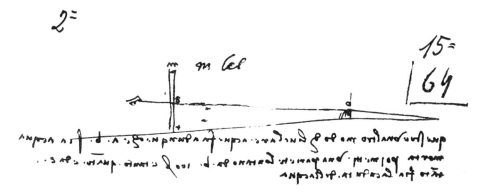

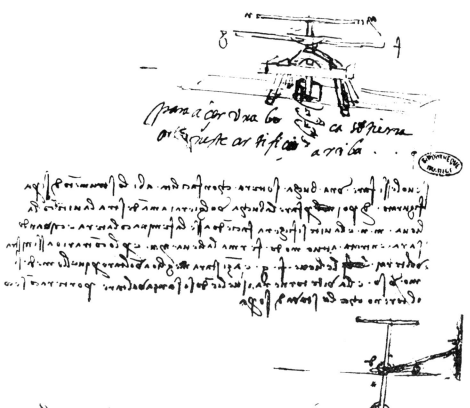

Fig. 1—Leonardo's Small Earth-boring Machine—Circa 1500

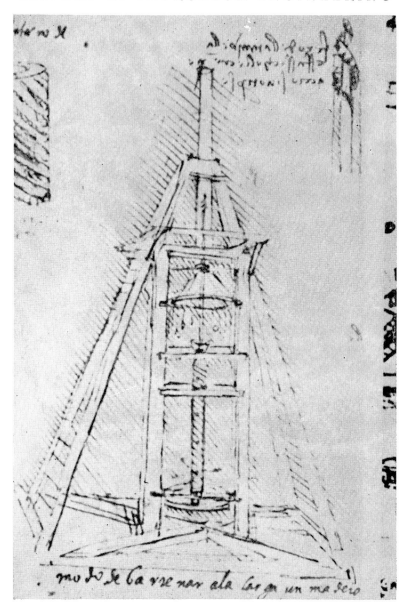

Fig. 2—Leonardo's Large Earth-boring Machine—Circa 1500

have been. Although this device has no particular bearing on modern rotary-drilling methods, it is very definitely related to the mechanical means used at the present time for boring holes for posts, poles, or other purposes, and to methods of feeding certain core drills. It is additionally interesting as being the first machine, for boring holes into the earth with a rotating tool, of which we have a description and sketch.

The second record of actual core drilling comes nearly 5,000 years after the earliest Egyptian borings, when the French engineer, Leschot, in 1863 drilled core holes in rock with a bit set with a hard mineral (diamonds) in a manner quite similar in principle to that of the Egyptians. Leschot circulated water to remove the cuttings. It is not known that the Egyptians used this principle but it is quite possible, and even probable, that they had to do so in order to cut a 20-ft core. Leschot's work was done in connection with the construction of the St. Cenis Tunnel in Switzerland where explosives were used to shatter the rock, rather than by fracturing the stone along lines of bore holes as is done in quarrying. Much coring and rotary drilling was doubtless done between the building of the pyramids and the St. Cenis Tunnel but no records of it are known, other than in small ornamental objects.

Early 1800's

Records of wells drilled by the percussion system during the early part of the 19th century and even earlier are found in the literature of both Europe and America; and it is recorded that rods and hollow tubes were used on some of the drilling machines, with water circulating through the tubes. This period is discussed in Chapter 5.

Prud'homme Wells, Drilled 1823

Mrs. J. Alphonse Prud'homme of Oakland Plantation, Bermuda, La.— near Nachitoches—relates a story* of the building of drilling tools and the boring of three wells on the plantation in search of potable water, in 1823. Gas was encountered in each of the wells, which were drilled to depths of about 400 ft. The gas was called "damp" (fire damp?) and would burn. Having no knowledge of the use of gas as a fuel at this early date, the wells were abandoned. This was many years prior to the discovery of either commercial oil or gas in the Southwest.

The land of which Oakland Plantation is composed was a grant from the Spanish Crown to Jean Pierre Emanuel Prud'homme in 1787. The present home was built by him in 1821 and has been occupied continuously by members of the family since that time. The present owner, Alphonse Prud'homme, is of the fifth generation. The information on which the story is based has been handed down directly through the family. In view of the importance of this material, including possible relation to relatively deep wells drilled in France circa 1800, Mrs. Prud'homme's story will be told at length. A few explanations and surmises are added.

During the early years of the 19th century, the principal source of potable water was, in many areas, from hand-dug wells—even as in recent years and at the present time. In 1823, Oakland Plantation was in need of additional good water. In consequence, Prud'homme made plans to dig a well in the customary manner. At that time a French engineer was a

*By letter to J. E. Brantly.

visitor at Oakland. The engineer suggested that the well be bored rather than dug by pick and shovel and offered to design the tools and rig. His design was for tools to be rotated through means of a solid iron drill stem or rods. No water or mud was to be circulated.

When the drawings were completed, they were turned over to the negro slave blacksmith who built the tools (Fig. 3), apparently under the guidance of the engineer. When the job was completed, the latter departed taking the drawing with him but leaving others for fishing tools. The tools show remarkable ingenuity in both design and workmanship. The old blacksmith was quite evidently an artist as well as a capable artisan.

When the tools were finished, at least three wells were drilled. They were then discarded beside the blacksmith shop, where they became covered with soil in the course of time. In 1924 they were recovered from their burial ground, cleaned, and placed on display in the museum at Oakland, where they now may be seen. Unfortunately, the writer has not had this privilege but has received an excellent summary story of them and the photographs of Fig. 3.*

The derrick consisted of a heavy timber tripod from which were suspended blocks and tackle to handle the drill rods. A heavy log was placed under the derrick, presumably attached to two of the tripod legs and with the necessary supports and bearings to serve as the hoist drum. In each end of the log drum, two holes were bored at right angles to each other to carry heavy iron bars that served as handles for the men who powered the hoist. The fast line or fall line from the blocks was spooled on the log drum or windlass.

The drill rods were solid iron bars 15 ft long and $1\frac{1}{2}$ in. in square cross section. By calculation, they must have weighed approximately 7.66 lb per ft or 115 lb for each 15-ft rod. They were connected by means of a "clevis" or two straps fastened or built on the bottom of the upper rod and into or between which the reduced upper end of the lower rod or of a down-hole tool was inserted (see photographs of tools). The rods were then made up into the "drill stem" by means of three matching holes in the three pieces through which bolts or pins were passed and secured. From the wide angle "V's" in the upper ends of the hole tools, it is probable that there were corresponding V-shaped lower ends within the clevis or straps on the lower ends of the rods. The rod joints so formed would have given a stronger and more rigid connection.

There is no suggestion as to how the rods were rotated, but probably by long handles attached to a "wrench" that slipped over the rods and could be moved as hole was made to keep the handles at a satisfactory working height above the ground. The line on the log drum could be played off as required. There is no mention of a brake. A timber brake with

---

*In March 1960, the writer visited Oakland Plantation, saw the tools, and discussed them and the wells with Mr. and Mrs. Prud'homme. There is no reason to change the story herein.

Fig. 3—Drilling and Fishing Tools Used to Drill Water Wells on Prud'homme Plantation, Louisiana—1823

or without a leather shoe could have been used. It is stated that 15 men were required to operate the rig or handle the drill stem, including rotating, hoisting, and making up. There is no mention of the manner of holding the string of rods when running in or pulling out of the hole. At a drilling depth of 400 ft the entire string must have weighed about 3,150 lb, considerable weight to handle by manpower.

Fig. 3 (left) shows 9 or 10 square drill-stem sections or rods and 22 down-hole tools of various types, including what appear to be—from right to left—a concave drilling bit, a reamer, a tool to square up the hold (on the drill rods), a helical or auger bit* with a guide, another concave drilling bit, an auger bit, another auger bit (on the rods) with flatter turns (both of these augers could have been friction-rod fishing tools), an underreamer, possibly a bailer or the upper section thereof, or a coring tool which is listed, another concave drilling bit, a steep spiral auger bit, a concave drilling bit, a larger steep spiral drilling bit, and other similar tools. Two bailers are reported, one with a ball valve and the other with a flapper valve.

The tools displayed are doubtless for drilling, reaming, and fishing. The square tool is for reaming the hole in which square casing made of cypress boards was run. It is 9 in. square. It seems likely that hole was made with under-gage auger bits and the rather long concave bits and then reamed with the two tools (left and center) shown in Fig. 3 (right-hand photo). In other words, a rat-hole was drilled and then reamed out—first round and then square—to take the casing.

While the drilling of a well 400 ft deep must have required considerable time and labor, there seems little doubt but that the tools listed in the account of the equipment and operation and shown in the photographs

---

*See Fig. 81, Chapter 5, for auger bits 1880 (France).

could have done the job. Although the tools were rotated to make hole, except for the square reamer, actually they must have operated otherwise more as do cable tools. It seems probable that water was dumped in, if the formation did not supply it, and the cuttings were removed by bailing. There is no mention of a bailing or sand line, so it is assumed that the bailers were run on the rods—a slow, laborious job. Possibly the bailer was run on a fiber rope sand line.

It is stated that the tools were designed by a French engineer. It is not likely that he invented and designed these tools and their method of operation while on Oakland plantation. It seems much more probable that he had seen such equipment operating in France before coming to America, or even that he had had such tools built and operated. Many wells were drilled in France in the late 1700's and early 1800's. (See chapter on percussion drilling, p. 154-157.) No records have been seen of the tools used, but they could have been of the Prud'homme type. No record of such tools having been used elsewhere in America has been found.

Although these tools were undoubtedly inferior to the percussion tools of the day in the areas in which the latter were used, in design and workmanship they are superior to any drilling tools of the day of which records have been seen. It seems quite possible that they could have been reasonably good hole makers in wet hole in the soft formations of the Gulf Coast. The rotating rods may have helped plaster and hold the walls of the hole in areas where cable tools could only be operated with considerable difficulty. The tools bear some resemblance to the Leonardo da Vinci earth-boring tools.

1844 - 1900

Beart Patent

The first reference found to a drilling machine using a rotating tool, hollow drill rods, and circulating fluid to remove the cuttings, is in English Patent No. 10,258 issued to Robert Beart of Godmanchester, England, on July 12, 1844. The first page of the patent is reproduced on p. 285. The patent discloses a method of boring the holes into the earth or into stone by means of rotating hollow drill rods through which fluid is passed to remove cuttings, or as expressed by Beart in his final claim of invention: "What I claim is so arranging apparatus for boring in the earth and in stone that the earth or matters cut or moved by the tools employed may be carried away by currents of water as herein described."

In his patent Beart describes two machines or methods of drilling or boring holes in the earth or stone. In the first, Fig. 4, he digs a shallow cellar in the earth and then builds an above-ground curb around it so that the top is appreciably higher than the level of the ground. The bore is started in the center of the tank. A second cellar is due at a point that will place it appreciably lower than the first tank. The bit is placed on the end of the hollow kelly joint with a stuffing-box swivel at the top.

A.D. 1844 . . . . Nº 10,258.

Apparatus for Boring in the Earth and in Stone.

BEART'S SPECIFICATION.

TO ALL TO WHOM THESE PRESENTS SHALL COME, I, ROBERT BEART, of Godmanchester, in the County of Huntingdon, Gentleman, send greeting.

WHEREAS Her present most Excellent Majesty Queen Victoria, by Her
5 Letters Patent under the Great Seal of Great Britain, bearing date at Westminster, the Twelfth day of July, in the eighth year of Her reign, did, for Herself, Her heirs and successors, give and grant unto me, the said Robert Beart, Her especial license, full power, sole privilege and authority, that I, the said Robert Beart, my exŏrs, admŏrs, and assigns, or such others as I, the
10 said Robert Beart, my exŏrs, admŏrs, or assigns, should at any time agree with, and no others, from time to time and at all times during the term of years therein expressed, should and lawfully might make, use, exercise, and vend, within England, Wales, and the Town of Berwick-upon-Tweed, my Invention of "IMPROVEMENTS IN APPARATUS FOR BORING IN THE EARTH AND IN
15 STONE;" in which said Letters Patent is contained a proviso, that I, the said Robert Beart, shall cause a particular description of the nature of my said Invention, and in what manner the same is to be performed, to be inrolled in Her said Majesty's High Court of Chancery within six calendar months next and immediately after the date of the said in part recited Letters Patent, as in
20 and by the same, reference being thereunto had, will more fully and at large appear.

Beart Patent—1844—First Page

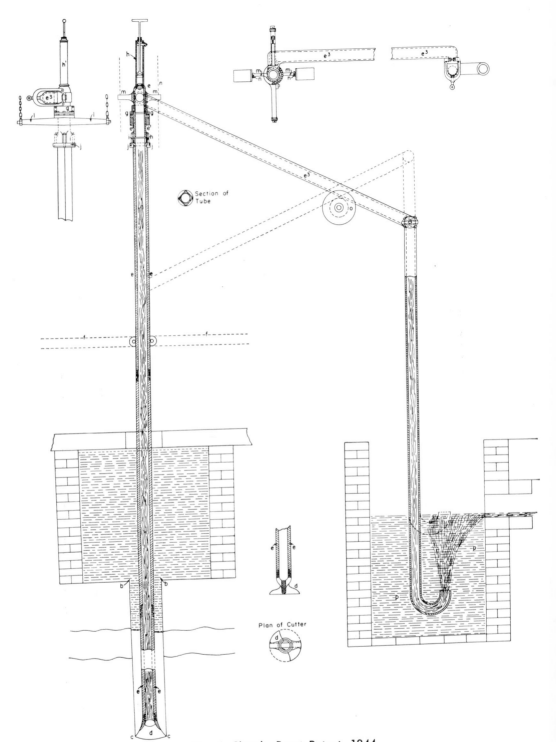

Fig. 4—Sketch—Beart Patent, 1844

286

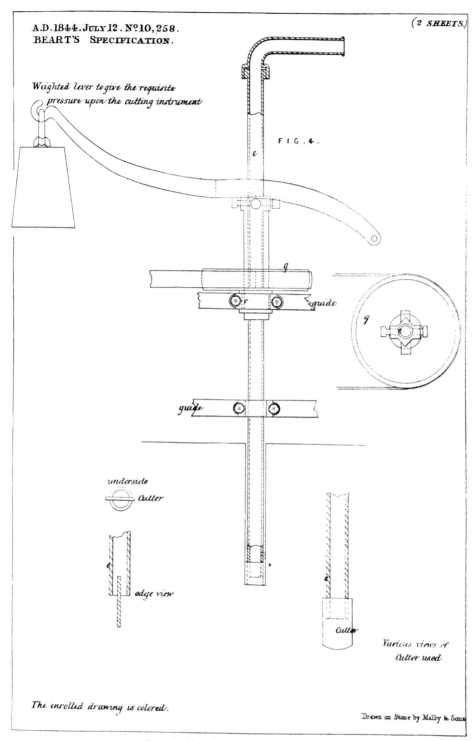

Weighted lever to give the requisite
pressure upon the cutting instrument

FIG. 4.

e

g

r

guide

q

guide

underside
Cutter

edge view

Cutter

Various views of
Cutter used

The enrolled drawing is colored.

Drawn on Stone by Malby & Sons

Fig. 5—Sketch—Beart Patent, 1844

An iron pipe with two flexible joints leads from the stuffing-box swivel to the lower tank. The upper or higher tank in which the hole is started is kept full of water. The pipe is primed and drilling begun by rotating the square hollow kelly with a long bar or by power. The fluid goes down outside the drill pipe and up through the drill pipe and, by the difference in height between the water in the two tanks or cellars and the syphon effect, circulation is established.

In the second method described the drill rods and bit are rotated by a belt-driven rotating device through which a splined quill passes. The square kelly is fixed to the upper end of the quill by a 4-set-screw chuck. The length of the quill is drilled and a new "hitch" is taken. In this machine the circulating fluid passes down the hollow drill rods and up the bore thus reversing the direction of flow from that of his first method. A stuffing-box swivel is used. Fig. 4 and 5 show the drawings in the Beart patent.

Insofar as the records go this very definitely establishes Beart as the inventor of the basic principles of the modern hydraulic rotary-drilling system for earth boring. His description includes a hydraulic swivel, a hollow square kelly, a belt-driven rotary machine, a splined quill and chuck as used in diamond drilling machines, hollow drill rods, a fishtail or drag-type bit, and circulation of fluid to remove the cuttings. A forerunner of the steel hose with flexible joints is also described. Beart makes several references to the percussion-drilling method and claims his device is an "improvement in apparatus for boring in the earth and in stone."

Fauvelle

The credit for inventing, developing, and using the first fluid-circulating rotary-drilling machine is accorded by many to a French engineer, M. Fauvelle, in 1845. Other references state that Fauvelle was assisted in building his machine by Beart. The principal features of the Beart patent issued in 1844 are given in preceding paragraphs.

In December 1846, the *Journal* of the Franklin Institute of Philadelphia published an article that is, in major part, an abridged translation (in English) of M. Fauvelle's own detailed account of the drilling of an artesian water well with a drilling machine invented and developed by himself. There is no mention of Beart in the article.

On the other hand Fauvelle makes the direct statement that, after starting the circulating pump and getting returns, "the boring tube is then worked like an ordinary boring rod" which probably meant a vertical reciprocating percussion motion with slight rotative movement between strokes solely to prevent the bit hitting in the same groove. This is still common practice with similar tools.

It is the opinion of the writer that the Fauvelle system was the forerunner of the Fauck hydraulic percussion-drilling system and not of the hydraulic rotary-drilling system. Had the Fauvelle system actually used the hydraulic rotary principle of drilling it would without doubt have continued as a useful well-drilling method, in view of the fine success attributed to it. The hydraulic-percussion system of drilling was continued and developed into the Fauck Rapid System, though it is not certain that it was derived directly from Fauvelle. No additional records of wells drilled with similar tools are found until the advent of the Fauck system, which is briefly discussed in the chapter on percussion drilling. It appears that the Beart inventions were incorporated in part in the Fauvelle system, and possibly into the Leschot and later diamond-drill machines.

Rotary-drilling methods are discussed by Professor August Beer of the Pribram School of Mines in Austria in a publication on drilling wells into the earth (Beer, August, Erbohrkunde Pribram, Austria, 1858). It seems probable there were hydraulic rotary-drilling tools of some description in use during the 1850's.

Leschot Diamond Drill

During the early part of the 1860's the first tunnel was being built through the Swiss Alps. One of the French engineers on the job was R. Leschot, who had had experience in the use of diamonds in cutting and polishing tools and had prob-

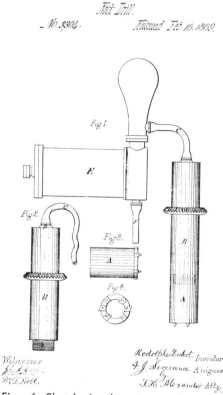

ably seen, heard, or read descriptions of Beart's or Fauvelle's rig or of some other actual or proposed rotary-drilling machine. He might have had descriptions of, or have seen, a Beart machine or he might have combined the Fauvelle hydraulic-drilling system with a rotating machine tool of the day. On the other hand his device may have been entirely original, but this seems doubtful.

Explosives were used in breaking down the rock in the tunnel bore and the first holes were probably drilled with hand steel and a heavy hammer, just as is done today when no other power is available. M. Leschot conceived the idea of a rotated tubular tool set with diamonds and with circulating fluid passing through it, as a means of faster and more economical drilling of the shot holes. On July 14, 1863, he received U. S. Patent No. 39,235 covering a rotary rock drill

Fig. 6—Sketch—Leschot Patent (Reissue) 1869

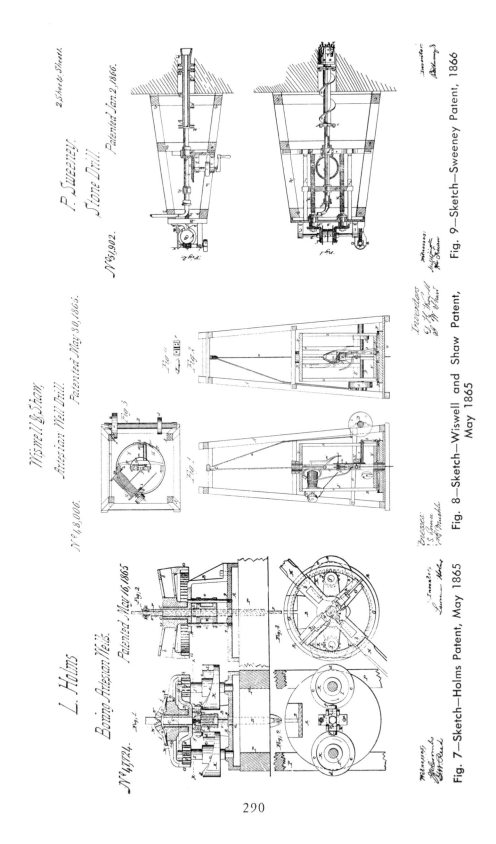

Fig. 9—Sketch—Sweeney Patent, 1866

Fig. 8—Sketch—Wiswell and Shaw Patent,
May 1865

Fig. 7—Sketch—Holms Patent, May 1865

set with diamonds or other satisfactory hard material and with the hydraulic-flushing method of removing cuttings, used while operating the tool. On February 16, 1869, Leschot received reissue Patent No. 3,304, Fig. 6, covering the basic features of his machine and of the drilling bit. The Leschot patents were assigned simultaneously to Asahel J. Severance of Middlebury, Vermont. It was on the descriptions and basic principles outlined in these patent papers that the modern diamond drill was based and developed.

Early Rotary Earth-boring Tools

Several patents were issued during the 1860's on drilling tools involving both the rotary principles of drilling and the circulation of fluid. The first of these to approximate modern machines was Patent No. 47,724 issued to L. Holms on May 16, 1865, covering a machine for imparting a rotary motion to drill rods with a cutting tool on bottom and a percussion motion by the use of cams properly positioned beneath the rotary machine. Holms states in his description that his machine either "drills or augers according to the varying character of the strata to be penetrated." There is no mention of a circulating fluid as a part of his invention though it would have been a simple matter, by using a hollow drill shaft, to have injected fluid into the tube and through the bit. The patent sketch is reproduced as Fig. 7. This device disclosed the quill and chuck later used in diamond core drill machines. This patent issued to Holms in 1865 does not claim invention of the rotary machine itself. This is good evidence that Holms knew that such devices were old, and were probably in use at the time. The Beart patent, previously mentioned, antedates Holms by 20 years.

On May 30, 1865, Wiswell and Shaw of Buffalo received Patent No. 48,006 covering an "improvement in Drills for Boring Wells &c." This patent, as did the Holms' patent, disclosed a machine that could impart either a rotary or percussion motion to the drill rods and bit (Fig. 8). The Holms and Wiswell and Shaw patents provide both rotary and vertical motion—apparently trying to improve on the cable-tool drilling rigs of the day. They were possibly influenced by Beart and Fauvelle although there is no mention of circulating fluid in either patent. On the other hand Sweeney, a year later, does provide circulation.

This patent granted to P. Sweeney on January 2, 1866, covered a stone drill with a bit using rolling cutters as the cutting elements, which was the forerunner of the modern rock bits (Fig. 9). In addition to the rolling-cutter-type bit, the Sweeney device used a hollow drill shaft and circulating fluid to remove the cuttings. The downward feed of the bit into the formation was regulated by a double screw somewhat similar to the screw feed of diamond-drilling machines of later years and remotely similar to a double-temper screw. The rotating device was a simple bevelled gear with a handle. Still another interesting feature of the Sweeney diagrammatic sketch is the 4-legged derrick and platform. Thus the Sweeney patent discloses a screw feed, a hydraulic swivel for fluid circulation, a rotary machine, a rolling cutter bit, and a 4-legged derrick. In addition, there is the ingenious helical screw above the bit to act as a pump and aid in the movement of drilling fluid and cuttings from the bottom of the bore to the surface. The pump pressure was doubtless very low.

In his patent application Sweeney claimed only an improved rock-boring machine. This is evidence that there were in existence, and known to Sweeney prior to the patent on his rather well-developed device, other fluid-circulating rotary-drilling machines. As far as known the Leschot diamond-drilling machines were not introduced into America until 1869-1870. An account of the Fauvelle machine was published by the Franklin Institute of Philadelphia in 1846, and the current literature may have described other rotary-drilling mechanisms. Later in 1866, patents were granted to David Morris for a rotary machine with a winged drag bit. Another was issued to John B. Root for a rotary-boring machine. A few years later, in 1869, a patent was issued to T. F. Rowland covering a drilling machine for use in shallow-water areas offshore. This device was a 4-legged tower resting on bottom with a platform for the drilling machine (Fig. 10). This patent anticipated offshore drilling platforms of today.

Development of Diamond Drills

Following a modest development of the diamond core drill machine in Switzerland and France by the French engineer Leschot, in the 1860's, a diamond drill was sent to and first used in the United States in the Vermont Dimension Stone Quarries about 1869. These operations were observed by M. C. Bullock, organizer of the Bullock Company, the forerunner of the Sullivan Machinery Company of Sullivan County, Vermont, (now Joy Manufacturing Co.). This led to the purchase of the Leschot patents and the building of diamond-drilling machines in the United States. Bullock introduced the new fluid-circulating diamond core drills into the coal fields of Pennsylvania near Pottsville in 1870. It is also related that in the preceding year the machine drilled a 130-ft hole in Michigan, probably for copper.

Core-drilling machines were developed soon thereafter for both surface and underground operations, using the single-cylinder hydraulic feed patented by A. Ball, 1884 (Fig. 11), assignor to Sullivan Machinery Company. The double hydraulic feed was patented by Atkinson in 1881 (Fig. 12) and by Bullock in 1883. The double hydraulic machine was the forerunner of the Longyear machines and of the hydraulic tables built by the Hydril Company and the Sheldon Machinery Company, circa 1930. Many small single and double hydraulic truck-mounted machines for structure drilling were built during 1920 and later. The single and double hydraulic machines were likewise commonly used in the mining industry for diamond drilling.

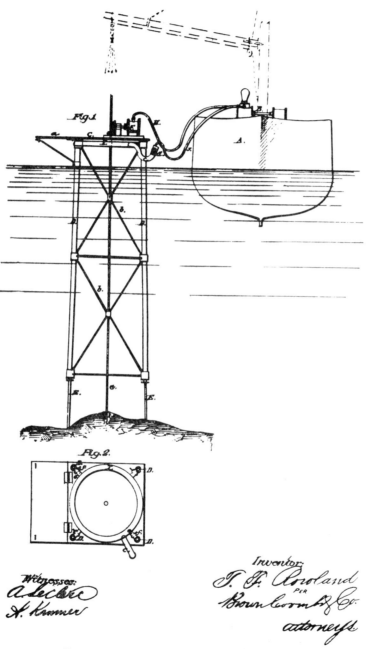

T. F. Rowland.

Rock Drill.

Nº 89,794.

Patented May 4, 1869.

Fig. 10—Rowland Patent, Offshore Drilling, 1869

A. BALL.

APPARATUS FOR SHIFTING DRILLING MACHINES.

No. 295,325.   Patented Mar. 18, 1884.

Fig. 11 (left)—Ball Single Hydraulic Diamond Drill (Sullivan Machinery Co.)

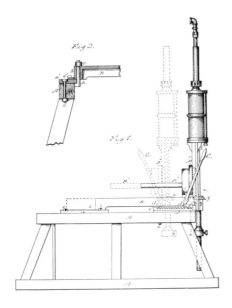

3 Sheets—Sheet 1.

J. ATKINSON.

WELL BORING AND ROCK DRILLING MACHINE.

No. 246,446.   Patented Aug. 30, 1881.

FIG. 1.

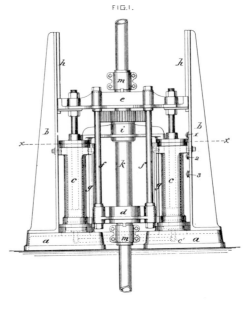

WITNESSES =   INVENTOR =

Fig. 12 (above)—Atkinson Double Hydraulic Diamond Drill

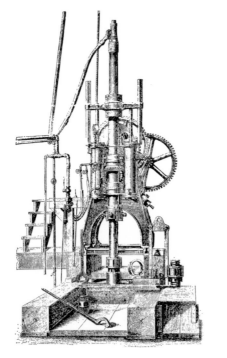

Fig. 13 (left)—Diamond Core Drill Shown at Centennial Exposition, 1876

The diamond core drill shown in the Centennial Exposition of 1876 (Fig. 13) was a double hydraulic diamond-drill machine built about 1875, probably after the Bullock double hydraulic patents. It seems unlikely that the hydraulic rotary system involving the use of diamond core drills could have been developed to the point of perfection indicated by this machine, within the 10 or 11 years succeeding Leschot's patent. This suggests that Leschot's basic principles may have been derived from systems invented and developed previously. This use of diamonds could have been original with Leschot, at least in the manner of application, although hard abrasives had evidently been used in Egypt as early as 3000 B.C.

Following the completion of the highly publicized Drake oil well in August 1859, numerous ideas were presented for the construction of rotary-drilling machines. The Sweeney and Holms patents, already mentioned, were two of them. They were succeeded by many others. During the late 1870's and early 1880's a number of patents were issued to individuals in the states of Iowa and South Dakota covering drilling machines. In the 20 years between 1860 and 1880 other patents were issued including No. 53,686 to Saffer of New York in 1868, No. 94,923 in 1869 to J. F. Summers, and No. 202,677 in 1878, also to Summers. The Summers patents anticipated much of the rotary-drilling machinery of the early part of the century. He also showed a square kelly, but it was solid, instead of being hollow to permit circulation through it. The Summers ideas were later incorporated into rotary quarry-drilling machinery. (M. A. Archer, long-time patent research and equipment engineer for The National Supply Co. in a letter to Prof. J. H. Pound, of Rice Institute, April 4, 1939.) The patents of these years made no claims as to gear-driven rotary machines, for they were old and well-known devices, but there were many claims of improvements and different applications.

Other patents that disclose forerunners of the gear-driven rotary machine were issued to W. H. Beach and C. H. Hausen in 1873, showing a square kelly, H. & J. Kelly in 1876, C. B. Hewett in 1877, and Haas and J. Manning in 1878. All of these disclose bevelled ring gear and pinion machines driving square or round drill rods. None include any mention of circulating fluid.

There are various references of the early 1880's to a hydraulic rotary-drilling machine using pipe for the drilling shaft carrying the bit, as developed by the brothers M. C. and C. E. Baker of South Dakota. The upper end of the drill pipe was kept some distance above the level of the ground and water was poured in to bring the cuttings up in the annulus between the pipe and the ground.* It is doubtful that many cuttings were actually brought to the surface, although thin mud or clay particles in water doubtless were; but the water probably facilitated the drilling progress. It was related that the success of the method was such that the water from a wind-

---

*See "Beart Patent," p. 284.

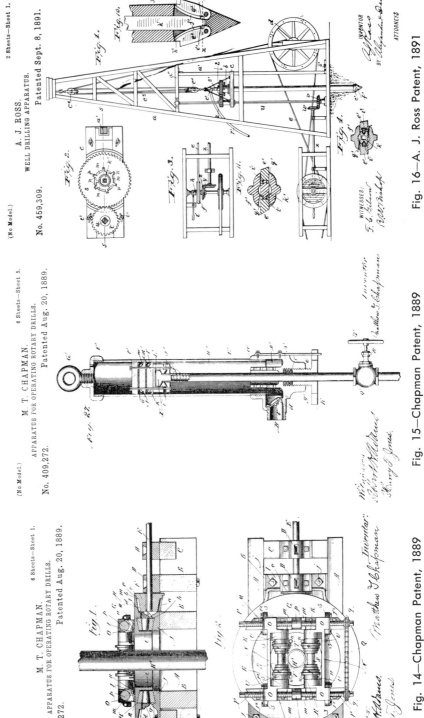

Fig. 16—A. J. Ross Patent, 1891

Fig. 15—Chapman Patent, 1889
Hydraulic Swivel

Fig. 14—Chapman Patent, 1889
Rotary and Grip Rings

mill was diverted into the drill pipe and a well or hole in the earth success-fully drilled in this manner. The Baker brothers reportedly drilled several wells throughout that section of the country with their new fluid-circu-lating rotary method. Several other patents of the 1880's were issued to citizens of South Dakota and Iowa, on comparable machines.

Developments 1889 to 1900

In 1889 Patent No. 409,272 was issued to M. T. Chapman to cover a rotary-drilling machine incorporating all the basic principles of the present-day rigs including mud-laden circulating fluid. Chapman, who may or may not have been familiar with the Baker brothers' equipment and operations, described the process in remarkable detail and applied for patent papers, receiving them on August 20, 1889. Fig. 14 and 15, the sketches accompanying the first application submitted by Chapman, show a rather modern-appearing rotary table with grip rings and a hydraulic swivel combined with a pressure and feed cylinder possibly borrowed from the diamond drill. A number of patents relating to rotary-drilling equip-ment were granted to Chapman in later years.

On September 8, 1891, A. J. Ross of South Dakota received Patent No. 459,309 covering a well-drilling apparatus (Fig. 16). These papers and diagrams disclose a rather novel rotating machine and swivel com-bination mounted on a cross member that moves up and down on a square rod carrying a pinion which rotates the gear that rotates the drill pipe. A vertical rod on the opposite side of the rotary serves as a stabilizer and guide. An interesting part of the sketch is the bit with wings designed to open into drilling position by pump pressure. This device is a forerunner of a type of hole-enlarging tool, wall scraper, and underreamer.

On June 29, 1891, A. Cameron received Patent No. 460,500 covering a "well-sinking machine." In the sketch and description he discloses a rotary table with the ring gear and pinion on top of rather than under the table, as in the Chapman and preceding patents. For rotation he used two guide posts attached to the table down which a clamp attached to the drill pipe moved as the bit was fed into the formation. Fig. 17 is a reproduction of the sketch accompanying the Cameron patent papers.

In 1890 Chapman received another patent, No. 446,039, in which he had changed the drilling-fluid intake from the outside to the inside of the drill pipe, as shown in Fig. 18. The sketch accompanying this patent shows a swivel which is approximately the same as was used in the early years of rotary drilling. A core bit is also shown. Fig. 19 shows the Douglass patent core barrel of 1891.

These patents and the machines illustrated, together with a few others, incorporate the basic ideas and principles upon which the hydraulic rotary-drilling machinery, equipment, and tools of today are designed and built. In more or less rudimentary form they include all of the essential items of the modern rotary-drilling rig.

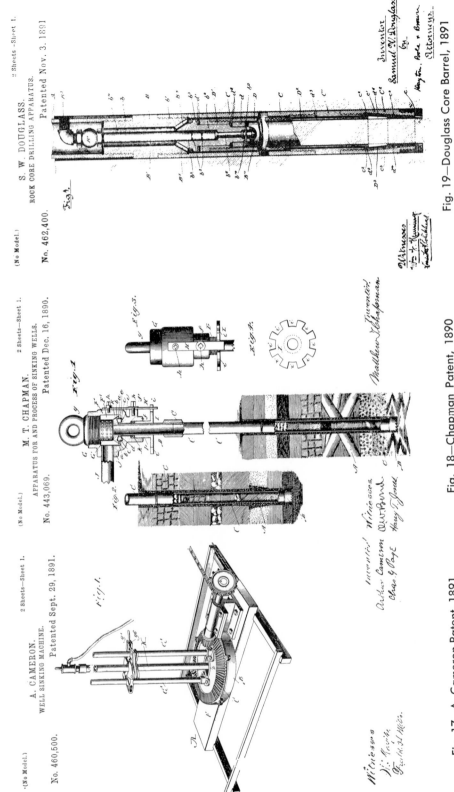

Fig. 19—Douglass Core Barrel, 1891

Fig. 18—Chapman Patent, 1890

Fig. 17—A. Cameron Patent, 1891

Fig. 20—One-horsepower Rotary and Hoist Brought to Corsicana by
Baker Brothers in 1895
(Bethlehem Supply Co. Photo)

There are several references to water-well drilling through South Dakota, Iowa, Kansas, Texas and Louisiana during the 1880's and 1890's on which rotary-drilling machines were used. Also a test well was drilled with rotary tools to 418 ft on Spindletop in 1893. On the salt dome, later to become famous, Patillo Higgins completed a small gas well during the same year.*

*Memorandum of Scouting Section of Humble Oil & Refining Co. dated December 20, 1955.

Fig. 21—C. E. Baker and Original Grip-ring Device
C. E. Baker, who, with his brother, M. C. Baker, designed what is believed to be the original rotary grip-ring device, is shown in the picture explaining the construction of his invention. This device, first used in the drilling of water wells in the early eighties, is still in existence at Corsicana, Texas. (Bethlehem Supply Co. Photo)

In 1895 the first oil well was completed near Corsicana, Texas, by John Galey and the Corsicana Oil Development Company. Immediately there was a rush of well-diggers with their equipment to the area. Among them were the Baker brothers from South Dakota with their 1-hp drilling machine and grip rings (Fig. 20 and 21). These photographs were made recently of the identical equipment brought into Corsicana by the Bakers. Worthy of notice is the driving device which consists of grip rings (Fig. 21) on a cross member between two upward-extending rods or pipes. This suggests a combination of the Cameron machine (Fig. 17) and the Chapman machine (Fig. 14).

When the Baker brothers arrived in Corsicana they found a machine shop operated by H. G. Johnston, E. H. Akin, and Charles Rittersbacker doing business with the well-diggers of the region. By that time the Corsicana oil field was under development. Soon after arrival, the Bakers conferred with the shop operators and together they designed and built the machine that became the Johnston rotary. The shop was the forerunner of the American Well and Prospecting Company, now a division of Bethlehem Steel Corp. Fig. 22 is a sketch of the original Johnston machine but it does not show grip rings. It closely follows the Cameron patent sketch with improvements incorporated in the clamp and gears.

A letter written by an old member of the American Well and Prospecting organization tells the story, as he recalls it being told to him, of the early days in Corsicana, particularly as it relates to the development of the Johnston rotary and the controversy with the American Well Company over the Chapman rotary. It appears there was considerable dispute over who had invented the rotary machine and grip rings—the

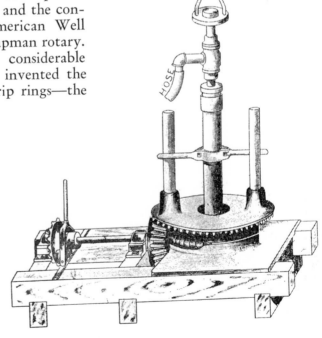

Fig. 22—Early Type of Rotary

Used for water-well drilling in the 1890's and for drilling oil wells in the Corsicana fields up to 1899. This machine follows design shown in Cameron patent papers of 1891. Also note similarity to Baker mule-powered table of Fig. 20, except this table uses clamps with limited stroke whereas Baker uses grip rings. Probably built by Johnson and associates.

Baker brothers or Chapman. The American Well Works, builders of the Chapman rotary, filed suit against Johnston, Baker, and associates when their early rotaries were built. After some years of litigation the decision was handed down that the Baker brothers had reduced to practice in the early 1880's the basic principles that were the subjects of the Chapman patents. This left the field open to all manufacturers.

The early rotary machines on fluid-circulating drilling rigs used either the grip rings of Baker and Chapman or the clamps with arms sliding down posts of Cameron (Fig. 17) to effect rotation of the drill pipe and bit.

The square kelly was disclosed in several patents during the period from 1844 to 1900. At least two included the circulation of fluid in their operation. On January 1, 1884, J. W. Hammett of Grant, W. Va., received Patent No. 292,485 covering a gear-driven rotary actuated by undisclosed power, carrying a square kelly with a driving recess and a boring tool of the auger type. With the same type boring tool, in 1886, J. E. Davis received Patent No. 333,931 on a gear-driven rotary machine with solid square kelly and a roller-bearing kelly bushing, all surprisingly similar to rotary tables of the early 1920's, although the roller-bearing bushings had not yet come into use (Fig. 23). On February 6, 1900, F. H. Davis received Patent No. 642,587 disclosing a square hollow kelly as shown in Fig. 24. This kelly operated through a gear-driven rotary machine.*

In 1884, George Westinghouse, father of the Westinghouse Electric Co. and the inventor of the Westinghouse air brake and many other mechanical and electrical devices, designed and patented a fluid motor—to be attached to the lower end of the drill pipe—that rotated the bit through the action of the circulating fluid in the motor. This submerged fluid motor was the forerunner of many similar devices of the years to follow.

In addition to the wells drilled from South Dakota to Corsicana with rotary tools during the 1880's and the 1890's, there is a record that "about 1889 Mr. B. Andrew, Sr. of New Orleans, La. was engaged in drilling wells by contract using the rotary system and soon discovered that thick plastic mud thoroughly mixed would wall up a hole being drilled and that in artesian water well drilling particularly, in which he was then engaged, the hole could be finished with one string of pipe and the casing set after the hole was drilled."†

Portable cable-tool machines had been built and used almost since the beginning of intensive oil-well drilling in the 1860's. In the 1890's, or even before, attempts were made to build portable rotary rigs. Diamond core drills were built in portable models; and in 1893 S. MacEachen patented a rotary rig on wheels consisting of all of the elements of such equipment—boiler, engine, hoist, pump, mast, crown pulley, swivel, rotary, and square kelly. It is not known that this rig actually drilled

---

*Note hose and swivel and cuttings basket above bit teeth in patent sketch.
†Carl A. Young, Lucey Manufacturing Corp. Catalog, 1920, and personal letter to writer.

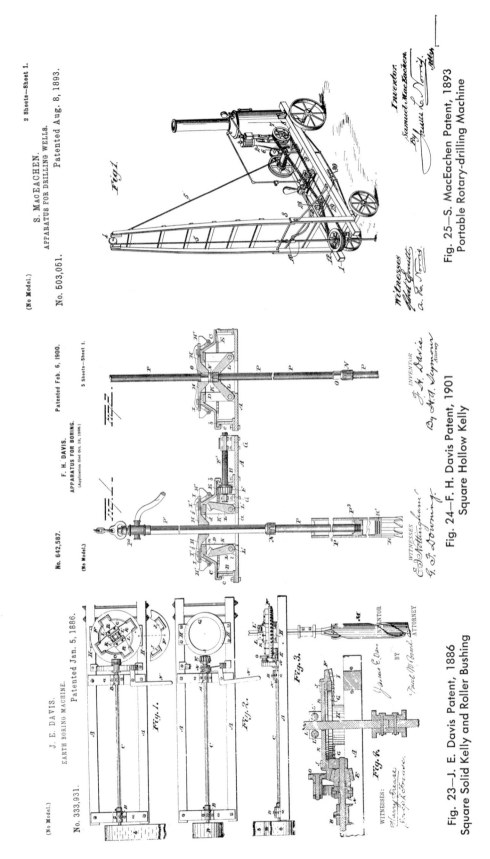

S. MacEACHEN.

APPARATUS FOR DRILLING WELLS.

Patented Aug. 8, 1893.

No. 503,061.

Fig. 1.

Witnesses
Geo. L. Gerritt
A. R. Norris

Inventor
Samuel MacEachen
By James L. Norris,
Attorney

Fig. 25—S. MacEachen Patent, 1893
Portable Rotary-drilling Machine

F. H. DAVIS.

APPARATUS FOR BORING.

(Application filed Oct. 12, 1898.)

Patented Feb. 6, 1900.

Fig. 1.

Fig. 2.

WITNESSES
E. J. Nottingham
G. F. Downing

INVENTOR
G. H. Davis
By A. F. Seymour
Attorney

Fig. 24—F. H. Davis Patent, 1901
Square Hollow Kelly

J. E. DAVIS.

EARTH BORING MACHINE.

Patented Jan. 5, 1886.

No. 333,931.

Fig. 1.

Fig. 2.

Fig. 3.

Fig. 4.

WITNESSES:
Harry Frost
Ralph R. Freeman

INVENTOR
James E. Davis
BY
Fred McBreed
ATTORNEY

Fig. 23—J. E. Davis Patent, 1886
Square Solid Kelly and Roller Bushing

wells, but with accessory tools it certainly could have bored shallow holes (Fig. 25).

Unfortunately the pre-1900 records are very limited and probably many of the stories that have been handed down are legendary. However, through the meager records available, patent papers, and the fact that a rotary rig was available in 1900 to drill to a depth of more than 1,000 ft in the Spindletop well, it is reasonably certain that many wells had been drilled with rotary tools and that many rigs had been built prior to 1900. In further support of this, in 1897, the Oil Well Supply Company* established a store in Corsicana, Texas, to supply and service area drilling operations, which at that time appear to have been almost entirely rotary.

During the last 60 years of the 19th century, there was undoubtedly extensive experimentation, trial, failure, and success in the development of both percussion and rotary-type drilling machines in the intensive search for tools with which both water and oil wells could be drilled. There were only a very few men who left records of their efforts. Their total contributions nevertheless covered the basic principles of fluid-circulating rotary-drilling equipment and practically all of the principal machines, tools, and equipment used today were "invented" by those early pioneers. Among these were:

1844-1845: Circulation of fluid to remove cuttings—Robert Beart of England and Fauvelle of France.

1844: Square hollow kelly—Robert Beart of England.

1863-1869: Diamond core drilling with circulating fluid—R. Leschot, France.

1865: Gear-driven rotary machine in combination with precussion motion—L. Holms, New Jersey, and Wiswell and Shaw, Buffalo.

1866: Rolling-cutter bit with circulating fluid, bevel gears driving rotating device, screw feed—P. Sweeney, New York.

1869: Bevel-gear-driven rotary machine with square kelly and gear-driven hoisting drum—J. F. Summers, Ohio.

1883: Gear-driven rotary, grip rings, circulating fluid—Baker brothers, South Dakota.

1885: Bevel-gear-driven rotary machine driving square solid kelly—G. Pech, Iowa.

1886: Solid square kelly with roller-bearing bushing—J. E. Davis, Ohio.

1889: Rotary machine similar to modern design, grip rings for continuous feed, circulating fluid—M. T. Chapman, Illinois.

---

*In 1952, this company became an operating division of United States Steel Corp., and is now "Oil Well Supply Division, United States Steel Corp."

These boilers are larger than other makes for the same power.

They are of the style universally used for drilling wells.

They are made of open hearth flange steel, having a tensile strength of 60,000 pounds per square inch, an elastic limit of 30,000 pounds, elongation of 20 per cent. in an 8-inch section, and will reduce in area 45 to 50 per cent., and turn over and close down solid when cold *without fracture*, will do the same after heating and plunging into cold water, and *will not blister*.

These boilers have unusual fire box surfaces, and storage room for steam. They are *double riveted* in the longitudinal seams. They do not foam or prime under any ordinary circumstances, even with quite foul water.

Every boiler is carefully inspected and tested at 160 pounds hydrostatic pressure and 125 pounds steam pressure per square inch.

SPECIFICATIONS OF DRILLING BOILERS.

Horse-Power		15	20	25	30	40
Diameter of shell	in inches.	30	36	40	42	44
Length of fire box	"	48	50	50	50	50
Height of fire box	"	30	36	40	42	44
Width of fire box	"	30	36	40	42	44
Diameter of dome	"	22	30	30	32	36
Height of dome	"	24	32	34	36	36
Diameter of smoke stack	"	16	18	20	22	24
Length of boiler	in feet.	13	14	15	16	16
Length of tubes	"	7	8	9	10	10
Length of smoke stack	"	24	27	27	30	32
Number of 3-inch tubes		30	36	43	48	54
Weight of boiler		4,400	6,400	7,600	9,000	9,800

Fixtures for boilers include lever safety valve, steam gauge complete, three gauge cocks, blow-off cock, feed valve, three nipples, one tee, grate bars, stack and guy wires.

Fig. 26—Locomotive-type Oil-field Boiler of 1890's

1890:   Two-drum hoist, hydraulic swivel, rotary with grip rings—
           M. T. Chapman, Illinois.
1891-1892: Gear-driven rotary machine with rotating clamp sliding on
           two posts extending up from table; principle used until early
           1900's—A. Cameron, Illinois.
1900:   Rotary machine with square hollow kelly for circulating
           fluid—F. H. Davis, New York (see Beart 1844).

Although there were many other patents on devices of similar principles, those listed seem to be the first in the fields from which the modern rotary rig is descended. Other essential parts of the drilling rig were borrowed from other operations, principally the cable-tool rig, which in turn had borrowed much of its machinery from other industries.

The boilers for rotary drilling were taken directly from the cable-tool rig which had borrowed from steamboats, sawmills, and locomotives. Both the locomotive fire-tube boiler and the shell-type return tubular boiler were used in early rotary days although the former, being much more portable and easily moved, seems to have predominated. By 1900 locomotive-type boilers were built in sizes from 15 to 40 hp and operated on steam pressure of about 75 psi. They were tested at 160 psi cold water and 125 psi steam. Fig. 26 illustrates an oil-field locomotive-type boiler of circa 1900, with specifications.

Engines were taken directly from the cable-tool rig and at the time varied in sizes 8 x 12 to 16 x 16, although it is not known that engines of the larger sizes were used on rotary rigs. The engine that drilled the Lucas Spindletop well was a 9 x 12 slide-valve, double eccentric, reversible cable-tool engine capable of delivering about 12 hp on 100-psi steam working pressure. The actual engine is illustrated in Fig. 27, which shows an assembly of the old machine, made up for the 50th anniversary celebration of the Spindletop well.

The drawworks in Fig. 27 shows a 2-shaft, single-speed, single-brake hoist that is said to be the unit that drilled the Lucas well. Fig. 28 shows the drawworks as manufactured in 1901. The drum was usually lagged with wood (Fig. 27). It is not certain that manila rope was used in the casing blocks but it is assumed so, since it was customary at the time. The worm-gear feed may be noticed beyond the brake in Fig. 28. This device was designed to impart a regular feed to the bit on bottom that was rather difficult with the single unlined brake band. It is not known whether the feed was ever used extensively.

The chain in general use was of the link-belt type as illustrated in Fig. 28, and in Fig. 27 showing the original Lucas Spindletop engine and drawworks. The chain on the low (and only) speed drive pictured in Fig. 36 is of the later pin type.

The rotary machine of Fig. 28, or "table" as it is customarily desig-

nated in the oil fields, is
a Chapman design, built
by American Well
Works of Aurora, Illi-
nois, and is quite similar
to the sketch in the
Chapman patent of 1889
as illustrated in Fig. 14.
Earlier rotaries of the
Baker and Cameron
types are illustrated in
Fig. 20 and 17.

The swivel in Fig. 28
was doubtless the last
word in such devices and
dates at least from 1900.
The open ball bearings

Fig. 27—Engine and Drawworks Used in Drilling
Lucas Spindletop Well in 1900

Showing relative position of all working parts.
The outfit may be used either with or without the worm feed, shown in outline.

Fig. 28—Drawworks—Rotary with Grip Rings, Swivel, and Travelling Block, 1900
(Oil Well Supply Co. Photo)

may be seen under the "C" link connecting swivel bail and the becket on the three-sheave traveling block. This block, together with its companion crown block, was borrowed directly from cable-tool stock. The sheave trunnions of the crown block ran in hardwood (probably live oak) bearings on wooden beams.

The circulating pump on the Lucas well is recorded as having been a Smith-Vaile, as illustrated in Fig. 29. These pumps were built for general industrial service in sizes up to 14 x 10 x 12, with a discharge capacity of about 500 gal per min at 50 rpm. The size used on drilling rigs was usually 8 x 5 x 10, having a capacity of about 150 gal. per min. This pump was of the piston-packed type and was of pre-1900 design and manufacture. In the small sizes it was used also as a boiler feed pump. The general design of this pump was changed very little for nearly 15 years. Pumps of other manufacturers were likewise in general industrial use in 1900; for example, Snow, Cameron (not the Cameron of modern oil-country goods manufacture), Fairbanks-Morse, Knowles, and doubtless others. It is not known which of these were used as circulating pumps prior to 1900—although they all were so used a little later.

Hose was of the outside wire-wrapped variety as shown in Fig. 30. Bits, as illustrated in Fig. 31, were entirely of the fishtail and diamond-point varieties; while a toothed bit cut in a collar or a toothed casing shoe (Fig. 30) was used to penetrate hard formations.

Drill pipe was lap-welded line pipe or ordinary merchant pipe. The driving joint or "grief stem" that worked in the grip rings was frequently, if not usually, a heavy-weight pipe such as extra-heavy, or double-extra-heavy. Pipe of standard thickness was not sufficiently strong to withstand the work after having been grooved by the grip rings.

The boilers, engine, drawworks, rotary, pumps, swivel, drill pipe, travelling block, crown block, casing line, drill pipe, and bits complete the principal items of the rotary-drilling rig of 1900. Only the drawworks, rotary, grip rings, swivel, bits, and a few minor items were designed, developed, and built especially for drilling wells, either water or oil. Other items of the rig were borrowed from various industries and adapted to rotary drilling. It seems apparent the development and

DUPLEX STEAM PUMP

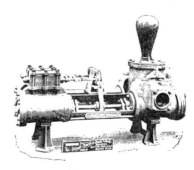

IN operating the Hydraulic Rotary Plant much depends on the Pump, as from the very nature of the process a constant stream of water under high pressure must be maintained.

Fig. 29—Smith-Vaile Pump of Type Used in Drilling Lucas Well, 1900

HOISTING APPARATUS
For Use in Connection With
Rotary Machine.

REVOLVING
and JETTING
SWIVEL.

Fig. 30 (left)—Items of the Rotary-drilling
Rig, 1900

Fig. 31 (below)—Rotary Bits, 1900

ROTARY DRILL

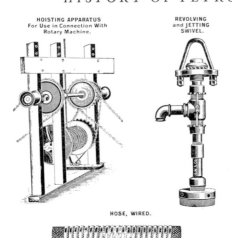

HOSE, WIRED.

HYDRAULIC AND JETTING
ROCK DRILL

SLIDE TONGS.

SWIVEL
BUSHING.

ROTARY
SHOE.

adaptation of all these machines and tools by 1900, when the Lucas Spindletop well was drilled,* had required many years and many wells to arrive at a rig capable of drilling a 1,000-ft hole in the soft formations of the Gulf Coast. More than 1,000 rotary-drilled oil wells had been completed between 1895 and 1901 in the Corsicana area. The drilling crews must have had experience on many previous wells and have fully understood the use of mud-laden fluid in drilling in soft cavey formations. The Spindletop well doubtless made the most of its mud as it was drilled. There is a legend that the mud used was mixed by driving cattle back and forth through a pit. Whether this is an exaggeration of fact or romancing, it is quite probable the hole was spudded with or used rig-site mud mixed in a pit—a common practice on the Gulf Coast for many years and certainly as late as 1933.

There has been some research and much speculation on who was responsible for the "invention" or the first realization of the value or necessity for mud-laden fluid in drilling wells in the soft-formation country to which the rotary was confined for the 25 years or more after the Lucas well was completed. Various individuals have been credited with discovery of its use. The M. T. Chapman Patent No. 443,069, filed in 1887, utilized "a stream of water and a quantity of plastic material." J. L. Buckingham in Patent No. 424,266 mentioned the use of "an unctuous substance"; and B. Andrews, Sr. of New Orleans was using "thick plastic mud to wall up the hole" before 1890. Mud-laden fluid was of necessity used in wells drilled with rotary tools for two reasons: First,

---

*Completed Jan. 10, 1901.

the formations drilled generally made considerable mud; and second, the well could have been drilled only with great difficulty without it. It seems safe to assume then that the discovery was made more or less independently by many intelligent drillers and others intimately associated with well-drilling even back to the early days of Beart and Fauvelle. The Baker brothers, Chapman, Andrews, Cameron, Sharp, and the Hamill brothers —to mention a few—must have realized its value and must have "conditioned" it as they thought necessary. With a matter of such vast importance in the industry there is credit enough for all.

As determined by factual historical records, legends, deductions, and surmises, it appears that by 1900 the rotary-drilling industry was a struggling infant but with experience enough behind it to have been able to drill a 1,000-ft well in that year and many more in the next 10 years with few changes in equipment.

In 1900 Patillo Higgins, who in years past had attempted and failed in the drilling of an oil well (although he had drilled a gas well) on the Spindletop dome, prevailed upon Capt. Anthony Lucas to undertake the drilling of a deep well for the purpose of finding the oil he believed to be there. Capt. Lucas was sufficiently persuaded and, with cable tools, got a first well down to 930 ft where the hole was lost. He then arranged with Guffey and Galey for the financing of an additional well and employed Al and Curt Hamill, rotary-drilling contractors of Corsicana, to drill the well with a rotary rig.

The rig was set up and with two helpers, Henry McLeon and Peck Byrd, they undertook to drill the well. The hole was carried without difficulty to a depth of 160 ft, where circulation was lost. Thereupon a string of 8-in. pipe was rotated and circulated as far as it would go. Next a string of 4-in. drill pipe with fishtail bit was run inside the casing, according to the report. They rigged up a drive block operated by the catline and, with drilling, circulating, and driving, the 8-in. pipe was carried to gumbo at 425 ft.

The formations were gumbo and clay with alternating soft sands from 425 ft down to about 800 ft. The heavy, highly colloidal drilling mud made from the gumbo walled up the sand to such an extent that little difficulty was encountered.

It seems from the reports that when the well reached the depth of about 800 ft, sand came in the hole and up into the 8-in. casing at 425 ft. In order to avoid difficulties with flow-back and sand entering the bottom of the drill pipe as it went into the hole or as connections were made, Capt. Lucas designed and made what is said to have been the first check valve or float valve used in a string of drill pipe. They had been used for many years in casing run in cable-tool wells.

At about 880 ft oil and gas were encountered and a string of 6-in. casing was run to that depth. They had been working during the daytime only; but after encountering the showings, they drilled during the day and kept the pumps running all night. After making 140 ft in 7 days, the fastest drilling in the hole, the well came in on January 10, 1901, at about 1,020 ft making an estimated 100,000 bbl daily. The oil industry as we know it was born.

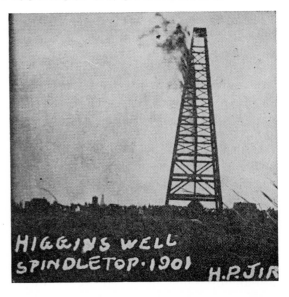

Fig. 32—Lucas Spindletop (Higgins) Well, 1901

Next to the Drake well, or even equally with it, this was the most important oil well ever drilled in the United States and its importance cannot be exaggerated. It established the presence of great deposits of liquid fuel, and it also established the rotary-drilling rig as equipment capable of drilling oil wells in soft formations where cable tools could not be successfully used except to very shallow depths. Although the rotary rig had been developed and perfected to the point that it could drill the Lucas well, the method was relatively unknown among the old oil producers. This first great gusher gave the needed impetus to its use in the search for oil in the Southwest, as well as in other soft-formation areas throughout the world.

Thus the hydraulic or mud-circulating rotary-drilling system had, by January 10, 1901, demonstrated its ability to drill and complete oil wells in the soft unconsolidated formations of the Gulf Coastal Plain.

1900 - 1915

After the completion of the Spindletop well (Fig. 32), the great oil boom of the Gulf Coast started. It extended into many states and countries where there were indications of petroleum in the less-consolidated formations in which cable tools could not be used successfully or with a reasonable degree of economy. The new areas included many additional parts of the Gulf salt-dome region, East Texas into northern Louisiana and southern Arkansas, across the river into Mississippi, and the San Joaquin Valley of California. Rotary-drilling rigs were sent abroad to Trinidad, Venezuela, Mexico, Colombia, Peru, Argentina, Roumania, Russia, and the Dutch East Indies.

At the time of the completion of the Lucas well the principal manufacturers of rotary equipment were the American Well Works of Aurora, Illinois, which built the Chapman equipment; H. G. Johnston and his associates who later founded the American Well and Prospecting Company of Corsicana, Texas, building the Baker and Johnston tools—apparently with some ideas from Cameron; the Parker Company which later became the Southern Well Works, the Lucey Manufacturing Company, and finally The Wheland Company of Chattanooga, Tennessee. Oil Well Supply Company also manufactured many items of tools and equipment and especially those used on both cable-tool and rotary rigs. Immediately following the Lucas well, The National Supply Company of Dayton, Ohio, formerly a manufacturer of cable tools only, entered the rotary field; and within the next few years was followed by other manufacturers including Boykin and the Beaumont Iron Works, both of Beaumont. Union Tool Company of California, later merged into The National Supply Company, began the manufacture of rotary equipment about 1910. In addition to larger organizations, there were many local blacksmith and machine shops that made various items for the rotary rig and drilling operation. Pumps were obtained from manufacturers such as Smith-Vaile, Snow, Cameron, Fairbanks-Morse, and others. For some years there was no pump made especially for handling mud-laden drilling fluid. Parker seems to have been first in 1905. Chain, both manila and wire line, hose, small tools, and pipe and fittings were standard articles of trade and were procurable from any well-stocked heavy hardware store. That left only the highly specialized rotary equipment such as bits, rotary tables, grip rings, swivels, and drawworks. The last mentioned was a simple machine built of two shafts, a drum for spooling the line, a brake, sprockets, and two catheads. It could be put together by any good machine shop and foundry.

Fig. 30 illustrates the rear view of the type drawworks that drilled the Lucas well, together with the swivel and hose of the day. A rotary shoe for rotating casing through bridges and past shoulders and also for drilling hard shells is likewise illustrated. The slide tongs were used for making up pipe.

Fig. 33 shows a Chapman patent rotary table, with grip rings, of about 1901. This table is remarkably similar to the sketch included in the Chapman patent papers of 1889 and was built in this model for some years following the Lucas well, with the exception of the improvements in the bearings, gears, and grip rings and a heavier machine. The rotary that drilled the Lucas well is said to have been a Parker rotary, 1900 model, shown in Fig. 34.*

Fig. 35 shows a Parker rotary rig drilling in the Spindletop oil field in 1901 or 1902. This illustrates a two-shaft, single-speed, single-

---

*Young, Carl A: Brief History of Rotary Drilling, Lucey Manufacturing Co. Catalog of about 1921.

brake drawworks with what appears to be a wire line on the drum, A Parker table with grip rings of the 1900 model is on the floor and the crew is coming out of the hole with what, from its size, appears to be casing although it could be 8-in. drill pipe. The two fishtail bits are standing in the rear right-hand corner, while the grief stem with the swivel on it is just extending into the **V** with the hose attached. The pipe is being racked behind a finger. The traveling block, C-link, hook, and Mannington elevator with bails are visible on the end of the pipe above the table. Chain tongs are being used to break out the pipe while a "calf head" is hammering the coupling to permit the tong man on the right to break the joint. The flambeaus, torches, or "stink pots" as commonly called—the common lights of the period—are visible. The "single-barrel" engine is to the left with a small segment of its fly wheel in view. The details of the derrick with its 20-ft floor are clearly seen. The two pumps are barely visible on the far side of the derrick floor. The similarity of this rig to the most modern steam-powered rotary-drilling rig in basic items is close. Otherwise there is no comparison.

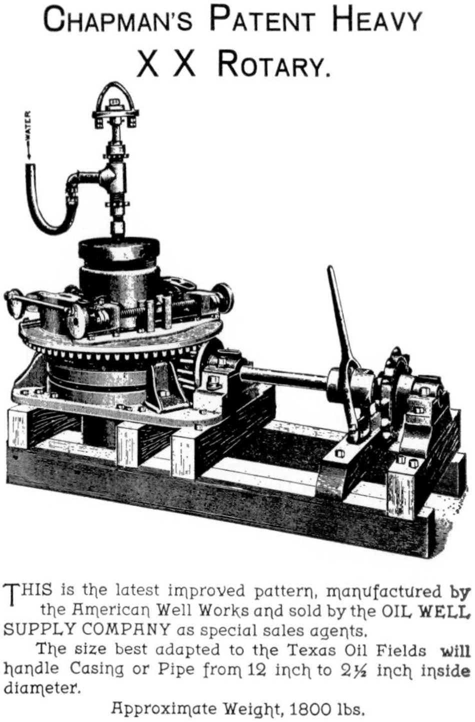

CHAPMAN'S PATENT HEAVY X X ROTARY.

THIS is the latest improved pattern, manufactured by the American Well Works and sold by the OIL WELL SUPPLY COMPANY as special sales agents.

The size best adapted to the Texas Oil Fields will handle Casing or Pipe from 12 inch to 2½ inch inside diameter.

Approximate Weight, 1800 lbs.

Fig. 33—Chapman Rotary Machine, 1901 (Oil Well Supply Co. Photo)

Fig. 34—1900 Parker Patent Rotary (The Wheland Co. Photo)

Fig. 36 shows a part of the derrick floor of a rig in use during the early part of the century. In the center is a Chapman rotary machine with grip rings mounted on a wooden-beam base structure. A link-belt chain, No. 1030 Ewart, of malleable iron is shown. The single-speed, single-brake drawworks is behind. By comparison in size with the catline, the

Fig. 35—Parker Rotary Rig of 1901-1902 in Spindletop (The Wheland Co. Photo)

casing line would appear to be manila rope and not steel. Both wire and manila line were in use in 1905. A pressure gage is visible on the mud line which, with the exception of the gages on the boilers, seems to have been the only instrument on the rigs. Many rigs as late as the mid-1920's had no gages except on the boilers. The drilling hose is visible between and behind the pipe, while a Mannington elevator with links is lying on the floor in the lower left near the washdown hose. It appears that the pipe is being racked behind a finger, as is now customary on the West Coast,

Fig. 36—Rotary Rig Chapman Rotary of Early 1900's, (Link-Belt Company Photo)

rather than in front of the drawworks as is customary in Mid-Continent and Gulf Coast operations.

The appearance of the rig suggests that 12-in. casing was run but would not go to bottom and had to be pulled. They have started somewhere up the hole and are now reaming and washing down to get the casing to bottom.

Fig. 37 illustrates a swivel-to-bit drilling shaft of 1900 to 1905.

Fig. 38 shows a diagrammatic view of a complete rotary-drilling rig of the very early years of the century.

There appears to be very little material in the literature on the early years of rotary drilling on the Gulf Coast and none has been found that gives a clear picture of the method of operation. The many photographs available, of which the several included are representative, together with the catalogs of the supply companies, do, however, permit a fair interpretation of the operating methods and drilling practices of the day.

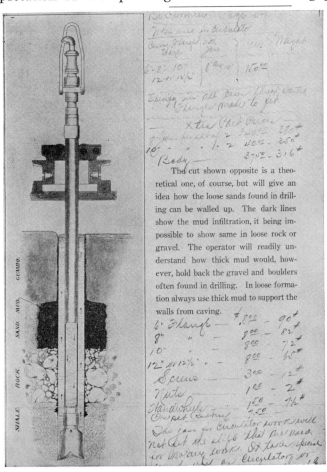

The cut shown opposite is a theoretical one, of course, but will give an idea how the loose sands found in drilling can be walled up. The dark lines show the mud infiltration, it being impossible to show same in loose rock or gravel. The operator will readily understand how thick mud would, however, hold back the gravel and boulders often found in drilling. In loose formation always use thick mud to support the walls from caving.

Fig. 37—Drilling Shaft—Conventional Drill Stem of Earliest Rotary Days, Circa 1902 (Oil Well Supply Co. Photo)

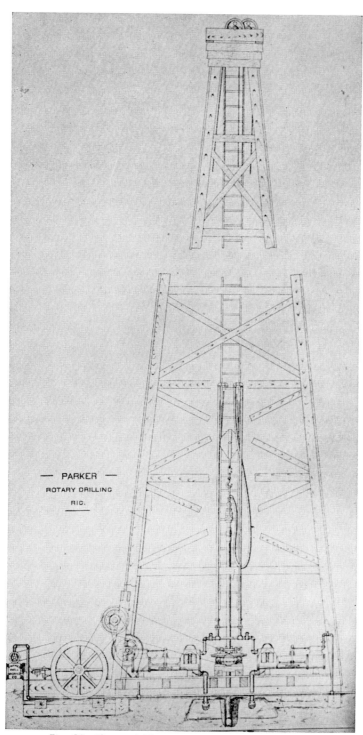

PARKER
ROTARY DRILLING
RIG.

Fig. 38—Elevated Plan, Parker Rotary Outfit, 1905
(Courtesy of The Wheland Co.)

Suffice it to say that the weight carried on the bit, the rotating speed, the fluid volume, and the bits were at the optimum allowed by the machinery, the tools, and the experience of the day. For the depths being drilled in formations of the character penetrated, the tools were reasonably satisfactory, although with the single addition of a larger fluid volume the rate of penetration could have been substantially increased. There were few changes in rotary-drilling equipment for the first 10 or 12 years after the Spindletop well, except the drawworks were made a little heavier and stronger and slightly larger boilers, pumps, and engines were used.

The critical machines in the development of the rotary-drilling rig were the rotary itself, together with its means of rotating the drill pipe, and the swivel. Even the swivel was in a way an adaptation of prior art. The rotary, however, involved a new application of the basic principle of rotating a cutting tool. The two problems involved were relatively slow rotation of a large drilling shaft carrying a large bit and a continuous though varying rate of feed of the bit into the formation. There were 3 means of accomplishing this feed in the various patent applications between 1844 and 1900. The first was by a square kelly passing through a rotating pulley (1844) and later by means of a drive bushing fitted in a rotary machine. This latter means of rotating the bit on bottom was disclosed in several previously mentioned patents. The second method was by grip rings operating on a tube or pipe, as already discussed and as disclosed in the Chapman patent of 1889. The third method was disclosed in the Cameron patent of 1891, involving a rotary machine having two posts extending upward from the rotating table. A clamp with two arms was attached to the pipe barely below the top of the posts; and with the rotation of the table, the posts rotated the arms of the clamp which in turn rotated the pipe. As the bit made hole the clamp arms moved down the posts. These posts determined the length of feed of the bit into the formation before the rotary must be stopped, the clamps released, and moved to the top of the post for another run or "hitch." This stroke was similar in length to the chuck-and-quill drive of the diamond core drill. The oldest method listed is the survivor.

The Chapman table with its grip rings, the invention of which was claimed by the Baker brothers, went into service in the late 1880's and after modest improvements and changes in design, went out of service about 1920. The Cameron rotary with 2 posts may have gone into service in the late 1880's, but certainly in the early 1890's, and was finally discarded for the more convenient Chapman table about 1900. The Baker table shown in Fig. 20 appears to have embodied features of both the Chapman and the Cameron type tables. Fig. 17 shows a diagrammatic patent sketch of the Cameron table with posts and clamps. What may be a sketch of the actual table is shown in Fig. 22.

Thus, during the 10 years 1890 to 1900 and possibly prior to this time there were 3 tables in use: the Baker rotary which used both grip rings and posts; the Chapman rotary which used grip rings only; and the Cameron rotary which used posts and clamps. The surviving rotary of the three was the Chapman. The grip-ring drive of this rotary was superseded, beginning in 1915, by the grooved, fluted, and square kellys with companion-drive bushings.

These three machines share the honor of being the first of their general type used in drilling wells for both water and oil. They were anticipated in basic principles of construction and operation by several patents dating back to Beart of 1844, but none of these early inventions are known to have been used for the actual drilling of wells, although it may be assumed that some were constructed and used for this purpose.

The oil wells completed in rotary-drilling areas from 1898 through 1906 are reported by Carl Young in the Lucey Manufacturing Company catalog of 1921 to have been as follows:

1898	374	1901		128
1899	268	1902		220
1900	373	1903		840
	———	1904		774
Total pre-Spindletop	1,015	1905		783
		1906		1,060
				———
				3,805

It will be noted that there was a very considerable decrease in number of wells drilled and completed in 1901 compared to 1900. During 1900 and the 5 preceding years, most of the oil wells drilled by rotary tools were in the shallow fields near Corsicana and in a few other shallow fields in Texas and Louisiana. With the discovery of Spindletop the play moved to the salt domes of the Gulf Coast where the wells were deeper and required considerably more time to drill. The increase in completions from 1901 to 1905 is remarkable. According to a copy of the *Oil Investors Journal* of Beaumont, Texas, published in 1907, there were 175 complete rotary-drilling rigs operating in the Gulf Coast of Texas and Louisiana at that time. There were also many cable-tool rigs in other parts of the Southwest.

Caddo Field

Owing to the fact that the actual drilling and completion of oil wells and the development of oil fields during these early years appear to have been accomplished with little or no assistance from engineers or technical men, there is very little material available describing drilling practices in engineering detail. The American Petroleum Institute had not as yet been organized and the American Institute of Mining Engineers had shown little or no interest in the oil industry. In 1908, however, Walter E. Hopper, a geology student from Cornell University went to the Caddo oil and gas field in extreme northwestern Louisiana for a 4-month study of the field and operations in it. As the result of his investigations he wrote a paper that was published in 1912 in *AIME Transactions,* Vol. XLII (1911). This is one of the earliest papers by an American engineer or geologist specializing in the oil industry to be presented before a technical society and published in its transactions. Some of the descriptions of drilling equipment are not entirely in accordance with what were probably the facts, no doubt due to the inexperience of the young geologist with rotary-drilling equipment and oil-field operations. Despite this, however, his descriptions are quite satisfactory and can be interpreted readily by those intimately familiar with drilling equipment and operations. They give a very clear picture of the operations of the day. Hopper's visit to the Caddo Field during the winter of 1908-1909 was under the direction of the Louisiana Geological Survey and the U. S. Geological Survey.

Attention was first attracted to the Caddo Field in 1895 by indication of gas in water wells from 40 to 60 ft deep. This led to the drilling of the Savage Brothers and Morrisell well or the Caddo Lake Oil and Pipe Line Company No. 1. The rig for this well was erected in May 1904 and drilling began in the following month. The well was bailed March 23, 1905, recovering a small amount of oil. It was deepened in July and converted into a gasser on January 3, 1906. In January 1907 it was abandoned, as far as is known. This was the first well drilled in that part of Louisiana, or in nearby Texas or Arkansas.

In consequence of the finding of oil in the Savage well, a number of strings of tools were moved in from the Gulf Coast and the first oil boom in this part of the Southwest was under way. The month following the finding of oil in the Savage well found four rigs drilling in the area; but before the field was to become an oil and gas field, there were many difficulties to be overcome. With the limited experience of the operators and the high pressures encountered, many wells blew out and cratered. Eventually, however, the field was developed into a substantial and important oil- and gas-producing area. It is still producing.

Hopper states that the derricks used during that early day were built of wood and were 84 ft high with 22-ft bases (Fig. 38). The boilers used, Fig. 39, were of the locomotive type with 125 lb steam working pressure. The size is not given but they were probably 30 to 50 hp. Engines were the single-cylinder slide-valve type used on cable-tool rigs with horsepower capacity varying from 20 to 28, as shown in Fig. 27. These prime movers cost $320 to $365. The hoisting gear or drawworks were 2-shaft, single-brake, single-speed, and weighed from 1,900 lb to 2,800 lb costing from $180 to $250. The pumps, size 8 x 5 x 10, usually

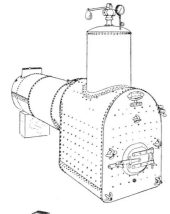

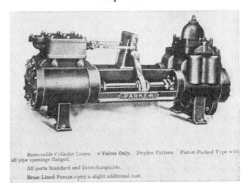

Fig. 39 (left)—Locomotive-type Boiler, Early 1900's

Removable Cylinder Liners. 8 Valves Only. Duplex Pattern. Piston-Packed Type with all pipe openings flanged.
All parts Standard and Interchangeable.
Brass Lined Pumps carry a slight additonal cost.

Fig. 40 (above)—Parker Slush Pump, Circa 1905

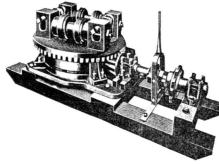

Fig. 41 (left)—Parker Patent Rotary, 1905
(The Wheland Co. Photo)

2 to each rig, were of several makes—Smith-Vaile, Knowles, Special Duplex, Gardner, and Parker rotary-drilling pumps. Fig. 40 shows a Parker mud pump, first built about 1905. These units were priced variously from $220 to $510. There were several rotaries in service, including those built by Parker, Fig. 41; American Well Works, Chapman, Fig. 33; and Oil Well Supply Company. These machines varied from 900 to 4,000 lb in weight and could handle pipe up to 20 in. in diameter. They cost from $225 to $1,600. Fig. 36 illustrates a rotary rig circa 1905.

Casing sizes were 10-in., 8-in., and 6-in. while the drill pipe was 4-in. It should be remembered that pipe sizes prior to standardization by API were designated by nominal inside diameters, as is present common practice with merchant pipe. These Caddo casing sizes were actually 10¾-in., 8⅝-in., and 6⅝-in. OD with 4½-in. OD drill pipe. This is one of the earliest records of the actual size of drill pipe. Old photographs suggest larger sizes on some wells. A back-pressure valve was commonly used in the drill pipe in the first coupling off bottom to prevent flow-back of the mud when running in the hole. A float valve was likewise used when running casing (see Fig. 42).

Two types of bits were used—the old fishtail type for soft formations and the core bit for harder beds. Diamond-point bits were used for

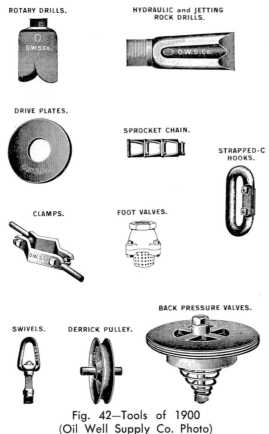

ROTARY DRILLS.

HYDRAULIC and JETTING ROCK DRILLS.

DRIVE PLATES.

SPROCKET CHAIN.

STRAPPED-C HOOKS.

CLAMPS.

FOOT VALVES.

BACK PRESSURE VALVES.

SWIVELS.   DERRICK PULLEY.

Fig. 42—Tools of 1900
(Oil Well Supply Co. Photo)

special jobs such as side-tracking. "Poor boy" core barrels, built of drill pipe or casing with hand-cut teeth or with steel-toothed shoes, were used for core samples and on hard shells. "Adamantine"* was used with plain-end pipe in a manner similar to the use of small steel balls in modern shot drills. According to W. E. Wrather (told in conversation) the hard Adamantine was in general use before 1910 in cutting the hard shells.

The surface casing string usually set was 12 in. in size and was carried down to a hard stratum, usually 500 to 800 ft below the surface. There is no mention of cementing and it is not believed that cementing was practiced on the Gulf Coast at this time. Following the $10\frac{3}{4}$-in. casing, $8\frac{5}{8}$-in. was run which, in turn, was followed by $6\frac{5}{8}$-in. Finally 2-in. tubing was run for production. Perforated liner was usually run into the producing sand. Drill pipe was pulled in thribles of 20-ft nominal length joints. Common short pipe couplings were used.

The crews consisted of 5 men to the 12-hour tour. Drillers received $5 to $6 daily, derrick men $3 to $5, and rig helpers or roughnecks $3.

The average time to drill a deep well—2,200 ft—was 120 to 180 days when a day crew only was used, an overall average of some $1\frac{1}{2}$ ft per hour or about 3 ft per hour of actual drilling time. Time required to drill shallow wells to about 800 ft was from 30 days with 1 crew to 18 days with 2 crews, an approximate average of $2\frac{1}{2}$ ft per hour overall working time, or 5 ft for actual drilling time—a quite creditable rate of penetration.

The complete rotary rig of the day cost about $2,825 exclusive of freight or transportation and weighed some 30,000 lb. (This is not believed to have included the derrick, which cost some $250 in addition and weighed about as much or even more than the rig.)

---

*Probably carborundum (silica carbide) or the mineral corundum, the hardest known mineral excepting the diamond.

California

The oil industry of California started some years prior to 1900, by which time a number of fields had been developed and many wells drilled. All work was done with cable tools. A rotary rig had been tried in 1889 by Western Prospecting Company in Pico Canyon but without success.* After the rotary rig had proved itself in the Gulf Coast and other parts of the Mid-Continent, it was concluded that it should be tried in the soft formations of the California fields where much difficulty was being encountered and heavy expenses incurred in the cable-tool holes. In 1908 James Patrick took a Parker rotary rig made by the Southern Well Works Company, originally of Beaumont and later of Chattanooga, to California (M. T. Archer, letter to Prof. J. H. Pound, Rice Institute, April 4, 1939; also Carl Young). This equipment was taken to the Santa Maria Field, rigged up and put to work. Because of the relatively hard formations in the area, the drilling operation was not highly satisfactory. In consequence, the rig was moved to the Midway district in the San Joaquin Valley where it became an immediate success. This operation was the beginning of rotary drilling on the West Coast. During 1908 Standard Oil Co. of California sent a representative to the Gulf Coast with instructions to hire six rotary drillers and to buy three complete rotary outfits. They were shipped to California and unloaded in the oil fields near Taft on the west side of the San Joaquin Valley. It is not clear if this decision was made before or after the Parker rig drilled at Midway.

When these early rotary rigs arrived there was considerable difference of opinion as to their adaptability to the California oil fields. As is usually the case, it took some time to accustom the operators to the new equipment, but after a few years the rotary was accepted, gradually supplanted the cable tools, and cable-tool men were trained in the operation of rotary rigs. At that time there were two tours run in California—daylight and night. The daylight driller was in charge of the job, took the place of what is now the tool pusher, and drilled for 12 hours.

In addition to the actual drilling of the well, the head driller had to build his derrick, rig up, catch samples, select casing seats, and finally complete the well. He filled all of those functions now filled by the driller, the tool pusher, and the petroleum engineer or geologist. Today the driller pays little attention to the logging of the formation through which he drills. On some rigs there is no requirement to record formation at all, but during those early years and for many years to come the work of the geologist in studying the subsurface geology of an oil field depended almost entirely upon the driller's interpretation of the materials through which the drill passed. Even as late as the early 1930's most of the regional and field contour maps were based on the driller's logs. After about 1920

---

*Earl Welty, Union Oil Co. of California.

the samples caught by the drilling crew were studied by office geologists who were able to locate formation changes with more accuracy. The electric-logging equipment, in use soon after 1930, gave important additional information on subsurface conditions. Finally, there came the well geologist who caught his own samples of cuttings and mud and studied them in an elaborate house-trailer laboratory equipped with all necessary instruments including bed, refrigerator, and cook stove (1945-50).

The rotary rigs moved from Texas to California included, among other items of equipment, 9 x 10 single-cylinder slide-valve steam engines, 8 x 5 x 10 duplex steam pumps of which 2 were used on each rig, and drawworks consisting of line shafts 2⅞ in. in diameter and drum shafts 2⅞ in. to 3⅞ in. in diameter. There was only a single brake flange and the steel brake bands, usually 3 in. or 4 in. wide, worked directly on the metal of the flange. There were no brake linings in those days. The brake flange on the drum was usually of cast-iron or cast-steel construction. The rotary tables in common use were of the Chapman and Parker patents with grip rings.

To drill a well from 2,800 to 3,000 ft with the light rotary outfit of that period required 60 to 120 days depending upon the difficulties encountered during the drilling, such as "twist-offs," blowouts, etc. Each twist-off meant a washover or side-tracking job. The circulating overshot had not yet been developed nor had the technique of circulating the drill pipe free with crude oil. This was a long period of time required to drill a well, but it was a very considerable improvement over the time of the cable tools then in use. As was customary with cable tools, rotary bits were sharpened or dressed on the derrick floor where the forge was located.

In addition to the other difficulties inherent in the equipment of that day, several of the fields along the west side of the San Joaquin Valley had a gas cap overlying the main producing oil zones. This gas was frequently under pressures of from 1,800 to 2,000 psi at depths of only 1,800 to 2,500 ft below the surface. With the light-weight and very poor-quality mud, and without adequate blowout preventers, blowouts were frequent.

In 1910 the oil-field operators and manufacturers of California undertook to improve the capacity and quality of the drilling machinery so that it might cope more efficiently with the drilling problems of the day. These efforts over the first few years resulted in the development of the two-plug cementing process, tool joints, long casing collars, internal-upset drill pipe, casing shoes, and other accessory items of equipment. Internal-upset drill pipe and tool joints were developed about 1911 and eliminated many fishing jobs. Also the four-way bit was built and used for reaming mud off the wall of the hole so that the string of casing would run to bottom. Many of the long 4-wing bits were still in use as late as 1934. Many other items of equipment were likewise improved but the principal drilling tool—the fishtail bit—remained the same and the Decker-type blowout preventers, Fig. 43, were not greatly improved.

The rigs themselves remained more or less the same until about 1915, except that a new swivel was developed that had a capacity of about 35 tons, and a clutch was put on the line shaft to replace the clutch that had formerly been used on the rotary table. Also the machines and tools were made heavier, or — in the language of the day — "more pig iron was used."

During those early days several very large wells were completed on the west side of the San Joaquin Valley. The Kern Trading and Oil Company completed one that, according to M. E. Lombardi, made 65,000 bbl of oil "day after day after day" flowing wild. Another well that blew out was estimated at 30,-000 bbl, and still another at from 30,000 to 35,000 bbl daily. A well in the old Buena Vista Field that blew out at 2,480 ft was estimated to make 65,000 to

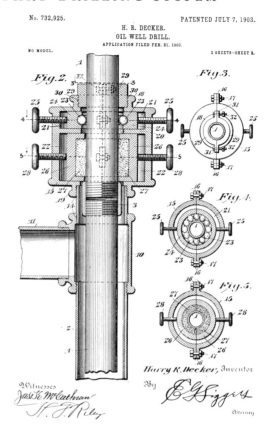

Fig. 43—Sketch—Decker Blowout-preventer Patent, 1903

75,000 bbl of oil daily. There were many wells of comparable size in the area, including the most famous of them all, the Lake View gusher. This well is estimated to have produced as much as 100,000 bbl of heavy black oil daily. It also made large quantities of sand, some of which was still piled around the well as late as 1935. The well was wild for a number of days.

L. B. Little, who retired about 1940 as superintendent of operations for the Southern District of California for Standard Oil Co. of California, was one of the men who came to California from Texas with the three rotary rigs already mentioned. Cyrus Bell, later of the contracting firm of Little and Bell and still later of Bell and Loffland, was another. He likewise retired from the drilling industry about 1940. On March 19, 1940, Little read a paper with slides before the spring meeting of the API Division of Production in Los Angeles in which he told the story of the early days of rotary drilling in California.

Union Tool Co. of California, Torrance, had been the important

323

manufacturer of cable-tool equpiment in California before the arrival of the first rotary rig. Shortly thereafter the company turned its attention as well to rotary-drilling equipment. One of the first machines built was a rotary table with grip-ring assembly built in accordance with the ideas of Cyrus Bell, the rotary being known as the "Bell rotary." This machine was of the open type that was used for many succeeding years and was lubricated by throwing crude oil or any heavy oil on the drive pinion.

During the early period of the rotary in California the Lake View Annex No. 2 in Sect. 26, T. 24 R. 32, south of Taft, was drilled to a depth in excess of 1 mile. (Carl Young, *op. cit.*) The well was drilled with a California-type Parker rotary rig. By this time the various manufacturers of oil-field equipment were building oversized and heavy tools for use in the deep, big-hole operations of California. Beginning about 1910 and until about 1927 the California manufacturers of rotary-drilling equipment and men in the industry with inventive turns of mind were largely responsible for the development and improvement of rotary-drilling machinery and tools.

The drilling division of the oil industry was handled exclusively by practical men during these years. Neither the geologist nor the engineer had anything to do even with locating the great majority of oil fields drilled until well after the turn of the century. The first record of trained professional engineers or geologists actively associated with the actual drilling of oil wells is about 1910. At that time (letter from Chester Naramore to John R. Suman, dated March 17, 1954), several oil companies operating in California had what were called "resident geologists" who were assigned to the superintendent of an oil field. The superintendent, being generally a practical man, was in need of much data he had not been trained to compute. In consequence the young geologist usually found himself devoting the greater part of his time to calculations of problems and sketching of equipment and tools having to do with the drilling of the wells. It was from this beginning that the oil-field or resident engineer-geologist started and developed over a number of years into the petroleum engineer. California, at least insofar as the records go, was well in advance of the Mid-Continent and Eastern states in training and using these engineers.

Chester Naramore, R. S. Haseltine, Ben K. Stroud, Paul Paine, Wm. C. McDuffie, Wm. A. Reinhardt, T. E. Swigart, R. P. McLaughlin, A. W. Ambrose, W. W. Scott, F. E. Rehm, R. R. Templeton, R. E. Collom, M. J. Kirwan, and H. H. Anderson were among those who became "petroleum engineers" or drilling engineers during this 1910-1920 period in California.

The great majority of the derricks used in drilling oil wells during these early years were built of wood, and did not exceed 84 ft in height, although a few steel derricks had been built of both angle iron and tubes and successfully used prior to 1900. They did not become popular, however, because of the lack of finished design and the prejudices of the drillers against them. In 1907 the tubular-steel derrick came into being when Lee C. Moore acquired a patent granted to T. A. Neill, a field superintendent for the South Penn Oil Company in Pennsylvania, on a method of joining tubular sections for the construction of steel derricks. The first of these was manufactured in 1908 (see Fig. 47 of the chapter herein on percussion drilling), and was the beginning of the steel-derrick era which some 25 years later had practically displaced the wooden derricks from the fields. Angle-iron derricks were also manufactured by several of the steel companies and sold rather extensively throughout the industry. One of the engineers responsible for the introduction of the angle-iron derricks was R. B. Woodworth of Carnegie Steel Company. Woodworth designed many cable-tool and rotary derricks, and in February 1916 prepared a very excellent history of derricks and cable-tool drilling machines that was published in the *Transactions* of the American Institute of Mining Engineers, Vol. LIV, 1917. Some of Woodworth's material is used in the percussion-drilling chapter. His paper is one of the best ever published on derricks and cable-tool drilling rigs.

Combination Rigs

Until about 1910 or 1911 the only drilling bits available on rotary operations were the fishtail, the diamond point for certain operations—particularly sidetracking, and the circular-toothed bit similar to the casing shoe. These tools limited the use of the rotary to areas containing formations that they could penetrate; and the hard "shells" of the Gulf Coast were drilled with considerable difficulty, time, and trouble with the tools available. In some areas, such as parts of California, some sections of the hole were too soft for cable tools and other sections were too hard for the rotary. This brought into use the combination rig with the rotary drawworks and its engine on one side and the walking beam, band wheel and its engine on the side to the right of the driller, and the bull wheel on the side to the left of the driller. The **V** was directly in front of the rotary drawworks. It is not known when and where these combination rigs first went into service, but probably somewhere on the Gulf Coast to enable the drilling of the cap rock on some of those domes where it was especially thick. According to Woodworth *(op. cit.)* the first combination steel derrick was sent to I. N. Knapp of Houma, Louisiana, in 1912 and the second to the Island of Trinidad. The California heavy-type combination derricks were built about 1912 or a little later. It is quite probable that combination wooden derricks were used earlier than 1910. Fig. 44 shows a portable combination rig of about 1906.

Although the combination rig enabled the drilling of both the soft formations and the hard formations, they were costly, cumbersome, and

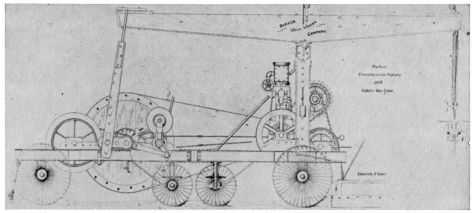

Fig. 44—Parker Combination Drilling Machine—Portable

sometimes required experienced cable-tool drillers as well as rotary drillers; and the former were not generally available within some hundreds of miles of the rotary operations such as on the Gulf Coast.

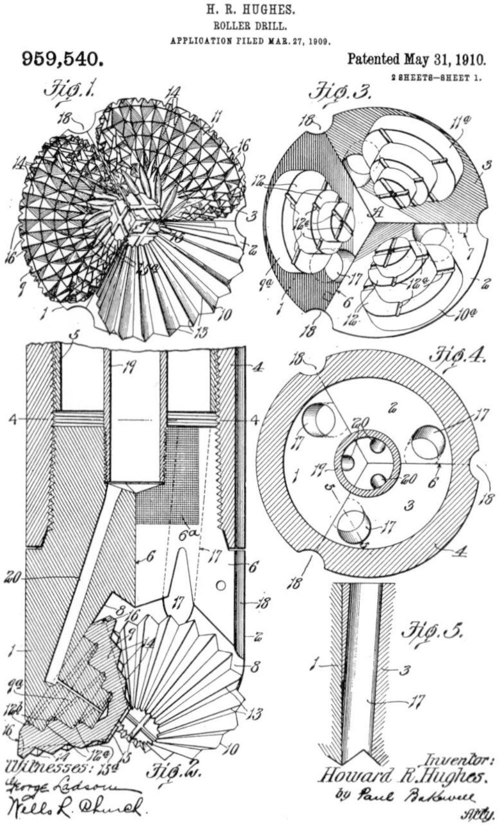

Rolling-cutter Bits

In 1908 Howard R. Hughes, a lawyer and inventor, designed the first tri-cone rock bit, Fig. 45, which was the predecessor of the Hughes cone bit of today. The Sharp-Hughes Tool Company was organized in 1909 to develop and market the tool. By 1914 numerous ideas had been tried, and during that year several 3-cone bits were manufactured and sold. The rolling-cutter rock bit was the second of the four great developments and inventions of the period, without any one of which, or an equally good substitute, the rotary-drilling industry of today could not function with its present efficiency.

H. R. HUGHES.
ROLLER DRILL.
APPLICATION FILED MAR. 27, 1909.

959,540.   Patented May 31, 1910.
2 SHEETS—SHEET 1.

Fig. 45—Sketch—Hughes Tri-cone Bit Patent, 1909

326

Prior to the Hughes rolling-cutter bit, there were several patents that described bits that operated in the same general manner. Some of these were the Catlin bit, Patent No. 9179 of 1852; the Sweeney bit of 1866 (see Fig. 9); the Reese bit, Patent No. 322,642, of 1885; the McLarty bit, Patent No. 633,974 of 1899; the Guttzeit bit, Patent No. 839,837 of 1907; the Frasch bit of about the same time; the Wittich bit, Patent No. 969,233 of 1910 (filed 1908); and the McLoughlin and Wynn bit, Patent No. 929,780 of 1909 (filed 1908). These several inventors preceded Howard R. Hughes with their ideas and patents, but it remained for Hughes to develop and manufacture the tool that was one of the most important contributions to the drilling of wells.

Fig. 46—First Humason Cross Roller Rock Bit, 1913
(Reed Roller Bit Co. Photo)

At about the time of the practical development and use of the cone-type Hughes bit, Granville A. Humason of Shreveport, La., filed application for patent (February 1913) on what was probably the first cross-roller rock bit of practical design and the forerunner of the Reed cross-roller bit. Fig. 46 shows the first Humason bit, built in 1913—another great contribution to the drilling industry. Both the cone-type rolling-cutter rock bit and the cross-roller cutter-type rock bit are presently manufactured by various companies.

Cementing

Casing had been cemented in cable-tool wells for some time prior to 1900. The first such job was reported in Ohio, and the process followed into other areas, including California where cable tools were used. Prior to the use of cement and even afterward, other materials such as bags of seed, beans, grain, balls of clay, soft lime, bark, and other substances were attached to the bottom length before running or were forced to the bottom of the well with the casing off bottom, and expanded to the walls of the hole. The casing was then lowered and driven into bottom in hopes that between the bottom contact and the material behind the pipe a water shutoff or seal would be obtained. It usually was.

When cement was used it was conveyed to the bottom of the hole in a dump bailer. After depositing the cement the casing, which had been held some feet off bottom, was lowered into the cement with the hope that a sufficient part of it would remain behind the pipe to shut off the water from above, upon hardening.

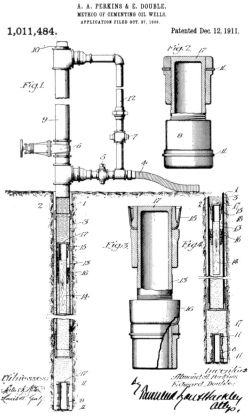

A. A. PERKINS & E. DOUBLE.
METHOD OF CEMENTING OIL WELLS.
APPLICATION FILED OCT. 27, 1909.

1,011,484.   Patented Dec. 12, 1911.

Fig. 47—Sketch—Perkins-Double Two-plug
Cementing Method Patent, 1909-1911

In 1904, F. F. Hill of Union Oil Co. of California (confirmed by letter from A. C. Rubel to the writer) conceived the idea of pumping the cement into the well and outside the casing. To do this job, he ran tubing with a packer set a short distance above the bottom of the casing. After establishing circulation, presumably, cement was pumped into the tubing and displaced outside and around the casing.

Although this method of cementing was reasonably satisfactory, particularly with the very small quantities of cement used at the time, the practice of pumping cement directly into the casing was more practical and involved less time, thus permitting the use of more cement.

In 1909 A. A. Perkins and E. Double filed application for patent on a method of cementing that used a top plug and a bottom plug directly in the casing and became known as the Perkins, or two-plug method of cementing. A patent was granted to Perkins and Double on December 12, 1911 (Fig. 47). This method of cementing became successful immediately and is, in basic principle, the system still employed. The patent sketch shows in diagrammatic section the well, wellhead connections, plugs, and the manner of their use. The bottom plug was placed in the casing, the cement was pumped in on top, and the top plug was inserted on top of the cement. Water or mud-laden fluid was then used to pump the top plug downward which carried the cement and the bottom plug ahead of it. The casing was held at a point sufficiently far off bottom to permit the bottom plug to pass entirely out into the open hole. In the early years of use the top plug had below it a spacer, usually a 4 by 4 timber, sufficiently long that when this timber encountered the bottom plug the top plug was still a few feet above the casing shoe.

Perkins' original method of cementing has been used continuously and in practically all of the wells that have been cemented by service

328

companies or by the rig crew, except that in later years no spacer has been used on most jobs and both plugs come to rest on a float shoe or on a float collar. On many early jobs a baffle plate or float valve (see Fig. 42) was used in the first coupling above the plain shoe, or coupling. No spacer was necessary with this device, both plugs coming to rest together on the baffle or float valve. The purpose of the spacer and baffle or float valve one coupling above the shoe was to have uncontaminated cement around the shoe. This is still an objective on all cement jobs. (See chapter herein by Millikan on cementing.)

Casing Shoes

In the beginning of the rotary-drilling industry, casing shoes for use on the lower end of the pipe were borrowed from the cable-tool operations. They were somewhat too heavy and thick for the usual rotary well, having been designed as drive shoes for carrying casing in cable-tool wells. The casing couplings, on the other hand, were not sufficiently heavy and did not protect the casing against bending and collapsing. This matter was discussed by the young engineers in the Coalinga Field with R. C. Baker who had previously designed and had built cable-tool casing shoes that were somewhat different from the old type, having a series of chisel teeth around the lower edge rather than one complete circular chisel. The original Baker rotary casing shoe was thereupon designed and made, and is still in use on some operations (Fig. 48).

This was the beginning of the manufacture of a long and varied list of devices of several types used in the running and cementing of casing in wells.

Couplings

At about the same time that Baker was designing his casing shoe, Chester Naramore—one of the young engineers referred to previously—observed the making up and running of casing with short couplings and devised a test to demonstrate their inadequacy. He and Baker made up 10-in. pipe with 6-in. collars, setting them up fast with chain tongs. Several joints were

Fig. 48—Baker Casing Shoe—First Built before 1910 and Still Manufactured

run in the hole leaving one joint standing in the derrick with the top at the stabbing board. From this position and with the lower joints hung in elevators resting on the rotary table, the upper joint, when rocked back and forth, jumped from the collar and fell to the floor. These results convinced Narramore and Baker that longer couplings were essential to the safe running of long strings of casing, and they arranged with Youngstown Sheet and Tube Company to have some made (Chester Naramore letter to writer). A few months later two carloads of pipe with these couplings were shipped to California and became known as the Coalinga-type collar, later the long collar of California DB-grade casing, and finally the API long couplings of the present day.

Tool Joints

There had always been much trouble with the threads on the line pipe, casing, or merchant pipe that was used as drill pipe. The cable-tool taper tool joint had been in service since the middle 1880's and was used exclusively on cable-tool drilling strings. As related by Naramore, one day in July 1912 M. H. Whittier drove into Coalinga to Al Guiberson's office where Naramore happened to be at the time and commented on the large piles of rotary drill pipe discarded because the couplings were worn thin. He said, "Al, the casing threads are too small to take so many make-ups. They should have heavier threads like the threads on our cable-tool drill stem and bits" (and thicker couplings).

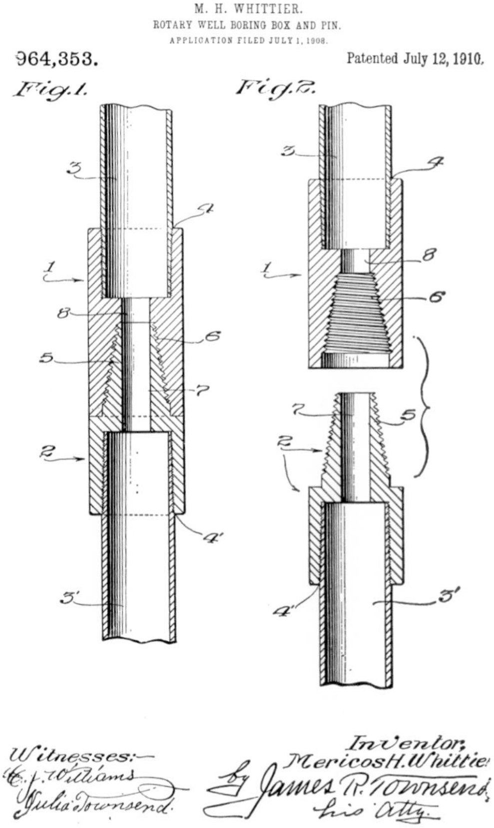

Soon after this discussion the first rotary tool joint was built

M. H. WHITTIER.
ROTARY WELL BORING BOX AND PIN.
APPLICATION FILED JULY 1, 1908.

964,353.   Patented July 12, 1910.

Fig.1.   *Fig.2.*

Witnesses:—
E. F. Williams
Julia Townsend

Inventor:
Mericos H. Whittier
By James R. Townsend
his atty.

Fig. 49—Sketch—Whittier Patent,
Rotary Tool Joint

by Guiberson using Whittier's design. This tool joint is presently in use and unquestionably has been one of the most important contributions to the industry. Whittier had received a patent on such a device in 1910 (Fig. 49). The early tool joints were quite similar to those in use 15 years later, except in thread design of the taper joint. Fig 50 illustrates the tool joint of the early years of its use. Fig. 51 shows the Hickman joint (1912) used largely to attach fishtail bits to the drilling shaft.

Kelly

The feed of the drill pipe and the bit into the hole since the commencement of rotary drilling, prior to 1900, had been by means of a grip with handles sliding down uprights on the Cameron-type table and by grip rings through which the grief stem (length of pipe) passed for its full length. The use of the grip rings and the tubular grief stem had many disadvantages, including the crushing of weak lengths of pipe and spoiling of all pipe so used by the vertical scoring. Slipping of the pipe in the grip rings and the difficulty of keeping them properly adjusted on the pipe were also serious problems.

In early 1914 Eugene Kibele, who had only recently gone with Southern Well Works in Chattanooga, Tennessee, as chief engineer and manager, called on Matthew Sweeney of the Sun Oil Company in Beaumont. Sweeney took Kibele to a Sun Company drilling well where they saw some of these several disadvantages associated with grip rings and tubular grief stems. Kibele promised Sweeney some thought would be given to the matter. Upon his return to Chattanooga he set up boring tools and drilled a hole through a round bar of iron. (Letters and documents in the possession of Mrs. Eric G. Schroeder of Dallas, daughter of Eugene Kibele.) This large rod was grooved to fit the wheels of grip rings and sent to Beaumont for use. Even though the device was not patentable because of a number of prior disclosures (before 1901), it was nevertheless one of the great contributions to the rotary-drilling industry. The grooves and grip rings were not entirely satisfactory so the fluted kelly with drive bushing was developed a short time later.

A recent article* states that C. E. Wilcox had the idea of a square stem to rotate the drill pipe on a Pacific Oil Company well near Taft in 1909. An unsuccessful attempt was made to interest manufacturers until he came in contact with Wilson and Willard. Patents were obtained but later were invalidated by the courts. The year that the first square kelly was built is not stated, but they were in use in California in 1915 (see p. 335). (see p. 335) The name is said to have been derived from the old baseball expression "slide, Kelly, slide."

It is reported by A. Beebe-Thompson that a square kelly was manufactured in England about 1914, for the Asiatic Petroleum Company. This kelly was $4\frac{3}{4}$-in. square and 28 ft long.

California Oil World, 2nd Issue, Nov. (1955).

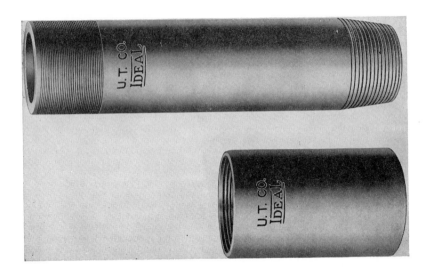

Fig. 51—Hickman Tool Joint to Attach Bits to Drill Pipe

Made at the Union Tool Company about 1912 and used mostly as a connection for fishtail bits.

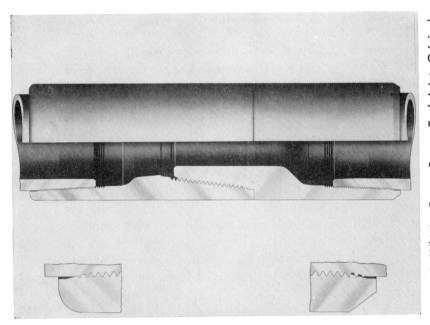

Fig. 50—Whittier Patent Rotary Tool Joint, Original Type

The two left of the cutaway sections shows machine fit, i.e., pipe screwed in on a machine, while the right-hand section shows the fit after string has been used for a short time.

Fig. 52—California Heavy-duty Rotary Rig, 1916
(Link-Belt Company Photo)

Fig. 52 shows a heavy-duty California rig of 1915 or 1916. The hoist is 2-shaft 2-speed, with double brakes. The three wooden posts and headboard may be seen. The square kelly is one of the earliest, supporting the opinion that the first kelly of this type was of California origin. This is doubtless a combination rig, although no part of the standard rig is visible. The chain is of the pin-and-bar type.

Swivels had shown some mechanical improvement by 1912 and were then capable of rotating 3,000 ft of 4½-in. drill pipe. Fig. 53 shows a hydraulic rotary swivel of 1912-1915.

The four developments of new tools and processes discussed in the preceding paragraphs—the rolling-cutter rock bits (Hughes and Humason), two-plug cementing (Perkins and Double), rotary drill-pipe tool joint (Whittier), and the kelly (Kibele)—were among the highly important contributions to the success and efficiency of rotary-drilling equipment. The long couplings and casing shoe were likewise important, but they were actually variations and improvements of then-existing tools. There were many other minor contributions during the interval between 1900 and 1915. The greatest accomplishment of the period was proving the usefulness of rotary-drilling equipment in drilling oil wells under conditions to which it was adapted. The development of oil fields in soft formations at any reasonable depth was made practicable.

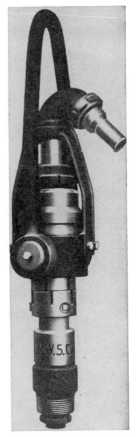

Fig. 53—Oil Well Supply Co. Swivel, 1912-1915

Drilling Fluid

Although patent files carry a number of patents concerning drilling fluid, the more important fact seems to be that the entire 1900-15 period was concerned in recognizing that a "mud laden," gelling, or thixotropic fluid was essential in drilling wells by the rotary system in soft formations. This can be said to be confirmed by Heggem and Pollard and Murray and Lewis, U. S. Bureau of Mines papers appearing toward the end of the period (*op. cit.*). The areas of extensive use of rotary tools were along the Gulf Coast and northward, and on the Pacific Coast. These were regions of generally unconsolidated and soft Tertiary and Cretaceous formations to which the rotary system of drilling was suited.

Along the Gulf Coast mud-making clays occur from the surface down, and any mud that the hole did not "make" was mixed in surface pits

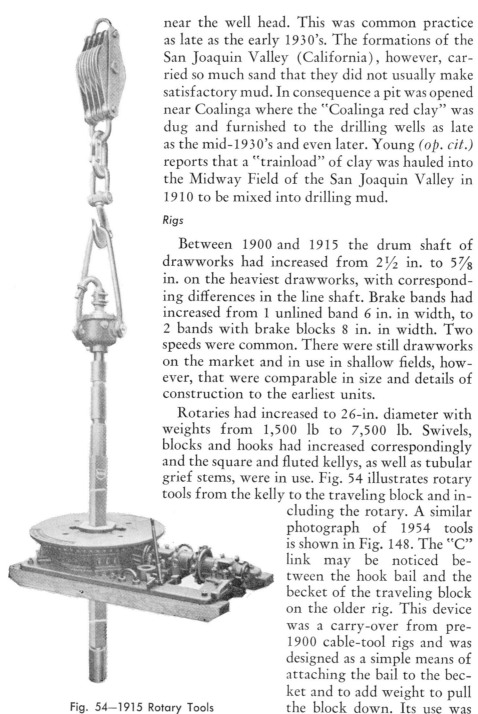

near the well head. This was common practice as late as the early 1930's. The formations of the San Joaquin Valley (California), however, carried so much sand that they did not usually make satisfactory mud. In consequence a pit was opened near Coalinga where the "Coalinga red clay" was dug and furnished to the drilling wells as late as the mid-1930's and even later. Young (*op. cit.*) reports that a "trainload" of clay was hauled into the Midway Field of the San Joaquin Valley in 1910 to be mixed into drilling mud.

Rigs

Between 1900 and 1915 the drum shaft of drawworks had increased from 2½ in. to 5⅞ in. on the heaviest drawworks, with corresponding differences in the line shaft. Brake bands had increased from 1 unlined band 6 in. in width, to 2 bands with brake blocks 8 in. in width. Two speeds were common. There were still drawworks on the market and in use in shallow fields, however, that were comparable in size and details of construction to the earliest units.

Rotaries had increased to 26-in. diameter with weights from 1,500 lb to 7,500 lb. Swivels, blocks and hooks had increased correspondingly and the square and fluted kellys, as well as tubular grief stems, were in use. Fig. 54 illustrates rotary tools from the kelly to the traveling block and including the rotary. A similar photograph of 1954 tools is shown in Fig. 148. The "C" link may be noticed between the hook bail and the becket of the traveling block on the older rig. This device was a carry-over from pre-1900 cable-tool rigs and was designed as a simple means of attaching the bail to the becket and to add weight to pull the block down. Its use was abandoned in the late 1920's.

Fig. 54—1915 Rotary Tools

335

Fig. 55—Heavy-duty California Combination Rig, 1915
[From *Union Tool* Co. (The National Supply Co.) *Catalog*]

Fig. 55 shows a derrick floor on a heavy combination rig in California in 1915. It will be noticed that in size of equipment there does not appear to be a great deal of difference between the tools shown and those 20 years later. The illustration shows a wooden combination derrick with bull wheels, 2 Mannington elevators nearby, and a 2-shaft, 2-speed, single-brake, 3-post drawworks. The casing line is doubtless wire, although it looks very much like the catline but of opposite lay. The swivel is of an unusual type and the square kelly is one of the first used. The open table is the grip-ring type to which the kelly bushings were adapted. The spider bushings and wedge pipe slips are among the earliest. Specifications for an extra-heavy California rotary-drilling outfit for drilling to depths of 5,000 ft are given in Fig. 55a.

Boilers had increased in size from 20 hp to 66 hp at 125 psi in largest size, although 40 hp at 100 psi was the unit in common use. Engine size used had increased from 9 x 12 of the Spindletop rig to 12 x 14 or 14 x 14. A 16 x 16 engine was built, but does not seem to have been used on rotary rigs. A "duplex" engine is listed in the Oil Well Supply Company catalog for 1900, but there is no record of its use.

The pumps of the Lucas rig were 8 x 5 x 10 (Fig. 29). The first pump built by a manufacturer of rotary-drilling equipment and especially for circulating rotary-drilling fluid seems to have been the Parker pump of about 1905. Hopper reports their use in the Caddo Field in 1908 (Fig 40). The Parker Company of Beaumont became the Southern Well Works of Chattanooga, which company later became the Lucey Manufacturing Company (now The Wheland Co.). By 1912 The National Supply Company, Oil Well Supply Company, American Well and Prospecting Company (Bethlehem Supply Co.), as well as Lucey, were building new, big mud pumps. Probably others also, including Union Tool Company of Los Angeles, were building these special "big" pumps for mud circulation.

Pumps, until about 1912, had shown little change in design from the originals of the early 1900's. Fig. 56 illustrates a Parker Pump of about 1910. The discharge valves are under the bonnet in the center of the fluid end. When the new and larger pumps were introduced about 1912, up to 12 x 6¾ x 14 in largest sizes, the bonnet was replaced by 4 valve caps with 2 single-bolt clamps (Fig. 57 and 58). Pumps of this size were the largest built until about 1927 and were in general use until the middle 1930's on relatively shallow wells. Probably the most of the wells of the great East Texas Field were drilled (1930-1934) with 12 x 6¾ x 14 pumps built by various manufacturers.

Floor tools, elevators, wire line, casing, and drill pipe—with the exception of the internal-upset and tool joints—and all other items around the rig were more or less the same as 15 years previously. Modern-type tongs and elevators were in the experimental and trial stage.

2 40 Horse Power Oil Country Boilers Complete with Smoke Stack (unmounted).
2 6 x 4 x 6-inch Duplex Boiler Feed Pumps.
1 14 x 14-inch 50 Horse Power Ajax Stripped Steam Engine with Sprocket and Heavy Rotary Fly Wheel.
1 National California Type Double Brake, Two Speed Draw Works, including Oak Uprights, Drive Shaft, Drum Shaft and Brake Shaft Complete.
40 Feet No. 1030 Sprocket Chain, Engine to Drive Shaft.
40 Feet No. 1030 Sprocket Chain, Drive Shaft to Rotary.
11 8/12 Feet No. 1240 Sprocket Chain, Drive Shaft to High Speed Drum Sprocket.
13 4/12 Feet No. 1240 Sprocket Chain, Drive Shaft to Low Speed Drum Sprocket.
40 Feet No. 103 Sprocket Chain, Drive Shaft to Mud Mixer.
1 National Mud Mixer with Two Sprockets.
1 23-inch National California Type Rotary with Flat Top, Bushing, Driver and Slips, or with Bushing and Gripping Device.
1 Round or Square Drill Stem with Subs to connect with Swivel and Drill Pipe.
2 12 x 6¾ x 14-inch National California Type Slush Pumps.
2 Lengths Wire Wound Rotary Hose, 2½-inch x 30 feet.
2 2½-inch Rotary Hose Couplings.
4 2½-inch Rotary Hose Clamps.
2 6-inch National Heavy Water Swivels.
1 National Structural Steel Crown Block with 5 Casing Sheaves.
1 40-inch National Quadruple Rotary Drilling Block.
1 4-inch Strapped C Hook.
1 4-inch Casing Hook.
1 6-inch Casing Hook.
1 15-pound Sucker Rod Hook for Cat Line.
1200 Feet ⅞-inch x 19 Roebling Wire Casing Line.
5000 Feet 9/16-inch x 7 Roebling Wire Bailing or Sand Line.
6 ⅞-inch Wire Rope Clips.
6 9/16-inch Wire Rope Clips.
1 National Sand Line Reel.
1 Set 4 and 6-inch Fair's Mannington Extra Heavy Wrought Iron Elevators with Long Links.
1 Set 6⅝, 8¼, 10, 12½, 15½-inch I. D. and 20-inch O. D. Fair's Mannington Extra Heavy Elevators with Regular Length Links.

Note:—If size of casing is changed or other than American Collar Casing is used, specifications will necessarily have to be changed.

2 Pair each No. 33½, 34, 35 and 16 Vulcan Chain Tongs.
1 National Double Chain Casing Tongs with 6⅝, 8¼, 10, 12½ and 15½-inch Jaws.
1 No. 8 Robbins Chain "Backup" Tongs.
1 Each 4, 6, 8¼, 10, 12½ and 15½-inch I. D. and 20-inch O. D. Slide Tongs.
Necessary amount of Rotary Drill Pipe to drill to required depth.
Necessary Tool Joints for Drill Pipe to drill to required depth. One Tool Joint is used between every third joint of pipe.
2 6 x 4-inch Swivel Bushings.
2 Each 6 x 8¼, 6 x 10, 6 x 12½ and 6 x 15½-inch Water Head Bushings.
Note:—Depends on size and kind of Casing used.
4 4 x 24-inch Drill Collars, 4-inch Pipe Thread Box x 3¾ x 4½-inch Tool Joint Box.
2 6 x 24-inch Drill Collars, 6-inch Pipe Thread Box x 3¾ x 4½-inch Tool Joint Box.
4 6 x 30-inch Drill Collars, 6-inch Pipe Thread Box x 5 x 6 -inch Tool Joint Box.

1 Each 6, 8¼, 10 and 12½-inch Rotary Shoes.
1 Each 6⅝ x 14 x ⅞-inch, 8¼ x 16 x 1-inch, 10 x 16 x 1¼-inch, 12½ x 16 x 1¼-inch and 15½ x 16 x 1¼ inch Plow Steel Casing Shoes.
3 22 -inch Rotary Bits, 5 x 6 -inch Taper Joint.
6 18 -inch Rotary Bits, 5 x 6 -inch Taper Joint.
10 16 -inch Rotary Bits, 5 x 6 -inch Taper Joint.
12 14 -inch Rotary Bits, 5 x 6 -inch Taper Joint.
10 12⅜-inch Rotary Bits, 5 x 6 -inch Taper Joint.
10 9⅞-inch Rotary Bits, 3¾ x 4½-inch Taper Joint.
6 7⅞-inch Rotary Bits, 3¾ x 4½-inch Taper Joint.

Note:—Specification for Bits will have to be changed if other than American Collar Casing is used.

1 4 -inch Wash Down Spear with Trip.
1 6 -inch Wash Down Spear with Trip.
1 12½-inch Overshot to run on 10-inch Casing, to catch 6-inch Pipe.
1 10 -inch Overshot to run on 8¼-inch Casing, to catch 6-inch Pipe.
1 8¼-inch Overshot to run on 6-inch Pipe, to catch 4-inch Pipe.
1 4 -inch Male and Female Case Hardened Nipple.
1 6 -inch Male and Female Case Hardened Nipple.
1 4 -inch Tool Joint Fishing Tap.
1 6 -inch Tool Joint Fishing Tap.
300 Feet 1¼-inch Manila Rope for Cat Head Line.
2 Lengths 1¼-inch x 25-foot, 4-ply Rubber Hose with Couplings, Clamps and Nozzle (for washing derrick floor and machinery).
1 Blow-Out Preventer.

Fig. 55a—Specifications for California Extra-heavy Rotary-drilling Outfit [From *Union Tool* Co. (The National Supply Company) *Catalog*, No. 25, 1917]

Derricks had been increased to 84 ft and in some cases to 96 ft in height. Wood was still commonly used, although both angle-iron and tubular-steel derricks were making their entrance into the oil fields.

Fig. 56—Parker Slush Pump, Circa 1910

Fig. 57—Mud Pump of New Type Built about 1912 in Sizes up to 12 x 6¾ x 14
An early steam slush pump made by A.W. and P. Co. (now Bethlehem Supply Co. at Corsicana, Texas).

"GIANT MUD HOG" PUMP

Fig. 7909

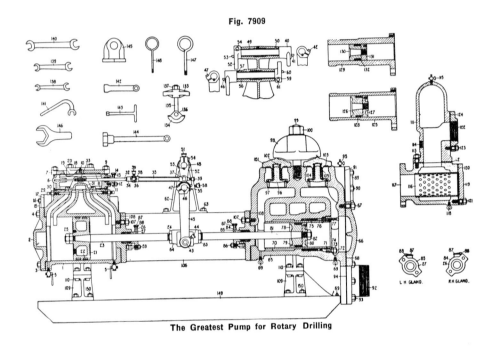

The Greatest Pump for Rotary Drilling

Diameter of Steam Cylinder inches	Diameter of Water Cylinder inches	Stroke inches	Gallons per revolution	Steam Pipe inches	Exhaust Pipe inches	Suction Pipe inches	Discharge Pipe inches	Discharge from Air Chamber inches	Weight lbs.	Price without Air Chamber	Price with Air Chamber
12	6¾	14	8.675	2½	3	8	6	5	6900	$775.00	$800.00

The "Giant Mud Hog" is designed along the lines of the "Mud Hog" Pump and will take care of 1000 lbs. water pressure.

All water valves are made of metal containing recesses to receive inserted packing rings. This brings the cost of water valves down to a minimum as these valves can be packed with hydraulic packing cut to size in cases where rings are not available.

This pump can also be used for pumping oil through pipe lines where large capacity as well as high pressure is required. When used for this purpose, brass valves can be furnished.

Fig. 58

(From *Oil Well Supply Co. Catalog*, 1916)

1915 - 1928

As previously stated, 1915-1928 was selected as an historical interval because of its being the period during which the many tools, machines, and practices that had been developed or invented prior to, or since the completion of, the Lucas Spindletop well were brought into general use and greatly improved. There were relatively few "inventions" during the period and few major changes of any kind.

Derricks

Derricks of the early part of the period were practically all built of wood, although the steel derricks, both tubular and angle, were coming into use. Fig. 59 shows the completion of a well in the northwest extension of the Burkburnett Field in October 1919. The wooden derrick in the foreground is an 84-ft cable-tool rig, but many of the towers in the background are rotary derricks of 96 ft to 122 ft in height. The Burkburnett Field saw the introduction of the rotary rig into that part of the Texas-Oklahoma area in 1918. Fig. 60 illustrates a wooden derrick in some detail, together with the rig layout of about 1916.

By the early 1920's wooden derricks were slowly but surely being replaced by steel. This replacement became more general in foreign fields, such as in Mexico, Venezuela, Colombia, and Peru, due in considerable part to the fact that these several countries had no lumber satisfactory for the construction of derricks; although Trinidad, Venezuela, and Colombia in particular did have very excellent hardwood timber for use as sills. By the middle 1920's practically all of the derricks built in these several countries and including Trinidad and Argentina were steel derricks, both tubular and angle steel being used.

At the same time most of the derricks being erected in the United States were still wood, the change to steel being first made in the timberless areas of the Mid-Continent such as Kansas, Oklahoma, and West Texas.

The great drilling campaigns of Oklahoma beginning in 1927 gave much impetus to the use of steel towers and the elimination of the weaker, less-durable, and usually more costly wooden derricks.

Specifications for wooden derricks of this period may be found in *A.P.I. Stds. No. 4 (1st Edition): A.P.I. Specifications for Standard Rigs and Derricks,* September (1927), or in *API Std 4B (14th Edition)* January (1952).

Boilers

Following the completion of the Spindletop well in January 1901, the locomotive-type boiler in general use on rotary-drilling rigs saw little change other than an increase in maximum size to about 50 hp by 1915 and up to 85 hp by 1927.

341

Fig. 59—Burkburnett Field, 1919, Wooden Derrick

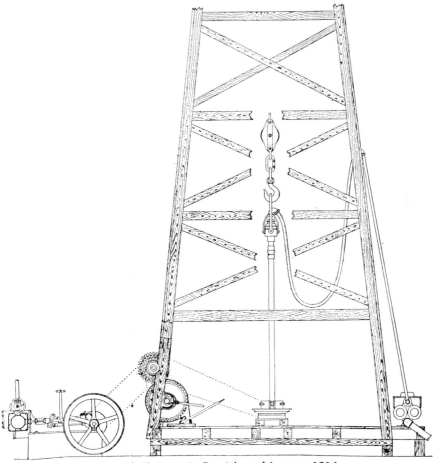

Fig. 60—Rotary-rig Derrick and Layout, 1916

Steam pressures increased from 100 psi in 1901 to 125 psi in 1915 and 175 psi in 1927. These increases in steam capacity and steam pressure permitted the use of somewhat higher-pressure pumps, although the sizes were not changed and the fluid delivery, theoretically at least, remained about the same. The increased steam output and pressure of the customary two boilers permitted the boiler plant to more nearly produce steam in sufficient volume to maintain the normal pressure. During these early years and even in later years, few rotary-rig boiler plants were capable of holding steam with the rig running at maximum capacity.

Although the locomotive-type boilers were used almost without exception in the Mid-Continent fields, shell-type return tube boilers were used almost as generally in California, where the maximum capacity was 100 hp at 150 psi working pressure.

Fig. 61 illustrates a locomotive-type oil-field boiler of 1927 having 85-hp capacity at 175 psi working pressure and built after API specifications of 1926.

Fig. 62 illustrates a 100-hp 150-psi shell-type return tube boiler of the California oil fields of 1927 and built in accordance with API specifications of 1926.

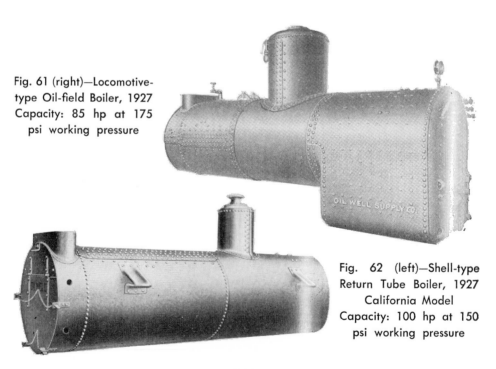

Fig. 61 (right)—Locomotive-type Oil-field Boiler, 1927 Capacity: 85 hp at 175 psi working pressure

Fig. 62 (left)—Shell-type Return Tube Boiler, 1927 California Model Capacity: 100 hp at 150 psi working pressure

Engines

The engine in most general use on rotary-drilling rigs throughout this 1915-1928 interval was almost the identical engine that had been borrowed from the cable-tool rig in the middle 1890's. Fig. 27 shows the 9 x 12 engine that completed the Spindletop well in January 1901. Fig. 63 illustrates a drilling engine of 1916, and Fig. 64 shows a single-cylinder, single-barrel or "mail-pouch" engine of 1927. These engines were built in sizes up to 16 x 16.

In 1918 the twin-cylinder reversible engine, which almost amounted to 2 of the smaller single-barrel engines with a common crankshaft and without a flywheel, came into use. As was the case with the single-barrel engines, they had slide valves and babbitt bearings on the crank-

Fig. 63 (right) — Single-cylinder Reversible Slide-valve Engine for Cable-tool or Rotary Rigs, 1916

Fig. 64 (left)—Single-cylinder Slide - valve Engine, 1927

shaft and bronze bearings on the crank pins. The primary purpose of the two-cylinder engine was to give smoother and more flexible power for moving the increasingly heavier drill-pipe loads and to eliminate stalling or stopping on center, as frequently happened with the single-cylinder engines. The heavy cast-iron flywheel and cast-iron rim weights with their several disadvantages, including explosions, were likewise eliminated. Fig. 65 shows a twin engine of about 1920.

There were considerable improvements in the twin-cylinder rotary hoisting engines between 1918 and 1927, including increase in cylinder

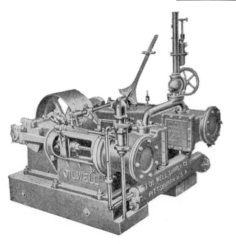

Fig. 65 (left)—Twin-cylinder Slide-valve Engine, 1920

Fig. 66 (right) — Fully En-closed Twin-cylinder Slide-valve Engine, 1927

sizes to 12 x 12, improved bearings, considerably improved materials, and enclosing the working parts of the engine for splash lubrication (Fig. 66).

Insofar as known, the first all roller-bearing piston valve fully enclosed twin-cylinder engine was built by Flory Hoist Co. of Bangor, Pa., for The Atlantic Refining Co. in 1926. This engine was built in a unit with a three-speed gear transmission and a free-running friction-clutch drum. The machine was used to drill several wells in Venezuela and Cuba. It operated in conjunction with a separate-drive rotary table and, though it was quite successful, no additional units were built.

Drawworks

In 1915 the heaviest drawworks had a 5⅞-in. drum shaft, two 6-in. brake flanges with a single brake lever, 2 shafts, and 2 speeds. The bearings were of babbitt and lubricated through an oil recess in the bearing cap. The chain was of the link-belt or, more generally, the pin-and-bar type. No. 4 (1240) chain was used on the engine and hoisting sprockets and No. 3 (1030) was used on the rotary drive. Fig. 67 shows part of a derrick floor of about 1921 including the hoist with pin-and-bar chain and grip-ring drive. There were still many single-brake, single-speed drawworks with 3⅞-in. drum shaft in use during the early part of this interval, and these were to be used for some years yet to come. In 1924 the all-steel hoist came into use, as illustrated in Fig. 68.

Fig. 67—Rotary Rig, 1921
Pin and bar chain and one of the last grip-ring drives.
(Link-Belt Company Photo)

By 1927 the 2 shaft drawworks had been increased in length to accommodate sprockets for a third speed. Drum-shaft diameters had been increased to 6 and 7 in., with line-shaft sizes an inch smaller. The three posts were generally steel, and bronze-bushed bearings had replaced the old babbitt bearings. Chain guards had not yet come into use except for the rotary chain. This type of guard, on some rigs, was made of sheet steel in a local shop, although more frequently it consisted of a 2-in. x 12-in. board held over the chain by brackets. Fig. 69 illustrates a 2-shaft, 3-speed drawworks. This drawworks developed complications on the standard 24-ft derrick floor, because of the width of the unit. The problem was solved by extending the derrick floor. Although this type drawworks was used quite extensively, it was never highly successful because of the length of the shafts and the difficulty encountered in keeping bearings tight and in alignment. With the increasing depths and the consequent heavier loads, the difficulties increased correspondingly and brought about the development of the so-called "jackshaft" drawworks having two posts, three shafts, and four speeds.

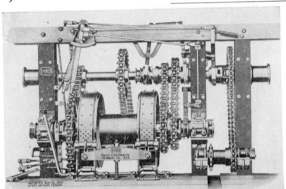

Fig. 68 (left)—Emsco All-steel Drawworks, 1924

Fig. 69 (right)—Two-shaft, Three-post, Three-speed Drawworks, 1927 Oilwell 353

Bits, Tool Joints, and Kellys

The rolling-cutter rock bits that had been invented in 1908 did not come into extensive and prominent use before 1915. Tool joints prior to 1915 were used on the inferior drill pipe of the day; and although the tool joints themselves were quite satisfactory compared to the old couplings, the lap-welded drill pipe was not adequate to permit the joints to reach the optimum of their usefulness.

The first bored kelly for oil-field service had been made from a round bar with grooves machined in it to fit the rotating wheels of the grip rings, and later a special bushing was used (Fig. 70). This scheme was not overly satisfactory so the fluted kelly was manufactured. This design was used for many years. The square kelly which seems to have been developed about 1915 in California (Fig. 55) finally superseded the fluted kelly during the early 1920's, except on some types of very small rotary rigs and on diamond drills, where both the fluted and the grooved kellys are still in use.

Thus the earliest of the square, bushing-drive kellys (Beart 1844) eventually became that which is presently in general use. A roller bushing is shown in Fig. 23, date 1886.

Pumps

After 1915 practically all the circulating pumps were designed specifically for oil-field service and built by manufacturers of other oil-field equipment such as The National Supply Co., Oil Well Supply Co., American Well and Prospecting Co., Gardner-Denver Co. and others. Lucey Manufacturing Company had acquired the Parker Company which built pumps for mud-circulating service about 1905. These pumps were of two sizes, viz., 10 x 5⅞ x 12 and 12 x 6¾ x 14. By 1915 well depths were increasing considerably, but few wells had been drilled to depths in excess of 5,000 ft. During that year the average Coalinga, California, big-hole well had casing set with rotary tools at 3,200 ft on top of the oil sand, and was drilled in with cable tools. The increasing well depths and the big holes drilled had rendered the old general-service pumps inadequate, and the oil-field equipment manufacturers were forced

Fig. 70—Frick-Reid Dreadnaught Drawworks, Circa 1920, with Grooved Kelly

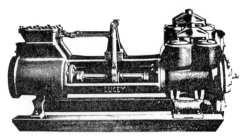

Fig. 71—Lucey Mud Pump of 1916 Used
into 1920's
(Note mud end)

to design and build pumps to balance the capacity of the more - powerful rotary equipment they were manufacturing.

Fig. 71 (Lucey pump) shows a typical 12 x 6¾ x 14 mud pump built about 1915. The slide valves were common to pumps of the time as was the method of securing the valve chamber caps by a water valve clamp and a single stud. Note caps over discharge valves in place of older bonnet.

Fig. 72 shows diagrammatic horizontal and vertical cross sections of a 12 x 6¾ x 14 pump of about 1915. Pumps of this design, size, and capacity were used on deep-well operations throughout the interval of 1915-1928, when they were replaced for deep wells by larger pumps. The water valve cap clamps with the single stud proved to be inadequate to hold the increasing pressures as deeper wells were drilled. In consequence, in the early part of the 1920's the valve cap and clamp were replaced by square valve caps having 4 studs, as is common practice in most modern pumps excepting those built for fluid-discharge pressures of 2,000 psi or more.

Power pumps came into service about 1922 (Fig. 73), but they were of little use for drilling. Fig. 74 illustrates an eccentric-type power end of a pump in use at the end of the 1920's.

Rotaries

There were no considerable changes in rotary tables between 1915 and 1920 excepting the change from grip-ring drive to kelly-bushing drive, discussed previously. About 1920, however, there were two considerable changes made. One of these was the development of the make-and-break table patented by H. G. Johnston in 1910 and 1912, later by C. L. Gross in 1920, Greve in 1921 and 1925, and B. Boykin, Jr. of Beaumont in 1921. The other major change was the shaft-driven rotary table.

Several manufacturers put make-and-break tables on the market in the early 1920's, and at the same time dropped a housing over the ring gear that at least partly protected it from the mud and water that came out of the drill pipe when trips were being made. The largest of the make-and-break rotaries were 20 in. in size; whereas the largest size of the plain rotaries was 27½ in., following the pattern and design of the machines of the previous several years. An idea of the difference in mechanism between the two tables may be gained from cost and weight. The list price of a

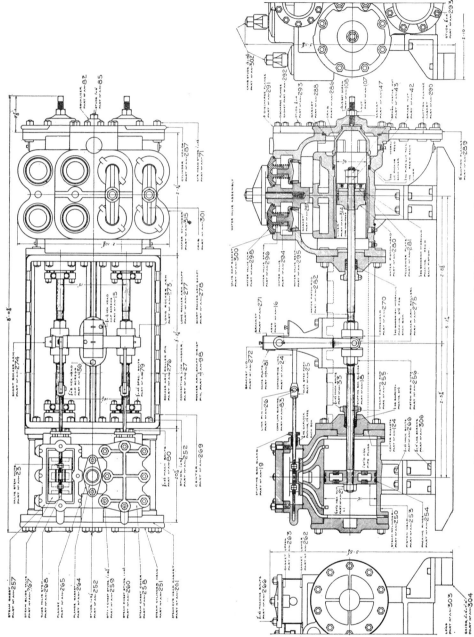

Fig. 72—Diagrammatic View of Mud Pump of 1915

Fig. 73 (above)—Power-driven Mud
Pump, 1922—Crank-type

Fig. 74 (above)—Eccentric-type Power
Pump Drive of Late 1920's
(Gardner-Denver)

Fig. 75 (left)—Grip-ring Table, 1916—
One of the Last Models

20-in. make-and-break rotary table in 1923 was $3,500 and the weight
was 9,400 lb. The list price of the open table was $1,800 with a weight
of 7,550 lb. These latter figures are for the table with bushing to drive a
square kelly as shown in Fig. 55.

Fig. 75 illustrates one of the last of the grip-ring rotary machines
manufactured (1916).

The grip-ring device, which was being used very little by this time,
added $725 to the cost and weighed 1,750 lb. This was doubtless an
additional reason for changing from grip-ring grief-stem drive to kelly
bushing and square or fluted kelly drive.

Fig. 76 shows a Greve patent make-and-break table engaged in
making up what appears to be 16-in. casing. The drawworks and table
drive are likewise illustrated.

The make-and-break table was a very useful machine, but for some
reason was not used extensively except in the Gulf Coast and southern
Mid-Continent. It went out of use practically entirely with the development of casing and drill-pipe tongs similar to those presently in use.
The use of the spinning line in making up drill pipe and casing likewise
militated against the make-and-break principle.

In 1918, 1919, and 1922 Victor York and Walter G. Black of
California, the latter for many years manager of the producing department for Standard Oil Co. of California, were granted several patents

Fig. 76—Make-and-Break Rotary Machine, 1922

on a shaft-drive rotary table. The 1918 patent is shown in Fig. 77. This table was driven by a shaft extending from the table drive shaft to a bevelled gear mounted on an extension of the engine shaft. This principle of table drive was not received enthusiastically by the industry and relatively few were manufactured. The York and Black basic principle of drive, however, was incorporated in machines built by Sheldon Ma-

353

chinery Company and the Doheny-Stone Company about 1928. It has been used again more recently in the National 160 hoist, first built in 1948. (See Fig. 124.)

Tongs and Elevators

Until about 1920, or even as late as 1925, the tongs most generally used in making up drill pipe were chain tongs of the single-jaw type. As the writer recalls it, 33's and 33½'s were the sizes generally used. The length of drill pipe was stabbed, the chain tongs were latched on, and the joint was then made up by three men passing the tong handles from one to the other. After the joint had been made tight by hand, one of the floor men tightened it by hitting the tong handle two or three blows with the back side of a 16-lb sledge hammer or, as commonly

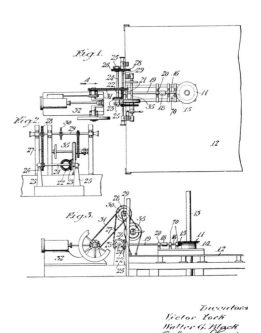

V. YORK & W. G. BLACK.
OIL WELL DRIVE.
APPLICATION FILED JULY 9, 1917.

1,277,166.

Patented Aug. 27, 1918.

Fig. 77—Sketch—York and Black Patent, 1918, Shaft-drive Rotary

called, "calf head." The joints were broken out in the same manner but in reverse order. If the joint was very tight, the cathead was used, with a tong line and the No. 16 chain tongs with a short handle, or "Maude."

Casing was made up with casing tongs or pipe grips consisting of the grip with a properly adjusted rope and a pole (see Fig. 78). Two or three 33's latched together around the pipe were likewise used. It was finally tightened with heavy chain tongs with chain of sufficient length for the pipe being run. During these years a number of pipe tongs were on the market including

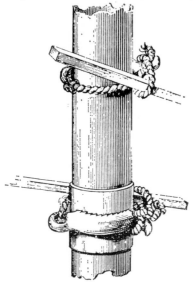

Fig. 78—Pipe Grip with Rope and Pole

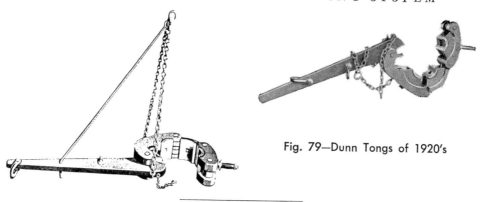

Fig. 79—Dunn Tongs of 1920's

both the Dunn (Fig. 79) and the Wilson (Fig. 80), but they had not yet come into general use.

The elevators in use were generally of the Fair and Mannington patents and a gate-type single-bail elevator made by a number of manufacturers. Slips were not yet in general use in the early 1920's thus necessitating two elevators to handle pipe.

Three of the men most instrumental in developing modern pipe tongs and elevators were Clem Wilson, Arthur G. Willard, and Web Wilson. In June 1954, the writer requested the only remaining member of this group, Web W. Wilson, to write an informal letter setting down his memory of the development of tongs and elevators with which he was and had been so intimately associated. He was the younger brother of Clem Wilson. On September 9, 1954, a long letter was received from Wilson, who died about 9 months later in June of 1955. Despite its interesting data and story, it is impractical to include the letter herein because of its length. Material from it is used.

The Wilson tongs and elevators, which are today used almost exclusively in the drilling industry, were an extremely important contribution to it (Fig. 80 and 81). There has been little change in design over the years. Those in the development of which both Clem and Web Wilson played the major part, have, since 1928, been manufactured and sold by Byron Jackson Company. Some years later, and after the death of his brother, Web Wilson organized his own company for the manufacture of other tongs and elevators.

Fig. 80—Wilson Tongs of 1920's

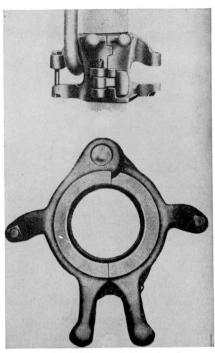

Fig. 81a—Wilson Elevator, Side-door
Type, 1916

Fig. 81b—Wilson Center-latch-type
Elevator, 1922

Bits

Until the early 1920's all drag bits, largely short to long fishtails, were heated in a hand forge at the rig, dressed or sharpened on an anvil with sledge hammers, and tempered in about 2 in. of water or oil. These tools would "make hole" rapidly for a brief period after which they would "slow up" and have to be pulled because of dullness or, not infrequently, breakage. This added considerably to well costs for it required several round trips daily. The steels of bits had been improved considerably over the old 0.30-percent carbon steels, as had the manner of dressing and tempering, but still the tools made little hole.

In 1922 hard-facing alloys such as stellite and stoodite came into use on drag bits. This proved to be one of the outstanding drilling-industry developments not only for drag bits and later rolling-cutter rock bits, but also in leading to the development of better, faster, and more efficient drilling machinery.

Although the untempered bits dressed with hard-facing materials were a vast improvement over the plain tempered steel bits in soft and medium-hard formations, they still would not drill hard rock. The later use of hard inserts was further helpful, but the drag bit still could not approach the efficiency of the short-toothed rolling-cutter rock bit or cable tools in the harder beds. In consequence the rotary in the early and middle 1920's could only compete with cable tools in areas of reasonably soft formations with possibly a few thin hard strata, which could be drilled by the early model rock bits.

Fig. 82 illustrates a forged-steel fishtail bit of the early 1920's. Fig. 83 shows a Hughes Simplex rock bit of the early 1920's. Fig. 84 shows a Reed cross-roller rock bit of about 1925. The short teeth of the cutters are clearly shown in the cuts.

About 1925, or a little later, new and greatly improved rock bits made their appearance. The improvements were first in bearings and tooth form. Whereas the old short-tooth cone-type bits would pack solidly with cuttings, the new bits were "self-cleaning". Both the cone-type and cross-roller bits had circulation nozzles so directed as to clean the teeth. This requirement for more fluid brought about the larger pumps of the late 1920's. The new rock bits had much longer teeth than the old hard-rock tools and were adaptable to drilling a much greater variety of formations—anything but soft plastic shales and clays—provided there was sufficient fluid circulation.

Following the use in the early 1920's of hard-facing materials (such as stoodite and stellite) on drag bits, these materials were likewise applied to the new long-toothed bits; and the cutting and wearing qualities of the tools were considerably improved. In 1928 the use of tungsten carbide in finely divided form was introduced as a hard-facing material. The first method of application was based on the use of the atomic hydrogen torch and was patented by Floyd L. Scott, presently (1955) chief research engineer for Hughes Tool Co. The later method of application was by common welding torch using an iron tube containing fine or coarse granular tungsten carbide. Fig. 85 illustrates an early model of the Hughes cone-type long-toothed rock bit, and Fig. 86 shows an early Reed cross-roller bit with long teeth. The teeth and cones of the Hughes bit were so designed and assembled that they were "self-cleaning". Both tools had water courses directed to clean the teeth.

In the beginning of the 1915-1928 interval, the bits in common use were—more or less in order of their importance—the fishtail, the disc bits, and two-cone rock bits. Diamond-point and long four-wing bits were likewise used for sidetracking and reaming. Throughout this period, as related, there were considerable improvements in these tools, especially rock bits, until at the close rotary rigs were capable of drilling substantial thicknesses of hard formation and rock in competition with cable tools. Combination rigs were in use in many areas, however, with cable tools being used in the hard formations and rotary tools in the softer beds. The rotary was introduced into the soft-formation areas of North Texas in the early part of this 1915-1928 interval. The Burkburnett Field north

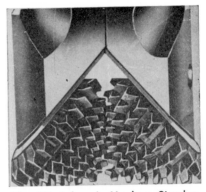

Fig. 82 (left)—
Forged Steel Fish-
tail Bit Used in
Early 1920's

Fig. 85 (above)—Hughes Simplex
Acme Self-cleaning Cones, 1925-
1933
Interfitting rows of long, narrow,
penetrating chisel teeth.

Fig. 86 (right)—Early
Cross-roller Bit
Cutters spaced apart for
drilling-mud circulation.

Fig. 83 (left above)—Hughes
Simplex Bit, 1920
Fig. 84 (right above)—Reed Bit
about 1925

of Wichita Falls was drilled with rotary, beginning in 1918. Rotary rigs
in combination with cable tools were introduced into Oklahoma from
this area in 1918. By 1927, because of the great improvement in rock
bits, rotary rigs started to play the most important part in the drilling of
oil wells in areas of varying formations.

Around 1921 or 1922 it was not expected that rotary rigs would
ever displace the cable-tool outfits in hard drilling. But the very rapid
improvement in rotary equipment, especially bits, enabled the newer tools
to displace cable tools in most of the fields of the world by about 1930,
except where cable-tool holes could be drilled without carrying pipe.

Beginning about 1920 or a little earlier, the value of the rotary-drilling system became apparent; and the changeover from cable-tool to rotary rigs as the more important equipment started. However, there were by 1927 few basic changes in machinery, tools, equipment, or practices, except that rock bits moved from the category of bits to drill relatively thin sections of hard rock to bits capable of drilling much greater thicknesses. The rotary rig had also become at least equally important with cable-tool equipment and had entirely supplanted the percussion rigs in softer-formation areas. There was a general modest improvement in practically all equipment and machinery and considerable improvement in those items that made for more efficient operation, such as bits, tongs, elevators, pump parts for fluid ends, slips, and cementing.

Cementing

The use of the Perkins 2-plug method for cementing oil wells was begun in California about 1910, based on the Perkins-Double patent described briefly on p. 328. It appears that very few wells of any kind were being cemented in the Mid-Continent oil fields during this period. T. H. Rakeshaw, in a letter to the writer, states that no cementing was done in any of the earliest rotary wells in Oklahoma but was well under way in the early 1920's. The 2-plug system was used with 2 blackjack oak plugs trimmed on the rig. This method was used in many areas, including the Tampico Basin of Mexico.

In 1919, Erle Halliburton undertook to establish a cementing service in Oklahoma comparable to the Perkins service in California and using the same Perkings-Double method. His first cementing wagon—horse-drawn—was in operation in 1920, as shown in Fig. 87. Halliburton made a deal with Perkins for an exclusive license to use his process east of the Rocky Mountains. This was the beginning in the Mid-Continent of the

Fig. 87—First Halliburton Cement Wagon, 1920

extremely important cementing service now offered by a number of companies throughout the oil-producing areas. (See Chaper 7, Millikan.)

Mud Lines

About 1923 L. S. Hamer in California entered well-cementing service and in so doing contributed the stopcock or plug valves to the drilling industry. Although this type of valve was one of the oldest in use—bronze valves having been found in the ruins of Pompeii—it apparently had not been used in the oil-well drilling industry. In connecting up cementing lines Hamer used three 250-lb stopcocks obtained in a local hardware store but these were not strong enough, so Hamer interested J. W. McClatchey in building heavier plug valves after drawings furnished him. (Letter from L. S. Hamer to J. E. Brantly, October 21, 1955.) All mud lines up to this time had used ordinary gate valves, clip gate valves and, later, high-pressure gate valves built by specialty companies for oil-well mud-line service. However the nature of the gate valve was such that it did not last and required frequent replacement, so there was a real need for the Hamer-McClatchey plug valve and later for similar equipment manufactured by others whose valves prior to this time had been used in refinery and many other services.

Fig. 88 shows the old Hamer hood-type cement gland with 3 stopcocks. These early plug valves were lubricated by removing the plugs, greasing all parts by hand and then reassembling. Grease-gun alemite lubrication was developed about 1932.

Fig. 88—Hamer Cementing Hood with First Stop Cocks Used on Rotary-drilling Rig, 1923

Hooks

Casing hooks had been borrowed for the rotary rig from cable tools where they were used in running casing. On a rotary rig, a device to jump the pin out of the box as soon as the tool joint was unscrewed when pulling a string of drill pipe out of the hole was extremely important as a time saver and to avoid wear and pull of the threads when the pin was hoisted out of the box by the drawworks. The answer to this problem was the spring placed in the hook above the swivel bearing. This was one of the many simple inventions that increased considerably the efficiency of the rotary-drilling rig during the first 25 years after the Lucas Spindletop well; and placed it, by 1927, at the point of usefulness where it could and was rapidly replacing cable tools in all but hard-formation areas where wells could be drilled with open dry holes. These inventions, developments, and improvements were in many if not most instances made or suggested by men on the rig or by "idea" men. Except for their work on bits and machinery, trained engineers played only a small part. The Wigle spring hook came into general use in the early 1920's and was the forerunner of today's hooks and connectors. Safety latches to prevent premature movement of elevators or swivel bails from the hook came into use about the same time (Fig. 90).

Rigs

Fig. 89 shows the upper end of the drill pipe, square kelly, rotary table, swivel, the hook without spring, the "C" link, and a 4-sheave travelling block without guards. This became standard equipment in the very late teens or about 1920. Fig. 90 shows similar items with improvements, 1924.

The discovery of the Signal Hill Field in California and its development in the early 1920's gave considerable impetus to the oil industry in that state. Intensive development was continued with the discovery of the Santa Fe and Dominguez Fields. These drilling campaigns promoted modest increases in the capacity of drawworks, the development and use of the twin-cylinder steam engine which had been introduced about 1918, the introduction of tongs and elevators similar to those presently in use, the use of somewhat higher steam pressure and slightly larger boilers, seamless drill pipe, and improved bits. One machine on the drilling rig that did more to control the rate of penetration than any other remained the same except for improvement in material and manufacture, and that was the pump. The 12 x 6¾ x 14 circulating pumps that had been brought into use about 1915 were still in use during 1927 on deep wells, although at that time they were beginning to be replaced in California by 14 x 7¼ x 14 pumps and by larger-cylinder, longer stroke, higher-capacity pumps in the Mid-Continent. Well-control heads and casing heads were vastly improved to meet the requirements of several strings of casing and multiple-sand production in California.

Fig. 91 shows part of the floor of a drilling rig in 1924. The fast tongs and elevators are shown. One wedge slip is lying off to the side and a 12 x 6¾ x 14 mud pump is on the derrick floor in the background. This is a California rig with 6-in. square kelly. The calf wheel on the left is used for spooling the dead line and doubtless has a single-cylinder engine connected to it by chain. It was probably used for running casing also. This is the type of rig that was used in the Signal Hill, Santa Fe Springs, Montebello, Long Beach, and Huntington Beach Fields during the middle and late 1920's. The 14 x 7¼ x 14 slush pump was added during the latter part of this period.

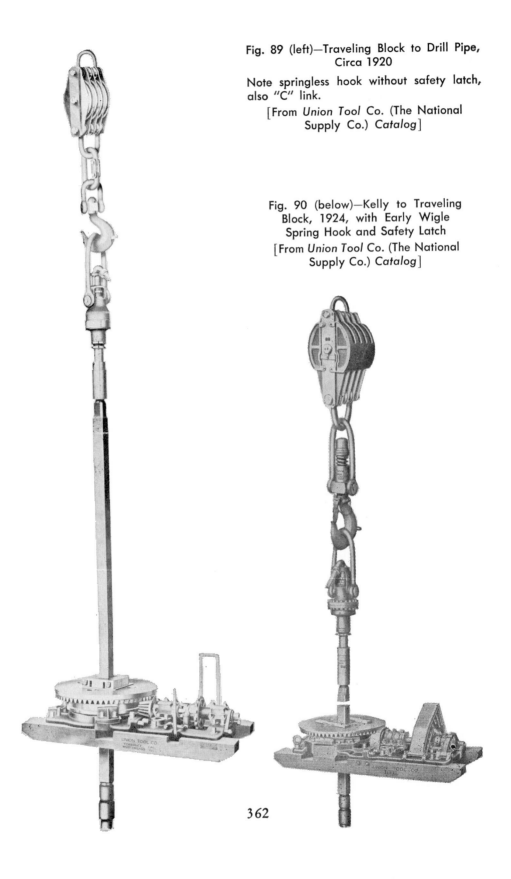

Fig. 89 (left)—Traveling Block to Drill Pipe, Circa 1920

Note springless hook without safety latch, also "C" link.

[From *Union Tool* Co. (The National Supply Co.) *Catalog*]

Fig. 90 (below)—Kelly to Traveling Block, 1924, with Early Wigle Spring Hook and Safety Latch

[From *Union Tool* Co. (The National Supply Co.) *Catalog*]

Fig. 91 (left)—California Combination Rig, Circa 1924

Fig. 92 (above)—Early Ram-type Blowout Preventer, 1915

Fig. 93 (below)—Cameron Ram-type Blowout Preventer, 1922

During this decade many important oil fields were discovered and developed in the Gulf Coast areas of Texas and Louisiana, in northern Louisiana, and adjacent Arkansas, where rotary tools were used. In these operations the equipment was generally lighter and cruder than that used in California.

Well-control Devices

As well depths became greater and higher pressures were encountered, the need for wellhead control devices to prevent blowouts became pressing. About 1915 Union Tool Company brought out a ram-type blowout preventer, as illustrated in Fig. 92.

Prior to this time the only blowout preventers were of the Decker and Hosmer head type that packed off around both the drill pipe and the grief stem or kelly. Beginning with cable-tool wells practically all holes drilled, except in known low-pressure areas, carried gate valves known as "drilling gates." These were made up on the surface casing. Next above the drilling gate was the flow-line nipple with a valve on the flow line, and above that was the Louisiana or Hosmer head type preventer. All of these early preventers were based on the ideas disclosed by H. R. Decker in his Patent No. 732,925 of 1903 (Fig. 43).

Fig. 94—Regan-Trout
Blowout Preventer,
1924

With the drilling of high-pressure wells in California and in the Gulf Coast, wellhead control equipment in addition to the Hosmer head became essential on many operations. The Cameron ram-type blowout preventer, Fig. 93, and the Shaffer blowout preventer of the same general type were developed during the 1920's. The second mentioned was built for wells in the Santa Fe Springs Field during the second drilling campaign in the late 1920's. The Cameron preventer was being developed for similar service in the Gulf Coast in the early 1920's. The Regan-Trout oil saver and blowout preventer was first built in 1924 (Fig. 94).

The ram-type blowout preventers, in their improved models, have been required safety devices on the great majority of the wells drilled within the past 25 years excepting those of known low pressures. Drilling gate valves were eliminated where either the Shaffer or Cameron control gates were used, but drilling gates with Hosmer heads continued in use for many years in important oil fields, e.g., the East Texas Field of the early 1930's.

During the great drilling campaign of the Tampico Basin in Mexico, just prior to and for a few years after 1920, the wells were drilled down to the reservoir limestone with rotary equipment, pipe was set, and the wells drilled in with tools through a cable-tool blowout preventer developed by Paul Weaver and Homer Craig. There was no control equipment on the wells as they were being drilled, other than the drilling gate. On wildcat wells that were drilled all the way with rotary, the drilling gate was likewise the only safety device carried on the well head. If an oil or water zone was encountered (there was little gas), there was usually time to loosen the joint between the kelly and the drill pipe, set the pipe on bottom, back off, and set the kelly in the rathole. The flow of the well could then be controlled by an extended handle on the drilling gate. There was no weighting material in the mud during those days and, in fact, there was little knowledge of the chemistry of mud-laden fluid. Drillers, however, had a practical knowledge of drilling mud and "conditioned" it accordingly with water, mud from the reserve pit, or fresh mud.

In these Mexican fields the casinghead pressure on closed-in wells was about 1,200 psi with wells about 2,000 ft in depth. The lightweight mud could not hold the pressure which accounted for blowouts such as Dos Bocas in 1908, Potrero del Llano No. 4 in about 1914, and Cerro Azul No. 4. There were many other wild wells during that great drilling campaign of 1919 to 1921. Three wells were on fire at one time in the Amatlan Pool in 1921. Extreme caution was necessary in selecting the point for the casing seat and in drilling in.

Drilling Fluid

The first material published on drilling fluid was in 1914 and 1915 by two Bureau of Mines engineers, Heggem and Pollard *(op. cit.).* Their work had to do with cable-tool drilling in Oklahoma and did not refer to rotary wells. Since the beginning of rotary-drilling operations, the value of or necessity for using mud-laden fluid in the soft formations then drilled was recognized by practically all drillers and operators, but little attention had been given to the chemistry of mud by the few engineers of the day and many blowouts and craters occurred in oil fields prior to the development and use of weighting materials. The Richland gas field was one of the several fields developed in northern Louisiana and southern Arkansas where a number of blowouts and craters occurred. The status of mud control at this period is revealed by the story of a driller who borrowed a pail and spring balance or milk scales from a dairy farm on the lease and commenced measuring the density of the mud when drilling in "dangerous territory." The distinction between weight or density and thickness or viscosity was, of course, important. Engineers and operators in this territory at the time were discussing some means of increasing the weight of the drilling fluid. The possibilities of the use of finely ground, high specific gravity minerals (barite, hematite) for increasing weight and "thickness" or viscosity was considered. Included was a discussion of the necessity for suspending properties in muds. At the time, Ben K. Stroud was chief engineer for the Louisiana State Conservation Commission. Stroud was a leading petroleum engineer, a graduate of Berkeley in 1904, and was coauthor with Paul Paine of the first textbook on petroleum engineering, published in 1913. Whether Stroud was solely responsible or not, he applied for and was granted the celebrated Stroud patent for the use of weighting material. Belonging to a somewhat later period is the Harth patent covering bentonite as a suspending agent. This apparently grew out of inquiries directed to Harth regarding the availability of barite for weighting material. Harth was chief chemist for the National Lead Company which had a considerable surplus of barite, used in some paints.

The earliest filtration studies in oil-well drilling were by Anderson and Kirwan of California. These were of great importance because they established that mud solids could not invade a formation of ordinary permeability because a mud cake is formed on all permeable beds. Unfortunately, this basic work was not continued and the subject was dropped for some 10 years.

In many areas the formations penetrated in the wells contained clay beds which would supply the mud needed for drilling the wells. In other areas it was necessary to use surface clays or shales that had to be mixed mechanically. Some mud mixers were horizontal, built after the fashion of the log trommel of the mining industry and clay mixers of the brick industry. Others carried the same mixing principle but, as a matter of conservation of space, were vertical rather than horizontal. Still others, and probably the major part of the drilling operations, used a section of the suction pit or a special mixing pit with a mud gun. The clays came out of the pits directly to the rig or mud-mixing plant. The use of the mixing jet for mixing prepared drilling-mud-making materials came some years after the mixing cone was used on cementing jobs.

Casing Heads

With the development of multiple-sand fields in California, together with the complication of the sections drilled, casinghead equipment that provided for running several strings of pipe became necessary. In the Santa Fe Springs Field as many as seven strings of casing and tubing were tied into the casing head. The Christmas trees also became more elaborate to handle dual-completion wells and large production. About the same time, in the middle 1920's, Gulf Coast wells were being drilled on which the old Louisiana pattern casing head or bradenhead would no longer serve. Wellhead equipment prior to this time had generally been made in local shops for the particular well, if the stock bradenheads were not satisfactory. With the discovery of new fields—many of them of high pressures—and fast development, it became necessary to standardize on suitable wellhead connections that could be stocked by the various supply companies. The manufacturers of such equipment during the middle 1920's were Hinderliter and Braden* in Oklahoma, McEvoy, Boykin, and the Beaumont Iron Works in Texas, and Regan and Shaffer in California. In addition to these specialized manufacturers of oil-field equipment, local shops still supplied a substantial number of casing heads.

With the use of the old bradenheads, little attention was paid to stretch and tension in the casing. Ordinarily there was only the surface string, the oil or water string, and the tubing. The bradenhead was made up on the surface pipe while the other string of casing was hung on the bradenhead. A pack-off between the surface pipe and the oil or water string hanging in the hole was obtained by packing expanded at least in part by the weight of the pipe. With running of multiple strings of casing it was realized by the operators that provision had to be made for expansion and contraction caused by varying temperatures.

The new heads were of two types—one in which the pipe was hung on threaded sections, Fig. 95, and the other on which the pipe was hung on slips, Fig. 96. Both types were used for a number of years; but because of the difficulty in obtaining the degree of accuracy required in cutting the

---

*The name "bradenhead" (derived from this manufacturer) was applied generally to casing heads in the 1920's.

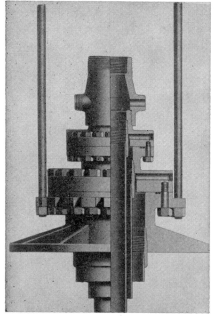

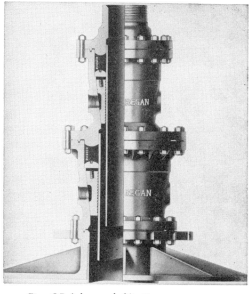

Fig. 95 (above, left)—Rasmussen-type
Santa Fe Head, 1923

Fig. 96 (above, right)—Slip-type Casing
Head, Shaffer, Circa 1930

Fig. 97 (left)—Louisiana-Pattern Casing
Head, 1915

pipe in the Rasmussen threaded type, it was superseded practically entirely by slip-type heads such as those used today. Fig. 97 illustrates the Louisiana pattern casing head used since the early days of the industry.

Practices

By this time — the 1920's — there were many petroleum engineers and geologists in the oil fields taking active part in certain phases of the drilling operations. They made the locations, inspected cuttings samples for oil shows, selected casing seats, and the size and number of strings of pipe to be run. There was some attention paid to mud control in a few areas in California and in the Gulf Coast fields. Otherwise the oil-company engineers took little or no part in the actual drilling of oil wells. That was to come some years later. Also the building of equipment was entirely in the hands of the manufacturers, with a few ideas from drillers, tool pushers, superintendents, and inventors who were observers of drilling operations rather than active participants. The engineers and geologists gave the most of their attention to the many and various problems of producing the oil. The basic training of most of these men was in geology, although a substantial number had engineering degrees, especially in mining. This subject is covered in the chapter in this *History* by Warner.

Coring

Until the early and middle part of this 1915-1928 interval, little formal coring of thick sections of sand or other formations had been attempted. The taking of cores was generally limited to a few inches obtained with the so-called "poor boy" core barrel, used at least since about 1905. This tool consisted of a 4-ft to 6-ft section of drill pipe with saw teeth cut in it with a hack saw or on an anvil, and later with the cutting torch. A hole about 1 in. in size was drilled 12 in. or more above the root of the teeth to permit the fluid to escape from the very slowly operating pump. The tool was run to bottom and rotated until a sufficient length of core was obtained. The pump was then shut off, weight put on the tool, and core was "burned in." The use of the term was quite well-chosen; the heat developed without fluid and—with the weight on the tools on a hard-formation bottom—frequently drove the oil out of the core, sintered the material close to the teeth of the core barrel, and at times partly welded the teeth together.

The geologist was now beginning to have some authority in certain phases of the drilling of wells. More, better, and longer cores and carefully taken samples were necessary to their studies of the formations. Microscopic studies of fossil forms and mineral content of beds drilled were used for correlation of formations.

Well-designed core barrels had been used with a great deal of success on diamond-core drills for many years. The tools used included single-tube barrels, double tube with both barrels rotating together, and a double tube with the inner barrel hanging on a swivel head. It was a relatively minor step from these excellent coring tools used on diamond drills, calyx, and shot drills, but there seems to have been no effort to adapt them to oil-field service until a short time prior to 1920.

One of the first companies to undertake the development of coring tools for the recovery of oil-well cores was Shell Oil Company of California. At that time the Department of Exploration and Exploitation of Shell was under the direction of B. H. van der Linden. J. E. Elliott, then a member of the oil-field engineering staff of the company in van der Linden's department, was assigned to a coring project. In the beginning they used a double-tube core barrel that had been developed by Dr. van der Gracht, at that time chief geologist for the Shell group, for taking cores in the coal fields of Holland. This seems to have been a double-tube core barrel of the diamond-drill type with very little clearance between the inner and outer tubes. The bit was designed for use in soft formations with the restricted circulation caused by inadequate space between outer and inner tubes. In consequence the bit would ball up rather badly, blocking the circulation holes and necessitating frequent round trips to clean the tool. Many changes were made in the shops of the company, but the resulting modifications did not improve the ability of the tool to do a satisfactory job of coring (letter J. E. Elliott to John R. Suman, May 11, 1954).

Elliott resigned from Shell Oil Company at the end of 1920 and, after a brief turn as Associate Professor of Petroleum Technology at Stanford University, returned to the oil industry, designed a core barrel and bits based on his past experience, and established a service for taking cores for various operators in California. His first contracts were with the Chanslor-Canfield Midway Oil Co., the Western Union Oil Company (subsequently Shell Oil Company), and Petroleum Midway Corporation (subsequently The Texas Company). Each of his three contracts called for five cores. Each core had to be at least 6 in. in length — otherwise the contract price was not paid for that particular core. Insofar as known, this was the first coring service offered to the oil industry. The contracts themselves were very enlightening in that they called for minimum length of 6 in. for each core, which gives a fair idea of the amount and difficulty of coring at the time. Elliott subsequently organized the Elliott Core Drilling Company and designed the core barrels and bits that were used in his coring service. In 1938 the Elliott Core Drilling Company was sold to Byron Jackson Company.

At about the same time that Elliott was starting his coring service, a core drill was developed in Mexico for coring the Cretaceous limestone of the producing formations. These formations, the San Felipe and Tamaulipus, carried considerable chert and soft bentonite. The double-tube swivel-type core barrel was patterned after core barrels used in diamond drilling, but so designed at the bit end that the cores were entirely free of contact with the circulating fluid and with more clearance between tubes. The bits were set with hexagonal tungsten carbide made in Germany and believed to be the first material of this kind ever used in the oil fields (1923). The tool worked very satisfactorily and on one well in 1926 (Aguada No. 26, Cortez Oil Co.) approximately 1,000 ft of formation were cored with practically 100 percent recovery. The materials cored were limestone, shale, bentonite, and chert. The cores would not fit in 1,000 ft of trays.

At about the same time, in the early 1920's, Hughes and Reed began the manufacture of their core barrels using both rolling-cutter bits and drag bits. The wire-line core barrel likewise came into service during this period, being manufactured and marketed by Reed Roller Bit Company. The previously mentioned barrel developed in Mexico was modified about 1925, and became a soft-formation tool for use in Venezuela. It became the standard double-tube-swivel-type core barrel manufactured by the Sullivan Machinery Company (Joy Manufacturing Company) and used especially in structure drilling.

Rigs

Although this period (1915-1928) saw few changes in the basic components of the drilling rig, it did see the introduction of a number of new and many improved tools and accessories. Boiler sizes increased from 60 to 85 hp at 125 psi working pressure in the locomotive type, and to 100 hp at 100 psi working pressure in the shell type. The largest-size pumps in use in 1927 were 12 x 6¾ x 14, which was precisely the same pump that came into service in 1915, although considerably improved in fluid-end design and in material and pressure rating. The 14 x 7¼ x 14 pumps built by The National Supply Co. and Gardner-Denver came in about this time, while the Wilson-Snyder 14 x 7¼ x 18 pumps were on the drawing boards and followed shortly thereafter.

A short time before 1920 internal-upset seamless drill pipe was introduced by Spang-Chalfant in Oklahoma. Sizes were 4½-in. to 6⅝-in. Tool joints were standardized by API committees in 1925. Bit-dressing procedures were greatly improved and three-way drag bits and disc bits were used. Tungsten carbide inserts and hard alloys such as stellite and stoodite came into use. In design the drag bits remained about the same, but rolling-cutter rock bits improved materially. Such tools as tongs, elevators, slips, and casing spiders also were improved during the interval and the changes accounted for a substantial decrease in round-trip time. Gripring tables went out of service entirely in the early 1920's, being superseded largely by the square kelly and bushings. Swivels and hoses were improved in materials and workmanship. The highest derricks in 1915 were 130 ft, though few of these were used. In 1927 they were about the same, with the 122-ft derrick in most common use.

Following is the inventory of a deep-well rig erected in California in 1927.*

122-ft by 24-ft derrick—galvanized steel.

Cellar 20 ft deep.

2 mud hoses 2 ½-in. diameter.

---

*Dievendorff, H. H. and Hertel, F. W: Deep-well Drilling Technique, *Petroleum Development and Technology in 1927*, 350, American Institute of Mining and Metallurgical Engineers (Incorporated), New York, 1928.

2 standpipes.

2 mud pumps (large) 14 x 7¼ x 14, 8-in. suction, 3-in. discharge.

2,000-lb pressure can be built up.

12 x 12 twin engine on hoist.

12 x 12 single engine on calf wheel, band wheel, and sand reel.

Drawworks—3-speed, extra-heavy, 2-shaft, 6½-in.—7½-in. drum shaft.

5 ⅞-in. to 7-in. line shaft.

Rotaries, chain drive, 25½ or 27½.

Swivels all-steel roller-bearing type.

Double-extra-heavy elevators, 2½-in. or 3-in. by 6-ft links.

8-in. Wigle spring hook—automatic safety latch.

Drilling line—1-in. 2,000 ft or 2,500 ft.

Dead line on calf wheel.

Weight indicator on dead line.

70- to 80-hp boilers (125-175 lb working pressure) 3 boilers per rig.

Mud-mixing plant, paddle mixer. Mud weight used 76 lb per cu ft-82 lb per cu ft.

18⅝-in. or 20-in. stove pipe or screw casing cemented at 650 ft-750 ft.

11¾-in.—13⅜-in. set at 3,000 ft-4,400 ft.

10¾-in., 9-in., or 8⅝-in. set at from 700 to 1,800 ft below next string above.

Well completed with 6⅝-in. or 5¾-in. casing.

Casing strings on a typical Ventura Avenue well were as follows:

Casing Size, Inches	Depth, Feet
13⅜	4,321
11¾	4,359
10¾	4,930
9	5,675
8⅝	6,055
6⅝	6,790
5¾	6,997

30-ft drill collar used. More weight above bit and easier to fish out.

Fishtail and disc bits faced with hard metal.

Used 6 drilling lines; 8 strung for heavy loads (running casing).

8⅝-in. or 6⅝-in. seamless upset drill pipe used in making surface hole; 6⅝-in. below surface pipe; 5⁹⁄₁₆-in. below next string; 4½-in. sets water string; 3½-in. drills in.

Coring cost—$20 per foot below 4,000 ft.

The rig equipment changes and improvements described were quite modest over the 12- or 13-year period. Casinghead equipment was great-

ly improved as were blowout-prevention devices; the chemical and physical characteristics of drilling fluid were being studied; and weighting
material and bentonite had come into use.

In summation, the only basic change or considerable improvement in
the principal parts of the rotary-drilling rig was in the engine, to which
one cylinder was added. In consequence of a small increase in steam working pressure and with mud-circulating pumps of the same or only slightly
increased size and discharge capacity, the increases in drilling efficiency
and rate of penetration resulted largely from better mud control, faster
round trips, fewer round trips because of better bits, and less lost time
occasioned by equipment failures. Therefore, although overall completion
time or drilling time improved during the interval 1915-1928, the actual
rate of penetration showed little improvement because the same type of
bits, the same fluid volume, same rotating speeds, and weight on the bit
were still in use. It may be said, then, that the interval from 1915 through
1927 was a period of improvement in accessories, tools, and machinery but
without material improvement in the basic items of the rig or considerable changes in the drilling practices used.

1928 - 1934

The years 1928 through 1933 are selected as a time interval of historical significance because, during that period, drilling equipment and
accessories were increased more in capacity and performance over the
equipment of prior years than in any previous or even later interval. It
was also during this interval that considerably increased numbers of oil-
field engineers took serious interest in the equipment, tools, and practices
used in drilling oil wells. The study of drilling statistics began, a few basic
experiments were carried out, and it was realized that the time consumed
and the cost of drilling wells were subject to great improvement. This
was the period of changeover from the old methods of drilling, based on
slow improvement of standard practices, to more modern practices based
on sound engineering principles—frequently at considerable divergence
from the standard practices of the immediate past.

Drilling machinery and practices in California prior to 1928 seem
to have been somewhat advanced over Mid-Continent and Gulf Coast
equipment and practices, according to the records available. It may be,
however, that the difference was apparent rather than real because of the
lack of comparable data.

During the period prior to 1928 it was customary for the driller to
use each item of his equipment to the maximum of which it was capable
regardless of other units. There was no thought of "balanced" rigs—frequently one inadequate basic item of the equipment would hinder and

delay the entire operation. The two weakest items were usually the boiler plants and the circulating pumps.

In the latter part of the 1920's several important oil fields were discovered in the Mid-Continent, particularly in Oklahoma. Highly competitive drilling campaigns developed, with every effort being made to get wells into production in the briefest time possible. These fields included Fitts, Oklahoma City, and the Seminole area. There was no proration in those days, at least in the beginning. Company tools and contractors' equipment were operated to complete wells as rapidly as possible and ahead of their offsets in order that the flush production might be the maximum obtainable. As a consequence of the intensive highly competitive drilling campaign and the demand for faster completion, the major items of equipment on the drilling rig were improved in design, materials, workmanship, and especially size and capacity. Boilers were increased in size and pressure from 85 hp and 125 psi working pressure in 1927, to 125 hp and 250 to 350 psi working pressure a year or two later. Pumps were increased in size from 12 x 6¾ x 14 and 14 x 7¼ x 14 delivering 300 to 450 gal per min, to 14 x 7¼ x 18 and 15 x 7¾ x 20 delivering in excess of 600 and 800 gal per min, respectively, and working pressures were increased correspondingly. Fig. 98 illustrates stream pumps of early 1930's. Pumps of this design, and even a few of these identical units, were still in use on steam rigs in 1955. Few changes in the design of steam pumps have been made since the 1930-1933 period other than a triplex pump brought out about 1935.

Fig. 98—Battery of 15 x 7¾ x 20 Steam Circulating Pumps, Circa 1933

The outstanding developments of the 1928-1934 interval, in addition to the improvement and great increase in capacity of the various basic items of the rotary-drilling rig, were:

1. The formation tester.
2. General use of plug valves or stopcocks for mud-pump manifolds.
3. The steel hose.
4. The beginning of mud control (3 technical papers on drilling mud were written prior to 1930, whereas in 1930 there were 23 such articles*).
5. Rock-bit improvements, including the unitized bit.
6. General use of tungsten carbide and other hard alloys in dressing all bits.
7. Hole-surveying instruments led by the acid bottle.
8. The requirements for drilling wells having inclinations not in excess of 3 deg from the vertical in some areas and 5 deg or somewhat more in others.
9. The 2-shaft, 4-speed drawworks, powered by twin-cylinder roller-bearing steam engines.
10. The hydromatic brake.
11. Automatic catheads.
12. Hard pump liners and rods.
13. Improved piston and valve packing.
14. The introduction of both internal-combustion engines and electric-powered rigs.
15. Full-hole tool joints.
16. The separate-table drive unit.
17. Drilling-feed controls, first on torque and later on weight on bit.
18. Higher-speed rotation.
19. Shale shakers.
20. Much greater fluid volume.
21. Drilling-control instruments, including drilling-weight indicators.
22. Improved pump-pressure gages.
23. Torque indicators.
24. Controlled directional drilling.
25. The entrance of trained engineers into the study of well drilling and the beginning of control of drilling practices by them.

Engines were redesigned and built in sizes up to 14 x 14. Oil bath, piston valves, and roller bearings were added features. These larger machines were of finest workmanship built to operate on 350 lb of steam. Fig. 99 illustrates a fully enclosed piston valve 350-psi working pressure horizontal engine. Fig. 100 shows a vertical engine of the same period.

*Louden, Baroid Co.

Rotary tables were improved in bearings, and were fully enclosed to exclude mud and water and to allow all bearings and gears to run in an oil bath.

Hoists were increased in capacity and improved in design to 2-post, 3-shaft, 4-speed units with 9-in. and 10-in. drum shafts and roller bearings on all shafts (Fig. 101). Toward the close of the period these hoists were unitized by the operators

Fig. 99—14 x 14 Fully Oil-bath Roller-Bearing Piston-valve Twin Engine of early 1930's

and covered for protection (Fig. 102). Then in 1933-34 the manufacturers of such machinery developed completely unitized, covered, 4-speed, 3-shaft hoists with roller bearings on all shafts, precision-cut sprockets, and chain running in oil. With rigid construction and precision built, the life of all parts of the units was greatly lengthened. Sprocket and chain wear, with precision alignment, was reduced to a fraction of what it had been in the past. The Parkersburg hydromatic brake, introduced about 1931, is shown in Fig. 102.

Swivels, which had always given considerable trouble, were redesigned with better bearings and better packing, thus materially length-

Fig. 100—12 x 12 Vertical Engine with Two-shaft Drawworks of Early 1930's

Fig. 101 (right)—All-steel Three-shaft, Two-post, Four-speed, All-roller-bearing Drawworks about 1930—Not Yet Unitized

(International Derrick & Equipment Co. Photo)

Fig. 102 (left)—Front View—Humble Unitized Three-shaft Drawworks, Mid-1930's, with Parkersburg Hydromatic Brake on Extreme Right

(Link-Belt Company Photo)

ening their life and reducing trouble time. Traveling and crown blocks were increased in size, capacity, and particularly in sheave diameter. The traveling blocks were guarded and had improved methods of lubrication. The Triplex and Wigle spring hooks were built in sizes up to 300-ton capacity, with considerable improvement in springing and bearings.

Rock bits, formerly built with bodies of considerable size with replaceable cutters, were unitized with much smaller bodies and sold or "rented" as a unit, Fig. 103a and 103b. The long fishtail bits were relegated to the junk pile or to reaming jobs, while very short fishtails or gumbo bits and 3-way and 4-way drag bits came into use (Fig. 104). Coring tools showed considerable improvement. Drill pipe was improved in tensile strength, and full-hole tool joints were brought into service. Drill-collar lengths were increased from the 24 to 72 in. of prior years to 30 ft.

Derricks for deep wells were first increased to 136 ft in height with 26-ft floors; but by 1933 with the same height derrick, the floor had been increased to 30 ft square. Angle silicon steel was generally used in derrick construction.

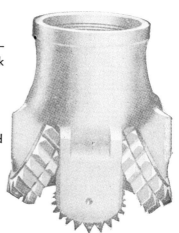

Fig. 103a (left)—
Hughes Tri-cone Rock
Bit, 1933

Fig. 103b (right)—Reed
Bit, 1933

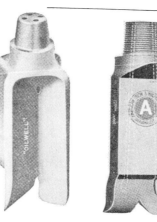

Fig. 104 (above)—Drag Bits of 1933

Development of this equipment was during the first half of the 1928-1934 interval, especially to meet the requirements of the new Oklahoma fields; but it spread immediately to the Gulf Coast and other parts of the Mid-Continent. The heavy new rigs did not reach California until the last 2 months of this time interval. The complete new rigs, excepting the unit hoists, were built and made available with all improvements shortly after 1930. The completely "balanced" rig with the unit, precision-built hoist did not come into use until late 1934. Such a rig required all new equipment, in proper sizes and capacities, to give balanced performance.

Despite these great improvements in equipment, probably the greatest of any comparable time interval in the history of the industry, drilling practices were changed only to the extent of using the maximum capacity of the various basic items of the rig. That is to say, the pumps were run at the maximum speed allowed by the steam available; as much weight was carried on the bit as the drill pipe would stand; rotating speeds were adjusted to the requirements of the cutting tool on bottom; and mud-laden fluid was that which could be made from the materials locally available, with weighting material added when high pressures were expected. These drilling practices in the Mid-Continent, controlled by the maximum capacities of the various items of equipment on the rigs, resulted in fast drilling, short-lived drill pipe, and crooked holes.

In California there was some improvement in the capacity of drilling rigs up to 1933, although the advancement did not compare to the Mid-Continent. On the other hand, by this time the petroleum engineers had begun their intensive studies of drilling practices and were entering into technical control of well drilling. Throughout the period 1928-1934 the drilling practices that were to result in such great improvement in rate of penetration in the next time interval were being developed in isolated fields rather than put into general practice. Mud control in particular was receiving a great deal of attention, and it was during these years that mud service companies entered the field in California and Gulf Coast areas. The first mud shaker screen was used in Oklahoma in 1930, but it was not until 1933 that this equipment saw considerable service.

The deep-sand development at Santa Fe Springs was well under way in 1929, with a production of 275,000 bbl daily. Wells were being drilled to depths between 6,000 ft and 7,000 ft with 200-psi steam pressure and 12 x 6¾ x 14 and 14 x 7¼ x 14 pumps. Table 1 indicates the marked improvement that was made in drilling time from 1923 to 1929.*

---

*Jensen, Joseph; Graves, McDowell; Gould, W. D; Gwin, M. L: Deep Sand Development at Santa Fe Springs, *Trans. Am. Inst. Mining Met. Engrs.*, 310 (1930).

Table 1
Drilling Time, Santa Fe Springs, on Carefully Selected Wells

Year	Depth, Feet	Zone	Average Feet per day	Associated Oil Co. Well No.
1923	4,741	Meyer	41.22	Green No. 2
1926	4,600	Meyer	59.74	Dewenter No. 5
1928	5,780	Buckbee	53.44	Green No. 3
1929	6,826	O'Connell	61.49	Dewenter No. 8

The greater part of the improvement was in overall average feet, rather than in feet per hour while the bits were on bottom; and was accounted for by the mechanical improvements and time saved on the surface, rather than by higher rates of penetration on bottom.

It was customary in California, prior to 1930, to use combination rigs on practically all drilling jobs, and this practice of using standby units—usually chain-driven calf-wheel—became common. On the rigs that used light drawworks in the 1920's, it was usual practice when running casing to lower it with the calf wheel (W. H. Farrand, communication to writer).

In the Santa Fe Field and other California operations of the middle and late 1920's and early 1930's there was a great development in casing-head equipment and Christmas trees. Where in the early days a well would have had two strings of casing and one string of tubing, in Santa Fe Springs many wells had six or seven strings with casing heads built to accommodate them. In a letter to the writer dated August 4, 1954, N. H. LeRoy of Shaffer Tool Works has the following to say concerning the deep-well development during the second Santa Fe Springs boom:

"The Santa Fe Springs deep drilling program probably brought more development in casing head equipment than any single field. It was for this high pressure field that flanged casing heads, the Shaffer gate and many such products were developed. The operators were likewise improving their drilling techniques and so the development of the well head business was synonymous with oil field drilling developments. Eight and nine thousand foot wells were being drilled with regularity which called for careful handling of casing, pressure control and other necessary precautions.

"It was during the second Santa Fe Springs boom that Mr. Shaffer conceived the idea of a ram type blowout preventer to seal around the drill pipe. Mr. Cameron in Texas was also developing a ram type preventer and both units were developed about the same time. The name SHAFFER or CAMERON immediately became associated with blowout preventers. A French oil operator recently told us that he thought the word 'SHAFFER' was an English word meaning preventer which is typical of how expressions originate in the oil fields. Braden Heads, Boll Weevils, Donuts, Santa Fe Couplings, etc., are typical expressions which originate from good selling, common usage, and advertising."

The drilling and development of the deep Santa Fe Springs sands did for the drilling industry in California what the Oklahoma fields had done for the drilling industry in the Mid-Continent, but in quite a different manner. In Oklahoma wells were drilled rapidly in relatively hard digging with the new, heavy rotary tools with rate of penetration and overall completion time greatly improved over prior years. In Santa Fe Springs the California operators accomplished deep drilling and completions in multiple high-pressures sands with substantially increased efficiency, but with practically the same rig machinery. This accomplishment resulted from improved accessory equipment and better-balanced drilling practices led by technically trained men. Round-trip time was helped by better and more-powerful twin engines and a few heavier drawworks, but the steam pressure and pumps were the same.

The major development of the East Texas Field occurred during the years 1932 and 1933. The drilling depths were $\pm$3,600 ft, while the formations were such that the first 2,500 ft were drilled by the usual rig in the field in less than 2 days after setting 100 ft of surface pipe. It was common practice among the crews to attempt to reach a depth of 2,500 ft within 24 hours after setting surface pipe, and it was frequently done.

The Austin chalk was encountered somewhat deeper and required 3 or 4 days of drilling time, after which more shales were drilled, and then into the Woodbine sands at approximately 3,600 ft. Normal drilling time, with 12 x 6¾ x 14 pumps and 125 lb of steam, was about 7 days. Overall completion time, including rigging up and rigging down, was approximately 15 days on the early wells; but during the latter part of the field development, as many as 3 wells could be drilled in a month with the same rig by moving in completion equipment after setting pipe and drilling out.

The drilling equipment used in the East Texas Field had generally been in use for several years, some of it dating from the middle or even early 1920's. The holes were not sufficiently deep nor did they offer problems that justified the use of the heavy "Oklahoma" rigs, although a few were brought into the field. The writer recalls a rig having three 350-psi steam boilers, two 20-in. pumps, a 3-shaft, 4-speed drawworks with 9-in. drum shaft, and other comparable equipment. A rig of this type had enough power to drill a well to the Woodbine sand in not to exceed 3 or 4 days.

Drag bits dressed with tungsten carbide and hard-facing alloys were used to and below the Austin chalk, while unit-type rock bits of greatly improved quality and dressed with tungsten carbide were used to drill the chalk. In the early days of rotary drilling the fishtail bits were dressed

Fig. 105—Zublin Bits,
Circa 1930

on the anvil at the rig; but with the development of 3-way and 4-way bits and disc bits in the middle and late 1920's, the service companies dressed the tools with a welding torch and hard alloys and rented the bits to the rig operators.

Zublin bits (Fig. 105), which had been used extensively in California and foreign fields, came into service in Texas during this period. The rolling-cutter rock bit manufacturers developed better bearings for the cutters; and discovered that mud-laden fluid, when reasonably free of sand, was a good lubricant for rock bits and the use of heavy oil could be eliminated.

There seems to be little question but that, by the year 1933, the Mid-Continent had considerably better drilling equipment than the best being used in California but was considerably behind California in drilling practices because of the greater use of engineers in this phase of the industry on the West Coast. Production engineers were plentiful in the Mid-Continent, but drilling engineers were less common. In California the petroleum engineers gave more of their attention to drilling; and finally, in the early 1930's, undertook intensive study and improvement of drilling practices. Some of these drilling engineers were Lot Bowen, Hy Winter, W. E. Gilbert, H. N. Marsh, A. C. Rubel, Ralph W. Marshall, M. W. Morris, Wm. H. Farrand, Roy A. Silent, Henry Grinnel, Clarence Froome, Martin Meers, Joseph Jensen, Jules Toussaint, Howard Cole, J. M. Bugbee, and J. E. Brantly. Working with them were engineers of the equipment manufacturers and other interested engineers and field men.

The Kettleman Hills oil field, which in its time was the classic drilling problem of them all, was undergoing intensive development in 1932 and 1933. Drilling costs were high because of the inadequacies of the equipment being used and of some of the drilling practices followed. Wells on the steep west flank required about 2 years to drill, and on the east flank, where formation dips were approximately 30 deg, took in excess of 1 year to complete. The top of the structure had relatively flat beds and was drilled in 6 months or somewhat more. The two primary problems were the 1,500 ft of hard, very tough, brown shale, and the Temblor formation in which the oil sands were interbedded with other hard tough shales. Hole-inclination requirements were within 3 deg of the vertical.

The upper formations offered no particular problems for drilling, other than the large hole and the inadequacy of the available mud pumps. The Brown shale was drilled with very little weight at a rate that rarely averaged as much as 1 ft per hour for the 24-hour day. With the relatively slow rotating speeds and little or no weight, the rock bits were kept on bottom for about 72 hours before they were pulled. The 1,500 ft of this formation on the flanks required as much as 6 to 9 months to drill in some wells. The Temblor sand was almost as difficult. Mud control had not yet been developed to any considerable extent, although bentonite and weighting material were used when needed; and the mud was treated with tannic acid to reduce viscosity when drilling some of the highly bentonitic zones in the formations.

In an attempt to reduce drilling time and costs in the North Dome Field, Kettleman North Dome Association, through a contractor, brought an "Oklahoma" rig into the field in November 1933. This rig is believed to have been the first heavy-duty "balanced" rotary-drilling rig ever assembled. Its capacity was equal to any but the very few heaviest rigs of today.

The well, 72-2P, was spudded November 25, 1933 and completed in late April 1934. The major items of this string of tools are as listed following.

1 — 136-ft x 30-ft angle-steel derrick.
4 — 125-hp, 350-psi working pressure, insulated boilers.
2 — 15 x 7¾ x 20 mud pumps — 350 psi working pressure, welded and flanged manifold, stopcocks (see Fig. 98).
1 — 14 x 7¼ x 14 service pump.
1 — 12 x 12 vertical steam engine (Fig. 100) (steam separator).
1 — 3-shaft, 4-speed drawworks, 9-in. drum shaft (not unitized on this well). Drip lubrication for all chains.
1 — 6-cylinder hydraulic drilling-feed control (first built).
1 — 27½-in. oil-bath rotary table.
1 — 300-ton hook.
1 — 250-ton travelling block, 5 sheaves.

1 — 250-ton crown block, in line.
1 — 150-ton, 6-in. swivel; 15-deg goose necks (first built).
2 — 4½-in. stand pipe, quick-relief valves.
2 — 3-in. 10,000-lb test hoses.
1 — all-steel calf wheel for dead line (standby) driven by
　　11 x 11 semi-enclosed steam engine.
1 — 2,500-ft 1⅛-in. plow-steel line.
2 — mud shaker screens.
1 — 250-bbl aboveground mud-suction tank giving flooded suction.
1 — 1,000-bbl mud-storage tank.
　　Mud-mixing pits for that area of field connected to well by 1,000
　　ft of 4-in. gravity line.
6,000 ft 6⅝-in. drill pipe with full-hole tool joints to drill surface and
　　14¾-in. hole.
7,000 ft 5⁹⁄₁₆-in. drill pipe with full-hole tool joints to drill 12¼-in.
　　hole.
9,000 ft 4½-in. drill pipe with full-hole joints to drill oil-sand zone.
240 ft 8-in. OD full-hole tool-joint 3140 steel drill collars.
180 ft 6-in. OD full-hole tool-joint 3140 steel drill collars.
　　(Note: First time multiple drill collars were used in such lengths.)
1 — junk-basket fishing tool, 7⅝-in. OD single-tube diamond-drill type
　　core barrel; 8¼-in. OD bit having teeth dressed with tungsten car-
　　bide inserts and stellite. Barrel 4 ft long. Diamond-type core catcher.
　　Tool was lowered over cones, cut 6-in. core, and pulled out. (First
　　such tool used.)

There were no recesses in drill collars, which were 30-ft double-box units with 10-ft double-pin subs between. Pin-up bits used double-box drill collar on bottom. Box-up bits used 10-ft double-pin sub on bottom. Fig. 106 shows the boiler plant of Kettleman Hills well 72-2P.

On the second location for this rig there was used for the first time in drilling history a rotary-drilling unit with 27½-in. oil-bath rotary driven by a 7¾ x 7 vertical, variable cutoff, reversible steam engine with 2-speed transmission; and the first recording and visual rate-of-drilling meter, showing pump pressure, rotating speed, and torque. Rotating speeds up to 400 rpm were used in the Brown shale. An additional boiler was added, making a battery of five to permit frequent washing while maintaining adequate steam. The boiler feed water was treated, but not very effectively. Tool joints were welded to drill pipe on later wells, following a similar job done by Associated Oil Company in Ventura.

On the first well drilled in the Kettleman Hills with this rig—72-2P in the Felix area—the bits used to the top of the Brown shale were 3-way and 4-way short drag bits, with fluid courses or nozzles designed for high-velocity fluid delivery on bottom, and Zublin bits. The drag

Fig. 106—Boiler Plant, Kettleman Hills Well 72-2P, 1933
Four 125-hp, 350-psi boilers, hot-water heater pump, water and fire controls. Rigging up.

bits were dressed with tungsten carbide inserts and stellite. Rotating speeds were approximately 125 rpm with conventional chain-drive rotary.

Rolling-cutter rock bits, both tri-cone and cross-roller types, were used in the Brown shale. Several types were tried with long-toothed bits rotated at the highest practical speed giving fastest hole—150 rpm with conventional chain-drive rotary. The Temblor formation was drilled with 8½-in. tri-cone and cross-roller rock bits at the same rotating speeds as in Brown shale. Drill collars were 160 ft to 240 ft in length with weights of 4 to 8 tons carried on bit in the upper hole, and 2 to 4 tons in Brown shale and Temblor. Six-cylinder hydraulic feed control was used from the top of the Brown shale to the bottom of the hole.

Fluid volume was 800 gal. per min* through the Brown shale to 7,200 ft and 600 gal. per min through the Temblor from 7,200 to 8,500. The well (72-2P) was completed in a little less than 6 months, as against 12 for the next fastest well in the Felix area.

In the early years of the development of the Kettleman North Dome Field the casing program approximated:

20-in. surface pipe—1,000 to 1,500 ft.

13⅜-in. intermediate string—5,000 to 6,400 ft, top Brown shale.

9⅝-in. water string—6,200 to 7,800 ft, through Brown shale.

---

*On later wells pumps were run in parallel, with reduced liners, giving 1,100 to 1,300 gal. per min in 14¾- and 20-in. hole.

384

6⅝-in. oil string with perforated joints opposite producing sands
—7,100 to 8,800 ft.

In the Gulf Coast and Mid-Continent oil fields, this last string would have been known as "full-length liner".

With the improved drilling practices, by early 1934 the casing program had been reduced to:

16-in. surface string—1,000 ft.

9⅝-in. water string—6,200 to 7,900 ft.

6⅝-in. combination oil string and liner—7,600 to 8,800 ft.

Well 72-2P was the first in the field in which the casing strings run were reduced from 4 to 3.

In the late 1920's and before the development of the Kettleman Hills Field started, H. N. Marsh was a field engineer for General Petroleum Corp. in the drilling of some of the deep tests in Lost Hills, California. The Brown shale was encountered at about 1,900 ft and contained salt water with an abnormally high pressure and some gas. Heavyweight muds were used to control the pressure. The high solids content of the mud, together with bentonitic shale encountered and gas cutting, offered considerable mud problems. In studying mud control, Marsh developed the funnel-type viscometer; and it was on his suggestion, or that of a close associate, that the Braun Corporation commenced making the mud-weight hydrometer for use along with the funnel, a very practical replacement for the pail and milk scales of the early days of mud control. The regular measurement of density and viscosity was a most important development, and 1930 found the industry using only these two instruments in the control of drilling fluids.

It appears that of all operating companies—in California at least—General Petroleum had had the greatest interest in drilling fluid, particularly in raw mud-making materials; and late in the 1928-1934 period a group of officials in that company organized the California Talc Company, as a supplier of mud materials. In the East, the National Lead Company in St. Louis, Missouri, had a very real interest in the same subject because of its position as a barite supplier in the paint industry and its interest in bentonite through the Harth patent.

After World War I, an industry-wide interest developed in the establishment of production research, including drilling fluids. In the 1920's it was agreed by leading engineers that drilling mud was a colloidal suspension and drilling-fluid research should therefore be directed by physical chemists. These discussions led to the assignment to mud research of, for example, Van Kampen in the Shell group; Loomis, Kennedy, Brown, and Ambrose in Gulf; and Cannon and others in Humble. The chemists brought to mud work from the ceramics art the first treating agents, sil and alkaline tannates. They also introduced the Stormer and McMichael viscometers, pH measurements, and settling tests. It is a continuing mystery to the writer* that titration for salt content of drilling fluids was not a required field-check procedure because this has so important a bearing on the physical state of colloidal suspension.

In the early literature, some mutually disagreeable properties were considered desirable, e.g., a mud should gel in the hole when circulation was suspended so that cuttings would not settle; but the same mud in the pits should have low gel strength to permit settling. The introduction of the vibrating shale screen about 1930 to remove cuttings from the returns was an important contribution. Also, further development and understanding has led to the practically universal use of low-gel-strength muds.

Conroe, with its near 1-billion-barrel reserve, was the most important field in the Gulf Coast being drilled up in 1933. The bottom-hole pressure bomb had reached a fair state of perfection at the time; and it was known, therefore, that Conroe was a normal-pressure field. Yet some 12 wells blew out—some of them making disastrous craters and fires—and all of these blowouts seemed to have some connection with the withdrawal of drill pipe. The Humble Company therefore decided to investigate—with a pressure bomb placed on bottom—the possibility of pressure reductions occurring with pipe movement. This investigation was carried out by George E. Cannon, and is incorporated in his classic API paper, *(Drilling and Production Practice, 1934)*. The recognition of "swabbing action" and the effect of gel strength and hole clearance was indeed of great importance. This work led to the recognition of low-gel-strength muds as being "safe" muds, and to the necessity for gel-strength measurements for control of muds at wells. It appears that the California engineers missed the significance of this work, although their mud studies were well-advanced for the time.

Water shutoff on all cement jobs in Kettleman Hills, beginning in 1934, was determined by setting a formation tester a few feet above the shoe of the string to be tested. The first well so tested was 72-2P on the 9⅝-in. string in February 1934.

Drilling-control Instruments

The basic developments of drilling-control instruments occurred during the interval 1925-1935. For that reason, the story is included here even though the records of invention extend well beyond the interval—both before and after.

Since the advent of rotary drilling, there has been almost continuous improvement in the methods and equipment used. Drilling-control instruments—the weight indicator, the mud gage, the torque gage, the rotary-table tachometer—have been conceived and developed and have taken many forms—from the simple to the complex, from the grotesque to engineering masterpieces.

*These paragraphs on drilling fluid from contribution by J. M. Bugbee, in 1934 with Standard Oil Co. of California in Kettleman Hills.

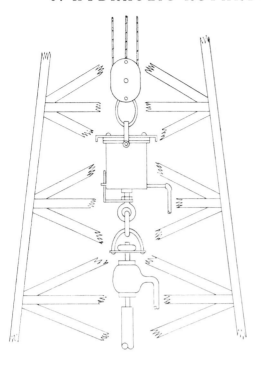

SHARP – NO. 839,656   1906

Fig. 107 (above)—Sharp Weight-indicator
Patent, 1906

Weight Indicators

As early as 1906 a hydraulic sensing element (cylinder), to be interpositioned between the hook and the swivel bail for measuring the direct load suspended from the traveling block, was patented by James R. Sharp (Fig. 107). Even before Sharp's invention some instrumentation was tried, as evidenced in his "Specifications of Letters Patent"... "The devices heretofore employed to accomplish these results are exceedingly large and have been secured upon the revolving table and are consequently inconvenient to the operator and tend to prevent the use of long pipe-sections and are therefore frequently omitted."

The first weight- or strain-indicating device actually to be used on a drilling rig may have

Fig. 108 (right)—
Fletcher Deadline
Weight-indicator Patent, 1924

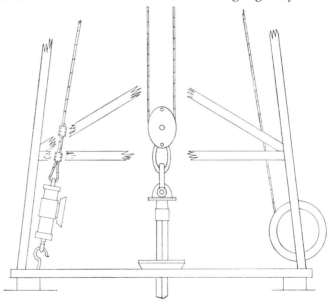

FLETCHER – NO. 1,483,426   1924

been a bailer tied back loosely to the "headache post" with the dart hanging a few inches from the floor. The movement of the bailer caused by the vertical deflection of the derrick when casing was being lifted could either have been measured or observed. This was rather a crude weight indicator but several patent applications were subsequently filed on inventions employing this principle.

It is believed the first weight indicator to be offered to the industry commercially was designed on the spring-balance principle. To handle the weights and take the abuse on a drilling rig, it had to be rugged. It used heavy coil springs, similar to those on railway cars, which were enclosed in a long steel cylinder. Extending through the coil springs was a piston rod with a follower plate on one end and an eye on the other, the latter

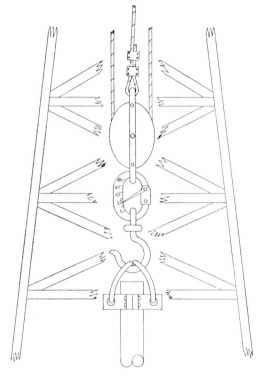

HUGHES – NO. 1,094,904   1914

Fig. 109—Hughes "C" Link Patent, 1914, Carrying Full Load of Pipe

being attached to the derrick sill and making the device a section of the dead line. As tension was put on the line, the piston and follower plate compressed the spring. A rack fixed to the piston rod drove a pinion on a shaft with a pointer which registered on a dial. The patent granted in 1924 to H. W. Fletcher was probably the first for measuring direct pull on the dead line (Fig. 108).

It is unlikely that any of the early-day inventors planned, or even foresaw, a world-wide drilling-instrument industry. They certainly did not envisage large control panels full of gages giving vital information to the drillers. Most of these men were merely trying to solve problems that affected their segment of the industry.

Following the efforts in 1906, a patent was granted to Howard Hughes, Sr. in 1914 on a calibrated "C" link to be interposed between the casing hook and swivel bail (Fig. 109).

Even a brief description of all inventions pertaining to weight indication from 1906 to the present (1959) would constitute a sizable volume. Suffice it here to point out the noteworthy fact that, during this period, more than 75 patents were issued pertaining to drilling weight indicators. Some of the designs for which patents were issued were not even reduced to practice—some were manufactured and submitted to the industry without commercial acceptance. Others were manufactured and tried without further development. Still others were preferred for a time in certain segments of the industry, and some were abandoned as a result of patent infringement or interference. The general principles of design were:

    a. Measuring the direct load suspended from the traveling block.
    b. Measuring the load applied on top of the derrick.
    c. Measuring direct pull on the dead line.
    d. Measuring vertical deflection of wooden derrick.
    e. Measuring a lateral component of the direct load on a dead line by producing an offset in the line.
    f. The combination weight indicator and wire-line anchor, in which the load is measured at the dead end with a lever system incorporated with a wire-line snubbing anchor.

Hughes, Fletcher, and Scott, all identified with the making of rock bits, recognized the importance of instrumentation—probably because of the damaging effect of excessive weight on rock-bit bearings and poor penetration when operated with too little weight. They used about all the principles cited except those of measuring a lateral component of the direct load on a dead line and the combination of a weight indicator and wire-line anchor.

The full impact of instrumentation on the industry was not felt until, in the deep-sand drilling boom on Signal Hill of 1926-1930, an inside well drilled to measured depth which should have made contact with the pay horizon did not do so. The hole was surveyed and the bottom found to be several hundred feet horizontally distant from the surface location, the course almost paralleling the dip of the formation for a considerable distance. Shortly after this incident a subterranean collision between a drilling well and an offset producer located several hundred feet away was reported in Seminole, Oklahoma. These and other incidents gave marked impetus to thinking and discussion of the crooked-hole problem, and the need for instrumentation soon became a reality.

During the 1930's and 1940's many companies tried their hands at weight-indicator design and manufacture but the majority of them soon gave it up. The main survivors are The Line Scale Company (Fig. 110), Cameron Iron Works (Fig. 111), Martin-Decker Corporation, and two manufacturers in Germany. The Line Scale Company and Cameron Iron Works manufacture unitized mechanical weight indicators which clamp to the dead line and take signals from line deflection. The original Martin-Decker weight indicator, Fig. 112, was also actuated by line deflection but used hydraulics rather than mechanical linkage, as did also the two

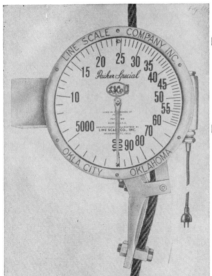

Fig. 110 (left)—Line Scale Weight Indicator

Fig. 111 (below)—Cameron Weight Indicator

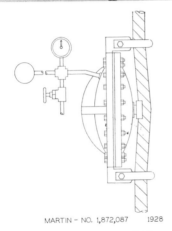

MARTIN - NO. 1,872,087   1928

Fig. 112 (above)—Original Martin
Diaphragm Weight-indicator
Patent, 1928

devices manufactured in Germany. One inventor, Joe Shimek, used steam or air to maintain deflection in the dead line with his diaphragm.

In 1945 John Spalding of The National Supply Company filed an application for patent on "Weight Indicator and Drilling Line Anchor." During the same year, John Spalding and E. L. Decker collaborated on the development of the wire-line anchor and weight indicator combination; The National Supply Company developed the anchoring device and Martin-Decker Corporation the companion weight indicator. In this combination the dead line is wound around a snubbing drum. The torque imparted to the drum is transformed to hydraulic pressure, the pressure being transmitted through a cylinder, piston, and hose to a gage at the driller's position. The piston and cylinder sensing element was abandoned in 1954 in favor of a stroking diaphragm developed in the drilling research department of Humble Oil & Refining Company and adapted to use in a diaphragm pressure transformer by an invention of Frank Crane, of Martin-Decker Corporation (Fig. 113).

Electronic instruments using strain gages adapted to links in the traveling-block system have been tried repeatedly and used with some success; but operating and maintenance problems thus far have rendered them ineffective as continuous-indicating instruments. As early as 1939 experiments were made with an electric strain gage for interposition

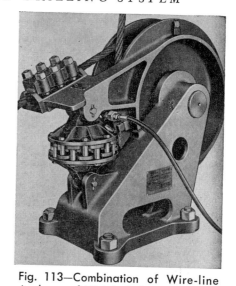

Fig. 113—Combination of Wire-line Anchor and Weight Indicator, Modern

The Ideal wire-line anchor provides a substantial tie-down for the dead line, and houses Martin-Decker's E-80 Sensater, the hydraulic pressure transformer that transmits signals to the weight indicator at the driller's position.

in the dead line. All electric, electronic, and hydraulic instruments can be, and have frequently been, equipped with recording devices.

In the early 1950's Gulf Oil Corporation developed a hydraulic and spring-actuated bottom-hole recording device in an effort to correlate bottom-hole weights with surface-indicated weights, but no general conclusions have yet been published.

Mud-pressure Gages

Following the acceptance of the weight indicator in its broader aspects, the mud-pressure gage became popularly accepted by the drilling fraternity. It was realized that, without adequate mud circulation and pressure, the rotary system could not function properly, although gas and air are being used successfully in some areas.

The development of mud gages was accelerated by an accident on a rig in the San Joaquin Valley in California. The mud end of a pump blew up and killed the driller. Immediately, company officials clamored for a pressure gage that could warn the crew of dangerous mud pressures.

The first mud gages were far from perfect. The ordinary bourdon-tube gage would function for a few minutes and then clog with mud. From 1927 on, continuous experimentation was undertaken. Cameron Iron Works, Fig. 114, Martin-Decker Corporation, Fig. 115, and others,

Fig. 114—Cameron Mud-pressure
Gages, Modern

Usually installed on the mud pumps
themselves for the benefit of the der-
rickman, as well as where visible to
the driller.

Fig. 115—Martin-Decker Mud-pressure
Gage, Modern

Usually installed in the instrument
panel for the driller's information.

eventually developed dependable gage protectors and damping devices
which permitted the operation of the pressure gages, and even recording
devices when desired. At the present, mud-pump pressure gages are quite
dependable, being designed to withstand the terrific vibration of the duplex pumps and hydraulic surges in the fluid system. All rigs are now
equipped with one or more mud gages of one type or another. Pressure-
relief valves have always been, and are still, essential safety devices.

It is worthy of mention here that ordinary stock instruments have
not been successful on drilling rigs. Extremes of temperature, corrosion,
vibration, humidity, and unusually difficult service, installation, and moving problems, require specially designed instruments; and invariably the
successful drilling-rig instruments have been so designed and built.

Today indicating and recording instruments are used in many processes and operations other than in the actual drilling operation—for example, all cementing, acidizing, and fracturing operations employ special indicating and recording instruments. More and more tubing and
casing is run with power tongs, on which torque gages and recorders are
used to record the foot-pounds of torque, and the time required to set
up each joint.

Torque Gages

About 1928, shortly after weight indicators and mud-pump pressure gages became generally accepted, engineers began investigating the
benefits of drill-pipe torque measurements. Inasmuch as most rigs were

Fig. 116—Martin-Decker Hydro-Mech Torque Instrument

The idler is installed under the rotary chain, and as torque is increased so does the pressure of the chain riding over the rubber-tired wheel. The more the idler is depressed, the greater is the pressure that develops in the hydraulic cylinder and in the hose leading to the gage on the rig floor.

steam-powered at the time, the most logical approach was the measurement of steam pressure in the manifold of the drilling engine. This, however, presented problems of plugging, condensate freezing, etc. since the lubricant injected into the steam line would accumulate in the lead-off tubing from the manifold to the pressure gage, and, under continued heat and pressure, would clog the line.

A gage-protecting device was designed, and gages capable of withstanding extremely rough usage were built. These steam-manifold gages —or torque gages as they were called—were fairly effective and popular until steam rigs were widely replaced by rigs powered by internal-combustion engines. A special type of heavy-duty vacuum gage was then designed to function as a relative indication of torque on gas or gasoline engines, but there were no such simple means of measuring the torque of diesel-powered rigs. Early in 1929 Walter Thompson, then superintendent for Standard Oil Co. of California in Huntington Beach, developed a chain-deflection instrument for torque measurement. At that time most rigs were steam-powered, and steam-manifold pressure gages were much cheaper and easier to install. Torque measurement became more and more important to the driller, especially on deep and crooked holes where weight sensitivity was impaired by hole friction. Therefore, diesel operators drilling such wells sought a means of torque measurement; and 17 years after the original design by Thompson, Martin-Decker perfected the present chain-deflection type mechanical hydraulic torque gage (Fig. 116).

Tachometers

What was probably one of the first rotary-table tachometers was used on the Standard of California Mascot Well (a deep test) in Taft in 1930. It was an electric-generator type designed for permanent installation and was set in a panel in combination with the weight indicator and a steam-manifold pressure gage.

This latter point is noteworthy because the first remote-indicating

Fig. 117—1954 Power Rig with Drilling-control Instruments
The driller can see what is happening on the rig floor, but he depends upon instrumentation to tell him what is happening hundreds of feet below the earth's surface.

weight gages were merely nailed to the wooden girt across from the driller. When mud gages were introduced, they were nailed alongside. Somewhere along the line—perhaps on this Standard rig in Taft—someone realized that drilling-control instruments were becoming too numerous and too awkward to move around when installed in a haphazard manner. Consequently, the instrument panel was born, and all the drilling-control instruments were mounted in one easy-to-transport steel box.

Electric tachometers were expensive. They cost from $300 to $500, depending upon whether or not graphic recording was included, and they required special adaptation for each rotary because of the variation of drive ratios. A device using a small gear pump, constant-viscosity fluid, and a pressure gage calibrated against rotary speeds was also built and used.

In 1933 Martin-Decker Corporation developed a simple calibrating system for the common magnetic-type tachometer and designed various types of convenient takeoff devices permitting easy adaption to any type of rig. During 1934 Martin-Decker introduced a drilling-control panel consisting of 5 instruments, viz., weight, vernier, mud pressure, torque, and tachometer, which was generally known as the Quintuplex. Fig. 117 shows a modern power rig with drilling-control instruments.

Future Outlook for Drilling-control Instruments

The future of drilling instrumentation will depend largely upon the demands of industry. In the early days it took the instrument manufacturers many years, many miles of travel, and many calls on drilling men to convince them that a simple $200 or $300 "stool pigeon" was a good investment. The first requirement is to make instruments that will, in the vernacular of the field, "stay together." Those that require special installation and treatment are frowned upon.

Considerable research work has been done by the Petro-Mechanics Division of Borg-Warner Corporation with an electronic bottom-hole recording instrument, which is reported to record weight, torque, mud pressure, speed, and other forces at the bottom of the hole. However, at this time the results obtained with this bottom-hole recorder have not been published; nor has there been any mention of its results as compared to those of surface measuring instruments. If the industry continues to use the rotary-drilling system substantially as it is today, and continues to seek oil below 16,000 ft, it will be found economical for the operator to use the most accurate and sensitive instrumentation available.

1934 - 1940

These years, 1934-1940, were selected as an historical time interval because it was during this period that deep-drilling jobs became carefully engineered and controlled operations. During the few preceding years of engineering research, experimentation, and trial, drilling equipment had been improved in capacity and dependability to the point that it could handle with efficiency any job of the day. In fact, the capacity of the heaviest-duty rigs of January 1934 were equal to the capacity of the heavy-duty rigs of today (1959), with the sole exception of a very few very large outfits. The heaviest hoisting equipment of 1934 had 300-ton working-load capacity or 20,000 ft of 5 ½-in. casing with 100 tons of spare capacity. Swivels were capable of rotating 15,000 ft of 4 ½-in. drill pipe.

Beginning in 1934 the combination of improved drilling equipment, increased drilling-crew skill, and drilling practices based on sound engineering principles gave rise to the greatest increase in overall rate of penetration (a fair measure of drilling efficiency) that had yet occurred in the industry. This rate of improvement continued through 1937. A rate-of-penetration curve (Fig. 123) gives a fair appraisal of the results obtained during the period. Quite naturally it was in those fields where the most difficult problems were encountered that the most intensive efforts for improvement took place—Kettleman Hills and Ventura in California and Gulf Coast fields of Texas and Louisiana were the leaders in this regard. From these areas the new equipment and practices spread rapidly throughout the oil fields, especially the more difficult ones.

In Kettleman Hills, beginning with the year 1934, overall drilling time was decreased by approximately one half over the wells drilled in the field prior to 1934. This was almost entirely due to increased rate of penetration occasioned largely by the use of more fluid and long drill collars, with weight concentration near the bit allowing more tonnage to be carried and still maintain a straight hole. Bits were likewise being considerably improved during this time and rotating speeds were increased. As already stated, it had been customary to keep a rock bit in the Brown shale for about 72 hours before it was finally pulled because of worn-out bearings. In 1934 and later, with increased fluid volume, a slight increase in weight on the bit and faster rotation, the same or more footage was obtained from the bit in 24 hours. The same was true in the Temblor, while the upper formations were drilled at greatly increased speed by using greater fluid volumes and higher nozzle velocity. Competition for the fastest wells was intensive and the engineers and drilling personnel of the various operators in the fields gave much study and effort to improving drilling efficiency.

During this same period the Ventura Avenue Field was being developed and the operators and engineers there carried on studies and improvements in drilling practices more or less parallel to those of Kettleman Hills, although the problems in Ventura were not so difficult.

Drilling engineering had been developing slowly since about 1930, but in 1934 much more intensive studies and efforts for improvement were started in California. The principal developments of the 1934-1940 period were in the use of long drill-collar strings allowing somewhat more weight on the bit, rotating speeds more nearly adapted to the formations being drilled, larger fluid volume, studies of performance, mud control, improved bits, and balanced drilling practices.

Monthly API chapter meetings attended by field engineers afforded an excellent clearing house for new ideas and practices. They were unselfishly related. Without such cooperation, progress in oil-well drilling would have been much delayed.

During this period of intensive effort there were many more drill-pipe failures and fishing jobs than had occurred prior to this time when the drilling string was subjected to less intensive work. As a consequence, pipe threads—both casing and drill pipe—and particularly means and methods of attaching tool joints, received much study and experimentation. Clarence Froome of Union Oil Co. of California was one of the leaders in this work. During the year 1934 in Kettleman Hills the hydraulic feed control came into use; but, as is the case with many other new developments, broad and general acceptance did not come until some 15 years later. Long drill collars and the principle of running drill pipe in tension were put into practice. Roy A. Silent wrote the first technical paper on these subjects.*

Rotary-drilling units or separately driven rotaries likewise came in-

*Drilling Mud and Full-hole Tool Joints, API Drilling and Production Practice (1934).

to use, thus permitting higher-speed rotation. This type of rig had been developed sometime previously in Mexico and Venezuela, but the first carefully designed and efficient unit was put in service on Well No. 32-29J in Kettleman Hills in 1934. The records of pump pressure, rotating speed, and weight on the bit—both recorded and visual—were shown on the rate-of-drilling meter chart put in service on this well. These instruments were very useful in studying down-the-hole performance and rate of penetration, but they did not come into useful general service until many years later; and, in fact, are not in extensive use even at the present time. Their principal use now is in formation correlation.

An important though simple change was made in the hydraulic swivel gooseneck. Until 1934 the gooseneck had always come out from the swivel at an angle of approximately 45 deg, and the sharp bend in the hose below the gooseneck caused hose failures. The angle was changed to about 14 deg to conform with the normal angle of the hose hanging in the catenary curve between the standpipe and the swivel, and these failures ended. This approximate angle was adopted immediately by most manufacturers, and is now an API standard (15 deg).

The boiler plants in California at the beginning of 1934 carried not more than 200 psi of steam, even on the deep wells. With the introduction of 350-lb boilers and with a need for almost double the fluid volume, special pumps having 20-in. steam cylinders were designed and built, to use on the old low-pressure boiler batteries and deliver a volume of fluid comparable to the output of a 15-in. or 16-in. steam cylinder on 350 lb of steam.

During the early and middle 1930's Gulf Coast wells were being drilled to continually greater depths, and the importance of the mud-laden fluid problems developed correspondingly. The Gulf Coast operations were using big rigs that had been built in the late 1920's and early 1930's for the Oklahoma operations; and because of the nature of the formations, long drill collars were not so important. The pumps provided large fluid volume and nozzle velocity was high. Therefore the principal efforts toward greater drilling efficiency on the Gulf Coast had to do largely with mud control and the handling and completion of wells in the soft sands. Much of this work was based on the studies of George Cannon in the Conroe Field in 1933, as already related.

An important contribution by the Gulf Coast operators was the unitization of the 2-post, 3-shaft, 4-speed drawworks. When these hoists were first built they had to be disassembled into shafts, posts, headboards, base, and chain guards on each location and reassembled on the next. Hu M. Harris of Humble Oil & Refining Co. is credited with having unitized the first of these drawworks by welding the posts to a base, replacing the headboards with a spacer between the tops of the

Fig. 118 (right)—Rear View of First Unitized
Drawworks, October 1932
Designed by H. M. Harris using 3-year-old
Union (or National) Tool, 5C3-B drawworks.

Fig. 119 (left)—First Unitized Drawworks,
1932
Designed by H. M. Harris of Humble Oil
and Refining Company, Houston, using a
Union (or National) Tool 5C3-B purchased in
April 1929 and operated three years before
being unitized in the fall of 1932 and
placed in operation on Oct. 21, 1932.
Harris and driller on derrick floor.

posts, and assembling the shafts, chains, and guards as a unit. This idea
was immediately copied by others and within a very brief period practically all hoists of this type had been unitized; and by 1934 the manufacturers
were building unit hoists. This was a vast improvement over all prior
drawworks for it permitted the building of a precision machine of rigid
construction that could be properly lubricated, whereas the older drawworks were anything but precision and rigid jobs and lubrication was
difficult. Trouble time and wear were greatly reduced. Fig. 118 and
119 illustrate the first drawworks unitized by Harris in 1932.

Fig. 102 (p. 376) illustrates a front view of a shop-unitized 3-shaft
drawworks, 1934. The one-piece or unitized drill-pipe slip that came
into use during these years is shown on the rig floor. The Parkersburg
hydromatic brake in general use by that time is likewise shown. The automatic cathead is visible. Safety precautions had not yet become general,
as may be noticed from the open rotary-drive chains.

The first steel substructure, according to Hu M. Harris, was built
in March 1930 by the Parkersburg Rig and Reel Company for The Texas
Company and was on location at Golden Meadows, Louisiana. It was
erected on a wooden mat in the swamp and was designed to support the
four corners of the derrick and keep it in line.

Harris obtained a drawing and photographs of the substructure
and redesigned it with a removable rotary-table support in order that
blowout preventers and Christmas-tree installations could be handled
from the derrick floor. After installing one on a dry-land location, the
advantages were quickly discovered. It was copied by different manufacturers and standardized by the API, and has been universally adopted
on all steel drilling derricks.

The first completely enclosed oil-bath rotaries were placed in service in late 1933 and during this 1934-1940 interval came into general use.

During this period the engineers who devoted their thought and effort to the drilling of oil wells were giving intensive attention to mud chemistry and control and were building up records of facts and theories on which the basic principles of mud chemistry and control could be founded. In 1932 an API committee in southern California prepared a paper, "The Effect of Drilling Mud on Production in California." A. C. Rubel was the principal author with John F. Dodge aiding in its preparation. It is said that in the course of their discussions, Dodge outlined the construction of a "performance tester," a laboratory filtration apparatus which reproduced, in some measure, down-the-hole conditions as to circulation, temperature, pressure, and filter medium. Early in 1934 Rubel authorized Dodge to select from the refinery staff of Union Oil Co. of California two chemists (Jones and Babson) to build and apply the laboratory equipment. In 1937, P. H. Jones published on the static filter tester, which is the present API standard tester. Jones and associates, in these publications, did not consider the theory of filtration; but in September and November 1938, D. H. Larsen published in *The Petroleum Engineer* his classic contribution on "Determining the Filtration Characteristics of Drilling Muds." J. M. Bugbee considers the summer of 1938, when the filter test came into wide application in the field control of drilling muds, as being the date when modern mud building and control first became possible.

A water-base drilling fluid or mud is considered to have three parts— a gel fraction, an inert fraction, and the fluid phase. The gel fraction is the essential one and most mud treatment is directed to it—to questions regarding its nature, amount, and physicial state. The filter test was and is, in effect, an overall test of the gel fraction and is, therefore, of greatest importance.

The early development in the Permian Basin was shared between rotary-drilling tools and cable tools. As was customary during those days, the rotary rigs used one 30-ft drill collar. The hard formations of that area required considerable weight for a reasonable rate of penetration; and the drill pipe had to supply the necessary weight on the bit in the absence of effective drill-collar mass. In 1936 a California contractor moved into West Texas with 240 ft of drill collar and drill pipe that had already seen considerable service. On rigs in which drill pipe had been run in compression, 25,000 ft of hole were considered to be good service and the usual accounting charge for drill-pipe depreciation per foot of hole drilled was $1; but with the longer drill collars and tension on the drill pipe, the service period was increased to as much as 100,000 ft of hole. Since that time the drill-collar lengths and consequent weight on the bit have been increased to the present 600 to 1,000 ft and more in some wells.

Power Plants

By the late 1930's it was recognized by many manufacturers, operators, and engineers that the use of steam as the source of power on drilling rigs was going into a decline, and might even disappear. There were many reasons for this, including the development of great oil fields in such areas as the Permian Basin where water was scarce and fuel expensive.

To forestall this decline several steam, water, and fuel-saving devices were developed and used. A power pump driven by a single-cylinder cable-tool engine was used in the summer of 1933 by Drilling and Exploration Company at St. Martinsville, La. A year or two later a new and greatly improved power pump was driven by engines especially built for the purpose. Both Oil Well Supply Company and The National Supply Company built these units. The power pumps were not yet of sufficient power-input capacity and otherwise developed to permit fullest success. Fuel and water savings of 30 percent to 40 percent were actually accomplished.

High-line a-c electric power and especially diesel-electric d-c power were built into many rigs. Internal-combustion engines had been greatly improved. Straight power rigs were used with diesel or spark-plug engines driving steam hoists through awkward transmissions that incorporated reverse gears. Friction clutches were not yet being used.

Steam pumps of the day were admittedly better than any power pump then made regardless of how driven, but electric-motor drive was without parallel for the hoist or drawworks. The steam pump of 1940 had about reached its maximum in size and efficiency, but the power pump was still relatively new and of low hydraulic-horsepower output.

Steam rigs, steam drawworks, and internal-combustion engines could be purchased over the counter, but electric rigs were all tailor-made jobs and required many months and even years for delivery. A war was going on in Europe and the manufacturers of heavy electrical equipment were overburdened with war orders. By 1941 no orders for electric rigs would be accepted and it was even difficult to keep the existing electric rigs repaired and operating. The oil-well drilling organizations were required to get along with what they had; and this they did to an admirable extent despite old equipment, shortages of repair and replacement parts, and inexperienced crews. Only that machinery and equipment directly useful in the war effort received study, redesign, and improvement. The internal-combustion engine was one of the principal items in this category. Power-transmission equipment likewise came in for much improvement.

At the end of the war practically all drilling rigs were either worn out or obsolete, and the question was what type of rig should be developed. Steam rigs were conceded to have seen their days of greatest usefulness. The drilling-rig manufacturers had on the boards new types of hoists especially adapted to internal-combustion engine drive. The engines had been greatly improved in power, efficiency, and ruggedness and the manufacturing facilities for them were extensive. At the end of World War II the manufacturers of heavy electrical equipment were deeply involved in atomic energy and new jet-engine work, as well as busily engaged in supplying machinery and equipment for new electric-power plants and other industrial operations. These companies had neither time for, nor interest in, promoting the manufacture of electric-motor-powered drilling rigs.

With the improved power pumps, internal-combustion engines, standardized engine-generator sets, and two-speed or even single-speed hoists built for the purpose, there is little question but that the flexibility of the d-c electric rig would have given it a field of usefulness in the oil-well drilling industry second to none. With high-voltage electric power, the new type wound-rotor a-c motors give almost equally satisfactory service.

As B. L. Moore (see bibliography) suggests in his contribution on electric rigs in the Mid-Continent and Gulf Coast areas, there is no reason why the use of electric rigs should not be greatly increased. It is believed that, with the elimination of costly transmissions, hydraulic power converters, greatly simplified hoists, and standardized controls and layouts, first costs should not exceed those for comparable "mechanical" rigs while operating and upkeep costs should be as low or lower.

The d-c electric rig adds an engine-generator power plant to the outfit but it eliminates a great weight of high-cost machinery between the driving motor and the drum shaft, and its flexibility is unsurpassed. Internal-combustion engine d-c generator rigs built as long ago as 1935 are still in service competitively with the most modern power or mechanical rigs. They have been improved from time to time and many have been rebuilt, but still they operate in competition with the latest power or mechanical rigs.

Tool Joints

During 1936 the Reed shrink-grip tool joint came into use. This had been anticipated in California in 1934, by a similiar joint shrunk onto hydraulic drill pipe that was run immediately above the drill collars. This joint was followed by the Hughes flash-weld joint and the Jones & Laughlin integral-joint drill pipe. The Hydril Company had previously manufactured a joint of this type, but generally for external-flush drill pipe.

In 1936 there were many types of tool joints and threads in service, including the Reed full-hole tool joint which had not yet become an accepted API standard joint. Tables 2 and 3 list the more important tool joints in use in the mid-1930's. The full-hole tool joint became an API standard joint in 1934.

401

Table 2

TOOL JOINT SPECIFICATIONS

Size of Drill Pipe (Ins.)	Type	O.D. of Tool Joint (Ins.)	Bore of Tool Joint (Ins.)	Dimensions of Joint (Inches) A	B	C	Taper per Foot (Ins.)	Threads per Inch	Approx. Length of Tool Joint (Ins.)	Approx. Weight of Tool Joint (Lbs.)
2 3/8	A. P. I. Regular	3 3/8	1	1 7/8	2 5/8	3	3	5	16	27
2 3/8	Union Tool	3 1/8	1 1/8	1 5/8	2 1/2	3 1/2	3	7	16	27
2 7/8	Union Tool	3 7/8	1 1/2	2 3/16	3	3 1/2	3	7	17	32
2 7/8	Regular Acme	3 7/8	1 1/4	2 1/32	3	3 1/2	3 3/8	4	17	34
2 7/8	*Reed Full Hole	4 1/4	2 1/8	2 3/4	3 3/8	3 1/2	3	5	17	38
2 7/8	A. P. I. Regular	3 3/4	1 1/4	2 1/8	3 1/8	3 1/2	3	5	18	35
3 1/2	Union Tool	4 1/4	1 1/2	2 7/16	3 1/4	3 1/2	3	5	18	40
3 1/2	Regular Acme	4 1/4	1 3/4	2 17/32	2 17/32	3 9/16	3 3/8	4	18	41
3 1/2	Acme Streamline	4 5/8	2 1/8				3 3/8	4	18	53
3 1/2	Acme Streamline	4 5/8	2 7/16	3.056	3.994		3	5	18	53
3 1/2	Reed Full Hole	4 5/8	2 7/16	2 9/16	3 1/2	3 3/8	3	5	18	50
4 1/2	A. P. I. Regular	4 1/8	1 1/2	3 7/32	4 1/2	3 3/4	3 3/8	5	18	41
4 1/2	Union Tool	5 3/4	2 1/4	3 13/32	4 13/32	4	3 3/8	4	20	80
4 1/2	Regular Acme	5 1/2	2 1/2				3 3/8	4	20	73
4 1/2	Acme Streamline	5 3/4	2 13/16				3 3/8	4	20	83
4 1/2	Acme Streamline	5 3/4	3				3 3/8		20	83
4 1/2	Acme Streamline	5 3/4	3 5/32	3.792	4.792	4	3 3/8		20	83
4 1/2	Reed Full Hole	5 1/2	2 1/4	3 9/16	4 5/8	4 1/4	3	4	20	72
4 1/2	A. P. I. Regular	6 3/4	3	4 3/8	5 41/64	4 1/2	3	4	22	122
5 9/16	Regular Acme	7	3 13/16				3 3/8	4	22	122
5 9/16	Acme Streamline	7	4				3 3/8	4	22	122
5 9/16	Acme Streamline	7	4	4.992	5.825	5	2	4	22	122
5 9/16	Reed Full Hole	7	2 3/4	4 3/8	5 1/2	4 3/4	3 3/8	4	22	120
6 5/8	*A. P. I. Regular	6 3/4	3 1/2	5 1/32	6 13/32	4 15/64	2	4	24	159
6 5/8	Regular Acme	7 3/4	5	5.920	6.753	5	3 3/8	4	24	161
6 5/8	Reed Full Hole	8	3 1/2	5.159	6	5	2	4	24	160
7 5/8	*A. P. I. Regular	8 7/8	4	5 11/16	7	5 1/4	3	4	24	251
8 5/8	A. P. I. Regular	10	4 3/4	6.608	8	5 3/8	3	4	24	323

*Union Tool Dimensions also.

The Hughes Acme Thread is a Truncated V-Form Thread.

The Doheny-Stone or Hydril is a Square Thread.

The A. P. I., Union Tool and Reed Threads are V-Form slightly Truncated

    See diagram, page 256.

Table 3

TOOL JOINT SPECIFICATIONS FOR USE ON EXTERNAL UPSET DRILL PIPE

O. D. Drill Pipe (Inches)	O. D. Pipe Threads (Inches)	O. D. Tool Joint (Inches)	Bore Tool Joint (Inches)	Size Box and Pin (Inches)	Threads per Inch	Length (Inches)	Weight (Pounds)
2⅞	3½	4¼	2⅛	2 ¾ x 3 ⅝	5	17	44
3⅞	4½	5¾	3 5/32	3 13/16 x 4 13/16	5	20	89
4¾	5 9/16	7, 6¾	4	5 x 5 13/16	4	22	148
5¾	6⅝	8, 7¾	5	5 15/16 x 6 ¾	4	24	198

UNION TOOL CALIFORNIA STANDARD TOOL JOINTS

O. D. Drill Pipe (Inches)	O. D. Tool Joint (Inches)	Bore Tool Joint (Inches)	Size Box and Pin (Inches)	Threads per Inch	Length (Inches)	Weight (Pounds)
2⅜	3⅛	1⅛	1¾ x 2½	7	14	25
2⅞	3⅞	1½	2 x 3	7	15	35
3½	4¼	1½	2¼ x 3¼	5	18	44
4½	5¾	2¼	3½ x 4½	5	20	88

HYDRIL INTERNAL FLUSH DRILL PIPE TOOL JOINTS

O. D. Drill Pipe (Inches)	O. D. Tool Joint (Inches)	Bore Tool Joint (Inches)	Weight Tool Joint (Pounds)
2⅜	3⅜	1¾	25
2⅞	3⅞	2⅛	30
3½	4½	2¾	37
3½	4½	2 9/16	42
4½	6	3 13/16	64
4½	6	3¾	66
5	6⅝	4 3/16	85

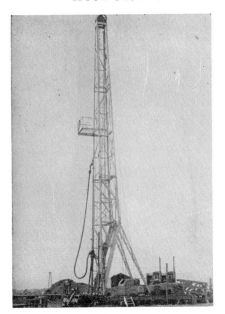

Fig. 120—Cantilever Mast of Late
1930's
(Lee C. Moore Corp. Photo)

Derricks

In the continuous and intensive search for time-saving devices and more efficient tools, it became obvious that the standard derrick, which was erected and disassembled on each job, was one of the time-consuming items of well drilling that could be improved. Single-pole masts and fabricated masts had been used on cable-tool machines and servicing units for many years, and it was relatively simple to change from this type equipment to a mast derrick for rotary rigs. About 1937 the Lee C. Moore Corporation brought out a jackknife cantilever-type drilling mast which has proved to be one of the fine and important contributions to the drilling industry. This first mast built was of tubular construction and 84 ft in height. It was still in service in Alberta, Canada, in October 1954. The next three masts built by Lee C. Moore were similar in design but constructed of angle iron and 92 ft in height. One of these early mast derricks was still in use in Oklahoma in October 1954. Fig. 120 shows a 1939 model (O. H. Dittmar letter to J. E. Brantly, October 16, 1954). The shortage of steel during World War II helped to popularize these drilling masts; and although at first they were used only for the drilling of comparatively shallow wells, they are now being used to drill wells to depths in excess of 15,000 ft. They are available in heights up to 142 ft of clear working space under the crown block, and in work-load capacity, up to 1,025,000 lb. For deeper drilling substructures up to 14 ft or more in height are used.

Boilers

In the late 1930's, as has already been observed, the operators and manufacturers realized that power rigs would eventually displace steam rigs because of expensive fuel and the shortage of good boiler water in many areas. In order to delay or prevent the disappearance of steam equipment, steam-engine-driven power pumps were brought into service and much work was done on the development of new boilers. At the beginning of the war several patents were issued covering flash-type and semi-flash boilers, one of which had been built in an experimental model, while another had gone through extensive technical and scientific analysis at the California Institute of Technology. The war stopped the building of even experimental working models; and by the time it ended, internal-combustion engines had been perfected to such a degree that steam rigs were on the way out.

One of these experimental boilers was of the vertical type with forced circulation with all heating surfaces receiving radiant heat. The superheater was built in the lower part of the venturi-type chimney with feed-water heater still higher, and an air jacket to raise the temperature of primary air before passing into the fire chamber. An atmospheric condenser through which all exhaust steam would pass was likewise designed. It was estimated that the boiler would produce about five times as much steam per pound of metal as would the conventional locomotive-type oil-field boiler. A somewhat similar unit was placed in experimental use on a Magnolia Petroleum Company well on the Gulf Coast and, it is understood, gave quite satisfactory results; but with the great number of conventional oil-field boilers in the hands of operators and contractors and the coming of power rigs, these new-type boilers were not built commercially.

The inventory of a heavy-duty steam rig of 1940 would not differ from a comparable rig of 1934 except in the unit hoist and a few accessory items. The service companies greatly expanded and improved their services and equipment during the middle and late 1930's. They kept pace with and provided much able and useful assistance to the efforts directed toward faster well drilling and lower costs.

Fig. 121 shows a battery of five 150-hp 500-psi working pressure drilling-rig boilers having full-automatic controls, including water-level regulators, low-water alarm, feed-water heater, fire and draft controls, and superheaters. This plant, erected about 1939, is said to have generated 62,000 lb of steam per hour. It was probably the largest steam-generating plant ever erected for a single drilling rig. Special pumps were built for the high-pressure steam. Equipment of this type was replaced by mechanical-power rigs following World War II. Except for developments during that war, many plants of this type doubtless would have been built. Fig. 122 shows a small diesel-electric rig erected in 1938 and with many changes still in use in 1955.

1940 - 1946

During the interval 1940 through 1945, World War II was in progress and included the United States beginning December 7, 1941. In the first two years of this period, an all-out effort was made in this country to drill as many wells as possible for the purpose of supplying oil to those nations with which America was friendly. There were 31,149 and 32,510 wells drilled during 1940 and 1941, respectively. At that time drilling equipment and machinery were being manufactured and developed more or less normally and the period saw the beginning of intensive develop-

Fig. 121—Five Broderick 500-lb SWP, 150-hp Boilers with Full Automatic Control
Superior Oil Co.

Fig. 122—Four Diesel-engine—Direct-current Generators on Continuous Shafts,
with Direct-connected Exciters, 1938
Drilling and Exploration Co.

Either or both may be driven by either or both diesel engines through V-belts. For
rotating and pumping the generators would be used in parallel, then connected in series
for heavy hoisting.

ment of internal-combustion engine-powered rigs or mechanical rigs and the decline of steam equipment. Power rigs of the day usually used hoists built for steam-powered rigs with an extra shaft carrying a reserve clutch, and an additional speed in some cases, located behind the drawworks and in front of the transmission. These units were rather crude in comparison with those to be developed later; and, because of the power characteristics of the prime movers, were rather difficult to operate with a reasonable degree of smoothness. However, there were many such rigs in use and it was evident at the time that steam rigs would be superseded by this type.

With the effective entrance of the United States into the war, there were only 21,990 wells drilled in 1942, a decline of approximately one third from the preceding year. In 1943 there was a further decline of about 1,500 wells, which was the low point in drilling activities in the nation for many years before and since.

In 1944 the consumption of oil increased materially because of war activity. Drilling was stepped up, and 1944 saw more than 5,000 wells added to the 1943 minimum figure, with an additional 1,000 or more in 1945. During these years very little new drilling machinery was manufactured and, in fact, it was extremely difficult for the operators to get more than bare replacement parts with which to keep the rigs operating.

In early 1942 the American Association of Oilwell Drilling Contractors was asked for an estimate of the number of wells that might be drilled before new equipment in quantity would be imperative. A questionnaire was mailed to all operators and contractors, with a 25-percent return. Upon compilation of these data it was estimated that approximately 75,000 wells to the then-average depths could be drilled with little more than replacement parts and a very modest amount of drill pipe. By the end of the war in August 1945, approximately 85,000 wells had been drilled; but the end came just in time, for practically all equipment was either worn out or in a very poor state of repair. Following the war there was a steady increase in the number of wells drilled until 1949, when a slight decline occurred. The increase was resumed in 1950 and continued through 1956, with declines since. Tables 4, 5, and 6, compiled by AAODC, show the number of wells drilled, total footage drilled, and drilling-cost trend for several years prior to 1960.

Table 4 shows drilling cost in 1935 at $5 per ft and the estimate for 1955 (20 years later) at $5.10 per ft, which is a truly remarkable performance in view of the decrease in the value of the dollar, and is accounted for by the increase in rate of penetration and the greater efficiency of personnel and equipment generally.

It will be noticed that there was an increase in drilling cost of approximately $1 per ft from 1941 to 1945, whereas there had been a decrease from 1935 to 1941 of a similar amount. From 1945 to 1955 the increased

Table 4
United States Drilling-cost Trends

Year	Total New Wells Completed	Average Depth per Well, Feet	Average Drilling Cost per Foot	Average Total Cost per Foot
1935	24,851	2,760	$5.00	$ 8.00
1936	28,962	2,797	4.75	7.75
1937	35,213	2,985	4.50	7.50
1938	29,127	3,110	4.25	7.50
1939	28,012	3,053	4.25	7.50
1940	31,149	3,088	4.00	7.50
1941	32,510	3,056	4.25	7.25
1942	21,990	3,088	4.00	7.50
1943	20,349	3,046	4.50	8.00
1944	25,786	3,272	4.75	8.25
1945	26,649	3,489	5.00	9.00
1946	30,230	3,345	5.00	9.50
1947	33,147	3,404	5.00	10.25
1948	39,477	3,463	4.75	10.75
1949	38,962	3,558	4.75	10.75
1950	43,204	3,689	5.00	11.00
1951	44,196	3,869	5.50	11.50
1952	45,879	4,060	5.85	12.00
1953	49,279	4,016	5.60	12.50
1954	53,650	4,025	5.10	12.75
1955	56,850	4,044	4.90	13.50
1956	58,271	4,022	4.75	13.50
*1957	53,472	4,107	4.60	13.60
†1958	48,312	4,031	4.50	13.25

*Revised   †Estimated

Table 5
United States Contractor Drilling Trends

Year	Total New Wells Completed	Total Footage Drilled	Average Depth per Well	INDICATED WORK BY CONTRACTORS Percent	New Wells Completed	Footage Drilled
1935	24,851	67,844,939	2,760	68	16,899	46,134,559
1936	28,962	80,996,816	2,797	69	19,984	55,887,803
1937	35,213	105,099,189	2,985	71	25,001	74,620,424
1938	29,127	90,585,158	3,110	71	20,680	64,315,462
1939	28,012	85,523,094	3,053	70	19,608	59,866,166
1940	31,149	96,182,605	3,088	71	22,116	68,289,650
1941	32,510	99,347,714	3,056	72	23,447	71,503,354
1942	21,990	67,903,053	3,088	70	15,393	47,532,137
1943	20,349	61,991,857	3,046	75	15,262	46,493,893
1944	25,786	84,378,457	3,272	78	20,113	65,815,196
1945	26,649	92,982,113	3,489	80	21,319	74,385,690
1946	30,230	101,124,813	3,345	81	24,486	81,911,099
1947	33,147	112,816,124	3,404	81	26,849	91,381,060
1948	39,477	136,709,153	3,463	82	32,371	112,101,505
1949	38,962	138,616,941	3,558	85	33,119	117,824,400
1950	43,204	159,393,997	3,689	88	38,020	140,266,717
1951	44,196	173,315,000	3,869	90	39,776	155,984,000
1952	45,879	186,389,000	4,060	91	41,750	169,614,000
1953	49,279	197,920,000	4,016	91	44,844	180,107,200
1954	53,650	215,940,250	4,025	92	49,358	198,665,030
1955	56,850	229,901,400	4,044	92	52,302	211,509,288
1956	58,271	234,350,550	4,022	93	54,192	217,946,012
1957	53,783	220,863,576	4,107	93	50,068	205,403,126
1958	48,670	195,083,688	4,008	95	43,836	185,229,504
1959	52,260	210,223,000	4,022	95	49,500	200,000,000
*1960	53,300	214,800,000	4,030	96	50,500	202,015,000

*Estimated.

Table 6

Comparison of Drilling Costs

	1941	1945	1947	1948	1949	1950	1951	1952	1953	1954	1955	1956	1957	1958
Labor costs, percent	100	140	150	170	180	190	196	197	198	200	202	204	208	208
Equipment costs, percent	100	110	132	145	160	175	180	183	188	190	195	200	205	208
Miscellaneous costs, percent	100	120	160	165	170	175	181	185	188	191	194	199	204	206
Total rotary drilling costs, percent	100	122	145	160	170	180	186	189	192	194	197	201	206	208
Drilling prices (footage basis), percent	100	115	110	105	101	100	103	103	102	99	96	93	90	88
Average drilling time (days), percent	100	95	95	80	75	65	60	59	58	56	56	54	54	52
Rate of penetration, percent	100	110	130	140	150	170	180	182	184	188	188	......	......	......

Table 7

Monthly Average of Rotary Rigs Actually Running in United States and Canada

Month	1942	1943	1944	1945	1946	1947	1948	1949	1950	1951	1952	1953	1954	1955	1956	1957	1958	1959
January	787	729	1,327	1,738	1,696	1,548	1,980	2,090	2,021	2,244	2,945	2,682	2,638	2,615	2,842	2,566	2,222	......
February	756	773	1,356	1,714	1,521	1,594	1,919	2,021	1,972	2,169	2,885	2,624	2,649	2,657	2,705	2,538	2,164	......
March	720	810	1,399	1,700	1,449	1,618	1,912	2,085	2,031	2,287	2,872	2,629	2,705	2,749	2,872	2,665	1,969	......
April	750	829	1,452	1,715	1,501	1,633	2,070	2,130	2,091	2,442	2,917	2,672	2,754	2,750	2,803	2,515	1,895	
May	789	869	1,517	1,790	1,479	1,686	2,189	2,181	2,145	2,578	3,007	2,700	2,677	2,773	2,906	2,512	1,926	
June	795	935	1,599	1,743	1,511	1,806	2,251	2,109	2,277	2,647	2,964	2,812	2,656	2,908	2,998	2,688	1,979	
July	861	1,036	1,665	1,730	1,515	1,896	2,302	2,027	2,295	2,740	2,658	2,788	2,632	2,906	2,867	2,735	1,946	
August	833	1,105	1,710	1,730	1,552	1,947	2,348	2,022	2,304	2,867	2,505	2,973	2,551	2,941	2,775	2,716	2,042	
September	789	1,156	1,754	1,756	1,639	1,978	2,335	2,001	2,297	2,937	2,585	2,796	2,474	2,966	2,777	2,700	2,072	
October	788	1,231	1,808	1,762	1,683	2,044	2,372	2,039	2,438	3,040	2,709	2,880	2,531	2,963	2,788	2,587	2,125	
November	788	1,293	1,849	1,796	1,674	2,056	2,437	2,197	2,500	3,008	2,835	2,941	2,713	2,058	2,822	2,559	2,237	
December	816	1,363	1,800	1,760	1,700	2,008	2,385	2,247	2,481	3,137	2,896	2,988	2,908	3,188	2,947	2,682	2,451	
Average	788	1,009	1,603	1,744	1,576	1,817	2,208	2,096	2,238	2,683	2,816	2,777	2,657	2,873	2,842	2,622	2,086	2,074

cost of drilling was only 25 cents per ft. The decrease in cost from 1935 through 1942 was accounted for by increased rate of penetration; the increase in cost from 1942 through 1945 was accounted for by a decrease in rate of penetration. From 1945 to 1955 the footage costs are approximately the same, although all operating costs and costs of materials and supplies have increased considerably. This again is accounted for by an increase in the rate of penetration.

Table 7 (AAODC and Hughes Tool Co.) shows the monthly average of rotary rigs actually running in the United States and Canada from 1942 through December 1958 with the averages for the year. It will be noted that there were approximately twice as many rigs operating in 1944 as in 1942 with an increase of less than 4,000 wells drilled, or 18 percent. In 1945 there was an increase somewhat in excess of 100 rigs over 1944 with an increase of approximately 1,000 wells or 3 percent, which appears to be more or less normal. It is difficult to explain the difference in the number of rigs operating between 1942 and 1944 except that the old equipment and the relatively inexperienced crews of the war years required more time to drill wells. From 1945 to 1954 there was an increase in the number of operating rigs of approximately 50 percent, with more than double the number of wells drilled.

Rate of Penetration

The percentage increase in the rate of penetration of wells drilled by the rotary method from 1932 to 1955 is shown in Fig. 123. The data for 1932-1947 are from a paper and an article as shown in the *Sources*, and that of 1948 to 1955 from the American Association of Oilwell Drilling Contractors, January 1956. The chart shows a sharp increase in rate of penetration from 1932 to 1941, then a drop during World War II with

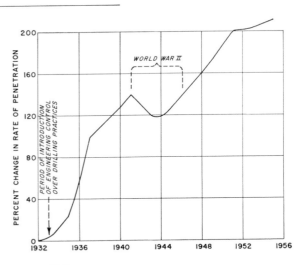

Fig. 123—Drilling Rate-of-Penetration Curve, 1932-1955

Sources:

1932-1939—A Preliminary Evaluation of Factors Controlling Rate of Penetration, J. E. Brantly and E. H. Clayton, *API Drilling and Production Practice*, 8 (1939).

1939-1947—Factors Governing Rotary Drilling Rates, J. E. Brantly, *World Petroleum*, March (1948).

1947-1955—American Association of Oilwell Drilling Contractors, January 1956.

a resumption of the increase after 1944. In the 23 years from 1932 to 1955 rate of penetration has increased 210 percent.

It has been stated to the writer by an engineer who has been closely identified with the Permian Basin for several years that his studies, though as yet incomplete, indicate little or no increase in average rate of penetration over the past 18 months in that region (June 1956).

During the period 1935 through 1954 average well depths increased 70 percent from 2,760 ft to 4,025 ft, and total footage drilled rose from 68,000,000 ft to approximately 216,000,000 ft—a 315-percent increase.

The number of rigs running in 1932 and 1933 are not definitely known, but in 1933 there were said to have been approximately 600 operating in the East Texas fields alone. The average number of rotary rigs operating in the United States during 1955 was 2,873, and in 1958 the average was 2,086.

1946 - 1960

The story of the developments and accomplishments during the period between the end of World War II into 1959, which covers a time interval of 14 years, can hardly be regarded as history because the industry is still engaged in the use, further development, and improvement of the major and accessory items that have been developed. It seems advisable, however, that the major accomplishments be recorded for the benefit of the time when the activities of today are in fact history.

As has been related and shown in Table 5, relatively few wells were drilled during World War II compared to the previous few years and to the subsequent years. At the same time the consumption of petroleum and its products was practically all that the producing wells of the world could furnish, even though all countries were on very restricted allotments. During the war years many countries attained a strong financial position that prepared them for considerable cultural and industrial advancement. This resulted in immediate demands for substantial increase in allotments of petroleum products, together with the purchase of much additional equipment to be fueled by petroleum; and intensive drilling campaigns were undertaken in the early post-war years, both in the United States and abroad. At this time drilling equipment in the hands of operators and drilling contractors was either obsolete or worn out, which necessitated early or immediate replacement of entire rigs or major parts—particularly of power plants. For five years the manufacturers of drilling equipment had been engaged in war work and had built relatively few major items of machinery, and no more repair and replacement items than were necessary to keep the drilling rigs in reasonably efficient operating condition. Many contractors and operators, particularly in foreign operations, were forced to build parts in local machine shops.

Even though the manufacturers had not been allowed to produce drilling equipment during the war, their engineers and designers had

Table 8
Drilling Depth Records

Year	Maximum Well Depth, Feet	Average Well Depth, Feet
1925	....	2,900
1926	....	2,800
1927	8,046	3,000
1928	8,523	3,000
1929	9,280	2,895
1930	9,753	2,900
1931	10,585	2,924
1932	10,944	3,011
1933	10,944	3,032
1934	11,377	2,731
1935	12,786	2,829
1936	12,786	2,861
1937	12,786	2,974
1938	15,004	3,144
1939	15,004	3,053
1940	15,004	3,088
1941	15,004	3,056
1942	15,004	3,088
1943	15,004	3,046
1944	16,246	3,272
1945	16,655	3,489
1946	16,668	3,345
1947	17,823	3,404
1948	17,823	3,463
1949	18,734	3,558
1950	20,521	3,689
1951	20,521	3,888
1952	20,521	4,060
1953	20,521	4,016
1954	20,521	4,025
1955	21,482	4,044
1956	22,570	4,022
1957	22,570	4,107
1958	25,340	4,031
*1959	25,340	4,163

*Estimated

Table 9
Average Wells and Footage Drilled Annually per Rig in the United States*

Year	Average Rigs Operating	Wells Drilled per Rig	Footage Drilled per Rig
1938	3,799	7.7	23,844
1939	3,683	7.6	23,221
1940	4,193	7.4	22,933
1941	4,446	7.3	22,345
1942	3,041	7.2	22,329
1943	3,041	6.7	20,385
1944	4,190	6.2	20,138
1945	4,387	6.1	21,195
1946	4,353	6.9	23,231
1947	4,741	7.0	23,796
1948	4,950	8.0	27,618
1949	4,290	9.1	32,312
1950	4,517	9.6	35,369
1951	4,844	9.5	36,490
1952	4,857	9.6	38,785
1953	4,784	10.3	41,478
1954	4,635	11.2	45,587
1955	4,867	11.5	46,955
1956	4,845	12.1	48,583
1957	4,791	11.2	46,100
1958	4,114	11.7	47,601

*World Oil, Feb. (1959)

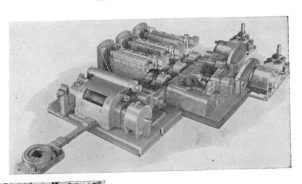

Fig. 124 (right)—National 160 Mechanical Rig, 1948 Six speeds with two pump drives.

Fig. 125 (left)—National 160 of Fig. 124 on location in Wyoming. Depth of hole drilled was 20,521 ft. 1,500-hp with Gyrol hydraulic couplings.

been busily engaged in placing on the drawing board new designs for practically all major items of machinery; and, with the exception of steam equipment, the rigs that were in service at the end of the war have disappeared from the fields and have been replaced by new types and models.

During the war transportation equipment of all kinds saw a great decrease in the use of steam-powered prime movers and an increase in internal-combustion engines and electric motors. For war purposes both diesel and spark-plug engines using gasoline and liquid petroleum gas were developed to a high point of perfection. The companies engaged in the manufacture of these machines had, in many cases, furnished products to the oil industry; and they were now prepared with much more efficient engines built in many additional sizes, particularly the larger. New hoists and power pumps designed and built by manufacturers of drilling equipment, together with the ability of manufacturers of internal-combustion engines to provide the new prime movers, resulted in the building of "mechanical" rigs almost exclusively. Very little steam equipment was manufactured subsequent to 1940, and at the present time the purchase of new steam-powered rigs is a very small fraction of the total. Manufacturers of electrical equipment made very little effective effort to place their products in the oil fields, although there was some evidence at the time that electric-powered rigs might have had an important future.*

In addition to the great number of wells being drilled the proportion of deep holes, or those in excess of 9,000 or 10,000 ft, increased rapidly; and the average rotary well depth has increased from 3,088 ft in 1940— which was practically the same as the average depth as far back as 1927— to about 4,163 ft as the estimated average for 1959. Thus in the 13 years from 1927 to 1940 there was little change in the average depths drilled, while from 1940 to 1959 there was an increase of 1,075 ft. Table 8 shows the deepest holes and average drilling depths from 1927 through 1958. Bearing in mind the great number of shallow wells drilled, the 1,075-ft increase in average depth in the past 19 years indicates a very substantial increase in the proportion of deep wells, and a corresponding change in the number of heavy-duty rigs in operation. Table 9 shows average wells and footage per rig from 1938 to 1958, incl.

In 1948 The National Supply Company exhibited at the Petroleum Exposition in Tulsa a new power rig which they designated as their No. 160. The rotary table, hoist, engines, transmission, and pumps are illustrated in Fig. 124. Fig. 125 shows this rig on location. The rotary table is shaft-driven beneath the drum from gears behind the hoist. The "console" controls are at the driller's position at the left of the hoist, together with the instrument panel. The over-speed brake is on the right. The 3 diesel engines furnish in excess of 1,500 hp, while the pumps have in excess of 700-hp power ends. This rig was purchased by the Superior Oil Company

---

*In 1958-59 electric rigs were beginning to appear in numbers in the oil fields.

Fig. 126—Exposed View of
Emsco Drawworks for Deep
Drilling—Early 1950's

of California and drilled a well 20,521 ft in depth, which held the deep-well record for several years.

Fig. 126 shows an exposed view of a somewhat smaller drawworks but one still rated as capable of drilling a well to 20,000 ft or more. Multiple chain between the line shaft and the drum shaft, together with the multiple sprockets for the line-shaft drive and the air clutch, are shown. Another feature is the lubrication system which permits the oiling or greasing of all bearings from a single position. Fig. 127 illustrates a still smaller-capacity modern drawworks with diesel engines and transmission and pump drives. Engines of the day vary up to 550 hp in 6-cylinder and twin 6-cylinder units. Fig. 128 illustrates a Marep V-type twin-six diesel engine rigged up for separate pump drive.

In response to the demand for more power, the friction clutch was

Fig. 127 (left)—Medium Duty
Power Rig, 1955

Fig. 128 (right)—Marep V-type
Twin-six Diesel Engine, 1955,
French

Fig. 129 (left)—Expanding-band Clutch

Fig. 130 (right)—Multiple-band Clutch

developed from something of a single-plate type to the expanding band (Fig. 129) and the multiple-plate type (Fig. 130). The expanding-band clutch has a flexible member between the operating band and the friction element which, when pressurized with air, expands gradually and applies an increasing force to the friction element. The multiple-disc clutch is air-operated through means of the same kind of reservoir which, when inflated, presses the friction elements together with an ever-increasing force. The proper operation of a mechanical rig with either of these clutches is a very delicate matter because too rapid an application of air pressure will stall the engine or throw great stresses on the train of chains, sprockets, bearings, etc. The driller has to be continuously on the alert when picking up a load with these clutches to prevent too rapid an applica-

tion of the moving power to the stationary load. In the use of either of these clutches, considerable slip is occasioned upon the acceleration of a load for the reason that the very nature of an internal-combustion engine is that, at very low speed, the torque characteristic is very unstable. Naturally the engine has to run at a certain minimum speed to develop the torque necessary to accelerate the load. Consequently, considerable slip is necessary each time the load is accelerated. This must of necessity occasion considerable maintenance of the equipment. The "slack" in the hoisting lines is likewise an important factor in starting the load.

Fig. 131—National Gyrol Hydraulic Coupling Also designated as Ideal Gyrol Fluid Drive. National started furnishing rigs with hydraulic couplings about 1937.

415

Fluid Couplings

To reduce the shock loads due to too rapid acceleration of the load, a fluid coupling to be installed between the prime mover and the clutch has found wide acceptance. One type is shown in Fig. 131. The action of the coupling imparts a resiliency to the operation of the friction clutch which makes it practically shockproof. This coupling, as the name implies, consists of a runner in an oil-filled housing which is connected to the load with the runner connected to the prime mover. Upon a sudden application of load there is a slip which is so gentle in its nature that the shock on chains, bearings, etc. is reduced very greatly as compared to the operation of a friction clutch alone.

For low-speed high-torque operations on a drilling rig, the torque converter is installed at the same location as the fluid coupling. The torque converter is capable of a torque multiplication brought about by an excessive slip inherent in its design. The torque converter will not allow the engine to stall, but will allow it to be loaded to full torque; and if the torque requirement of the load is sufficiently great, there will be a slip in the torque converter. As the slip occurs the torque on the output shaft will be increased until, at a stalling position, the torque may be as much as several times the input torque. This is a very necessary item of transmission for certain applications, which include pulling or working loose stuck casing, stretching pipe when locating the level of cement on the outside of the casing, etc. In addition to this, it makes possible a limited simplification of the drawworks, viz., from perhaps six speeds to two speeds.

Electromagnetic Couplings

This coupling is known as the eddy-current coupling and its operation is similar to the well-known dynamatic brake which is used extensively for braking service. The transmission of energy through this coupling is entirely dependent upon the strength of the magnetic field, which is variable. At normal power, transmission through this coupling is very resilient—consequently there is even less shock than with the torque concerter. Slippage can also be regulated from about 3 percent to 100 percent.

Fig. 124 illustrates somewhat of a novel idea in the transmission of energy to the rotary machine, and is similar to the York and Black principle of 1920 (Fig. 77). This is done through rapid shifting from a special jack shaft and gearing connected to the prime mover through a friction clutch. This rig, illustrated in Fig. 124 and 125, uses three 600-hp engines with fluid couplings. It is to be borne in mind that these rigs, with their compounding by means of chains, shafts, sprockets, bearings, etc., are reasonably expendable. As a rule, the life of this transmission equipment is about five or six years. The cost of replacement is high. Another feature of clutches, fluid couplings, and torque converters is that regardless of whether the duty at the moment of the operation be at full speed or static level, the engine is always, at full speed or little less, loaded to full torque.

416

Fig. 132—1,000-hp Fabricated Steel Pump, 8¼ x 18, 1952

Fig. 133—Oil Well 220-P Power Pump, 8 x 20, 1952

Power Pump

The pumps used on the first mechanical rig, built in the mid-1920's, were of the order of 6 x 12 operating on not in excess of 500 to 600 lb discharge pressure. They were seldom, if ever, compounded. At the present time the power pumps in use are capable of operation at a maximum pressure of as high as 2,400 lb. The dimensions of the present largest pumps are of the magnitude of 22-in. stroke with 8¼-in. fluid cylinders, operating at as high as 75 strokes per minute, with an input capacity of as high as 1,000 hp. Fig. 132 and 133 show pumps of the early 1950's.

Humble Oil & Refining Co., working in conjunction with several manufacturers of oil-field equipment, experimented with a semi-automatic drilling rig during the early 1950's. The rig utilized automatic

Fig. 134—Automatic Slips in 1952, Rotary

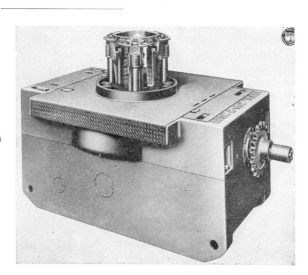

power slips, tongs, and pipe-racking devices. A drilling-feed control of the walking-brake type, together with "pushbutton" operation of the working parts of the rig, were included. Fig. 134 shows a 1952 rotary table with automatic slips. Fig. 135 illustrates power tongs of the same period.

Feed Controls

Beginning in the late 1920's, drilling-feed controls based on the torque principle were built by several manufacturers, including the Halliburton built by National and the Hild drive built by Oil Well. Fig. 136 shows Halliburton control together with steam engine and drawworks of the day—about 1928. Fig. 137 shows the Hild drive. Both of these devices regulated feed of

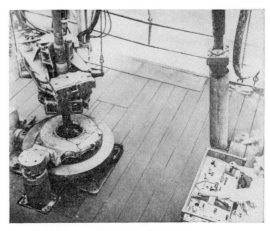

Fig. 135—Power Tongs, 1952

Fig. 136—National-Halliburton Drilling Control, 1928

the bit into the formation on the principle of torque acting through differential gears.

In 1934 a hydraulic feed control using a 6-cylinder double-acting pump and based on the weight principle was put in service. This unit, although in use for over 20 years, has only come into extensive use in the past 5 years in the heavier rigs (Fig. 138).

Within the past few years Humble developed its Walking Feed-off brake and The National Supply Company developed its Micromatic drilling control, Fig. 139, similar to the Brantly patent of 1936. The basic principle of the hydraulic pump drilling-feed control of 1934 was suspension of the load on the fluid of the discharge line and the regulation of the downward feed by the rate of discharge of the fluid. The Micromatic control is based on the principle of holding the load within the mechanism with feed-off promoted by actuation of the control with outside power.

Fig. 137—Oil Well Hild Drive, 1928

Fig. 138 (left)—"Oil Well" Brantly
Hydraulic Drilling-feed Controls
Based on Weight on Bit,
(Original, 1933)
1952

For drilling to 10,000 ft.   For drilling over 10,000 ft.

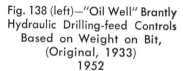

Fig. 139—National Micromatic Drilling-feed Control
Based on Weight on Bit, 1952

Fig. 140 — Reed Drill-
collar Joint, Circa 1950

Fig. 141—Rig Layout Showing Mud Ditches, Tanks, and Pumps, 1953

Modern heavy-duty rigs of today generally use a control for the smooth and regular feed of the bit into the formation.

Drill pipe and tool joints have seen only minor changes during the past few years except in alloy steels used in their manufacture. The sole exception is the development and use of external-upset drill pipe to give internal-flush fluid passage. Drill collars have shown no changes in basic design other than the development of the Reed drill collar, a cutaway of one end of which is illustrated in Fig. 140.

Drilling practices have changed very materially within the past 10 years in mud control, fluid volume and velocity; and the arrangement of the mud-circulating system as illustrated in Fig. 141.

Fig. 142 illustrates a simpler rig layout of 1953 with the older type mud-circulating system still in use on the Gulf Coast.

Instruments have been considerably changed and improved for drilling control, hole surveying, and rig performance. Rock bits have been continually improved with a number of different forms and styles of cutters developed, including the hard-rock button type. The rolling-cutter bits have been so developed that they can be used in practically any type

420

Fig. 142—Rig Layout and Mud Pits, Gulf Coast, 1953
(Continental Photo)

formation, with the sole exception of gumbo, by the use of high-velocity fluid from the nozzle and with tooth forms suitable to the formation. Drag bits have practically gone out of service except in soft-formation areas where the short jet-type fishtail is used. Diamond core barrels and full-hole bits have been developed and are used extensively in areas of hard formation. Fig. 143 illustrates bits of 1920 and 1934. Fig. 144 and 145 show bits of the early 1950's.

The use of long drill collars, first started in 1934, has been continued and expanded until, in hard-rock areas such as the Permian Basin, as many as 20 or more 30-ft lengths are used. Much excellent work has been done on the use of long drill collars and straight-hole drilling by Arthur Lubinski and H. B. Woods (see bibliography). Oversized drill collars— i.e., those which have insufficient clearance to permit the use of outside fishing tools—have likewise been used to some extent immediately above the bit as a means of lowering the center of gravity of the concentration of weight above the bit and also to promote straight-hole drilling by the small angle of deviation that the oversized drill collars will allow.

A number of new drilling-fluid materials have been developed and the chemistry of mud has improved to the point where control is almost absolute within the desired and necessary limits.

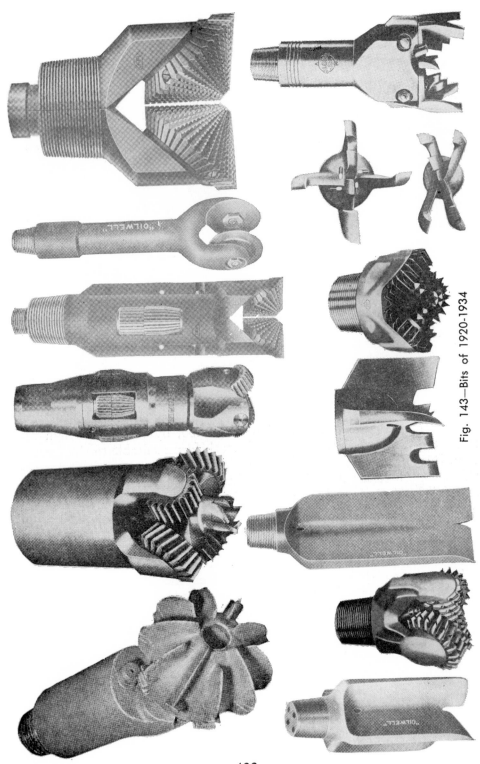

Fig. 143—Bits of 1920-1934

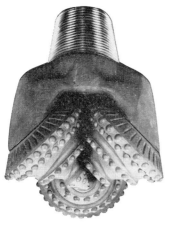

(a) Tri-Cone Chert Bit with
Hard Alloy Buttons

(b) Cross-Roller Bit

(c) Modern Two-blade
Drag Bit

Fig. 144—Bits of Early 1950's

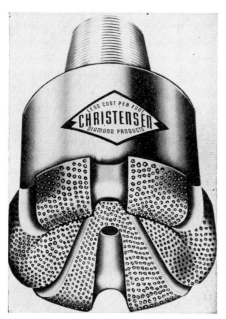

Fig. 145a—Type HSF Drilling Bit
Developed in 1952 in which the fluid
is discharged through ports in the
center, or concave cone portion of the
bit. Used during 1952 and early 1953.

Fig. 145b—Large-size Simplex Bit
Top hole for Aramco (Arabia), 1955

Fig. 146 and 147 illustrate a portable rotary-drilling rig constructed in 1954. This machine may be used for drilling, completion work, and clean-out jobs. It will drill holes in excess of 3,000 ft.

Fig. 146—Portable Drilling Rig, 1954
Over-the-road view of Franks Clipper drilling and workover unit.

Fig. 147—Franks "Pioneer 52" Trailer-mounted Rotary Rig
Has its own telescoping 102-ft derrick, 600-hp twin-engine power unit, pump drive from the trailer power unit as well as the drawworks drive— drawworks equipped with hydromatic brakes. Unit operating near Mt. Pleasant, Michigan, for E. V. Hilliard, 1953.

This period since World War II has seen the practical disappearance of the conventional 4-legged derrick except on a few very deep holes, on barges, and on marine platforms. Their place has been taken almost entirely by mast derricks of various types built by various manufacturers as illustrated in Fig. 148 to 154, inclusive.

Fig. 148 illustrates one of the few conventional derricks in use today with 400-ton hoisting equipment. Fig. 149 shows a modern rig layout with a mast

Fig. 148 (above)—400-ton Hanging tools in Conventional Derrick, 1954

Fig. 149 (right)—1954 Rig with Lee C. Moore Mast Derrick

derrick, 1954. Fig. 150 illustrates a 1,250-hp Ideco rig with full-view mast. Fig. 151 illustrates a drilling barge with a conventional derrick. Fig. 152 illustrates a drilling platform with drilling mast. Fig. 153 illustrates a drilling platform with a 6-well derrick. Fig. 154 illustrates a different type of drilling platform with 140-ft by 30-ft by 952,000-lb derrick.

Fig. 155 through 172 are photographs of rotary-drilling equipment now in use (1960). Table 10 lists the weights for transportation of a helicopter rig.

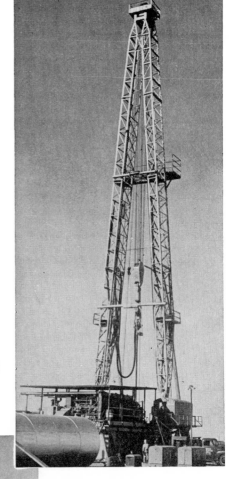

Fig. 150 (right)—1,250-hp Ideco Rig with Full-view Mast, 1955

Fig. 151 (left)—Drilling Barge with Conventional Derrick (Courtesy Oil Well Supply Div., United States Steel Corp.)

Fig. 152—136-ft Mast, Offshore Location Drilling Platform, 1955

Fig. 153—Drilling Platform for 6 Directionally Drilled Wells, 1954
(Lee C. Moore Photo)

Fig. 154—140-ft x 30-ft, 952,000-lb. Derrick on Platform, 1954

Fig. 155—Retractable Trailer-mounted Drilling Mast on Trailer Drilling Floor, 1959
(Lee C. Moore Corp. Photo)

Fig. 156—Cantilever-type Mast and Substructure for 10,000-ft Drilling Range, 1959
Can be transported by helicopter or conventional aircraft.
(Lee C. Moore Corp. Photo)

Fig. 158 (right)—Drawworks Converted to Electric Drive, 1959

Many drilling contractors are finding it economical to convert their present engine-driven drawworks to modern electric drive. This is a recently converted drawworks with 2 duplicate 1,000-hp d-c gear motors. There is no increase in drawworks width. Pumps on the rig have independent motor drives.

(Photo by Oil Well Supply Div., United States Steel Corp.)

Fig. 157 (left)—Drawworks for Helicopter Rig, 1959

Drawworks components for disassembly of the new helicopter rig were designed by The National Supply Co., Pittsburgh, for flexibility in handling. Ten major units—the lower frame; drum shaft assembly; drum brake rims, clutch parts, and sprocket; catshaft and sand reel; drawworks counter shaft; hydromatic brake assembly; upper frame section; cathead assemblies; and rotary counter shaft—average 2,200 lb each.

(The National Supply Co. Photo)

Fig. 160—Multiple-well Derrick Designed posed of Welded Sections and Designed Specifically for Drilling from a Floating Vessel, 1959

(Lee C. Moore Corp. Photo)

Fig. 160—Multiple-well Derrick Designed for Drilling 25 Wells from LeTourneau Offshore Platform, 1959

(Lee C. Moore Corp. Photo)

Fig. 161—Remote Control of Drilling Machinery on Mobile Offshore Platform

Many interesting adaptations and modifications of standard rotary-drilling machinery are found on offshore installations. On this mobile platform, the driller controls all drilling operations from his derrick-floor console (top right). The main drawworks, together with its prime movers, compound drive, and hydraulic feed control, is below deck (bottom right) where it is protected from salt spray. An independently driven drawworks on the derrick floor (below) serves as a combination catworks and sand reel and drives the rotary. It requires an operator only for sand-line spooling; other operations are controlled by the driller from his derrick-floor console.

(Photo by Oil Well Div., United States Steel Corp.)

Fig 162 (right)—Rotary-drilling Unit, 1959

Accurate control of drill-stem rotation, lessened danger of twistoffs, and reduced wear and tear on drawworks parts are advantages provided by this drilling unit. This independent unit, complete with prime mover, releases up to 300 hp from the drawworks compound for driving the mud pumps.

(Photo by Oil Well Div., United States Steel Corp.)

Fig. 163 (left)—Hydraulic Gate, 1959
(Ram-type Blowout Preventer for
Ultra-high Pressures)

This hydraulic gate is designed for 10,000 psi working pressures and is tested to 15,000 psi in the factory. The rams are changed by swinging the ends open on hinges, which exposes the rams completely.

(Shaffer Tool Works Photo)

Fig. 164 (right)—Blowout Preventer, 1960

Cameron 6-in. 10,000-psi working pressure single, open-face flanged Type "F" blowout preventer with side outlets below the rams. The blowout preventer is equipped with a Type "L" low-pressure operating device that may be actuated with air or a liquid, or a combination of the two. Maximum operating pressure is 1,500 psi.

(Cameron Iron Works, Inc., Photo)

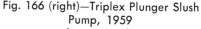

Fig. 165 (left)—Drilling Control Panel
Unit, 1960

Cameron drilling-control panel unit designed to operate three blowout preventers with hydraulic pressure and gate valves on choke and kill lines with rig air pressure. The unit is equipped with an air-driven hydraulic pump as well as a manual hydraulic pump for emergency purposes. Type "J" remote-reading pressure gages, operating on only 15 psi air pressure, are used to show actual high pressures in the hookup.

(Cameron Iron Works, Inc. Photo)

Fig. 166 (right)—Triplex Plunger Slush
Pump, 1959

In pump applications where volume is less important than pressure—such as in slim-hole drilling—considerable interest is being shown in plunger pumps. This triplex, for example, develops pressures to 10,000 psi from 700 input horsepower, yet weighs less than 8,300 lb.

(Photo by Oil Well Supply Div., United States Steel Corp.)

Bottom View

Showing Nozzle

OSC-3A-J Rock Bit

This new (1959) Hughes Tool Co. jet bit with conventional water courses, and the OSC-2A-J jet bit, are built for drilling in top-hole formations. By using fewer teeth, deeper grooving, and increasing the average intermesh, this self-cleaning bit is designed to increase rate of penetration. Recommended drilling weights range from 1,000 to 4,000 lb per inch of bit diameter, with rotary speeds decreasing from 150 to 75 rpm as weight is applied.

Bottom View

Side View

OWV Jet Bit

OWV is recommended for use when formations become slightly too hard for softer-formation bits, but before use of OWC or harder bit is indicated. Its geometry assures maximum cutting action and bit life in medium to medium-hard formations such as the harder shales, sandy shales, shales alternating with streaks of sand and limestone. Yet cutting structure is versatile and bit has been found most economical in drilling various formations containing anhydrite and gypsum. Drilling weights commonly used range from 1,000 to 7,000 lb per inch of bit diameter, with rotary speeds decreasing from 150 to 75 rpm as weight is increased.

Fig. 167—Rock Bits, 1959

Bottom View

Side View

W7R-2-Jet

Designed for use in extremely hard formations in a range between those ordinarily drilled with Hughes W7 and W7R. Has the following design features: 1. Steel web extended to join two teeth minimizes premature breakdown of gage surface at "B" diameter. 2. New hard-facing pattern, in which type and location of hard-facing guide ribs are important factors, minimizes amount of gage-point breakdown. 3. On 8¾- and 9-in. sizes, rate of penetration has been increased through elimination of 1 row of teeth. 4. Stronger cutting structure has been achieved by lengthening tooth crest.

Bottom View

Side View

RG1-Jet Bit

"Hugheset" Type RG-1J rock bit is designed to drill extremely hard abrasive formations, such as chert, quartzite, granite, flint, novaculite, taconite, pyrite-bearing quartzitic formations, and basalt. Does not have conventional teeth. Instead, sintered tungsten carbide and forged alloy steel are combined to produce high resistance to abrasion. In the hardest formations known, subsurface fracturing occurs beneath each insert as it contacts the bottom. The rows of closely spaced inserts on the gage points of each of the three cones assure drilling a full-gage hole. Experience to date indicates the best operating procedure in drilling chert or chert-bearing limestone is to carry a weight of approximately 4,000 lb per inch of bit diameter, with rotary speed approximately 35 rpm. All this weight should be applied with drill collars.

Fig. 167—Rock Bits, 1959

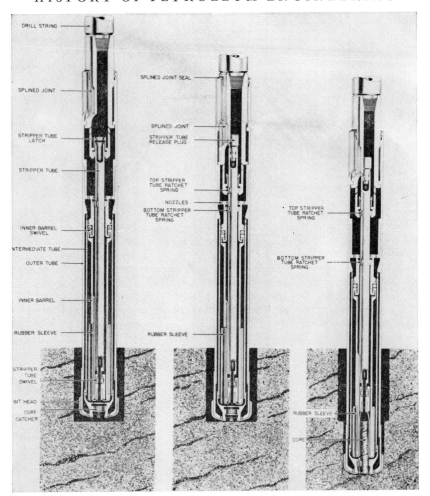

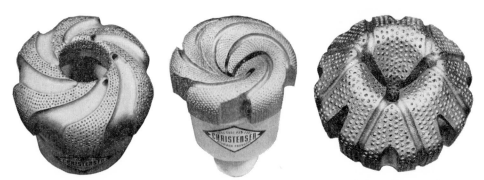

Fig. 168—Rubber-sleeve Diamond-bit Core Barrel for Rat-hole Coring with
Bit for Core Barrel and Three Full-hole Diamond Bits, 1959
(Christensen Diamond Products Photos)

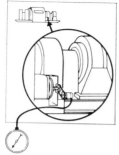

V-BELT PULLEY DRIVE
FROM ANY SHAFT TURNING
IN DIRECT PROPORTION
WITH THE ROTARY

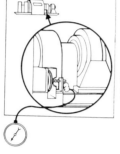

DIRECT CONNECTION
TO ANY SHAFT TURNING
IN DIRECT PROPORTION
TO THE ROTARY

Fig. 169—Martin-Decker Electric Rotary
Tachometer, 1959

The small a-c generator is mounted in some manner to the drawworks or rotary table and the rotary speed indicator installed in the weight-indicator panel. A ratio adjustment is provided at the head so that the instrument can be set for any required installation.

Fig. 170—Martin-Decker Pump Speed or
Volume Indicator, 1959

The small a-c generator is attached in some manner to the pump turning in direct proportion to the pump speed. The indicator is mounted in the weight-indicator box with a ratio adjustment for setting the instrument for any installation.

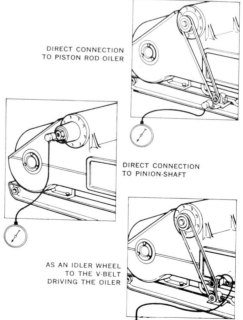

DIRECT CONNECTION
TO PISTON ROD OILER

DIRECT CONNECTION
TO PINION-SHAFT

AS AN IDLER WHEEL
TO THE V-BELT
DRIVING THE OILER

Fig. 171 (left)—Martin-Decker Ezy-Vue
Pressure Gage, 1959

This instrument can be mounted directly
to the standpipe or pump and uses a
beryllium copper probe for separating the
mud or cement from the fluid required
to actuate the gage. The instrument can
be dampened in the field by screw-
driver adjustment at the top of the gage.
The Ezy-Vue is fluid-filled to provide a
rugged, accurate gage for operations.

Fig. 172 (right)—Martin-Decker Electric
Drilloger Recording System, 1959

For remote recording of any of the following signals: Weight on the bit; rate
of penetration; rotary speed; pump pressure; pump speed; torque. This equipment
can be installed in the toolpusher's shack
or doghouse and the complete drilling
record provided for immediate study of
operations or for later evaluation.

Table 10

The National Supply Co. Type 4-10 Helicopter Rig
Weights for Transportation
(From *The National Supply Co. Catalog*)

	Pounds
Drum shaft assembly with brake rims, clutch parts and sprocket removed	3,500
Brake rims, clutch parts and sprocket from drum shaft	2,200
Catshaft, complete with sand reel with 9/16 Lebus grooving, less catheads	3,000
Foster 62MH spinning cathead, levers, and adapter	850
Foster 63AD breakout cathead and bracket	765
Hydromatic brake complete with dual Airflex clutch and skid base	2,000
Drawworks countershaft, complete	2,100
Rotary countershaft, complete	665
Drawworks frame, lower section	4,000
Drawworks frame, upper section	1,250
Transmission line shaft, complete	2,300
Transmission jackshaft, complete	953
Transmission housing	1,600
Transmission cover	400
Compound section No. 1 with shafts and air compressor	3,080
Compound section No. 2 with shafts	2,810
Compound section No. 3 with shafts and air compressor	3,200
Compound section No. 4 with shaft	1,300
2 compound skids at 800 pounds and 650 pounds	1,450
2 engine skids at 700 pounds each	1,400
4 engines at 4000 pounds each (approximate)	16,000
6 Universal joint sets	800
Miscellaneous guards and loose items	3,500
TOTAL WEIGHT—with sand reel	59,123
TOTAL WEIGHT—less sand reel (2400 pounds)	56,723

C-150-B Pump—Airborne

Frame only	4,000
Cover	1,600
Adapters, crossheads, lock nuts, intermediate rods, cylinder heads, sprockets, etc.	1,670
Crankshaft and connecting rods	2,700
Fluid end with studs and seats	3,980
Pinion shaft complete, less drive sprocket	775
Pump skid	1,930
Pump drive countershaft, complete with housing	430
Pump drive chain guard	380
TOTAL for one pump	17,465

Addendum

Pneumatic Rotary Drilling

The term "pneumatic drilling" is used to describe rotary drilling accomplished with an aeroform fluid as the circulating medium, in distinction to the liquid medium used in hydraulic rotary drilling.

Although the first widely described and probably the actual first application of pneumatic drilling was in 1938, the development of this method was deferred until about 1950 and then became the most publicized and significant drilling innovation of the period 1950-60. In this decade thousands of wells were drilled at least partially with air or natural gas as the drilling fluid. The literature of the period is replete with accounts of large and often spectacular economies credited to the method. Nearly all accounts, however, contained warnings that removal of cuttings was difficult-to-impossible in the presence of moderate-to-heavy flows of formation water. The conception prevailing by 1960 was that pneumatic drilling was superior to hydraulic drilling under certain favorable conditions, with a more universal application being dependent upon the solution of the water-incursion problem.

Initial incentives for the development of pneumatic drilling were four major disadvantages which are characteristic of hydraulic drilling under certain widely occurring conditions. These were: 1, the formation damage by water or particle incursion which often resulted from drilling-in with pressures exceeding those in the formation; 2, the difficulty of obtaining absolute or even relative indications of the potential productivity of different members or intervals of a formation; 3, the expense, often the impossibility, of combating lost circulation; and 4, the time and expense of cleaning out during completion. Early in the development of the pneumatic method two other prime advantages—faster penetration and longer bit life—were observed and soon became important criteria in the choice between hydraulic and pneumatic drilling.

Although the equipment and techniques of cable-tool and pneumatic drilling have nothing in common, the use of cable tools for drilling-in may be considered the first stage in the evolution of pneumatic drilling. The second or intermediate stage was the use as a circulating medium of oil or water aerated by natural gas to lessen the pressure exerted by the fluid column on the bottom of the hole. This method was referred to as "pressure drilling" or "reduced-pressure drilling".

Pressure drilling was described in at least 3 instances in the literature of the 1930's. The first reported use of natural gas as a deliberately introduced and carefully controlled drilling-fluid component was by the Big Lake Oil Co. in the Big Lake Field of Reagan County, Texas, in 1932. As described by E. V. Foran the effort here was to complete 8,800-ft wells, with gasified water, in a flowing condition so as to avoid formation damage. It was essential to keep pressure on an 8,200-ft pay at or below the 1,900-lb formation pressure. This was accomplished by introducing 800 cu ft of gas per barrel of water. The gas was metered into and out of the drilling fluid, with the metering providing close indications of the productivity of different members of the producing formation. Other equipment used included a hydraulic rotary table, flush-joint drill pipe, pressure drilling head, a 1,200-lb water knockout, and 500- and 125-lb permanent separators. Makeup of the drilling head was as shown in Fig. 173.

Beginning in 1934, with Big Lake experience as a guide, E. H. Moore, Inc. used pressure drilling to drill-in 50 wells, and to deepen 32 others, in the Fitts Pool of Pontotoc County, Okla. Here, as related by K. R. Teis, oil or water was aerated with natural gas for use as the drilling fluid. Pressure drilling at Fitts resulted in the recognition of the McLish

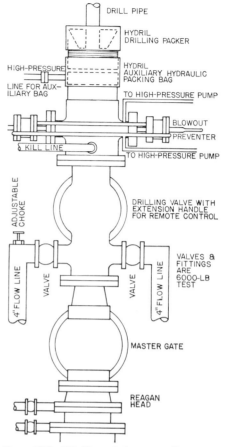

Fig. 173—Wellhead Layout Showing Connections for Pressure Drilling Big Lake Oil Field, Reagan County, Texas, 1932

and Wilcox formations as highly productive and touched off an extensive campaign of deepening Hunton, Viola, and Bromide wells. The equipment used was similar to that at Big Lake, with the flow diagram as it appears in Fig. 174. Essentially the same system was used by Phillips Petroleum Co. and others in the Oklahoma City Field in 1935 and possibly earlier.

At Dominguez, California, in 1937, Union Oil Co. of California used equipment and methods adapted from Fitts Pool experience for subpressure completions in the depleted middle Pliocene and upper Miocene. With gas-input pressures of 175 to 340 psi, gas-oil ratios (in the drilling fluid) of 370 to 430 cu ft per bbl, and oil rates of 175 bbl per hour, bottom-hole pressures as much as 100 psi below the formation pressures were achieved. In describing this operation S. Grinsfelder and Jan

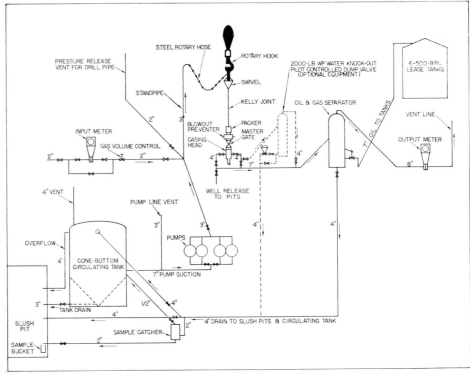

**Fig. 174—Flow Diagram for Pressure Drilling
Fitts Pool, Oklahoma, 1934**

Law had more to say than earlier reporters on the influence of drilling rates, gas-oil ratios, and rates of circulation on the lifting power of the fluid.

The drilling fluid in the aforementioned pressure-drilling operations was in the liquid phase at all times, never in the gas phase. Pressure drilling, therefore, despite its probable strong influence on the emergence of pneumatic drilling, must be considered as a special case of hydraulic drilling. Those who used it appeared to consider it of no consequence or advantage except in avoidance of plugging of productive formations. Increased bit life and faster penetration were mentioned briefly or not at all, either because the intervals drilled were too short to afford comparisons or because these advantages did not materialize until the full transition from a liquid to an aeroform circulating medium was made.

Although N. C. Wells refers without particulars to pre-1938 drilling-in in limestone formations with gas, no account of these instances can be located, nor is it certain that the operations referred to were not pressure-drilling completions on the order of those just described. With this possible exception, it appears that the first instance of pneumatic drilling was its use for 2 completions by The Texas Co. in the Brown zone at

Signal Hill, California, in 1938. The practice here, however, was not a total departure from pressure-drilling methods, since oil at the rate of 20 bbl per hour was circulated with 2,000 Mcf per day of gas. The 2 completions penetrated the Brown zone 888 ft and 793 ft, respectively. Wells observed that drilling through loose sand members was accomplished mostly through jetting action, with little or no weight on the bit, and that total volume of sand recovered measured 152 percent of the calculated volume of the hole. Input pressures were 250 to 500 psi, with return pressure at the surface being 30 psi.

Following the Signal Hill operations there was a 12-year lapse, complete at least so far as the literature is concerned, in the utilization of pneumatic drilling. The hiatus during World War II can possibly be attributed to scarcity of compressors and to other wartime factors which reacted against the use of methods not completely proved. When resumed it was in 1950 or 1951 at the South Mountain and Oat Mountain Fields in California. Here Standard Oil Co. of California, Shell Oil Co., The Ohio Oil Co., and Union Oil Co. of California drilled surface hole for 14 wells with air as the circulating medium. The fractured shales and broken volcanic rocks which made up the formations to 1,200 ft presented a lost-circulation problem which could not be overcome with hydraulic drilling. Previous practice was to drill the surface hole with cable tools, with much time consumed and crooked holes resulting. Equipment used for the air drilling included 7 to 9 construction-type compressors with aggregate free air capacity of 3,000 to 4,500 cu ft per min at from 100 to 110 psi, connected as shown in Fig. 175. K. M. Nicolson reported not only the satisfactory solution of the lost-circulation problem but increases in rates of penetration, as compared to drilling with mud, of up to 237 percent, and increases in bit footage of 36 to 348 percent. He also advanced a formula, based on Newton's law of turbulent resistance, setting out the relationship between air velocity, air density, particle shape, and particle size, and enabling the calculation of particle-size lifting capacity. Nicolson also commented extensively upon the importance of hole size, drill-pipe size, compression capacity, and pressure as factors affecting the design of a system for optimum use of horsepower. Reverse circulation was experimented with and promised two major advantages, viz., increased lifting capacity with the same pressure or the same lifting capacity with reduced air volume, and less difficulty with wet cuttings, in that these were returned inside the drill pipe and not permitted to contact and plaster the walls of the hole. Two air-drilling holes were stopped by sloughing formations which were not a problem with mud and many delays resulting from inability to lift wet cuttings were encountered.

The earliest extensive use of natural gas as a circulating medium was in the San Juan Basin of New Mexico, where between May 1951 and

441

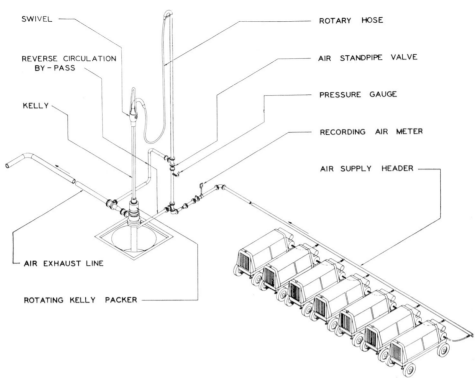

SWIVEL

REVERSE CIRCULATION
BY–PASS

KELLY

AIR EXHAUST LINE

ROTATING KELLY PACKER

ROTARY HOSE

AIR STANDPIPE VALVE

PRESSURE GAUGE

RECORDING AIR METER

AIR SUPPLY HEADER

Fig. 175—Schematic View of Air-drilling Facilities
South Oat Mountain, California, 1951

March 1954 several hundred wells were drilled, with 300 of these belonging to El Paso Natural Gas Co. Gas drilling was confined to surface hole and the Mesa Verde formation between 5,000 and 5,800 ft. Pressures used were from 80 to 450 psi, with 250 psi noted as the minimum pressure effective where water was present. Weight on bit was held to 6,000 to 8,000 lb in $6\frac{1}{4}$-in. hole; 20,000 lb in $8\frac{3}{4}$-in. hole. L. S. Fuller reported the following advantages as compared to other methods of drilling:

1. Reduction of drilling time to 27 hours as compared with 3 to 8 weeks for cable tools.
2. An increase of 85 percent in rate of penetration compared to hydraulic drilling.
3. Elimination of mud contamination of producing zone.
4. Ability to test in stages as wells were drilled and cleaned out.
5. Cleaning-out time reduced to a few hours, as compared to weeks when hydraulically drilled.
6. Savings of $20,000 per well.

Among the difficulties noted by Fuller were the danger of stuck drill pipe from closure of the annulus (in either cased or open hole) by water-soaked cuttings, necessity for frequent inspection of blowout equipment, and the need for rigorous fire-prevention measures at the surface.

It was the opinion of many that the extensive gas fields of the San Juan Basin could not have been economically developed except for pneumatic drilling.

Air drilling was introduced to the Appalachian area in March 1954 by Delta Drilling Co. as contractor for New York State Natural Gas Co. An attempt to air-drill surface hole in the Benezette gas field of Elk County, Pa. was thwarted by water incursion and mud was used to 723 ft, where the drilling reverted to air and continued to the top of the Oriskany pay at 7,138 ft where air was replaced by gas for drilling-in. The following penetration advantages as compared to wells hydraulically drilled were reported by H. J. Magner:

	Hydraulically Drilled Wells, Range	*Air-drilled Wells, Range*
Feet per bit	111-318	194-793
Feet per day	91-289	295-510
Feet per drilling hour	7-17	27-36
Footage rates	$8.50	$6.00

An interesting and probably unique application of air drilling took place in the Bartlesville sand fields of Nowata County, Okla., beginning in February 1955. Here, Overby Drilling Co., contractor for Brundred-Climax Waterflood Division of Climax Molybdenum Co. successfully drilled 588 shallow wells, totalling 305,500 ft, in less than 2 years, using only a Mayhew Model 1000 rig for part of the period, then adding a Mayhew Model 2000 rig. Most of the drilling with the smaller rig was performed with 2-man crews, with 3-man crews on the larger rig. After early minor troubles were overcome L. L. Brundred reported that the operation was so systematized that wells spudded at 4:00 p.m. one day were drilled, shot and cleaned out, and the rig torn down and rigged up at a new location, by 4:00 p.m. the next day.

By 1958 there was general agreement that, subject almost entirely to the limitations imposed by its inability to handle considerable flows of formation water, pneumatic drilling had a tremendous potential for speed, economy, and protection of producing zones and could be considered to be one of the most significant advances in the history of rotary drilling. By 1958 the method had been widely tested in the Permian and Delaware Basins, the Rocky Mountain area, California, the Mid-Continent, the Appalachian area, and in Canada. From a survey covering 226 widely scattered air-drilled wells, comprising 419,407 ft of hole, Gordon Jackson reported that 85 percent had reached their objective depth. Eighty-two of these operations encountered no water or wet formations;

while of the 144 wells in which water had been encountered, 110 were successfully completed, with a forced reversion to mud on the remaining 44.

In the earlier days of pneumatic drilling, casing-off and squeeze cementing were the principal means of combating formation water flows. In the latter part of the 1950's intensive attention was paid to other means of attaining a water shutoff, and to chemical additives which would diminish the stickiness and thus resist the balling tendencies of wet cuttings. Among the mechanical means used was a length of plastic pipe cemented opposite the weeping zone with an epoxy resin. Numerous tests were made of chemical liquids of low viscosity which could be squeezed into the formation to set up either on contact with the water or through a chemical timer. One of the more successful of these was a water gel hardened by a combination of chemical timer, temperature, and dilution with water. Also fairly successful was a liquid plastic which hardened on contact with water. Other means included the injection of liquid, followed by injection of a gas to form an insoluble precipitate, and injection only of a gas—e.g., silicon tetrafluoride—which formed a gel on contact with water.

Chemicals added to the air or gas stream to create foaming on contact with water were of various composition, with some of them being so successful with moderate to heavy water flows as to enlarge the practical range of air drilling. Disadvantages noticed were an accelerated corrosion of drill pipe and a reduced penetration rate as compared to dry drilling. In general, quantities of the foaming agent required were proportional to the amount of water inflow.

In 1960 the problem of water shutoff and/or lifting of wet cuttings was reduced, but still present in a degree to prevent anything like universal use of pneumatic drilling.

ACKNOWLEDGMENTS

Following is a list of those individuals and companies who prepared editorial material to be used in the text of this chapter, and a list of individuals who contributed or confirmed information—either through letters or conversations. Although all of those listed as contributors furnished material, only a very small part of their contributions could be used and little or no reference has been made here to many of the items discussed. The material from these valuable contributions, some of which are classics, will be used in an extended volume now in preparation.

Listed also are publications and literature from which information was obtained and catalogs consulted—particularly those published prior to 1930—in the preparaton of this chapter and that entitled "Percussion-drilling System." The publications listed furnished information included in these chapters, although few direct quotations or passages from any of them are used. Many technical and trade journals were studied, but again the material used was of a general nature with relatively few direct quotations. The same is true of the catalogs listed, from which illustrations and data on progress of equipment were obtained.

For the periods prior to 1920, the material was gathered largely from non-technical articles, a few technical papers, catalogs of several companies, and, particularly, the U. S. Patent Office. Beginning about 1930 numerous fine technical papers have been published in various association and institute transactions and in the trade journals. Information has been drawn from many of these papers, but specific references have been made only to the few most closely related to the history of rotary drilling. Much of the material used for the years 1920 to 1952 is based on the writer's personal experience.

The contributors of illustrations have made available a great many that could not be used in this chapter. Credit is usually given only in cases of prior publication.

Contributors of Material Used in Text

Ashton, A. A., Emsco Mfg. Co: Pumps

Baker, Ray, The Texas Co: Drilling barges

Ballagh, J. C., Los Angeles: Casing protectors

Barkis, Bruce, B & W Inc: Casing accessories

Berman, M., & Skinner, C. W., Hewitt-Robins Inc: Rotary-drilling hose

Brantly, M. M: Air and gas drilling

Bugbee, J. M., Shell Oil Co: Development of drilling fluid

Cannon, George E., Humble Oil & Refining Co: History of drag-type drilling bits

Decker, E. L., Martin-Decker Corp: Drilling-control instruments

Dittmar, O. H., Lee C. Moore Corp: Derricks and photographs

Dunlop, C. A., Humble Oil & Refining Co.

Eastman, John, Eastman Oil Well Survey Co: Well surveying
Emerson, James L., Chiksan Co: Steel hoses
Farr, A. P., Hughes Tool Co: Tool joints
Haines, C. S., Hewitt-Robins Inc: Hose
Hamaker, Rex G., Reed Roller Bit Co: Cross-roller bits
Harris, Hu M. (retired), Humble Oil & Refining Co: Unitized drawworks
Hilker, F. C., Eastman Oil Well Survey Co: Directional drilling
Johnston, M. O: Formation testing
Jones, R. D., Hughes Tool Co: Tool joints
Justice, George E., Houston Oil Field Material Co., Inc: Fishing tools
Kilgore, Grover, Halliburton Oil Well Cementing Co: Formation testing
Kirby, John H., II, K & O Oil Tool Services: Magnetic fishing tools
Losey, Tom, The Guiberson Corp: History of swabs
Mahan, J. R., The National Supply Co: Power plants
Marsh, H. N. and associate: Development of instruments used for measuring the properties of drilling fluid
Mills, Brad, AAODC: Safety and educational work
Moore, B. L., Humble Oil & Refining Co: Power plants and mechanical rigs
Morgan, A. J., John A. Roebling's Sons Co: Wire line
Nicholson, G. F. and Horner, V. C., Byron Jackson Tools, Inc: Derrick tools
Noble, Wiley B., Reed Roller Bit Co: Wire line, core barrels, drill collars, tool joints, and reamers
Nolley, R. H., Hughes Tool Co: Core barrels
Redman, Wm. J., Wilson Snyder Works, Oil Well Supply Div., U. S. Steel Corp: Pumps
Reinhold, B., Abbegg & Reinhold Co: Pump liners and kelly drive bushings
Rogers, Walter F., Gulf Oil Corp: Control of drilling fluids
Scott, Floyd L., Hughes Tool Co: Tri-cone bits
Siegle, J. C., Youngstown Sheet & Tube Co: Drilling shaft
Sweeney, R. T., Link-Belt Co: Chain
Uren, Lester C., University of California, Berkeley: Drilling fluid
White, Carl Jr., Franks Mfg. Co: Portable rigs
Works, Madden, Cameron Iron Works: Blowout preventers
Young, Forest, The National Supply Co: Feed controls
Zubin, John, Universal Engineering Co: Zubin bits

Letters and Conversations

Alred, Cyril, Associate Curator, Dept. of Egyptian Arts, Metropolitan Museum of Art
American Well & Prospecting Co. (Bethlehem Steel Corp.)
Archer, M. T., The National Supply Co: Letter to J. H. Pound
British Museum, Egyptian Section, London, England

DeGolyer, E: Letters to J. E. Brantly

Dittmar, O. H., Lee C. Moore Corp.

Elliott, J. E: History of core barrels

Farrand, W. H., Petroleum Engineer, formerly Manager of Foreign Operations, The Texas Co.

Hamer, L. S., Hamer Oil Tool Co., Los Angeles

Ideco, Division of Dresser Industries

Jillson, Dr. Willard R., formerly State Geologist of Kentucky

Kilgore, Grover, Halliburton Oil Well Cementing Co., Duncan, Okla: Cementing

Knox, Earl S., Los Angeles: Electric power plants

LeRoy, N. K., Shaffer Tool Works, Los Angeles

McDuffie, Wm. C., Los Angeles

Messeranti, Mario, Messeranti Oil Field Equipment, Italy

Naramore, Chester: Personal letters to John Suman and J. E. Brantly

Navarre, M. Rene, Director Institut Francais du Petrole: Letter on Fauvelle drilling system and wells drilled in France, pre-1850

Quayle, A., Oil Well Supply Co: Letter on make-and-break rotary tables

Rakeshaw, T. H. (retired), Oklahoma

Rubel, A. C., Union Oil Co. of California: Letters to J. E. Brantly

Schroeder, Mrs. Eric G: Letters from Eugene Kibele on development of kelly

Spalding, John D., The National Supply Co: Letters on various items of equipment

Suman, John R. (retired), Standard Oil Co. (N. J.): Letters to J. E. Brantly

Sutter, T., Baker Oil Tools, Inc., Los Angeles: Casing accessories

Swanson, E. B., Washington, D. C.

Swigart, Theodore E., Shell Oil Co: Letters to John R. Suman

Welty, Earl, Union Oil Co. of California

Wilson, Web A: Letter on tongs and elevators

Wrather, W. E., Director, U. S. Geological Service

Young, Carl: Personal letters to J. E. Brantly

Publications and Literature

Am. Assoc. of Petroleum Geologists Bulletin, various.

American Institute of Mining and Metallurgical Engineers and *AIME Transactions,* various.

American Journal of Science, 2nd Series, 15 (1853); Swallow, G. C: Geology of Kentucky (1955).

American Petroleum Institute, *RP 29* (formerly designated *Code 29*): *Standard Field Procedure for Testing Drilling Fluids,* 1st Ed., 1938; 2nd Ed., 1942; 3rd Ed., 1950; 4th Ed., 1957.

American Petroleum Institute, *Drilling and Production Practice,* various.

American Petroleum Institute Specifications, various.

Anderson, H. H.

Andros, Stephen O: *The Petroleum Handbook,* 1919.

Anon: *Arts and Crafts*, Fig. 89 (1909).

Anon: Early Drilling Machine, Employees Monthly Magazine, The National Supply Co., Dec. (1922).

Appleton: *Cyclopedia of Applied Mechanics*, 1882.

Aristotle

Arnold and Garfias: Cementing Process of Excluding Water from Oil Wells, *U. S. Bur. Mines TP 32* (1913).

Baroid Div., National Lead Co., various publications.

Arrault, Paulin: *Outils et Procedes de Sondages*, Paris, 1890.

Ball, Max: *This Fascinating Oil Business*, Bobbs-Merrill Co., New York, 1940.

Baroid News Bulletin: March-April (1954).

Bawawy, Dr. Alexander, British Museum on Egyptian coring.

Beebe-Thompson, A: *Oil Field Exploration and Development*, Crosby Lockwood & Sons, London, 1925; *Oil Field Development and Petroleum Mining*, 1910 and 1916.

ibid: Treatises on oil-well drilling, early 1900.

Beer, August: *Erdbohrkunde Priebam*, Austria, 1858.

Bielstein, W. J. and Cannon, George E: Factors Affecting The Rate of Penetration of Rock Bits, *API Drilling and Production Practice*, 61 (1950).

Bignell, L.G.E: Evolution of the Oil Field Derrick.

Brantly, J. E: Factors Governing Rotary Drilling Rates, *World Petroleum*, March (1948); *Rotary Drilling Handbook*, 1st Ed., 1936; 2nd Ed., 1938; 3rd Ed., 1942; 4th Ed., 1948; 5th Ed., 1952.

Brantly, J. E. and Clayton, E. H: A Preliminary Evaluation of Factors Governing Rate of Penetration in Rotary Drilling, *API Drilling and Production Practice*, 8 (1939).

Brantly, M. M. and Moore, Stanley C: Straight-hole Drilling, *Drilling Contractor*, Dec. (1955).

Brundred, L. L: Rotary Drilling with Air in Shallow Water—Flood Development, *API Drilling and Production Practice*, 448 (1956).

Burkesville *Courier*, Burkesville, Ky., Oct. 11, 1876.

California Oil World, 2nd Issue, Nov. (1955).

California State Mining Bureau, various bulletins from office of the State Oil and Gas Supervisor.

Cannon, George E: Changes in Hydrostatic Pressure due to Withdrawing Drill Pipe from the Hole, *API Drilling and Production Practice*, 42 (1934).

Carll, J. F: *The Geology of the Oil Regions of Warren, Clarion and Butler Counties, Pennsylvania*, Second Pennsylvania Geological Survey, 1875-79, III (1880).

Clark, H. H: Electric Lights on Rigs, *U. S. Bur. Mines TP 79* (1914).

Clarke, S. and Englebach, R: *Ancient Egyptian Masonry*, 202-204, Fig. 245-249 (1930).

Collom, R. D: Mud-Laden Fluid for Rotary Drilling, *Summary of Operations, California Oil Fields*, 8 [7].

Confucius.

Coldre, Louis: Chinese Brine Wells at Ssu-chan *Western Engineering*, Dec. (1914).

Crew, Benjamin J: *A Practical Treatise on Petroleum*, Henry Clay Baird & Co., 1887.

Ctesias.

Cumming, J. D: *Diamond Drilling Handbook*, Toronto, Canada, 1951.

Cunningham, Craig: Treatises on oil-well drilling, early 1900's.

da Vinci, Leonardo.

Curtin, Thomas: Casing and Fishing, *U. S. Bur. Mines Bull. 182* (1920).

Dartmouth Alumni Magazine: April (1951).

Degousee, M. J: *Guide du Sondeur*, Paris, 1847.

Deneca.

deThury, Hericart: *Consideration Geologiques et Physiques sur la Cause du Jaillissement des Eaux des Puts Fores*, Paris Firmin Didot, 1829.

Dievendorff, H. H. and Hertel, F. W: Deep-well Drilling Technique, *Petroleum Development and Technology in 1927*, American Institute of Mining and Metallurgical Engineers, Inc., New York, 1928.

Diodorus Siculus.

Discordies.

Drilling Contractor, various issues.

Drilling Magazine, various issues.

Encyclopedia Brittanica, Vol. 2 and 28, 1911.

Fauvelle: A New Method of Boring for Artesian Springs, *Journal of Franklin Institute,* [6] Dec. (1846).

Foram, Wm. T: Oil from the Garden of Eden, *Petroleum Engineering,* Oct. (1942).

Foran, E. V: Pressure Completions of Wells in West Texas, *API Drilling and Production Practice,* 48 (1934).

Fuller, L. S: Drilling with Air and Natural Gas, *API Drilling and Production Practice,* 82 (1954).

Giddens, Paul H: *The Birth of the Oil Industry,* 1938.

ibid: Early Days of Oil, Princeton University Press, Princeton, N. J., 1948.

Goodrick, H. B: Easy Exploration Methods, *World Petroleum.*

Grinsfelder, S. and Law, Jan: Recent Pressure Drilling at Dominguez, *API Drilling and Production Practice,* 74 (1938).

Guiberson, W. R: Drilling Wells in California, *Oil Gas J.,* May 20 (1915).

Habets, M. (Professeur a l'Universite de Liege): *Rapport sur L'industrie des Sondages,* Paris, 1889.

Hale, J. P: West Virginia Historian.

Hazel, M. F: Rotary Drilling Equipment, 1951, *Oil Gas J.* (1951).

Heggem, A. G. and Pollard, J. A: *U. S. Bur. Mines TP 66 and 68* (1914).

Henry, J. D: *Oil Fields of New Zealand,* 1911; *Oil Fields of the Empire.*

Herodotus.

Holy Bible: Genesis, 15th, 18th, and 19th verses, 26th chapter.

Hopper, Walter E: The Caddo Oil Field in Louisiana, *Trans. Am. Inst. Mining Met. Engrs.,* **XLII** (1912).

Howell, J. V: How Old Is Petroleum Geology? *Am. Assoc. Petroleum Geologists Bull.* **14** [5] May (1930).

Isler, C: *Well Boring for Water, Brine and Oil,* London, 1902.

Jackson, Gordon: An Analysis of Air Drilling, *The Drilling Contractor,* **XV** [4] 57, June-July (1959).

Jeffrey, W. H: *Deep Well Drilling,* Gulf Publishing Co., Houston, 1st Ed., 1921; 2nd Ed., 1925; 3rd Ed., 1931.

Jensen, Joseph: Recent Developments Related to Petroleum Engineering, *Trans. Am. Inst. Mining Met. Engrs. (Petroleum Development and Technology)* **123,** 63 (1937) (reprint, p. 241).

Jensen, Joseph, and Robertson, Glen D: Problems of Southern California Oil Fields, *Am. Assoc. Petroleum Geologists Bull.,* **8** [2] March-April (1924).

Jones, P. H: Field Control of Drilling Mud, *API Drilling and Production Practice,* 24 (1937).

Jones, P. H. and Babson, E. C: Evaluation of Rotary-drilling Muds, *API Drilling and Production Practice,* 22 (1935).

Josephus.

Kemler, Emory N: Rotary Percussion Drilling.

Keystone Well Drillers' Manual, 1927.

Kirwan, M.J: Cities Service Oil Co.

Knapp, A: Action of Mud Laden Fluids in Wells, *Trans. Am. Inst. Mining Met. Engrs.,* **69,** 1076 (1923); *Trans. Am. Inst. Mining Met. Engrs.* (1922).

Kurtin, Thomas: Casing Trouble and Fishing Methods in Oil Wells, *U. S. Bur. Mines Bull.* 82 (1920).

Larsen, D. H: Determining the Filtration Characteristics of Drilling Muds, *Petroleum Engineer* (in 2 parts): Part 1, 42, Sept. (1938); Part 2, 50, Nov. (1938).

Lauer: J. Ph. *La Pyramide a degres, L'Architecture,* I.II, Pls. XCV-XCVI.

Leonard, Charles C: *History of Pithole,* 1867.

Lewis, J. O. and McMurray, W. F: The Use of Mud-Laden Fluid in Oil and Gas Wells, *U. S. Bur. Mines Bull.* 134 (1918).

Little, L. B. (retired), Standard Oil Co. of California.

Lombardi, M. E: Deep Drilling at Coalinga, *Trans. Am. Inst. Mining Met. Engrs.,* **51** (1915).

Louden, E. W: *Rotary Drilling Fluid,* Baroid Div., National Lead Co., Houston.

Lucas, A: *Ancient Egyptian Materials and Industries,* London, 1948, 3rd Ed.

Lubinski, Arthur, and Woods, Henry B: Factors Affecting the Angle of Inclination and Dog-legging in Rotary Bore Holes, *API Drilling and Production Practice,* 222 (1953); Practical Charts for Solving Problems on Hole Deviation, *API Drilling and Production Practice,* 56 (1954); Use of Stabilizers in Controlling Hole Deviation, *API Drilling and Production Practice,* 165 (1955).

Lyman, B. S: *Reports on the Geology of Japan,* 1877.

Magner, H. J: Progress of Applachian Rotary Drilling through Air and Gas Methods, *API Drilling and Production Practice,* 282 (1955).

Marsh, H. N: Properties and Treatment of Rotary Mud, *Trans. Am. Inst. Mining Met. Engrs. (Petroleum Development and Technology)* 234, (1929).

Mayborn, T. W: *Drilling Magazine,* several issues including June 1950, Sept. 1950, May 1951, and May 1952.

McLaurin, J. J: *Sketches in Crude Oil,* 1898, 2nd Ed.

Memorandum of Scouting Section of Humble Oil & Refining Co., Dec. 20, 1955.

Meyer, P: *J. Inst. Petroleum Technology* (1934).

Mineral Resources, U. S. Geological Survey, 1886.

Mitzakis, Marcel: *Oil Encyclopedia,* New York, 1922.

Nicolson, K. M: Air Drilling in California, *API Drilling and Production Practice,* 300 (1953).

Niles' Register, (s) xiii, 4, 1929.

Noel, Col. E: Quanats, *Journal,* London, May (1944).

Nolley, J. P; Cannon, George E; and Ragland, Douglas: The Relation of Nozzle Fluid Velocity to Rate of Penetration with Drag-type Rotary Bits, *API Drilling and Production Practice,* 22 (1948).

Oil and Gas Journal, various issues.

Oil Region Reminiscences, issued by Oil Men's Assn. of Butler County, Pa., 1907.

Oil Weekly, various issues.

Owsley, Wm. D: *Drilling Practice,* 1937.

Pamphlets published by The Burmah Oil Co., Ltd.

Pardee, Harold N: Causes and Prevention of Crooked Cable Tool Holes, *Petroleum Engineer,* Feb. (1930).

Peckham, S. F: Report on the Production, Technology and Uses of Petroleum and Its Products, *Miscellaneous Document No. 42,* Vol. XIII, Part 10, 47th Congress, 2nd Section.

Pennington, J. V: The History of Drilling Technology and Its Prospects, *Proc. Am. Pet. Inst., Sect. IV (Prod. Bul. 235)* 48 (1949); also *Drilling Contractor* **6 [1]** 73, Dec. (1949).

Petrie: *Tools and Weapons,* 44-45, pl. LII, 58-73 (1917).

Petrie, W. F: On the Mechanical Methods of the Ancient Egyptians, *J. of the Anthropological Inst.,* Aug. (1883).

Petroleum Engineer, various issues.

Petroleum—Its History and Development, D. Appleton & Co., New York.

Petroleum Review: Vol. XXIV (1911); Aug. 18 (1899), published in London, England.

J. *Petroleum Technology,* Am. Inst. Mining and Metallurgical Engineers, Petroleum Branch, Dallas, Texas.

Petroleum Times, London.

Phelps and Lake: *Petroleum Engineering,* Gulf Publishing Co., Houston; 1st Ed., 2nd Ed. 1927.

Pliny.

Plutarch.

Pollard, J. A. and Heggen, A. C: Mud-Laden Fluid Applied to Well Drilling, *U. S. Bur. Mines TP 66* and 68 (1914).

Polo, Marco.

Pope, Capt. and Humphreys, Capt. A. (Topographical Engineers, U. S. Army): Letters.

Price, Paul H: Evolution of Geologic Thought in Prospecting for Oil and Natural Gas, *Am. Assoc. Petroleum Geologists Bull.,* April (1947).

Read, Thos. T: Deep Well Drilling 2000 Years Ago, *World Petroleum,* Jan. (1932).

Redmayne, R.A.S: *Modern Practice in Mining,* Vol. 1, London, 1908.

Redwood, Boverton: *A Treatise on Petroleum,* Charles Griffin & Co., London, 1922 (enlarged from 1906 and 1913); rev. ed., 1926.

ibid: Petroleum and Its Products, Charles Griffin & Co., London, 1906.

Rizzone, M. L: Power Transmissions of Rotary Rigs by Friction, Fluid, and Electro-mechanism.

Rogers, R. H: Preliminary Design of Drilling Barges and Deep-Water Drilling, *Petroleum Engineer,* Oct. (1929).

Rogers, Walter F: *Composition and Properties of Oil-Well Drilling Fluids,* Gulf Publishing Co., Houston.

Romance of American Petroleum and Gas, Vol. 1.

Rubel, A. C. (for Pacific Coast Dist. Subcommittee on Drilling Practice): The Effect of Drilling Mud on Production in California, *Proc. Am. Pet Inst., Sect. IV (Prod. Bul. 209)* 33 (1932).

Scott, B. H: Rotary Fishing Tools, Calif. State Bureau of Mines, **13 [1]** July (1927).

Silent, Roy A: Drilling Mud and Full-hole Tool Joints, *API Drilling and Production Practice,* 140 (1934).

Smith, E. C: Ancient Drilling Equipment, *World Petroleum,* June (1938).

Spon, Ernest: *The Present Practice of Sinking and Boring Wells,* London, 1885.

Strabo.

Stroud, B. K: Mud-Laden Fluids and Tables of Specific Gravities and Collapsing Pressures, *Tech. Paper #1,* Louisiana Dept. of Conservation (1922); Use of Barytes as a Mud Laden Fluid, *Oil Weekly,* June 5, 1925.

Suman, John R: *Petroleum Production Methods,* Gulf Publishing Co., Houston, 1922.

Symers, Major Michael: Reports in the *Journal of the British Embassy.*

Tacitus.

Techlenburg: *Handbuch der Tiefbohrkunde,* Vol. IV.

The Rig and Reel: Cement a Big Factor, Nov. (1923).

ibid: Digging Shafts to the Oil Sands, Feb. (1922).

ibid: Drilling Equipment History, April, May (1919).

ibid: Drilling with a Spring Pole, Aug. (1924).

ibid: Early Drilling in Ohio and Kentucky, April (1923).

ibid: Issues of June (1919) and July (1920).

ibid: Russian Drilling Methods, Oct. and Nov. (1923), Jan. and Feb. (1920).

ibid: The Petroleum Region of America, June and Aug. (1920).

The Yellow Strand: Aug. (1908), Oct. (1909), published by Broderick & Bascom Rope Co.

Teis, K. R: Pressure Completion of Wells in the Fitts Pool, *API Drilling and Production Practice,* 23 (1936).

True, Martin E: Semi-Automatic Power-operated Drilling Machinery, *API Drilling and Production Practice,* 38 (1952).

True, M. E. and Stone, B. L: Semiautomatic Power Operated Drilling Machinery, *Trans. Am. Inst. Mining Met. Engrs. (Petroleum Development and Technology)* **186,** 27 (1949).

U. S. Bureau of Mines, various publications.

U. S. Patent Office.

U. S. Steel News, May (1937).

Uren, Lester C: *Petroleum Production Engineering,* McGraw-Hill Book Co., Inc., New York, 1st Ed., 1924; 2nd Ed., 1934; 3rd Ed., 1946.

Van Couvering, M: Circulating Mud Laden Fluid in Connection with Cable Tool Drilling, *State Oil and Gas Supervisor,* Aug. (1920).

Wells, N. C: Pressure Drilling at Signal Hill, *Petroleum World,* 19, Oct. (1938).

Wheeler, H. A: The Illinois Gas Fields, *Trans. Am. Inst. Mining Engrs.,* **XLVIII** (1914).

Whiteshot, Charles A: *The Oil Well Driller,* Mannington, W. Va., 1905.

Woodworth, R. B: The Evolution of Drilling Rigs, *Trans. Am. Inst. Mining Met. Engrs.,* **LIV** (1916).

World Oil, various issues.

World Petroleum, various issues.

ibid: Ancient Chinese Drilling, Jan. (1932).

Catalogs
Prior to 1930
Baker Oil Tools

Emsco Manufacturing Co.

Lucey Manufacturing Co.

National Supply Co.

Oil Well Supply Co.

Paulin Arrault (France)

Regan Oil Field Equipment Co.

Shaffer Tool Works

Union Tool Co.

Subsequent to 1930
Various advertisers from the *Composite Catalog,* Gulf Publishing Co., Houston, Texas

The author is very grateful to the foregoing contributors of data and photographs, and also to the members of the Editorial Board, *History of Petroleum Engineering,* especially its chairman, D. V. Carter, and to E. L. Estabrook, for editorial assistance. I am particularly appreciative of the tedious job of paging and placing illustrations in Chapters 5 and 6, done by Mrs. Marjorie S. Kibben of the API Division of Production. To Wm. H. Strang, Director of the API Division of Production, I express grateful appreciation for his advice, assistance, and encouragement.

Chapter 7

CEMENTING

C. V. MILLIKAN

CHARLES VAN ORMER MILLIKAN, a native of Noble County, Oklahoma, received a degree in 1917 from Oklahoma Agricultural and Mechanical College by combining a chemistry major with courses in petroleum geology and development. Brief employment in the oil fields was interrupted by World War I naval service. Upon release he entered the University of Pittsburgh for further study of geology and petroleum engineering. Upon graduation in 1920, he was employed as an evaluation engineer by the Pittsburgh consulting firms of Johnson, Huntley, & Somers, and Ralph E. Davis. In 1922 he joined the geological department of Amerada Petroleum Corporation. His earliest assignments there were concerned with reserves estimation; torsion balance exploration; gas-oil ratios, and controlled flow of wells. Experiments in the latter resulted in his design and development of the first practical bottom-hole pressure gage, the application of which had great significance in future analyses of reservoir mechanics. He is currently the chief engineer of the corporation.

Mr. Millikan is an Anthony F. Lucas medalist of AIME and was chairman, in 1930, of AIME's Petroleum Division. He has been prominent in the fundamental research and drilling and production practice activities of the API; is a recipient of API's Certificate of Appreciation, and has participated in research and activities of the AAPG. He is the author of numerous geological and engineering papers, with those on bottom-hole pressures and productivity indices being considered particularly significant.

7

Oil-well cementing and cementing practice are important factors in the completion of oil wells. Cementing is the means whereby oil- and gas-producing horizons are separated from each other and from water-bearing strata. Adding strength to the casing and protecting it from corrosion are more recent requirements. It was the problem of the source and movement of water into oil wells and the technique of using cement to prevent such movement that led to the first employment of petroleum engineers in the oil fields.

Water produced with oil has been one of the serious problems of oil-well operators since the beginning of the petroleum industry. Sometimes the water came from the formation that contained the oil, but more often its source was an upper sand. The first oil wells had no casing or, at most, a tube or hollow log set through the surface gravel. Then an iron tube was run to the top of the sand. Even if successful in shutting off water, it was all to do over when the tube had to be pulled to repair downhole equipment. In the late 1860's an outer large tube was run through the upper water sands as a permanent casing and a smaller tube was run for pumping. The permanent tube or casing was a great improvement, but a tight casing seat was still a problem on every well. Many methods were used to obtain or insure a casing seat that would hold: wrapping various seeds, which swelled when wet, in heavy canvas or leather around the bottom joint of the casing, setting the casing on a hard formation, driving the casing into shale—sometimes by drilling a few feet of slightly smaller hole just before running casing, and leaving the heavy mud made by the last "screw" before running casing.

John R. Hill patented in 1871 "Improved Mode of Closing the Water Courses Encountered in Drilling Oil Wells".[1] The patent provided that ". . . as soon as the drill has passed the water course the drill is withdrawn and a sufficient quantity of hydraulic cement or other suitable material that will harden under water to fill the bore to above the level of the water course is poured into the said bore. When the cement or other material is fully set . . . the drill cuts out the cement from the bore of the well but leaves the water courses closed with said cement." The cement was not used in combination with casing, as he states, "I am aware that wells have been drilled dry by means of casings, seed bags, &c. These modes of separating the superfluous water from the oil &c., below, I do not claim." Hardison and Stewart are reported to have put cement in a well in Pico, Calif. in 1883.[1a] A news report in October 1902 stated that " (In Spindletop, Texas) . . . a fund of $3,000 was raised

---

[1] References are at the end of the chapter.

for the purpose of cementing the bottom of those wells to stop the entrance of salt water . . .", but no further reference or information was found.[1b] The use of portland cement in oil-field practice for shutting off water that could not be held with a casing shoe began in 1903.

The Lompoc Field in California was being developed and operators were having great trouble shutting off the water from a sand just above the oil sand. Early in 1903 Frank F. Hill, with Union Oil Co. of California, mixed 50 sacks of neat portland cement and dumped it in a well with a dump bailer of his own design, then set the casing down into the cement on bottom.[2] After waiting 28 days, the cement was drilled out and the hole drilled on into the oil sand without further trouble from the water. Cementing casing quickly became an accepted practice in that area and spread to other California oil fields where the operators were having difficulty in shutting off water above oil sands.

The cement was dumped from the cloth sacks into a wood mortar box usually about 4 ft wide, 8 to 10 ft long, and about 1 ft deep. Water was dumped in and two to four men with mortar hoes did the mixing, then shoveled the thick grout into the dump bailer. The bailer was lowered to bottom, dumped, and pulled up for another load. While the first box of cement was being dumped, a second box was being mixed. Twenty to thirty-five sacks were mixed at a time, and 50 to 100 sacks were used for a job, the lower number being more frequent.

Late in 1905, over 2 years after the first cement was used and on the same lease, dumping the cement failed to get a shutoff. Hill ran tubing with a packer to the bottom of the casing and pumped in the cement. This method forced most of the cement outside the pipe, thus obtaining better probability of a successful water shutoff and saved drilling so much cement. It had the disadvantage of frequent trouble getting the tubing and the packer loose.

The first use of cement, and particularly pumping cement through tubing, was commemorated in 1952 when a monument was placed on the Hill lease in the Lompoc Field, by the Petroleum Production Pioneers and Union Oil Co. of California.[3]

The next improvement in cementing oil wells was to add enough water to completely fill the hole, pack between the casing and tubing at the surface, pump the cement through the tubing, then lower the casing to bottom. A number of tubing heads were designed to hold the pressure at the casing head when the pipe was lowered. Trouble with tubing heads, doubts about the use of thinner cement, and an occasionally cemented string of tubing resulted in slow adoption of the improved method of pumping cement.

Neat cement slurry, to be handled by a pump, had to be mixed with more water than for dumping and a thinner cement had less strength. It was contended then—and maintained for more than 30 years—that a primary requisite of a cement job was the strength of the cement. Pumping cement through tubing resulted in some degree of contamination, both ahead of and behind the cement. Nevertheless, saving in cementing time was important enough in many wells to overcome the disadvantage of the small amount of contamination.

Packing off between the casing and tubing at the bottom of the hole was easier than at the surface. The practice was developed of setting the packer, circulating water down the tubing and up around the casing and following with cement. This permitted a greater quantity of cement to be used and, therefore, a higher probability of a successful water shutoff. Some operators made an effort to cement the water string to the surface, and had reasonable success in rotary-drilled wells but rarely accomplished it in wells which had been drilled with cable tools. Pumping cement down through casing was rarely tried because of the fear of excessive contamination of the cement with mud and water.

R. C. Baker, at the time an independent oil operator and later founder of Baker Oil Tools, Inc., invented the cement retainer in 1912 to pack off between the casing and tubing when pumping cement through tubing (Fig. 1).[4] It was a cylindrical cast-iron shell, flared at the bottom, some 30 in. long, having a rubber sleeve with slips above and containing a back-pressure valve. The retainer was attached to the tubing with a left-hand thread, and was run to the bottom joint of casing then pulled up against the slips to expand the packer. After the cement was pumped to bottom, the tubing was unscrewed and excess cement circulated out. The cement retainer was of greatest value when the casing could not be set on the bottom of the hole. It did not gain wide use until many years after its invention. The big improvement of adding circulating "jars" or valves in 1927, later adding a second and opposing set of slips, and then tripping by hydraulic pressure made it a more versatile tool. When high-pressure squeeze cementing became a practice in the middle 1930's, a cement retainer, built to withstand the high pressures, was used on almost every job.

The Baker cement plug (Fig. 2), later known as the "Sure Shot" plug, was put on the market in 1913.[5] A majority of wells were still cemented with a dump bailer. The hole was completely filled with water and after the cement was placed, a cap was put on the casing which was then lowered to bottom. If the hole would take water, this procedure would leave much of the cement inside the pipe. The Baker plug would insure forcing all cement up behind the pipe. After the cement was dumped, this cast-iron plug was tied with wire or soft rope to the dart of a bailer with which it was pushed down through the casing to below the shoe. The bailer was then pulled up, wedging in the bottom of the shoe, and further pulling broke the wire or soft rope permitting with-

457

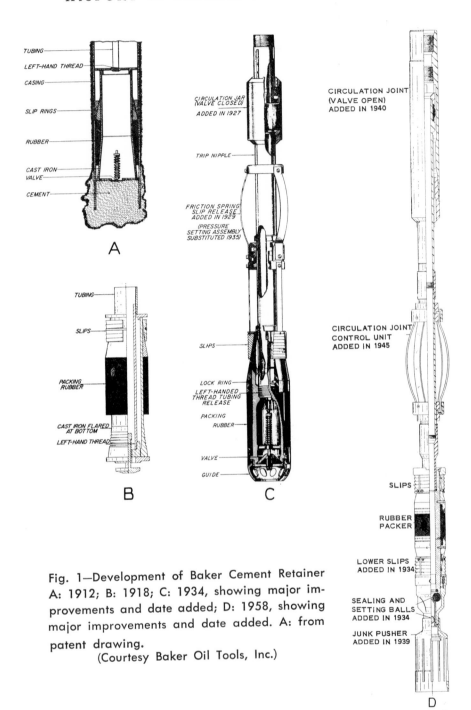

Fig. 1—Development of Baker Cement Retainer A: 1912; B: 1918; C: 1934, showing major improvements and date added; D: 1958, showing major improvements and date added. A: from patent drawing.
(Courtesy Baker Oil Tools, Inc.)

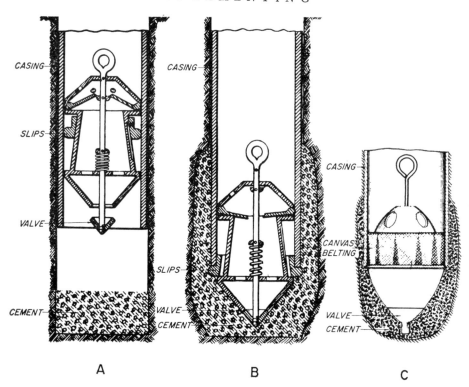

Fig. 2—Baker Cement Plug
(A and B from patent drawings, 1912; C from patent drawing, 1920)
A: Running in near bottom of casing; B: set in bottom of casing; C: slips replaced by canvas belting.

drawal of the bailer. The casing was then lowered to bottom, forcing all cement up around the pipe. Other plugs designed for the same purpose were less widely used.[6]

California operators were much concerned about the damage resulting from failure to obtain a water shutoff. Damage was not confined to the well in which the failure existed, for such water would migrate to adjacent wells and cut off or overpower oil production. The first of several associations of operators cooperating to obtain greater assurance of water shutoffs was formed in Santa Maria in 1910. Most of the operators joined the association and it was supported by assessments on a well basis and was staffed by experienced and capable men. Such associations continued until the Oil and Gas Division, State Mining Bureau, was created in 1915. It was staffed with competent inspectors and a witnessed water-shutoff test was required on the water string in every well drilled in the state. This law and its strict and competent enforcement were important factors in the development of better well-completion practices in California and did much to promote that phase of petroleum engineering.

The larger operators devoted a great deal of attention to cementing casing. It was the concern—in fact, necessity—for obtaining shutoff that gave employment to the first petroleum engineers in the industry. A satisfactory shutoff was not exclusively a problem of properly setting casing—with or without cement. Where the casing was set was of equal importance. If too shallow, a second string would have to be run to shut off water. If too deep, part of the oil sand would be behind the casing, a condition of much more concern then than now. Graduate engineers and geologists were employed to study the well logs and subsurface geology to determine casing points and analyze the problems of setting the casing, including cementing, to obtain a water shutoff.

In 1904, Almond A. Perkins came to Taft, Calif. from the oil fields at Bradford, Pa., by way of Spindletop. He worked on pipelines for some time before joining Standard Oil Co. of California, where he was soon assigned to water problems in the wells in the area. After a few years he was transferred to Los Angeles. Soon thereafter he left the company, but took with him the frustrating water problems on which he had spent so much time. He reasoned that a means of separating the cement and the displacement water while being pumped into the well would be an improvement on the cementing practice, and he and Edward Double received a patent in 1911 on the use of "barriers" or plugs ahead of and behind the column of cement.[7] Such barriers would prevent dilution of the cement and indicate when it was all out of the casing; and, therefore, the cement could be pumped through the casing without the necessity of running tubing. Rather than license the use of plugs on cementing jobs, Perkins elected to establish a cementing service. He furnished the steam pump, mixing equipment, and the plugs for a fixed service fee.

March 15, 1910, was an important day in the history of the petroleum industry because of two occurrences, both near Taft. Union Oil Company's Lakeview No. 1, in the Maricopa area south of Taft, blew in wild making an estimated 75,000 bbl of oil per day; and Al Perkins cemented his first well for an independent operator, using the "Perkins Method." He cemented about 60 wells that year. The second event was not spectacular and received little or no publicity at the time, but was to have a far greater impact on the industry than the Lakeview gusher.

The first plugs, or barriers, used by Perkins were cast-iron with belting discs on top of each and a leather cup also on top of the second plug (Fig. 3). The first plug was short and was pumped through the casing to the bottom of the hole. Ahead of the second plug a spacer timber, usually 3 to 5 ft long, was used so that when its lower end hit the bottom of the hole, the upper end would stop the upper plug with the pressure cup still in the pipe. When all of the cement was out of the pipe, the plug stopped and the increase in pressure would stop the steam pump. It was a definite means of determining when the cement was in place and more reliable than measuring the displacing water. It did not, however, completely eliminate the measuring of water as this was considered a desirable check on the position of the plug. The original cast-iron plugs or barriers had been used only a short time when wood was substituted and served equally well. These wooden plugs, in numerous shapes and lengths, were used even for some time after float collars and rubber plugs came into use late in the 1920's (Fig. 3).

There was no stampede for Perkins' cementing services. Most operators had substantially as good cementing equipment as did Perkins and there was little to gain for them to let their own equipment remain idle and call Perkins. On most jobs the value of the two-plug system was not sufficient reason to call him. There was the danger that a plug would freeze; and furthermore, the cement could be pumped to bottom through tubing in less time than through casing. However, the fact that Perkins' pumps could work against higher pressure than most of the pumps in use at drilling wells gave him many jobs on deep wells or where higher pressures were anticipated. The higher pump pressure was also an assurance of continued circulation if there was danger of the pipe freezing off bottom while cementing because setting the pipe on bottom after placing the cement was, at that time, considered an essential part of a successful job.

The Perkins-Double patent specified the use of two barriers or plugs. Some of the operators attempted to avoid the patent by using only one plug which followed the cement. The courts ruled that any barrier which prevented mixing of the cement with contaminants, whether used ahead of or back of the cement, was covered by the patent.

Perkins' services were limited to the San Joaquin Valley until 1918 when he established an office and service point at Whittier, Calif. in the Los Angeles Basin. The big drilling boom at Santa Fe Springs, Signal Hill, and Huntington Beach in the early 1920's justified additional expansion, as did the coastal area. An agreement was made with another company to establish a similar cementing service in Wyoming for which a royalty was paid; but it was not a financial success, and Perkins expanded into the Rocky Mountain area.

All of the early uses of cement were developed in California. Except in the Gulf Coast area, rotary-drilling equipment was little used in the entire Mid-Continent until southern Oklahoma became an active area in 1914. Even there cable tools predominated in the earlier development. Water sands were numerous, but there were also many formations competent enough to furnish casing seats which would give a water shutoff with a casing shoe. If water trouble did occur,

461

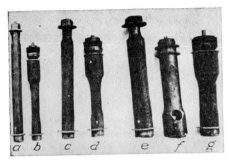

Perkins Cementing Plugs: a, b—4½-in.
15-lb casing; c, d—6⅝-in. 28-lb casing;
e, f, g—8¼-in. 36-lb casing.

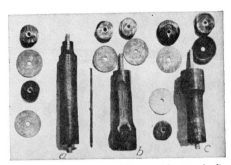

Perkins Cementing Plugs (dismantled):
all for use in 8¼-in. 36-lb casing: a—
when no float plug is used on casing
shoe; b—when plug is used; c—upper or
second plug, always of same design.

Wooden Plugs Used in 1927

Wooden Plugs Used in 1930's

Wooden Plugs Used in Late 1930's

Rubber Plugs from 1930's

Modern Rubber Plugs

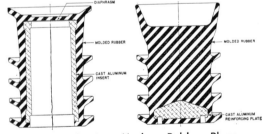

Cross Section, Modern Rubber Plugs

Fig. 3—Representative Cementing Plugs
Two top pictures reproduced from *U. S. Bur. Mines Bull. 163*, Plate XII (1918).
Others courtesy Halliburton Oil Well Cementing Co.

underreaming a few feet and resetting the pipe would usually cure it. On the few wells in which the pipe was cemented the job was done with a dump bailer. Gas breaking through a casing seat was more difficult to stop than was water. Other areas which were developed later in southern Oklahoma had more trouble getting casing seats to hold.

In the Mid-Continent fields cement was first used for plugging back wells to shut off water. The work was encouraged by the United States Bureau of Mines, which made studies of the application in various fields by engineers who had had experience with similar practices in California. This work was initiated about 1916 and had become quite generally used before cementing casing became an accepted practice in the early 1920's.

Fig. 4 shows photographs of the Perkins equipment in use from 1912 to 1938.

In 1916 Perkins employed a young man by the name of Halliburton who gained experience quickly and who, in less than 2 years, was an area manager. This, however, did not satisfy his ambition nor stop his itching feet. The big excitement in oil at the time was in North-Central Texas. When Perkins would not consider establishing a branch in the Mid-Continent area, Erle P. Halliburton went to Burkburnett, Texas—in 1919—where he found many drilling wells but no demand for cementing. He proposed to create that demand. With borrowed money and credit he acquired a wagon on which was mounted a steam pump, mixing boxes, and other equipment and was ready to provide oil-well cementing service. His first effort was with the operators of wells being drilled in the bed of the Red River, to whom he pointed out that the hazards of possible floods justified the better protection. He got a few jobs there and an occasional job on a well that had trouble getting casing to shut off water, but his one-man organization was not overworked cementing wells. The use of cement was not common and each superintendent appeared to be satisfied that when a cementing job was necessary, he and his men could do as good a job as anyone.

The Hewitt Field in Carter County, Okla. was being developed in 1920 and it had reached the point for Halliburton where any new area looked better than where he was, so he moved to New Wilson, Okla., the boom town in the Hewitt Field. The productive sand or sands were lenticular and, for the Mid-Continent area, steeply dipping. Upper formations that could be recognized were scarce and never definite. It was the practice to set casing on top of the sand; but frequently, especially in rotary-drilled holes, casing was set much too high or considerable sand was drilled before casing was set. One well that got into more than usual trouble was Skelly Oil Company's No. 1 Dillard, which had drilled into the oil sand and blew out while running casing with 133 ft yet to run to set on bottom. Several efforts to control it

About 1912—Steam Pumps on Truck with Solid Rubber Tires

1934—Steam Pump, Motor Pump, and Measuring Tank
on Truck, Jet Mixer and Sacked Cement

1938
Fig. 4—Perkins Equipment

failed. Halliburton asked for the opportunity to cement it and, with some skepticism, W. G. Skelly gave him the job. He connected a pump to the casing and mixed and pumped in 250 sacks of neat cement. After setting 10 days, the cement was drilled out and the well put on production without water or excessive gas. So far as records are available, this was the first time casing had been cemented off bottom intentionally. During the next several months, 61 wells were cemented with the casing swinging 20 ft or more off bottom with no difficulty reported. For the first time, Halliburton found demand for his services.[8]

Throughout the oil fields there was always concern during the cementing operation whether the increase in pressure indicated that the plug had reached bottom or whether it had lodged higher in the casing. Some operators measured the displacing water as insurance— or perhaps just for the satisfaction of knowing that the plug was moving. Many had observed that the cement left in the casing was usually soft; but that, if there was a larger amount, the lower part was much harder. It appeared that the better cement would be around the casing shoe if several feet were left in the pipe. Halliburton used a measuring line through a stuffing box to measure the depth to the upper plug during its travel down the casing.[9] By knowing the position of the plug at all times, pumping could be stopped to leave any amount of cement that the operator desired in the casing.

The first measuring line was clothesline purchased from a local hardware store, and run through a rebuilt cable-tool oil saver. Later flat steel measuring lines and then flat aluminum lines were used. In 1926 Halliburton invented a "well-sounding device" which used a round plow-steel wire around a measuring wheel with a counter and run through a stuffing box.[10] Halliburton would not sell this equipment to operators at first; and as late as 1930, when acid bottles and other hole-deviation instruments and bottom-hole pressure gages came into use, he would only license its use.

The same types of equipment and methods used by Perkins in California were used by Halliburton. The amount of cement used commonly ranged from 50 to 125 sacks, the lesser amount being more frequent. The neat cement was mixed in a wooden or metal box or tank by a high-pressure stream of water and with mortar hoes, and pumped into the well. From 25 to 50 sacks were mixed at a time, and for larger quantities two mixing tanks were used alternately. There was nothing special about the equipment; all of it was on each lease or easily available for any operator wishing to do his own cementing. It was a laborious task, however, made more so by the necessity of getting the cement down the hole and up around the casing before it set.

Halliburton recalled having seen steam jets used to remove cinders from the boiler room on steamships while serving as a seaman and reasoned that the same principle might be used for mixing cement. He experimented with such equipment while in the Hewitt Field, and in the summer of 1920 was using a jet mixer as a part of his cementing service (Fig. 5). After further improvement in details of design and operation, he applied for a patent in 1922 on "A Method of Hydrating Cement and the Like."[11]

Drilling in the Hewitt Field was declining by the end of 1920, but the Empire Field near Duncan, Okla. had been discovered. In early 1921 drilling in the Empire Field became as active as Hewitt and was increasing. Halliburton expanded his operation and in March moved to Duncan. He established an office, purchased a truck, and employed help. After two years of effort, much of the time with Mrs. Halliburton working with him instead of hired help, his service had become a small but established business.

Halliburton had been using the patented Perkins "two-plug" method of cementing without a license. Perkins sued Halliburton for patent infringement, but the case was settled out of court; and in December 1922, Halliburton obtained an exclusive license to use plugs in the Mid-Continent states then producing oil. As a part of the consideration, Perkins was given the right to use Halliburton's patent on the method of measuring the depth of the top plug while it was being pumped down. Exclusive use of plugs, the measuring line, and the jet mixer gave Halliburton advantage over operators who might be inclined to do their own cementing. Halliburton licensed Perkins to use the jet mixer in March 1924.

The jet mixer was not a considerable improvement in the method of mixing cement. For the small amount of cement used, rarely over 150 sacks, the saving of time was not substantial. Perhaps more cement would have been used in many cases, but there was a limit on the time between mixing the cement and the time it would set. In general, comparatively few wells had the casing cemented, and in most instances

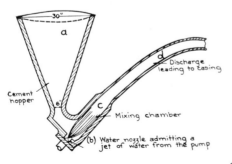

Fig. 5—Halliburton's Jet Cement Mixer (From "Petroleum Engineering in the Hewitt Oil Field," U. S. Bur. Mines, 1921)

operators did their own cementing. Halliburton's future lay in a demand for a greater amount of cement to be used on each job. The limit had already been reached for manual mixing. If a greater quantity was used, his faster mixing equipment would have to be used. He successfully sold the operators on the idea that more cement gave greater insurance of a good job. After all, what was the cost of a few hundred sacks of cement compared to the additional cost of a failure.

During this same period rotary drilling was on a rapid increase in the north Mid-Continent area: Tonkawa in 1923, Wewoka in 1923-24, and Cromwell in 1924 in Oklahoma, and Powell and Mexia in central Texas in 1923 were among the most active fields. Assurance of a water shutoff with a casing shoe alone in a rotary-drilled hole was far less than in a cable-tool-drilled well. This combination of the accepted advantage of using more cement and the increase in the number of rotary-drilled wells rapidly expanded the demand for cementing services. Business was good but income was not sufficient to provide the capital to finance the rate of expansion necessary to meet the demand for cementing services. Halliburton incorporated in 1924 as Halliburton Oil Well Cementing Company with main offices at Duncan, Okla. Those companies who had been doing their own cementing frequently used methods patented by or licensed to Halliburton. It was of mutual advantage for many of them to purchase stock in the new company. This was the source of a large part of his new capital.

Halliburton in the Mid-Continent and Perkins on the West Coast were the two main cementing-service companies. Local competition appeared from time to time, and in some areas gained as much or more work than the larger company. In 1940 Halliburton Oil Well Cementing Company purchased all the equipment and business of Perkins Cementing, Inc. and associated companies and now services the entire domestic oil-development industry and operates in many foreign countries. Fig. 6 shows Halliburton cementing equipment from 1920 to 1958.

From the beginning of cementing in oil wells there was a great variety of equipment and methods used in mixing and placing the cement. Mechanical mixing was used soon after cementing became a practice and various methods were tried from time to time; but, until the Halliburton jet mixer was developed, none gained wide use.

One of the more popular was the Scott mixer.[6] A sheet-iron conical hopper was set on a piece of pipe 8 or 10 in. in diameter, and a shaft with paddles was run through the pipe and directly connected to a steam engine and all mounted on a wagon. The mixed cement discharged into a box from which it was picked up by the pump and forced into the well. The weight of the cement was governed by the amount of water introduced at the base of the hopper. There is no evidence that this was used very far from the Taft area; and even there it was not

1920: Tank for Mixing Cement with High-pressure Water and Mortar Hoes; One Steam Pump Mounted on Horse-drawn Wagon

1934: Two Steam Pumps and Water Tank on Truck

1958: Bulk Cement Delivered Direct to Jet Mixer

Fig. 6—Halliburton Equipment

used extensively. Shell Oil Company and others used a conventional concrete mixer which discharged into a flume where further mixing was done with mortar hoes before reaching the tank serving as a suction pit for the pumps.

Cementing plugs were designed in many sizes, shapes, and materials. The first cast-iron plugs soon gave away to wooden plugs. The lower plug was made smaller at its upper end in order that the belting disc would bend down to bypass the cement more easily if the plug should stop before going completely out of the pipe. The upper plug was necessarily long enough to insure the upper end remaining in the pipe. After a few years, its length was increased, or a timber—sometimes 20 ft or more in length—would be inserted just ahead of the upper plug to insure that amount of cement being left in the pipe. In Louisiana most operators preferred several cement sacks for a plug, or two or three sacks on top of a loose-fitting wooden plug. In the late 1920's molded rubber plugs were introduced and have been used since with only minor changes. A plug was frequently used when cementing through tubing, either measuring the displacing water or by putting a swage nipple on the bottom of the tubing to stop the plug when all the cement in the tubing had been displaced. Whatever its shape or material, it was a "barrier" against contamination of the cement.

There were special ways of mixing and placing cement for plugging off bottom water that gained popularity in some districts. In Illinois, where the fluid levels were very low, the McDonald method consisted of running tubing close to the bottom of the well and slowly adding dry cement to a continuous flow of water. At the bottom of the hole the water filtered into the water-producing section of the sand leaving the cement to set and develop a water shutoff.[12] Considerable success was claimed for the method. In the Gulf Coast, sacks partially filled with mixed cement were inserted in the casing, pushed to bottom, and tamped with tools to break the sacks. Some operators placed a thick grout of cement, either neat or with sand, lowered to bottom in tin cans—probably nitroglycerin containers—and tamped with tools, presumably placing the cement with minimum contamination. The McPherson method used a loose-fitting canvas packer on the bottom of the tubing which was lowered into the shot hole. The sides of the shot hole were washed, then the cement pumped to bottom, the tubing raised to the top of the shot hole, after which pressure of 200 to 300 psi at the surface would insure better bond of the cement to the water sand.[13] Some claimed merit by the "cement shot," wherein a small charge of nitroglycerin was exploded immediately after the cement was dumped. Despite the advantages claimed for the special methods, the dump bailer was used on most jobs.

During the early years almost every man who directed cementing jobs had his own particular procedure and particular equipment which he felt essential to a successful job. Soon after the jet mixer came into general use, the operation of cementing casing became quite uniform throughout the industry. Methods of plugging back wells continued to vary for another 10 or more years. When higher-pressure squeeze cementing came into practice, high-pressure equipment was required which was usually furnished by a cementing service company and the operation became about as standard as for cementing casing.

Cement was packed in cloth bags from the beginning of the industry until about 1925. Paper bags were used some during World War I but this practice was discontinued. Multi-walled moisture-resistant paper sacks were introduced in 1924 and became generally used in the oil country in 1927. These had the advantage of being disposable, and of giving the cement better protection against mosture. The job of dumping cement was made much easier when a narrow table was set against the hopper of the jet mixer, with a knife extending up through the table an inch or so to cut the cement sack as it was pushed along the table toward the hopper of the mixer.

About 1916 or 1917 a few operators were using a "float plug" which was a drillable cast-iron plug screwed into the steel casing shoe. The hole in the plug was too large to obtain appreciable floating of casing weight, but it did serve as a guide shoe. It was 1922 when W. L. McLaine of General Petroleum Corporation designed a workable float shoe by using a cast-iron poppet back-pressure valve mechanism in a guide shoe.[14] In 1926 Don Burch, with Barnsdall Oil Company,* built the body and valve into a special casing collar and the float collar came on the market.[15] A year later he replaced the cast iron with concrete;[16] and shortly thereafter Baker Oil Tools, Inc., licensee of McLaine and the Burch patents, incorporated a plastic valve mechanism. The float shoe and float collar were first used to obtain a floating effect or buoyancy to control the rate of fall and the weight on the casing hook of long heavy strings of casing; but later they became equally valuable as a part of the cementing equipment. In cementing, the first plug was so shaped that the belt disc would collapse and bypass the cement under the pressure built up when the plug hit the float collar. Later, plugs were drilled straight through and the hole was closed with a diaphragm which would break under the pressure. The second plug was solid. The float collar was placed from one to three joints off bottom, depending upon the amount of cement the operator desired to leave above the casing shoe. This use did away with the necessity of following the plug with a measuring line.

---

*Later became part of Sunray Mid-Continent Oil Company.

Waiting on cement to set was largely lost time and anything which would reduce that time was of interest. If a cement job failed, it was invariably blamed on too-short waiting time or bad cement. Chemicals which would increase the early strength of cement were considered perhaps as early as 1918, but most of them proved of little value and some were harmful. Huber obtained a patent on the use of an accelerator in oil-well cement—and chlorides of the alkaline earth in particular— in 1923,[17] but a year or so later it developed that the chemicals had been used for the same purpose much earlier. In fact the effect of calcium chloride on setting time of cement appears frequently in the cement industry literature prior to 1922. In 1914, Franklyn W. Oatman,[18] commenting on calcium chloride, stated "If over 2% . . . likely to hasten the set as to make the cement difficult to handle." The same paper notes that at a temperature of 142 F. cement will set in one-half the time at normal temperature. In California the chemicals supplied under the Huber patent application were referred to as "Huber's chemical," "McDuffy's reagent," and some other names characteristic of oil-field parlance. Perkins advertised a "four-day setting cement" in 1922 using calcium chloride under the Huber patent application. Accelerators gained wide use quickly. Calcium chloride proved to be the best, and during the early years a very large amount of it reached the industry under various trade names.

Waiting time for cement to set was reduced sometimes to as short as seven days but only in the intense competitive drilling in California was it as short as four days, and then largely by smaller operators. Late in 1924 the Corporation Commission of Oklahoma proposed a rule to require a minimum of 10 days waiting on cement, but would reduce it to 7 days if an approved accelerator was used. Some operators claimed that accelerators were more dangerous than helpful. An excess of accelerator would decrease the strength of the cement; and because of the working conditions under which the accelerators were added, there was no assurance that a uniform mixture was obtained. The use of accelerators reached a peak about 1925, and trade-name accelerators decreased in favor of calcium chloride which was purchased in quantity by the operator.

As accelerators became popular the cement-manufacturing companies became interested and several made "special oil-well cements." Some of them used a slightly different composition, but in most cases it was only a finer grind. There was a general change in the composition of construction portland cement from about 1926 to 1933 which increased the early strength primarily by increasing the tricalcium silicate with a corresponding decrease in the dicalcium silicate. A finer grind also increased the early strength. Prior to 1927 for the average construction portland cement about 83 percent passed a 200-mesh screen.

471

The fineness increased gradually until in 1941 about 97 percent passed 200-mesh; then it decreased and since 1943 has been an average of about 95 percent. The average for the same cements through 325-mesh showed an increase from 82 percent in 1934 to 92 percent in 1941, and since 1942 about 90 percent. Specific area expressed in square centimeters per gram became a measurement of fineness of cement about 1934, at which time the average was 1,400 sq cm. Construction cements now average over 1,700 sq cm (turbidity method).[19]

About the same time that the composition of cements was undergoing a general change, several plants in Europe were producing a higher-early-strength cement by increasing the tricalcium silicate to a high percentage and grinding to a specific area of 2,500 sq cm. Lone Star Cement Company was the first to make this high-early-strength cement in the United States at a plant in Indiana in 1927, giving it the trade name "Incor." It was first made to supply a demand of the construction industry and was used in that industry over a year before it reached the oil fields, where it found a ready market. As manufactured high-early-strength cements became available, the use of accelerators declined. Concurrently, knowledge of the temperatures in wells and the effect of higher temperatures on the early strength of cement was increasing, and therefore the realization that the time then allowed for cement to set was sufficient for construction cement.

The first wells cemented had been shut down 28 days for cement to set, in accordance with the accepted practice at the time for construction work. It was some 10 years before oil-field operators were willing to reduce the time to 3 weeks, although some of the more venturesome had been resuming operations as soon as 2 weeks. In another 10 years, a waiting time of 10 days was considered sufficient; and 10 years later, i.e., some 30 years after cement was first used, most operators accepted 3 days as sufficient time for the cement to be hard enough to serve its purpose. Conservation laws in effect in most of the states by that time provided, among many other requirements, a minimum waiting time for cement to set; and since 72 hours was the general practice at that time, such time was an almost uniform provision in the rules for each pool, or in a statewide rule.

The earlier cementing work was judged exclusively by testing for water shutoff. If no water showed on the test, the cement job was successful. That was final. Failure of cement jobs was frequent, by whatever standard they might be judged. The number of oil companies who assigned engineers to the problems of completing wells, including cementing casing, was increasing. As the problems of cementing were studied, there developed a position that the cement must reach a certain hardness in order to assure a successful job. Such an attitude came from the observation that, in a high proportion of instances where water broke in, the cement had been soft. In 1927-28, Humble Oil & Refining Company cut and tested several hundred cement cores from Gulf Coast wells and found that, if judged solely on the basis of the strength of the cement, 60 percent of the jobs on wells less than 1,000 ft deep should be called failures, 80 percent of the jobs from 1,000 to 3,000, and 100 percent of those in wells deeper than 3,000 ft.[20] This study appeared to confirm the necessity of high strength of cement. More important, though, was information that in most cases the low strength was determined to result from contamination of the cement, mostly by drilling mud. Precautions against contamination were developed—such as giving more attention to conditioning the mud before cementing, circulating longer before cementing, making mud lighter (or, rather, thinner or less viscous), pumping a few barrels of water either ahead of or following the cement or both, and holding the second plug in a container to be released as soon as all of the cement was in the pipe. The column of cement was usually heavier than the mud, and when the casing was opened to insert the plug, the vacuum pulled in a substantial volume of air to become trapped between the plug and the cement. Holding the second plug in the casing to be released after the cement was in the pipe had been tried several years earlier but was discontinued because of the frequency of the plug getting down into the pipe ahead of the cement, thus leaving all of the cement in the casing. These better practices improved the results of cementing, but there was still much trouble.

During the first 10 years cement was used, production from 2,000 ft was considered deep; and at the end of the second 10 years 3,000 ft was deep. By the late 1920's several fields had been developed below 6,000 ft and temperatures at that depth were high enough to cause trouble when using the same cement as for shallower depths. The first of these deeper developments was the Clark zone in the Santa Fe Springs Field, California, at about 7,000 ft, which was developed in 1929.[21] In some of the early wells all of the cement could not be pumped out of the pipe; and in some which had high-pressure equipment to place the cement, it did not set. Temperatures were determined to be about 212 F and laboratory tests proved that most cements mixed and set at such temperature could not be expected to give reliable service in a well. Tons of ice placed in the pits to cool the circulating mud did not help. Speed of mixing and placing the cement was the best insurance, but not a guarantee. Otis D. Small, chemist with the Pacific Portland Cement Company, used an ice cream freezer with an electric heater in the water around the mixing can to demonstrate how quickly cement would become too thick to be handled with a pump.[22, 23]

This related to the time of initial set; if stirring continued a few minutes longer, the cement would never harden. The Pacific Portland Cement Company, in the fall of 1929, supplied a retarded-setting cement made by increasing the iron, decreasing the tricalcium aluminate, and quenching the hot clinker with oil. It carried the trade name "Goldengate High Temperature Oil Well Cement." Retarded cement, combined with the speed of mixing and placing that had been developed, largely eliminated trouble in that pool.

Some operators had long made a practice of testing cement as provided by the ASTM standards for construction work, which provided for cement mixed with 20 to 24 percent water; although for oil wells, cement was mixed with 40 percent or more water. L. T. Bachman, with Santa Cruz Cement Company, in 1921 proposed testing such a thinner mix with ASTM equipment after setting 24 and 48 hours immersed in water.[24] His proposal gained some following. Most field men accepted a test made by mixing some cement to the usual consistency in a convenient can and determining the hardness from time to time with a handy stick or, more handy, a finger. In the late 1920's some work was reported on the effect of temperature and pressure on setting time and strength of cement, but it made no immediate impression on the industry.

Halliburton Oil Well Cementing Company in 1929 set up a laboratory for testing cement under the direction of Claude P. Parsons. First investigations were on such problems as effect of water-cement ratios on volume, weight, and strength, effect and limitations of accelerators, comparison of different cements for oil-well use, development of retarders, etc. Parsons continued to maintain close contact with new developments both in the laboratories and in the fields, and published numerous technical papers that influenced acceptance of improved practices throughout the oil fields.

B. C. Craft and students reported extensive testing of cement in 1934. They showed the apparent practical maximum water-cement ratio was about 50 percent, that high temperature materially decreased both the time for initial set and the compressive strength, and that high pressure increased the compressive strength but reduced the time for the initial set some although not in proportion to the pressure.[25] In general their tests confirmed earlier reports and were the most extensive that had become available to the oil industry up to that time.

The cementing trouble that had been experienced at Santa Fe Springs, and comparable conditions at Kettleman Hills at 8,000 ft and deep wells in Ventura, emphasized the need for better understanding of just what cement did under bottom-hole conditions. Small's ice-cream-freezer test was informative in a qualitative way. Standard Oil Co.

of California, under the direction of Silcox and Rule, undertook making it an instrument. First work was with a modified small electric-motor-driven ice cream freezer in 1930. It was not a satisfactory instrument and equipment using the same principle was designed which, with experience, was improved until the torque required to turn the mixer paddles in a can of cement immersed in a temperature bath could be measured and give reproducible results. The torque was related to the pumpability or thickness of the cement and, for the particular design of "thickening-time tester," a torque pull of 40 oz was considered the limit of pumpability. The instrument was increasingly used to test cement to be used in high-temperature wells, and was made available to other oil companies and to the cement-manufacturing companies. D. E. Silcox and R. B. Rule presented a description of the tester and a discussion of test results in July 1935.[26]

Halliburton Oil Well Cementing Company, under the direction of J. E. Weiler, in 1937 built a "consistometer" for testing the fluidity or pumpability of cement slurries under elevated temperatures which worked on the same fundamental principle as the ice cream freezer of Small and the thickening-time tester of Silcox and Rule; but it was more compact, built to test two samples simultaneously for comparative purposes, and to indicate thickness or viscosity in terms of poises. A viscosity of 100 poises was considered the limit of pumpability.[27]

Stanolind Oil and Gas Company, under the direction of R. F. Farris, constructed a cement tester in 1939 that would test the thickening time under controlled temperature and under pressure as high as 5,000 psi.[28] His results in general confirmed the effects of temperature and pressure on neat cement, but were more detailed and covered a much wider range of conditions. His work also showed that continued movement of cement after substantial increase in viscosity, even though still pumpable, would decrease the strength. The instrument was rebuilt in 1947 to permit testing up to 10,000 psi.

The requirements of cement for cementing casing and means of testing to determine if a given cement would meet such requirements were gaining more widespread interest, and more companies were assigning engineers to both laboratory and field work to increase the ratio of successful jobs. The most complete and practical discussion of requirements and testing procedures up to that date was presented by E. L. Davis to the API in 1938.[23]

The American Petroleum Institute, Division of Production, in 1937 established a committee on cements, with the objective of establishing a code to cover testing of oil-well cements. A progress report was presented at the annual meeting of the Institute in 1939,[29] but it was not until 1947 that the first *API Code for Testing Cements Used in Wells*

(API Code 32)[30] was approved. The delay was due to many factors. The standard tests for cement used for construction were not satisfactory for cement used in oil wells, and the instruments that determined the length of time that a slurry would remain pumpable had not been used extensively enough to obtain agreement on standards.

During this period—1937 to 1947—cements for oil wells continued undergoing changes, as did engineers' specifications. Hardness in 72 hours was considered to be of primary importance at the time the committee was formed, but decreased in importance before the first code was accepted. Accelerated cements were decreasing in use and were therefore less important from a testing standpoint, while demand for retarded cement was increasing and specifications were needed. In fact, methods of testing cements and specifications of operators were undergoing changes so rapidly that a code which appeared to be acceptable at one meeting was out of date by the next annual meeting of the committee. The first code covered only testing procedure, with no requirement as to strength.

In June 1952, responsibility for maintenance of *API Code 32* was transferred to the Committee on Standardization of Oil-well Cements, reporting to the Central Committee on Standardization of Oil-field Equipment of the API Division of Production. Designation of the code was changed to "recommended practice," and the third edition (dated April 1953) was published as *API RP 10B: Recommended Practice for Testing Oil-well Cements.*[31] This publication was in its seventh edition in 1958. The first API specification for oil-well cements, designated *API Std 10A*, was approved in 1952 and the first edition published in March 1953. The most recent edition of the standard (fifth, 1958)[32] contains specifications for seven classes of portland cement, in regular and sulfate-resistant types. The primary difference in the classes is the early strength at different temperatures.

Trouble with cementing deep high-temperature wells and the many laboratory tests demonstrating the quicker setting and substantially higher earlier strength of cement set under higher temperature created a broad interest in cementing problems, but for several years there is little evidence that it had any influence on the thinking as to the amount of time necessary for the cement to harden enough to accomplish its purpose of preventing movement of fluids behind the pipe. Seventy-two hours for the cement to set around the water or oil string had become general practice. Perhaps this was reassuring to those who shortened to 72 hours reluctantly. At the same time many operators were drilling out of the surface pipe in 48 hours or less, in face of the knowledge that the temperature was higher around the oil string and the cement should set faster than at the surface. The impacts of drilling through the shoe of the water or oil string are light compared to the banging while drilling with drill pipe in compression through and several hundred feet below the casing shoe on the surface pipe.

As the years passed it became generally recognized that 72 hours was much longer than necessary to wait for cement to set around the water or oil string, especially in the deeper wells. However, not only was the practice well-established, but in those states which had regulations the 72-hour period was almost universal. R. F. Farris,* in order to determine a reasonable minimum waiting time, made an extensive investigation of the rate of increase of the strength of cement under pressure and temperature in the laboratory and confirmed his findings in the field. He published the results in 1946[33] and soon thereafter presented them to some of the conservation commissions, particularly the Railroad Commission of Texas. The rules were changed to reduce the waiting-on-cement time to 24 to 36 hours for several fields then being developed. The shorter waiting time proved entirely satisfactory in the field and such time and even shorter waiting periods are now widely accepted.

Deeper fields were increasing both in number and in depth. The higher temperatures were causing some trouble, but in general faster cementing operations by better planning and operating with larger equipment made the use of construction cement practical in wells that a few years earlier would have required a retarded cement. The first data from the thickening-time testers had shown the short time that cement would remain pumpable under high temperatures and also that it would fail to set if it was moved too long. There was need for a cement that would remain pumpable for a longer time—a slower initial-setting or retarded cement. Yet quick setting and accelerated cement had been emphasized so many years it was difficult to reverse thinking and practice.

Cement with a delayed initial set was new only to the oil industry. Rye flour was used to retard cement-setting time in 1882. Borax was used to delay the setting of plaster of paris in 1895 and gum arabic in 1904; and years later both were used in portland cement. Dextrin was used in 1908 and several gums and other materials were used in 1927.[34] It will be noted all of these were additives. Increasing the iron content to retard setting was developd in 1921, but was less effective. The first retarded cement for oil wells was made by Pacific Portland Cement Company by some change in the raw materials and a coarser grind. The first retarded cement in the Mid-Continent area was Universal Atlas Portland Cement Company's "Unaflo" in 1935, which was made with additives of borax, boric acid, and gum arabic.[35] Lone Star Cement Company's "Starcor" was put on the market in 1936 and was

---

*Research Laboratories, (former) Stanolind Oil and Gas Company.

made by controlling the raw materials to increase the iron and reduce the tricalcium aluminates. All of the retarded cements were a coarser grind, having a specific area of about 1,300 sq cm per gram, compared to regular cement with 1,700 sq cm and high-early-strength cement with 2,500 sq cm. As wells were drilled to continually increasing depths, with corresponding increases in temperatures where the cement was placed, the demand for delayed-setting oil-well cements increased. As demand increased, other chemicals which would retard setting were discovered. Boric acid, borates, and gum arabic were already in commercial use; and during the next few years some of the chemicals recommended were tartaric acid, numerous organic salts, sodium bicarbonate, casein, sodium phosphates, starch and carboxyl celluloses, and tannic, gallic, humic, quercitannic, lignic, and carbolcyclic acids in sodium hydroxide.[34] It was usually recommended that a combination of two or more chemicals be added to obtain best retarding effect.

The composition and grind of cement will not alone retard setting enough for present highest-temperature wells, and retarding additives are in general use. The use of bulk cement has made it more practical to add the retarding agent at the bulk plant in the amount necessary for the conditions in the well to be cemented. The most commonly used retarder is the calcium salt of lignin sulphonic acid which has the additional property of acting as a dispersing agent, and is especially valuable when bentonite is added and in pozzolan-cement mixtures.

The 1930's was a period of great advances in policies relating to and practices of drilling and producing oil, and engineering in the development and operation of oil fields was more generally accepted. It was a period, particularly in the early part, of over-production, proration, and minimum drilling. It would appear that reduced field activities afforded opportunity to direct mental energy to new and improved means of drilling, completing, and producing oil wells. Many of the new developments materially influenced cementing. The more important were retarded-setting cements and laboratory investigations of properties of cements under simulated operational conditions which have been discussed. There was also formation squeeze cementing, gun perforating, electric logging, temperature surveys to determine the amount of cement behind the casing, open-hole calipers, and improved drilling muds. These were all being developed concurrently and came into field use largely from 1933 to 1937.

Applying pressure to the neat cement after it was in place in the well was practiced from the beginning of the use of cement. The earlier practice was to fill the hole with water on top of the cement. Later it was recommended that pump pressure be used in addition to the hole full of fluid to obtain better contact of the cement with the walls of the hole. Where several hundred sacks of cement were used, the column of cement behind the pipe and the head of fluid above the cement column were heavier than the hydrostatic pressure inside the pipe and pump pressure was necessary to place and hold the cement behind the casing. By the time such large quantities of cement were used, most long strings of casing were run with back-pressure valves; but very few operators would trust the back-pressure valve or even check to see if it would hold. The pump pressure was held until the cement had more than reasonable time to set. In plug-back jobs it was argued that the more pressure put on the cement, the more firm would be the bond between the cement and the sand. "Squeezing" the cement meant, up until the middle 1930's, putting pressure on the cement in addition to the column of fluid.

The Conroe Field in South Texas had a large gas cap and was under a substantial water drive. The wells were completed by cementing the casing on top of the sand and setting a screen through the producing sand. Many wells had a high gas-oil ratio or produced much water, and some had both. A high gas-oil ratio meant a penalty on allowable oil production, and water production meant high lifting costs and the problem of disposal. Cementing under pressure was usually successful in reducing the excess gas or in shutting off water, and probable success was correlated with higher pressure. This resulted in higher and higher pressure being used until it became high enough to pump a large amount of cement into the formation, i. e., it was "squeeze cemented". The first well into which substantially more cement was pumped than could be contained in the hole was a General Crude Oil Company well, with operations under the direction of Thomas W. Pew, in 1934. Experience soon showed that those wells to which the highest pressures had been applied and, generally, in which the most cement had been pumped into the formation, had the highest probability of successful shutoff of the excess gas or water. Pew obtained a patent on the method[36] but no licenses were given for its use nor were royalties collected. It was, in effect, dedicated to the public. The same "squeeze-cementing" procedure was tried successfully in other areas and soon became an accepted practice.

What took place undergound when several hundred sacks of cement under high pressure could be pumped into a well when there was no apparent place for it to go caused much discussion. Some contended that it displaced mud behind the pipe that was not displaced by the original cement job, some that the exposed formation was merely compressed, and some that the formation fractured, more likely along bedding planes. Although all three conditions may be present to some degree, the artificial fractures probably take most of the cement.

High-pressure formation squeeze-cementing jobs required heavy equipment that could deliver a cement slurry at a much higher pressure

479

than had been commonly needed. Cement retainers, although greatly improved since they were introduced in 1912, had not been widely used. Squeeze-cement jobs which often required pressures higher than the safe working pressure of the casing made the use of cement retainers essential. Screwing a plug into the bottom of a retainer made a very satisfactory bridge plug and with a retainer above, the high pressure inside the casing could be confined to a short interval.

Cement retainers could be removed only by drilling up. Retrievable cement retainers came on the market about 1939. Halliburton Oil Well Cementing Company acquired the Yowell tool which was used for washing screens and perforations, and redesigned it as a retrievable cement retainer. Friction slips are set by hydraulic pressure. The packing elements are cupped and, by using opposing elements, the high pressure on the casing can be confined to a short interval. Baker Oil Tools retrievable retainer has opposing slips which are released from neutral position by rotating the tubing, and set by either raising or lowering the tubing. Reverse movement and rotation will release and lock them in neutral position. Packing rubber is expanded against the casing by weight on the slips. Retrievable cement retainers were used where it was not necessary to hold the cement under pressure until it set. The saving was in the initial cost and in the time required to drill out a regular retainer.

Stage cementing is used where the amount of cement may cause pressures high enough to result in lost circulation, and failure to get the cement high enough for the protection desired. It is also used for greater insurance of a good cement job through an upper producing formation. Early in the 1920's it became a practice in some California fields to run the oil string to total depth, the lower part through the producing zone being perforated or slotted. Ports in the casing at the top of the zone permitted circulation and cementing. A drillable plug inside and a canvas "bootleg" packer outside prevented cement from going down into the producing zone. Special equipment was designed to simplify the operation and increase probability of a successful job. A collar which would serve as a part of the casing was built so that a plug pumped into it would open ports for circulation and simultaneously stop circulation below. Such equipment was modified in the early 1930's and used for stage cementing. After the quantity of cement is pumped into the casing for the lower part of the hole, followed by sufficient mud or water to clear the cement in the casing below the collar, the plug is inserted followed by cement for the second stage. In some cases a third stage is used.

Gun perforating was introduced in California in 1932* and into the Gulf Coast in 1934. The orginal use was for perforating casing opposite upper sands in wells in which the original completion had become depleted, but in the Gulf Coast area it was soon used for original completion. A well was drilled to total depth, casing was cemented on bottom, and the producing interval gun-perforated. The practice of completing wells through gun perforations spread rapidly; and within three or four years, it was almost universal practice on the Gulf Coast and a large percentage of the wells in the better fields in the Mid-Continent area which produced from harder formations were so completed. Wells completed through perforations were in better condition for cementing off any intrusion of water or free gas.

Electric logging, commercially introduced in California in 1932 and in the Gulf Coast area in 1933, may not have directly affected cementing practices but it did bring about completion and recompletion practices in which the cementing operation was an integral part. Electric logging grew rapidly; and within a few years the industry gained very high confidence in the interpretation of probable productivity of sands, particularly in the Gulf Coast area. This confidence, combined with other improved practices—especially side-wall coring, led to the practice of drilling wells—even wildcat wells—to the greatest depth to be tested, electric logging, side-wall coring, then cementing casing through the deepest sand considered worthy of a production test. This put still more responsibility on the cement job. At first it had only been necessary to get a good cement job around the shoe. Then, with setting casing through the sand and completing by gun perforating, it was necessary to have a good cement job through the sand. Now it became necessary to have a good cement job through all prospective producing sands in hundreds or even thousands of feet of hole, and cementing methods were not that good.

When a well was completed through perforations and produced unexpected water or excess gas, it was squeeze-cemented, drilled out, and reperforated. The frequency of squeezing and reperforating was so high, particularly along the Gulf Coast, that most operators would "protection squeeze" or "block squeeze" a sand before perforating for completion. Protection or block squeezing involved perforating a foot or two of the casing with 4 to 12 holes just below the gas-oil contact and also just above the water level and then squeeze cementing, drilling out, and perforating for completion. It was not uncommon to squeeze three or four times before obtaining a completion free of water or excess gas. Some operators maintained that some certain high pressure had to be reached on a squeeze job to obtain a successful shutoff, and would continue to pump cement until such pressure was reached. If such pres-

---

*By William Lane and Walter Wells who formed Lane-Wells Company.

sure was not reached, the cement was drilled out, the casing perforated again, and more cement pumped in. Another way of reaching the desired high pressure was by interrupting the job by shutting down the pump for a short time, then resuming pumping. A job might be shut down or interrupted several times for one to several minutes before reaching a maximum pressure acceptable to the operator.

The amount of cement to use on any job was always a problem and especially on a casing job. There had been no way to determine how far up behind the casing the cement moved; and when that could not be determined, there was no assurance that the amount of cement used accomplished what the operator desired in addition to preventing movement of fluid around the casing shoe. Did it cover the sand that was suspected of carrying corrosive water? Did it reach the sand that contained oil and gas to protect it from upper water or prevent it from dissipating into other sands? Did it come high enough to obtain the additional casing strength? These uncertainties added an element of anxiety to every cementing job.

The hydration of cement is an exothermic reaction, and when Conrad Schlumberger* found that sufficient heat was generated by the cement behind casing to obtain distinct change in the temperature gradient, he applied for a patent on "A Thermometric Method of Determining the Top of Cement Behind Casing" in 1934.[37] After some testing Amerada Petroleum Corporation, commencing in 1935, made a practice of determining by recording thermometer the top of cement behind casing on all intermediate and oil strings. Humble Oil & Refining Company mixed a small amount of carnotite with the cement and used a gamma-ray log to determine the top of the cement behind the pipe in 1939.[38] The great variation between the calculated top and the actual top of the cement back of the casing, as shown by these tests, added to the general concern as to the effectiveness of cement in accomplishing the purposes for which is was used. It created wider interest in the actual conditions between the casing and the walls of the hole and the influence of such conditions on the effectiveness of the cement job. The height to which cement will rise between the casing and the hole is dependent upon the amount of cement, the diameter of the pipe and the hole, and effectiveness of mud displacement. The volume of cement and the diameter of the pipe are known and the diameter of the drilling bit is known, but not the diameter of the hole after drilling is completed. Some holes hold reasonably close to bit size, but many of them slough or cave—severely in some areas.

The diameter of a shot hole after shooting with nitroglycerin or gelatin was a problem that aroused the curiosity of every man who

---

*Who, with his brother, Marcel, started what became the Schlumberger Well Surveying Corp.

worked around such wells and is one that is important if the well is to be plugged back. Myron M. Kinley invented a caliper in 1935[39] for determining the size of shot holes, but its design would not permit using it in a hole full of fluid. It was redesigned to operate on an electric cable[40] and was used first in 1940; and on the whole, the results were not unexpected. In the beginning it was run on an experimental basis—or, one might say, to satisfy curiosity—but with greater interest in better cement jobs, the caliper became a valuable tool. If cavities existed, there was less chance of a good cement job in such intervals; and improved mud and drilling practices could reduce and perhaps eliminate many of the irregularities, thereby increasing the probability of a good cement job. The volume of the hole could be calculated, and the quantity of cement run to fill to the desired level.

There was a marked increase in the success of cementing of casing during the 1930's as a result of improved cements and cementing practices and drilling equipment and practices. If any one of these contributed more than another, it was the drilling mud. Prior to about 1932, drilling muds received little attention except from the driller. He made the mud "heavier" or "lighter" by the amount of water added, which actually referred to viscosity rather than density. In areas where upper zones having high gas pressure were present, a weighting material—first iron oxide and later barite—was added for increasing density. By 1932 study of drilling mud had been initiated by several companies; and from these studies came improvement in viscosity and density control, gel strength, amount of filtrate, and thickness of mud cake. It was the latter that had most effect on the cement job.

Looking back in the light of our present knowledge, perhaps one should marvel at the number of successful—or apparently successful—cement jobs rather than the number of failures. Nearly all drilling muds were affected by cement, usually by increasing gelation. When the cement came in contact with a thick mud cake the already stiff or tough mud was increased in strength by the chemical action of the cement, thus obtaining the same objective as if *all* of the drilling mud had been replaced by cement, as was commonly believed to be the condition.

By the end of the 1930's the improved drilling muds had lower viscosity, left a much thinner mud cake on porous formations, reduced sloughing of the walls of the hole, and, in most cases, were less affected by contamination with cement; and, if contaminated, chemical treatment would restore them to good condition. All of these factors contributed to better placement of cement, permitting a closer contact with the walls of the hole, particularly through sands or other porous formations, and less hole enlargement where the cement might channel through instead of replacing the drilling mud.

Union Oil Co. of California had been having trouble cementing casing in one area in 1939; and, under the direction of P. H. Jones, set up experimental equipment to simulate the hole conditions at the producing sand. Heavy canvas was wrapped inside a large perforated pipe to act as a porous formation. The canvas and outer pipe were split lengthwise so that, as each test was completed, it could be taken apart and the results of the cement job observed. Mud was circulated under pressure through the annular space between the casing and the canvas, later followed by cement. Many tests were run to show the effect of equipment and methods available to improve a cement job, and the effect of various thicknesses of mud cake, removal of mud cake, casing centered in the hole and against the side of the hole, movement of casing—both reciprocated and rotated, and other conditions that might be expected or created at depth in a well. Jones and Berdine presented the results of the work to the American Petroleum Institute in the spring of 1940.[41] Briefly, they showed that it cannot be expected to wrap casing with cement when it is against the side of a well bore, as it is certain to be at the bottom of a deep hole, and a thick mud cake is present. Centering the casing in the hole, removing the mud cake as much as possible and moving the casing, either by reciprocation or rotation while the cement is moving, are all important to obtain a completely successful cement job.

Testing drilling mud for mud cake had become common practice and the existence of mud cake on the face of the sands in every rotary-drilled well was generally recognized. It seemed logical that if the mud cake could be removed at the time the oil string was run, a better completion could be expected. Kenneth Wright and Bruce Barkis, petroleum engineers with many years of oil-field experience and concerned with the ever-present problem of oil-well completions, designed a "wall scratcher" to be attached to the casing to remove the mud cake while the casing was being run.[42] The wall scratcher was a loose-fitting collar with steel-wire bristles, free to move between brazed or welded lugs some 3 ft apart to permit the casing to move through the scratcher collar as each joint was added. Two to four scratchers were recommended for each joint of casing near the bottom. The first commercial scratchers were run in California late in 1939. Cementing casing through the producing formation and completing through gun perforations was not yet practiced in California; but results of one of Jones' tests indicated the advantage of removing the mud cake to improve such a cement job, and wall scratchers were first used on a cement job in California in the summer of 1940.

No centralizers were used with the first scratchers nor was the casing moved after cement equalized, i. e., when pressure first showed at the surface. Centralizers in various forms had been available for many years but never gained wide use. The earliest centralizers were welded to the casing. In 1930 Irvine, and Steps and Hartman each patented the use of a stop between two loose-fitting collars holding the centralizing springs bows.[43, 44] Many other arrangements were used but it was the Steps and Irvine design that became the accepted centralizer. Scratchers were used in the field for five or six years before general use of centralizers with them was accepted.

Movement of casing while placing cement to improve the cement job was admittedly a desirable part of the operation many years before 1940. In the early days in California it was the practice to keep the casing moving up and down, but this was more to prevent freezing than for distribution of cement. F. B. Tough, with the U. S. Bureau of Mines,[6] recognized in 1918 that "the ultimate shape of the cement mass when set and its distribution, radially as well as vertically, have much to do with its effectiveness," and "that a string of casing will not hang concentrically within a hole." Tough also noted that mud plastered on the formation might interfere with placement of cement. He suggested moving the casing while cementing to reduce such hazards. A few operators in California did sometimes rotate casing while cementing but it was in wells considered shallow even for that time. As depth of wells and the usage of rotary drilling increased, with thicker drilling muds—often loaded with sand—and lower safety factors for casing, movement was discontinued. Operators were reluctant to risk damaging the casing by moving it once it was run to the depth at which it was to be cemented. Despite this general opposition, a few operators did move the casing in areas that required dangerously high pressures to place the cement. It reduced the maximum pressures and a few engineers recognized that it would improve the distribution of the cement.

The improved drilling mud and drilling practices during the 1930's and on into the 1940's substantially reduced the dangers of moving casing. But who would break the practice barrier of such long standing when the safety of a deep hole and a long string of casing was at stake? Even if the casing could be moved, what about the danger of its freezing at the upper point of movement, thus forcing its being cemented 15 to 30 or 40 ft off bottom? It was invariably observed that with scratchers on the casing, circulation after the pipe was on bottom would bring up stringers and balls of stiff clay removed from the walls of the hole by the scratchers. If one pass of the scratchers would remove so much mud cake, surely several passes would clean the walls of the hole. Finally casing was raised and lowered or "reciprocated" through the length of a joint until the cement equalized, i. e., until the pressure started to increase at the surface. It was another long step to continue moving the casing until the cement was in place, which would improve distribution. It took time to recognize that the risk of parting or freezing casing by moving it while placing cement was less than the risk of a poor or unsuccessful cement job.

The use of scratchers, as is true of most new equipment, did not increase rapidly. It was necessary to overcome fear that projections on the pipe might interfere with getting it to bottom, and fear of moving the pipe. Scratchers had come onto the market only a short time before World War II and shortage of material and manpower and restrictions of development had their effect. Operating companies were concerned with the real value of such equipment and compared the effectiveness of wells cemented with scratchers, centralizers, and movement of pipe while cementing with those which had been completed without such equipment. Among the first reports published was one by Tepliz and Hassebroek on results in Louisiana[45] and J. L. Rogers on results in Illinois,[46] both in 1946. Experience was showing a much higher success ratio, particularly where producing zones were some distance above the casing shoe.

As was mentioned previously, rotating casing to improve distribution of cement around casing was practiced to some extent prior to 1920 but was discontinued. Quintana Petroleum Company rotated casing in some 50 wells, while cementing at about 5,600 ft, in Tom O'Connor Field in southwest Texas in 1936.[47] A few others in the area followed the practice but it did not become general or extend to other areas. Rotating scratchers patented by Carl E. Reistle, Jr. and George Cannon were not on the market until 1946,[48] by which time reciprocating scratchers were widely used. They were generally accepted, and gained in use as did the reciprocating scratchers. Scratchers or centralizers, and usually both, are used on a large majority of the deep casing strings; and the casing is moved continuously until all of the cement is in place behind the pipe.

Since 1940 several substitutes and modified portland cements have become available to the industry. The first of these was gypsum cement (plaster of paris) which was introduced by Halliburton Oil Well Cementing Company in 1940. Gysum cement is one of the oldest cements known to man, but its time of hydration was short. An improved method of controlling the setting or hydration time was developed, permitting sufficient time after mixing with water to place it in a well. Its use has been limited almost entirely to drilling wells and to wells being worked over. It is particularly useful for holding junk at the bottom of a hole while it is being drilled up.

Dowell Incorporated put on the market in 1943 a phenol-formaldehyde thermo-setting plastic, the polymerization time of which could be controlled. It is a liquid placed by a dump bailer; and under pressure will penetrate mud cake and porous formations which a neat cement will not do, or additives can be used to prevent its penetrating the porous formation. It was used primarily for plug-back jobs to shut off bottom water, and was satisfactory in some areas, especially the East Texas Field; but in general the necessary close control of the conditions under which it has to be run has limited its use.

Pozzolan is the oldest known mineral cement and was used for construction until the development of quicker-setting and harder portland cement about 1825, but did not become a general construction material until the last decade of the 19th century. A common pozzolan alone is not suitable for oil-well cementing because of its low early strength. Halliburton Oil Well Cementing Company, after more than 3 years of testing in the laboratory and in the field, in 1953 introduced "Pozmix," a mixture of a pozzolan and portland cement and several pozzolan mixtures are now available. The mixture makes a lower-weight slurry which is an advantage when there is danger of lost circulation. It has lower strength than portland cement, but is much higher than necessary except where reinforcement of the casing is important, and also is less brittle, which may reduce fracturing by bullet or jet perforating or other impacts. It is estimated that over two-thirds of the cement used for casing jobs in 1957 were portland-pozzolan mixtures. The most common proportion is equal parts but others are in demand, especially higher proportion of pozzolan, up to 80 percent.

Bentonite was brought into the oil fields as a rotary-mud conditioner in 1930. It was soon learned that addition of bentonite to neat cement would increase viscosity, and the mixture might have an angle of repose as high as 60 deg and still be pumpable. Such mixture has been useful in cementing large cavities penetrated in drilling wells. Adding bentonite to the cement slurry has gained wide use. A neat-cement slurry mixed with over 4½ gal. to the sack (over 50 percent water by weight) will separate or settle, leaving clear water on top. This can be prevented by the addition of 3 to 4 percent bentonite without appreciable decrease in strength.

Loss of circulation while cementing is troublesome in some areas. Addition of various fibrous materials to cement to prevent or reduce lost circulation while cementing has been practiced since such materials were introduced to the industry as drilling-fluid additives in the middle 1930's. Perlite, made available to the industry in 1951 as a drilling-mud additive to prevent lost circulation, is added to cement for lost circulation both directly and for its lowering of the specific gravity of the slurry. Granulated walnut shells, a development in the Research Laboratory of Stanolind Oil and Gas Company for the same purposes, were put on the market in 1953. Phillips Petroleum Company has sponsored the use of diatomaceous earth to reduce weight. Recently, Magnolia

Petroleum Company (now Mobil Oil Company) has reported adding powdered silica to reduce the loss in strength where excessive diluent additives are necessary to meet minimum weight limits. Granulated gilsonite is being used both to reduce weight and to block loss into porous formations. Many other substances have been suggested and experimented with, either to reduce the cement weight or to prevent lost circulation.

Adding rock salt to the cement in slight excess of amount necessary to saturate the mixing water at bottom-hole temperature gives a better contact of the cement with the walls of the hole through salt sections.

Halliburton Oil Well Cementing Company made bulk cement available to the oil industry in early 1940 and, by the end of the year, had bulk stations in many of the larger active areas and expansion continued. By 1957 well over 75 percent of the portland cement used in the domestic oil wells was furnished from bulk plants. Bulk cement trucked to the well where it is to be used has the advantage, in addition to convenience and speed of handling at the well, that additives can be much more efficiently blended with the cement at the bulk plant than at the well. The more common additives now mixed at the blending plant as ordered by the operators are pozzolan, bentonite, and lost-circulation materials. In areas having deeper wells and higher temperatures not only are retarded cements used, but the pumping time can be further increased by blending a retarding agent in the amount needed for the existing conditions.

Several cementing materials have been introduced recently but it is too early to know what effect they may have on the future of cementing. Among them is use of a slurry of oil and portland cement in a well producing water. Cement being selectively wet by water will hydrate or set on contact with the water zone and the remainder will be carried out with the oil when the well is put on production again. Another is a pozzolan developed by Halliburton Oil Well Cementing Company for use in very high-temperature wells. Dowell Incorporated has put on the market "Cealment," a portland cement-latex slurry recommended where better bonding to the formation or pipe is desired.

Progress in effective use of cements in oil wells has maintained pace of improvement with drilling and producing progress or, more appropriately, as a part of that progress. Acceptance of improved materials and practices has—looking back upon them—been slow at times. As means of correlating and calculating — means of seeing down the hole, so to speak — have been developed, better materials and methods have had a shorter period from introduction to common practice or discard. Cementing, as in all other phases of drilling and producing, went through its periods of fads or styles — or the popular thing to use or way to do. It worked in that well; it appealed to the men; it became the practice. Time was considered too valuable and wells too costly to justify investigation and study. Times have changed.

More is expected of a cement job than ever before. At first it was only to prevent movement of water under the casing shoe. Now it must prevent movement of any fluids behind the pipe; and, in addition, it should reinforce the casing and protect it from corrosion. For the petroleum engineers working on these problems, there is no end to progress and seldom even an interruption.

ACKNOWLEDGMENT

Acknowledgment is gratefully made of the assistance of the members of the Editorial Board, *History of Petroleum Engineering,* and of the Special Committee on Cementing Practices Volume.

Appreciation is expressed to those who furnished so much of the information and background that is the base of this history of cementing: Frank F. Hill, Manager of Operations (retired), and W. S. Eggleston, Manager of Reserves and Valuation, Union Oil Co. of California; Erle P. Halliburton, Founder, W. D. Owsley, Vice President, and Phil Montgomery, Technical Coordinator for Cementing Services, Halliburton Oil Well Cementing Company; R. C. Baker, Founder, Ted Sutter, President, and R. C. Glover, Foreign and Domestic Sales Engineer, Baker Oil Tools, Inc.; Bruce Barkis, B & W, Inc.; Otis D. Small, Senior Chemist (retired), Pacific Portland Cement Company; D. E. Silcox, Senior Chemical Engineer, C. C. Scharpenberg, Chief Engineer Producing Department (retired), and L. B. Little, General Superintendent Southern Division (retired), Standard Oil Co. of California; Lewis Whitney, formerly with Perkins Cementing, Inc.; E. L. Davis, Petroleum Engineer; R. P. McLaughlin, first Oil and Gas Supervisor, California State Mining Bureau; Joseph Jensen, Consulting Engineer and Geologist, Tidewater Oil Company; Thor Germundsen, Manager Structural and Railways Bureau, and Harold H. Steinour, Assistant to the Director of Research, Portland Cement Association; E. Gruenwald, Manager "Incor" and Technical Service, Lone Star Cement Corporation; and to the many others who were helpful.

REFERENCES

[1]Hill, John R: Improved Mode of Closing the Water Courses Encountered in Drilling Oil Wells, U.S. Patent No. 112,596, March 14, 1871.

[1a]American Petroleum Institute: *California's Oil,* 12 (1948).

[1b]*National Oil Reporter,* **3 [9],** 7, Oct. 9 (1902).

[2]Hill, Frank F: Personal letter to Union Oil Co. of California, Public Relations Department, July 8, 1940. See also Ref. 3.

[3]Union Oil Co. of California: *On Tour,* Nov.-Dec. (1952).

[4]Baker, R. C: Cement Retainer, U.S. Patent No. 1,035,674, Aug. 13, 1912, filed Jan. 29, 1912.

[5]Baker, R. C: Plug for Well Casings, U.S. Patent No. 1,392,619, Nov. 18, 1913, filed Nov. 20, 1911.

[6]Tough, F. B: Methods of Shutting off Water in Oil Wells, *U.S. Bur. Mines Bull. 163* (1918).

[7]Perkins, Almond A. and Double, Edward: Method of Cementing Oil Wells, U.S. Patent No. 1,011,484, Dec. 12, 1911, filed Oct. 27, 1909.

[8]Swigart, T. E. and Schwarzenbek, F. X: *Petroleum Engineering in the Hewitt Oil Field, Oklahoma*, 63, U.S. Bureau of Mines in cooperation with the State of Oklahoma and the Ardmore Chamber of Commerce, Jan. 1921.

[9]Halliburton, Erle P: Method and Means for Cementing Oil Wells, U.S. Patent No. 1,369,891, March 1, 1921, filed June 26, 1920.

[10]Halliburton, Erle P: Well Sounding Device, U.S. Patent No. 1,692,037, Nov. 20, 1928, filed June 15, 1926.

[11]Halliburton, Erle P: Method of Hydrating Cement and the Like, U.S. Patent No. 1,486,883, March 18, 1924, filed June 20, 1922.

[12]Kay, F. H: Petroleum in Illinois in 1914 and 1915, *Illinois Geological Survey Bull.* 33, 87 (1916); also Ref. 6.

[13]Hager, Dorsey, and McPherson, G. W: Water Troubles in the Mid-Continent Oil Fields and Their Remedies, *Trans. Am. Inst. Mining Engrs.* **61**, 580 (1920).

[14]McLaine, W. L: Float Plug, U. S. Patent No. 1,491,915, April 29, 1924, filed Sept. 28, 1922.

[15]Burch, D. D: Casing Shoe, U.S. Patent No. 1,603,447, Oct. 19, 1926, filed Feb. 25, 1926.

[16]Burch, D. D: Apparatus for Cementing Oil Wells, U.S. Patent No. 1,712,948, May 14, 1929, filed June 21, 1927.

[17]Huber, Frederick W: Method and Composition for Cementing Oil Wells, U.S. Patent No. 1,452,463, April 17, 1923, filed May 24, 1922.

[18]Oatman, Franklyn W: Water Intrusion and Method of Prevention in California Oil Fields, *Trans. Am. Inst. Mining Met. Engrs.* **48**, 627 (1915).

[19]Gonnerman, H. F. and Lerch, William: Changes in Characteristics of Portland Cement as Exhibited by Laboratory Tests over the Period 1904 to 1950, *Portland Cement Association Research Department Bull. 39*; also *ASTM Special Publication No. 127*.

[20]Doherty, W. T. and Manning, M: Gulf Coast Cementing Problems, API Southwestern District Meeting, Dallas, Texas, April 3-4, 1929; *Oil Gas J.* 48, April 4, (1929).

[21]Jensen, Joseph; Graves, McDowell; Goold, W. D; and Gwin, M. L: Deep Sand Development at Santa Fe Springs, *Trans. Am. Inst. Mining Met. Engrs. (Petroleum Development and Technology)* 310 (1930).

[22]Personal communications, Otis D. Small, July 1956; D. E. Silcox, July 1956.

[23]Davis, Eugene L: Specifications for Oil-Well Cement, *API Drilling and Production Practice*, 372 (1938).

[24]Discussion on Cements and Mitigating Influences Related to their Use for Shutting off Water in Oil Wells, Llewellyn T. Bachman, Directing Chemist, Santa Cruz Portland Cement Company, Davenport, Calif., September 17, 1921 (mimeographed report).

[25]Craft, B. C; Johnson, T. J; and Kirkpatrick, H. L: Effects of Temperature, Pressure, and Water-Cement Ratio on the Setting Time and Strength of Cement, *Trans. Am. Inst. Mining Met. Engrs. (Petroleum Development and Technology)* **114**, 62 (1935).

[26]Silcox, D. E. and Rule, R. B: Special Factors Must be Considered in Selection, Specification and Testing of Cement for Oil Wells, *Oil Weekly*, July 29 (1935).

[27]Weiler, J. E: Apparatus for Testing Cement, U.S. Patent No. 2,122,765, July 5, 1938, filed May 15, 1937.

[28]Farris, R. Floyd: Effects of Temperatures and Pressures on Rheological Properties of Cement Slurries, *Trans. Am. Inst. Mining Met. Engrs. (Petroleum Development and Technology)* **142,** 117 (1941) (reprint, p. 306).

[29]Robinson, W. W: Cement for Oil Wells: Status of Testing Methods and Summary of Properties, a report of the Special Subcommittee on Oil-Well Cements, *API Drilling and Production Practice,* 567 (1939).

[30]*API Code 32: Code for Testing Cements Used in Wells,* American Petroleum Institute, Dallas, Texas, 1948, 1st Edn.

[31]*API RP 10B: Recommended Practice for Testing Oil-well Cements,* American Petroleum Institute, Dallas, Texas, Jan. (1958) 7th Edn.

[32]*API Std 10A: Specification for Oil-well Cements,* American Petroleum Institute, Dallas, Texas, Jan. (1958) 5th Edn.

[33]Farris, R. Floyd: Method of Determining Minimum Waiting-on-Cement Time *Trans. Am. Inst. Mining Met. Engrs. (Petroleum Development and Technology)* **165,** 175 (1946).

[34]Hansen, W. C: Oil Well Cements, Third International Symposium on the Chemistry of Cement, London, 1952. Cement and Concrete Association, 52 Grosvenor Gardens, London, SW 1.

[35]Weiler, J. E: Method of and Composition for Retarding the Setting Time of Portland Cement, U.S. Patent No. 2,006,426, July 2, 1935, filed December 5, 1934.

[36]Pew, Thomas W: Method of Shutting off Water Sands in Wells, U.S. Patent No. 2,087,297, July 20, 1937, filed April 24, 1935.

[37]Leonardon, E. G: The Economic Utility of Thermometric Measurements in Drill Holes in Connection with Drilling and Cementing Problems, *Geophysics,* **1** [1] 115, Jan. (1936).
Deussen, Alexander, and Guyod, H: Use of Temperature Measurements for Cementation Control and Correlation in Drill Holes, *Am. Assoc. Petroleum Geologists Bull.,* **21** [6] 789, June (1937).

[38]Howell, Lynn G: and Frosch, Alex: Detection of Radioactive Cement in Cased Wells, *Trans. Am. Inst. Mining Met. Engrs. (Petroleum Development and Technology)* **136,** 71 (1940) (reprint, p. 69).

[39]Kinley, M. M: Well Surveying Device, U.S. Patent No. 2,102,080, December 14, 1937, filed December 23, 1935.

[40]Kinley, M. M. et al: Surveying Caliper, U.S. Patent No. 2,267,110, December 23, 1941, filed July 18, 1940.

[41]Jones, P. H. and Berdine, Denis: Oil-Well Cementing—Factors Influencing Bond Between Cement and Formation, *API Drilling and Production Practice,* 45 (1940).

[42]Wright, Kenneth A: Method of Conditioning Well Bores, U.S. Patent No. 2,338,372, January 4, 1944, filed August 19, 1939; also, Well Production Equipment, U.S. Patent No. 2,374,317, April 24, 1945, filed December 10, 1940.

[43]Irvine, Herschell R: Casing Centering Device, U.S. Patent No. 1,778,830, October 21, 1930, filed June 18, 1927.

[44]Steps, Robert Alexander, and Hartman, William Walter: Cement Equalizer, U.S. Patent No. 1,775,376, September 9, 1930, filed July 8, 1929.

[45]Teplitz, A. J. and Hassebroek, Willard E: An Investigation of Oil Well Cementing, *API Drilling and Production Practice,* 76 (1946).

[46]Rogers, J. L: Casing-Cementing Practices Improved in Illinois, Indiana and Kentucky Completions, *Oil Gas J.,* 98, July 13 (1946).

[47]Mills, Brad: Rotating While Cementing Proves Economical, *Oil Weekly*, 14, Dec. 4 (1939).

[48]Reistle, Carl E., Jr. and Cannon, George E: Cementing Oil Wells, U.S. Patent No. 2,421,434, June 3, 1947, filed November 27, 1944. See also Wright, K. E: Rotary Well Bore Cleaner, U.S. Patent No. 2,402,223, June 18, 1946, filed June 26, 1944.

Chapter 8

LOGGING, SAMPLING, AND TESTING

Eugene G. Leonardon

EUGENE G. LEONARDON was born at Montaigut, Central France, in 1888. He received a degree in engineering from the Ecole Polytechnique, Paris, in 1912, and a degree in law from the University of Paris in 1914. He served throughout World War I in the French artillery, attaining a captaincy and the Croix de Guerre. His affiliation with Conrad Schlumberger, which began in 1913, was interrupted by military service and by supervision of a steel plant and mining operations in the Saar.

Mr. Leonardon rejoined Conrad and Marcel Schlumberger in 1919, serving as staff engineer from 1921 to 1926 and as manager of the United States branch from 1926 to 1934. He became a vice president of Schlumberger Well Surveying Corporation upon its incorporation in 1934, advancing to the presidency in 1939 and serving in that position until 1946, when he became a director of the corporation.

Professional affiliations include AAPG, SEG, AIME, AIEE, American Geophysical Union, Seismological Society of America, and the European Association of Exploration Geophysicists. He has made numerous significant contributions to technical literature, mainly in geophysics.

8

INTRODUCTION

At the beginning of the present century, the art of drilling oil wells was quite simple—it consisted mostly of "making hole". Little effort was made to learn about the conditions on the way down or at the bottom of the well, other than to watch for the presence or absence of oil or gas. The only knowledge of the stratigraphy came from the bailing operations which gave, at best, a crude record of the formations penetrated. This state of affairs was not surprising, and went hand in hand with the limited overall knowledge of the practical oil man of those days. Similar conditions have existed at the birth of other industries or sciences. Mineralogists, for instance, began examining their samples with the naked eye. Later they applied the magnifying glass and the microscope. They further enlarged their knowledge by measuring the density, hardness, and electrical properties of the rocks and by making chemical analyses of them.

An evolution of the same character took place in the drilling and completion of wells. As the industry grew to major proportions, every segment of the activity had, of necessity, to become more efficient and more precise. Hence, there was a constant drive toward the trial and adoption of new scientific methods and new mechanical devices. This continual process of refinement will be recited in other chapters of this history, each author discussing the manner in which it affected his particular sphere.

Who was mainly responsible for this advance—the old-timer or the scientific-minded new comer? This is, in our opinion, a moot question, akin to the classical one of whether the chicken or the egg came first. The fact is that the industry was starting from rudiments, and that the blending of practical experience and scientific knowledge brought about tremendous progress, spectacular in its rapidity.

A field in which this progress has been particularly impressive is that of logging, sampling, and testing, which we are about to discuss. We shall first give a definition of it: It comprises those processes and methods which propose to tell about the conditions inside a well or at the site of the drilling tool. Of course, it is a difficult proposition to try to know what happens down the hole, at depths of 2 or 3 miles and even more—to extract messages from earth formations so far away from eye and reach. Yet this has been achieved with an amazing degree of success and accuracy.

The techniques of logging, sampling, and testing are made up of a series of varied and independent procedures which are now integral

495

tools of one or several basic branches of the industry, such as drilling, exploration, or production. For this reason, it is but natural that mention of these techniques be made in other chapters of this book, in order to allow a comprehensive presentation of the subject at hand. Such overlapping, if kept within reasonable limits, is indeed desirable.

We propose to discuss in the following pages the most significant procedures of logging, sampling, and testing, and their evolution, viz.:

> Sampling and coring in percussion drilling
> Sampling and coring in rotary drilling
> Diamond core drilling
> Micro-paleontological analysis
> Heavy-minerals correlations
> Drilling-time logging
> Mud logging
> Side-wall sampling
> Electrical logging
> Induction logging
> Nuclear logging
> Velocity logging
> Caliper logging
> Temperature surveys
> Testing for fluid samples

A few comments are in order. Percussion- and rotary-drilling systems are fully covered by other chapters of this book, but it seems desirable to discuss here the history of the practice of sampling with both systems through the years.

Diamond drilling calls for a similar observation. In many respects it is an adaptation of the rotary system, and should properly be discussed under drilling methods. There is, on the other hand, the matter of the progress in the art of coring which pertains to this chapter.

Micro-paleontological analysis, heavy-minerals correlations, and drilling-time logging are especially tools of the geologist, with which he establishes stratigraphic correlations and maps subsurface structures. The balance of the services listed are of a much more complex nature. Not only are they useful to the geologist for stratigraphic purposes, but their power of analysis goes much further—they furnish clues or precise data about the nature of the formations traversed, the quality of the fluids contained therein, their pressure, temperature, and other bottom-hole data. Such information is of great value in many phases of petroleum engineering—exploration, exploitation, and reservoir operations. The use of these services is, therefore, discussed also in other parts of this history, particularly in the chapters on production techniques and control and on reservoir engineering.

SAMPLING AND CORING IN PERCUSSION DRILLING

More than 2,000 years ago, the Chinese drilled brine wells and reached depths of 3,000 ft. They used a primitive procedure from which our cable-tool method or churn drilling has evolved. Basically the two systems do not differ.

In those ancient times, as today, it was desirable to have some knowledge of the materials penetrated by the hole. Up to a point, this is easy to achieve in cable-tool operations, since the hole has to be cleaned every few feet of depth drilled. This is the function of the bailer (or sand pump, as it has also been called). The mixture of cuttings and water is brought to the surface and dumped on the ground. It is examined and a record of it may be kept.

Another source of information comes from the experience of the driller. The nature and characteristics of the rocks encountered are first determined roughly by the "feel" of the tools when drilling. Much of this information is entered in the driller's log. Back in the 1870's or 80's, such records were quite sketchy, as the following example illustrates:[1]

Tar Creek No. 1

1887

     25 ft—Wooden conductor
     82 ft—8-in. drive pipe: 5 pieces
    115 ft—Struck sand and a little oil. Gravity: 26.5
    196 ft—Total depth (February 23, 1887)

1888

    371 ft—Drilled deeper; 8″ hole. Got more oil and mud; cased
              off oil and mud with 5⅝″ casing; 21 pieces
    400 ft—Struck gray sand; verry *(sic)* sharp sand
    560 ft—Struck red sand
    695 ft—Struck a little light oil
    730 ft—More oil and gas
    775 ft—Through the red sand into soft red rock
    960 ft—Finished drilling and pulled 5⅝″ casing; 25 pieces:
              386′ 8″
              Perforated 36′ from bottom, and 200′ from top
              Tubed May 1st; started off at 75 bbls.

---

[1]References are at the end of the chapter.

Such meager description was the rule. Many similar records abound—for instance, those cited by Carll.[2] In those days the economic aspect of the drilling business could only discourage any serious interest in this type of investigation. Carll[3] laments on this situation in these terms:

"It is said that about four thousand well shafts were sunk in the oil fields of Pennsylvania and New York in the one year 1877. Never before in the history of the enterprise were wells put down so rapidly—allowing these wells each to average 1056′ (and this is undoubtedly too low an estimate), every five wells aggregated one mile of rock, making altogether 800 miles of bore holes drilled in one year . . . of this large number of wells there has not been preserved a special record of one in a hundred, and but few of those that have been preserved can be obtained in a shape to be of any use to the Survey . . . proper records for geological study cannot be obtained. Every interest of the business is against it. The contractor is drilling to make the best time possible, that he may reap the largest profit on his contract. The well owner cares nothing for the structure, except as it relates to the oil producing sand, and with him too, time is of great importance. The work cannot be delayed by superfluous measurements and washing of sand pumpings, to satisfy what they consider to be only scientific curiosity."

However, such habits were bound to change. Geology and its relationship to the presence of oil came progressively to be understood. In this respect, Carll did a fine work of pioneering, relentlessly bringing the attention of the oil operators to the necessity of collecting samples regularly, comparing them, and identifying the formations traversed. A circular sent by the Survey to the owners and contractors asked them to compile reliable well records and send them to the Survey. Carll reports with satisfaction that, on one of his visits to Pittsburgh, "the owners of the well kindly made a donation of the whole collection of sand pumpings. . . With the drilling record in hand, I put the specimens in paper bags, marked them in agreement with the record, and shipped the whole to Pleasantville. I have since filled a set of bottles and labeled them, so that each specimen may be examined separately and compared with any other in the large collection prepared in the same manner for the State Museum."[4] In this work, Carll did a bit of geological correlation. He preserved with particular care the sand pumpings of 6 wells in Petrolia (1876), enclosing the specimen in square bottles, each containing ½ oz of material. They were labeled with numbers, depths, etc., and the bottles were put in proper position on a rack formed of six separate vertical strips (one for each well). Six inches of the strips represented 100 ft of the well, so that the exhibit gave a cross section of the subsurface to scale.[5]

The routine of sampling with churn drilling did not vary for a long period of time. Harris[6] in 1910 discussed logs which differed little from records 35 years older. Slowly, however, the gathering, examination, and conservation of cuttings received more attention and care. In 1914, Udden[7] issued the following instructions, which give a measure of the progress made: "In collecting samples for examination, it is of course desirable to take them at as close intervals as possible. Large samples are not necessary. An ounce of cuttings taken from each bucket, or from every five feet of drilling, will be ample for the study of 'coal measures' in this State. Where the well is passing through the thicker limestones of the Silurian or Ordovician, an ounce of cuttings taken every 10 feet is quite sufficient. . . For keeping and shipping samples, bags of light cloth are very suitable."

In this same paper, Udden formulated a set of directions for the full examination of the samples collected. He went into it in great detail, considering the structure and texture of the rocks, the examination of the sand grains, the use of the acid test for calcareous materials, the search for fossils and unusual minerals.[8]

In addition to the bailing of cuttings, fragments of rocks are now and then brought to the surface because they cling to the bit, especially if the formation is sticky. This haphazard way of removing a rock sample from the bottom is of small moment. The idea became a feature of interest, however, when various core barrels or "biscuit cutters" were developed. The early tools appeared more than 70 years ago. Brantly, in the chapter herein on percussion drilling, mentions such old tools and shows them in Fig. 81 and 83; but it was not until the 1920's that efficient devices were put on the market. Among them, the Keystone and the Baker cable-tool core barrels deserve particular mention. The first device was invented in 1905 and perfected in the Mid-Continent area in 1925.[8a] The Baker tool[8b] was also built in 1925 and used extensively in California, West Texas, and Colorado in the latter part of the 1920's. Both tools were very successful in the coring studies of the Bradford sand, Bradford Field, Pennsylvania, in the summer of 1928. Among the interesting jobs performed with the Baker core barrel should be cited the coring of early bore holes on Bahrein Island, around 1932. The Baker cable-tool core barrel is still used by the industry today.

The cores brought to the surface can be experimented upon and analyzed in the laboratory. Such examination furnishes valuable data for production studies and reservoir evaluation, dealt with in other chapters in this history. This remark applies not only to cable-tool drilling, but to rotary and diamond drilling as well.

499

SAMPLING AND CORING IN ROTARY DRILLING

Rotary drilling came into use in the oil fields around the beginning of the century. It was with a rotary drill that the oil at Spindletop was discovered near Beaumont, Texas, in 1901. Although the rotary system had long been known and used in mining and water-well work, it did not gain rapid acceptance in the oil fields until sometime around the 1920's. The old-timers preferred cable-tool drilling. Johnson and Huntley[9] point out concisely the reasons therefor: "The churn drill accustoms the driller to watching the variations in the formations through which he is passing, since he drills usually with a dry hole and runs the bailer frequently. . . On the contrary, the wash of the rotary machine furnishes an obscure record as to the formations passed through, and it is difficult to keep an accurate log."

It was well-recognized that the rotary was a hole maker, but it was also evident that it could easily pass through zones of interest without giving much of any indication of their contents—particularly beds carrying water, oil, or gas. These drawbacks explain why the rotary system was not favored by the oil industry for quite a long time, in spite of its speed. Collom[10] reports that during the period of 1914-18, approximately 100,000 of the 109,000 wells estimated as completed in the United States were drilled with cable tools. The situation nowadays is completely reversed. In 1957, 86.5 percent of the drilling activity for oil and gas in the United States was due to the rotary.[11] Several factors made this evolution possible, in particular improvements in bits and mud control. Also, the practical old-timers dropped their prejudices, and the introduction of coring tools in the 1920's came to the rescue. Last but not least, electrical logging and allied techniques began to provide an adequate amount of information about the character and fluid content of the formations traversed by the rotary bore hole.

Notwithstanding this evolution, formation samples taken during the drilling are still a very valuable source of information, and it would be unthinkable not to collect them. The routine is simple. The essential tool is a box or keg, the bottom of which has been sawed off and replaced by one or several wire nets. The box is inserted under the flow of the drilling mud, and after a lapse of a few minutes is removed and another one is inserted in its place. The cuttings in the box are then washed with clear water, while still wet, and inspected by the driller. He then pours them into a bottle for future reference.

In sampling work, there is a feature which should be emphasized, viz., the necessity of a close collaboration between the petroleum engineer or geologist and the driller. The latter, in his own way, knows and can tell a great deal about the conditions at the bottom of the hole— from the manner in which the tool behaves, the way the pump works.

He observes whether the formations are hard or soft, sticky or clean, etc. His guess about their nature is generally correct. What he has to say is decidedly good to know. On the other hand, he can easily be confused by this sampling business and its purpose. It is the job of the engineer to educate him and sell him on the importance of this activity. Team work is essential. This collaboration will be especially productive if the engineer or geologist has his representative—the sampler—present at all times on the location to take care of the sampling work, particularly if the well is a wildcat. The sampler has been a familiar figure in the oil fields since the early 1920's.

As mentioned, mechanical coring has been successfully practiced with the rotary system since the early 1920's. The first core barrels were rugged and simple tools which cut out a small sample from the bottom of the bore hole. Numerous more efficient instruments have since been built by the industry. (See in this respect Chapter 6 on the hydraulic rotary-drilling system, p. 368 and following.) However, special mention should be made here of the two pressure core barrels developed by The Carter Oil Company[12] and the U.S. Bureau of Mines-American Petroleum Institute[13] in the late 1930's. These instruments not only can cut a sample of the formation but seal it at the same time. When brought to the laboratory, the sample is representative of the conditions at depth, and makes possible the determination of valuable reservoir data. This is an ingenious development which will be cited later, in connection with testing.

DIAMOND CORE DRILLING

For efficient core recovery—often 100 percent—diamond drilling is unsurpassed. Provided the tools are properly selected and applied, the diamond drill will core soft and hard rocks equally well, irrespective of depth and at any angle. These qualities make the process especially useful in mining and quarry work, mineral prospecting, coring at dam sites, etc. It has been so utilized for about a century.

Diamond drilling also has made a place for itself in the oil industry. First, there is the field of core or exploratory drilling where the objective is the accurate knowledge of the rocks, their nature, their attitude, etc., and not the drilling of a hole to produce oil and gas. In this case, lighter rigs are used. The second field is production drilling or wildcat drilling with standard rotary rigs, where the diamond bit is used for the harder parts of the hole. In this instance the process is advantageous for economic reasons. Finally, diamond cores provide excellent material for the operations of core analysis, because of their high degree of conservation and percentage of recovery. On this subject, we refer the reader to the chapter on reservoir engineering.

As mentioned in the chapter on the hydraulic rotary-drilling system, the idea of diamond drilling is that of the French engineer Rodolphe Leschot who obtained a patent in 1863.[14] At the time, Leschot was employed on the Mont Cenis Tunnel. He had noticed that the chisels and boring bars used to drill holes for blasting wore out rapidly. In his youth he had been a watchmaker, and was well-informed about the hardness of the jewels in watches. He conceived the idea of setting diamonds in the bits "because the wear is almost imperceptible, in operating on the hardest substances." The tool "was composed of a series of diamond edges attached to an annular or tubular stock or crown." It "bore an annular groove or hole, leaving a central core or kernel, which is easily detached . . ." Although many details have changed, this description is still valid to outline the principles of today's diamond drilling.

The first use of diamond drilling in this country took place in connection with the cutting out of blocks of marble in the Vermont quarries in the 1860's. A series of small diamond drill holes, closely spaced, was bored along a line of the slab so that such slab could be easily separated in two parts along the line. The bit used for this particular work was solid and did not take any core.

At about the same time, the first attempt to use diamond drilling in an oil field took place. It is mentioned in a book by Edmund Morris, published in 1865, in the following manner:[15]

> "A new plan has just been introduced, and I had the satisfaction of witnessing its operation at the experimental well, which has gone down about ten feet into the first rock. This is in reality, as well as in name, a drill, being a thin circular tube, set around the edge with six small stones of a species of diamond. A powerful engine with proper machinery causes the drill to revolve with great velocity, cutting down into the rock and leaving a central core standing, which is jerked out with clamps let down for the purpose."

A few years later, in 1872, the system was used for sinking two vertical shafts near Pottsville, Pennsylvania. Numerous holes of $1\frac{3}{4}$-in. diameter were drilled at the bottom of the shafts to a depth of 250 to 300 ft for the purpose of blasting the rocks, which were subsequently removed.[16]

Exploring for Oil by Diamond Drill

In prospecting for oil and gas, diamond core drills were first used for exploration work during late 1919 and early 1920 in eastern Oklahoma and southern Illinois. This was key-bed drilling. As the expression implies, it consisted in drilling down to a known stratum from which cores were obtained. These cores served to establish the top and bottom depth of the key stratum, and made it possible to draw contour maps of the horizon. It was customary, even in hard-rock drilling areas, to drill the soft formations—which were not generally used as key beds— with drag bits of the very short fishtail type. Diamonds were used only in core bits to drill the hard rocks.

In the early 1920's, the cutting material used in the drilling tests was Brazilian black diamonds (carbonados) which were relatively expensive, compared with the cost of rock bits surfaced with hard metal. For this reason, diamond drilling was sparse in the oil fields for several years. However, experiments in the use of African bort were started in 1926, and resulted in the utilization of these diamonds which were cheaper than the carbonados. This gave an impetus to diamond drilling, particularly when mechanical methods for setting the bort were devised around 1930 to replace the hand-setting practices which were excessive in cost. Also, with a view to lowering costs (particularly with large diamond bits), tungsten carbide and other diamond substitutes were introduced to the industry. They worked satisfactorily, but of course did not compare with diamonds. Thanks to the merits of the method and to the foregoing improvements, diamond drilling developed rapidly and was extensively used in many oil provinces, both in the United States and abroad.

Drilling conditions in the oil fields differ from those in mining districts. For instance, rocks are generally softer in oil territories, and mud liquid is usually circulated instead of clear water because it minimizes caving, etc. Much research was carried out in oil-field diamond drilling both by diamond-bit manufacturers and by oil operators. The patterns and sizes of diamonds had to be changed continuously to fit operating conditions. The matrices in which the diamonds were set were revised. The diameter of the cores was increased (in mineral drilling the large barrels did not produce cores exceeding 2 in. in diameter); the core barrels were redesigned to allow mud circulation. All these facts, and many more, had to be determined by trial and error. The same era of the 1920's, which saw the successful development of this exploratory work, witnessed also the coming of age of a new science—applied geophysics. Torsion balance, seismic surveys, electrical-logging measurements became regular tools of the engineer and geologist, and displaced to a great extent the diamond drill as an exploration tool.

Diamond Drilling and Production Work

During the same period, interest began to be shown in the use of the system for oil-production work, as an adaptation of rotary drilling. It appeared that the cost of drilling wells might be substantially reduced with this technique. Edson[17] pointed out in 1921 that diamond drilling is not a new and untried tool, having been used for "over 50 years" in the coal and metal field. He emphasized the value of the cores as a source of accurate information and the economy of the method, which "gives the operator larger value for the money spent".

One province where the process was put to work was the oil fields of Mexico. The first company to use this equipment was Panuco Boston Oil Company, an affiliate of The Atlantic Refining Company. The operations were successful and the drills were later moved to another property belonging to Cortez Oil Company. Fishtail bits were used down to the limestone, at which point diamond core bits were run into the hole to drill into the prospective zone. Excellent discussions are given by Edson[18] and Longyear[19] of a well completed as a producer in 1922. The depth reached was 2,153 ft, and the initial production 1,200 bbl. The cost was low and the core recovery 85 percent. Similar work took place in California and in the Mid-Continent around 1924. Large machines were designed for the purpose. They were not always successful—the fact is that they had to be competitive with conventional rotary drilling.

When World War II came, it had its effects on oil reserves. They were substantially reduced at the end of the conflict. The search for oil was vigorously resumed after 1945—holes were pushed deeper, and new fields were drilled which previously might have been considered uneconomical. At the same time, new horizons were achieved in the field of metallurgy. Drilling diamonds became cheaper. Thanks to these factors and to the building of better equipment, a new era was opened to diamond drilling.

Diamond Coring for Reservoir Evaluation

In water flooding, no operator can decide about a program without studying carefully the characteristics of the sands. Actually, all the details of the project—type and size of the pumping equipment, setting of packers, spacing of the wells, etc.—depend upon a detailed knowledge of the producing horizon. For this purpose, diamond coring is far superior to conventional coring; it has been used extensively for the exploitation of the Bradford sand.[20]

It was primarily in the West Edmond Field, Oklahoma, that the economic value of diamond coring was firmly established in 1945. The results achieved became known to the operators of the Rangely Field, Colorado, where an important reservoir problem involving unitization and pressure maintenance was posed. The productive section is the Weber, which lies at a depth of about 6,000 ft and is 600 to 700 ft thick. It is made up of hard, dense, dry dolomite and dolomitic sand, hard shales, and sands. It is comparatively difficult to drill with the rotary system; and in a particular well, 60 days were required to core 400 ft. The first diamond coring was performed by Stanolind Oil and Gas Company in August 1946.[21] The results were so satisfactory that in

less than a year the superiority of diamond coring was fully demonstrated. It was recognized that the operations were twice as fast and much
cheaper than with rotary drilling. Core recovery was almost 100 percent.

As a result, diamond coring and drilling have become commonplace in many oil provinces of the world. Diamond-bit manufacturers,
drilling operators, and engineers continue to improve and to perfect the
process. At present, it is estimated that 95 percent of all cores cut in the
oil fields are cut with diamonds, and approximately 25 percent of the
footages drilled below 12,000 ft during 1958 were drilled with diamonds.

MICRO-PALEONTOLOGICAL ANALYSIS

Prior to 1920, microscopic examination of well samples and cuttings played practically no role in petroleum engineering. The investigation of samples was conducted with the naked eye or, at best, with
a hand lens.[22] In conclusion, a name would then be suggested such as
shale, clay, slate, limestone, sand, or sandstone. The material would also
be characterized as to color and texture, but no effort would be made
to classify minute fossils and organic remains for geological or stratigraphic purposes. There was, however, an early investigation which constituted a departure in this direction. It occurred in 1891-92. At that
time, the City of Galveston was endeavoring to increase its supply of
fresh water and, rather than obtain it from the mainland, decided to
sink a well to a depth of 3,000 ft. Actually, the well was stopped at
3,070 ft and no suitable supply of fresh water was found. J. A. Sing-
ley of the Texas Geological Survey had been instructed by his superior,
Dr. E. T. Dumble, the state geologist, to watch the drilling of the
well and secure all possible information therefrom.[23] Many hundreds of
samples were taken. They contained numerous fossils which were submitted to G. D. Harris, then with the United States Geological Survey
(USGS), for study. Harris identified 77 different species of fossils, and
wrote a preliminary report on them in 1893.[24] This was amplified and
completed in 1895 by a detailed description of the fauna from this well.

No practical conclusions were drawn from this valuable work,
and more than a decade elapsed before fossils were mentioned again by
various authors. First, the same Harris,[25] in studying the structure of
the Jennings Field, Louisiana, examined the fossils of 31 wells and identified 13 of them as mostly of Miocene geologic age. Blatchley,[26] in Illinois,
used as a key stratum "the *Fusulina* limestone" after J. A. Udden's
recognition of fusulinds in well cuttings and the outcrop. In other
studies, Udden[27] examined older rocks and used a spore, *sporangites hur-
onense,* "almost too small to be seen by the unaided eye" for some stratigraphic correlations. He advocated the use of the microscope for the
determination of the mineral content of the shales.

This line of research was further stimulated by the publication, in 1914, of a USGS paper on the Charleston deep well. This paper by Stephenson,[28] with a separate report on the mineralogy of the water by Chase Palmer, discusses the geology of a well drilled near Charleston, South Carolina, early in 1911. The well went to a depth of 2,001 ft, penetrating formations from the Pleistocene to the Upper Cretaceous. The study of the fossils was made by Dr. J. A. Cushman, who identified as many as 81 Foraminifera.

First Micro-paleontological Laboratories

Around 1920, there was a pressing need for subsurface information in the salt-dome area of Texas. No stratigraphic data were available, so to speak; even the age of the reservoirs in the producing fields was not known. Dr. E. T. Dumble, then vice-president and manager of the Rio Bravo Oil Company and consulting geologist for the Southern Pacific Railroad, was particularly interested in the possibilities of paleontology in connection with this problem because of his previous successful experience on the Galveston well. In addition, his interest was stimulated by various papers which were presented at the meeting of the American Association of Petroleum Geologists (AAPG) in Dallas in 1919, and by the discussions by Charles Schuchert, Dr. J. A. Udden, Wallace E. Pratt, and others, which took place.

In September 1920, Dumble opened a laboratory at the Rio Bravo Oil Company in Houston, for the purpose of using paleontology in the study of well samples. Esther E. Richards, now Mrs. Paul L. Applin, was appointed paleontologist. Three other companies (Gulf Oil Corp., Humble Oil & Refining Company, and The Texas Company) agreed to cooperate in the initial support of this project. However, in November of the same year, the Humble Company decided to set up their own laboratory, and Alva C. Ellisor was put in charge. The Texas Company followed suit a year later, appointing Hedwig T. Kniker to its paleontological laboratory. Other girls joined the new profession soon—Laura Lee Lane (1923) worked for Alexander Deussen; Grace Newman (1922) for the Rio Bravo Oil Company; Emma Jane Coffman (1923), now Mrs. John Miller, for the Humble Oil & Refining Company; and Elisabeth Stiles for Gulf. "With the exception of Emma Coffman, all of this group shared an apartment, and, believe it or not, lived peaceably together and did not divulge company secrets".[29]

The year 1921 was a period of experimentation in the paleontology laboratories. Samples of similar size were soaked overnight, washed by hand, the concentrates dried and packaged. A careful description was made of each sample, so that the compiled records would form a complete detailed report on every well.

Soon a micro-fauna was discovered in the sediments. The first characteristic faunal zone to be identified was the one which later became known as the Het. (*Heterostegina*) zone. It was found around December 1920-January 1921, in deep Oligocene wells drilled by Humble Oil & Refining Company at Goose Creek. Soon afterwards, the same fauna was located by the Rio Bravo Oil Company. Later on, a number of faunal zones were identified in rapid succession.

The early work progressed slowly. Acceptance by most geologists was difficult. They believed that such organically simple forms of organisms as Foraminifera must have evolved very slowly, and therefore would extend unchanged through many stratigraphic levels, thus making it impossible to establish sharp correlations. This assumption proved to be incorrect. In fact, because of the abundance of the microscopic fossils, it soon became possible to collect groups or complete faunas which had a short time range.

There were many practical difficulties or drawbacks to overcome. For instance, cores and cuttings were usually of poor quality, and the descriptive literature of Foraminifera was meager. The means of filing and preserving the micro-fossils had to be perfected. Initially the slides were made of glass with a saucer-shaped depression in which the fossils were placed. They were covered by a sheet of mica fastened down with small seals. Later the glass was replaced by cardboard; the depression was given a black background which made the observation of details clearer.

During the years 1922-24, numerous data were accumulated, and the value of the work was clearly demonstrated. Matching assemblages and sequences of assemblages could be traced from well to well. This information, combined with the detailed lithological records of non-fossiliferous nature, formed the basis from which stratigraphic correlations and structural maps were prepared.

The results achieved were effectively publicized at the March 1924 AAPG meeting in Houston. Two papers, in particular, were influential in engaging the interest of the profession—one by Schuchert,[30] and the other by Miss Ellisor, Miss Kniker, and Mrs. Applin.[31] The demonstration of what had already been accomplished was the motivating factor for the greatly increased demand for the work in the Gulf Coast and for the extension of the method to other areas with the opening of laboratories in California, Oklahoma, North and West Texas, etc. The value and reliability of the use of Foraminifera were naturally variable according to the area and to the age of the rocks studied. This led to the use of other types of micro-fossils and to some variations in the technical procedures.

The economic value of micro-fossil examinations for working subsurface geology having been demonstrated, the academic institutions were prompt in offering courses in micro-paleontology. The University of Texas announced its course in 1923, with Dr. F. L. Whitney in charge. Columbia University, too, offered a course in 1923, under Dr. J. J. Galloway. Stanford University followed in 1924 with a course by Dr. Hubert Schenck. Even though the initial laboratory work was started by women, the profession of micro-paleontologist is definitely a career for men. With the rapid expansion of the activity, many men entered the occupation.

In the professional field, the new activity resulted in the founding of a new scientific association—the Society of Economic Paleontologists and Mineralogists. Created in 1927 by 89 charter members, this new body grew rapidly. The following membership figures, at 5-year intervals, demonstrate its vitality:

1930	254
1935	255
1940	318
1945	343
1950	677
1955	1,092
1958	1,364

The first publication of the Society was issued in July 1927.

HEAVY-MINERALS CORRELATIONS

More than a century ago, a British geologist named Sorby[32] had the idea of using thin sections and the Nicol prism for the study of sedimentary rocks. However, it was in the investigation of igneous rocks that he was particularly successful. After him, the petrographic study of sedimentary rocks rested quite a while. Cayeux noted in 1916[33] that certain stratigraphic horizons could be characterized by unique assemblages of heavy minerals within certain geographical limits, remarking, in particular, that ". . . the study of the heavy minerals is an inexhaustible mine of information in regard to the history of the currents of the ancient seas . . ." In 1923, Henry B. Milner published an article on the same subject,[34] which was reviewed by K. C. Heald in the first 1924 number of the *AAPG Bulletin*.[35] Heald's quotation of Milner stresses the line of thought: "And investigation of the petrography of certain sediments . . . has conclusively shown that for limited areas . . . horizons are broadly characterized by heavy minerals assemblages."

Heald indicates that there are about 25-odd mineral species in detrital deposits which could be examined by the petrographer, but that such number can be greatly reduced "by discarding all that have a specific gravity less than that of bromoform solution, which is 2.90". He continues with Milner's suggestion of applying petrographic methods to oilfield problems in outcropping rocks "or deeper strata that may be penetrated in wells drilled for oil . . . It is far from improbable that thin layers with distinctive aggregates of heavy minerals may be recognized wherever they are penetrated in restricted areas".

The growing interest of geologists in the possibilities of utilizing heavy minerals for correlations was heightened by the publication in 1924 of a report by Tickell[36] on heavy minerals, with numerous photomicrographs. In short order, also in 1924, two other reports were published by Reed.[37, 38] Reed and Tickell had been associated in a project of Stanford University, for the study of "heavy-minerals residues". This project was financed by the Stanford Petroleum Research Fund, contributed by several oil companies. Their studies were concerned with samples of outcrops in the vicinity of the oil fields of Ventura and Coalinga. They concluded that this line of work had hardly been explored, and that it offered interesting possibilities.

During the same year, an effort was taking place in the Mid-Continent area. Fanny Carter Edson, at the Roxana Petroleum Company (now Shell Oil Company), undertook the assignment of defining the sedimentary formations and unconformities of the region. She had done graduate work at the University of Oklahoma and at Stanford University where Tickell and Reed were researching on the problem of heavy-minerals correlations. Mrs. Edson herself was an experienced petrographer. In her work for Roxana she made heavy-minerals determinations in well samples a basic procedure for some years. She prepared and published a public manual on their identification.[39]

This period of the early 1920's was one of enthusiastic work and progress. At the same time, some of the limitations of the process were foreseen. Reed, for instance, writes:[40]

"It may, therefore, be worth while to list, in conclusion, some of the advantages and disadvantages that these minerals may be conceived to offer for this important task" (the problem of correlations).

The disadvantages listed were inconspicuousness of heavy-minerals zones, repetition of zones, and restrictions of identified zones to single depositional basins, thus precluding long-distance correlations. The advantages were the omnipresence of at least some heavy minerals, their excellent preservation and easy identification, and the probability of their concentration in zones thinner than most fossil zones.

Be that as it may, correlations often can be made by the use of heavy minerals. Reed himself and Bailey gave good proof of this feasibility in correlating satisfactorily 29 core holes in Pliocene sediments buried at depths of 500 ft or more.[41] Heavy-minerals correspondences have been used in stratigraphic geology with more or less intensity, but do not seem to have become regular routine for well-to-well correlation. The reason, probably, is that there are other processes more rapid and less costly at present.

However, it is in the elucidation of marine depositions that the study of heavy minerals may find its most efficient use. Cogen[42] in 1940, discussing heavy-minerals assemblages of certain surface and subsurface Gulf Coast sediments, concluded that the detritus from several mineralogically different provinces had been distributed laterally coastwise in one or both directions by longshore marine currents. He demonstrated that "mineral-zone boundaries may transect formations and paleontologic horizons". Thus, he reverts to Cayeux's thought-provoking assumption as quoted by Reed:[43]

"In addition (to certain other uses) several of these heavy minerals are means incomparably more sensitive and certain than organisms to determine currents, and their introduction into a given region is often the work of currents."

Referring to the conditions in the Upper Cretaceous of the Paris Basin, which he has studied for many years, Cayeux says:

"It is known that a surface current came into the basin through the Strait of Poitou, and that another came down from the North.

"The first carried certain materials of which one finds not even a trace in the deposit of the second . . . There is no doubt that we have here the principle of a method . . . called to render the greatest services to paleo-oceanography."

This opinion is shared by Rittenhouse, who wrote in 1948:[44]

"Even though present in small amounts, such heavy minerals . . . may be exceedingly useful in correlating sands, outlining petrographic provinces, indicating sources and past history of the source material, and in helping to decipher geologic history."

To summarize, the study of heavy minerals has not been of paramount value in the finding of oil. Nevertheless, under certain circumstances, it has furnished excellent help for correlations. Furthermore, it has considerable potentialities for elucidating the historical geology of a province and the direction of the currents during the process of deposition. Such studies, therefore, accumulate valuable data concerning the distribution and formation of possible source and reservoir rocks.

DRILLING-TIME LOGGING

The drilling tool exhibits a characteristic way of behaving, according to the formations traversed. In rotary drilling, "any driller can detect such formations as hard rock, hard shell, sand (hard or soft), shale, and gumbo, by the way the engine runs, the action of the rotary table and the tune of the mud pumps."[45] In cable drilling, "experienced drillers become very adept at judging the formations by the feel of the drilling cable. The blow transmitted from hard and cemented rocks is quite different from that coming from soft and unconsolidated ones . . . The speed of drilling also varies . . ."[46]

Most interesting is the informative and interpretative value of the drilling speed. It is studied by measuring one of the following factors:

1. Length of time necessary to drill 1 ft (or 2 ft, as the case may be) of formation. This is the *drilling time.*

2. Length of hole drilled in 1 min of time. This is the *drilling rate.* When the rock is hard, drilling time is large, drilling rate small. Between the two quantities there is a simple relationship—one is the inverse of the other. They are interchangeable for practical purposes, even though not necessarily equally convenient in matters of interpretation.

In the 1920's—and even earlier—it was common practice to mark the kelly in 5-ft and occasionally 1-ft intervals, and to measure the time elapsing as each consecutive mark passed through the rotary table. Such a procedure did not give an accurate record of the speed of drilling, as applied to individual beds, but it was a useful and valuable part of the driller's log.

In 1936 F. B. Nichols, who was employed as a development geologist in the Seminole area for the Indian Territory Illuminating Company, saw that the foregoing procedure could be improved, if the human element were minimized. In 1937, he built a recording device which consisted essentially of a measuring wheel, a recording drum carrying a strip chart, a clock, a magnet, and two recording pens. The instrument was actuated by a flexible steel cable which was tied to the top of the rotary swivel, passed over

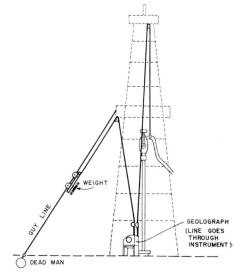

Fig. 1—"Geolograph" Hookup
(After Leroy, L. W: *Subsurface Geologic Methods,* Colorado School of Mines, Golden, 1950, 2nd Ed.)

DRILLING TIME
hours & minutes

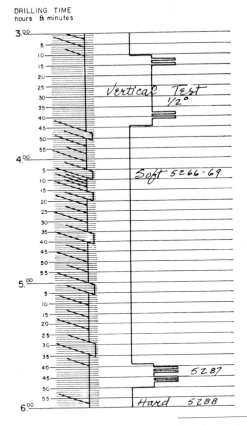

Fig. 2 (left)—"Geolograph" Chart
(After pamphlet of Geolograph Co.,
Composite Catalog, 1958)

Fig. 3 (below)—"Geolograph"
Recording Unit
(Courtesy of Geolograph Co.)

a pulley near the top of the derrick, thence down around the measuring wheel in the device and back up into the derrick over a second pulley to a weight which traveled on a guy line (Fig. 1).[47] The device was called a Geolograph by Nichols. The recording machine is equipped with two inking pens supplied with inks of different color. These pens each trace a diagram. The right-hand diagram indicates by horizontal and vertical lines the amount of time that drilling is in progress, when it has been stopped, or when the bit is off bottom. The record on the left is made up of slanting lines, each line marking the time at which 1 ft of hole (or sometimes 2 ft), exactly, has been completed (Fig. 2). In other words, it marks on a linear scale the time it took to drill each successive foot. Nichols' primary aim was to record the drilling breaks. However, the down-time record proved valuable because, for the first time, the drilling contractors had an opportunity to study with some accuracy the performance of the bit.

The Geolograph was first used in the Oklahoma City Field in December 1937 (I.T.I.O. Well #8, Alice Bodine). The results agreed well with the data obtained from sampling and electrical logging. Until

512

1941, the instrument was used by I.T.I.O. on its own wells, but occasionally the company would let contractors rent the service. In 1941, Cities Service Oil Company took over the I.T.I.O.; and in November 1942, Nichols purchased from the new company their interest in the process. He founded the Nichols Geolograph Company, which became the Geolograph Company in 1943. This organization has been constantly in operation since then. Fig. 3 shows a picture of the instrument used at present.

Another instrument is the Log-O-Graf. It was placed in commercial field operation by Warren Automatic Tool Company early in 1946, and was retired in June 1950. Its general principles were similar to those of the Geolograph. In particular, the same cable arrangement as shown on Fig. 1 is used to trigger the instrument. A spring-wound clock was used to drive the recording-stylus pen across the chart. The advance of the depth would automatically stop when the bit was picked up at the bottom. Similarly, the clock would halt when the drilling was interrupted. On the chart, the drilling times were shown in abscissae, in minutes per foot, while the depths were marked at a given scale (1, 2, or 5 in. per 100 ft) in ordinates (Fig. 4). Thanks to this feature, no redrafting of the depth was necessary to compare the chart with the electric log, or other well log. This was a distinct advantage because, not unnaturally, the spontaneous potential (SP) log is often quite similar to the drilling-time curve.

A third instrument is the *rate-of-penetration recorder*, built by the Martin-Decker Corporation. Martin-Decker became interested in Nichols' ideas at a very early date, and exchanged views with him. Finally, however, they decided to develop an instrument proposed to them by Yeatman,[48] a mechanical engineer with the Shell Oil Company.

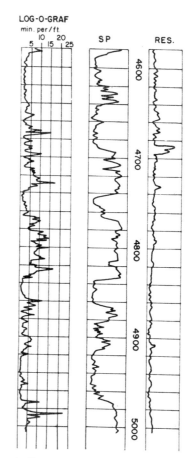

Fig. 4—"Log-O-Graf" Chart (left) Shown with Electric Logs (center and right) (After pamphlet of Warren Automatic Tool Co., Houston)

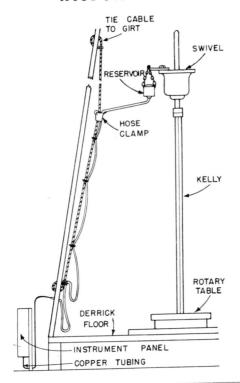

TIE CABLE
TO GIRT

SWIVEL

RESERVOIR

HOSE
CLAMP

KELLY

ROTARY
TABLE

DERRICK
FLOOR

INSTRUMENT PANEL
COPPER TUBING

Fig. 5 (left)—Setup of Rate-of-Penetration
Recorder
(After pamphlet of Martin-Decker Corp.,
Long Beach)

Fig. 6 (below)—Polar Chart of Martin-
Decker Recorder
(After Yeatman, C. A., U. S. Patent
No. 2,230,280)

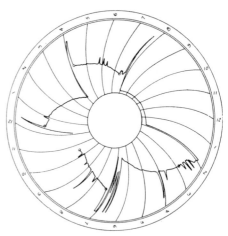

He had already built a few instruments of his own when Martin-Decker agreed to take a license on his patent, on April 19, 1939, and to market the process. In the Yeatman patent (Fig. 5), a hydraulic reservoir is attached to the swivel block at some place where it is not subject to rotation. This reservoir is connected by a flexible hose to a container located preferably below the derrick floor. The hydraulic head between the two varies with the height of the swivel block, and serves as a means of measuring the rate of progression of the drill. This datum is registered on a polar chart in feet or in meters (Fig. 6). A transparent template with curves corresponding to various speeds of drilling may be superimposed over the chart in order to read directly the speed per hour at all points along the well. The Martin-Decker-Yeatman recorder is manufactured by the Martin-Decker firm and sold to many foreign and domestic operators.

Finally, mention should be made also of the research and development work by Thomas A. Banning, Jr. of Chicago, and G. F. Shepherd of Dallas. Shepherd was one of the early users of, and believers in, the study of the drilling speed. Together with Banning, he recognized the desirability of accurately measuring successive increments of new drilling, and producing a log which would register and plot automatically the foot-time (time required to drill each foot) at successive depth locations. These men started their work jointly in the fall of 1943. The physical development had progressed considerably about the spring of 1945. A patent was filed by Banning on May 28, 1946, and another on April 21, 1955.[49] The first equipment, with signaling unit, was ready to operate early in 1946; and the first field test took place successfully at that time, near Baton Rouge, Louisiana, in the University Field. Other successful field tests have since been made, the most recent being during the fall of 1957 and spring 1958, in California. The tool, which has not seen commercial use yet, is very accurate and eliminates human errors in operation. It requires no attention in the form of re-setting or the like during all normal drilling operations. It certainly will constitute a useful progress when it is available commercially. Fig. 7 shows the most recent form of the instrument.

Fig. 7—Banning's Apparatus for the Study of Drilling Speed
(Courtesy of Thomas E. Banning, Jr., Chicago)

MUD LOGGING

The examination of cuttings provides the basic information which the driller enters on his driller's log. This record is never sufficiently detailed or complete; and in order to make it more accurate and more useful, it is often desirable to resort to mechanical coring. There is a drawback to this, however—coring is too costly to be used continuously, throughout the well. A constant effort has, therefore, been made during the years to get all the data which can possibly be obtained from the cuttings brought to the surface. As early as 1922, Collom[50] proposed to investigate the presence of oil, gas, water, or sulfur in the cuttings by treating them. He pointed out also the desirability of knowing with some accuracy the depth of the cuttings in rotary drilling; he showed how their travel time (or lag) can be measured with the aid of dye tracers and expressed in numbers of strokes of the pumps. George O. Suman[51] recommended gas sampling: "Sometimes on prospect wells, a simple gas trap is installed at the point of discharge into the circulation ditch." This gas can be put into bottles for the purpose of testing and analyzing, and "in view of the simplicity of the process, it is unusual that such a plan is not oftener used." The observation of bubbles, foam, and decrease of drilling-mud weight was mentioned as possible evidence of gas. With respect to oil, he proposed to detect it either by visual observation or by making extracts of cuttings with acetone or ether.

The use of ultra-violet light, which affords a sensitive, rapid, and practical test for the presence of small amounts of oil, was described by Bentz and Strobel.[52] The same process was commented upon and recommended by Melhase[53] a few years later.

An excellent summary of all the procedures available around 1933, with the exception of fluorescence, is given by Schnaebele.[54]

From this literature, the basic elements of mud logging were emerging, but their sporadic use could hardly be called a well-logging method. The development of mud logging in its present form received its impetus from the work of John T. Hayward. There is no record before him of a continuous mud-analysis log showing the combined results of drilling-mud analysis for gas and oil, and for relating these to such useful factors as drilling rate and depth. His work is well-described in papers by Bignell,[55] Mills,[56] Sawdon,[57] and by Hayward himself.[58]

Hayward had spent many uncomfortable hours, sleeping under boilers and in the back of automobiles, waiting for core barrels to be run and pulled. Remarking that "it is for the fluid contents rather than for the rock itself that wells are drilled," it had struck him that "the circulating mud formed a good means of communication, during drilling, with the bottom of the hole." However, discussing the matter with others, he was always told that he could not reasonably hope that the returns would appear, at the surface, in the order of their depths. For instance, the cuttings drilled from 3,000 ft might arrive later than those drilled at 3,100 ft. Hayward, of course, did not accept such opinion. He performed a series of crucial tests in a number of wells which proved that he was right—when new drill-pipe joints were added, he would "place a telltale in the drill pipe" dropping together a pint of casinghead gasoline, a handful of oats, and some fine colored gravel obtained from pet shops. All these things returned to the surface simultaneously.

From this, Hayward knew that his new line of investigation would work, the more so because he was not actually interested in the cuttings but rather in the gases and liquids. By appropriate measurements at the surface, he succeeded in determining the content in oil and gas of the formations traversed. He then needed only to correlate these observations with the depth to obtain a continuous diagram, giving a picture of the oil and gas content while drilling was in progress. It was Hayward's idea that, if this work could be done reliably, mechanical coring could be mostly eliminated and cores taken only when a show would make it advisable. Hayward was then chief engineer for the Barnsdall Oil Company.

The first complete equipment designed for mud logging was used at the Kate Edwards No. 2 in the Lamar Peninsula, Texas, during August 1937. This was a crude apparatus barely related to today's equipment. It was portable, was transported to the well site in an automobile, and set up in a dog house. The equipment used consisted primarily of two pump-stroke counters, a centrifuge machine, a vacuum jar and vacuum pump, and a paddle-wheel device for automatically taking a composite

Fig. 8—Mud-sampling Device
(Courtesy of Baroid Div., National
Lead Co.)

sample of the mud. This sampling device was a series of dippers mounted on the spokes of a wheel (Fig. 8). It operated in such a manner over the mud ditch that the flow of mud caused the wheel to rotate and, at each turn, to dip up a small sample of mud and deposit it in a container to be collected by the operator.

A portion of the mud sample was centrifuged to determine the presence of oil by separation from the mud. Later it was discovered that such a close control of the quality of the mud samples was not necessary. The paddle wheel was discarded around 1942 or 1943. At present, samples of the flowing mud are taken with a container or with a small pump.

As to the presence of gas, the inventor made use of a peculiar property applying to liquids in which gases are suspended or occluded[59]— such liquids expand or contract in terms of the pressure applied to them, and the variations of volume are substantially in direct relation with the amount of gas contained therein. Therefore, a given volume of mud was poured into a graduated glass container and the pressure was then reduced by means of a vacuum pump. The gas content was deduced from the variations of volume measured. This was the so-called "bottle method." It was quite sensitive, but had certain drawbacks. First, it was a batch method rather than a continuous recording method; but the main trouble was that it did not distinguish between air, carbon dioxide, and petroleum gases. It was soon replaced by the "hot-wire method," discussed following.

The lag (travel time of the mud from the bottom to the mouth of the well) was determined in number of strokes of the mud pump required to bring the samples to the surface from the bottom. This factor was used to correlate the samples of mud with the depth from which they were coming. Thanks to these procedures, representative curves could be drawn as the hole progressed. However, the equipment was cumbersome and the operations were time-consuming. Furthermore, the results were not continuous.

During 1938 and 1939, the efficiency of the system was considerably improved. First, an apparatus was built for detecting oil in the drilling mud and in the cuttings, by studying them under ultraviolet light for fluorescence. This was an advance over the separation by centrifuging. This phase of the process is still not continuous today. In gas detection, progress was also achieved. A gas separator or trap was mounted on the mud flow line.[60] It consisted of a short length of 12-in. diameter pipe which fitted over the end of the flow line, with a hinged lid, through which the mud passed. This pipe had a 2-ft length of smaller-diameter riser attached to it, to form a chamber for gas separation. The arrangement caused the gas to break out of the mud and be collected. Air was continuously drawn through the trap, and the gas-air mixture passed across hot wire filaments where the gas was burned. The quantity of gas burned (or intensity of combustion) was proportional to the percentage of combustible gas in the air. This was measured electrically in terms of the resistance of the hot-wire circuit. Thus a continuous reading was obtained.

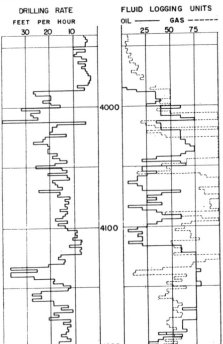

DRILLING RATE
FEET PER HOUR
30   20   10

FLUID LOGGING UNITS
OIL ——— GAS ------
25   50   75

4000

4100

4200

Fig. 9—Typical Early Mud-logging Record, 1940
(Courtesy of Baroid Div., National Lead Co.)

During the early stage of the process, the curves offered were the rate of penetration and oil and gas content of the mud. No doubt it was because of this phase that the term "mud logging" became common in reference to the service. The term still persists, although it is somewhat obsolete considering the number of data studied. To date, mud-logging procedures measure and record oil in the mud and in the cuttings, total gas and methane in the mud, total gas in the cuttings (a standard feature since 1945), methane and heavy gases (hexane and heavier) in the cuttings, rate of penetration, and drilling-fluid characteristics (in particular, variation in salt content). Also lithology and microscopic examination of cuttings are often included; mineral fluorescence of the cuttings is checked. All these data are compiled and plotted on a final log. Fig. 9 and

518

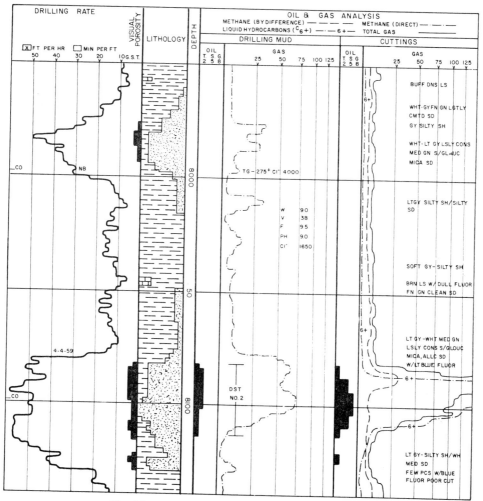

Fig. 10—Present-day Mud-logging Record, 1959
(Courtesy of Baroid Div., National Lead Co.)

10 show two logs, one measured in the early 1940's, the other recently.

By far the greatest part of mud-logging work takes place on wildcat operations, wells of an exploratory nature, because it is in such case that control and information are most needed. In the development of a field, it is often useful also when the stratigraphy or geology is complicated. Even on inside location it may sometimes be desirable. Finally, the log constitutes a complement to electrical and radioactive logging, and similar techniques, because there can never be too much information for solving the problems of testing and completing a well.

As said before, mud logging was started and developed by the Barnsdall Oil Company on its own wells. The company was neither organized for nor wished to get into the servicing business. In June 1939, Baroid obtained an exclusive license on the process and entered the field with one unit in August 1939. Meanwhile—also in 1939—Barnsdall, not wishing to be involved in the patent business itself, created a subsidiary for the logging of their own wells, Barnsdall Research Corporation, with Hayward in charge. Later, this subsidiary was purchased by him. At about the same time, in May 1950, Baroid's exclusive license was changed to a non-exclusive one. Many companies entered the field, to the extent that there were in December 1957 about 85 mud-logging companies operating in the United States and Canada, with a total of 350 logging units available.

At present, a mud-analysis log furnishes a whole series of useful data such as amount of methane in the drilling mud, total combustible gas and methane in the cuttings, liquid hydrocarbons (C_6^+ hydrocarbons) in the cuttings, oil in the drilling mud and in the cuttings, rate of penetration, etc. Further refinements in analytical methods have led to recent experimental use of such instruments as the mass spectrograph, infrared absorption spectrometers, and gas chromatography. Mud logging is still in a development stage, and it is likely that further progress or new refinements will take place. It is not possible now to predict the form of future instrumentation or the range of its applicability.

SIDE-WALL SAMPLING

If the cost were not a factor, drill holes for oil or gas would be cored throughout their length. This is not feasible, however, for reasons of economy; and cheaper procedures are utilized. Some have already been discussed. An interesting one consists in taking samples from the sides of the well. In this respect, several lines of approach were followed. One was the idea of a deflector, by means of which a tool or knife would be pushed obliquely away from the axis of the hole and thus drill or cut a sample out of the wall, at any chosen depth. Patents by Mitchell[61] and Mason[62] illustrate this principle. The idea of a deflected drill resulted many years later in the side-wall core barrel, of the type leased or sold now by A-1 Bit Company and Hunt Tool Company.

An apparatus of a more intricate nature consisted of lowering into the hole a housing containing a miniature drilling tool, which could be operated from the surface. It could be projected laterally, penetrate a few inches into the formation, and take a sample. Afterward it would be retracted and brought to the surface. Spencer, Nichols, Williston, and Mennecier[63] patented tools of this nature. The Mennecier hard-formation sample taker was used commercially by Schlumberger for several years. It was designed to core hard formations and did not work well in unconsolidated ones.

Another idea is that of a cup which is forced into the walls of the hole by appropriate mechanical means. Upon being retrieved, the tool brings to the surface a small cylindrical sample of the formation.

Among the numerous inventors, special mention should be made of Perry, Williston, Burt, and C. Schlumberger.[64] In one of his improvements, C. Schlumberger introduced the action of an explosive charge to trigger the mechanism of the sampler. Not all of these inventions saw commercial development. Burt's invention, however, deserves special comment. In late 1933, he began sketching means whereby the two-bladed underreamer used by Baker Oil Tools, Inc. could be adapted for taking side-wall cores, in portions of the hole which had been overlooked or in which core samples taken with conventional core barrels on the drill pipe were unsatisfactory.[65] The first test of the instrument took place in the Montebello well, Community No. 1, on April 24, 1934, and was a success. From this point on, the use of the Baker wall sampler gained considerable acceptance until it met competition from other devices in the late 1930's and early 1940's, in particular the core-taking bullet.

Other inventors, among them Bannister, Piggot, and M. Schlumberger, proposed firing a hollow bullet against the formations, thus tearing off a cupful of them. Piggot was not oriented toward the business of well drilling but had in view the sampling of ocean bottoms. His apparatus has been effectively used for this purpose.[66] Bannister's mechanism[67] fires a bullet through the drill bit against the bottom of the well. The bullet is washed to the surface by the circulating fluid and brings a sample to the driller. The most comprehensive and successful invention is the work of M. Schlumberger.[68] Basically, the tool is similar to a gun perforator; and, like the perforator, is lowered into the hole by a cable. It fires a bullet into the walls of the well, but this bullet is in the form of a cylindrical sleeve or a cup and performs the function of a core barrel. It is fastened to a wire or cable the other end of which is attached to the housing, so that when the supporting cable is pulled upward, the bullet is pulled out of the formation bringing a sample to the surface.[69]

This type of side-wall sample taker was introduced in the Gulf Coast in April 1936. Acceptance by the industry was slow at first. There were 24 experimental operations performed between April and September 1936. The first commercial job was in Southwest Texas in September 1936.

Since then, the oil industry has fully recognized the value of side-wall coring. Guns originally built to recover three cores on each trip in the hole have been re-designed and enlarged to recover as many as 30 samples per trip. A very large number of operations are performed every day by several service companies, among them Lane-Wells, Pan-Geo Atlas Corporation, Schlumberger, Welex, etc.

ELECTRICAL LOGGING

The inception of electrical logging goes back to 1912, when Conrad Schlumberger, then professor of physics at the Ecole des Mines in Paris, France, began studying the problem of exploring the underground by means of surface electrical measurements. Up to that time, magnetic permeability, only, had been used practically for this purpose. Conrad Schlumberger thought that electrical conductivity should prove particularly rewarding because it varies between very large limits.

The procedure applied consisted of sending an electrical current into the ground between two points called "power electrodes." If the soil is homogeneous, the electrical conditions (potentials, paths of the lines of current) are known, *a priori*, at every point of the medium. On the other hand, if the ground is not homogeneous (conductive ore body lying at depth in the vicinity, presence of folded or stratified layers, etc.), the electrical flow will undergo perturbations. The study of these perturbations, at the surface, furnishes a means of predicting certain features of the underground.[70] To this end, Schlumberger at first traced equipotential curves at the surface of the earth (method of the map of potentials). Then he soon adopted the more rapid and efficient technique of the resistivity map.[71] For this purpose, a resistivity-measuring device is used. It comprises two power or current electrodes, A and B, through which the electric current is sent; and two probing electrodes (or secondary electrodes), M and N, between which the differences of potential are measured. Usually the probing electrodes are near the center of the line AB (Fig. 11). This is by no means the only arrangement. For instance, MN may be located in the vicinity of A, while the other power electrode is at a great distance from the region AMN. In such a case, the influence of B is negligible and the equipotential surfaces are half spheres centered on A.

In case of a homogeneous ground, there exists a simple relationship between the intensity of the current flowing through the power electrodes, the drop of potentials between the probing electrodes, and the resistivity of the medium; the latter quantity can be readily computed. It is plain, however, that if the ground is not homogeneous, the data obtained do not give the true resistivity. They are affected by the material in the area of the measurement and give what is called the

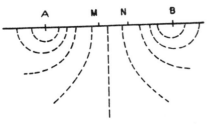

Fig. 11—Electrode Arrangement for Measuring Surface Resistivities

"apparent resistivity." It is the plotting of such apparent-resistivity measurements, over a whole area, which constitutes the method of the resistivity map. As a geophysical process of surface exploration, it met with great success.

However, the interpretation of the resistivity figures very often could have been made more definite, or simple, had the true resistivity of the underground been known at a few points. It was for this purpose that attempts were made at Besseges, France, in 1921, to measure actual resistivities at depth in mine shafts, galleries, and open holes.[72] However, it was not until 1927 that the idea of making measurements in drill holes took substance and matured into an invention. The first experiments took place at the Pechelbronn oil field, Alsace, on September 5, 1927 (well Diffenbach 2905). Fig. 12 shows the diagram obtained. As soon as enough data were accumulated, it was realized that these measurements constituted an efficient process of identifying the formations traversed — a new and promising approach had been found toward a more detailed and accurate knowledge of the conditions in open, uncased drill holes.[73]

Such is the story of the beginnings of electrical logging. It came out of experiments intended to achieve another purpose, a feature which is not uncommon in scientific research.

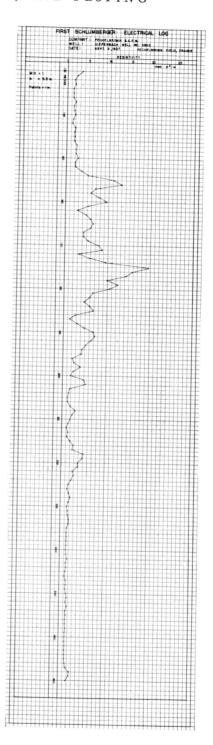

Fig. 12—First Resistivity Log Run at
Pechelbronn, Sept. 5, 1927
(Courtesy Schlumberger Organization)

ELECTRICAL LOGGING, FIRST PHASE

Resistivity Log

The procedure used at Pechelbronn was crude and of makeshift nature. Fig. 13 and 14 show the hand-operated winch then in use, and the sheave which served to lower the cable and electrodes into the well. Basically, however, it was not very different from the one still in use today. It consisted of lowering into the hole three insulated conductors, at the end of which were attached the power electrode A and the two measuring electrodes M and N (Fig. 15).[74] The other power electrode, B, was grounded at the surface. The conductors were three separate cables of the type used for lighting fixtures, tied together here and there by friction tape. A battery, E, sent the current into the AB circuit; the differences of potentials between M and N were measured by a potentiometer P. The conductors were lowered into the hole by means of a sheave operated by hand. Point by point, measurements were made at intervals of 3 ft or thereabout. Shortly thereafter, the equipment was installed permanently on a truck. At first, the resistivity log was used for stratigraphic correlations, for which it was invaluable even in its primitive form. Soon, however, it was recognized that it could spell out the character of the rocks to some extent. Clays have a low resistivity; porous sands are conductive if saturated with salt water, moderately resistive if the water is fresh, quite resistive if the impregnating fluid is oil. Therefore, valuable information and clues were added to the knowledge of the well. As for oil beds, some sort of relationship—even though not precise—was observed to exist between their resistivity and their oil potential. In a given formation, the higher the resistivity, the

Fig. 14—Sheave and Tripod Lowering
Cable in Well

Fig. 13—The Winch

First Electrical-logging Equipment, Used at Pechelbronn in 1927
(Courtesy of Schlumberger Organization)

better was the production. This correspondence was demonstrated in Cabimas (Venezuela), Grosny (Caucasus), and Tintea (Roumania) in 1930-31.[75]

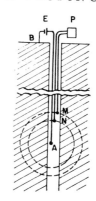

Fig. 15—Sketch Illustrating the Process of Measuring Resistivity in Drill Holes (After Schlumberger, C.)

Spontaneous Potentials

After the resistivity measurements were introduced, another discovery was made late in 1931 when it was noticed that differences of potential existed naturally in open (uncased) holes.[76] The new diagram recording these differences was named the SP diagram (SP standing for spontaneous potentials). Spontaneous potentials are of physical and chemical origin. They are caused by the movements of fluids between the open hole and the formations (filtration) and by the difference of ion concentrations in the electrolytes filling the hole and the formations. Such potentials do not vary along a shale (impervious) section of the well. On the other hand, they usually show large and negative values with respect to a point at the surface, when measured in front of a porous bed. The combination of the resistivity and of the SP log increased considerably the possibility of their interpretation in geological terms, as Table 1 shows summarily. It should be noted that the conclusions arrived at are only *qualitative, not quantitative.*

It has been explained that the apparent resistivity depends upon the volume and nature of the ground encompassed by the measurements. It also varies with the size and configuration of the measuring device — the *sonde.* Not only this, but the hole is filled with mud, and certain por-

Table 1

Resistivity Log	SP Log	Probable Conclusion
Low resistivity	No SP	Shales
Low resistivity	Large SP	Salt-water sand
High resistivity	Low SP	Fresh-water sand
Good resistivity	Moderately large SP	Possible oil sand
Very high resistivity	No SP	Hard rock; very compact sand with sweet water

ous beds may be invaded by the drilling fluid. Truly there are many apparent resistivity values. Depending upon the purpose of the investigation, the man skilled in logging will select the proper sonde from the available tools; more likely he will use several for better understanding. A brief listing and discussion of the various devices follows.

1. In their experiments on uncased drill holes at Besseges in 1921, M. Schlumberger and his co-workers were using a single-conductor cable, one end of which was grounded at the surface; the other moved up and down the hole. This movable electrode was the only part of the circuit which did not remain the same during the measurements. Its resistance depended, to a certain degree, upon the nature of the neighboring rocks. Should the voltage be maintained constant, the variations of the intensity of the current would furnish useful indications regarding the nature of the formation encountered. Such arrangement did not produce accurate data, but gave an idea of the changes in resistivity of the formations, and was useful. It was called a "debit" sonde (debit means *flow* in French), because it measured the flow of the current into the formations. The name of *mono-electrode* or *power electrode* is quite descriptive of this system.

Such debit sonde was improved in France in the fall of 1927 by C. Schlumberger, as illustrated in Fig. 16. The electrode lowered into the hole comprised three separate sections—two of sizeable length on top and at bottom, with a short one between, this center electrode being connected to one of the long electrodes by means of a very low impedance. In such arrangement, the current issuing from the middle section (the intensity of which can be measured) flows horizontally into the formations. Its volume is affected only slightly by the mud filling the hole, and its measurement gives a satisfactory value of the resistivity of the formations in front of the short section. The name "guarded electrode" has been given to this system of focusing.

2. Two electrodes, only, are in the well—one current electrode A and one measuring electrode M. The other two electrodes are at the surface (Fig. 17). Should the ground be homogeneous, the equipotential surfaces are spheres centered on A.

If the distance AM is not great with respect to the diameter of the hole, the resistivity is affected by the nature of the mud filling the hole and also by the volume of the invaded zone. Thus the resistivity obtained may not be highly representative of the formations traversed. On the other hand, this arrangement, when AM is small, gives a fine response with respect to individual beds. The curve obtained is called a "short normal." If the distance AM is rather great with respect to the diameter of the

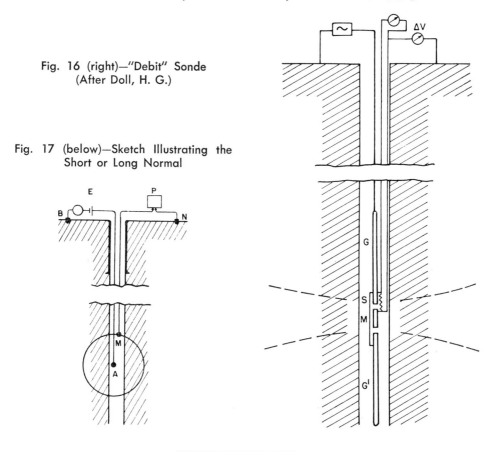

Fig. 16 (right)—"Debit" Sonde
(After Doll, H. G.)

Fig. 17 (below)—Sketch Illustrating the
Short or Long Normal

hole, a larger volume of formations is taken in. The device is less responsive to thin individual beds, but taking a larger bite into the virgin formations behind the invaded zone gives a better representation of them. The curve is called a "long normal." Short and long normal curves are also designated in terms of the AM spacing—16-in. normal, 18-in. normal, etc. This system has been in field use since 1932.[77]

3. Three electrodes are in the well (see Fig. 15)—one current electrode A, two measuring electrodes M and N. The second current electrode is at the surface. The distance AM is large with respect to the diameter of the hole. MN is small. Such sonde deals with a large volume of virgin formations and gives a good idea of their true resistivity, provided the bed is fairly homogeneous over a large thickness (at least 40 ft). Furthermore, it is sensitive to the character of the individual beds when MN passes in front of them. It is known as the "lateral" device. It has been in use since the early period of electrical logging.

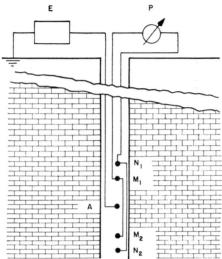

Fig. 18—Schema of the Limestone Sonde

4. There is a current electrode A in the well, and two pairs of measuring electrodes $M_1 N_1$ and $M_2 N_2$ symmetrically located with respect to A (Fig. 18). The second current electrode is at the surface. Electrodes $M_1 M_2$ and $N_1 N_2$ are short-circuited. Such a sonde is well-adapted for logging thick beds of high resistivity. The abnormal readings taken, for instance, at the boundaries of a resistive bed are minimized by the symmetrical character of the arrangement. At the same time, a good representation of details within the resistive bed, although *qualitative*, is obtained, provided the length of the arrangement is comparatively smaller than the bed thickness. This setup is called a "limestone sonde", a name suited to the purpose.[78] It was introduced commercially early in 1946.

5. There may be three current electrodes—A_0, A_1, A_2—and two pairs of measuring electrodes—$M_1 M_2$, $M'_1 M'_2$—in the well, positioned as shown in Fig. 19, with a second current electrode and another measuring electrode at the surface. The pairs of electrodes—$A_1 A_2$, $M_1 M_2$, $M'_1 M'_2$—are respectively short-circuited. A current of constant intensity is fed through electrode A_0. Electrodes A_1 and A_2 are also fed with a current of the same polarity. The intensity of these currents is automatically adjusted during the measurements, so that the difference of potentials between $M_1 M_2$ and $M'_1 M'_2$ is maintained equal to zero. The potential prevailing at any of these four electrodes is recorded. The apparent resistivity measured with this arrangement is proportional to the value of this potential.

In this system, the current issuing from A_0 cannot flow upward or downward past $M_1 M'_1$ and $M_2 M'_2$. It is as if the hole were plugged by insulating disks, extending a distance from the hole. It is a *focusing* device. The sheet of current flowing

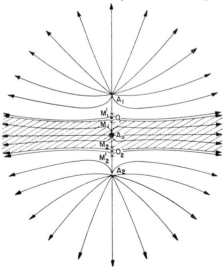

Fig. 19—The Laterolog—Lines of Current in Homogeneous Medium
(After Doll, H. G.)

from A_0 is indicated by a shaded area on the figure. The contrast between the flow of current with a normal device and this focused system is illustrated on Fig. 20. The arrangement—called "laterolog," "guard log," "focused log"—is well-adapted for the investigation of thin beds, because the lines of current are forced more readily into the formations. Also, under certain conditions the apparent resistivity measured is quite close to the actual resistivity of the formation, a factor quite desirable to know when attempting quantitative interpretation. This focusing device has been in commercial use since October 1950.[79]

Two types of laterolog are currently used. One makes use of point electrodes as shown on Fig. 19 (laterolog 7); the other (laterolog 3) has elongated electrodes as in Fig. 16, and the same automatic controls as laterolog 7.

6. A miniature unfocused device is mounted on an insulated pad (Fig. 21). It makes two sets of measurements, corresponding to two

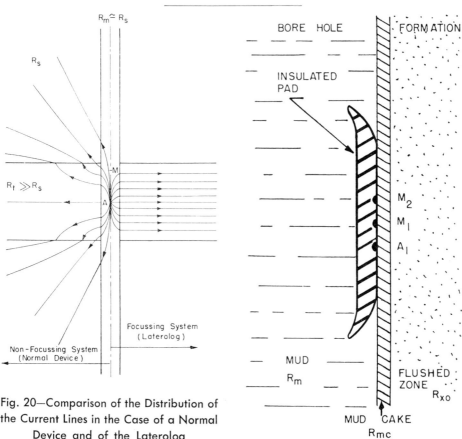

Fig. 20—Comparison of the Distribution of the Current Lines in the Case of a Normal Device and of the Laterolog (After Doll, H. G.)

Fig. 21—Schema of the Microlog Sonde

529

depths of penetration. The pad is pressed against and maintained in contact with the walls of the well during the whole survey. Such a device serves to perform a very shallow investigation of the conditions at the periphery of the well bore. It will show where the mud cake is present and well-built, hence the permeable zones. Also because of its diminutive size, it will differentiate very thin beds with accuracy. Finally, it reaches the flushed zone just beyond the mud cake and makes it possible to evaluate its resistivity—a datum of interest in quantitative interpretation, particularly with respect to porosity. The technique is known under different names, according to service company—microlog, microresistivities, minilog, contact log. This type of log was put into practice industrially in December 1948.[80] A basic aim of micro-devices (microlog and micro-laterolog) is the measurement of porosity.

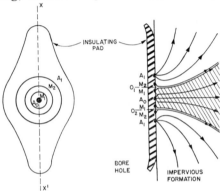

Fig. 22—Schema of the Microlaterolog
(After Doll, H. G.)

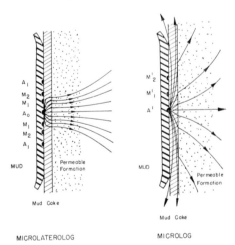

MICROLATEROLOG   MICROLOG

Fig. 23—Comparison of Distribution of Current Lines for Microlaterolog and Microlog in Homogeneous Medium
(After Doll, H. G.)

7. A miniature focused device (Fig. 22) employs both an insulated pad and a focusing current for a deeper investigation. In consists of two current electrodes, one of very small size at the center of the pad A_o, the other circular A_1, and two circular measuring electrodes M_1 and M_2. These three ring electrodes are concentric with A_o. A current of the same polarity is fed to A_o and A_1, and the intensity of such current is regulated continuously so that the potentials of M_1 and M_2 are the same. As is the case with the laterolog, the current is focused; also it cannot spread sideways (Fig. 23). This system is called "microlaterolog", "minifocused log", "microfocused log", "forxolog". It penetrates the formations almost horizontally. The mud cake, if it is less than $1/4$-in. thick, does not influence the measurements. Neither do formations which are at a distance of more than 3 in. from the walls of the hole. The main usefulness of the microlaterolog is to give the re-

sistivity of the flushed zone of permeable formations. This datum is valuable in determining the formation porosity and also the true resistivity of the formations beyond the invaded zone. The system was introduced in November 1951.[81]

How the Resistivity and SP Curves Were Pressed into Service

The whole array of resistivity curves went into commercial use step by step. During the period 1927-31, only one diagram of resistivity was run. It was not continuous but measured point by point, and had the appearance of a broken line. Then the SP curve was added, and two diagrams were produced in the course of a single run. Meanwhile, different types of resistivity sondes were experimented with, both in the laboratory and in the field. Soon it became common practice to re-run a well in order to obviate the limitations of a given set-up. Generally one normal and one lateral curve were the choice. In the next step, two resistivity curves were registered simultaneously, together with the SP. These added runs were made easier, thanks to the incorporation of more conductors in the cable lowered into the well. The first cables comprised 3 conductors; this number was increased to 4 in 1938, and to 6 in 1947. When World War II came, it had become customary to produce in a single run one SP curve and two resistivity curves, generally one short normal and one long normal. If more curves were desired, additional runs had to be made. The number of sondes and curves increased in the ensuing period. Now a regular run quite often comprises four or five curves. They are not all necessarily resistivity and SP curves, since now nuclear, induction, and velocity logging techniques have been added to the arsenal of well logs.

The Geometry of Electrical Logging

Recording many diagrams of apparent resistivities is only part of the job of electrical logging. It now remains to utilize the complex measured values to evaluate the true resistivities of the formations surrounding the hole. This phase has been under study since the early 1930's, and has gained momentum as the process has become more and more an essential tool of petroleum engineering. Thanks to the computing machines now available, problems which would have required years of conventional operations can be solved in a few weeks or less. Furthermore, analog resistor network systems have been built for the determination of the response of logging tools, under conditions too complex for mathematical treatment. Albums of "departure curves" have been published which correspond to almost any conceivable set of conditions in a drill hole. In this geometry of electrical logging, Doll and his co-workers at Schlumberger played an essential and considerable role from the start.[82]

ELECTRICAL LOGGING, SECOND PHASE

During the whole period of the 1930's, there was much elation among the specialists in electrical logging and some frustration, too. The data produced were very valuable, but they were qualitative only. For instance, in the case of an oil sand, its porosity could not be determined nor its oil potential. And these were the data which the petroleum engineer wanted. However, although he wanted them badly, he himself had very little base to start from in order to get them. It is true that a few interesting observations had been made, but they had not been investigated thoroughly or correlated.

One of them, already pointed out, pertained to the relationship which appeared to exist between the magnitude of the resistivity of an oil bed and its oil potential—the higher the resistivity, the greater the production. However, the rule was somewhat vague. Sands saturated with oil did not have an infinite *true* resistivity but a finite one, sometimes not very high, indeed. Was it possible that some interstitial saline water was present in the sand and that such water accounted for its conductivity? An observation of this nature had already been made by Lindtrop and Nicolaeff in their study of the oil and water content of oil sands at Grosny, U.S.S.R.[83] The conclusion of the authors was that for an oil sand with 25 percent porosity, the percentage of connate water was in the order of 5 percent to 7 percent. Further evidence of the fact was offered by Lewis and Horner, and Pyle and Jones.[84]

If the foregoing is generally true, an oil sand is conductive electrically. The conductivity is proportional to the percentage of water present, and to the salinity of this water. In other words, there is a relationship between the oil saturation, the concentration of the saline water, and the true resistivity of the sand. This point was demonstrated satisfactorily by experiments conducted in 1935 by the Petroleum Institute of Azerbaidjan (AZNI) at Baku, U.S.S.R.[85] They are reported thoroughly by Martin, Murray, and Gillingham.[86] They consisted of saturating a sand of a given porosity with varying proportions of a mixture of oil and water of a known resistivity. "The testing instrument was a cylinder, on the ends of which were placed two electrodes. The resistivity was measured very simply by using a Wheatstone bridge." Numerous measurements were made and the relationship between oil saturation, salinity, and resistivity was established. Fig. 24 illustrates the results. It represents the variations of resistivities in terms of saturations (saturations in abscissae, resistivities in ordinates). There is, of course, a curve for each particular value of porosity studied. Curve I, for instance, corresponds to a sand of 20 percent porosity; Curve II, to a porosity of 45 percent. *If the poros-ity and the resistivity are known,* the saturation can be read on the diagram. Therefore, a method of evaluating the oil saturation of a sand had been found. There is no denying that the procedure was lengthy and expensive, but it was a step in the right direction.

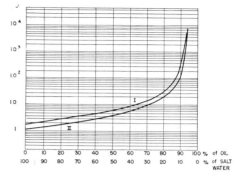

Fig. 24—Variations of Resistivities in Terms of Saturation

Beginning in 1941, G. E. Archie approached the same problem and reported on his work in two illuminating papers.[87] His first concern was to explore the question of the resistivity of the formations, when all the pores are filled with water. This is "of basic importance in the detection of oil and gas by the use of an electrical log. Unless this value is known, the added resistivity due to oil and gas in a formation cannot be determined". He established the following simple relationship:

$$R_o = F R_w \qquad (1)$$

Wherein: R_o is the resistivity of the formation when all pores are filled with a brine of resistivity R_w. He called the quantity F, the formation resistivity factor. There is a simple physical explanation of the formation factor. Let ϕ be the porosity of the formation (it is a fraction, less therefore than 1). If the ions of the brine could travel in full freedom, as they do in an electrolyte, the following relation should obtain:

$$R_o = R_w \, (1/\phi) \qquad (2)$$

But this is not the case. The movement of ions is restricted at the connections between pores, and we shall write instead:

$$R_o = R_w \, (1/\phi^m) \qquad (3)$$

m is related to the shape, size, and distribution of the void space. It is comprised between 1.3 and 2.1, and is determined by experience. Its value can also be derived from core analysis. The porosity being smaller than 1, ϕ^m is smaller than ϕ and the value of R_o in equation (3) is actually greater than the value shown in equation (2). Comparing equations (1) and (3), we have:

$$F = (1/\phi^m) \qquad (4)$$

Now if we write $\phi^m = \phi_a$, equation (3) may be written:

$$R_o = R_w \, (1/\phi_a) \qquad (5)$$

Comparing with equation (2), we see that we can call ϕ_a the apparent or electrical porosity, and F is the inverse thereof.

533

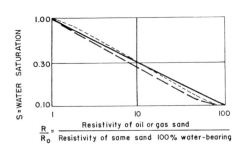

Fig. 25—Relation of S to R/R₀ According to Investigations by Jakosky, Leverett, Martin, and Wyckoff

Archie analyzed and correlated the investigations previously published by several authors—Jakosky and Hopper, Wyckoff and Botset, and Leverett.[88] He came to the conclusion that, for water saturations down to 15 percent or 20 percent, the following relationship applied:

$$S_w = (R_o/R_t)^{1/n} \text{ or } R_t = R_o S_w^{-n} \quad (6)$$

Wherein: S_w is the water saturation of the sand; R_o is its resistivity when filled 100 percent with water; and R_t is its resistivity when saturated with a percentage S_w of water (Fig. 25). For clean consolidated or unconsolidated sands, the value of n is close to 2, so that, for most practical purposes:

$$S_w = \sqrt{R_o/R_t} \quad (7)$$

Replacing R_o by FR_w, there is this additional expression of the saturation:

$$S_w = \sqrt{FR_w/R_t} \quad (8)$$

In certain instances, R_o and R_t can be deduced from the electrical log:

R_o, if there is a water sand in the vicinity of the oil sand; and if, as is quite probable, the lithologic features and the salinity of the connate water in this sand are substantially the same as in the oil bed.

R_t, if the bed is thick. A good approximation to true resistivity can be obtained from an appropriate device, if the invasion is not deep.

But in most cases, R_o and R_t are not always available with the desirable accuracy. At this juncture, the SP diagram comes to the rescue. A simple relationship exists between the value of the SP and the resistivity R_w. It is, however, a relationship which took time to be established, as the following historical discussion will show.

The SP phenomenon was discovered in the latter part of 1930, and thorough experiments about its nature were undertaken at Pechelbronn in December 1930. The conclusions reached around May 1931 were to the effect that "neither the casing nor the metallic part of the sonde seem to play an important part; the SP curve appears to be remarkably stable with respect to time, composition of the muds, etc.; it is not caused by stray currents or vertical currents; it is due to electrocapillarity" (filtration of liquid from the bore hole into the permeable formations).[89]

In September 1931, the following instructions were issued to the Schlumberger field personnel: "The first results in Russia and Venezuela are remarkable. It has been decided to run the SP surveys in all wells."[90] At that time, the SP was supposed to be the result of electrofiltration only, and given by the following expression:

$$E = a \ (R_m \ p/v) \qquad (9)$$

a being a constant depending upon the nature of the permeable zone, the filtration, and the mud cake; *p* the difference of pressure between that in the hole and that in the formation; R_m the resistivity of the liquid; and *v* the viscosity of the fluid. However, this explanation did not prove satisfactory. There were instances when no difference of pressure existed, yet the SP was large. Another cause was then added to the previous one, viz., the electrochemical effect. This effect is quite well-known in the textbooks. When a difference in ion concentrations exists between the fluids in the hole and in the formation, a difference of potential takes place. If c_1 is the concentration of dissolved salts in the fluid of the well and c_2 the same figure in the fluid of the formation, *R* the constant of perfect gases, *T* the absolute temperature, *F* the Faraday (96,600 coulombs), this liquid-junction potential, as it is called, is equal to:

$$E = [(RT/nF)] \ [(v-u)/(v+u)] \ [log \ (c_1/c_2)] \qquad (10)$$

Wherein: log is the Naperian logarithm; *n* is the valence of the dissolved salts; and *u* and *v* are the mobilities of the cations and anions. This is the Nernst equation which holds only for different concentrations of similar salts. More accurately, the concentrations should be replaced by the mean activities of the electrolytes in the two solutions:

$$E = [(RT/nF)] \ [(v-u)/v+u)] \ [log \ (a_1/a_2)] \qquad (11)$$

Wherein: a_1 and a_2 are the activities in question.

This general relationship takes a simpler and more concrete form if a certain temperature (approximately 75 F.) is specified. In such instance, and for sodium chloride solutions of low concentration, equation (10) becomes *(E in millivolts)*:

$$E = [-11.5 \ log_{10} \ (c_1 \ /c_2)] \qquad (12)$$

c_1 and c_2—the concentrations—can be replaced, as an approximation, by the respective resistivities of the fluids in the hole R_m and in the formation R_w, giving then:

$$E = [-11.5 \ log_{10} \ (R_m/R_w)] \qquad (13)$$

Laboratory experiments and field work confirmed the importance of the chemical effect. Early in 1933, many of these results were made public.[91] In April of the same year, Schlumberger operators were definitely advised that "if filtration plays a role, the chemical effect is, at least, just as important".

At this point, it was, however, apparent that the knowledge of the SP phenomenon needed further clarification. For one thing, as seen from the foregoing, a simple relationship did not obtain between the electro-filtration potentials and the permeability of the formations as measured directly on cores. As to the chemical effect, it showed a discrepancy in magnitude when experimenting in the laboratory and in drill holes. It is true that in the laboratory the experiments had been conducted on decomposed and hydrated surface clays.

The matter rested more or less stationary for quite a number of years. In 1943, Mounce and Rust analyzed the inconsistencies of the situation in a very lucid paper, pointing out the following facts:[92]

1. It had been known for quite some time that formation permeability had little or no effect upon the filtrate loss. Hence, the electrofiltration effect depends chiefly upon the nature of the mud cake.

2. This effect is probably less than 10 percent of the total SP observed.

3. What causes the other 90 percent? Certainly an electro-chemical effect, but one in which the shales play an essential role. To illustrate this point, the authors experimented on a chain of electrolytes constituted as follows: "A circular trough was divided into three sections by partitions of unglazed porcelain. These sections were then filled with three different electrolytes. Two carefully prepared non-polarizing electrodes were placed in one of the sections. It was always found that when the electrolytes differed only in concentration, the electrodes remained at the same potential. Similar results were obtained with many combinations of electrolytes. If clean sand cores were used as partitions, only small potentials were observed. But when shale was used for the partitions, quite large potentials were observed."

Mounce and Rust pointed out the similarity between the conditions of the experiment and those existing in a well when a bed of shale is in contact on one side with a porous sand containing saline connate water, and on the other side with a mud fluid of different salinity. During the same period, Tixier—then engaged in the interpretation of electrical logging in the Rocky Mountain region—came also to the conclusion that "the SP potential was mainly a chemical potential, with only a small and sometimes negligible filtration potential".[93]

It remained for Wyllie to furnish a comprehensive explanation of the electrochemical SP. In the paper which he made public in October 1948,[94] Wyllie showed that it consisted of two different effects.

1. The EMF developed at the boundary of the mud in the hole and the interstitial water in the porous formation. This effect has been discussed previously, and its value is given in equation (11). It is approximately:

$$E = [-11.5 \ log_{10} \ (R_m/R_w)]$$

2. Another EMF at the boundaries of the shale bed with the electrolytes in contact therewith. Quoting research work by Marshall and Krinbill,[95] he indicates that membranes made from certain clays "developed a potential difference between their faces, if interposed between salt solutions of different concentrations . . . The potentials so developed were very sensitive to concentrations of monovalent cations." With such cations, the EMF followed the Nernst equation and was approximately equal to:

$$E = [-59.15 \ log \ (R_m/R_w)] \tag{14}$$

Thus the value of the total chemical effect is the sum of equations (13) and (14), and is approximately:

$$E = [-70.65 \ log \ (R_m/R_w)] \tag{15}$$

More accurately, it can be written:

$$E = [-70.65 \ log \ (a_w/a_m)] \tag{16}$$

a_w and a_m being the mean activities of the interstitial water and mud, respectively, when these are considered to be sodium electrolyte solutions. With these expressions, the problem of computing the saturation is at hand. Already it has been stated that the filtration effect is not large; actually, it is generally of little moment. Therefore, equation (15) makes it possible to compute R_w. Then using equation (1), the formation factor $F = R_o/R_w$ will be computed; whereas, of course, ϕ will be given by $\sqrt[m]{1/F}$. In fact, a good value of F is often available from other sources (neighboring well, velocity logging, etc.).

Completing Wyllie's papers are the very exhaustive and clear analysis of the geometry of the SP by Doll,[96] the important contribution of Gondouin, Tixier, and Simard,[97] and the study of filtration potentials by Scala and Gondouin.[98] This latter paper seems to substantiate the fact that the part played by electrofiltration in the total SP is minor. Such filtration does not take place across the mud cake only, but across the shales as well, as suggested at first by Schenck.[99] Sometimes the foregoing relationships will not permit one to achieve a satisfactory quantitative interpretation, because some of the desired data may not be available with the desirable accuracy. Other approaches can be tried, however, utilizing other data of the electrical diagrams.[100]

As electrical logging gained acceptance, the equipment had to move toward industrial efficiency. In the early days, the various components and apparatus were of the experimental or laboratory type. The sonde was stopped at regular intervals in the hole and a reading was taken. At the end of the day, resistivities were computed and plotted on a discontinuous diagram. Such plotting became more and more tiresome and called for more time when the SP curve began to be recorded late in 1931.

A decided improvement took place in 1932, when continuous hand recording was introduced. The log became available at the well in the form of resistivity and SP diagrams traced on coordinate paper by a pencil or pen. The next progress for this part of the equipment was the introduction of photographic recording in 1936. The first recorders comprised two galvanometers, and delivered a two-curve survey only. In the following advance, several resistivity curves of different character were produced—hence the increase in the number of galvanometers, which quickly jumped to 3, 5, and finally 9, allowing the recording of more and more curves in a single trip.

The cable was gradually improved with respect to tensile strength and insulation. It initially was a rubber-covered, multi-conductor cable; it has been replaced by an armored multi-conductor. The recording truck also ceased being an all-purpose do-all platform (Fig. 26), to become gradually a streamlined laboratory. Its appearance has not changed greatly in the past 10 years; even though now—with its impressive array of costly and intricate electrical instruments, its load of 20,000 ft of armored cable—it represents a large investment.

Commercial Development of Electrical Logging

Fig. 26—Electrical-logging Truck Used in California in 1929
(Courtesy of Schlumberger Organization)

As said previously, electrical logging was first used by Schlumberger in Pechelbronn, Alsace, France, in the latter part of 1927. It was introduced in Venezuela on March 6, 1929 (Well R-216, Shell Oil Company, La Rosa Field), in U.S.S.R. (Baku) in August, and in the Dutch East Indies around the end of the same year. Several attempts took place in the United States in 1929-30 to demonstrate the process.

538

The first one was on August 17, 1929, in California (Boston Land Company, Well B, West Haven area). The test did not arouse much interest, the reasoning being that the equipment was too experimental and not of the type to give a fine performance. Two other better-organized and more exhaustive demonstrations were undertaken a few months later. One in the Oklahoma-Kansas area was initiated by R. S. Knappen of the Gypsy Oil Company (now Gulf Oil Corporation), and conducted by H. G. Doll of Schlumberger. It lasted 3 months (September 18-December 25, 1929), logging 28 wells in the Seminole Field, 3 in the Oklahoma City Field (Oklahoma), and 2 wells and 46 core holes in the region of Anthony-Kingman (Kansas). At Seminole, the Pennsylvanian oil beds were quite conspicuous; so were the hard beds of Devonian age, such as the Hunton and Viola limestones. However, the engineers and geologists were not interested in the Pennsylvanian oil beds. They were drilling for the Wilcox sands; and the Viola being an excellent marker, no other one was needed. In Kansas, the shallow stratigraphy—Permian and more recent sedimentation—was outlined very satisfactorily by the resistivity log; but the knowledge of such stratigraphy was of no interest because the oil fields were below the Permian, and there was an unconformity at the base of this member. To conclude, there seemed to be no need of the method in the Mid-Continent area for the elucidation of the immediate field problems at hand, and the test program was abandoned.

The other demonstration took place in the Gulf Coast and lasted from January 27 to August 3, 1930. It was performed for the joint account of the Gulf Oil Corporation, the Humble Oil & Refining Company, and the Shell Petroleum Corporation, under the supervision of Paul B. Leavenworth, L. P. Teas, and John C. Myers. The operators were G. Deschatre and R. Henquet. The first run was made on January 29, 1930 (Siadous #1 at Mykawa, Harris County, Texas). By June 15, 1930, 53 electrical resistivity logs had been run in 45 drill holes, the locations of which were scattered over the Gulf Coastal plain from the Alta Verde area, Brooks County, in the Rio Grande Valley, to the Whitecastle Dome near the Mississippi River. With the exception of Raccoon Bend, the number of wells in a given field never exceeded three; often it was only one. Nonetheless, attempts were made to establish stratigraphic correspondences between not-too-distant wells, in particular at Raccoon Bend. The results—even though quite plausible—were not very convincing, particularly because geological correlations were not very certain either. There is no question but that a much more exhaustive and persevering examination of the process would have been necessary either to disprove or prove the process. The test was again abandoned. Of course, the period of 1930 was not favorable, economically. The country was in the throes of a depression and decidedly not in a spending mood.

In 1932, Shell Oil Company in California (Los Angeles), on the strength of the good results achieved in Venezuela, contracted with Schlumberger for an experimental crew for a full year. The work started in the spring of 1932, and was of such quality that at the end of the year the contractor decided to stay on his own. In the Gulf Coast, the Shell organization hired an experimental crew in 1933, at the behest of T. E. Swigart. At the end of the year, the usefulness of the process was fully demonstrated.

Once the initiation period was over, the commercial development of electrical logging proceeded rapidly. At the end of 1933, there were already 32 crews in the field—2 in France or Morocco, 2 in Europe, 5 in Venezuela, 4 in the United States, 1 in the Far East, and 18 in the U.S.S.R. Since then, electrical logging has had tremendous success and spectacular development, of which the foregoing figures cannot give an idea. Including all logging systems, the number of crews at work in the free world is in the order of 760. Many service companies are offering electrical logging in the United States and abroad, among them Lane-Wells, Pan-Geo Atlas Corporation, Schlumberger, Seismograph Service Corporation, and Welex.

Of course, the Iron Curtain countries also have their activity. Several comprehensive manuals have been published by the Russians on electrical as well as nuclear logging. Frequent articles on the same subject appear in scientific and trade journals such as *Neftianoe Khosiastvo, Geophysica,* etc.

INDUCTION LOGGING

In spite of its versatility, resistivity logging will not operate satisfactorily under all conditions. For instance, in holes drilled with cable tools, there is no liquid filling the hole to establish contact between the electrode and the formations. It is true that such contact can be achieved by scratcher electrodes, but the procedure is not too practicable; and measurements are often unreliable. Another instance is that of drilling with non-conductive oil-base muds. In both cases, induction logging can be very useful. It does not require any direct contact between a sonde and the formations for the passage of the current.

The use of the induction process was first proposed in connection with surface exploration by Mason, C. Schlumberger, and Sundberg—among others—many years ago. The process has been a regular feature of shallow ore exploration for more than a quarter of a century, with a certain number of positive successes to its credit.

In 1942, during World War II, Doll and his associates were engaged in a military research project for the War Department. It consisted of building an automotive vehicle which could detect enemy mines ahead of its path and automatically come to a stop when such a mine was encountered. The assignment was successfully completed in spite of its difficulty. Thus a nucleus was formed around him of engineers specialized in the problems of induction, as applied to the ground. Doll envisioned that this know-how could be utilized in the study of conditions in an oil well, and made plans to start on this peaceful application at the earliest possible moment.

The principle of induction logging is shown in Fig. 27.[101] An alternating current of constant magnitude and frequency is fed from the oscillator to a coil T, called transmitter. This transmitter is mounted at one of the extremities of the sonde O. The alternating magnetic field resulting from this current induces eddy currents in the surrounding medium. These eddy currents follow circular paths centered on the axis of the sonde. They, themselves, create a secondary magnetic field, which in turn induces an electromotive force—a"signal"—in a second coil R, called the receiver. Since the current in the transmitter is constant, the intensity of the eddy currents is proportional to the conductivity of the ground. It follows, then, that the secondary field and the "signal" generated in the receiver are also proportional to the same conductivity (i.e., the inverse valve of the resistivity). No particular difficulty arises in using one quantity or the other.

The "signal" is amplified and rectified to direct current, then transmitted to the surface where it is registered in the form of a continuous log.

In practice, the equipment incorporates now more than two coils. As the original technique was perfected, additional coils were added for the purpose of "focusing" the measurements, i.e., minimizing the influence of the mud column or of the material above and below the sonde. Several types of such "focusing" sondes have been put into service.

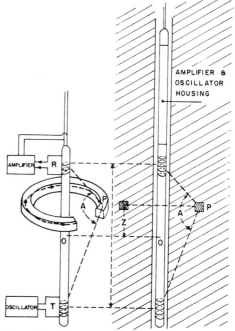

Fig. 27—Schema of Induction Logging Sonde
(After Doll, H. G.)

541

The first commercial operations with induction logging took place in 1946, in wells drilled with oil-base muds. At this stage, induction logging was viewed as a supplementary tool destined to analyze wells which did not respond satisfactorily to conventional electrical logging. However, as soon as a satisfactory focusing equipment was developed, it was quickly recognized that the system was superior to conventional electrical logging in many respects. For instance, the mud column and the adjacent formations have a comparatively small and even negligible influence on the induction curve. Unless the invasion is deep, the induction-log values correspond to the true resistivity of the formations.

In front of a given bed, the measurements show less distortion than is the case with conventional electrical-logging devices; the definition of boundaries is more accurate. Interpretations are particularly facilitated when a short normal is associated with the induction curve, inasmuch as this short spacing reflects the characteristics of the invaded zones of the beds.

From an auxiliary tool, the system has moved into the general practice of electrical logging, accounting now for more than 50 percent of the logs run in the United States. A combination in a single run of an induction log, a short normal, and an SP curve (styled "induction-electrical" log) [102] is standard practice in many areas.

Induction logging, associated with the crop of more recent logging devices (micrologging, focusing tools, velocity logging), represents an impressive expansion of logging techniques.

NUCLEAR LOGGING

Radioactivity was first discovered by H. Becquerel in 1896, when he observed that even in the absence of light, and without previous excitation, a preparation of uranium affected a photographic plate which had been wrapped in black paper and in addition covered with aluminum foil. Continuing these investigations still further, Becquerel observed another, and still more important, property of the rays emitted by uranium, i.e., their ability to render air conductive and cause the discharge of electrified bodies—*the phenomenon of ionization*. This ionization of the air means that the molecules of air are broken into positively and negatively charged fragments called ions. Nearly all present-day instruments for studying radioactive phenomena depend directly or indirectly upon this ionization for an excitation effect.

The spontaneous emission of radiations was soon found to be a property of other substances. In examining a number of uranium minerals, Pierre and Marie Curie noticed that some of them—in particular pitchblende—were more radioactive than their uranium content justified. They succeeded in 1898 in isolating two radioactive elements hitherto unknown, which they called polonium and radium. Thus was born the new branch of physics called nuclear physics, the industrial developments of which have been spectacular. Never before in such a short period have the established concepts concerning war, survival, industrial fuel, and energy for the future been so profoundly altered.

In the early 1900's, it became generally evident that practically all terrestrial materials contained measurable quantities of radioactive elements, even though in extremely minute quantities. A basic reference, replete with information, is Ambronn's *Elements of Geophysics*, translated by Margaret C. Cobb in 1928.[103] Among many other results, the tests along borings, tunnels, or galleries, are worth reporting.

"... The radiation varies considerably with the kind of formation. Such a series has been investigated by Joly along the Gothard Tunnel, by Mache and Bamberger along the Tauern Tunnel, by Poole along the Loetschberg Tunnel, by Gockel and Wolf along the Simplon Tunnel, by Fletcher along the Trans-Andes Tunnel, by Buechner in a well at Baarlo in Holland-Limburg, and by Eve and McIntosh in a well at Beachville (Ontario)."

Ambronn himself carried out radioactivity measurements on a series of samples from an oil well at Celle, Hanover, in 1921. Plotting such measurements together with the geologic section of the well, he traced, in a general sense, the first radioactivity well log ever produced. Ambronn saw also that radioactivity measurements could be used for surface exploration, and published examples of such work.

Numerous investigators have undertaken the very necessary task of measuring the radioactivity of different rocks and formations and classifying them. Such activity has been expressed generally in terms of the radium (or thorium) content of the rocks, per gram of rock. This equivalent has been used in many geological papers and is well-understood. The average radium and thorium content of rocks of the upper crust is possibly equivalent to 2.10^{-12} grams of radium per gram of rock. Many excellent papers have thoroughly reported on this subject, among them those of Westby and Scherbatskoy,[104] Bell, Clark, and Whitehead,[105] Green and Fearon,[106] and Russell.[107] Fig. 28, taken from the Russell paper, gives a graphic representation of the activity of various sedimentary rocks.

In disintegrating, a given radioactive element is transformed into another element (generally of lower atomic weight), and this transformation is accompanied by the emission of energy. For certain radioactive substances, it takes several billion years to disintegrate completely.

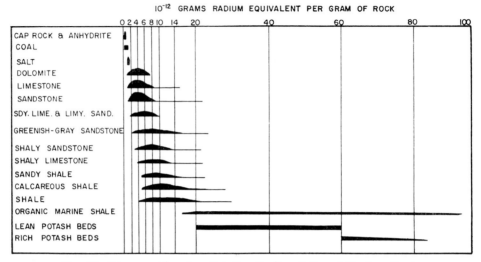

Fig. 28—Diagram Showing Relative Radioactivity of Various Rocks
(After Russell, W. L.)

For instance, the 3 important elements—uranium 238, thorium 232, and potassium 40—have, respectively, a "half life" of 4.5, 14, and 1.4 billion years. The "half life" is the time required for half of the original atoms to disintegrate. Other radioactive elements are so unstable that they exist only for a fraction of a second.

During the course of these transformations, the radioactive elements give off three different types of rays, viz., the alpha, beta, and gamma rays. Alpha rays consist of nuclei of the rare gas, helium, which are expelled at high speeds (up to about 1 percent of the speed of light); they are much less penetrating than the beta or gamma rays. A sheet of paper or a few centimeters of air will stop them. Beta rays are electrons traveling at speeds approaching the speed of light; they can traverse several millimeters of metal, and as much as 10 ft of air. Gamma rays are electromagnetic waves like radio or light waves; but their wave length is very small, in the order of 20 trillionths of an inch instead of 20 millionths of an inch for visible light. They are very much like X-rays, except that they are of shorter wave length and far more penetrating. They can go through a thickness of several inches of steel.

The principal radioactive elements belong to three different groups: the uranium series, which includes radium; the actinium series; and the thorium series. Starting from these three parent elements, the radioactive substances spontaneously disintegrate successively from one material into another, following three separate sequences. The end products are three isotopic forms of lead. In addition, some radioactivity is produced by potassium, rubidium, and samarium.

Measuring the radioactivity of the rocks at the surface constitutes, of course, a method of geophysical exploration. Two types of measurements are used for the purpose. One procedure measures the radiation emitted by the ground; the other the activity of the air pumped from the soil. An exhaustive discussion of the processes (ionometric method), with a wealth of references, will be found in Rothe's treatise on geophysical prospecting.[108] Among other results, the location of faults and identification of formations are cited. The early work of Ambronn on faults deserves special mention. Among other things, he observed a notable increase in alpha-radiation at the outcrop of a fault near Blankenburg, Germany, in 1918.[109] The process, however, found little practical use or commercial progress for many years, owing possibly to the excellence of competing procedures. Of late, however, it has experienced an extensive and successful development in the exploration for radioactive ores in this country (Colorado plateau, in particular), Canada, and many other foreign countries.

Gamma-ray Logging

By 1937-38, electrical logging had gained general acceptance by the oil industry. Its great usefulness in exploration and exploitation had been fully demonstrated. It was, therefore, but natural to think that the knowledge thereby obtained could be enlarged by the use of other processes of a similar nature. In particular, the recording of the natural radioactivity (practically represented by gamma rays) in bore holes looked interesting, since it was feasible even if the hole were lined with a steel casing—a condition under which electrical logging could not be used.

Two groups of investigators, working independently, attacked the problem of making gamma-ray logs. One of these groups comprised Lynn G. Howell and Alex Frosch of Humble Oil & Refining Company, Houston, Texas. They started their work in 1935, and had accumulated considerable experience when they reported on their work in two papers in 1939. The first one[110] shows ionization measurements made in May 1937 in the Crook No. 1 well and the Brown B-4 well in the Hastings Field; continuous surveys made with two Geiger-Mueller tubes in October 1937 in the J. D. Walton B-8, and in November 1937 in the Colby C-22 well, both in the Kermit Field in West Texas; and finally three other continuous logs made in July 1938 in the Friendswood and Thompson Fields of the Gulf Coast of Texas. These logs were made in both cased and uncased holes. Characteristic variations of radioactivity were observed which were correlated with geology as well as with the conventional electrical logs. The second paper[111] discusses a particular application of the process to cementing. By incorporating in the cement a certain quantity of radioactive material, it became possible to detect this radioactive cement behind the casing, measure its thickness, etc. The method is more flexible than a temperature survey.

The other group included W. G. Green, S. A. Scherbatskoy, R. E. Fearon, L. M. Swift, and J. Neufeld of Engineering Laboratories, Tulsa, Okla. They made their first gamma-ray log on October 29, 1938, in the Barnsdall Oil Company's Dawson No. 1 well in the Oklahoma City Field The unpublished record demonstrated clearly that it could reveal lithology. Subsequent to this work, this group—together with Socony-Vacuum—founded a new corporation, Well Surveys, Inc., for the purpose of furnishing gamma-ray logging service to tne industry. Practical demonstrations were given during the year 1939, and the results achieved were made public by Westby and Scherbatskoy early in 1940.[112] The first commercial survey was performed for Stanolind Oil and Gas Company in May 1940, at Spindletop. In April 1941, the company had four logging crews in operation. Meanwhile, one crew was also established in Trinidad. This crew eventually moved to Venezuela.

Because shales are much more radioactive than other formations, particularly clean sands and limestones, a gamma-ray log on a newly drilled well will show a clean sand or limestone to have a low radioactivity, whereas a shale bed, a shaly sand, etc. will cause a stronger reaction. In many instances, there is a great similarity between the spontaneous-potential log and the gamma-ray log—both discriminate between shale and sand sections. Gamma-ray logging is generally excellent for the purpose of bed definition, spelling out the geology and establishing correlations. In addition, it constitutes an excellent substitute for the SP curve in the case, for instance, of hard formations or of salty muds. As will be seen later, its usefulness is enhanced in combination with the neutron log. Of course, both logs can be run in a cased hole. This is not possible with conventional electrical logging.

The Neutron and Neutron Logging

While Well Surveys, Inc. was experimenting on gamma-ray logging, the idea of a companion service was advanced by Fearon in July 1938.[113] It was subsequently perfected by Pontecorvo, who described it for the first time in September 1941.[114] The process consisted of bombarding the formation along the bore hole with neutrons and measuring the intensity of the secondary gamma-ray activity generated by such bombardment.

A neutron, in the arsenal of atomic artillery, is a particle of matter bearing no electrical charge. It has a large mass, approximately that of a proton (hydrogen nucleus), and it travels at high speed. Because it is not charged electrically, like an electron or an alpha particle, it does not behave like them. A charged particle exerts electrical forces which produce ionization of atoms located along its path of travel. Part of its energy is dissipated in this process. The energy lost by the particle is equal to that taken up by ionization. On the other hand, a neutron will be affected only by very short-range forces which come into play when the neutron meets an atomic nucleus. In other words, a free neutron will travel unchecked at high speed until it hits such a nucleus. When this collision occurs, the neutron will undergo a loss of speed. The circumstances are comparable to the collision of two elastic balls. Both atom and neutron will recoil with a transfer of momentum. As a result of such collisions, the neutron will lose energy until it reaches a speed at which it is as likely to get energy in a collision as to lose it. It will have gradually become a slow neutron or a thermal neutron (i.e., a neutron with a speed of particles of its mass and temperature). When neutrons have reached such a stage, they can be readily absorbed by most materials, in particular by hydrogen, chlorine, silicon, sodium, indium, etc. This absorption or "capture" is usually accompanied by the emission of very energetic gamma rays, called "gamma rays of capture." Because hydrogen has a mass similar to that of a neutron, it is more effective than any other element in slowing down neutrons. As a result of the predominant effect of hydrogen on neutron log response, the log can be considered essentially a recording of the hydrogen content.

Neutrons, for well logging, are produced by bombarding beryllium with alpha rays emitted by a radioactive element. The beryllium and the radioactive elements (generally radium) are intimately mixed, thus providing excellent conditions for the alpha particles to spend their energy on beryllium. When the nucleus of a beryllium atom is hit by an alpha particle, both gamma rays and fast neutrons are emitted. The latter, as explained before, result finally in the emission of gamma rays of capture, the intensity of which is measured in the logging process.

The detector measuring the gamma-ray intensity will be subjected to the action of three kinds of radiations: first, the gamma rays caused by the natural radioactivity of the rocks; second, the gamma rays contributed by the radium-beryllium capsule; and third, the gamma rays resulting from the neutron bombardment. Fortunately, the latter are much more energetic than the first two, so that, for a properly designed logging instrument, the radioactivity which is measured in this instance is that resulting from the neutron bombardment.

Some experimenters are not content with this neutron—gamma-ray logging. They observe that a certain quantity of slow neutrons, scattered through the formations surrounding the bore hole, bounce back toward the hole and that the measurement of this fraction should also characterize the porosity of the material subjected to the bombardment. As a source of fast neutrons they use a capsule of beryllium-polonium, and the radiation detector is of such nature that it is affected by the neutrons only, not by the gamma rays—natural or of capture. This is the neutron-neutron logging technique which was introduced to the trade in 1950.[115]

Other experimenters also record the neutron intensity before they are slowed down to the thermal level (epithermal neutron logging).

Recently active research and testing have been carried out on gamma-ray spectral analysis and artificial neutron generation in bore holes. This field of investigation may lead to very useful developments.

William L. Russell suggested a radiation logging process which proposed to measure the density of the formations. Various adaptations of the method have been described by Campbell,[116] Baker,[117] and Caldwell and Sippel.[118] They are based on the principle that when gamma rays traverse a material, their intensity along the path decreases as an exponential function of the length of the path and of the density of the material.

The method utilizes a source of gamma ray such as radioactive cobalt (cobalt 60) or cesium (cesium 137). It has to be separated from the detector by a shielding, so that the scattered rays—passing through the mud, for instance—do not reach the detector directly. Furthermore, in order to minimize the effect of the bore-hole fluid on the readings, the source and the detector are placed on the same side of the tool and this side is pressed against the bore hole by a bow spring. Finally, the source and the detector may be collimated, or made directional, so that the path of the radiation through the rocks is more or less along a narrow beam conforming to the exponential law. The method is called density logging, and the diagram a densilog, or gamma-ray log. Its accuracy is good in smooth holes. It should prove valuable with respect to the determination of density and porosity.

Nuclear-log measuring devices are comprised of an ionization chamber, a Geiger-Mueller or a scintillation crystal detector, enclosed in a cylindrical housing. This device is lowered into the hole by means of an insulated cable, which connects it to the measuring devices located at the surface. These instruments deliver a photographic or a pen-recorded graph similar to that of the electrical log. The logs are of the type shown on Fig. 29.

During the early phase of nuclear logging, the data obtained were of a qualitative nature, i.e., no endeavor was made toward a quantitative interpretation; in fact, there was no zero line on the diagrams. Improvements appeared in the late 1940's. Zero lines were indicated on the logs and numerical scales of gamma-ray and neutron intensities were added.

If a source of radiation is required for the operations (neutron logging, density log), such source is included in the device. Sometimes great care must be taken to shield the detector from the source, so it will not capture any energy directly from the source.

A casing-collar locator is part of the equipment. Its function is to define the depth of each casing joint with respect to the formations, when a survey in a cased hole is performed.

Gamma-ray and neutron logs are excellent investigation tools which may confirm, supplement, or replace electrical logging. They can operate inside an empty hole or a cased hole, something which electrical logging cannot do. This latter feature is very useful for depth control in perforating work.

The gamma-ray curve is useful for correlations and bed definitions. In hard formations it establishes an easy differentiation between shales

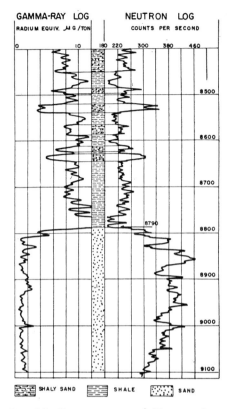

Fig. 29—Gamma-ray and Neutron Logs
(After Schlumberger, Document #8)

and other hard formations. It is not affected by the salinity of the mud, and will give a readable record in very salty muds in which the SP shows a flat diagram.

The variations observed on the neutron log are governed principally by the hydrogen content of the formations. In other words, they are an approach to the measurement of porosity—a quantity of very great interest, as we have seen in electrical logging. This is one of the most important applications of the neutron log.

VELOCITY LOGGING

In view of the remarkable results obtained with resistivity logging, it was logical to study other physical properties of the rocks to ascertain if they might be equally valuable in the investigation of open holes. One of these is their elasticity. Actually, the quantity measured is not the elasticity, but the travel time of elastic waves which are sent through the formations; but inasmuch as distances are known, the velocity of propagation of such waves can be computed. When the medium is elastic and homogeneous, there is a simple relationship between its velocity, elasticity, and density. In the case of geologic layers, however, the velocity is influenced also by such factors as the nature of the matrix, the temperature, the pressure of the medium, the nature of the saturating liquids or gases, and particularly by the porosity. These influences are far from being clarified, and comprise the subject of intense study at the present time.

Early Velocity Measurements for Seismic Exploration

The early investigations of velocities in drill holes were not concerned with well logging. They were prompted by the necessity of interpreting more accurately the results of seismic exploration. Seismologists badly needed some technique capable of furnishing them with accurate data on the speed of propagation of the seismic waves at all depths. Without such data, they were unable to compute accurately the depth of their reflecting horizons, and in many instances had reached the point of no return in their interpretation. In terms of priority, therefore, velocity layering of the underground was the original purpose of the velocity measurements. It aimed to determine the elastic characteristics of formations of rather large thicknesses.

Such time-depth measurements were successfully performed by seismic crews of the Amerada Petroleum Corporation as early as 1927[119] (Fig. 30). Many wells shot for velocity in the early 1930's are mentioned in a 1944 number of *Geophysics*.[120] Weatherby applied for a patent on the subject in 1934.[121] Schlumberger Well Surveying Corporation initiated a service of this type on a commercial basis in April 1935, furnishing the truck, the cable, and the personnel necessary for the lowering of the pick-up in the hole, while the oil or seismic company supplied the seismic equipment. The technique consisted of lowering geophones into a drill hole at different depths by means of an electric cable, and measuring the times of arrival of explosions created at the surface. (The reverse process could be used as proposed by Weatherby.) Initially, the geophones were of the velocity type, similar to those used in surface exploration. However, it was necessary to wait a considerable time before shooting in order to establish conditions of stability in the hole. In 1946, the Humble Oil & Refining Company and others started to use pressure detectors, which are less sensitive to the foregoing defects, for both deep-well and marine seismic work. This trend was followed generally by other operators.

Up to 1954, these geophone surveys were normally performed by a mixed crew, as explained previously. However, contractors who specialize in electrical logging were in a position to supply complete,

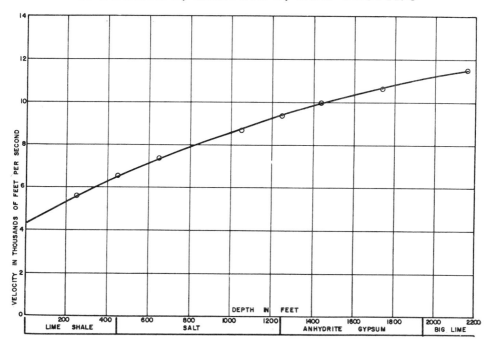

Fig. 30—Time-depth Measurements
(After Peacock, H. B.)

efficient, and economical service. For this reason, many of these service companies now perform entirely most of the conventional or abbreviated geophone surveys. As of January 1957 some 4,300 wells in the free world were listed as shot for velocity. A vast majority of these were in the United States and Canada.

During the period 1950-53, the feasibility of shooting perforator guns at various depths for measuring velocities was investigated.[122, 123] In this technique, the explosions take place in the hole while geophones are planted at the surface. This has been called the reverse method. Incidentally, the Weatherby patent mentioned proposes a reverse method. The limitation of the process is, apparently, the depth. However, this drawback can be circumvented if both the geophone (or geophones) and the perforator gun are lowered into the hole, the geophone or geophones being placed on the cable several hundred feet above the gun. This last technique, due to F. P. Kokesh and his co-workers, has been styled the "long-interval" method.[124] It has not met with extensive use thus far. It may, however, prove of prime interest in certain seismic investigations, when the measuring set-up needs to be large with respect to the diameter of the hole, and when no detailed logging is required.

551

There is no question but that, by 1940, time-depth measurements were an established necessity in seismic exploration. Cooperative well-velocity surveying groups were promoting the accumulation and dissemination of velocity data. While this development was going on, there were scientists who were thinking of a different proposition, viz., the logging of a hole by measuring the velocities of the formations traversed—exactly after the manner of an electrical log. Actually, the first descriptions of this technique bear a striking similarity to that of electrical logging. A transmitter plays the role of the power electrode, and one or several receivers replace the secondary electrode or electrodes.

Beginning in the mid-1930's, a large number of U. S. patent applications concerning this new phase were filed by numerous inventors. It is pertinent to remark that these patents are very general in character. Be that as it may, little practical development took place before the end of World War II. The fact is that the necessary electronic techniques for handling the measurements of very short time intervals were not available. They were a consequence of the tremendous developments realized during the war, and became public knowledge only at its end. It must be recognized, also, that geologists and petroleum engineers were quite happy with electrical logging then, and did not feel strongly the need of another tool performing a similar service.

Quite a number of companies engaged actively in the investigation and development of velocity logging at the end of World War II, viz., Humble Oil & Refining Company, Magnolia Petroleum Company, Shell Oil Company, The Texas Company, United Geophysical Company, and others. The first papers made public on this new field of activity are those of Mounce, Hubbard, Charske, and Kuppers (Humble),[125] Summers and Broding (Magnolia),[126] and Vogel (Shell).[127] They constitute the first detailed discussions of velocity-logging techniques. It is proper to mention that some of these concerns had devices in operating order as early as 1949.

Humble logged its first deep well in the Clay Creek Field, Washington County, Texas, on March 5, 1951. The first commercial log under Magnolia license was made in March 1954 by Seismograph Service Corporation. United Geophysical performed its first routine commercial job in Canada in July 1954. Humble licensed its instrument to Schlumberger in 1955, and the first commercial log by that company was made in July 1957. Shell also has equipment which has been in operation for many years and is licensed to well-logging companies.

The distances involved in the process are small; the interval between the transmitter and the receiver or receivers is of a few feet (3 ft or 4 ft). This means, in turn, that the travel time measured is in the order of tens of microseconds, a minute quantity indeed. Many devices are equipped with a two-receiver arrangement. The advantage of this dual feature is that it makes possible the measuring of the difference of time in the arrival of the sound pulses to the receivers. Thus, the perturbances caused by the quality of the mud or the size of the hole can be eliminated. Fig. 31 represents a schematic view of the instrument, which is equipped, in addition, with an SP electrode and a gamma-ray detector.

Velocity logging is now offered on a contracting basis by several service companies. As of September 1957, some 1,000 logs had been run. Many of them were accompanied by conventional or abbreviated geophone surveys, so as to satisfy the special requirements of the geophysicists. Fig. 32 shows a sonic log, together with a porosity log obtained by core analysis. The agreement of the results is quite remarkable.

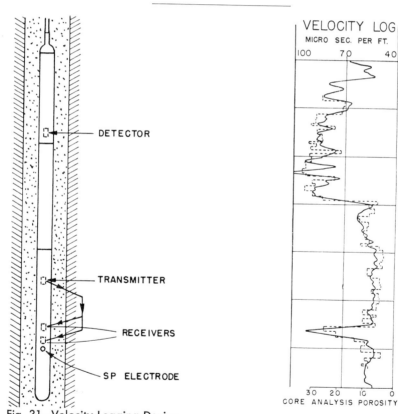

Fig. 31—Velocity Logging Device
(Combined with Gamma-ray Device)
Schema of Sonde Used for Velocity
Measurements
(After Tixier, M. P., Alger, R. P., and
Doh, C. A.)

Fig. 32—Comparison of Velocity Log (—)
with Core-analysis Porosity (---)
(After Tixier, M. P., Alger R. P., and
Doh, C. A.)

As explained, the primary purpose of velocity measurements was a more accurate interpretation of seismic data for more efficient surface exploration. It was achieved by procedures encompassing substantial thicknesses of formations. When the more difficult technique of detailed logging was adapted to usage, the seismologists discovered that they could use the high resolving power of the logs for detailed studies of the source and form of the seismic reflections.

In the field of well logging, the petroleum engineer and the geologist find that these logs constitute excellent correlation curves with a tremendous amount of detail. Recently, these logs have attracted considerable attention because they provided an excellent method of determining the porosity of the formations, and this with a good accuracy. Interest in this phase is increasing rapidly.[128] As a result, velocity logs were run at the rate of about 500 per month in the United States and Canada at the end of 1958. Velocity logging has given impetus to the study of transmission of vibrations through porous media. In this new field, it is to be expected that interesting results will ensue that will benefit petroleum engineering.

CALIPER LOGGING

The first investigations of the condition of the wall of a bore hole were made for the purpose of locating crevices. Carll[129] reports that, in the late 1870's, "the theory of rock crevices obtained great currency". It was believed at that time that all oil was produced through fissures in the formations; and consequently drillers, owners, and geologists were intensely interested in locating crevices.

"The crevice furore", says Carll, "became so prevalent that an instrument was devised and patented called 'crevice searcher'. It was lowered into a well by means of poles, like sucker rods, and designed to indicate how many, where located, and how deep were the crevices in the oil sands. The cylindrical body of the searcher was about two feet long and nearly filled the bore hole. In lowering it, whenever a crevice was reached, a little finger about an inch long (which was kept pressed out against the wall of the well by a spring) snapped out into the opening and checked the downward movement."

Later, operators discovered that the diameter of bore holes was not constant all along the depth. At certain places, formations disintegrate and cause the hole to become enlarged. Although these variations were known to exist, it was only occasionally that their presence was verified with certainty.

This was the case when Ryder[130] undertook the measurement of the diameter of a well in connection with secondary-recovery work in which he was engaged in Pennsylvania. His purpose was to achieve better control of shooting. He explains his problem as follows:

> "The purpose of a shot is to get more oil and to get it sooner. It can function solely through its ability to enlarge, in the well, the effective exposure of the pay sand face."

In order to investigate the efficiency of a shot, he made a rough survey of a hole which had been shot with $3\frac{1}{2}$-in. shells. He dropped crushed limestone into it by small quantities at a time, and successively determined the height filled thereby. He was thus able to trace a curve of the mean diameter of the well at the site of the shooting. This was done as early as 1928.

Guyod[131] reports that, in 1933, he was engaged in electrical logging in Germany. With his instrument, he determined the thickness of a coal seam which had been penetrated by a bore hole; this thickness was 165 cm. However, in the mud returns, the drillers recovered a volume of coal cuttings which corresponded to a thickness of 285 cm for the seam. Obviously, the coal—being very friable—had caused the hole to cave in. From these data, Guyod was able to determine the average enlargement of the hole in front of the coal bed.

Such ingenious but painstaking processes can be of service only in special circumstances. For an efficient and systematic survey of the diameter of bore holes, a technique was necessary—it is calipering. The *caliper* or *section gage* consists of a cylindrical housing which is lowered into the hole. Once it has reached its lowest position, several arms—which were retracted within the housing while going down—are released and come in contact with the walls of the well. These arms, by appropriate instrumentation, measure the distance between the center of the hole and its walls. Thus the mean diameter of the bore hole can be recorded for its whole length.

The first to have the idea of a caliper was Cabot with his cave finder,[132] patented in 1929. The housing of the tool was provided with two diametrically opposed links which would expand to follow the contours of the well. The instrument was equipped with electrical means of signaling. It certainly looked like a workable apparatus. There is, however, no known record of its having been successfully used.

The man to build a caliper commercially and use it in the oil fields was Myron Kinley, the oil-well fire fighter of world fame. His invention was disclosed by Beckstrom in 1935[133] and covered by two patents in 1937 and 1941.[134] The original instrument had four expanding arms. It had a length of 9 ft, all the lower 6 ft of which consisted of a 5-in. pipe in which the 4 arms were locked as the tool went down the hole. The upper part contained the recording instruments in a liquid-proof case. When released, each arm operated a ratchet which raised and lowered a recording stylus. The stylus in turn traced a curve showing the diameter of the hole. There were, therefore, four curves showing the continuous measurement of two diameters of the hole, at right angles. Later, this complicated recording was replaced by electrical methods of recording at the surface. Fig. 33 shows a type of caliper built by Kinley in the early 1940's. The first tools were equipped with a tip or rod at the lower part. This rod would release the arms of the instrument when hitting bottom. However, it would not operate reliably when the bottom was filled with soft mud. In present measurements, the arms can be released mechanically or electrically.

Kinley worked successfully in many areas (Oklahoma, New Mexico, Kansas) in the 1930's; but because he was himself engaged in other activities, he experienced considerable difficulty in managing the sales end of this business. He therefore entered into an agreement on a royalty basis with the Halliburton Oil Well Cementing Company on August 1, 1940. Later, on January 1, 1947, he sold his patents outright to the same firm. The caliper service was offered to the industry commercially by the Halliburton Oil Well Cementing Company about January 1, 1941.

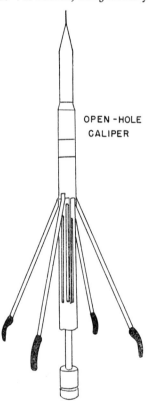

OPEN-HOLE
CALIPER

Fig. 33—Sketch of Caliper
(After Parsons, C. P.)

Working independently — and knowing little or nothing of Kinley's activity—Bossler, in the oil fields of Pennsylvania, built a caliper which—like the first edition by Kinley—was crude but very effective. Good descriptions of it were made public in 1938.[135] Illustrations showed that the data were transmitted electrically to the surface.

At first, calipering was used for controlling shooting and making it more efficient. Soon, however, it appeared that the knowledge of the "cavities and constrictions" of an oil well were of interest for other purposes. Bossler[136] pointed out that in secondary-recovery work it is important to set packers at a place where the diameter is regular, not in front of caves. Salnikov[137] reports that in 1936 The Carter Oil Company had difficulties in the South Burbank Field in Oklahoma, in trying to exploit it by pressure maintenance, because of high gas-oil ratios. They made an attempt to shut off upper gas zones by means of specially designed underset formation packers.[138] There was a need of a tool to assist in selecting the proper spots in the open hole, below the casing shoe, where packer rubbers could effectively seal off a gas. As a result, a caliper log by Kinley was run in a well preliminary to setting the packers. It worked successfully. This was in the latter part of 1936. Other uses followed, e.g., the surveying of the contours of a well after an acidizing operation, the controlling of heaving shales, the computing of the amount of cement necessary for a casing cementing. Finally, the caliper log is helpful in production testing and for a more complete interpretation of the electrical log.

Since the early 1940's, activity in calipering work has increased greatly. Caliper logs are run routinely in a considerable proportion of oil wells. The fact is that the knowledge of the diameter of the well is useful for many purposes, as already mentioned—cementing, testing, heaving-shale control, acidizing, electrical-log interpretation. Many excellent papers have been published on the subject.[139] Most electrical-logging companies perform caliper logging on a contracting basis.

TEMPERATURE SURVEYS

It has been known for a long time that the temperature of the sub-surface rocks increases with depth. Observations to this effect were made by Gesanne, in Alsatian mines, as early as 1740. The heat does not flow everywhere with the same intensity through the earth's crust. It varies from place to place according to the nature of the rocks and the geology. It is convenient to characterize this intensity in measuring the variation of depth which corresponds to a variation of temperature of 1 deg. This is the *geothermal gradient.*

Drill holes provide a convenient way to gain access to temperature data. Before making a measurement, however, it is necessary to wait until the well is in thermal equilibrium, a condition which may entail considerable waiting time.

In 1869, Lord Kelvin measured the temperature down to a depth of 347 ft in the Blythswood well, using for the purpose an electric thermometer made of copper and iron.[140] Johnston and Adams[141] studied the temperatures at different locations. After unsuccessful measurements in a well near Charleston, West Virginia, in June 1912, they experimented in a bore hole near Findlay, Ohio, in November of the same year. They went to a depth of 3,000 ft and measured regular geothermal gradients, except for an anomaly at 770 ft caused by a gas flow. In both cases they operated with maximum thermometers. In 1916, they studied the same problem in a well—Hibbs No. 4—near Mannington, West Virginia. The instrument was an electric thermometer, utilizing a coil of nickel wire, the accuracy of which was a little less than 0.01 C. The results were excellent; the geothermal gradient was about 5 C. per 1,000 ft between 1,000 and 2,500 ft. Shortly thereafter, van Orstrand[142] investigated eight deep wells in West Virginia, and one deep well near Bessie, Oklahoma. The thermometer, of the resistance type, was made of platinum. Readings were taken to a maximum depth of 3,000 ft, with results which were very satisfactory. Mention should also be made of Arctowski,[143] who built a measuring wheel and reel in 1924 with which he lowered maximum thermometers into deep wells; and of Kraskowski,[144] who developed a similar device a few years later.

Considerable material has been accumulated on the subject of geothermal gradient. It varies from one place to another. Among other things, it has been demonstrated that such gradient is influenced not only by the nature of the formations, but also by their structural features. For instance, isothermal curves traced on structures like the Salt Creek Dome, Wyoming, the Long Beach Dome, California,[145] the Humble Dome, Texas, and a fault in the Powell oil field, Texas,[146] are in very good accordance with the geological contour curves outlining these structures. A paper by Heald is of particular interest because of its generality.[146a] Thus, geothermal prospecting appears as a basic method of geophysical exploration; it has been so recognized and recommended. It has never been used extensively, because of the excellent commercial success achieved by other methods (gravimetry, seismology, magnetometry, electricity). The fact is that thermal prospecting is slow and painstaking. The parameter sought is the true temperature, i.e., the temperature which exists at the point of observation if the earth has not been disturbed. Conditions of equilibrium are paramount in such investigations, and they necessitate time.

As said previously, the conditions in a drill hole do not correspond to an equilibrium of temperatures. The earth has been penetrated by a drilling tool; a large tonnage of mud or water has been circulated in the hole. At places this mud or water has invaded the formations; at others the reverse may have taken place, and fluids from the porous strata have been discharged into the well. Abnormal temperature conditions have been created; and equilibrium will be reached only after quite a long period of time (transitional period). Nonetheless, spot measurement of temperatures—particularly bottom-hole temperatures— even though they may differ from the true temperatures, are routine practice. They furnish information which is of value in connection with the operations in the hole, particularly perforating. The Amerada Petroleum Corporation initiated subsurface measurements of temperature in 1931, in connection with the recording equipment of their bottom-hole pressure gage. Other companies did the same thing. Coming back to the unstable conditions of temperature in the hole, they may be exploited to good advantage in studying the thermal evolution which takes place during the transitional period, until equilibrium is reached. The procedure is, generally, as follows.

First, the well is conditioned. Mud or water is circulated for an hour or more, so that the temperature will be fairly uniform throughout. In the upper part of the hole, the temperature of the fluid will be greater than that of the rocks; at the bottom the converse situation will prevail, while at some intermediate depth the fluid and rocks will be in thermal equlibrium. The drill pipe is then pulled out, and a first temperature run is made. This temperature curve should be very uniform (Fig. 34), roughly in the shape of a straight line (Curve 1), with little difference from surface to bottom—a proof that the conditioning is satisfactory. After this, the hole is left idle for a few hours,

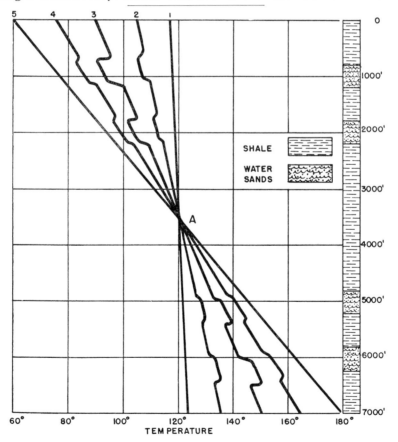

Fig. 34—Variations of Temperature in a Bore Hole, after Circulation Has Ceased
(After Leonardon, E. G.)

during which the mud temperature at each level gradually tends to adjust itself to the temperature of the rocks surrounding it (Curves 2, 3, 4). Should this period of idleness be long, the adjustment would be total (Curve 5) and the true temperature of the earth would prevail at all depths. During the transitional period, the change in the difference of temperature at each level proceeds at a pace which depends upon the heat conductivity of the surrounding rock. For instance, sands usually have decidedly greater heat conductivity than shale. These changes depend also upon the volume of the mud, i.e., the presence or absence of caving along the hole. Be that as it may, the pace of temperature exchanges varies with depth, and the temperature logs taken during the transitional period yield valuable information.

This type of temperature survey was initiated by the Schlumberger organization in Pechelbronn, Alsace, in 1932. They introduced the service in February and March 1935, respectively, in California and the Mid-Continent. Temperature surveys are now a regular part of the services furnished by many logging contractors.

The applications of temperature logs are covered by many excellent papers.[147] A brief outline of these applications follows.

1. *Cementation Control.* Cement, while setting, generates a considerable quantity of heat. A temperature survey will locate the top of the cement behind the casing; it will also detect channeling if such has occurred, etc. Amerada and Carter established the policy of using temperature surveys to determine the height of the cement behind the oil string in 1935-36.

2. *Location of Water Flows, Lost Circulation.* In case of lost circulation, mud or water will be fed to the well. In case of a water flow, water will be taken out from the well—the water level will be depressed. A break in the temperature curve will be noticeable at the place where fluid is flowing out or in.

3. *Locating Gas-producing Horizons.* While gas is produced, a strong cooling effect takes place because of its expansion. A temperature log will locate the point of entry with precision. Such effect takes place also—to a lesser degree—when an oil sand is in production, as a result of the expansion of the gas dissolved in the oil.

4. *Correlations.* Even though this phase is not too important, it is worth mentioning. The same formations act in the same manner in neighboring wells; the logs have similar silhouettes, which make correlating possible.

In the same well, the sections where caving is pronounced will have much in common with the caliper log. Very useful correspondence may be established also between temperature and the electrical logs. This can be used, in particular, for depth control in perforating work.

TESTING FOR FLUID SAMPLES

The economic purpose of drilling oil wells is to produce oil or gas. From the early days of the industry, it has been recognized that the testing of the contents of the porous strata was an essential function of drilling. The various components of the present testing tools have been developed over a considerable period of time. For instance, early packers in the form of seed bags and other substances, which expanded when wet, were known to be used when drilling and production were confined to brine that was produced for the manufacture of salt.[148] In the year 1867, Patent No. 68,350, entitled "Improvement in Apparatus for Testing Deep Wells,"[149] was granted to Burr and Wakelee by the U.S. Patent Office. That patent disclosed a straddle packer with a bypass which was designed to release gas pressure from below the bottom packer to prevent gas blowing the unit from the well. That device had no retaining valve. It was a significant step in the development of testing packers.

In 1880, Stewart invented a packer[150] consisting of a single rubber cylinder mounted on the tubing. This cylinder could be expanded by the action of a mobile conical wedge mounted also on the tubing. In the position of expansion of the packer, the lower part of the well could be tested for fluids. The interesting feature of the system was that apertures were provided in the tubing establishing connection between the inside and outside of it. These apertures were closed by the wedge when the packer was expanded and the well below was being tested for fluids, but they were open when the packer did not operate. Thus, the system was equipped with a sort of *equalizing valve*.

In 1882, Franklin[151] invented a "device for controlling and regulating the flow of oil wells". This tester could be opened or closed by rotating the tubing. The tool, which could be run above a packer, was quite operable. In between 1867 and 1882, the straight-hole rubber packer was invented and was offered for sale by oil-tool companies in their published catalogs. Such packers were also mentioned in the bulletins of the Pennsylvania Geological Survey for the same period. This development of packers and testers went on until the first commercial testing tools were introduced, in about 1926.

At that time, the Johnston brothers were working in the area of El Dorado, Arkansas. Frequent tests were necessary, owing to the irregular nature of the formations and their thinness. There was no way to accomplish this without setting casing. The cost of such testing was, therefore, very great. After a number of improvisations, E. C. and M. O. Johnston conceived the idea of a spring-controlled *retaining valve*, which would be run above a packer of some sort. They finally built a packer, conical in form, which would be lowered at the end of the pipe and set on a shoulder at the bottom of the hole (Fig. 35).[152] The material used for the packer was cut from discarded belting; the reason for selecting such used belting was that it would rupture more easily when pulling the tool out. Also it was plentiful and easily accessible in the oil fields. Other parts of the tool were a heavy spring secured from a railroad box car and a poppet valve. The idea was to run the drill pipe into the hole, with the valve closed on the bottom of the pipe to prevent any drilling fluid from entering the pipe, and set the packer on the shoulder in the hole to hold the column of drilling fluid away from the formation to be tested. Then, by movement of the pipe, the pipe would open and thereby expose the formation below the packer to atmospheric pressure. This would permit the formation fluid from below the packer to flow into the drill pipe without any back pressure due to the drilling fluid. The valve was prevented from opening, while going into the hole, by metal straps fastened to the outside of the housing so that the spring could not compress. When on seat, however, the metal straps were sheared by the weight of the pipe and the valve opened. When the tester was coming out of the hole, the valve would close under the action of the expanding spring, and the fluid which had entered the pipe would remain there, hence the name *retaining valve*.

The device was satisfactory and successful. However, it did not permit much spudding of the equipment to set the packer on the seat, or to pass crooked sections of the hole, and crooked holes were then frequent. The inventors recognized the necessity of equipping the device with a valve that would not allow the drill pipe to take in fluid while going down into the hole; in other words, with a valve that would not be operated by the movement of the pipe. This was the reason for the *trip valve* which could be opened only by a blow from above, on a plunger located at the bottom of the pipe. In practice, an iron bar was dropped down the drill pipe and struck the plunger of the valve. This valve was put into operation between 1926 and 1928, and was run on top of the retaining valve which now had the metal straps removed and was held shut only by the heavy spring.

Testing was initially confined to formation testing in open hole, and generally on a shoulder, for quite a long period of time. That work

Fig. 35—Early Johnston Testing Tool, 1927
(Courtesy of Johnston Testers, Inc.)

was performed with the cone packer, to which a short perforated pipe was attached below. The reason for this procedure was that the use of the straight-hole rubber packer, which required an anchor or support all the way to bottom, was not safe. The condition of the mud was such that settling sand would usually stick any long anchor. That condition was changed by the progress of mud engineering, years later, and the steady increase in knowledge obtained by continued drilling under careful supervision. With that improved condition, the cone packer to all intents disappeared and the straight-hole packer became the accepted method. In this respect, there is no question but that improvement of the quality of the rubber was a decisive factor in the success of the straight-hole packer. In the early days, the rubber companies did not know how to make the type of rubber needed to stand the pressures encountered in the hole. This problem was successfully solved, thanks to the cooperation of the rubber manufacturers. However, with the very great depths reached by the drill nowadays, new difficulties are cropping up and experimenting is again in order.

With each test, there came to notice some additional improvement which seemed necessary. One thing that became evident at a rather early date was the need for some method of *equalizing* the pressure above and below the packer after a test. It was realized that the pressure below the packer was that of the formation fluid, whereas the pressure above the packer was that of the weight of the whole column of drilling fluid which might be many times greater than the formation pressure. To pull the packer loose from the seat, it was necessary to lift the entire column of fluid resting above it, or have some way of letting the upper column have access to the space below before trying to pull the packer off the seat. M. O. Johnston reports several instances when a 5-in. drill pipe collapsed under the strain, even though sometimes not very much fluid had accumulated above the packer. As the depth of testing increased, the problem became more acute. This difficulty was responsible for the development of the *equalizing valve*, which was put into use in 1931.[153] The initial work took place in California, where holes were deeper than in other districts. The first successful test was made in the North Belridge Field in the San Joaquin Valley, California, in 1931. This valve was an immediate success. Actually it is still in use, even though in a slightly modified form.

Naturally, all drill-stem tests are not positive. They sometimes will yield no oil or gas or water. In such instance, a doubt arises as to whether the valve functioned correctly. In the early 1930's it was realized that such a failure of performance might result, among other causes, from the conditions in a crooked hole. Holes were crooked then, and there was no way to determine the extent of their crookedness. Therefore, the problem was to make sure that a negative result was really negative. With this in view, Luther Johnston bought a pressure recorder from the Standard Oil Company and attached it to the tail pipe below the packer. His purpose was to record the change of pressure in the space below the packer, caused by the opening of the valve. Two runs were made, one at White Castle, Louisiana, and one at Cameron Meadows, Louisiana, in late 1933 or early 1934. These two runs were gratifying— so gratifying, in fact, that this feature rapidly became a regular procedure in testing. Pressure-chart recorders now show every successive change of pressure taking place below the packer (Fig. 36). The method has assumed such importance that two, and sometimes three, recorders are run as a security factor.

The testing of water shutoffs is an important operation. This was particularly so in California where it was an obligation made compulsory by the State Mining Bureau. Prior to 1931, such testing was done by bailing or swabbing the fluid down and letting it stand for 12 hours. Then the level of the fluid would be located by running a bailer. If the rise amounted to more than $1\frac{1}{2}$ bbl in 24 hours, the test had to be done over. The operation was time-consuming and costly. One could well visualize the use of a packer which would operate satisfactorily inside the casing. The clearance of such packers is small (3/16 in. to 3/8 in.) and not sufficient to allow it to be forced down through the mud without some sort of bypass. M. O. Johnston built such a packer in 1931. It was provided with slips strong enough to support the weight of the pipe plus the column of mud resting on the top of the packer while the test was made. The first test was performed on December 31, 1931. The process proved successful and was accepted by the state organizations, and the first test approved by the State of California was run in March 1932. The new procedure required from 3 to 8 hours and represented great saving in rig time. It is still in vogue, even though the cement plug is not drilled out to 5 ft below the shoe any more—perforations are used instead.

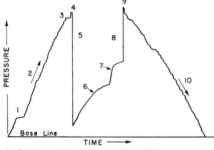

1. PUTTING WATER CUSHION IN DRILL PIPE
2. RUNNING IN HOLE
3. HYDROSTATIC PRESSURE (WEIGHT OF MUD COLUMN)
4. SQUEEZE CREATED BY SETTING PACKER
5. OPENED TESTER, RELEASING PRESSURE BELOW PACKER
6. FLOW PERIOD, TEST ZONE PRODUCING INTO DRILL PIPE
7. SHUT IN PRESSURE, TESTER CLOSED IMMEDIATELY ABOVE PACKER
8. EQUALIZING HYDROSTATIC PRESSURE BELOW PACKER
9. PULLED PACKER LOOSE
10. PULLING OUT OF HOLE

Fig. 36—Diagram Illustrating the Series of Operations Performed in Testing a Well (Operations are Numbered 1 through 10) (After Kirkpatrick, C. V.)

During the foregoing developments, many operators felt that the shock of opening a testing tool too suddenly was detrimental to the walls of the well. This led the testing specialists to open the tool against a choke. Furthermore, as wells were getting deeper and deeper, the possibility became increasingly serious that an empty string might collapse. This brought about the practice of running a certain amount of water or mud in the pipe so as to prevent such mishap. Some operators have set a maximum figure of 6,000 ft for the length of the dry pipe. To summarize, this meant that the test must commence through a choke, against a fluid cushion (or water blanket, as it is also called), and it is desirable that the flow of the choke may be regulated. This resulted in the development of the *adjustable flow bean* in which several small openings can be opened or closed by a rotation of the pipe. This type of choke was accepted in the 1930's, and is still used in an improved form.

Twenty years ago, petroleum engineers were satisfied with the measurements of flow pressures only. As time went on, however, some of them—specialized in reservoir studies—began to insist on more accurate depth-pressure records, not only of flow pressures but also of shut-in pressure at the end of the test. To achieve this, it was necessary to let the well stand for a pressure buildup. This could be done easily as far as the retaining valve was concerned. It could be kept closed but it proved difficult to do that without opening the equalizing valve. The answer was to put a lock on the latter valve, so that it would remain closed until the tool was pulled up and the retaining valve closed. Although that helped, there were still cases when the bypass valve in the casing was opened when the retaining valve was closed. This resulted in the development of a shut-in pressure tool which could be operated without picking up the device at all.

For years the test had been allowed to proceed on the derrick floor, without any type of flow head on top of the drill pipe. Just a wet rag was draped over it, which would puff up when the flow headed and drop back if it declined. If the rag indicated that the well was going to flow and if the owner wanted to let it flow, then the fires were extinguished. It was not uncommon, then, to close the valve, put on the Christmas tree and lead lines, and let the well flow into the pits and tanks. All of this certainly afforded little protection against fire, particularly when spark-plug engines were introduced at the rig. The *swivel flow head* was developed to direct the flow away from the derrick. However, it did leave the platform in the same condition when pulling out the hole and breaking off stands of pipe full of oil and gas. The matter was corrected with the *back circulating tool* which was introduced in the 1940's. Thus, oil and gas can be pumped out of the pipe under control, leaving the drill pipe full of mud or water. A good deal of mud is thereby saved.

For the purpose of bringing a well in gently, a hydraulic test tool has been invented. It combines in a single device the operations of the retaining valve, the equalizing valve, trip valve, adjustable bean, and shut-in tool. Of course, for the optimum success of the testing operations, the exact knowledge of the diameter of the hole is essential. This makes the caliper part and parcel of the equipment. Setting a packer should not be attempted in zones where there are irregularities and cave-ins. A packer can expand only so far, and if it does not press against the walls with sufficient pressure, it will not do its job.

It is now more than 15 years since testing reached the status of a useful and accepted practice. In 1958, the number of operations in North America was of the order of 30,000. New problems are, however, cropping up as a result of the constant progress of petroleum engineering and also of the increasing depths which the drill is now reaching. At 20,000 ft or more, there is a need for a very high-pressure packer. Also the equipment should be able to stand temperatures of 300 to 400 F. There is every expectation that these new problems will be solved as they present themselves.

In another chapter of this history, Reistle stresses the importance of the examination of core samples in the following terms, which we deem worth quoting: "Most of the properties of oil-bearing formations which are pertinent to oil production . . . can be determined by the analysis of core samples of reservoir rocks." It would be difficult to state in clearer terms how essential it is to obtain a true representation of the conditions at depth. The drawback to this core analysis is that the samples are costly and difficult to secure; they are soiled or invaded by the mud, and they are not brought back in the conditions of pressure, temperature, etc., which prevailed at depth. It is for these very reasons, as this chapter illustrates, that so many indirect approaches are being made to augment the knowledge of the formations reached by the drill.

There have been direct approaches, however, and a very ingenious and attractive one is that of the pressure core barrel. Two tools of this type were developed in the late 1930's—the Carter pressure core barrel[12] and the Bureau of Mines-American Petroleum Institute core barrel.[13] These two tools can cut a core of the producing formation and seal this core in an inner core barrel, while still at the bottom of the hole. Thus, the sample can be brought to the surface under the conditions *in situ* and be studied in the laboratory. There is no question but that this procedure would have met with great success, had it not been for the fact that other systems of information were already in existence at the time. The limitations in acceptance resulted from economic factors.

In 1938, M. Schlumberger offered another way of sealing the material extracted from the formations.[154] He proposed to add a front valve to the open cup of the side-wall coring bullet so that the sample, when brought to the surface, would be at the pressure existing at the site of the shooting.

A tool of this character, a sucking bullet, was built. It performed successfully in the Po Valley, Italy, during the year 1953, and in this country shortly thereafter (March 3, 1954, in the L. W. Phillips A. T. Walton #1, in the Carthage Field, Panola County, Texas). However, no effort was made to introduce this instrument commercially to the oil operators. The reason is that considerable research and experimental work was also carried out by the Schlumberger organization along another line, during the same period. It resulted in the building of two tools—a fluid sampler and a formation tester.[155]

The fluid sampler (Fig. 37) operates in a manner similar to that of the sample taker. It fires a bullet which is connected with a flexible metal tube to a 330-cc reservoir. It does not take a sample of the formation, but a sample of the fluid only. It is used in open holes. The first field test took place in the Blue Ridge Field, Fort Bend County, Texas, on June 14, 1953 (well Earl T. Mackey, Bassett-Blakely B-8).

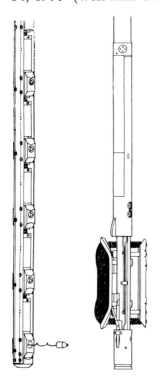

The formation tester is shown in Fig. 38. The initial version was proposed by Chambers.[156] Several years of development by Chambers and Schlumberger Well Surveying Corporation took place before a successful tool could be manufactured. The instrument is equipped with a rubber pad and a back-up shoe. When these two parts are expanded, they position the tool securely in the hole at the depth required. Then a shaped charge is fired through the pad into the wall of the well. The formation fluids flow through this perforation and connecting tubing into a container housed inside the tool (approximate capacity 1, 2.75, or 5.5 gal.). When the container is filled, a valve thereon is closed, sealing the fluid sample at the rock pressure. The pad and back-up shoe are then retracted, but the

Fig. 37 (far left)—Side-wall Fluid Sampler
(Courtesy of Schlumberger Organization)

Fig. 38 (near left)—Side-wall Formation Tester
(Courtesy of Schlumberger Organization)

packer frequently remains fixed to the wall of the hole by the excess of hydrostatic pressure over formation pressure. In order that it may be disengaged, two shots are fired which open the face of the packer to the mud pressure. The tool is then brought to the surface, where it can be examined. The information obtained is, on the whole, both as correct and specific as that resulting from drill-stem testing, if not better.

All the steps of the testing operations with these two instruments are observed and registered at the surface in a manner similar to the procedure used in conventional testing.

CONCLUDING REMARKS

Drilling and producing oil wells is difficult and costly. One reason for this is that the true conditions inside the bore hole are poorly known, as a rule, at all depths—hence a considerable element of trial and error affects the venture. Any approach which may improve this situation, extract more data from the well formations, will be an economic progress. Every scrap of information, however small, helps. To attain it is the function of logging, sampling, and testing. For this purpose, numerous processes and methods, some of them related to very modern physics, have been resorted to. An array of tools has been introduced in the well for running measurements and performing operations. Research being constantly pursued and new ideas proposed every day, this phase is in a state of flux. Although the achievements of the past have been surprisingly rewarding, there is no reason to suppose that the future will be static. Quite the contrary, one should expect that better tools and new techniques will be developed which will advance further the efficiency of petroleum engineering.

The purpose of drilling is to reach the formations containing hydrocarbons and to exploit them. A most important goal is to know the conditions which prevail in these beds—porosity, saturation, rock pressure, temperature, etc.—because these data will allow one to compute the true conditions of the reservoir. The goal has been attained to a considerable degree.

Logging, sampling, and testing were practically non-existent 30 years ago. Their development since 1930 has been spectacular. The assets of the service companies engaged in such work were practically nil then. At present they represent a sum in the order of a quarter billion dollars at least, a non-negligible percentage of the assets of the whole petroleum industry.

ACKNOWLEDGMENTS

The author could not have written this chapter, which embraces many diversified and specialized techniques, without the good will and generous cooperation of many organizations and individuals. He wishes to gratefully acknowledge this very helpful assistance. The list which follows gives the names of companies and persons to whom he is especially indebted; it should be understood that said list is by no means limitative.

Amerada Petroleum Corporation: Faust, L. Y. and Weatherby, B. B.

Baker Oil Tools, Inc: Glover, R. C; Hilton, Paul E; and Sutter, T.

Bank of the Southwest: Vance, Harold

Baroid Division, National Lead Company: Choate, Lee R; Gray, George R; Pixler, B. Otto; and Wilson, R. W.

Christensen Diamond Products Company: Christensen, Frank L.

Core Laboratories, Inc: Koepf, E. H.

DeGolyer & MacNaughton: MacNaughton, Lewis W.

Drilling & Service Company: Deely, C. and Short, L. W.

Electrochemical Laboratories: Fearon, Robert E.

Geolograph Company: Nichols, P. B.

Gulf Oil Corporation: Hanna, Marcus A.

Gulf Research & Development Company: Wyckoff, R. D. and Wyllie, M. R. J.

Halliburton Oil Well Cementing Company: Greer, Walton J.

Hamilton Well Log Consultants: Hamilton, R. G.

Hayward-Wolff Research Corporation: Hayward, J. T.

Humble Oil & Refining Company: Howell, Lynn G; Mounce, W. D; and Rust, W. M., Jr.

Johnston Testers, Inc: Bettis, W. F. and Johnston, M. O.

Joy Manufacturing Company: Fitchie, J. F. and Martin, J. B.

M. M. Kinley Company: Kinley, Myron M.

E. J. Longyear Company: Longyear, R. D.

Martin-Decker Corporation: Decker, E. L. and Knowlton, J. W.

Mineral Industries Library, Pennsylvania State College

Mobil Oil Company: Alexander, C. I; Carter, D. V; and Cortes, Henry C.

Monarch Logging Company, Inc.: Rochon, R. W.

Pan-Geo Atlas Corporation: Castel, J. H. and Charrin, P.

Schlumberger Well Surveying Corporation, and Schlumberger Limited: Alger, R. P; Allegret, A. M; Biggs, W. P; Griswold, G. A; Kokesh, F. P; Martin, M; Rieke, R. R; Sherman, W. R; Tixier, M. P; Watson, M. C; and Wallick, E. W.

Shell Development Company: Smith, Noyes D., Jr., and Vogel, C. B.

Shell Oil Company: Archie, G. E. and Lister, J. B.

Societe de Prospection Electrique: Delacour, J.

Southern Methodist University

Standard Oil Co. of California: Walstrom, John E.

Standard Oil Co. (New Jersey): Salnikov, I. S.

The Texas Company: Herzog, Gerhard

Tidewater Oil Company: Armstrong, Lloyd, and Roth, J. E.

Union Oil Co. of California: Stuckey, Charles W.
United Geophysical Corporation: Peterson, R. A.
Warren Automatic Tool Company: Taylor, J. W.
Welex, Inc.: Walker, Terry
Well Instrument Development Company: Guyod, Hubert
Well Surveys, Inc.: Swift, Gilbert
Applin, Mrs. E. R.
Banning, Thomas A., Jr.
Bentz, A.
Bossler, Robert B.
Brantly, J. Edward
Ellisor, Miss Alva C.
Flood, H. Lee
Jakosky, J. J.
Sawdon, Wallace A.
Schell, F. A.
Shepherd, G. F.

Finally, the author wishes to express his warm appreciation and thanks to D. V. Carter, L. E. Elkins, E. L. Estabrook, C. E. Reistle, Jr., W. H. Strang, Harold Vance, C. A. Warner, and others on the Editorial Board, for their suggestions and corrections.

REFERENCES

[1]Rubel, A. C: Personal communication. Tar Creek No. 1 was drilled in 1887-88 on the Sespe oil claim in Ventura County, California.

[2]Carll, John F: *The Geology of the Oil Regions of Warren, Venango, Clarion and Butler Counties, Pennsylvania*, Second Geological Survey of Pennsylvania, 1875-79, **III** (1880).

[3]*Ibid:* 165.

[4]*Ibid:* 116.

[5]*Ibid:* 211

[6]Harris, G. D: Oil and Gas in Louisiana Sections of Chicago Jennings No. 2 and No. 8, 62, *U.S.G.S. Bull. 429* (1910).

[7]Udden, J. A: Some Deep Borings in Illinois, *Ill. State Geological Survey Bull. No. 24,* 13 (1914).

[8]*Ibid:* 18.

[8a]Fettke, Charles R: Core Studies of the Bradford Sand from the Bradford Field, Pennsylvania, *Petroleum Development and Technology in 1928,* 221, American Institute of Mining and Metallurgical Engineers (Incorporated), New York, 1929.
Composite Catalog, 186, Gulf Publishing Co., Houston, Texas, 1929.

[8b]Uren, L. C: *Petroleum Production Engineering—Development,* 166, McGraw-Hill Book Company, Inc., New York, 1956, 4th Ed.
Composite Catalog, **1,** 608, Gulf Publishing Co., Houston, Texas, 1960-61, 24th Ed.

[9]Johnson, Roswell H. and Huntley, L. G: *Principles of Oil and Gas Production,* 115 (1916).

[10]Collom, R. E: Prospecting and Testing for Oil and Gas, *U. S. Bur. Mines Bull. 201,* 52 (1922).

[11]*Oil Gas J.,* 155, Jan. 27 (1958).

[12]Sewell, Ben W: The Carter Pressure Core Barrel, *API Drilling and Production Practice,* 69 (1939).

[13]Taliaferro, D. B. and Heithecker, R. E: Bureau of Mines—American Petroleum Institute Pressure Core Barrel, *API Drilling and Production Practice*, 53 (1939).

[14]Leschot, Rodolphe: Tool for Boring Rocks, U. S. Patent No. 39,235, July 14, 1863.

[15]*Derrick and Drill*, or an insight into the discovery, development, and present conditions and future prospects of petroleum, by the author of *Ten Acres Enough* (Morris, Edmund), p. 127-8, James Miller, New York, N. Y., 1865. Personal contribution of E. De Golyer.

[16]Coxe, Eckley B: A New Method of Shaft Sinking, *Trans. Am. Inst. Mining Met. Engrs.* **1-2**, 261 (1871-74).

[17]Edson, F. A: Drilling Oil Wells with the Diamond Drill, *Am. Assoc. Petroleum Geologists Bull.*, **5 [3]** 386, May-June (1921).

[18]Edson, F. A: Diamond Drilling for Production, *Am. Assoc. Petroleum Geologists Bull.*, **6 [2]** 91 (1922).

[19]Longyear, R. D: The Diamond Drill in Oil Exploration, *Am. Assoc. Petroleum Geologists Bull.*, **6 [2]** 98 (1922).

[20]Newton, William C. and Philippi, Paul M: Diamond Core Drilling in the Pennsylvania Oil Fields, *Oil Gas J.*, Jan. 19 (1939).

[21]Christensen, Carl J: Diamond Coring in the Rangely Field, Colorado, *Trans. Am. Inst. Mining Met. Engrs.* (*Petroleum Development and Technology*) **174**, 206 (1948).

[22]*Loc. cit:* Udden, J. A., ref. 7, 18.

[23]Dumble, E. T. and Harris, G. D: The Galveston Deep Well, *Am. J. Sci.*, 46 (1893).

[24]Harris, G. D: Preliminary Report on the Organic Remains Obtained from the Deep Well at Galveston, Together with Conclusions Respecting the Age of Various Formations Penetrated, *Texas Geological Survey Annual Report No. 4* (1893).

[25]Harris, G. D: Oil and Gas in Louisiana, *U.S.G.S. Bull. No. 429* (1910).

[26]Blatchley, Raymond S: The Oil Fields of Crawford and Lawrence Counties, Illinois, *Ill. State Geological Survey Bull. 22* (1913).

[27]*Loc. cit:* Udden, J. A., ref. 7, 13 et seq.

[28]Stephenson, L. W: A Deep Well at Charleston, South Carolina, *U.S.G.S. Professional Paper 90-H* (1914).

[29]Ellisor, Miss Alva C: *Rockhounds of Houston*, an informal history of the Houston Geological Society, Houston Geological Society (1947).

[30]Schuchert, Charles: The Value of Microfossils in Petroleum Exploration, *Am. Assoc. Petroleum Geologists Bull.*, **8 [5]** (1924).

[31]Ellisor, Miss Alva C; Kniker, Miss Hedwig T; and Applin, Mrs. Paul L: Subsurface Stratigraphy of the Coastal Plain of Texas and Louisiana, presented at a meeting of the American Association of Petroleum Geologists, Houston, March 1924.

[32]Sorby, H. C: On the Microscopical Structure of the Calcareous Grits of the Yorkshire Coast, *Quarterly J. of the Geological Soc. of London*, **VII** (1851).

[33]Cayeux, L: *Introduction à l'étude pétrographique des roches sédimentaires, Text et Atlas*, Paris, 1916.

[34]Milner, Henry B: The Study and Correlation of Sediments by Petrographic Methods, *Mining Magazine*, Feb. (1923).

[35]Reviews and New Publications, *Am. Assoc. Petroleum Geologists Bull.*, **8 [1]** 97, Jan.-Feb. (1924).

[36]Tickell, F. G: The Correlative Value of the Heavy Minerals, *Am. Assoc. Petroleum Geologists Bull.*, **8 [2]** 158 (1924).

[37]Reed, R. D: Some Methods for Heavy-Minerals Investigations, *Econ. Geology*, **19 [4]** June-July (1924).

[38]Reed, R. D: Role of Heavy Minerals in the Coalinga Tertiary Formations, *Econ. Geology*, **19 [8]** Dec. (1924).

571

[39]Edson, Fanny Carter: Criteria for the Recognition of Heavy Minerals Occurring in the Mid-Continent Fields, *Oklahoma Geological Survey Bull. 31* (1925).

[40]*Loc. cit:* Reed, R. D., ref. 38, 748.

[41]Reed, R. D. and Bailey, J. P: Subsurface Correlations by Means of Heavy Minerals, *Am. Assoc. Petroleum Geologists Bull.*, **11** [**4**] 359 (1927).

[42]Cogen, W. M: Heavy Mineral Zones of Louisiana and Texas Gulf Coast Sediments, *Am. Assoc. Petroleum Geologists Bull.*, **24** [**12**] 2069 (1940).

[43]Cayeux, L: As quoted by Reed, R. D., *loc cit.* (ref. 38).

[44]Rittenhouse, Gordon: Analytical Methods as Applied in Petrographic Investigations of Appalachian Basin, *U.S.G.S. Circ. 22*, March (1948).

[45]Collom, R. E: Prospecting and Testing for Oil and Gas, *U. S. Bur. Mines Bull. 201*, 64 (1922).

[46]Ziegler, Victor: *Oil Well Drilling Methods*, 235, John F. Wiley & Sons, Inc., New York, 1923.

[47]Nichols, P. B: Device for Recording Drilling Operation, U. S. Patent No. 2,287,819, June 30, 1942. Also Mizell, G. P: Depth Recorder for a Well Drill, U. S. Reissue Patent 21,297, Dec. 12, 1939.

[48]Yeatman, C. A: Hydraulic Head Integrator of Relative Vertical Motion, U. S. Patent No. 2,230,280, Feb. 4, 1941.

[49]Banning, Thomas A., Jr: Measuring and Recording Various Well Drilling Operations, U. S. Patent No. 2,671,346, March 9, 1954; Measuring and Recording Various Well Drilling Operations, U. S. Patent No. 2,856,692, Oct. 21, 1958.

[50]*Loc. cit:* Collom, R. E., ref. 45.

[51]Suman, George O: Characteristics Which Determine the Value of Oil Zones, *Oil Weekly*, Dec. 12 (1930).

[52]Bentz, Dr. A. and Strobel, E: Anwendung von Utravioletem Licht in der Erdoelgeologie, World Petroleum Congress, London, July 19-25, 1933.

[53]Melhase, John: *Fluorescence as an Aid in Correlating Oil Sands*, The Mineralogist Publication Co., Portland, Ore., February 1936.

[54]Schnaebele, R: Les moyens de déceler les couches pétroliferes dans les sondages à Pechelbronn, *Science et Industrie*, Special Number 239-bis (1933).

[55]Bignell, L. G. E: *Oil Gas J.*, 57, Feb. 17 (1938).

[56]Mills, Brad: Continuous Determination of Oil and Gas Content of Drilling Mud Helpful, *Oil Weekly*, 18, Aug. 1 (1938).

[57]Sawdon, Wallace A: Mud Analysis Used to Log Wells While Drilling, *Petroleum Engr.*, Aug. (1939).

[58]Hayward, J. T: Continuous Logging at Rotary Drilling Wells, *API Drilling and Production Practice*, 8 (1940).

[59]Hayward, J. T: Detection of Gas in Drilling Fluids, U. S. Patent No. 2,280,075, April 21, 1942.

[60]Hayward, J. T: Method of Detecting Gas in Well Drilling Fluids, U. S. Patent No. 2,489,180, Nov. 22, 1949.

[61]Mitchell, J. S: Method and Apparatus for Drilling Holes, U. S. Patent No. 1,570,518, Jan. 19, 1926.

[62]Mason, Arthur J., Jr: Earth Sampler, U. S. Patent No. 1,599,140, Sept. 7, 1926; Earth Sampler, U. S. Patent No. 1,674,117, June 19, 1928; Earth Sampler, U. S. Patent No. 1,705,623, March 19, 1929.

[63]Spencer, E. A., Jr., et al: Side-wall Drilling Organization, U. S. Patent No. 1,804,819, May 12, 1931.

Nichols, Charles R: Method of Determining Angle and Direction of Dip of Geological Formations, U. S. Patent No. 1,891,628, Dec. 20, 1932.

Williston, S. H: Method of Obtaining Cores and Instrument Therefor, U. S. Patent No. 1,932,612, Oct. 31, 1933.

Mennecier, M: Side-wall Sample Taker, U. S. Patent No. 2,558,452, June 26, 1951; Side-wall Sample Taking Apparatus, U. S. Patent No. 2,599,405, June 3, 1952.

[64]Perry, Leroy A: Formation Thief, U. S. Patent No. 1,635,340, July 12, 1927.

Williston, S. H: Side-wall Sampler, U. S. Patent No. 1,683,642, Sept. 11, 1928: Side-wall Sampler, U. S. Patent No. 1,815,661, July 21, 1931.

Burt, C. E: Apparatus for Extracting Cores from the Side Wall of Well Bores, U. S. Patent No. 2,013,457, Sept. 3, 1935.

Schlumberger, C: Apparatus for Sampling the Rocks in Bore Holes, U. S. Patent No. 2,015,873, Oct. 1, 1935; Core-taking Device, U. S. Reissue Patent No. 20,120, Sept. 29, 1936.

[65]Uren, L. C: *Petroleum Production Engineering—Development,* 346, McGraw-Hill Book Company, Inc., New York, 1956, 4th Ed.

[66]Piggot, C. S: The Technique of Securing Undisturbed Core Samples of the Ocean Bottom, *Am. Philosophical Soc. Proc.,* **79**, 1, April (1938).

Piggot, C.S: Core-taking Apparatus and Method of Exposing Cores, U. S. Patent No. 2,227,198, Dec. 31, 1940.

[67]Bannister, C. E: Device for Taking Cores or Samples from Wells, U. S. Patent No. 1,955,166, April 17, 1934.

[68]Schlumberger, M: Core-taking Device, U. S. Patent No. 2,055,506, Sept. 29, 1936.

[69]Leonardon, E. G. and McCann, D. C: Exploring Drill Holes by Sample Taking Bullets, *Trans. Am. Inst. Mining Met. Engrs. (Petroleum Development and Technology)* **132,** 85 (1939) (reprint, p. 141).

[70]Schlumberger, C: Process for Determining the Nature of the Subsoil by the Aid of Electricity, U. S. Patent No. 1,163,468, Dec. 7, 1915.

Schlumberger, C: Etude sur la prospection électrique du sous-sol, Gauthier-Villars, Paris, 1920.

[71]Schlumberger, C. and M: La méthode de la carte des résistivités du sous-sol, *Annales des Mines,* (Paris), Sept. (1930).

[72]Schlumberger, M. and Leonardon, E. G: Survey at Mines de Besseges, Gard, France, March (1921). Personal communication.

[73]Schlumberger, C. and M: Communication sur le carottage électrique, Deuxième Congrès International de Forage (Paris), Sept. (1929). A summary in English was published by H. G. Doll and S. F. Kelly, *Mining and Metallurgy,* Nov. (1929).

[74]Schlumberger, C: Electrical Process and Apparatus for the Determination of the Nature of Geological Formations Traversed by Drill Holes, U. S. Patent No. 1,819,923, Aug. 18, 1931.

[75]Schlumberger, C. and M., and Leonardon, E. G: Electrical Coring; A Method of Determining Bottom-hole Data by Electrical Measurements, *AIME TP 462,* Feb. (1932).

[76]Schlumberger, C. and M., and Leonardon, E. G: A New Contribution to Subsurface Studies by Means of Electrical Measurements in Drill Holes, *AIME TP 503,* Feb. (1933).

Schlumberger, C: Electrical Process for the Geological Investigation of Porous Strata Traversed by a Drill Hole, U. S. Patent No. 1,913,293, June 6, 1933.

Schlumberger, C: Process for the Reconnaissance of Geological Formations and Study of Porous Strata Encountered by a Bore Hole, U. S. Patent No. 1,970,342, Aug. 14, 1934.

[77]Schlumberger, C: Electrical Device for the Determination of Specific Resistivity, U. S. Patent No. 1,894,328, Jan. 17, 1933.

[78]Doll, H. G. and Martin, M: Electrical Logging in Limestone Fields, Third World Petroleum Congress, The Hague, Holland, 1951.

[79]Doll, H. G: The Laterolog: A New Resistivity Logging Method with Electrodes Using an Automatic Focusing System, *Trans. Am. Inst. Mining Met. Engrs. (Petroleum Development and Technology)* **192**, 305 (1951).

[80]Doll, H. G: The Microlog—A New Electrical Logging Method for Detailed Determination of Permeable Beds, *Trans. Am. Inst. Mining Met. Engrs. (Petroleum Development and Technology)* **189**, 155 (1950).

[81]Doll, H. G: The Microlaterolog, presented at a meeting of the American Institute of Mining and Metallurgical Engineers, Houston, Texas, Oct. 1952.

[82]Schlumberger Well Surveying Corp: *Document 8, Introduction to Well Logging* (1958).

[83]Lindtrop, Norbert T. and Nicolaeff, V. M: Oil-water Content of Oil Sands, Grosny, U.S.S.R., *Am. Assoc. Petroleum Geologists Bull.*, **13**, 811 (1929).

[84]Lewis, A. and Horner, W. L: Interstitial Water Saturation in the Pore Space of Oil Reservoirs, *Geophysics*, **1**, 353 (1936).
Pyle and Jones: The Connate Water Content of Oil Sands, *Oil Weekly*, Nov. 16 (1936).

[85]Kogan, I: Utilization of Electric Logging Data for the Determination of Oil Reserves, *Azer. Neft. Khoziatzvo*, Oct. 11 (1935).

[86]Martin, M; Murray, G. H; and Gillingham, W. J: Determination of the Potential Productivity of Oil-bearing Formations by Resistivity Measurements, *Geophysics*, **3**, July (1938).

[87]Archie, G. E: The Electrical Resistivity Log as an Aid in Determining Some Reservoir Characteristics, *Trans. Am. Inst. Mining Met. Engrs. (Petroleum Development and Technology)* **146**, 54 (1941) (reprint, p. 54).
Archie, G. E: Electrical Resistivity, An Aid in Core Analysis Interpretation, *Am. Assoc. Petroleum Geologists Bull.*, **31**, Feb. (1947)

[88]Jakosky, J. J. and Hopper, R. H: The Effect of Moisture on the Direct Current Resistivities of Oil Sands and Rocks, *Geophysics*, **2**, 33 (1937).
Wyckoff, R. D. and Botset, H. G: The Flow of Gas-Liquid Mixtures through Unconsolidated Sands, *Physics*, 325, Sept. (1936).
Leverett, M. C: Flow of Oil-water Mixtures through Unconsolidated Sands, *Trans. Am. Inst. Mining Met. Engrs. (Petroleum Development and Technology)* **132**, 149 (1939) (reprint, p. 381).

[89]Societe de Prospection Electrique, internal company publication, May 1931.

[90]*Ibid*: Sept. 1931.

[91]*Supra* ref. 76, TP 503.

[92]Mounce, W. D. and Rust, W. M., Jr: Natural Potentials in Well Logging, *Trans. Am. Inst. Mining Met. Engrs. (Petroleum Development and Technology)* **155**, 49 (1944) (reprint, p. 47).

[93]Tixier, M. P: Inter-company report.

[94]Wyllie, M. R. J: A Quantitative Analysis of the Electrochemical Component of the SP Curve, *Trans. Am. Inst. Mining Met. Engrs. (Petroleum Development and Technology)* **186**, 17 (1948).
Wyllie, M. R. J: Statistical Study of Accuracy of Some Connate Water Resistivity Determinations Made from Self-potential Log Data, American Association of Petroleum Geologists, St. Louis, Mo., March 1949.

[95]Marshall, C. E. and Krinbill, C. A: The Electrochemical Properties of Mineral Membranes, *J. Am. Chem. Soc.*, **64**, 1814 (1942).

[96]Doll, H. G: The SP Log: Theoretical Analysis and Principles of Interpretation, *Trans. Am. Inst. Mining Met. Engrs. (Petroleum Development and Technology)* **179**, 146 (1949).

Doll, H. G: Selective SP Logging, *Trans. Am. Inst. Mining Met. Engrs. (Petroleum Development and Technology)* **189,** 155 (1950).

Doll, H. G: The SP Log in Shaly Sands, *Trans. Am. Inst. Mining Met. Engrs. (Petroleum Development and Technology)* **189,** 205 (1950).

[97]Gondouin, M; Tixier, M. P; and Simard, G. L: An Experimental Study of the Influence of the Chemical Composition of Electrolytes on the SP Curve, *Trans. Am. Inst. Mining Met. Engrs. (Petroleum Development and Technology)* **210,** 58 (1957).

[98]Gondouin, M. and Scala, C: Streaming Potentials and the SP Log, *Trans. Am. Inst. Mining Met. Engrs. (Petroleum Development and Technology)* **213,** 170 (1958).

[99]Schenck, K. D: An Investigation of the Streaming Potentials Developed in Formations of Low Permeability, M.S. thesis, University of Oklahoma, Norman, Okla., 1955.

[100]Poupon, A; Loy, M. E; and Tixier, M. P: A Contribution to Electrical Log Interpretation in Shaly Sands. *Trans. Am. Inst. Mining Met. Engrs. (Petroleum Development and Technology)* **201,** 138 (1954).

[101]Doll, H. G: Introduction to Induction Logging and Application to Logging of Wells Drilled with Oil-base Muds, *Trans. Am. Inst. Mining Met. Engrs. (Petroleum Development and Technology)* **186,** 148 (1949).

[102]Dumanoir, J. L; Tixier, M. P; and Martin, M: Interpretation of the Induction-Electrical Log in Fresh Mud, *Trans. Am. Inst. Mining Met. Engrs. (Petroleum Development and Technology)* **210,** 202 (1957).

[103]Ambronn, Richard: *Methoden der angewandten Geophysik,* T. Steinkopf, Dresden and Leipzig, 1926. Translated by Margaret C. Cobb, *Elements of Geophysics,* McGraw-Hill Book Company, Inc., New York, 1928.

[104]Westby, G. H. and Scherbatskoy, S. A: Well Logging by Radioactivity, *Oil Gas J.,* Feb. 22 (1940).

[105]Bell, K. G; Goodman, Clark; and Whitehead, W. L: Radioactivity of Sedimentary Rocks and Associated Petroleum, *Am. Assoc. Petroleum Geologists Bull.,* **24 [9]** Sept. (1940).

[106]Green, W. G. and Fearon, R. E: Well Logging by Radioactivity, *Geophysics,* **5 [3]** (1940).

[107]Russell, William L: Well Logging by Radioacticity, *Am. Assoc. Petroleum Geologists Bull.,* **25 [9]** Sept. (1941).

[108]Rothe, Edmond, and Rothe, J. P: *Prospection Geophysique,* **1,** Gauthier-Villars, Paris, 1950.

[109]*Op. cit:* Ambronn, Richard, ref. 103, 127.

[110]Howell, Lynn G. and Frosch, Alex: Gamma-ray Well Logging, *Geophysics,* **4 [2]** March (1939).

[111]Howell, Lynn G. and Frosch, Alex: Detection of Radioactive Cement in Cased Wells, *Trans. Am. Inst. Mining Met. Engrs. (Petroleum Development and Technology)* **136,** 71 (1940) (reprint, p. 69).

[112]*Loc. cit:* Westby, G. H. and Scherbatskoy, S. A., ref. 104.

[113]Fearon, R. E: Well Logging Method and Device, U. S. Patent No. 2,308,361, Jan. 12, 1943.

[114]Pontecorvo, Bruno: Neutron Well Logging—A New Geological Method Based on Nuclear Physics, *Oil Gas J.,* Sept. 11 (1941).

[115]Russell, J. H. and Bishop, Bryan O: Quantitative Evaluation of Rock Porosity by Neutron-neutron Method, *Petroleum Engr.,* April (1954).

Brons, F: Process and Apparatus for Exploring Geological Strata, U. S. Patent No. 2,220,509, Nov. 5, 1940.

[116]Campbell, John L. P: Density Logging in the Gulf Coast Area, *AIME J. Petr. Tech.,* 21, July (1958).

117Baker, P. E: Density Logging with Gamma Rays, *Trans. Am. Inst. Mining Met. Engrs. (Petroleum Development and Technology)* **210**, 286 (1957).

118Caldwell, Richard L. and Sippel, Robert F: New Developments in Radioactive Well Logging Research, *Am. Assoc. Petroleum Geologists Bull.*, **42 [1]** Jan. (1958).

119Peacock, H. B: Personal communication, Report on Velocity Determination at Amerada, Hughes #3, Sept. 7, 1927.

120*Geophysics*, 540, Oct. (1944).

121Weatherby B. B: U. S. Patent No. 2,062,151, filed Nov. 16, 1934.

122Smith, Neal J. and Claudet, A. P: New Method for Measuring Seismic Velocities, *Oil Gas J.*, Sept. 14 (1950).

123Kokesh, F. P: The Development of a New Method of Seismic Velocity Determination, *Geophysics*, **XVII**, July (1952).

124Kokesh, F. P: The Long Interval Method of Measuring Seismic Velocities, *Geophysics*, **XXI**, July (1956).

125Mounce, W. D; Hubbard, C. L; Charske, C. J; and Kuppers, H. P: Seismic Velocity Logging, Fifth Annual Midwestern Geophysical Meeting, Dallas, Texas, Nov. 19-20, 1951.

126Summers, G. C. and Broding, R. A: Continuous Velocity Logging, *Geophysics*, **XVII**, 592 (1952).

127Vogel, C. B: A Seismic Velocity Logging Method, *Geophysics*, **XVII**, 586 (1952).

128Hicks, W. G. and Berry, J. E: Application of Continuous Velocity Logs to Determination of Fluid Saturation of Reservoir Rocks, *Geophysics*, **XXI [3]** (1956).

Brandt, H: A Study of the Speed of Sound in Porous Granular Media, *J. App. Mechanics*, 479, Dec. (1955).

Wyllie, M. R. J; Gregory, A. R; and Gardner, L. W: Elastic Wave Velocities in Heterogeneous and Porous Media, *Geophysics*, **XXI [1]** (1956).

Wyllie, M. R. J; Gregory, A. R; and Gardner, G. H. F: An Experimental Investigation of Factors Affecting Elastic Wave Velocities in Porous Media, *Geophysics*, **XXIII [3]** July (1958).

Tixier, M. P; Alger, R. P; and Doh, C. A: Sonic Logging, *Trans. Am. Inst. Mining Met. Engrs. (Petroleum Development and Technology)* **216**, 106 (1959).

129*Op. cit:* Carll, John F., ref. 2, 245.

130Ryder, Harry M: Well Shooting with Reference to Secondary Recovery, *Oil Gas J.*, May 6 (1937).

131Guyod, Hubert: Personal communication.

132Cabot, J. J: Cave Finder, U. S. Patent No. 1,708,354, April 9, 1929.

133Beckstrom, C. E: Open-hole Diameter Changes Located and Measured by Recording Calipers, *Oil Weekly*, May 27 (1935).

134Kinley, M. M: Well-surveying Device, U. S. Patent No. 2,102,080, Dec. 14, 1937.
Kinley, M. M. et al: Surveying Caliper, U. S. Patent No. 2,267,110, Dec. 23, 1941.

135Bossler, Robert B: Feeler Device for Recording Extent of Shot Hole, *Producers Monthly*, 11, May (1938).
Bossler, Robert B: A Shot-hole Recorder, *Oil Gas J.*, June 30, (1938).

136*Ibid.*

137Salnikov, I. S: Personal communication.

138Salnikov, I. S. and Haider, M. L: Pressure Maintenance and Unitization, South Burbank Pool, *API Drilling and Production Practice*, 91 (1937).

139Guyod, Hubert: Caliper Well Logging, *Oil Weekly*, Aug. 27, Sept. 3, 10, 17 (1945).
Parsons, C. P: Caliper Logging, *AIME Petr. Technology*, May (1942).

140van Orstrand, C. E: Temperature of the Earth in Relation to Oil Location, *Temperature, Its Measurement and Control in Science and Industry*, a Symposium of the American Institute of Physics, New York, Nov. 1939.

[141]Johnston, John, and Adams, L. H: On the Measurement of Temperature in Bore Holes, *Econ. Geology,* **II** (1916).

[142]van Orstrand, C. E: Temperature Measurements, West Virginia Geological Survey, County Reports (1918).

[143]Arctowski, Henryk: Nouvelles Recherches sur les gradients thermiques dans les puits á pétrole de Boryslaw, Krosno et Bitkow, Institut de Géophysique de l'Université de Leopol, Communication No. 7, Leopol (1924).
Geothermal researches made at Borislaw, *The Geographical Journal,* (London), **66,** July-Dec. (1925).

[144]Kraskowski, S: Geothermische Messungen in den Bohrlochern des Donetzbecken, *Erganzungs Hefte fur Angewandte Geophysik,* **3** (1932).

[145]van Orstrand, C. E: On the Correlation of Isogeothermal Surfaces with the Rock Strata, *Trans. Soc. Petroleum Geophysicists (Physics)* March (1932).

[146]van Orstrand, C. E: Some Possible Applications of Geothermics to Geology, *Am. Assoc. Petroleum Geologists Bull.,* **18 [1]** Jan. (1934).
Terry, M. C. and Burney, J. H: Thermal Prospecting for Oil, *Temperature, Its Measurement and Control in Science and Industry,* a Symposium of the American Institute of Physics, New York, Nov. 1939.

[146a]Heald, K. C: The Study of Earth Temperature in Oil Fields on Anticlinal Structures, 1, *Prod. Bul.* 205, American Petroleum Institute, New York, Oct. 1930.

[147]*Earth Temperature in Oil Fields (Prod. Bul. 205),* American Petroleum Institute, New York, Oct. 1930.
Leonardon, E. G: The Economic Utility of Thermometric Measurements in Drill Holes in Connection with Drilling and Cementing Problems, *Bull. Soc. Petroleum Geophysicists,* Jan. (1936).
Schlumberger, M; Doll, H. G; and Perebinissoff, A. A: Temperature Measurements in Oil Wells, Institute of Petroleum Technologists, Nov. 1936.
Deussen, Alexander, and Guyod, Hubert: Use of Temperature Measurements for Cementation Control and Correlations in Drill Holes, *Am. Assoc. Petroleum Geologists Bull.,* **21 [6]** June (1937) (Los Angeles meeting, March 1937).
Gillingham, W. J. and Steward, W. B: Application of Electrical-Logging Methods to West Texas Problems, *API Drilling and Production Practice,* 97 (1938).
Mounce, W. D: Problems of Temperature Measurements Concerning Petroleum Production, *Temperature, Its Measurement and Control in Science and Industry,* a Symposium of the American Institute of Physics, New York, Nov. 1939.
Millikan, C. V: Temperature Surveys in Oil Wells, *Trans. Am. Inst. Mining Met. Engrs. (Petroleum Development and Technology)* **142,** 15 (1941) (reprint, p. 77).
Guyod, Hubert: Temperature Well Logging, *Oil Weekly,* Oct. 21-Dec. 16 (1946).
Kunz, K. S. and Tixier, M. P: Temperature Surveys in Gas-producing Wells, *AIME J. Petr. Tech.,* **7 [7]** July (1955).

[148]*Op. cit:* Carll, John F., ref. 2.
Op. cit: Ziegler, Victor, ref. 46, 144.

[149]Burr, T. and Wakelee, T: Improvement in Apparatus for Testing Deep Wells, U. S. Patent No. 68,350, Sept. 3, 1867.

[150]Stewart, L: Oil-well Packer, U. S. Patent No. 230,080, July 13, 1880.

[151]Franklin, B: Device for Controlling and Regulating the Flow of Wells, U. S. Patent No. 263,330, Aug. 29, 1882.

[152]Johnston, M. O: Oil-well Testing Device, U. S. Patent No. 1,842,270, Jan. 19, 1932.

[153]Johnston, M. O: Equalizing Valve, U. S. Patent No. 2,129,216, Sept. 6, 1938.

[154]Schlumberger, M: Side-wall Formation Sampler, U. S. Patent No. 2,119,361, May 31, 1938.

[155]Lebourg, M; Fields, R. Q; and Doh, C. A: A Method of Formation Testing on Logging Cable, *Trans Am. Inst. Mining Met. Engrs. (Petroleum Development and Technology)* **210,** 260 (1957).

[156]Chambers, Lawrence S: Side-wall Formation Fluid Sampler, U. S. Patent No. 2,674,313, April 6, 1954.

Chapter 9

COMPLETION METHODS

Harold Vance

Harold Vance was born in Geneva, Indiana and graduated from the University of California in 1923 with the degree of B.Sc. in P.E. In 1939 he received the LL.B. degree from Houston Law School.

Earliest employers included United Oil Company and the U. S. Bureau of Mines. He was associated with the oil discoveries at Borger and Wink, Texas and served as division petroleum engineer and division production superintendent with Marland and Continental Oil Companies from 1926 to 1929. He became an independent producer and consulting engineer in East Texas in 1931. In 1934 he became head of the department of petroleum engineering of A&M College of Texas and in 1952 assumed a vice presidency and the managership of the oil loan department of the Bank of the Southwest, in Houston, Texas.

Professional and industrial affiliations include API, SPE of AIME, AAPG, IPAA, and TIPROA. Mr. Vance is the author of numerous technical papers and of the book *Petroleum Subsurface Engineering*, and was co-author with E. DeGolyer of *Bibliography of the Petroleum Industry*.

9

INTRODUCTION

The proper completion of the oil and/or gas well is essential for the control and maximum recovery of production from a reservoir. The advances in completion techniques have kept pace with the improvements in the method of drilling to the producing reservoir. There are certain procedures in well-completion practices which are dependent upon the drilling method used during the completion process. The cable-tool drilling method, the first used in drilling and completing wells, had certain inherent advantages—if properly employed—in completing an oil or gas well. Extraneous fluid seldom entered the producing formation because the pressure differential in the hole was usually in favor of the formation fluids entering the hole. This pressure differential could, however, be detrimental when the pressures within the reservoir were excessive and the flow of oil or gas during completion could not be controlled.

Advances in well-completion practices have now brought to the rotary drilling system most of the advantages of the cable-tool method and, at the same time, the advantages of rotary drilling have been retained. In either method, the casing program is very important. Since the cable-tool method was the first used in completing oil wells, it will be discussed first, although certain procedures are common to both methods.

In addition to the completion practices inherent to cable-tool and rotary drilling methods, the following subjects are included in well-completion practices and are discussed in detail: shooting of the pay formation; acid treatment; fracturing formations; sand control in the oil and gas wells; multiple completions; and permanent-type completions.

CABLE-TOOL WELL COMPLETIONS

It is believed that David and Joseph Ruffner,[1] in the drilling of salt wells, developed some of the well-completion methods which were later used in the oil development which started in 1859. In January 1808, in the completion of a salt-water well at "Great Buffalo Lick" on the Kanawha River, above Charleston, W. Va., the brothers were confronted with shutting off some of the fresher salt-water sands in order that they could produce a more concentrated salt water which had been opened at the bottom of the hole. In this connection, there was need for a pipe or a conductor to reach from the bottom of the hole to the surface and some packing device to shut off the shallower water sands so that only the deeper sands would be produced through the conductor. No metal tubes were available at that time so they whittled out of two long strips of

[1]References are at the end of the chapter.

581

wood, two long half tubes of the proper size, fitted the edges closely together, and then wrapped the whole from end to end with small twine. This wooden tube was then prepared with a bag near the lower end to fit as closely as practical, water tight, in a 2½-in. hole and was carefully pressed in place. Thus, the brine flowed freely through the tube and excluded the less-concentrated upper waters. Brine wells were drilled as deep as 465 ft during this period.

The necessity for metal tubing of the type that Ruffner had constructed of wood was apparent; and soon a tinsmith was preparing convenient lengths of tin tubing, and these lengths were soldered together as they were run in the hole. The screw joint was to come later and tubes with screw joints were first made out of copper and later out of iron. In order to form a tight seal at the bottom of the tube, a method called "seed bagging" was developed and was used for a long time. The "seed bag" was made of buckskin or soft calfskin and sewed up like the sleeve of a coat. It was some 12 to 15 in. long, about the size of the well hole, and open at both ends so that it could be slipped over the tube. One end was securely wrapped above knots on the tube to prevent slipping. Some 6 or 8 in. of the bag were then filled with flaxseed, either alone or mixed with powdered gum tragacanth—then the top end of the bag was tightly wrapped like the bottom end and the tube was ready for the well. When in place, the water would swell the seed and the gum, and thus pack off between the tube and the hole to form a water-tight joint. This seed bag was probably the first "packer" used in this country.

Casing Program for Cable-tool Completions

During the period 1859 to 1865,[2] it was common practice in oil-well drilling to use no casing in the hole—neither for the purpose of keeping the walls of the hole from caving nor to shut off the water, and many times the hole had some water or was full of water at the time the oil sand was encountered. The pressure within the oil measure was sufficient to cause the well to flow both the oil and the water which was in the hole, or which had access to the hole, until finally the oil was exhausted and the water could reverse the process by entering the oil sand.

Later, the drillers began to set a joint or two of pipe to keep the hole from caving at the surface, then run a string of tubing which served as a conductor through which the oil could be produced. This tubing was packed off, usually, by seed bags which would shut off any water in the hole above the oil measures and also prevent any cavings of the hole from dropping down opposite the producing formation. The tubing thus served as an oil string and as a conductor to the surface for the oil and gas which was to be produced. Small casing, 3¼-in. in size, was first introduced in 1865. This casing held a seed bag at the lower end and extended below the fresh-water sands so that the tubing could be inserted and withdrawn without letting the water, which was back of the pipe, down on the oil sand. The use of the full string of casing through which tubing could be run and withdrawn is believed to be the most important advancement in completion practices up to 1865. Without the full string of casing, the continual removal of the tubing and seed bags let the water and cavings down on the oil sand until finally the hole itself was ruined and the well had to be abandoned.

In 1873,[3] it was the practice to run casing of about 6 to 6½ in. in diameter to a sufficient depth to shut off the fresh water. It was also the practice to drill to the top of the oil-bearing sand with a hole of sufficient size to run the casing, with a seed bag on the bottom so that the fresh water would be shut off, and then drill ahead through the casing into the oil sand in a reduced hole. After the hole had been drilled through the sand, tubing with a working barrel on the bottom was run in the hole to a point somewhere below the top of the producing oil sand and the well was placed on the pump.

The principle of the seed bag as a packer was improved upon in a number of instances. One method was to place canvas around two telescoping sections of the bottom of the casing shoe so the weight of the pipe on bottom would telescope the tubes, which, in turn, would shorten the length of the canvassed section and push it out to contact the walls of the hole. This same principle was applied with a rubber section wrapped around the pipe outside a telescoping section of the pipe.

Considerable educational work was necessary to convince the operators it was important to exclude extraneous water from the oil sand, and much of the early work done by the U. S. Geological Survey in California and later by the U. S. Bureau of Mines engineers had to do with stressing the importance of proper exclusion of extraneous waters before drilling into the oil-bearing horizons. The packer was always considered as a temporary method of excluding water, and one of the advantages of this packer method of shutting off water was that usually the casing could be salvaged after the well had ceased to produce profitably. In many formations it was found that a proper water shutoff could be accomplished by setting the casing—which had been equipped with a reinforced section at the bottom known as the "shoe"—directly into the formation, which was impervious to water. The contact between the casing shoe and the formation itself formed a shutoff and drilling was continued inside the casing in a reduced hole. This type of shutoff is commonly referred to as a "formation shutoff" and was reasonably satisfactory where the proper formation served as a seat for the shoe.

It was also found, in some instances, that a heavy mud fluid back of the casing would improve the percentage of successful formation shutoffs, because the particles of mud fluid would settle around the shoe on the bottom of the pipe and form an impervious layer outside the casing.

Later on it was found that a more permanent job of excluding water could be secured by placing cement around the shoe and up back of the casing. The subject of cementing as a method of excluding water is covered in another chapter of this history and will not be discussed here.

Connections on Cable-tool Wells During the Drilling-in Process[4]

After setting the last string of casing above the oil sand, a "bell nipple" was screwed into the top collar at about the level of the derrick floor, Fig. 1. Drilling was thus continued and if oil or gas were encountered, the "bell nipple" was removed and the screw fittings for closing in the well were applied.

The usual method of connecting up an oil well was to place a casing-head tee on top of the inner string of casing and connect the flow line to the side outlet, then extend the line to the flow tank. The top opening of the tee was closed by a casing stop which was usually a wooden plug on top of the tee and held in position by 4 set screws placed radially through the top of the tee, Fig. 2.

Sometimes the well produced oil or gas, or both, at such a high rate that there was need for some method of controlling the flow while the well was being deepened. This was done by using a "control head" with an oil saver on top which provided a packing gland around the drilling cable and a side outlet through which the oil flowed during the process of deepening. Fig. 3[5] shows the types of oil savers available as early as 1907 for controlling the flow of oil and gas while drilling-in with cable tools.

Fig. 1 (left)—Gas Wasting from a Well Being Drilled[4]

Fig. 2 (below)—Oil Well Connected to Flow line, Showing the Tee Casing Head and Flow Line Connected to Side Outlet[4]

OIL SAVERS

FOR WIRE LINE

CAIRO PATTERN
Fig. 2588

RIGBY'S PATENT
Fig. 2589

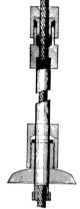

Weight, 30 lbs.

Cairo Pattern, Fig. 2588 - - - - - - - - each	$15 00
Rigby's Patent, Fig. 2589, for ¾″ wire line - "	15 00

Weight, 50 lbs.

PATENT BARREL OIL SAVER AND PARTS

Fig. 2587

For drilling in the oil sand while the well is flowing. The drilling cable is put through the tube and packed with rope yarn. The tube works up and down with the cable through the cap in the casing head. The oil is carried off through the pipes in the sides of the casing head. The cap is fastened to the head by the set screws.

Size casing head for - - inches	5⅝, 6¼	5⅝, 6¼	5⅝, 6¼	6⅝, 7⅝	6⅝, 7⅝
Size of barrel - - - - inches	2½	2¾	3	2½	2¾
Weight - - - - - lbs.	48	49	55	53	49
Complete - - - - - - - -	$16 50	23 00	24 00	17 00	29 00
Base, complete - - - - - -	8 00	10 00	10 50	8 75	13 25
Base only - - - - - - - -	3 75	4 50	4 50	5 00	8 50
Barrel and ring - - - - - -	11 00	16 00	16 50	11 00	16 00
Stuffing box - - - - - - -	2 50	2 75	3 00	2 50	4 00
Follower - - - - - - - -	1 10	1 15	1 30	1 25	1 50
Top nut - - - - - - - -	1 25	1 50	2 00	1 25	1 50
Size casing head for - - inches	6⅝, 7⅝	8¼	8¼	8¼	....
Size of barrel - - - inches	3	2½	2¾	3	....
Weight - - - - - lbs.	55	53	49	55	....
Complete - - - - - - - -	$30 00	21 50	30 50	31 00	....
Base, complete - - - - - -	13 75	10 50	14 00	14 50	....
Base only - - - - - - - -	9 00	7 00	9 00	10 00	....
Barrel and ring - - - - - -	16 50	11 00	16 00	16 50	....
Stuffing box - - - - - - -	4 50	3 00	5 00	5 50	....
Follower - - - - - - - -	2 00	1 25	1 50	2 00	....
Top nut - - - - - - - -	2 00	1 25	1 50	2 00	..

SAND LINE CAP

FOR MANILA OR WIRE ROPE

Fig. 2585

Fastened in the casing head. The sand pump line is put through it. Used while the well is flowing.

Fig. 3—Oil Savers Available as Early as 1907[5]

Fig. 4[6] shows a well being deepened with surface equipment developed after 1907 while the well was flowing at the rate of 250 bbl per day.

In the Yates Field, Pecos County, Texas, the flow of oil was so large that wells had to be deepened by stages. When the flow of oil began to hold the tools up to the extent that the line would go slack on the derrick floor, the tools would be pulled out of the hole and the well produced until the flow decreased to the extent that deepening operations could be continued. Some of the wells in the Yates Pool produced at the rate of 5,000 bbl per hour; and while flowing at such high rates, some actually "drilled" themselves in.

Homer Craig,[7] in 1921, while employed by the Huasteca Petroleum Company in Mexico, developed a high-pressure oil saver which was used to complete the larger oil producers in the Tampico area of Mexico. This oil saver was similar to those available through supply stores as early as 1907, but was designed to handle high pressures. This same oil saver was used, in a few instances, for drilling-in wells in the Hendricks Field, Winkler County, Texas, in 1927. Here, deepening operations were conducted with the well entirely closed in and pressure on the oil saver, at times,

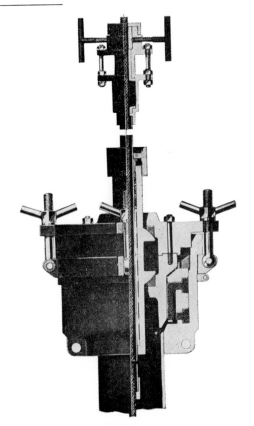

Fig. 4 (above)—Method for Drilling in Flowing Oil Wells with Cable Tools without Waste[6]

Fig. 5 (right)—Kerotest High-pressure Oil Saver[8]

amounted to 1,500 psi. A. S. Feild, then superintendent for Shell Oil Company in the Hendricks Field, designed certain modifications to the Craig high-pressure oil saver and the Kerotest Valve Company built and sold this new equipment, shown in Fig. 5.[8] The last sale of this oil saver was in 1935. The hazards connected with completing and deepening high-pressure wells by the cable-tool method made a change to the rotary-drilling system of completion necessary.

The method of bringing in a well wherein there was open hole through the producing formation was known as bringing the well in "barefoot".[9] There was no need for a liner or perforated pipe of any kind opposite the producing formation if it did not cave. If the producing formation was unconsolidated, perforated casing or a liner was placed opposite the producing sand. Many types of screen, or button-perforated pipe, formed the casing or liner and sometimes it was necessary to pack off between the liner and the water string. A lead seal was often used to pack off between the packer and the liner. This method of packing off was later improved by using a hook wall line packer with slips from which the liner was suspended in the last string of casing. Fig. 6[10] shows the method of setting the lead seal which was commonly used until the advent of the hook-wall packer. This lead seal is being used at the present time in completing water wells.

In some areas, cavings would block the flow of oil into the hole. To correct this condition, it was common practice—where there was no water immediately below the producing horizon—to extend the hole 20 to 30 ft, thus providing a "sump" into which the cavings could fall.

Perforating Casing in the Hole

In some areas the final string of casing was set through the oil measures and the casing perforated in the hole. It was possible, in some instances, to run the casing after the total depth had been reached; but usually the casing was carried along as drilling progressed. In this latter case, the tools operated through the casing and joint by joint was added as drilling progressed. At times, it was necessary to underream the hole ahead of the casing shoe because the bit, in some formations, tended to cut a hole smaller than the outside of the casing shoe.

If blank pipe had been run through the producing formation, it was necessary to provide an opening through the pipe. It is believed the first patent[11] for an in-the-hole mechanical casing perforator was issued to J. C. Swan on October 25, 1910. During the period 1910-1919, some 14 patents were issued on casing perforators.

The most common perforator was the single-knife casing "ripper" or splitter, which cut a slit any desired length. Fig. 7 shows the operation of a single-knife perforator which was most successfully operated when

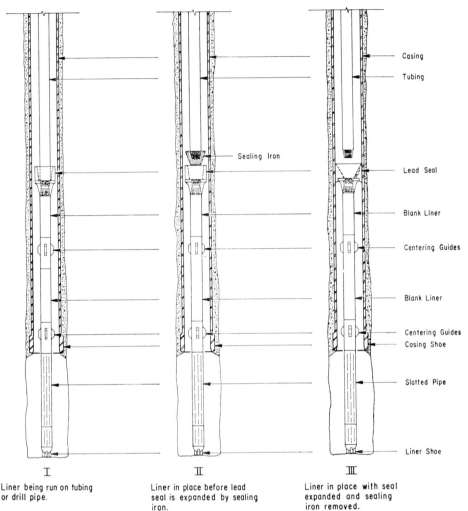

Casing

Tubing

Sealing Iron

Lead Seal

Blank Liner

Centering Guides

Blank Liner

Centering Guides
Casing Shoe

Slotted Pipe

Liner Shoe

I
Liner being run on tubing
or drill pipe.

II
Liner in place before lead
seal is expanded by sealing
iron.

III
Liner in place with seal
expanded and sealing
iron removed.

Fig. 6—Illustration of Liner Setting Using Lead Seal[10]

run on a string of tubing. The weight of the tubing forced the knife blade
out through the casing.

The Mack perforator, sometimes called the Graham perforator, was
one of the first to perforate two holes simultaneously. The mechanical
action was similar to that of the single-knife perforator shown in Fig. 7,
but the knives were made by placing cutting points on a wheel, which
points could be any size or shape. An improvement to the double-knife
perforator had four knives which punched four holes at right angles.

Experiments were conducted on the flow of sand through different
shapes and sizes of perforations and the following statement is by E. W.
Wagy:[11]

". . . . When sand is wet, the natural slope is 2 to 1, hence the slot would not need to be so wide before the sand would start to run in; the minimum being about one-fourth of an inch for pipe one-half inch thick. Obviously, horizontal perforations tend to hold out sand more than vertical perforations would. For the same reason, the various types of 'shutter' perforations will keep the sand out of the well unless it is forced in by gas pressure and fluid pressure. These two factors are always unknown quantities and are also constantly changing. For this reason, the choice of screen and perforated pipe has to be a matter of trial."

Results Obtained with Mechanical In-the-hole Perforators

An examination of in-the-hole perforated pipe revealed great irregularity in the size of openings punched in the pipe and the location of these openings. Measurement errors resulted in the perforation being located in casing joints which weakened the string, and the non-uniform method of perforation also weakened the walls of the casing. Not all the difficulties could be blamed on the perforator itself, as the character of the pipe perforated certainly had something to do with the nature of the perforations. Continual improvements in mechanical in-the-hole perforators tended to

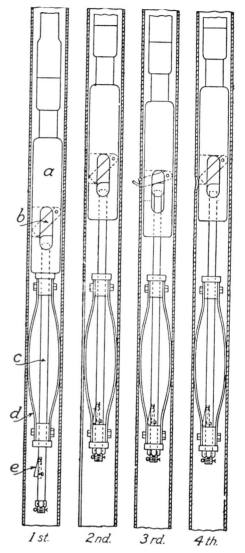

1st.   2nd.   3rd.   4th.

Fig. 7—Single-knife Perforator[11] Shows perforator in four different positions during the procedure of cutting a casing. a: Body; b: Knife; c: Mandrel; d: Spring; e: Lug.
(Courtesy of Paul Paine, Tulsa, Okla.)

eliminate some of the shortcomings of the earlier models.

Use of Shop-perforated and Screened Pipe in Cable-tool Completions

In a number of instances, shop-perforated pipe and later screened pipe were run on the bottom of the oil string as drilling proceeded, although it was not always known just where the perforated or screened pipe would be needed in the oil measures until the well was completed.

Another method of placing shop-perforated or screened pipe was to run blank pipe as an oil string to the bottom of the hole, then run a liner to bottom through this oil string. The liner would consist of shop-perforated or screened pipe with a joint of blank pipe at the top. After the liner had been run to the bottom, the oil string itself was pulled up far enough to leave the blank portion of the perforated liner inside the oil string. The patented-type screened pipe was used in place of shop-perforated pipe where the character of the producing sand required its use.

The important thing to consider was just how much sand could be handled economically. Screened pipe was designed for wells which produced more sand than could be handled economically with the use of ordinary in-the-hole perforated or shop-perforated casing.

During the period January 9, 1917 to July 29, 1919, some 14 patents were issued for screened pipe. The names of O. A. Layne and M. E. Layne appear very prominently in the list of patentees.

Fig. 8 shows various types of button-type screens and wire-wrapped screens in use in the 1920's.[11]

Some of the information just given concerning the use of screened pipe and shop-perforated pipe liners can also be applied to rotary completions, but with rotary a wash pipe must be made available to remove the mud solids from the annulus between the liner and the hole.

In-the-hole Gun Perforator

The idea of shooting through the casing with bullets was shared by many people. A basic patent was issued in 1926 to Sid Mims, a Los Angeles, Calif. oil man. Several years later, Walter T. Wells and Wilford E. Lane[12] were much impressed by an article they read concerning the efforts of a man in Romania to fire bullets through oil-well casing. After several attempts on their part to construct a gun to shoot through oil-well casing, they finally developed one

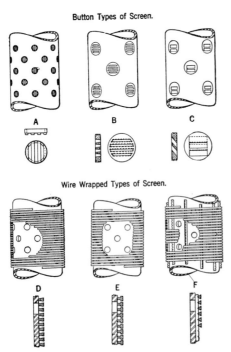

Button Types of Screen.

A   B   C

Wire Wrapped Types of Screen.

D   E   F

Fig. 8—Types of Screen Pipe[11]
A, McEvoy Screen; B, Layne & Bowler button screen, keystone opening: C., Layne & Bowler button screen, shutter openings; D, Layne & Bowler Keystone wire-wrapped screen; E, Getty screen; F, Stancliff screen.

which successfully shot a bullet through three strings of casing. They constructed an electrical conductor for suspending the gun from the surface, through which electrical current is passed, for the purpose of firing the bullets; and in December 1932, the first well was perforated. This well was located in the Montebello Field, Los Angeles County, California. Union Oil Co. of California owned the well and considered it to have reached its economic limit. Eleven runs were made for shooting and 87 shots were fired. The well, after perforating, started producing 40 bbl of oil per day and continued to do so for several years.

Lane and Wells, while preparing to perforate the Union Oil Co. well, acquired the patents which had been issued to Sid Mims in 1926. They continued to develop the gun perforator and offered it on a service basis under the name of Lane-Wells Company. The perforator consisted of an alloy-steel cylinder, in which were inserted chambers containing the powder charge and bullets. The gun was lowered into the hole on an armored insulated cable and the shots could be fired individually or as a group by operating electric controls at the surface. Much development work was necessary to provide a satisfactory method of sealing the powder against the hydrostatic pressure to prevent the powder from becoming wet, also to develop a suitable insulated electrical cable. A method of locating the collars on the casing in the hole was also developed, making it possible to perforate within the body of the joints of casing.

Special-purpose guns were developed which could run in the tubing, perforating it but not the casing. High-temperature powders were developed which permitted perforation at depths where the temperature reached 340 F, eliminating the possibility of premature detonation.

The Shaped-charge Principle Applied to Casing Perforating

The principle of the cavity effect of explosives, known as the Monroe effect[12] or shaped-charge principle, was first disclosed by Prof. Charles E. Monroe in the 1880's. This principle was utilized in World War II in projectiles and rockets. After the war, a number of individuals and concerns investigated this principle in connection with gun perforations. It was first offered as a service by Well Explosives, Inc.

The shaped-charge process required no bullets and the perforations were effected by focusing high-velocity force streams against the casing. In smaller guns this method improved the depth of penetration.

The same principle has been applied in developing a casing or tubing cutter which involves ring charges, so that a complete cut can be made in one trip on an electric cable (op. cit.).

Running Tubing under Pressure in Wells Drilled with Cable Tools

In 1927, during the development of the Yates Field in Pecos County, Texas, no thought was given to running tubing in the hole, and it would have been impossible to do so, in a number of instances, with the equipment available at that time. The first equipment made to run tubing in flowing wells was a tubing oil saver which was set on top of the usual cable-tool control head. A cast-iron disc was placed in the bottom joint of tubing and this disc was usually the top of a piston out of a Model T Ford engine, which had been turned down to the proper size. There was no flow up through the tubing on account of the disc, but oil and gas could flow through the outlet from the control head. When the desired amount of tubing had been run in the hole, the tubing oil saver was flanged up permanently as part of the wellhead connections. The disc was knocked out of the tubing by dropping from the surface a Ford axle which broke the cast-iron disc, permitting the well to flow through the tubing. The annulus between the tubing and casing was then shut off. This crude method of running tubing in flowing wells was only applicable where the pressures encountered were low and the flow of oil was not of any great consequence. However, the problem of tubing such wells as those encountered in the Yates Pool simply meant that in a number of cases the tubing could not even be started in the hole without some sort of snubbing device.

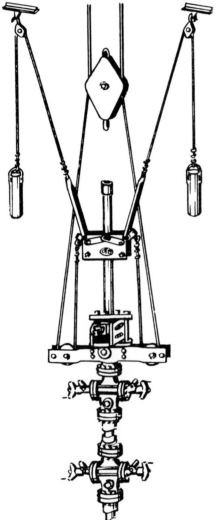

Fig. 9—Completely Hand-operated Equipment Used from about 1929 to 1934[9]

It is believed that H. C. Otis[9] was the first to develop equipment for running tubing in high-pressure flowing wells. This equipment involved a snubbing device which was used on the tubing until the weight of the tubing in the hole would prevent it from being blown out of the hole.

Otis *(op. cit.)* was given the job of running a syphon line into a 1,000-ft Nacatosh sand gas well in the Bethany Field, Panola County, Texas, in 1926. This well had a large open-flow volume but was making considerable salt water. He used what he called a "stripper", which is believed to be the same as the tubing oil saver discussed previously, and he designed a snubbing device to push the tubing in against the well pressure. After this experience, he redesigned his stripper or oil saver and snubbing equipment so that he was able to run coupled tubing into wells having a surface pressure as high as 350 psi with virtually no gas escaping from the stripper or through the tubing.

Fig. 9 shows the completely hand-operated equipment that was used from 1929 to 1934. The traveling snubbers were operated by handles attached to the line, forcing the slips against the pipe in a scissor-like action. Both of the blowout preventers were of the hand-operated type and no safety head was used.

A number of patents were secured by Otis during the period 1931 to 1934. The original one was Patent No. 1,837,990 titled "Well Tubing Snubber", issued December 22, 1931.

It was necessary to leave the stripper *(op. cit.)* which Otis first designed as a permanent part of the wellhead equipment, since he had not developed a means of removing it.

Not only was it necessary at times to run tubing in the hole under pressure, but it was also necessary to remove tubing from flowing wells. In this connection, Otis developed a method of placing a plug in the tubing which was run in and set by the use of a Halliburton line. The first plugs were not removable; but later he designed a type which could be removed and, at about the same time, developed a plug through which a hole was drilled. Thus he had, in effect, a bottom-hole choke which could be changed or removed at will.

SHOOTING OF PAY FORMATION TO INCREASE PRODUCTION

It is believed the idea[13] of shooting a well to increase production must have been in the minds of several persons at about the same time. In 1860, Harry H. Dennis exploded a shot of black powder alongside a string of tools stuck in a water well he was drilling. The shot was for the purpose of loosening the tools, but there was a noticeable increase in water production following the shot. The results obtained may have been responsible for William Reed's experiments in 1863 in shooting 3 of his oil wells. Reed lost interest in the idea when the shots failed to increase production.

First Torpedoes[2]

In 1862, Col. E. A. L. Roberts—then an officer in the volunteer service, with his regiment in the Army of the Potomac—conceived the idea of exploding torpedoes in oil wells to increase production.

The first torpedoes were constructed by building a tin case which was filled with gunpowder, with a percussion cap at the upper end. The line which held the torpedo in place opposite the productive sand was used to guide a metal cylinder dropped from the surface. This metal cylinder hit the percussion cap which, in turn, exploded the charge of gunpowder. In the early shooting, water was used to tamp the shot to make it more effective.

In the fall of 1864, Col. Roberts constructed 6 such torpedoes; and in January 1865, visited the Titusville area to arrange for an experimental shot. His idea met with great disfavor because no one wanted the risk of possible damage to his well by exploding such a shot. However, he soon persuaded Capt. Mills to permit him to operate on the Ladies' Well at Watson Flats, near Titusville. After two torpedoes had been exploded in this well, it commenced to flow oil and paraffin. Notwithstanding the success of the first experiment, the operators were still skeptical; and it was not until the fall of 1865 that they would permit the inventor to operate on wells to any extent for fear the explosion would cause the hole to cave and destroy the well's productiveness.

In December 1866, Col. Roberts exploded a torpedo in a well known as "Woodin Well". This was a dry hole, never having produced any oil. The result of the shot increased the production from zero to 20 bbl per day, and then the following month—January 1867—the second torpedo was exploded which brought the production up to 80 bbl. This established the torpedo beyond question to be all that Col. Roberts had claimed, and there was an immediate demand for shooting throughout the general area.

Introduction and Development in the Use of Nitroglycerin

In 1846, Ascania Sobrero, an Italian chemist, discovered the explosive now known as nitroglycerin while experimenting with nitric acid and various organic substances. Sobrero's product was called "pyroglycerin", but in 1854 Williamson and Railton pronounced this product to be trinitrate of glycerin.[14] In 1859, Emmanuel and Alfred Nobel began experimenting with this explosive which by then was called nitroglycerin. Their experiments had to do with finding a means of detonating it in its original liquid form. They enlarged the percussion gun cap which was filled with mercury fulminate to make the modern blasting cap, and these were in use by 1864 *(op. cit.)*.

The first recorded use of liquid nitroglycerin in boreholes[13] occurred in New York in 1865, where a quantity was exploded in a hole using a gunpowder primer and an ordinary fuse.

In 1875, Nobel perfected and patented a jelly-like product which he called "blasting gelatin" *(op. cit.)*. It was prepared by mixing 7 to 10 percent collodion cotton with liquid nitroglycerin. This explosive had a tremendous shattering power, was less sensitive to detonation, and more convenient to handle than liquid nitroglycerin. In oil-well torpedo work, Nobel's explosive gelatin was referred to as "solidified nitroglycerin."

In 1926, during the early development of the Permian Basin in West Texas, it was the general practice to use liquid nitroglycerin in shooting oil wells. Thereafter, there was a gradual change-over in this area to the use of solidified nitroglycerin, although some operators continued using liquid nitroglycerin because they believed better results were obtained.

The container or "shell" which carried the liquid explosive to the bottom of the hole—or the point at which the shot was to be exploded—was made of tinned sheet metal, cylindrical in shape, with a conical top and bottom. The early shells were made of a single thin wall, but later a double-walled shell was used because the single-walled shell was sometimes ruined in running it into the hole and there was a possibility of leakage and premature explosion. The shells were made in 20-qt joints of various diameters and were designed to hold 20 qt, regardless of the diameter; therefore, the length of the shell varied with the diameter. These 20-qt shells could be placed one on top of the other as the conical top and bottom served as a means of guiding one shell to the one already in the hole, so that any number of shells—one on top of the other— could be run in. The shells used for solidified nitroglycerin were similar to single-wall shells first used for liquid nitroglycerin.

Placing the Shots

Great care had to be taken in measurements in order that the shot could be placed where needed, and the location of the shot had to be known with respect to the casing in the hole. Sometimes the nitroglycerin was dumped in the bottom of the hole, rather than exploded from the 20-qt can. In such cases a "dump shell" was used which was provided with a releasable false bottom, so that when the shell reached bottom the nitroglycerin contained in the shell was drained out. This method of running nitroglycerin in the hole was naturally very hazardous and had to be done with extreme care.

If the shot to be exploded was too close to the casing in the hole, it was necessary to pull several joints of casing out of the hole; and here difficulty was encountered, depending upon what was back of the casing. Cavings back of the casing would drop in on top of the shot already in the hole and any water would cover the shot and help tamp it.

The formation to be shot had to be directly exposed to the shot, and any other than an unconsolidated formation was considered one from which an increase in production might be expected. There were a great variety of opinions as to just what happened when the formation was "shot"; but everyone conceded that there was an enlargement of the hole, and thus there were a lot of cavings which had to be recovered from the hole. It could take days to clean out the hole to the bottom, using ordinary cable tools and bailers. About 1928, there was developed in the Chalk Field, Howard County, Texas, a method[15] of cleaning out wells after shooting which proved economically beneficial. It was found that, by utilizing a stuffing-box casing head and a shop-made bit on the bottom of the tubing, cuttings could be easily removed by circulating oil down the annulus and up through the tubing. A clean-out operation which usually took 8 to 10 days with the cable tools required only 1 day by this method.

Methods of Detonation

The "sand firing" head was an early method of detonating shots, but is now obsolete in most areas. This "firing-head" shell contained gun caps fitted on the lower end of a plunger and when the shell was filled, the nitroglycerin extended up into the firing tubes sufficiently to cover the gun caps. The firing-head shell, always the top one in a torpedo, was detonated by dropping a cast iron go-devil down the hole.

The "jack squib" was another method of detonating the shot and is still used in some instances. The jack squib is a tin tube with a cartridge of 60-percent nitroglycerin dynamite primed with 2 blasting caps and sufficient lengths of waterproof fuse. The fuse is lighted and the squib dropped into the hole so it will explode on top of or opposite the shot already in the hole.

The "line squib" was a detonating device similar to the one which was exploded by dropping a go-devil from the surface, but this device was lowered to the top of the shot which was already in the hole by means of a wire line. A tubular go-devil was placed around this wire line; and when the go-devil was dropped from the surface, it was guided to the detonating device.

The "bumper squib" was a detonating device containing a weight which was designed to strike a firing pin by quickly slackening the line used to run it in the hole.

The "electric squib" was a small shell about 12 in. in length, containing a tube of nitroglycerin to which was added an electric blasting cap. The blasting cap was connected to the surface with duplex insulated copper wire. Extra weight was added to the small shell and the insulated wires were attached at intervals to the shooting line used to lower the detonating device from the surface to the top of the shot already in the hole. The explosion was controlled from the surface by means of an electric current generated by a plunger-type battery.[14]

Any method of exploding the shot in the hole by dropping something from the surface meant there could be no obstruction in the hole to keep the detonating device from reaching the shot. Any cavings above the torpedo in the hole would prevent this happening. Therefore, in 1920 a time bomb was placed in the last torpedo run in the hole. This time bomb was exploded electrically, using dry-cell batteries as the source of electricity; and the time of the explosion was controlled by a watch or clock which actuated the detonating mechanism. The time bomb had been known for many years, but until 1920 it was looked upon by torpedo companies and producers as an "infernal machine".

In the early 1920's, several time bombs were on the market; and up to January 1, 1928, an estimated 3,200 had been used for detonating shots in the Cromwell and Seminole Fields of Oklahoma and the Amarillo Field in Texas, with only three premature explosions involving the loss of life.[14] The "Zero-Hour Electric Bomb" was one of the first. Its principal parts consisted of a watch, a small dry cell, 2 electric blasting caps, and 1½ lb of nitroglycerin dynamite or gelatinized explosive. The "Bolshevik" and "King" were mechanically operated bombs which were actuated by clocks; and although there was some difference in the mechanical arrangement, they operated on the same principle. The time bombs were all enclosed in a cast-iron shell and/or a shell tube with cast-iron top and bottom.

C. O. Rison (op. cit.) lists 17 premature explosions of nitroglycerin in wells and at the surface. This is by no means a complete list of accidents, but it is representative of the type which advances in technique have helped to prevent. The wire shooting[16] lines with depth measurements and weight-indicating devices have replaced the old manila rope, and the single-slotted hook which instantly released the shells when they touched an obstruction or bottom has been replaced by a safety hook which requires manipulation to release the shell.

Tamping and Size of Shot

The amount of water tamping depended upon the possibility of injury to the casing in the hole. Table 1 shows the amount of water tamping with relation to the casing shoe and size of shot which was in general use throughout the Mid-Continent area.

Table 1

Distance from Casing Shoe to Top of Shot, Extent of Tamping, and Size of Shots in Mid-Continent[14]

Distance from Casing Shoe to Top of Shot, Ft	Tamping (Water) on Top of Shot, Ft	Size of First Shot (Nitroglycerin), Qt	Size of Second Shot (Nitroglycerin), Qt
30	20	10	20
50	40	20	40
70	50	40	
80	60	60	
90	70	80	
100	75	100	

In the early 1920's, a number of devices were developed to bridge the hole between the top of the shot and the casing shoe. The bridge prevented the shot energy from being dissipated up the hole. Halliburton Oil Well Cementing Company initiated the use of Cal-seal in the late 1930's, which proved very successful as a bridging agent. Instruments were developed to record at the well head the explosions below the bridge which might not be detected otherwise.

ACID TREATMENT

In 1894, Herman Frasch,[17] who was chief chemist at the Solar Oil Refinery in Lima, Ohio, was attracted by the great differences in productive capacity of the wells in the fields near Lima, which were producing from limestone. He concluded that these differences resulted from variations in size and continuity of the pores containing oil. J. W. Van Dyke,[17] general manager of the Solar Oil Refinery at the same time, working with Frasch, agreed that an acid treatment might enlarge the pores and develop connecting channels by dissolving out parts of the formation. Both of these gentlemen applied for patents on the use of acid solvents in wells, one of which covered the use of hydrochloric acid and the other sulfuric acid. The inventors assigned one-half of each of their patents to the other, indicating they were not certain at that time which acid would give the best results.

Frasch discussed with G. N. Talcott of the Ohio Rubber Company at Cleveland, Ohio, the problem of corrosion of casing and tubing caused by contact with the acid, with the idea that tubing might be lined with rubber. Talcott suggested that a rubber hose might serve just as well.

In the Oil City, Pa. *Derrick*, dated October 10, 1895, there was a report on the first acid treatments; and on March 21, 1896, the *Derrick* said the method was ". . . beyond the experimental stage . . . production can be increased where all other methods failed." In spite of these apparently good results, the method was soon forgotten and the records do not indicate why the inventors failed in their attempt to make a commercial success of their process.

In the great Lima-Indiana oil field, there is no record that any acid treatment to increase production was conducted, although many men were interested in any method which would increase the production of the rapidly declining limestone production. There is some evidence that acid was used on fishing jobs.

Acid was used in wells in the Glenn Pool in Oklahoma for the purpose of dissolving out limestone which had been deposited from the waters, and it did prove to be successful for this purpose. The Gypsy Oil Company initiated this cleanout work, which started in 1928. A short time before this, another subsidiary of Gulf Oil Corp. experimented with uninhibited hydrochloric acid to increase the production from their limestone wells in Lee County, Kentucky. It is reported that the project did not prove profitable and was abandoned after the treatment of some dozen wells in the latter part of 1930.

In the latter part of the 1920's, The Pure Oil Company began to explore for oil in the Central Michigan Basin and found production in the Dundee limestone, but the productive capacity of the wells varied widely from well to well and sometimes what appeared to be good locations proved to be dry.

The Dow Chemical people had a large plant in the immediate area and they, too, were interested in possible new uses for hydrochloric acid as they produced large volumes of it at their plant. The Dow Chemical plants also produced large amounts of acid waste which were disposed of underground and they had observed that acid treatment of disposal wells had increased the injection rate of these wells. These tests had been conducted under the supervision of John Grebe and Nolan Poffenberger of Dow's research department. It was only natural, then, that these men would get together with W. A. Thomas, division geologist for The Pure Oil Company, and Howard Humphry and R. H. Carr of Pure's engineering department, to complete plans for the first oil-well acidizing experiment late in 1931.

On February 11, 1932, the first treatment[17] was made on The Pure Oil Company Fox #6 well, in the Greendale Pool of Midland County, Mich. The hydrochloric acid concentration was 15 percent by weight and with the addition of arsenic acid—which Dow also made—served as an excellent inhibitor against corrosion of steel pipes and tubing. It was decided the well should be treated in two stages, using 500 gal. of acid in each stage with adequate testing of the well after each stage. Fox #6 produced 16 bbl of oil per day after acidizing, which was an increase of about 12 bbl per day.

Acid treatment was continued on additional wells and the results obtained are shown in Table 2 *(op. cit.)*.

The Pure Oil Company and Dow Chemical Company lost no time in filing applications for patents. Pure's patents were filed in the name of R. H. Carr and covered the technique of introducing chemicals into the well by the balanced fluid column method. Before the first experimental well was acidized, John Grebe and Ross T. Sanford, both with

Table 2[17]

Well	Daily Production before Treatment, Bbl	Daily Production after Treatment, Bbl	Number of Treatments
Pure Oil-Root #2	30	800	3
McClanahan Oil Co.- Shaeffer #1	75	334	?

Dow, did considerable work on the optimum acid concentration and methods of inhibiting the acid against corrosion of the metal parts of the well; and they filed claims covering the treatment of wells with chemicals containing a corrosion inhibitor. Both applications were received in the patent office on the same day. Grebe and Sanford were granted Patent No. 1,877,504 on September 13, 1932; and Carr's patent was No. 1,891,667, granted December 20, 1932.

The inventors were thinking primarily of the greatest benefit which could be obtained by treating all wells which had almost reached their economic limit, of which there were thousands in hundreds of different pools scattered through the states of Michigan, Ohio, Indiana, Illinois, Kentucky, West Virginia, Pennsylvania, and the Province of Ontario.

By the middle of 1932 it seemed certain that the acid process had real commercial possibilities, and Dow Chemical Company formed a subsidiary called Dowell Incorporated to handle the new chemical service. By the end of January 1933, wells were being acidized by various individuals and organizations throughout the areas where limestone was the producing horizon. Many of these companies soon left the field, but Chemical Process Company, founded by Paul Pitzer and C. K. West of Breckenridge, Texas, survived and prospered. Pitzer and West, in the spring of 1932, experimented with acid on some of their own wells which were completed in the Breckenridge (Caddo) lime and were ready for abandonment at the time the tests were made. Their first experiment was made by pouring some 230 gal. of 15-percent hydrochloric acid down the casing, with negative results. The second well was treated with 750 gal. of acid followed by some oil to force the acid into the limestone. This second well, which produced 1½ bbl per day before treatment, began to flow at the rate of 125 bbl per day after treatment.

Fluoride chemicals[18] were first added to the acid used in treating Michigan wells in 1933 to speed up the rate of reaction on dolomites and siliceous rocks. In 1937, this fortified solvent—to which had been added various surface-active agents, demulsifying compounds, and corrosion inhibitors—was used by Dowell on California wells to dissolve silicates present in the oil-bearing formations and drilling fluids. In 1939, this well-treating mixture, now known as "mud acid", was used successfully by Texas Gulf Coast operators for the same purpose.

FRACTURING FORMATIONS TO INCREASE PRODUCTION

It has long been recognized that formations could be occasionally "broken down"—by water in water-injection wells, by cement slurries, mud or water in the case of a cement squeeze, and by acid in the case of acid treatment of some wells. Generally, the breaking down of a formation was indicated by a pressure reduction, usually abrupt, while pumping these fluids into the well; but the mechanics of the phenomenon were little understood.

It is of interest to note that J. J. Grebe and S. M. Stoesser[19] in 1935, stated:

"In experiments in treating wells with acid for the production and disposal of brine . . . it was discovered that a fluid pressure at the bottom of the well sufficient to counterbalance the weight of the rock above it plus an additional pressure required for actually breaking (cracking) the formation, makes possible the introduction of fluids into new crevasses thus created."

In 1939, Paul D. Torrey[20] mentioned the "fracturing" in squeeze-cementing operations and in the injection of water or brines during oil-field flooding operations. Grebe again discussed "earth lifting" in 1943,[21] and S. T. Yuster and J. C. Calhoun, Jr.[22] mentioned "pressure parting" and gave detailed information on conditions observed in certain wells under water flood in the Bradford Field.

During the 1940's, the Research Department of Pan American Petroleum Corporation (then Stanolind Oil and Gas Company) performed experiments aimed at increasing the knowledge of this "breakdown" phenomenon. It was during this experimentation that the hydraulic-fracturing method for improving the productivity of wells was envisioned.

R. F. Farris of Pan American Research[23] first suggested that hydraulic fracturing with a "low-penetrating fluid" (defined by Farris as a fluid which, with respect to the natural fluids in the well such as water or crude oil, has a considerably retarded tendency to filter through the formations) might increase the effective drainage capacity of an oil or gas well by providing an improved system of flow channels from the formation into the well proper. J. B. Clark, also of Pan American Research, in October 1948[24] announced to the industry the original version of the hydraulic fracturing (hydrafrac) process in which napalm soap (an ingredient in making jellied gasoline, a World War II incendiary material) could be used to thicken crude oil or kerosene as both a fracturing fluid and as a carrier for sand in the process. This technique created a fracture in the formation and deposited sand as a propping material to keep the fractures from closing. The napalm gels being relatively unstable, the viscous solution will revert to approximately that of the base oil after the fracture is formed and, further, the time of reversion is controllable within definite limits by the addition of small amounts of water to the napalm gasoline gel. This greatly facilitated subsequent displacement of the treating fluid from the formation by reservoir crude oil. The process was described and the results of field tests were reported. These showed that treatments in 23 wells had resulted in sustained production increases in 11. The process was first commercialized early in 1949 by Halliburton Oil Well Cementing Company under exclusive license from Pan American. In 1953, the exclusive license was terminated and all service companies who desired to sell fracturing services and who were capable of supplying a reputable service were licensed.

Many variations of the process were soon developed. The most significant were the use of: *1*, special refined oils which have inherently low-fluid-loss characteristics; *2*, special additives to reduce fluid loss of oils or water; *3*, low-penetrating acid which not only fractures but acidizes calcareous formations; *4*, spaced batches of oil-soluble bridging materials or ball sealers to cause multiple fractures in a formation; *5*, large-volume high injection-rate treatments where lease crude or water is the fracturing fluid; and *6*, the development of techniques of fracture placement at specified points in a formation.

As much as a quarter of a million gallons of fracturing fluid have been injected into a formation from a single well, at a rate as high as 4,000 gal. per min and containing a total of 125 tons of sand. A majority of the treatments are in the range of 20,000 to 40,000 gal. of fracturing fluid carrying 10 to 20 tons of sand. Many changes and improvements have been made in the type of equipment used to carry on the fracturing operations, principally directed toward providing pumps of higher capacities so that the fracturing process can be completed in as short a period of time as possible.

The growth of the process, including these variations, has been phenomenal. Starting with no commercial jobs in 1949, the rate of usage increased to a maximum of about 4,500 jobs per month in 1955. Treatments declined in the recent recession to a low of about 2,300 jobs per month early in 1958 and have since leveled off at about 3,000 jobs per month.

The fracturing process has been the most important engineering contribution to the maintenance of maximum productivity and to the increase in ultimate recovery of oil from the reservoir that has been offered to the industry in recent years.

ROTARY METHOD OF WELL COMPLETION

The cable-tool drilling method had certain inherent advantages in well completion which have now been brought to the rotary system of drilling through the advancements in technique and new equipment. The one inherent disadvantage of the rotary system for drilling through the oil-producing formation is the fact that there must be a differential pressure in favor of the liquids out of the drilling fluid entering the producing formation, otherwise the well would be out of control.

All water-base drilling fluids lose some filtrate to the producing formations and often clay particles and weighting materials are carried into the formation, reducing the permeability. This reduction in permeability is known as "water-blocking" or "mudding off" and, in many cases, the effect is permanently detrimental to oil production. Some producing formations contain bentonite clays which become hydrated and increase in volume in contact with water. These hydrated clays sometimes reduce to zero the permeability of the sandstone exposed in the hole.

To overcome the detrimental effects of water infiltration into the producing formation, cable tools were often used to drill in, especially when the formation pressure was low. In some cases, the well was drilled in dry with rotary, and in high-pressure areas special flush-joint drill pipe and an effective stuffing-box oil saver were essential to prevent blow-outs. The Sheldon-Burden rotary and the Hydril rotary, which are described in another chapter, provided the necessary equipment.

In some areas, where conditions permitted, the water-base drilling fluid was removed before drilling into the producing formation and crude oil was then used as the circulating fluid.

The idea of using an oil-base instead of a water-base mud for drilling the producing formation was probably in the minds of many persons at about the same time. However, it appears that R. D. Dawson and P. H. Huisman of Shell Oil Company were the first to put into practice the use of an oil-base drilling fluid. They applied for a patent on air-blown asphalt for use in oil-base muds in the Netherlands on June 2, 1938. In the latter part of 1938, George Miller[25, 26] prepared an oil-base mud using air-blown asphalt, with lamp black as a settling inhibitor, which was successful on an 8,000-ft test in the Ten Sections Field, Kern County, Calif. In April 1942, George Miller started a concern known as Oil Base, Inc., which was the first to offer an oil-base drilling mud to the petroleum industry. A number of individuals and companies have since developed oil-base muds and many patents have been issued. In the majority of cases, use of oil-base muds in drilling oil formations subject to damage by water from mud filtrate has resulted in high initial and higher ultimate well production.

Methods of Removing Water-Block

As already stated, the formation of water-blocks when using water-base mud in drilling the producing formation had long been recognized, but a study of the methods of removing the water-block probably started with the work of L. C. Chamberlain, Jr.

Chamberlain reasoned that the Jamin effect—wherein there was a resistance to the flow of fluid through a capillary tube containing alternating drops of fluid and bubbles of gas—might explain why some wells did not react favorably to acid treatment and, further, that the addition of surface-tension-reducing agents to the well-treating chemical might reduce or eliminate the Jamin effect.

In 1935, Chamberlain[17] was granted a patent involving the use of certain surface-tension-reducing agents in well-treating acids. In 1937, a well which was producing 48 bbl of oil daily from the Simpson sand at Seminole, Okla. was reworked. Light mud fluid was used in the rework job and it was found that, after reworking, the well produced at a much lower rate. To remove the water-block, about 1,000 gal. of low-surface-tension fluid was then injected into the oil sand. When placed on production after this treatment, this well started producing some oil and increasing amounts of water. Finally, the water volume began to decline and the oil production increased until the well was producing at the rate of 90 bbl of oil per day free of any water.

In 1938, Monson[27] was granted a patent which covered the use of sulfonates and other agents for removing drilling water from the formation. L. C. Chamberlain *(op. cit.)* in 1943 was granted a patent which provided for the use of non-acid fluid containing suitable surface-tension-reducing agents for the removal of water-block. It was well-known that a reduction of the water saturation of a reservoir rock would increase its permeability to oil and decrease the permeability to water, thereby promoting a more efficient flow of oil into the well bore.[28] These high water saturations may be the natural free water saturation of the producing formation—or may be induced by the water out of the drilling fluids, or from casing leaks, or various other causes, increasing the saturation of the producing formation close to the hole. Torrey *(op. cit.)* stated that a chemical known as "Orchem M-14" was developed during the early part of 1953 for the specific purpose of removing water-block. Orchem M-14 was a cationic wetting agent which, it was claimed, would preferentially oil-wet the reservoir surface within the treated area increasing permeability to oil and reducing permeability to water; and, also, would break down and remove water-blocks which had been created in the reservoir in the immediate periphery of the well bore. The first field test with this chemical was in the East White Point Field, San Patricio County, Texas, in August 1953. It was used in a well where the producing sand had been penetrated and saturated with water from another horizon. Before treatment, this well produced 8 bbl of oil per day; and after treatment, it produced 110 bbl per day. In 1954, A. W. Garst[29] reported the development of a treatment involving certain non-ionic surface-active agents by which water-block is removed from wells by lowering oil-water interfacial tension to a very low value. The treatment had then been used in 90 wells, with successful results obtained in 39 wells representing 7 formations in 9 fields. A number of oil-wetting chemicals are now available and, generally, good results have been obtained by use of such chemicals on wells in other fields in Texas where the formations had been saturated with extraneous water.

Casing Program for Rotary Completions

The casing program is of utmost importance in the proper completion of the well with the rotary system as well as with the cable-tool system. There are two casing programs used in completing wells drilled with rotary tools when production is from a single horizon. In both of these programs, it is customary practice to set and cement surface casing to protect the fresh-water sands from contamination and for pressure control. In one casing program, it is the practice to set and cement a string of casing immediately above the producing horizon either before or after drilling through the producing sand, and set a perforated liner if needed. The other casing program is to drill through the producing sand, set and cement casing entirely through the producing sand and perforate opposite the producing sand, then set a perforated liner if needed. California practice, at one time, was to run a full oil string with blank pipe at the top and perforated pipe on the bottom opposite the producing horizon, but the present general practice is to use only a perforated liner opposite the producing zones.

In the development of the Long Beach Field in the Signal Hill area, Los Angeles County, Calif. in 1921, it was customary practice to set the water string at the top of the oil measures which were encountered as shallow as 2,300 ft. After making a successful water-shutoff test, drilling was continued with rotary through some 2,500 ft of alternating sands and shale, the sands being oil-bearing. An oil string, which consisted of some 2,300 ft of blank pipe on top and 2,500 ft of perforated pipe on bottom, was run to the bottom of the hole. With this type completion, the well often produced water even though there was no water present in the oil sand at the location where the well was being drilled. Various tests indicated that its source was from behind the water string, which had been worn through by the rotation of the drill pipe. It became customary practice to pump cement up back of the oil string, tying the oil and water strings together by forcing cement out through the topmost regular perforations. Numerous devices were developed to keep the cement from dropping inside and outside the casing, and also for centering the oil string in the hole.

The knowledge that the water string was being worn through by rotating drill pipe led to the invention of various types of "casing protectors" which were placed on the drill pipe. A number of these were made of ball bearing, or bronze, but the one most widely used was the rubber protector developed by J. C. Ballagh in about 1928. It was sold under the trade name of "Bettis Protector" and was produced by the Patterson-Ballagh Corporation. This protector was expanded over the tool joints and it held firmly on the pipe below the tool joints. The outside diameter of the rubber protector was slightly larger than the tool joints, thus eliminating the wear on the water string.

605

In multiple-sand oil and gas fields, a satisfactory in-the-hole perforator and the electric well log used in conjunction with accurate measuring devices have made possible the practice of setting and cementing casing through all producing sands and completing the well to produce initially from one or more of the deepest sands. After the lowermost sands have ceased to produce profitably, they can be cemented off and the casing perforated opposite upper sands. This has made it possible to deplete multiple-sand fields through a minimum number of wells. In most areas where there is only one producing sand, it is common practice to set and cement casing through this sand and perforate the casing opposite the sand for completion.

Improvements in cementing practices, such as casing-centering devices and methods of providing a satisfactory bond between the cement back of the casing and the formation by the use of scratchers pioneered by Bruce Barkis and Kenneth Wright in 1940, have made possible satisfactory recompletions in multiple-sand fields.

SAND CONTROL IN OIL AND GAS WELLS

The use of screen pipe and perforated liners to control sand production has already been discussed under the heading of shop-perforated casing used in cable-tool completions.

Gravel Packing of Oil Wells[30]

Gravel packing for the purpose of controlling sand production in a water well was first used in 1878 by James Dallard, and it became common practice to complete water wells in this manner. It was a simple matter[31] to gravel pack water wells, as they were customarily of large diameter and relatively shallow so that gravel could be dumped in at the surface. The gravel supported the walls of the well and prevented caving against the casing, as well as excluding the sand production.

L. C. Uren *(op. cit.)* is believed to be one of the first persons to give serious consideration to the problem of gravel packing oil and gas wells. He was impressed with the theoretical advantage of large-diameter wells from the standpoint of initial production and ultimate recovery, and conceived the idea that reservoir rock might be underreamed below the casing point to a sufficient size to permit gravel in quantities to be placed between the liner and the walls of the hole. Uren was granted a patent in 1924 covering such a process and also a patent covering the equipment for accomplishing this gravel-packing operation. The oil industry was not impressed with the method, but the Layne-Atlantic Company was granted a license to use the process and successfully applied it in gravel packing wells in the Gulf Coast area in 1932. The Texas Company began experimenting with gravel packing in some of their wells in Coalinga and Wilmington Fields in California during the mid-30's, and the results of this gravel-packing operation were brought to the attention of the oil industry. The Texaco Development Corporation purchased Uren's basic patent and also acquired patents which had been issued to Layne and were junior to those of Uren. Uren then helped them to develop two other patents covering details of the circulation method of gravel packing. The Texaco Development Corporation has licensed several other companies and service organizations to use these methods. Fig. 10[32] is a sketch illustrating the method of gravel packing wells by reverse circulation.

The development of the prepacked liner retarded the use of gravel packing by the methods finally developed by the Texaco Development Corporation. This prepacked liner was constructed by placing gravel of the size desired in the annulus between two perforated liners.

The use of the prepacked gravel

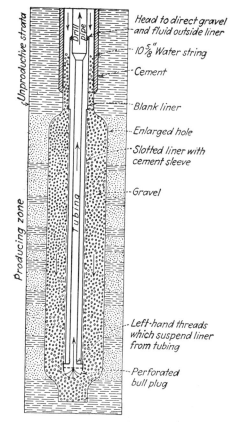

Fig. 10—Sketch Illustrating Method of Gravel-packing Wells by Reverse Circulation[32]

liners[33] reached its peak during the development of the Wilmington and Long Beach Harbor oil fields in California in the middle 30's. The principal problem was mud clogging in the screen and gravel. Salt-water washing and mechanical scratching were helpful, but the rapid decline of oil production resulted in a change back to open-hole gravel-packing techniques.

Gravel packing *(op. cit.)* has been proved to be a possible means of controlling sand entry, but the related problems of fluid contamination in the reservoir and of mud contamination in the gravel have offset —in many cases—the advantages of continuous oil production. However, in about 1950, petroleum engineers developed improved methods of gravel packing and well-completion practices to facilitate use of clean well fluids to avoid mud contamination and the resulting limited well productivity.

Plastic-coated Walnut Shells Used for Sand Control

Recently, plastic-coated walnut shells—which are designed to form a bonded, permeable filter bed in perforations or opposite the producing formation—have been used in controlling sand production. After the shells have been coated with plastic at the surface, they are circulated into position with carrier fluid or viscous low-gravity oil.[34] The plastic coating on the shells will harden and bond the shells together, forming a bridging medium to prevent sand production.

Field placement procedure has involved either or both of two techniques: *1*, the use of penetrating fluid and low pressure to allow the shells to filter against the sand face; and *2*, the use of high pressure to fracture the formation and leave the shells in the fracture as a propping and filtering medium. If a thick mud cake covers the sand face, the high-pressure technique must be used. In some cases, an aluminum screen and liner have been used in conjunction with an annular ring of bonded shells inside the casing to prevent sand entry.

Use of Adhesive Materials to Consolidate Sand

Halliburton Oil Well Cementing Company is believed to have first introduced plastic material which would bind together the sand grains of a poorly consolidated formation exposed in a well without materially affecting its permeability to oil. This use of phenolformaldehyde resin plastics to consolidate incompetent formation sands apparently was an outgrowth of the use of plastics for water exclusion *(op. cit.)*, which was done in the East Texas Field in November 1942, to control water entry from the Woodbine sand.

The first commercial applications of plastics to consolidate formations were begun by the service companies in late 1945 or early 1946. Three of the early patents covering the use of plastics for sand consolidation were issued to C. Irons and S. M. Stoesser on February 24, 1942, to G. G. Wrightsman and S. E. Buckley on June 19, 1945, and to P. H. Cardwell on October 18, 1949. One of the first treatments on record was performed on January 17, 1946, on the Gulf-E. R. Taylor #37 in the Pierce Junction Field, Harris County, Texas. Initial results were encouraging and, by 1947, the treatment was being used extensively along the Louisiana-Texas Gulf Coast.[35] Most formations which had a combination of an effective reservoir drive plus high permeability could be successfully consolidated; but when the reservoir drive was not effective or the permeability of the sand was low, the chances of securing desired producing rates with effective sand consolidation were reduced.[36]

Essentially, there are two basic methods of consolidating sand with plastics. In the first method, plastic is squeezed into the sand, followed by a larger volume of crude or diesel oil to remove the excess plastic, leaving permeable paths through which fluids can enter the well bore.

The well is then shut in until the remaining plastic has hardened; and a second treatment is applied, in some cases, before the well is put on production. [34-37, incl.] The second method involves squeezing plastic containing a shrinking agent into the sand, after which the well is shut in. The plastic shrinks as it hardens, opening permeable paths to the well bore. [34]

Recently, improvement has been achieved in plastic consolidation of sands through use of permanent completion methods which permit perforating the casing and the placement of the plastic in the presence of clean well fluids. Use of mud during perforating, or at any time prior to the consolidation treatment, fills the perforations with mud filter cake and prevents adequate treatment of an entire interval. A variation of the plastic technique was to squeeze the formation with Ottawa sand suspended in a viscous gel, followed by a treatment of plastic to bind the Ottawa sand grains.

MULTIPLE-WELL COMPLETIONS

In many areas in the United States it has been illegal to produce more than one reservoir through the same hole. Therefore, two, three, and sometimes four complete wells at each location were needed to produce from that many separate reservoirs at the same time. It was not uncommon in the early days of oil development in this country to complete a well temporarily, so that gas could be produced between strings of casing and oil produced through the oil string. This was commonly termed "bradenheading" off the gas between strings, and the gas supply made available was generally used for fuel in completing the same well or others. This gas supply, which was entirely separated from the oil, was a highly desirable fuel supply for development purposes. In September 1913, [4] a well in the Wicey Pool near Bixby, Okla. was completed so that gas could be produced between strings of casing and oil produced through the oil string which was $5\frac{3}{16}$-in. casing. The gas sand was encountered at about 1,700 ft after $6\frac{5}{8}$-in. casing had been set. The gas volume was such that no further drilling could be conducted. The well was killed by lubricating mud in the hole, then drilling continued through the gas sand. A string of $5\frac{3}{16}$-in. casing was fitted with a packer at the lower end and, on September 9, 1913, the fluid was bailed from the well and the gas allowed to clean out the hole. The casing was then seated below the gas sand, thus excluding the gas from inside the casing, and open-hole drilling was resumed. A stuffing-box casing head was placed on top of the $6\frac{5}{8}$-in. casing and packed around the $5\frac{3}{16}$-in. casing, thus controlling the gas between strings. The well was finished by drilling to the lower oil sand and bringing the oil up through the inside of the $5\frac{3}{16}$-in. casing, while the gas was recovered between strings. A well completed by this method was known as a "combination well".

In 1926, cable tools were being used to drill and complete all wells in the Panhandle Field of Texas. N. O. Miller devised a method of completing these wells without wasting the upper gas in drilling to the underlying oil-producing zone. The purpose of his invention was two-fold: first, to prevent the waste and hazard of drilling through the gas horizon; and second, to eliminate recementation of the dolomite pay horizon when carrying a hole full of water, so that the gas pay could be successfully brought in as a dual completion with the oil. He invented a stuffing-box type casing head through which casing collars would pass without gas leakage. This casing head was installed on the water string and the oil string was run through it. Additional joints were added as drilling progressed through the gas zone. The gas pressure was sub-normal, so a 1,200-ft column of water carried in the hole was sufficient to balance the gas pressure and keep the gas in place with a minimum time of formation contact with water; and the casing head was closed in, so there was gas confined back of the oil string and water in the oil string. Before the oil zone was encountered, the oil string was landed for a formation shutoff and the wells were completed to produce oil through the oil string and gas through the casing annulus.

In the middle 1930's, several operators in the Wilmington Field, Los Angeles County, Calif.[40-42, incl.] made dual completions by separating the Upper and Lower Terminal zones using shop-perforated casing and a special cementing device which permitted the cementing of the shoe and the blank casing between the producing zones, with tubing landed in these special tools. The purpose of these dual completions was to prevent the commingling of production from these two zones, as there was a substantial difference in the gravity of the oil produced and in the price differential paid. These completions were made several years before the introduction of the perforating gun which proved that, while the gun perforator is not essential to a dual completion, it certainly is the simplest method of accomplishing what one needs to accomplish in making a dual completion.

It is believed that the petroleum engineering section of Continental Oil Company was the first to make application to the state conservation authorities for multiple completions in Texas and Louisiana sometime during 1936. In 1938, Continental completed wells in the Ville Platte Field in Louisiana so that gas could be injected into the producing zone near the top while oil was being produced from the bottom of the same zone. This is believed to have been the first instance of one hole serving both as a producing well and as an injection well into and from the same formation. World War II was partially responsible for a notable increase in multiple-well completions. Several deep multiple-sand fields happened to be discovered during that period and the supply of casing was limited. The conservation commission authorized multiple completions as a means of obtaining the maximum amount of oil with the minimum use of steel for oil-well casing.

The ordinary dual completion would be a case in which a tubing packer separated the lowermost producing formation from a producing formation back of the tubing and above the packer. This would permit producing the lowermost formation through the tubing and the formation back of the tubing through the annulus between the tubing and the casing. This method makes production from the annulus almost impossible after the well ceases to flow. Another type of dual completion would have a packing device—as mentioned previously—but with a second string of tubing alongside the one which goes through the packer, through which the oil producible through the annulus could be brought to the surface. In this latter case, it would be possible to pump oil from either one or both of the formations after the wells had ceased to flow.[43]

PERMANENT-TYPE WELL COMPLETION

Recompletion in multiple-sand fields was always expensive and often detrimental to the producing formation by adding extraneous fluids to the producing formation. This was the case in both single completions in multiple-sand fields and dual completions, but more particularly in the latter. It was apparent from the beginning that, in order to accomplish recompletions in multiple-sand fields without the usual procedure of installing workover equipment and killing the well, it would be necessary to find tools capable of operating through tubing which could be kept in place during recompletion operations. To recomplete a well with tubing in place, it was necessary to develop a tubing-type perforator, which was first used late in 1950. This was a jet-type gun perforator of such size that it would run through the tubing and perforate both tubing and casing, and could also be run outside the tubing to perforate the casing below the tubing. Tubing perforators have since been developed so powerful that they are equal to a conventional 4-in. jet gun, and this perforator service is now offered throughout most of the United States.

In order to vary the length of the tubing in the hole where the bottom of the permanent tubing was set above all producing horizons, a method was devised whereby small tubing was inserted through the regular tubing to extend to a depth beyond the bottom of the permanent tubing. This extension was accomplished by suspending various predetermined lengths of 1¼-in. steel tubing from the lower end of the 2-in. production tubing, using a landing nipple and mandrel. This method permitted successive recompletions at higher intervals after plugging off with cement and reperforating higher, and was employed shortly after the development of the tubing gun. Later, the 1¼-in. steel tubing was discontinued and a 1-in. aluminum tubing used instead. This aluminum tubing was easily handled by light wire-line equipment.[44]

In the development of the permanent-type well completions, it was necessary to make some type of arrangement wherein the cement would plug only the perforations to be abandoned and any excess could be circulated out. A modified cement—which was a common cement containing a large amount of bentonite and a small percentage of calcium lignosulfonate—was found to accomplish the desired results without becoming dehydrated, except adjacent to the formation. It was found that high pressures were not necessary in cementing off perforations through which oil and gas had been produced. It was also found that the cementing operation should not be done in the presence of mud fluid which would deposit a filter cake on the sands, and that much better results were obtained by using salt water in the hole.

Set cement in the hole can be removed by placing a nozzle on the lower end of the tubing extension which directs a flow of acid against the cement. The solution formed by the chemical reaction on the cement is removed by circulation *(op. cit.)*.

Continued development of permanent-type well-completion equipment and techniques has improved and broadened the application and method to the extent that almost any type of completion or recompletion, except deepening, can be performed through the tubing. Included in operations that may be performed on permanently completed wells are: *1*, removing sand from within the well bore by utilizing telescoping joints in the tubing extension which automatically lengthens the extension as sand is washed from the well by reverse circulation; and *2*, squeeze cementing and perforating in connection with recompleting the upper and lower zones of dual wells, as well as single completions *(op. cit.)*.

CONCLUSION

The importance of proper well completions cannot be over-emphasized. The reservoir must have every opportunity to deliver oil and/or gas to the conductor which makes the connection between the reservoir and the surface. This conductor, whether casing or tubing, should offer an unobstructed passage and permit workovers as the need arises. The conductor should not wear out on account of corrosion before the reservoir has been depleted.

Satisfactory in-the-hole perforators and electrical well-logging methods, coupled with accurate measuring devices, have made it good practice in some areas to set and cement the casing entirely through the producing formation and perforate to produce from any desired section.

Circulating fluids are available with rotary drilling to prevent the formation of water-blocks in the producing formation. The discovery of chemicals for removal of water-blocks, when formed, has reduced the number of unsatisfactory completions.

Difficulties in controlling sand produced with oil have been partially eliminated by using specially designed slotted screens and liners prepacked with gravel. The method of gravel packing used for water wells has been applied to oil wells. Plastics have been successfully used to consolidate the oil sands and reduce production of sand in the oil.

Methods of increasing the production by shooting, acidizing, and fracturing the producing formation have been responsible for higher initial well production and greater ultimate recovery.

Multiple-well completions have materially reduced development costs. It is now possible to produce from five different reservoirs through the same well bore.

REFERENCES

[1]Petroleum Investigations: Hearings before a Subcommittee of the Committee on Interstate and Foreign Commerce, House of Representatives, 73rd Congress, H. Res. 441, printed in U. S. Government Printing Office, Washington, 1924, 876 (1800-1924).

[2]Carll, John F: *The Geology of the Oil Regions of Warren, Venango, Clarion, and Butler Counties, Pennsylvania,* Second Geological Survey of Pennsylvania, 1875-79, **III** (1880).

[3]Henry, J. T: *The Early and Late History of Petroleum,* published in 1873. A copy is in the Drake Well Museum, Titusville, Pa.

[4]Heggem, A. G. and Pollard, J. A: Drilling Wells in Oklahoma by the Mud-laden Fluid Method, *U. S. Bur. Mines TP 68, Petroleum Tech.* 15 (1914).

[5]*Oil Well Supply Company Catalog:* Section A, No. 21, p. 203-204 (1907).

[6]Swigart, T. E. and Beecher, C. E: Manual for Oil and Gas Operations, *U. S. Bur. Mines Bull.* 232 (1923).

[7]Craig, Homer: Personal communication with H. K. V. Tompkins, Houston, Texas, in April 1958, regarding the invention of the Craig oil saver about 1921.

[8]*Kerotest Catalog:* Nov. 1930, Kerotest Manufacturing Co., Pittsburg, Pa.

[9]Otis, H. C: Development of Running and Pulling Pipe under Pressure and Use of Side Door Choke, submitted to Harold Vance by letter dated December 7, 1954.

[10]*The Layne and Bowler Company Catalog:* Aug. 1959, The Layne and Bowler Company, Houston, Texas.

[11]Wagy, E. W: Perforated Casing and Screen Pipe in Oil Wells, *U. S. Bur. Mines TP 245, Petroleum Tech.* 55, April (1920).

[12]Campbell, John L. P: History of Perforating, submitted to Harold Vance upon request, December 29, 1954.

[13]Rough, Robert L: Letter dated April 11, 1955, to Harold Vance. Rough with U.S. Bureau of Mines, Morgantown, W. Va.

[14]Rison, C. O: Manufacture of Nitroglycerin and Use of High Explosives in Oil and Gas Wells, *Trans. Am. Inst. Mining Met. Engrs. (Petroleum Development and Technology)* 240 (1928-29).

[15]Vance, Harold: Development and Production Methods in West Texas, *Proc. Am. Pet. Inst. (Prod. Bul. 202)* 105 (1928); also *The Oil Weekly,* June 22 (1928).

[16]Miller, R. G: Letter dated October 18, 1955, to Harold Vance, regarding methods employed for detonating nitroglycerin.

[17]Fitzgerald, P. E: The Development of Chemical Treatment of Wells, furnished to Harold Vance upon request, May 1955.

[18]Heath, S. B. and Fry, William: U. S. Patent No. 2,011,579, issued December 17, 1935. First use of fluoride chemicals in acid treatment of wells in Michigan (1933).

[19]Grebe, J. J. and Stoesser, S. M: Increasing Crude Production 20,000,000 Barrels from Established Fields, *World Petroleum*, Aug. (1935).

[20]Torrey, Paul D: Selective Exclusion of Fluids from Wells, *API Drilling and Production Practice*, 205 (1939); also *Oil Weekly*, May 22 (1939) and May 29 (1939).

[21]Grebe, J. J: Tools and Aims of Research, *Chem. and Eng. News*, Dec. (1943).

[22]Yuster, S. T. and Calhoun, J. C., Jr: Pressure Parting, *Producers Monthly*, **9[4]** Feb. (1945).

[23]Farris, R. F: U. S. Patent Re. No. 23,733, Nov. 10, 1953.

[24]Clark, J. B: A Hydraulic Process for Increasing the Productivity of Wells, *Trans. Am. Inst. Mining Met. Engrs. (Petroleum Development and Technology)* **186,** 1 (1949).

[25]Miller, George: Oil Base Drilling Fluids, *Proceedings of the Third World Petroleum Congress, Section II,* The Hague, 1951, published by E. J. Brill, Leiden, Holland (1951).

[26]Miller, George: Letter to Harold Vance, dated March 20, 1958, giving additional data regarding oil-base drilling fluids.

[27]Monson: U. S. Patent No. 2,135,589, 1938.

[28]Torrey, Paul D: Letter to Harold Vance, dated September 23, 1957, regarding chemical treatment for water-block removal (1953).

[29]Garst, A. W: A Low-cost Method of Production Stimulation, *AIME J. Petr. Tech.*, 10, Nov. (1954).

[30]Curry, Carter: Gravel-Packing Techniques on Gulf Coast, *Oil Gas J.*, June 22 (1953).

[31]Uren, Lester C: Letter dated December 27, 1954, to Harold Vance.

[32]Uren, Lester C: *Petroleum Production Engineering—Exploration*, McGraw-Hill Book Co., Inc., New York, 1953, 3rd Ed.

[33]Barkis, Bruce, Sr: Personal communication regarding all phases of completion practices.

[34]Burpee, G. E. and Ring, Kenneth: Article on the use of plastics, written for Harold Vance upon request and submitted April 16, 1958.

[35]Cardwell, P. H: Plastic Used to Consolidate Incompetent Formations, *Trans. Am. Inst. Mining Met. Engrs. (Petroleum Development and Technology)* **170,** 174 (1947).

[36]Smith, R. H. and Polk, A. C., Jr: Use of Plastics in Consolidating Loose Sands in Wells, *Trans. Am. Inst. Mining Met. Engrs. (Petroleum Development and Technology)* **170,** 243 (1947).

[37]Townsend, A. A. and Smith, R. H: Well Completion and Remedial Work with Plastics, *Oil Gas J.*, **46 [1]** May 10 (1947).

[38]Wrightsman, G. G. and Spain, H. H: Consolidation of Sands in Oil and Gas Wells, *Oil Gas J.*, **46 [11]** 73, July 19 (1947).

[39]Tausch, G. H. and Corley, C. B., Jr: Sand Exclusion in Oil and Gas Wells, *API Drilling and Production Practice*, 66 (1958).

[40]Sanders, T. P: Several Benefits Gained from New Type Well Completions, *Oil Gas J.*, April 7 (1938).

[41]Mills, B: Multiple Zone Producing Practices at Wilmington, California, *Oil Weekly*, June 27 (1938).

[42]Bell, Olin G: Multiple Oil-Zone Completions, *Am. Assoc. Petroleum Geologists Bull.* **23,** 1273, Aug. 9 (1939).

[43]Bennett, E. O: Letter dated December 3, 1954, to Harold Vance, regarding development of multiple zones.

[44]Huber, T. A: History of Permanent-type Well Completions, submitted to Harold Vance upon request, October 27, 1954.

BIBLIOGRAPHY

Atchison, T. C., Jr; Duvall, W. I; and Grant, B. F: Progress Report on Well-shooting Research, *API Drilling and Production Practice*, 63 (1952).

Bailey, J. E. and Dimit, Charles E: Plug-back Work with Plastics in the East Texas Field, *API Drilling and Production Practice*, 82 (1943).

Benckenstein, C. H: U. S. Patent No. 2,354,570, July 25, 1944, covering use of sand in the treating fluid where it acts as a propping agent.

Cabeen, W. R. and Bemis, E. G: Field Performance of Sand-control Liners in California, *API Drilling and Production Practice,* 271 (1949).

Chamberlain, L. C., Jr: U. S. Patent No. 2,327,017, 1943, covering use of non-acid fluid containing suitable surface-tension-reducing agents.

Chenault, R. L: Experiments on Fluid Capacity and Plugging of Oil-Well Screens, *API Drilling and Production Practice,* 296 (1938).

Clark, W. A: Economics of Gravel Packing in California, *API Drilling and Production Practice,* 327 (1939).

Clark, W. A: A Resumé of the Application of Gravel Packing in California, *Trans. Am. Inst. Mining Met. Engrs. (Petroleum Development and Technology)* **136,** 15 (1940) (reprint, p. 13).

Coberly, C. J: Selection of Screen Openings for Unconsolidated Sands, *API Drilling and Production Practice,* 189 (1937).

Coberly, C. J. and Wagner, E. M: Some Considerations in the Selection and Installation of Gravel Pack for Oil Wells, *AIME Tech. Paper 960, Petr. Tech.,* Aug. (1938).

Cunningham, J. M: Theoretical Consideration of the Perforation Pattern in a Screen Pipe, *API Drilling and Production Practice,* 307 (1938).

Eastman, H. J: Lateral Drain-Hole Drilling, *Petroleum Engr.,* B-57, Nov. (1954), and B-44, Dec. (1954).

Evinger, H. H. and Muskat, M: Some Theotretical Considerations on the Problems of Well Shooting, *Trans. Am. Inst. Mining Met. Engrs. (Petroleum Development and Technology)* **142,** 216 (1941) (reprint, p. 405).

Foran, E. V: Pressure Completions of Wells in West Texas, *API Drilling and Production Practice,* 48 (1934); also *Petroleum Engr.* (title: Deep Well Drilling under Pressure Control), Sept. (1934).

Garten, J. P: Investigation of the Production Characteristics of Wells Completed with Gravel-Screen Liners, *AIME Paper No. 683-G,* Oct. (1956).

Grant, B. F; Duvall, W. I; Rough, R. L; and Atchison, T. C: Research on Shooting Oil and Gas Wells, *API Drilling and Production Practice,* 303 (1950).

Gumpertz, B: Screening Effect of Gravel on Unconsolidated Sands, *Trans. Am. Inst. Mining Met. Engrs. (Petroleum Development and Technology)* **142,** 76 (1941) (reprint, p. 265).

Henderson, J. K; Salle, W. L; and Stout, C. M: How Plastic-coated Walnut Shells Control Loose Sands, *World Oil,* 271, April (1956).

Hill, K. E: Factors Affecting Use of Gravel in Oil Wells, *API Drilling and Production Practice,* 134 (1941).

Howard, R. A. and Watson, M. S., Jr: Relative Productivity of Perforated Casing, *Trans. Am. Inst. Mining Met. Engrs (Petroleum Development and Technology)* **189,** 179 (1950).

Jamin, M. J: Memoir on Equilibrim and Movement of Liquids in Porous Substances, *Comptes rendus,* **50,** 172 (1860) and *Comptes rendus,* **50,** 311 (1860).

Ladd, B. J. and Terrell, K. E: Newest Method to Control Unconsolidated Sands, *Petroleum Engr.,* B-112, Dec. (1955).

Lake, Frank W: Well Completion Practice, *Petroleum Engineering Handbook,* published July 15, 1930 by *Petroleum World,* 1st Edn.

Lewis, P. F: Oil-field Explosives, Their Characteristics and Use, *API Drilling and Production Practice,* 73 (1934).

Lewis, P. F: The How and Why of Well Shooting, *API Drilling and Production Practice,* 278 (1938).

Miller, A: Liners, Perforated and Screen Pipe, *J. Inst. Petr. Tech.* (London), 34 (1934).

Miller, E. B: Plug-back Work with Plastics, *API Drilling and Production Practice*, 97 (1944).

Miller, F. G: Pressure Distribution about a Slotted Liner in a Producing Well, *Trans. Am. Inst. Mining Met. Engrs. (Petroleum Development and Technology)* **142,** 137 (1941) (reprint, p. 326).

Muskat, M: Effect of Casing Perforations on Well Productivity, *Trans. Am. Inst. Mining Met. Engrs. (Petroleum Development and Technology)* **151,** 175 (1943) (reprint, p. 381).

Perrine, R. L: Well Productivity Increase from Drain-Holes as Measured by Model Studies, *AIME J. Petr. Tech.*, 30, Feb. (1955).

Rembert, William E: Casing Perforating Gun Used Successfully in Arkansas, *Oil Weekly*, Aug. 29 (1930).

Robinson, Reginald, and Caldwell, Blake M: Two Decades of Gun Perforating, *AIME J. Petr. Tech.*, Sept. (1953).

Rodgers, C. J: Some Aspects of Gravel Packing, *Trans. Am. Inst. Mining Met. Engrs. (Petroleum Development and Technology)* **201,** 15 (1954).

Sage, B. H. and Lacey, W. N: Effectiveness of Gravel Screens, *Trans. Inst. Mining Met. Engrs. (Petroleum Development and Technology)* **142,** 89 (1942) (reprint, p. 131).

Smith, R. H. and Polk, A. C., Jr: Use of Plastics in Consolidating Loose Sands in Wells, *Trans. Am. Inst. Mining Met. Engrs. (Petroleum Development and Technology)* **170,** 243 (1947).

Stormont, D. H: Increasing Drainage of Oil into Wells by Drain-Hole Drilling, *Oil Gas J.*, 105, Aug. 17 (1953).

Uren, L. C: Increasing Production of Petroleum by Increasing the Diameter of Wells, *Trans. Am. Inst. Mining Met. Engrs.*, **71,** 1276 (1925).

Uren, L. C: Sand Control in Oil Production, *Petroleum Engr.*, April (1934).

Uren, L. C: Domercq, J., Jr; and Mejia, J: Influence of Well Diameter Upon the Pressure Gradient and Rate of Flow of Oil Through the Reservoir Rock in the Vicinity of a High-Pressure Flowing Well, *Trans. Am. Inst. Mining Met. Engrs. (Petroleum Development and Technology)* **114,** 25 (1935).

Uren, Lester C: Part II — Sand Control and Formation of Well Cavities, *World Petroleum*, Oct. (1957).

West, T. S: A New Well Completion Technique, *Trans. Am. Inst. Mining Met. Engrs. (Petroleum Development and Technology)* **170,** 250 (1947).

West, T. S: A Gravel-Pack Completion for Exclusion of Gas and Water, *Trans. Am. Inst. Mining Met. Engrs. (Petroleum Development and Technology)* **192,** 183 (1951).

Western Company, The, Midland, Texas: Letter to Harold Vance, dated October 23, 1957, regarding acid treatments in the oil fields of West Texas.

Wilson, G. S: Selection and Use of Screen Pipe, *Trans. Am. Inst. Mining Met. Engrs. (Petroleum Development and Technology)* **103,** 116 (1933).

Winterburn, Read: Application of Gravel Packing to Unconsolidated Sands, *Oil Weekly*, Jan. 11 (1943).

Winterburn, Read: Control of Unconsolidated Sands in Wilmington Oil Field, *API Drilling and Production Practice*, 63 (1947).

Zublin, C. W: The Theory, Application and Mechanics of Drain Hole Drilling, *AIME Paper No. 446-G*, Oct. (1954).

Chapter 10

PRODUCTION EQUIPMENT

C. J. COBERLY

C. J. COBERLY was born in 1892 in Cameron, Missouri and, after preparatory education in Los Angeles, was graduated from Stanford University in 1915 with an A.B. degree in mechanical engineering. His oil-
industry connection began in 1912 as a draftsman for Wilson and
Willard Manufacturing Company, and was continued after graduation
with Southern California Edison Company and California Compressed
Gas Company. In 1923 he organized Kobe, Inc. for the production of
perforated pipe. In 1926 the company began the development of hydraulic oil-field pumps. Field testing, begun in 1932, was followed by
quantity production and sales. He is currently president of Kobe, Inc.
and of Wulff Process Company, and a director of California Cotton
Oil Company.

Academic honors include Tau Beta Pi. Professional affiliations include
API, AIME, ASTM, and a life membership in ASME. Mr. Coberly
has made numerous contributions to the engineering literature, principally
through presentations before API, AIME, and ASME.

INTRODUCTION

The obvious antecedents of the petroleum industry's production equipment and techniques were those employed in developing fresh-water and, more directly, salt-water wells. Possibly the earliest activities were carried out by the Chinese, who reportedly were completing water, gas, and salt wells more than 1,000 years before Christ. In Western civilization annals, the plunger pump was described by Hero in 120 B.C.

Some development stages of the equipment included Leonardo da Vinci's suggestion, in the 15th century, for a plunger pump in which the piston was reciprocated in a cylinder by a grooved drum to lift water from a well and discharge it at the surface. In 1705 Thomas Newcomen[1] built an atmospheric engine for pumping wells (Fig. 1), and it was so arranged that the engine piston connected to a pump rod through a pivoted beam having a sector end to which the piston rod and pump rod were fastened by chains to give a straight-line motion to each. In 1798 Richard Trevithick made a direct-acting steam pump (the famous "Cornish" pump) with the cylinder directly over the well, but with a beam attached to the pump rod to which weight was applied to balance the rod load (Fig. 2).

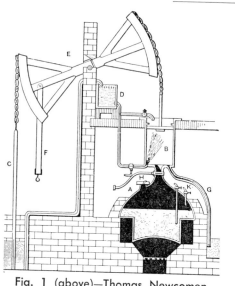

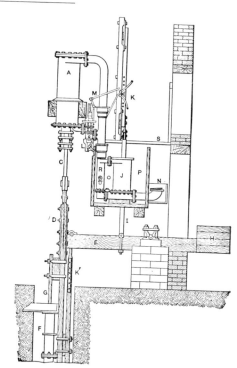

Fig. 1 (above)—Thomas Newcomen Atmospheric Engine Pumping Unit, 1705

Fig. 2 (right)—Cornish Pumping Engine of 1798

[1]References are at the end of the chapter.

The greatest influence on the initial production equipment used by the oil industry, however, was a result of the use of cable tools to drill the wells. The oscillating walking beam, a simple and effective means of lifting and dropping the bit, was also well-suited for operating the bottom-hole plunger pump once the well was completed. Both drilling and pumping loads were small enough to permit the use of wooden structural elements with a few pieces of iron to serve as bearing points. As crude as the rig was, it was effective and inexpensive.

Actually, the effectiveness of this equipment has been considerably underrated by those who assume that Drake's well, completed at 69½ ft, was an all-out effort for the times. Literature[2] indicates that the equipment had been used to drill and pump several water wells more than 500 ft deep, a well having been drilled in Paris, France, to a depth of 1,798 ft in 1832. At one stage of his negotiations for a drilling contractor, Drake stated that he expected the driller to guarantee to drill at least 1,000 ft.[3] This is supported by the fact that, within 5 years after Drake's discovery, there were many oil wells being completed and pumped in the "third sand" at 900 ft with essentially the same equipment used by Drake.[3] A real record for the equipment was a well drilled in 1867 by Jonathan Watson, in Titusville, to a depth of 2,130 ft.[4]

Thus the production end of the fledgling oil industry was able to launch its phenomenal expansion with the almost-identical tools and techniques that had been developed in the water-well industry.

EARLY REPORTS OF PRODUCTION OPERATIONS

There can hardly be a more vivid and descriptive picture of the early producing operations than that furnished by J. H. A. Bone in his book, *Petroleum and Petroleum Wells*, published in 1865.[3] Concerning the drilling rig, which of course served for subsequent pumping and servicing operations, he gives the following description:

"The exact spot being determined, a huge derrick is erected immediately over it. This is a square frame of timbers, substantially bolted together, making an enclosure about forty feet high, and about ten feet at the base, tapering somewhat as it ascends. This is generally boarded up a portion of the distance to shelter the workmen. A grooved wheel or pulley hangs at the top, and a windlass and crank are at the base. A short distance from the derrick a small steam engine, either stationary or portable, is fixed and covered with a rough board shanty; a pitman rod connects the crank of the engine with one end of a large wooden walking-beam, placed midway between the engine and the derrick, the beam being pivoted on its center about twelve feet from the ground. The walking-beam is a rude imitation of that of a side-wheel steamer. A rope attached to its other end passes over the pulley at the top of the derrick, and terminates immediately over the intended hole. A cast-iron pipe, from 4½ to 5 inches in diameter, is driven into the surface ground, length following length, until the rock is reached. In the older wells the ground was dug out to the rock and a wooden tube put in it. The earth having been removed from the interior of the pipe, the actual process of boring or drilling is commenced."

The production operations Bone *(op. cit.)* reported as follows:

"When the hole has been sunk to a sufficient depth and 'strike oil', the next thing is to extract the oil from the well. If a flowing well has been struck, all the trouble on this head is saved, as the oil and gas rush out in a stream, sometimes with such violence that the men have to make their arrangements with considerable rapidity, or the precious fluid runs to waste. The first business is to tube the well. An iron pipe, with a valve at the bottom like the lower valve of a pump, is run down the entire depth of the well, the necessary length being obtained by screwing the sections firmly together. If the oil does not flow spontaneously, a pump-box, attached to a wooden rod, also made of sections screwed into each other, is inserted in the tube, and the upper end of the rod attached to the 'Walking-beam'. The well is now ready for pumping.

"One important feature in the tubing process must not be forgotten. In boring for oil, springs of water are of course cut through and the water falls into the hole. Being heavier than the oil, it lies at the bottom, and would enter the pump-tube but for a very ingenious contrivance known as the seed-bag. This a leather bag, in shape something like a boot-leg, filled with flax-seed, which is fastened around the iron tube at what is considered the proper point, and crowded down with it. When the seed-bag becomes wet it swells and thus forms a water-tight packing between the tube and the rock. At times the seed-bag slips or bursts, the well at once fills with water, and the tubing has to be pulled in order to refix the seed bag.

"More or less gas accompanies the oil in its passage to the surface. If a flowing well, the gas is allowed to escape, there being no use for it, and it can be distinctly seen puffing out of the pipe, generally with labored breathings or panting, the cause of which is known among the operators as the 'Breathings of the earth', in reality being the irregular obstructions to its passage by the unequal flow of oil in the bottom of the hole. The passage of the oil from a large flowing well is a curious and interesting sight.

"In many of the pumping wells the gas is saved and used, either by itself or with coal, as fuel for the engine. To save it, the mingled gas, oil and water—for in spite of all precautions some water will come up from nearly every pumping well—is conducted by a pipe from the well tube into a tight barrel. The oil and water fall into the bottom of the barrel, and run off by a pipe near the bottom into a huge tank or vat, where another separation is caused by the different gravities of the two fluids, the water sinking to the bottom of the vat. The gas escapes by a small pipe at the top of the barrel, and is conducted into the furnace, where it burns with a fierce and steady flame. The engine of the Forest City well, as also many other wells, is run entirely by gas, the jet being spread into a broad and waving flame by passing through a piece of sheet iron pierced with holes. Its steadiness is shown by the fact that the engine house is lit with several jets of gas, of a steadier and purer flame than that furnished by some gas companies."

"The oil, as it flows into the tank, is a dark green fluid. When sold for shipment it is drawn off by a faucet in the bottom into barrels. In the larger wells, where a considerable quantity of oil is kept on hand before sale, ranges of vats are built, the oil flowing from one to the other. The vats are covered with boards, and at the larger wells roofed in to prevent evaporation.

"At the gassy wells great care has to be taken with regard to fire, as a lighted cigar might set fire to the gas and blow up the whole concern. In the early days of the flowing wells, before their nature was thoroughly known, serious conflagrations took place from this cause. Should a well take fire, water not only fails to extinguish it, but seems to add to the fury of the flame."

Fig. 3 is a photograph of a typical rig, used in 1868.

As for costs and general problems of operating an oil property, Bone (*op. cit.*) states:

"After the well is sunk, should it flow, the expense is merely nominal. If it is a pumping well, two engineers, one or two extra hands, and the fuel, will make the ordinary daily expenses from ten to twenty dollars, according to circumstances. The breakage of the wooden pump-rods, giving out of machinery, delays by slipping and bursting of the seed-bag, and the frequent difficulty of obtaining fuel, even at a high cost, will frequently increase the expenses and diminish the receipts at the same time."

EVOLUTION OF EQUIPMENT

General Summary

In attempting to trace the development of production equipment, it has been possible to identify the "first" of many innovations and,

Fig. 3—Typical Old Rig—Fee Well at Shamburg, 1868

in some cases, to identify strong trends in equipment developments. The nature of the subject is such, however, that it is impossible to identify a date when any given class of equipment came into universal usage.

One phase of the problem is the fact that normally production equipment is exceptionally long-lived. Traditionally, operators try to install equipment far stronger or better than the well will require and then obtain a run-life of 15 to 50 or more years from it. So, if the historian attempts to establish that in a given interval of time—say 10 years—there was an almost universal trend toward a given class of equipment, it means that at the end of that period not more than 20 to 25 percent of *all* wells had that equipment in use. Thus, if production equipment is to be considered expendable, it is at a very slow rate. Its life in most wells is extended by reduced duty on the equipment as the production rate declines. Its abandonment in favor of more modern and efficient equipment is strongly influenced—if not dominated—by the economics of a field or well just barely paying its keep, without any possibility of justifying a re-equipping program.

623

Despite this time-lag factor, which tends to obscure the evolutionary development of equipment, there are some trends which can be identified and which strongly influenced development. A discussion of some of them here will help provide a background for the evolution described in the separate sections which follow.

Within 10 years after Drake's discovery well in 1859, "conventional" pumping equipment was well-established as consisting of what is now known as the "standard rig front." Essentially, it is just as Bone described it in 1865—the cable-tool drilling rig left on the well so that the walking beam can be used for operating the pump, and with the bull wheels and sand reel which can be used for servicing the well. Except for "rig irons", which were principally the bearings for moving parts, all elements were wooden and the universal motive power was steam.

The first major production-equipment innovation developed by the industry was the central pumping power, in about 1880. This provided a means of pumping a number of wells from a central point on the lease by connecting a steam-powered eccentric to jacks at each well head through shackle or rod lines. The major advantage of these systems was the elimination of the quite high cost of maintaining steam engines at each well head. Their application was limited to shallow, low-volume wells. Although central powers had several operating disadvantages, they were widely applied until the 1940's.

In about 1900, there were several developments which were later to have a major effect on the production-equipment evolution. Most important, perhaps, was the fact that rotary drilling was coming into its own and thus began eliminating the economic appeal of standard rig fronts made of wood to serve for both drilling and pumping. Also in 1900, internal-combustion engines were beginning to replace steam engines, and iron sucker rods were supplanting wooden sucker rods.

In spite of these developments, there was little actual change in surface equipment until the early 1920's. The standard rig front had had a 60-year record of performing satisfactorily; it was familiar to all operators, and could be erected at a low cost. The problem, however, was that wells were getting deeper, pumping loads were getting heavier, and operators were finding that maintenance of standard rig fronts was growing increasingly more difficult and expensive.

From events that followed, it seems there must have been a pent-up and almost universal demand for a pumping mechanism to replace the standard rig front. If any generalization can be made, it is that between 1922 and 1932 the petroleum engineers developed and the industry standardized on beam pumping units. It was a remarkably fast transition after its slow start, particularly considering the wide variety of experimental equipment introduced to solve the problem.

There were two major factors which led to the development and acceptance of the unit pumper which represented a modernized version of the tried and familiar beam pumping system. The first was the evolution of efficient gear reduction units (and these, in turn, permitted the introduction of multi-cylinder, high-speed gas engines). The other was the development of efficient mobile well-servicing units, which eliminated the need for providing power and hoists at each well.

It is also remarkable that, although this equipment adequately kept up with the demands on it, neither the petroleum engineers nor the manufacturers fully understood the mechanism of transmitting power with an elastic rod system and the loads it imposed on the pumping mechanism.

The problems of transmitting power with sucker rods were increased in geometric proportion as wells were drilled deeper. The urgency of this problem resulted in studies which Joseph Zaba describes as the "golden age" of engineering.

The problems of sucker-rod pumping fostered a search for and development of alternate methods of artificially lifting oil, and the first commercially accepted substitute for mechanical transmission of pumping power seems to have been the electric submersible pump, in about 1930. Also in the early 1930's, a system for using hydraulic power transmission was introduced and proved to be commercially successful. In the latter 1930's, gas-lift devices—stage lift valves, bellows-type pressure-charged gas-lift valves, and plunger lift—were marketed, and proved capable of greatly increasing the applicability of gas lift as a device for artificially lifting oil.

Lease facilities for collecting, storing, and shipping the produced oil were at first very crude and usually consisted of wooden barrels which served all three purposes and also provided a means of measuring the production.

For many years the lease men were on their own to improvise methods and equipment for the separation and handling of gas, oil, sand, water, and oil-water emulsions. This became a difficult task with increased flow rates, high pressures, and large amounts of sand and water mixed with the oil. Wooden barrels gave way to large wooden tanks, then to riveted iron and, finally, to bolted steel and welded tanks.

Petroleum engineering applied to lease facilities was notable for its absence until around 1900 and, as in most other phases of the oil industry, made its major contribution after 1920. However, there were basic advances started in gas separation, electrical and chemical emulsion treatment, and in water handling between 1900 and 1920.

Modern facilities still retain some similarity in design to early equipment but with emphasis on improving the "housekeeping" of the oil field and reducing the field labor through the use of better facilities and in recent years by semi-automatic lease operation, including in some cases the shipping of production.

Well Equipment

Although the petroleum industry was able to start operations with tools and techniques which had been proved in drilling and producing water and salt wells, it quickly ran up against the realization that oil wells had some specialized problems that had to be tackled. One which caused considerable concern was the phenomena of gas-locked pump valves. Standard completion procedures called for running a string of tubing with a seed-bag packer to seal off upper water, so that all production—including gas and oil—had to come through the pump; and it was a fairly common occurrence to get a slug of gas between the standing valve and the traveling valve, which would expand and compress as the pump reciprocated and would have enough pressure when expanded to keep the standing valve from opening. Robert Cornelius,[5] in 1866, received a patent (Fig. 4) on an idea for providing an enlarged area at the top of the plunger stroke which would allow the production column to drop into the plunger barrel and displace the gas. On the same date, S. H. Early[6] was issued an important patent on tubing the well to allow gas to be produced through the annulus between the tubing and the casing and on what has become known as the "poor man's" gas anchor.

The problem of handling gas seems to have had a part in the adoption of casing as a means of producing gas separately from the oil. Its use was a new and revolutionary procedure, and it is not clear from the literature where it was first employed. *The Derrick's Hand Book*[7] contains the following notation under date of December 1861: "Casing first used by Julius Hall at well on Tidioute Island." The same reference, under date of August 3, 1865,

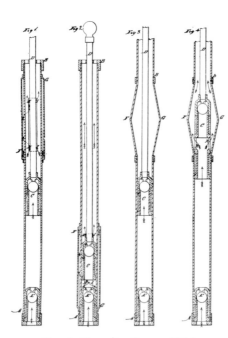

Fig. 4—Cornelius Pump, 1866

states: "Upon the Blood farm, Oak Creek, the new system of casing the wells with artesian tubing to the second sand rock has been adopted."

C. A. Whiteshot, in the *Oil Well Driller*, states that 1865 was the year casing was introduced. These references indicate that the well was drilled through the formation, casing equipped with a seed-bag packer was lowered to a point above the sand, and tubing was run inside without a packer. According to John J. McLaurin, in *Sketches in Crude Oil*, the setting of casing above the formation and then drilling through was first done on Benninghof Run in the summer of 1868.

The great importance of the use of casing was probably not realized by those who were the first to adopt this practice. Nearly all of the advances in drilling and producing methods rely either directly or indirectly on the use of casing. In production it is inconceivable that wells could be produced successfully for any appreciable time without casing, even though rotary-drilling developments have made it possible to run tools in a large amount of open hole under favorable formation conditions. The isolation of surface water, gas, oil, and bottom water and the control of sand are essential to successful and economical production of a single zone, to say nothing of the problems of multiple productive zones.

The problem of finding a better packer to replace the seed bag was given early attention, as is indicated by the quotation from *Derrick's Hand Book (op. cit.)* under date of December 5, 1864: "J. R. Cross, the inventor, has on exhibition at the Jones House an apparatus intended to supersede the clumsy leather seed-bag used to shut off water in oil wells." By 1884 rubber packers were a common supply-house item.[8] These were operated by compression, being expanded when the casing was landed. There were also available cup-type packers for use on tubing strings. The earliest record of a tubing packer, as well as a tubing anchor which could be set by rotation, is that shown in a catalog dated 1892.[9] Self-setting tubing catchers were disclosed in at least 5 patents in the period 1915 to 1918, and were being advertised extensively in the trade journals in 1922.

It is probable that at least some of the tubing first used in oil wells was brass,[10] but iron—and later steel—has been available from the beginning of the industry. Straight couplings with **V** threads were standard until upset tubing was patented in 1899 and advertised for sale in the Oil Well Supply Co. catalog of 1900. Sands,[11] in 1922, stated that: "Quantities of upset end tubing are now being used in deep well production . . ."; and Hager,[12] in 1921, reported that it was common practice in Kansas and Oklahoma to run a tubing packer to force all gas to be produced through the tubing. Tubing of wells, however, apparently was not a universal practice as indicated by Kraus'[13] statement: "During 1929 the practice of tubing-run wells to conserve gas energy was greatly stimulated."

In the early 1920's the petroleum engineers were experimenting with tubing in flowing wells as a means of conserving gas energy and regulating the rates of production. Studies of gas-oil ratios were undertaken on a broad scale during this period and the methods of control which were used were dependent upon the use of tubing during the natural-flow period. Also, all methods of production following the flowing period are basically tied to the use of tubing with the possible exception of casing pumps used for handling large volumes of fluid under certain conditions.

In early practice flowing wells were brought in without tubing and it was not run until after the flush-production period. Later practice seemed to be to run tubing when the well was completed. C. V. Temple[14] reports that the Hobbs Field, New Mexico, was probably the first to have tubing in all wells at the time of completion. He also states that in the Yates Pool, Texas, a large number of wells were completed before the practice of tubing the wells on completion was started.

In 1930, according to Wallace,[15] the most commonly used tubing was seamless with a tensile strength of 48,000 to 75,000 psi, and was equipped with the "new long collar" with tapered threads which provided a great improvement in collar sealing.

Sucker-rod Pumping Equipment

Pumps

The first bottom-hole oil pumps adopted the designs used for pumping water. Before the start of the oil industry, pumps not very different from those used today—except for materials of construction —were common, and the engineering principles were understood. This is indicated by Patent No. 1615 issued to Joseph Evans on May 25, 1840, from which the following statement is quoted:

"By this construction I obtain several advantages over the common pump. The ample water way through the lower box gives great relief to the lift; the increased length of stroke causes fewer openings and closings of the valves and less frequent arresting of the momentum of the water."

By a few changes in terminology, this could well be used by the petroleum engineer in describing present-day equipment.

Although the patent record shows that most of the features of the modern pumps were conceived in the early days of the oil industry, the pumps most commonly used until after 1900 were of the type now classed as "tubing" pumps, in which the pump barrel is run on the tubing string (Fig. 5). The standing valve was at first run with the tubing and could only be retrieved by pulling the tubing. The plunger—run on the rods—was short, and usually was equipped with four

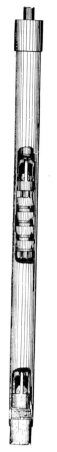

Fig. 5—Early Sucker-rod
Pump
*(Oil Well Supply Company
Catalog, 1884)*

leather cups. Leather flap valves were used in shallow wells, but ball valves were more generally used. The pump barrels, or common working barrels, were made of brass, cast iron, or wrought iron. In describing their cast barrels, Eaton and Cole in 1872[16] stated: "These barrels are made from the finest grained gun metal; are bored from solid bars, and for finish, hardness and perfection are unequalled."

Reports of early experience in pumping oil indicate that gas and sand were major problems. Before the use of separate strings of tubing seed bags sealed the tubing to the formation, forcing all the gas to go through the pump, and gas lock was common. To relieve the gas, the plunger was pulled above the pump barrel. Sand traps either below or above the pump were generally used, but these could not have sufficient capacity to be useful for very long without cleaning.

A study of the patent record brings out interesting developments which were made to answer these and other problems. Many of these developments apparently did not come into general use, as the early catalogs of manufacturers do not show them.

T. J. Lovegrove[17] in 1865 described a downpass gas anchor to give gravity separation of the gas and oil. Reinhold Boeklen[18] designed a pump having mechanically operated standing and working valves which would be effective in preventing gas lock. Robert Cornelius[19] provided an auxiliary slide valve actuated by the plunger, which bypassed the working valve on the downstroke to prevent gas lock.

Nearly all of the early patents described some form of sand trap in connection with other features of the pump. These were located at various points. Some were below the pump in connection with the gas anchor; others were in the pump chamber above the standing valve, around the pump barrel, above the working valve, or in a tubular rod section above the pump. Sand traps have continued to be the subject of patents—since 1920 twelve patents have been directed primarily to this problem. In 1952 a patent issued to O. H. Crabtree[20] showed a pump construction for preventing the sand from packing around an insert pump. Other inventions have been made relating to handling of sand, which will be described later.

Many patents were directed to the problem of having to pull the tubing to replace the standing valve of tubing pumps. Three different methods have been used—screw-on devices, latch-on tools, and lost-motion connections between the pump plunger and the standing valve —which would permit the normal stroke of the pump.

Nineteen patents show different forms of screw-on devices, of which the following are representative. In 1862 T. J. McGowan[21] disclosed a right-hand screw-on device for a standing-valve assembly having a left-hand threaded connection to the bottom collar of the pump barrel. J. H. Davis[22] screwed the plunger on to the standing-valve cage and then pulled the valve from its seat. In 1884[8] equipment catalogs illustrated this type of puller. To prevent damage to the threads of screw-on devices by bumping down, one of the threaded members was spring-loaded in a keyed holder which took the direct blow of the plunger. Rudolph Conrader[23] showed a construction of this type. Also with the idea of avoiding bad threads, the male member was a tap which formed its own thread. This was used by C. D. Ballard[24] in 1907. H. L. Nolan[25] used a tap with a protecting threaded sleeve over it, and with a jaw clutch and shear pin. The clutch engaged the standing-valve cage, the pin was sheared by turning the rods, and the tap advanced into the hole in the standing-valve cage. Similar devices have also been the subject of recent patents.[26]

The earliest latch-on puller was a **T**-tool device designed by J. Q. Adams[27] in 1876. In 1879[28] a tee-bolt was used with rectangular hole in the closed end of a cylindrical mating piece. Some 19 patents have been directed primarily to this construction, and many other patents use this in connection with other pump features. Eleven patents have been issued since 1920 on this type of standing-valve puller, with the latest in 1943.

Lost-motion pullers were first used in 1867.[29] A number of different constructions have been used. The one which has become commonly known as the "Garbutt rod"[30] is used with a tubular plunger having the working valve on top of the plunger. The rod attached to the standing-valve cage extends into the plunger, and has a tee-head on its upper end which is longer than the internal diameter of the inside shoulder on the lower end of the plunger tube. These were in commercial use in the early 1900's.[31] Fifteen patents show this type of puller, six of which were earlier than Garbutt.

Wear of plunger cups was an important problem in oil pumps, which led to many innovations. One is a spare plunger[32,33] which could be put in use by lowering the normal plunger with the rods until it rests on the spare, which is then screwed on by turning the rods.

Packed plungers in place of cups appeared in 1871.[34] This was an outside packed plunger in which the packing was tightened by turning the tubing. John Sparks[35] adjusted the packing by engaging a jaw clutch on the standing-valve cage, and then turned the rods to tighten the packing. Nelson Perkins[36] in 1887 used an outside packed plunger depending upon column pressure for sealing, and provided a means of balancing the pressure across the packing before pulling the plunger to prevent damage to the packing. James Horsley[37] in 1902 made a traveling-tube pump with spring-loaded packing rings. A. G. Willard[38] made a contracting ring outside a packed pump with the rings at the top of the working barrel. J. M. Eastham used a spring-loaded outside packed plunger. E. C. Wilson[39] in 1924 made an insert pump with spring-loaded packing on the plunger. A similar pump was made by D. W. Hoferer[40] in 1940 with multiple packing sections, each spring-loaded.

Pumps with a close-fitting metal plunger and metal barrel date back in the patent record to 1866.[41] This was a grooved metal packing collar with a tubular plunger and with no packing or cups. In 1877[42] G. C. Merrill made a metal-to-metal pump with a grooved plunger to reduce the leakage. R. Branham[43] in 1891 used split metal rings on the plunger. Thompson and Penrod[44] used a close-fitting plunger above a cup stand. Trade catalogs[45] indicated that metal-to-metal pumps were relatively common in 1900, with both smooth and grooved plungers.

In 1905 the D + B Pump Company brought out sectional liner pump barrels[46, 47] which contributed to the success of close-fitting pumps by making these close-tolerance parts more practical to manufacture. John Hahn,[48] E. A. Hardison,[49] and C. C. Scharpenberg[50] also made close-fitting metal-to-metal pumps. S. B. Sargent, Jr.[51] and E. E. Stevenson[52] assembled sectional liners in a tube with end pressure and fastened the tube in the outer pump tube at its lower end so the column pressure would be applied to the outside of the liner tube. E. E. Stevenson[53] assembled the pump with resilient spacing and aligning rings between liners.

Double standing and working valves used in series appear to be credited in the patent record to R. B. McMakin[54] in 1907.

Insert pumps which may be pulled as a complete unit with the rods had their beginning in the early days of the oil industry, but were not used extensively until the 1920's. The first patent showing the insert construction was issued to J. B. Root[55] in 1865. In this pump the tubing was composed of wood staves with outside bands of metal, and the pump barrel was a metal tube equipped with a plunger and a standing valve and sealed into the wooden tubing and arranged to be pulled with the pump plunger by pulling the rods. Theophilus Mayhen[56] used a chain- or rope-operated pump with a sinker bar to pull the plunger down. The pump was an insert unit with a top latch and a bottom seal with a rubber sleeve sealing against an internal shoulder in a tubing collar. J. H. Devirs[57] used a wire-line insert pump with a top latch and a drop bar to release the latch. This pump seated in a taper shoe. J. F. Carll[58] made a top-seal insert pump held down by column pressure, and used a second standing valve below the pump so that the fluid in the tubing would not backwash the formation when the pump was pulled. J. T. Whipple[59] used an insert pump having a bottom seal which could be made tight in the tubing at any point by turning the rods, which expanded a packing with a taper thread. W. J. Wright[60] in 1897 made a traveling-tube insert pump with bottom holddown and seal. W. A. Springer[61] in 1899 and A. B. Gahagan[62] in 1902 made solid plunger insert pumps with bottom intake and discharge valves. These pumps had cup holddowns and the produced fluid was discharged into the annulus between the pump casing and the tubing. W. A. O'Bannon[63] in 1934 made a small-capacity insert pump intended to seal off in a common working barrel. This pump had a spring-loaded packed plunger and used bottom cup seal.

Traveling-tube pumps are essentially also insert pumps. The earliest pump of this type shown in the patent record was made by W. J. Wright and has already been described under insert pumps. W. W. Warner[64] made a combined traveling-tube and traveling-plunger pump in which the traveling tube is on top and prevents sand from contacting the cups of the plunger. W. E. Ellis[65, 66] used a cup-packed traveling-tube pump which was claimed to reduce the wear on the cups.

W. B. Robb[67] produced a close-fit traveling-tube pump. W. A. O'Bannon[68] made a traveling-tube pump combining spring-loaded soft packing and a cup stand. J. A. Yerkes[69] in 1932 designed a bottom-lock pump of this type. W. A. O'Bannon[70] produced a traveling-tube pump with an outer casing for the traveling tube, having the space between filled with oil which leaked by the packing and which would have less sand and smaller particles than the produced fluid. D. W. Hoferer[71, 72] in 1938 designed a bottom-lock traveling-tube pump which also had a traveling plunger in the tube contacting a shoulder at the end of its stroke and then causing the traveling tube to move, thus dividing the total stroke by two. Hoferer's second patent was the same construction with dash pots to prevent shock when the moving plunger hit the end of the traveling tube.

Multiple-tube pumps in which three or more telescoping tubes are used to increase the length of leakage path are generally known as "fluid-packed pumps." The first patent on this type of pump was issued to E. T. Adams[73, 74] in 1925. This pump had spring-loaded relief valves to bleed the fluid and sand from the annulus between the two stationary tubes and the moving tube between them. H. M. Green,[75] in the same year made a 4-tube fluid-packed pump with 2 stationary and 2 moving tubes. I. B. Winsor[76] used check valves between the first and third tubes to produce a vacuum on the upstroke and to bleed leakage fluid on the downstroke. E. W. Patterson[77] ported the space between tubes to the discharge column above the working valve with restricted ports to give a pressure increase on the upstroke and a decrease on the downstroke.

C. M. Peters[78] made a top-lock fluid-packed pump with no vents between tubes. This is a five-tube pump with three stationary and two moving tubes. C. M. O'Leary[79] in 1936 also made a top-lock fluid-packed pump with grooved tubes to reduce the slippage.

Many of the patents on insert pumps are directed to the means of latching and sealing the pump to the tubing. Seventeen patents have been issued on top-latch constructions, fourteen on bottom-latch, and twelve on top-seal pumps.

The first top-latch patent was issued to John Nicholson in 1867.[80] This pump had pivoted latch fingers with flat leaf springs which engaged an internal shoulder of the top collar. The pump rod had a collar which disengaged the latch when the plunger was pulled above the normal working position. In 1903 O. L. Clark[81] made a top-seating pump with a bottom seal so that column pressure was applied to the outside of the pump casing to balance the internal pressure on the working stroke.

John Hahn[82] in 1912 made a spring top latch with a bottom seal, and W. G. Black[83] in 1917 used jars both for seating and loosening a top-latch top-seal pump. A. L. Ligon[84] designed a pump with a top lock and bottom seal in which the lock collar had a series of serrations to permit locking at one of several points to accommodate variations in the length of the pump. R. W. Gunn[85] made a top-seat bottom-latch pump with a spring tube split longitudinally into multiple sections as a friction holddown which was forced into a bottom collar. E. W. Ostrom[86] in 1937 made a top latch, top seal of a type now in quite general use with insert pumps.

The patent issued to Earl Derby[87] in 1926 is of interest in the problem of handling gas. This is a casing-type gas anchor which takes advantage of the casing volume above a packer to give sufficient time to obtain satisfactory separation of gas from the liquid before it enters the pump.

The desirability of high compression ratio in pumps was probably first recognized by the engineers who designed the traveling-tube insert pumps. Neilsen[88] in 1929 designed a multi-tube insert pump with this in mind, and Kork Kelley[89] in 1950 made a traveling plunger pump with a bottom working valve and a poppet-type standing valve without a cage for close spacing.

A number of pumps[90-92, incl.] were made with mechanical devices to open the working valve and break a gas lock by bumping the plunger down.

633

Mechanically actuated valves have been the main objective of many patents, but the literature does not give any evidence of their being used commercially. The first of these dates back to 1865,[18] on the Boeklen pump which had both the standing and working valves mechanically operated. In 1866 Robert Cornelius[19] designed a pump with the mechanical working valve, and in 1869 C. H. Duncan[93] made a pump with the standing valve operated by the friction of the pump plunger cup against a loose liner connected to a poppet valve. Since then other means for operation of the working valve, standing valve, or both valves have been designed—the latest in 1942,[94] which was a traveling-tube pump with both valves mechanically operated.

Casing pumps were in fact the first type to be used, as there was no tubing in the first oil wells. This type has come back into use for low-head, high-volume pumps. Since 1920 a number of these pumps have been developed. Most of the designs related to the means of setting and releasing the packer. J. Penrod[95] in 1922 was one of the first, and his design used a wire-line-operated casing pump. The latest was patented by E. J. Mullins,[96] and was a rod-operated pump with tubing-rod guide and a slip-joint valve in the tubing to open into the casing.

Double-acting pumps have been the subject of over 50 patents since 1870, but most of these have been for shallow water wells rather than for pumping oil. Because the rod string has practically no column strength, some means of pulling the rod down must be provided. This gives double-acting pump action but has very little to recommend it, as all the work is done by the rod system on the upstroke.

A number of methods have been devised for balancing part of the rod load at intermediate points to reduce the maximum load at the polished rod. This is advantageous in wells of extreme depth. Scott[97] was one of the first to engineer a balance of this type. In the Scott device, however, the balance pressure was supplied through the casing annulus and therefore was not applicable to wells producing much gas. G. E. Behnke[98] in 1936 designed a rod balance which overcame the objections to the Scott design, as the pressure was supplied by the producing column and several balances could be used, if desired, at spaced locations.

A similar development uses spaced pumps[99] to reduce the elongation of the rods. This, however, does not reduce the polished-rod load; but, since the pumps are in series, it does reduce the load on each pump and reduces the length of the rod subjected to maximum stress.

Numerous devices[100] have been developed to reduce the stress in the tubing by transmitting the load to the casing. Recent engineering has shown that column buckling of the tubing near the bottom results in increased tubing and rod wear.[101] This is overcome by means of slip-type holddowns to lock the tubing to the casing near the bottom.

Another development of interest is the use of multiple pumps to increase the displacement in a given tubing size. E. W. Patterson[102] used pairs of tubular plungers arranged in multiple to increase the stroke. Mock in 1952[103] used a plurality of short-stroke sections in series to increase the stroke, and Sutton[104] made a traveling-tube insert pump with dual pistons in tandem.

Oil containing high sand cuts has been a problem to engineers, particularly in producing low-gravity shallow wells; and, in addition to bottom-hole traps, means have been developed to handle the sand with the oil and pump it to the surface. J. E. Hall[105] and M. J. Morton[106] introduced agitation in the pump barrel to keep the sand in suspension, and early designs used tubing for rods with the production through this tubing to give a higher velocity for this purpose. M. N. Lotta[107] used large-diameter rods to give a high velocity in the tubing. C. S. Boden[108] used tubing for rods and circulated clean oil down the well tubing and up this rod tubing to assist in removing the sand. In the 1920's the "Kynro"[109] and other circulation pumping systems were marketed. This system was further developed in the 1940's in the Santa Maria Field in California, using a low-viscosity fluid for circulation to both dilute and reduce the viscosity of the production and to keep the sand in suspension.

A number of other developments should be mentioned which prevent sand—and also corrosive water—from contact with the plunger and liner. C. G. Upton[110,111] in 1939 used a grease chamber at each end of the packed section to exclude abrasives and lubricate the plunger. R. L. Chenault[112] used filters to supply clean oil to the packing cups, and B. F. Schmidt[113] used grease confined between two mercury seals for this purpose. J. R. Brennan[114] used a chamber built into the pump to give gravity separation of produced oil which is fed to the plunger fit in place of the oil-water-sand mixture of the well fluid.

Another development which relates to pumping systems[115] rather than rod pump construction is the use of a control choke to limit the formation withdrawal rate on intermitted wells. A packer is used to form a chamber between the tubing and casing. Fluid from the formation enters this chamber through a choke of a size selected to give the desired maximum formation withdrawal rate with no fluid over the packer. During the shut-down period, fluid enters through this choke and builds up in this casing chamber to the static fluid level. The pump inlet connects with this chamber, and during the pumping period the rate of withdrawal from the chamber depends upon the capacity of the pump used. The formation withdrawal rate increases as the fluid level above the packer is drawn down, but never exceeds the selected maximum rate controlled by the capacity of the choke.

Sucker Rods

The sucker rods used by the oil industry until the 1890's were of selected hickory and usually equipped with riveted iron fittings on each end with a box-and-pin type joint, as shown in Fig. 6. Rods were round, square, or octagonal depending largely upon the type of end fitting used. Early efforts to improve wooden rods were directed to means of coupling the rods together. In some cases the rods were provided with the same threads on both ends, with a couple having either double pin or double box threads. In others the ends were bolted or had interlocking transverse keys and keyways, with sleeves slipped over the outside to hold the mating parts together. In the period from 1866 to 1895 there were 20 or more patents issued covering these connections. An important feature was the method of attaching the rod ends to the wooden rod. The earliest patent found was issued in 1866 to R. N. Allen.[116] This disclosed a box-and-pin threaded joint in a round fitting, having a forged flat extension on the center line with transverse ridges across both sides. The wood had a slot milled to fit over this extension. The outside was then wire-wound in grooves in the wood between these cross ridges. H. D. Parker,[117] also in 1866, made a joint with an internal thread in a tube having an outside diameter the same as the wooden rod. The inside of this tubing had a reverse taper, and the end of the rod was turned to fit the small

Fig. 6—Wooden Sucker Rod with Pin and Socket Ends Riveted to Rod
(Oil Well Supply Company Catalog, 1884)

diameter. A round tapered wedge was driven into the end of the wood to expand it into the taper tube. A double pin thread coupling was used.

Daniel Jones[118] provided a tubular coupling in which longitudinal and transverse grooves were provided in both the outside of the wood and the inside of the tube. After the coupling was driven on, molten lead was poured into the grooves through the end of the coupling, locking the wood in place.

Although many different joints are disclosed by the patent record, the type most generally used has either 2 or 4 straps with rivets through the straps and rod, as illustrated in Fig. 6.

An indication of at least one of the problems encountered with these rods was the item recommended in the 1884 Oil Well catalog called a "rivet catcher"—a metal, cup-shaped device placed at the bottom of the sucker-rod string. One objectionable feature of wooden rods reported was their buoyancy, which limited the speed at which the well could be pumped.

One of the earliest patents on metal rods was issued to W. C. Allison[119] in 1881, and revealed "well poles" consisting of tubing with forged box-and-pin ends and flattened near each end to accommodate wrenches. Steel sucker rods of various cross-sectional shapes were patented,[120] some of which were straight and others twisted for guiding and scraping effect in the tubing. In 1884, iron sucker rods and small iron pipe for use as hollow sucker rods were offered by Oil Well Supply Company. Another manufacturer claims to have first patented iron sucker rods in 1890.[121] In a letter dated March 22, 1900, an operator states: "The iron sucker rods are going to come into general use before long. I am not going to buy any more wooden sucker rods."[122] A phase of the development of iron sucker rods as described in the aforementioned patents was the marketing of "stub ends"—shown in a 1900 catalog[46]— which were forged box-and-pin fittings to be welded onto either solid or hollow "rods". Carbon-steel rods of the box-and-pin type appeared in the early 1900's. The Oil Well catalog of 1904 lists them, in dimensions shown in Table 1, although other manufacturers state that steel rods first appeared in 1908.

The weight of iron rods was later recognized as a problem in the deeper wells and efforts were made to offset this weight. In 1917 C. O. Salberg[123] provided a composite rod consisting of steel strap welded to the rod ends with half-round wood pieces riveted to both sides of the strap to form a round section. C. F. Rigby[124] in 1920, F. M. Nevins[125] in 1926, and E. V. Watts[126] in 1940 proposed hollow tubular rods closed at the top end or both top and bottom, and filled with gas under pressure to prevent collapse. In some cases the gas pressure was graduated with depth to balance the hydrostatic head.

In the early 1920's rod failures were increasing rapidly—probably because of increased well depths and heavy pumping—and many opera-

Table 1
Solid Iron Sucker Rod
Round iron or steel for small tubing

Rod Size, In.	Size of Box and Pin, In.	For Tubing Size, In.
$9/16$	$3/4$	$1\frac{1}{4}$, $1\frac{1}{2}$
$9/16$	$1\frac{1}{8}$	2
$5/8$	$1\frac{1}{8}$	2
$11/16$	$1\frac{5}{16}$	2, $2\frac{1}{2}$
$3/4$	$1\frac{5}{16}$	$2\frac{1}{2}$
$7/8$	$1\frac{1}{4}$	$2\frac{1}{2}$, 3

Fig. 7—Modern API Sucker-
rod Joint, 1959

tors began looking for causes. One effort to minimize failures was an attempt—in about 1923—to relieve internal strains induced by upsetting, by heat-treating the ends of the rods;[127] but this left a point of strain at the end of the heated section farther down the rod. Apparently full normalizing was essential, and this was first done in 1927.[128] By 1930, at least two manufacturers were offering full-heat-treated rods which were oil or water quenched and drawn. Low-alloy manganese steel rods were introduced in 1926 *(op. cit.)*.

Corrosion and corrosion fatigue were recognized by Blaine B. Wescott[129] and others as a problem in sucker rods, particularly under high loads. In addition to nickel-alloy rods, some use has been made of heavily nickel-plated rods and couplings. V. B. Browne[130] proposed a method of manufacturing rods with a stainless-steel sleeve drawn and forged over the outside of the rod to resist corrosion.

Adoption of the API sucker-rod joint, which was ratified in 1927, and strict adherence by the manufacturers to API dimensional specifications—together with improvement in field joint-makeup practices, resulted in a substantial reduction in pin failures of sucker-rod joints. Fig. 7 is a modern API sucker-rod joint. A prestressed rod has also been shown in the patent record,[131] but it is not known whether or not this has been used commercially.

In conjunction with the use of rods, numerous devices have been offered to scrape paraffin from the tubing.[132] Some of these have been applied to the rod, and others are in the form of a special coupling.[133]

Also, rod guides of metal[134] and with rollers[135] have been provided. Plastic has been used for the purpose, both in the rigid type[136] and elastic oil-resistant rubber materials. Rod catchers which expand and grip the tubing, in the event of rod breaks, have been developed.[137]

Swivel joints[138] to prevent unscrewing have been developed, as well as cushion joints[139] to reduce peak loading of the rods.

Rod Substitutes

Methods have been suggested for eliminating the threaded connection of sucker rods, but none has had any important commercial application. There were at least three patents[140] in the 1880's related to arrangements for running pumps on strips of strap iron welded together as the pump was first run, and then to subsequently spool the strap iron on a reel when it was necessary to pull the pump. No record has been found of the commercial use of this arrangement. Oil Well—in its 1904, 1907, and 1916 catalogs—offered types of wire-line pumping "outfits" which substituted wire line for rods, and hence allowed the "rod string" to be spooled when pulling the pump. Wire-line pumping was not widely used, however, as it was found that the stretch of the line was too great to give efficient pumping in deep wells. To avoid this Roy Chadwick[141] in 1907 proposed a pre-stressed wire line with short tubular cylinders over the wire, with a means of tightening the line against the compression of the cylinders to form a rigid sucker rod and relieving this tension on the line to permit reeling it on a drum. R. A. Smith[142] used cables in 90-ft lengths fastened into rope sockets. Sections had alternate right and left lay to prevent twisting under load.

Surface Equipment for Beam Pumping

Since the beginning of the oil industry the most common type of equipment for lifting oil involved the use of a sucker rod to operate a single-acting bottom-hole pump, and some device at the surface to raise and lower the sucker rod. This section is concerned with those surface lifting devices which are primarily mechanical in operating principle. Central powers and some "long-stroke" units are described in separate sections of this chapter.

The almost-universal rod-lifting mechanism is the walking beam of the standard rig front (Fig. 8)—an element common to both Drake's first pumping rig and today's most modern unit pumper. Although it would appear to be a simple matter to apply power to one end of the walking beam to cause it to oscillate and thereby raise and lower the sucker rods, there actually is a quite complex relationship between the motions and loads involved. This complexity was not generally recognized until the 1920's, and is not fully understood even today. As a

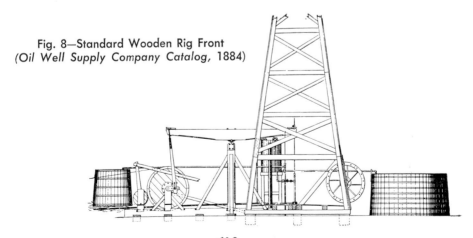

Fig. 8—Standard Wooden Rig Front
(*Oil Well Supply Company Catalog,* 1884)

result, the evolution of beam pumping equipment reveals many trial-and-error type innovations, most of which did not gain general acceptance.

A study of the patent record prior to 1920 shows very few significant changes in the standard rig front for pumping. A. E. Nickerson and L. C. Streeter[143] in 1875 disclosed means of back-side pumping with shackle lines to other wells. The engineering during this period seems to have been directed to pump jacks and central powers, which are discussed later. John S. Klein[144] in 1894 (Fig. 9) designed a pumping unit which was used to pump water from the bottom of gas wells using small tubing in place of sucker rods to operate the pump, and discharging the water through the tubing. This unit was all iron construction, with belt drive for the first reduction with a spur gear second reduction to the crank.

In 1915 a pumping unit was patented by J. P. Coffman[145] and assigned to National Transit Company. The construction shown provided a webbed main gear with several bosses at different distances from center, bored for a crank pin. The pitman connected to a metal beam about midway between the samson post and the end which carried the counterweights in the form of metal disks assembled on each side of the beam and held by a single heavy bolt through their centers and the beam. A metal frame with bearings for the main gear shaft, and pinion and bandwheel shaft, provided for a pivoted samson post and had an arm extending nearly to the polished-rod hanger. A short pivoted strut connected the beam to the end of this extension to provide a straight-line linkage.

Fig. 9—John Klein Geared Pumping Unit, 1894
(Oil Well Supply Company Catalog, 1904)

From 1920 to the present the records show some 75 patents have been issued directed principally to construction details to insure trouble-free operation, and to give easy adjustment of counterweights, rod hangers, and unit position relative to the well. Many were directed to straight-line linkages for beam hangers. Counterbalance features have also been given much attention. A review of some of these may be of interest. Also, there have been a number of designs to modify the polished-rod motion to improve the operation. Very few of these have found favor.

Straight-line linkages for the beam have been proposed, but very few have been adopted. The most generally accepted means of imparting a direct straight-line lift to the polished rod is still the familiar horsehead which was shown in water-works pumps of Newcomen (Fig. 1), Watt, and Trevithick (Fig. 2) in the 18th century. R. Brannon,[146] E. E. Stevenson,[147] W. L. Borough,[148] T. F. Watson,[149] R. E. Stickel,[150] and Carl Eurit[151] devised various linkages for giving a straight-line motion to the rod hanger. W. J. Gourley and F. H. Barney,[152] and A. N. Porter[153] provided link-type hangers which contacted strut supports at selected points in the travel to compensate the motion to approximate straight-line action. R. G. Hamaker,[154] J. B. Ratigan,[155] W. C. Trout,[156] S. Bullum,[157] H. A. Winland,[158] A. R. Maier,[159] C. R. Athy,[160] and G. S. Comstock[161] were issued patents on various features of horsehead straight-line motions. These included position adjustment, swing back for pulling, spherical mounting, single and double cable and fastening means, and other details.

Patents relating to different means of counterbalancing were prominent. William Clarkson, Jr.[162] provided a second beam pivoted at its outer end and connected at the inner end to the beam end with a second pitman, and having counterweights attached to the second beam and adjustably positioned near the pitman. W. G. Corey[163] designed a gear-driven beam unit with a combination beam balance and a rotary balance of unique characteristics. This balance was carried by a second gear with a 2:1 ratio so the counterbalance came in phase with the beam, and therefore gave its maximum effect at 180 deg of crank motion. W. M. Jones[164] built, and tested at Santa Fe Springs, Calif., a unit in which the motor and gear reduction served as the counterbalance weight and revolved around a stationary gear in planetary action, and had a pitman attached to an adjustable-position crank pin. The power was supplied to the motor through slip rings. The action of this unit could be 1:1 or 2:1 to give the same results Corey obtained. J. C. Slonneger[165] designed a counterbalance carried by a second hinged beam and attached to the pump beam by a second pitman. A. N. Porter[166] designed beam balances with a means of changing the position of the counterweights with the stroke of the pump.

Many of the other patents covered, among other things, means of mounting and adjusting both crank and beam counterbalances. W. C. Trout[167] showed a skid-based pumping unit with **A** frame, samson post, steel beam, belt drive to gear reduction, double crank arms with counterweights adjustably mounted in ways on each side of crank arms, and with a yoke-type double pitman. A. R. Maier[168] designed a single-pitman unit with a back-crank disk on the other end of the shaft, and with counterweights on the main crank fixed in radius but adjustable through 360 deg relative to the crank pin.

A number of units for straight-line linkage to control the beam motion have been patented. R. C. Baker[169] designed a parallelogram straight-line motion with an adjustable beam counterbalance. Fred McCrosky[170] used a parallelogram motion with roller arrangement on the pitman to change the lever arm and give a quick return. C. M. Livingston[171] provided a vertical guide post with a cam to give a straight-line motion to the beam end. This unit had a double pitman in compression with a hinged samson post at the rear end of the beam. J. B. Picard[172] used a standard form of beam with a samson post lever suspension for the beam and a guide-link from the **A** frame samson post to the beam to produce approximately straight-line action. Fred Graham[173] designed a similar straight-line beam suspension.

G. T. Humphrey[174] mounted the beam on a roller trunnion, with either a cam or a linkage to cause the beam to move endwise as it oscillated to give an approximately straight-line action. A. N. Porter[175] devised a somewhat similar unit with an upper beam mounted on rollers on a lower beam with the rod hanger attached to one end and the beam balance on the other. A front-side compression pitman operated the lower beam hinged on a samson **A** frame. The **A** frame had a linkage to the upper beam, causing it to shift endwise on the rollers to give a straight line to the polished rod. A variation in this unit is shown in a later patent.[176] C. G. Hopkins[177] pivoted the beam on a short column hinged to an **A** frame at its lower end with a toggle linkage between **A** frame and column which was operated by a link from the beam. A. N. Porter[178] disclosed a rigid post near the beam end with a cam guide similar to Livingston's design *(op. cit.)*. H. A. Holzer[179] used a suspension link from the **A** frame with a linkage to the beam to give it a straight-line motion. An unusual feature of this unit was a scotch yoke beam driven from the crank and pivoted on one end on the **A** frame near its base, with a pitman connecting the end of this beam to the regular beam above it.

Several patents were related to means of altering the rod motion. A patent to E. G. Willrich[180] used a standard beam with a special cam in place of a crank. W. F. Reschke[181] used gearing to obtain a quick return, with the ratio adjustable. E. W. Patterson[182] used a round-end double rack and pinion built into the pitman to give slow acceleration at the ends of the stroke, with uniform velocity for about 70 percent of the stroke. W. H. Wineman[183] modified the stroke with a cam-operated linkage which moved the beam fulcrum. C. W. Hall[184] made a mechanism for altering the motion of the rods with a horsehead pivoted on the beam end having a special cam shape on the rear half, with a cable anchored to the base of the samson post. The shape of the horsehead adds or subtracts to get the desired motion.

Other means of altering the motion of pumping units have also been proposed. W. J. Crites[185] provided a flywheel on the prime mover, with a hydraulic coupling drive to the unit to allow the speed to vary with the load. E. O. Bennett[186] built an electro-magnetic coupling which was tried in Oklahoma. The magnetic coupling was controlled with a motor generator which had a cam-operated control to vary the coupling on a pre-selected basis with relation to the crank position.

Springs have been used for counterbalancing, both during the ends of the stroke and throughout the full stroke. J. M. Hartgering and Charles M. Perkins[187] used one or more springs which came into action as the beam approached each limit of its travel. H. H. Raulerson[188] used a spring counterbalance pulled by a cable from a cam-shaped sheave to give a variable lever arm with polished-rod position and spring compression. J. T. Phipps[189] designed a similar unit.

C. M. O'Leary[190] designed a number of pumping units, all based on an internal gear drive inside a large-diameter pitman bearing.

Other engineers who contributed details of pumping units, which were the subject of patents, are J. R. Mahan, C. R. Athy, J. F. Eaton, C. E. Anderson, C. E. Bridwell, R. G. De La Mater, R. P. Vail, G. A. Fullerton, E. E. Stevenson, J. B. Sperry, L. A. Rawson, A. R. Maier, R. R. Bloss, W. W. Erlewine, W. Schweinlein, Harold G. Durnell, S. T. Steel, P. C. Jackson, J. A. Lyne, F. J. Young, and G. Tremolada.

Effort has also been directed to stroke increasers, the most important of which are described under long-stroke units. E. D. Smith et al.[191] proposed a chain attached to the polished rod and carried over a sprocket on the beam end with the other end fastened to the pitman near the crank end. T. E. Braly[192] used a samson post with a bull post ahead having levers pivoted to it and straddling the beam, with a shaft through the beam engaging slots in the levers. Compound levers are thus provided to increase the stroke produced by a given crank throw. E. A. Kliewer[193] used a beam unit with either a chain or rack and gear device for doubling the stroke. R. E. Whittlesey[194] proposed a unit with a stationary sector gear and a moving sector gear with a gear between, and with a pitman attached for increasing the stroke.

H. A. Thompson[195] made a duplex pump with two beams, two pitmans, and one samson post with two crank pins 180 deg out of phase, for operating two wells. J. A. Lyne[196] designed a double unit, with a single gear reduction, which used crank arms at 90 deg with a single pitman to each beam and having two samson posts, either on the same or opposite sides of the gear reduction, for the purpose of pumping two wells closely spaced.

One early substitute for the bandwheel was the Crocker Pumping Outfit, shown in the National Supply Company catalog of 1901 (Fig. 10). It was a unit which provided double reduction through cast-iron spur gears. It had a relatively small bandwheel, which was belt-driven by a small (2½-hp) gas engine; and the gear wheel of the second reduction had crank holes in one spoke, to which the pitman was attached. This unit was designed for installation on a standard front to replace the crank and bandwheel.

The 1916 Oil Well Supply Company catalog described two completely unitized pumpers, including a mounting for direct connection of a gas engine or electric motor to the spur-gear double reduction.

In 1919 Marion Machine, Foundry, and Supply Company was manufacturing a unit pumper with double reduction spur gears, but this

Fig. 10—Crocker Pumping Unit
(National Supply Co. Catalog, 1901)

unit had a wooden beam and pitman and conventional rig irons. In 1921, Spang and Company advertised a similar unit. The need for these and other improvements was shown by Marsh[197] in 1928. He made power measurements on standard ends having a jack shaft for a second belt reduction to permit the use of electric-motor drives, and found the efficiency of the drive to be 15 to 65 percent, depending upon the load.

A patent issued to C. M. Heeter[198] in 1917 described an improvement in standard end samson posts and rig irons.

J. R. Suman[199] invented a pumping unit which was the first to show a double pitman with an equalizing yoke bolted to the beam, with pitman bearings on each end (Fig. 11). This unit, which was described by H. C. George[200] in 1925, had the pitman rods in compression and connected the beam yoke about midway between the samson post and rod hanger. The pitman bearings had hinged bearing caps for quick removal from the crank pins to swing the beam out of the way for rod pulling. The shaft carrying the crank arms had a hoisting drum and brake for well servicing.

S. E. (Red) Manning and Dick Cason, Jr., superintendent and engineer, respectively, of Humble Oil & Refining Company in the Orange Field, Texas, built a gear pumping unit in 1922, using a worm-gear rear end of a tractor with a crank on the axle and an electric motor on the drive shaft.[201] R. S. Sterling, then president of Humble, became interested in this home-made unit and approached the Lufkin Foundry and Machine Company with the idea of producing the units commercially (Fig. 12). The first units were delivered by Lufkin to Humble's Goose Creek Field in the latter part of 1923. By 1925 these units were used in quantity, primarily in the Gulf Coast. A standard stock worm gear reducer was used with an extended shaft and outboard bearing to mount the crank. Difficulties were encountered with this reducer and Lufkin

Fig. 11—J. R. Suman Double Pitman Pump Saratoga, Texas, 1916

Fig. 12—First Worm-gear Unit Built by Red Manning and Dick Cason, Jr., 1922

Produced commercially by Lufkin Foundry and Machine Co.

Fig. 13—National Double-reduction Single-crank Unit, 1927

Fig. 14—O.C.S. Company Chain-drive Rig Front, 1928

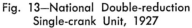

designed their own gear box. In 1929 Lufkin discontinued worm gear reducers and started building reducers with herringbone gears.

Other engineers and manufacturers had an important part in developing double reduction units. The August 1927 issue of *Rig and Reel*[*] reported introduction of the Ruf-Nek Pumping Unit, designed and built by the Link Belt Company and distributed by the Parkersburg Rig and Reel Company.[202] This unit, equipped with herringbone gears and powered by a directly connected electric motor, was adapted to a standard steel rig front. Emsco Manufacturing Company's first worm-gear unit was built in 1928.[203] In 1930 arrangements were made with Falk Gear Corporation to build speed reducers for Emsco's units. The first all-Emsco unit was built in 1937 and was placed in use in California. Bethlehem Supply Company's first commercial pumping unit was installed in Kilgore, Texas, in April 1937, and had a double helical gear reducer.[204] Their units were changed to herringbone gear reducers in 1940. The National Supply Company's first crank and reduction gear type unit was built in 1927[205] (see Fig. 13). Their first unitized pumper with herringbone gears was built in 1932 and used in the East Texas Field.

Paralleling the use of gear reducers was the development of the chain reducers pioneered by the O.C.S. Company, now a division of the Parkersburg Rig and Reel Company,[206] and by Emsco, who introduced the silent chain drive in 1928. In 1928 the O.C.S. Company placed their No. 35 Rig Front (Fig. 14) on a lease near Seminole, Okla. This was a single reduction open chain drive with regular beam, samson post, and pitman of a standard rig. Also in the same year the company designed, built, and placed on test in Oxford, Kans. their No. 2 Pumping Unit, which was a double reduction chain drive with a single crank. A number of other developments were made by this company, and in 1935 they came out

*Magazine of Parkersburg Rig and Reel Co., Parkersburg, W. Va.

with a complete line of single and double reduction chain-driven units in different sizes. Emsco also was active in the development of chain-drive units and, as stated, introduced the first silent chain drive in 1928. In 1938 the single reduction chain-driven unit of The Happy Company made its appearance,[207] and in 1950 they introduced the eccentric adjustment of the primary shaft of the unit, which facilitated taking the slack out of the chain.

To some degree the literature of the 1920's reveals the extent of the transition from bandwheel to gear reducers. George,[200] in 1925, stated that some supply companies had available unit pumpers of either wood or steel construction, with beam counterbalance, driven by a small motor or gas engine, and using belt, chain, or gear reduction.

Marsh,[197] in 1929, stated that in California the power was usually transmitted through a belt to the bandwheel using standard rig elements. He further stated, however, that some operators were driving the bandwheel by chain, and reported that single-reduction units were often used to replace the motor, belt, and countershaft of electric-drive rigs. These reduction units—according to Marsh—were usually gear-type, but chain and V belt were also being used. He further stated that early reduction gears were unsatisfactory because the engineers and manufacturers were not sufficiently familiar with the load requirements of pumping. He reported that double reduction gears were being tried on a limited scale and gave promise of offering solution to the speed-reduction problem.

Haury,[208] in 1931—in making some generalizations about operations in the Mid-Continent—said the trend was toward all-steel standard ends with speed-reducing pumping units coming into favor. He indicated that various types of drive, including spur gear, worm gears, herringbone gears, silent chain, and V-belt drives were being used; and reported that, in some cases, these were directly connected to multi-cylinder gas engines or electric motors, and that all of them had more-or-less readily adjustable rotary counterbalances.

A strong trend developed in the 1920's toward the use of all-steel standard fronts. Such a unit had been offered by Oil Well in 1892, primarily for export, but the literature does not mention use of such rigs in this country until 1919 when Lee C. Moore began advertising them. By 1925 there were at least three manufacturers selling them. These units were, of course, superseded by the unit pumper which came into general acceptance in the early 1930's. The counterbalancing of pumping rigs appears to have been a fairly casual operation until the 1920's. Pictures of standard-front units of the early days frequently show various pieces of scrap iron hanging from the end of the beam. The Klein Gas Well Pumper, brought out in 1903, and the two Oil Well unit pumpers of 1916 all had cast-iron weights attached to the beam. In the early 1920's bandwheel and pitman counterbalances were used, but reports indicate that they caused serious maintenance problems on wooden standard-front units. Kirwan and Covell[209] in 1929 reported that at Seminole, where nearly all wells were equipped with standard fronts, the most widely used counterbalance was the "grasshopper", as illustrated by the Crocker unit, Fig. 10. In this arrangement, the counterbalance weight was carried by a second beam having one end hinged to a ground support and the weighted end suspended by wire rope from the walking beam.

W. C. Trout of Lufkin Foundry and Machine Company is credited with designing the first adjustable crank counterbalance, which was installed on a beam unit in 1925 (Fig. 15). Other designs have followed, but it was not until after 1950 that all crank counterbalances manufactured were adjustable by either a screw or ratchet arrangement.

In 1921 E. W. Patterson[210] conceived the idea of an air counterbalance which was first applied to a long-stroke pumping unit, described under that heading. In 1929 the air counterbalance was first applied to beam units. The Shaffer Tool Company of Brea, Calif., under the direction of E. W. Patterson, built the first unit of this type which was placed in operation in California. Late in 1931 Lacy Oil Tool Company, under license from Patterson, placed their first air-balanced unit (Fig. 16) in the Venice Field.[211] Several patents were issued to Patterson[212] and also C. M. O'Leary[190] covering the basic idea and details of construction. It was originally of chain-reducer type, but in 1934 this was changed to double reduction herringbone gear. In the following years the unit underwent many changes in design under the direction of William G. Corey. For a short period prior to World War II, the Reed Roller Bit Company of Houston, Texas, built air-balanced pumping units under arrangement with Lacy Oil Tool Company. In 1943 the Parkersburg

Fig. 15 (above)—Lufkin Adjustable Crank Counterbalance, 1925

Fig. 16 (right)—Patterson Air-balanced Unit, 1929

Rig and Reel Company also started building air-balanced units, and in 1955 the Lufkin Foundry and Machine Company entered the field.

Other air-balanced units also have been patented. K. T. Penick[213] made a hydraulic, pneumatic counterbalance with a tubular samson post as reservoir, having a cylinder between samson post and pitman, which is connected to the beam with a horsehead. W. E. Saxe[214] designed an air-balanced unit with the air cylinder

Fig. 17—Emsco All-steel Standard End with "Camelback" Steel Beam, 1930

acting as a sliding guide for a beam pivot point. A hinged samson post and a front-side pitman were used.

Although the engineers who designed the early prototypes of unitized pumpers were concerned primarily with the method of speed reduction, other features were developed which are now quite generally used. Many of the designs shown in the foregoing patents never reached commercial use. Also some have not survived the rigor of field use. One of the early Emsco units made use of a planetary system to keep the wrist pin in a straight vertical motion while the pinion rotated on the inside of the ring gear. A National Supply unit used a double reduction unit with two main gears, two cranks, and two pitmans attached to a polished-rod hanger to give a straight-line motion.

The design steps leading to the modern pumping units include the twin-crank unit, a feature of the Suman unit previously mentioned (Fig. 11). Such a twin-crank and pitman unit was designed and placed on a lease in Oklahoma in 1929. Lufkin designed a twin-crank unit in which the wishbone-type pitman was attached to the beam by means of a ball-and-socket joint. Emsco in 1930 sought to improve the geometry of the unit with the so-called "camelback" walking beam, in which the center iron, the pitman bearing, and the carrier bar were in a straight line (Fig. 17). Bolted-on power assembly bases, ground-level lubrication systems for tailboard and saddle bearings, wide-base portable units and reducer substructures were developed in the 1940's. Cabot Shops Inc., in 1948, introduced the rubber tail bearing to provide a shock-resistant equalizer assembly.

Fig. 18—Double Pinion-gear Reduction Pumping Unit—D. V. Carter, 1940

A double pinion gear reduction was developed by D. V. Carter[215] which divides the gear tooth load and increases the capacity of the unit. A unit of this type, Fig. 18, was built by Lufkin and installed by

Magnolia Petroleum Company in the Rodessa Field in 1940 and successfully carried heavy pump loads.

API Specifications

Rapid evolution of surface beam-pumping machinery was helped to a great extent by the work of various standardization committees of the American Petroleum Institute. These committees were composed of engineers, representatives of manufacturers, and production men. For a considerable period of time, this work proceeded along three lines—development of specifications and ratings for rig irons, structural portions of pumping units, and speed reducers.

The API Committee on Standardization of Rig Irons, organized in 1923, worked out detailed specifications for the rig-iron components of standard rigs. In 1936, the committee was merged with the API Committee on Standardization of Standard Rigs and Derricks. In that year, the manufacturers subcommittee of the Committee on Standardization of Standard Rigs and Derricks proposed a method of rating the rig portions of pumping machinery. In 1938 the manufacturers recommended a name-plate marking for the rig portion of pumping units, the rating to represent the weakest element between the beam hanger and the crank. In 1941 a suggestion was made for the establishment of standard sizes of pumper structures, the increases in capacities being based on equal percentage increments. This study was correlated in 1942 with the study of standard sizes for reducers, with two subcommittees working jointly on the problem. However, when the action on speed reducers was finalized in 1945, the matter of standard structures was dropped. Current API specifications for pumping units give rating for the walking beam by a specific formula, and by general stipulation for other components—including samson post, pitman, and hanger. Use of a name plate is prescribed, giving pound rating of the unit structure.

As far as the reducer is concerned, Bowman Thomas, in 1932, was probably the first engineer to call attention to the need for a uniform method of rating for pumping machinery.[216] At that time different manufacturers rated the pumping units by different criteria—such as size of crankshaft, horsepower, horsepower per revolution per minute, pounds of crank pull, feet of given size of tubing a unit can handle, and torque. Thomas suggested two ratings, viz.:

1. Horsepower per rpm so that the operator knows the limits to which the unit can be loaded at any given speed.
2. Working torque capacity, to define the crank pull capacity for given stroke lengths.

Work on standardization of reducers was conducted by the API Committee on Standardization of Pumping Equipment and Engines. A Subcommittee on Rating of Pumping Machines was formed under the chairmanship of Hallan N. Marsh (who was succeeded in 1939 by Emory

N. Kemler). In 1935 the subcommittee proposed a method of rating of speed reducers based on the American Gear Manufacturers Association code, *Proposed Recommended Practice for Rating of Helical and Herringbone Gear Speed Reducers Used for Oil Well Pumping Units.* A name plate was proposed showing peak-torque rating at 20 rpm and 9 rpm, and nominal horsepower rating at 20 rpm and 9 rpm. The specifications became tentative in 1935 and final in 1937. As early as 1938 it was pointed out that horsepower rating of reducers was misleading and might easily lead to overloading of the reducer because of possible change of relationship between torque and horsepower resulting from change in operating conditions of the unit, and because the fly-wheel effect of the system might impose power peaks injurious to a reducer of the same horsepower rating as the prime mover. The horsepower rating of the reducer was, therefore, dropped from the name plate. In 1938 the manufacturers of chain speed reducers presented proposed ratings of their reducers. The specifications were adopted as tentative in 1939 and as final in 1941.

As previously stated, in 1942 cooperative committee work was in progress on establishment of standard sizes of pumping structures and reducers. The part of the work dealing with reducers resulted in final acceptance in 1945 of a number of groups of reducers of various sizes. This grouping forms the basis of present nomenclature of API sizes of pumping units.

When the work on the rating of speed reducers was conducted in 1935, J. C. Slonneger's formula for calculation of polished-rod load was included in specifications for arriving at peak torque. Because of development of other formulae for determining the polished-rod load, differences of opinion arose as to which of these formulae gave results most accurately agreeing with actual conditions; and in 1938 a proposal was made to remove the formula from the API specifications. In 1940 a committee was appointed—consisting of Eugene Hosford, J. C. Slonneger, and Kenneth N. Mills—to study the problem. The matter was on the agenda of the appropriate API committees for a number of years, and the discussions led eventually to the elimination of the well-load formula from the specifications, leaving to the user's judgment which of the formulae he should use and what factors possibly affecting the well loads he should consider.

Central Pumping Powers

The origin of central pumping powers is not clearly defined by literature or patents, but apparently they became an accepted commercial item in the period 1875 to 1884. The demand for them was prompted by the expensive and difficult-to-maintain alternative of operating a steam engine and boiler at each well head to supply power for pumping.

The first patent found relating to central pumping powers was issued in 1875 to A. E. Nickerson and L. C. Streeter.[217] This patent proposed operation of a number of wells from a more-or-less conventional standard-end pumping unit by transmitting motion from the walking beam of the standard end to other wells through wooden shackle lines. At the outpost wells, the pumping rig consisted of a simple wood walking beam mounted on a wood samson post. Several outpost wells could be operated from the "power" well by simply hooking on to any shackle line.

The earliest type of power consisted of a large bandwheel on a vertical shaft, belt-driven with a quarter-twist belt from a small pulley on a jack shaft with a second belt drive from a steam engine (Fig 19). A belt tightener was usually located between the bandwheel and the jack shaft. The vertical shaft had a step bearing below, with a tail shaft bearing on top with wire-line guys to suitable anchors. The vertical shaft had one or more eccentrics with hook-on points on the eccentric straps for a number of rod lines.

In April 1880, E. D. Yates[218] was issued a patent on a push-pull type central power (Fig. 20) ; and in the Oil Well catalog, 1884, there is shown

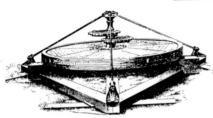

Fig. 19 (left)—Bandwheel Central Power
(*National Supply* Co. Catalog, 1901)

Fig. 20 (below)—Push-pull Central Power
E. D. Yates, 1880

a power of this type, as illustrated in Fig. 21. This was made largely of wood, but had iron for cranks, pins, and connections. There was a large bandwheel mounted on a horizontal shaft which had a crank at each end, with the crank throws opposed. A pitman was connected to each crank and the two were tied to opposite sides of a pull wheel. Shackle lines to wells were tied to spokes on the pull wheel, which oscillated through a short arc as the bandwheel was rotated. The same catalog also illustrates the "grasshopper" jack, designed specifically for shackle operation.

After 1880 almost all the patents issued related to gear drives with single and double reduction and to the arrangement of cranks, eccentrics, straps, bearings, and means of attaching pull rods (Fig. 22).

In 1885 four patents[219-222, incl.] were granted to George Allen relating to details of crank and eccentric units with bevel-gear drives, with two additional patents in 1889[223] and 1898.[224]

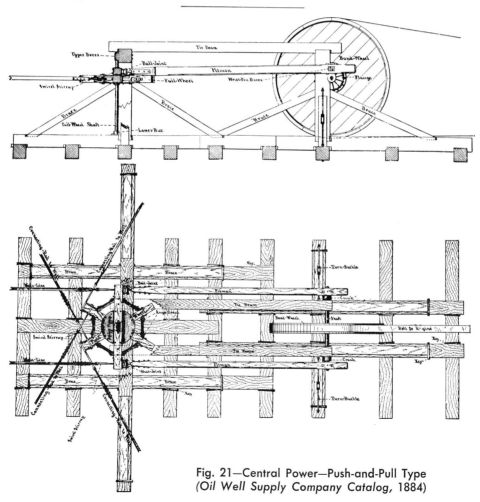

Fig. 21—Central Power—Push-and-Pull Type
(Oil Well Supply Company Catalog, 1884)

653

Fig. 22—Gear-driven Central Power
(Oil Well Supply Company Catalog,
1900)

Fig. 23—Fully Enclosed Gear-driven
Modern Central Power
The National Supply Co., 1936

In 1896 and 1897 eight patents were issued to G. W. Grimes, all of which relate to vertical shaft powers. The first[225] had a bevel-gear drive with adjustable stroke eccentrics on the shaft. The most elaborate[226] used four eccentrics on the main shaft with two other vertical shafts each having two eccentrics.

A number of other patents were issued on variations of the push-pull type. J. N. Maher[227] used a bevel-gear drive to a vertical shaft, with crank and pitman to oscillate a drum, with multiple grooves and multiple points for attaching rod lines in each groove.

J. J. Kivis[228] used a spur gear reduction with horizontal shafts, and having a crank and pitman on the main gear with ball-and-socket bearings to an oscillating wheel mounted on a vertical shaft, with notched points in the rim for bolting on pins to which wooden pull rods are attached with strapped ends.

C. E. Sutton[229] used a double-spur reduction gear with horizontal shafts with double crank, spaced 180 deg apart, with pitman to horizontal rack and gear drive on a vertical shaft, with disk for attaching rod lines.

Several patents were issued to E. D. Yates[230, 231] during this period, all relating to bevel-gear drive vertical-shaft units with two crank throws and four pull rods on each. Kenton Chickering[232] was the first to show a worm-gear drive. From 1900 to 1924 sixteen patents were issued on bevel-gear and bandwheel powers. W. G. Corey et al.[233] were the first to show enclosed gears with bevel- and spur-gear reductions running in oil. L. F. Burnham et al.[234] of the Westinghouse Company produced a helical-gear first reduction, bevel-gear second reduction, with anti-friction bearings and with motor drive—all totally enclosed in oil.

C. M. Anderson[235] of the Oil Well Supply Company made a bevel-gear first reduction spur-gear second reduction with all bearings, including eccentrics, with force-feed lubrication.

J. R. Mahan and J. B. Picard of National Supply Company[236] (Fig. 23), and Oswald Duda of American Well and Prospecting Company, both built bevel-gear spur-gear units with roller bearings totally enclosed, with force-feed lubrication to all bearings.

The earliest patent found for a well jack was issued in 1877 to W. F. Plockrass.[237]

There was essentially no standardization of auxiliary equipment used on central-gear pumping systems. Hook-ups for a given lease would be dictated by terrain, well-pumping problems, possible locations for the central power plant, and—most of all—by the operator's degree of ingenuity. As a result, there have been

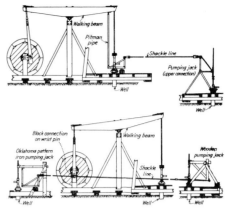

Fig. 24—Back-side Pumping
(From L. C. Uren)

developed an exceptional number of versions for "hook-ons", "hook-offs", holdups, holddowns, multipliers, butterflies, line supports, and counterbalances.

Since 1930 the trend to deeper pumping, multi-cylinder engine and motor drives, and satisfactory beam-pumping units in a wide range of sizes has resulted in their use in place of central powers on most new installations. Since 1940 only a small number of powers have been installed.

During the 1930's, back-side pumping (Fig. 24) was given considerable attention, primarily because of the need for economy measures in a time of low crude prices. This system was, in effect, a version of some of the earliest patents (Nickerson and Streeter, 1875[145]) in that a "jerk line" was tied to the crank of a pumping unit and was used to operate one to three other wells. The popularity of this arrangement was short-lived, however, because of the inherent limitations of the method—such as lack of flexibility, difficulties of counterbalancing, and loss of production of all wells when the power well was shut down.

The first attempt to work out API specifications for multiple sucker-rod installations was in 1939. J. C. Slonneger prepared the outline of the proposal, but no agreement could be reached on the details.

Long-stroke Pumping Units

Pumping units in this classification cover three general types: hydraulic, pneumatic, and mechanical—or a combination of two or more of these types. All have the common requirement of imparting a straight-line motion to the polished rod.

Although interest in long-stroke pumping did not materialize until the 1920's, when the maximum well pumping depths reached 5,000 to 5,500 ft,[197] the basic concept of this type of equipment dates back many centuries. (See Introduction and Fig. 2.) Bailing and swabbing might also come within this heading, but those methods of production have not been generally used in the United States except as a temporary expedient or as a means of determining well capacities. In the mining industry steam-actuated or water-actuated long-stroke cylinders, directly over the shaft or with a mechanical connection to the rod system, have been used for handling large volumes against high pumping heads. Pumps of this type were used for mine de-watering long before the start of the oil industry.[1]

Thomas M. Fell[238] in 1865 showed a steam cylinder connected with a chain linkage to the pump sucker rod and also to a counterbalance weight. Condensation of the steam with the pump liquid—in this case, water—was used to produce a vacuum to add to the lifting capacity of the unit. In 1874 M. Lytle[239] described a steam pump directly over the well (Fig. 25) or, as an alternate, the steam cylinder was connected with a pitman to a beam at a point between the pump rod and the samson post.

W. P. Barclay[240] devised a mine pump with an engine cylinder operated with water under pressure, with intake and exhaust valves actuated by collars on the piston rod. P. J. Thayer and M. J. Seymour[241] in 1881 showed a similar arrangement applied to an oil well, with the cylinder directly over the well and with a rod having valve-operating stops at each end of the stroke for opening the valve to pressure for the power stroke and to exhaust for the return stroke to allow the rods and pump plunger to fall by gravity (Fig. 26). S. B. Connor et al.[242] in 1881 invented a hydraulic-deadweight counterbalance for the rod load of mine pumps. C. C. Worthington[243] in 1886 disclosed a counterbalance for a vertical direct-acting steam pump in which either a hydraulic-pneumatic or a hydraulic-deadweight system was used. John S. Klein,[244] of Oil City, Pa., developed a pump in 1894 for keeping water out of gas wells. His design consisted of a beam-operated rod pump having a counterbalance and with a gas cylinder between the well and the fulcrum point, with gas from the well being used to operate the unit. M. W. Quick,[245] of Titusville, Pa., in 1897 used a vacuum-operated engine cylinder connected by a pitman to the outer end of a beam; and in 1900[246] he provided a similar device which was pressure-operated.

J. G. Steiner[247] in 1903 devised a multiple-well hydraulic unit with a cylinder over each well and a tube from each well to one end of an operating cylinder having a similar number of wellhead cylinders connected to the opposite end of this cylinder, and having a crank and pitman mechanical drive for operating the cylinder. The rod load of one group of wells was therefore balanced against the other group, and the operating cylinder was double-acting.

R. J. Hoffman and E. H. Hollingshead[248] in 1904 provided an air-operated cylinder directly over the well head and operated from a central plant. Frank W. Davis and Albert W. King[249] in 1905 disclosed an operating cylinder in which the piston rod of the engine extended through

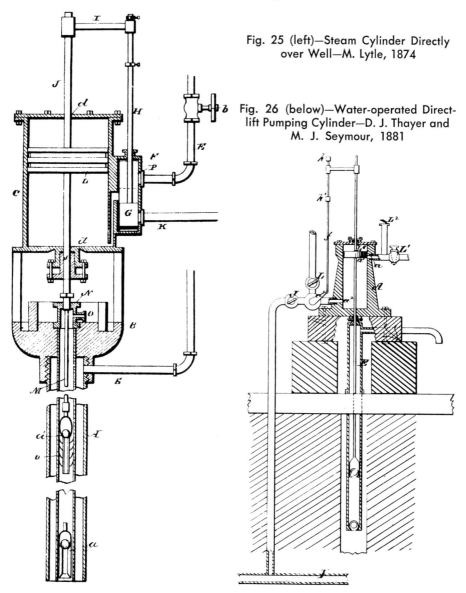

Fig. 25 (left)—Steam Cylinder Directly over Well—M. Lytle, 1874

Fig. 26 (below)—Water-operated Direct-lift Pumping Cylinder—D. J. Thayer and M. J. Seymour, 1881

the tubing head and performed the function of the polished rod of the system. This made it possible to obtain a long stroke without the necessity of elevating the power cylinder. M. W. Quick[250] in 1906 developed a pumping unit with a gas cylinder, using gas from the well, and having the piston rod connected to the polished rod by means of a cable over a large-diameter sheave to provide a straight-line motion for both the polished rod and the piston rod of the operating cylinder (Fig. 27).

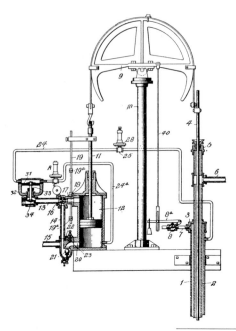

Fig. 27 (left)—Pumping Unit Operated with Casing Gas—M. W. Quick, 1906

Fig. 28 (below)—Segelhorst Hydraulic Long-stroke Unit with Direct-lift Cylinder over Well Head, 1926

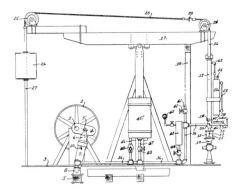

A. L. Segelhorst,[251] an employee of Standard Oil Co. of California,[252] proposed a direct-lift cylinder in 1918 which would give a long stroke and utilize the bandwheel crank, beam, and other parts of a standard-end pumping unit (Fig. 28). A cylinder, having a large-diameter piston, was connected to the bandwheel crank and was connected to the small-diameter cylinder mounted on the tubing head. The piston in this cylinder was connected to the polished rod, and also had a cable attached which extended through the upper end of the cylinder and over sheaves on each end of the walking beam, with a counterweight attached to the end of the cable. The beam was blocked in a stationary position and acted merely as a support for the two sheaves. This unit acted as a stroke multiplier, in the ratio of the area of the large operating cylinder to the small cylinder at the well head, and any desired stroke could be obtained by changing this ratio. The polished rod, therefore, had a simple harmonic motion produced by the bandwheel crank.

The various devices shown in the patent record—here discussed briefly—show all of the basic elements of the hydraulic, pneumatic, hydraulic-pneumatic, and hydraulic-mechanical devices found in present-day long-stroke units. However, inasmuch as the need for the long stroke had not yet become apparent for oil-well pumping, the primary object of the inventors of these devices was to provide a straight lift over the well or to utilize a particular source of power—steam, gas from the well being pumped, or, in a few instances, water or hydraulic fluid supplied by an actuating pump. Those applications—although directed to mine de-watering, such as the develpoments of Barclay *(op. cit.)*—did have the need for high-capacity high-head pumping and took advantage of the long stroke, but these were intended primarily for shallow water wells.

The historical record shows very little information on the application of these devices. George[200] reports the application of air cylinders at the well head in Bradford, Pa. fields. Steam units[253] have been used and were offered for sale in the Oil Well catalog of 1903.

H. L. Wood[254] reported that the first long-stroke unit was used to pump a well in Terre Haute, Ind., about 1891, and was still in operation at the time of his article in 1926. This pump had a stroke of 11 ft 7 in.

W. H. Clapp,[255] Professor of Mechanical Engineering at California Institute of Technology, designed a gas-operated beam unit in which particular attention was given to the control of acceleration to minimize the stress in the sucker-rod system.

A hydraulic stroke multiplier was developed by E. W. Patterson[256] and commercialized by the Pacific Oil Tool Company (Fig. 29).[257] This unit is based on the same principle as that used by Segelhorst *(op. cit.)*, with an important added feature of a hydraulic-pneumatic counterbal-

Fig. 29—Pacific Oil Tool Long Stroke
(From *California Oil Fields,* 1926)

ance. This was accomplished by making the operating cylinder double acting, with one side of the piston applying pressure to the fluid to direct it to the wellhead cylinder and the other side supplied with fluid under substantially constant pressure from a counterbalance tank. The air pressure in this tank was held at a value that would balance all of the rod load and approximately one half of the fluid load. The wellhead device consisted of a pair of cylinders spaced apart a sufficient amount to clear the casing head and its connections. Ram-type plungers were used, with a beam attached to their top ends having its mid-point directly over the well. A polished-rod clamp was carried by this beam.

One feature claimed for this unit was that it retained the simple harmonic motion of a crank-actuated device and could be conveniently made for any desired stroke. These machines were run successfully at 20 spm with a 10-ft stroke, or an average polished-rod speed of 400 ft per min.

A later model of this device used a single cylinder at the well head with a crosshead guided in a structural frame and having a cantilever extension carrying the polished-rod clamp over the well centerline. It was reported that about 100 of these machines were sold and operated in California and Texas. Problems developed with the mechanical drive, and its manufacture was discontinued.

Intensive development of long-stroke units started in the 1920's. W. E. Hubbard devised and engineered a number of different designs and, although none of his units became a commercial success, he should be given credit for pioneering this development (Fig. 30). E. H. Musser[258] reported on trials of a Hubbard long-stroke unit built by General Petroleum Corp. in their shops in Vernon, Calif. The first installation was made in the Signal Hill Field in 1925 and operated successfully.

Hubbard built other designs of hydraulic long-stroke pumps and probably did more to pioneer units of this type than any other one man. Several patents[259] were issued in his name covering important features. The Hubbard units were all well-engineered and, if available today, would probably have the high commercial standing which the designs merited.

A Hubbard long-stroke unit, built under Patent No. 1,879,262, was financed by the Guiberson Corporation and a pump of this type was installed in the Signal Hill Field in 1928 (Fig. 31). This unit had a single cylinder directly over the well head, a counterbalance tank, and a specially designed multi-cylinder operating unit with a four-way valve to direct the flow from the counterbalance tank to the operating pump and from there to the cylinder for the upstroke, and from the cylinder to the pump and from there to the counterbalance tank for the downstroke. Provision was made for controlled acceleration and speed limitation in the event of failure of the pump rod or other parts of the equipment. As far as can

Fig. 30 (left)—Hubbard Unit, 1926

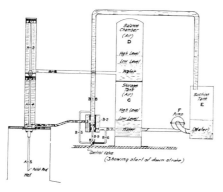

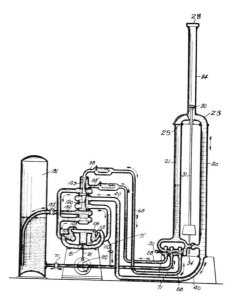

Fig. 31—(right)—Hubbard Hydraulic
Pneumatic Pumping Unit
Built by Guiberson Corporation, 1927

Fig. 32 (left)—Hubbard Hydraulic Unit
with Pneumatic Counterbalance
Using Radial Operating Pump
Built by Hydraulic Pumper Company,
Tulsa, 1941

be determined, only one of these units was installed. The construction was rather elaborate and the manufacturing cost, even in quantity, would have been high.

A small Hubbard unit was built by Pacific Pump Company and installed in 1938. This also had a positive-displacement operating pump. A larger version of this same unit was also built with a centrifugal pump for power supply. Another Hubbard unit, as covered by Patent No. 2,277,761, was built by the Hydraulic Pumper Company of Tulsa, Okla. (Fig. 32); and the first unit was installed in a well of the Skelly Oil Company in Polo, Okla. in 1941. Ten of these units were installed in various fields in the Mid-Continent and their operation was reported as satisfactory. They were similar to the previous Hubbard designs, but incorporated a radial-type 9-cylinder pump as the operating unit. Hubbard also built a small unit for stripper operation in which the stroke was controlled with electric-limit switches operating through relays to reverse the direction of the operating motor. The Hydril Company built this unit in limited quantities about 1940.

A long-stroke pumping unit was built by the Vernon Oil Tool Company under patents held by John H. Suter[260] using a centrifugal pump as the operating unit, in which a double-intake impeller was provided with two involute discharge passages in close axial arrangement. A control cylinder was provided with a pilot valve which served to shift the pump impeller axially to align the pump runner with one of the pump-discharge involutes. The skirts of the double-intake impeller were made extra long and acted as valves when the impeller was shifted. Thus, both the intake and discharge of the operating pump were reversed by simply shifting the pump impeller. Both of these developments were later acquired by Axelson Manufacturing Company as a basis for further work on long-stroke units.

In 1929 Andrew Youngquist, John V. Box, and Charles A. Dailey—of Standard Oil Co. of California—proposed a gas-operated unit which was engineered and produced by Kobe, Inc., which had twin power rams connected with a beam over the well head, with a second set of counterbalance rams inside the first set (Fig. 33). A hydraulic-pneumatic counterbalance system applied a pressure to this second or inner set of rams to balance about 90 percent of the rod load. Gas pressure applied to the annular area between the inner and outer rams supplied the lifting force for the fluid load and 10 percent of the rod load. Provision was made for control of both speed and acceleration in each direction of the pump stroke. These units had a maximum stroke of 10 ft and a maximum polished-rod load of 35,000 lb. H. A. Brett[261] reported on the construction and operation of this unit.

In 1928 W. G. Corey and Charles A. Trow[262] invented a multiple-well hydraulic central power unit, in which each well was controlled by

Fig. 33—Kobe Gas-operated Unit with Hydraulic Pneumatic Counterbalance First Installed in California, 1929

Fig. 34—Early photo of Salentine Unit without Counterbalance

an automatic valve. H. M. Salentine,[263] starting in the 1920's, pioneered hydraulic units for stripper production without counterbalance and with relatively low horsepower input (Fig. 34). Lane-Wells and others manufactured these units, and they are currently being produced and sold by the S. C. Carter Company in Los Angeles. The important features of the Salentine unit were its low-cost construction and its design for quick return and slow power stroke.

The first Vickers unit was installed for Ed Stanton at Long Beach, Calif. in August 1937. Vickers[264] produced and installed at Santa Fe Springs, Calif., in December 1948, the first long-stroke unit of the general type which they later manufactured. This pump had an 18-ft stroke and used as an operating unit the Vickers balanced-vane type pump. The controls and operating pump were, to a large extent, standard units developed for machine-tool hydraulics, for which the Vickers Company has become famous. Others in the Vickers Company, now a division of Sperry Rand, contributed improvements (Fig. 35).[265] Patent No. 2,347,-302 discloses the details of the type of Vickers units now being produced. In this unit an intensifier is provided so that high pressure can be applied to the wellhead cylinder with moderate pressure on both the operating pump and the counterbalance system, thus permitting the use of a small cylinder at the well head and small connecting lines, with large lines only in the closely coupled intensifier and counterbalance tank.

Gas-operated long-stroke pumping units were applied on a substantial scale by The Pure Oil Company and others. A. E. Carr and K. A. Covell, petroleum engineers with The Pure Oil Company, took an important part in the development and application of this equipment, although the construction and basic ideas should be credited to W. H. Wineman[266] of the Sullivan Machinery Company. P. D. Cornelius[267] also contributed to this development. A distinguishing feature of the Sullivan pump head (Fig. 36) was a single cylinder suspended and braced in the derrick by cables, with a piston rod below the cylinder which could be attached to the polished rod with clamps. Controlled operating and exhaust pressures determined the speed in each direction. Gas under suitable pressure for operating was supplied from any source, or a compressor was used with gas or air in a closed circuit.

Fig. 35—Vickers Long-stroke Unit with Dead-weight Counterbalance, 1944

Fig. 38—Modern Axelson Long-stroke Unit

Fig. 37—Pelton Modern Long-stroke Unit
with Hydraulic-Pneumatic Counterbalance

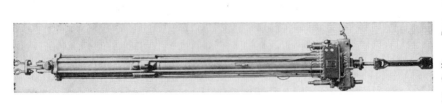

Fig. 36—Sullivan Pneumatic
Long-stroke Unit, 1936

The application of the Sullivan head offered particular advantage in deep wells with heavy rod loads where the ratio of the load on the power stroke to the return stroke resulted in a low compression ratio for the compressor, hence a relatively high thermal efficiency for gas operation. Since single-stage compression was used, the pressure on the compressor suction was determined by the counterbalance load. To further improve the thermal efficiency and to prevent icing in cold weather, the operating gas was run through a gas-fired super-heater.

Other important features of the Sullivan pump are the constant force characteristics of the unit and the absence of a heavy dead-end mass attached to the rod system. The result of this combination is a very favorable rod load throughout the cycle. The constant-force feature produces a somewhat variable velocity cycle as contrasted to hydraulic or mechanical pumps, in which the rods are constrained to a fixed-velocity cycle with a resultant variation in rod load. Sullivan units were produced for total loads of 30,000 lb and maximum stroke lengths of 15 ft. The first installations were made by The Pure Oil Company in the Navarro County, Texas, Powell Field in 1931.[268] Several hundred installations were made and many of these are still in operation.

The Pelton Water Wheel Company entered the long-stroke pumping unit business in 1940, based upon inventions of S. C. Kyle,[269] Morgan White,[270] F. H. Rued,[271] and E. T. Billings and T. E. Garrison.[272] (See Fig. 37.) The important features of the Pelton unit are the single counterbalance tank, balancing of all the rod load and approximately one half of the fluid load, a positive-displacement gear pump as the operating unit, adjustable stroke, controlled acceleration, and safety controls to prevent damage in the event of failure of any of the equipment in the system which would either stall the unit or suddenly release the load. Pelton units have pioneered heavy pumping with long-stroke units, principally in wells from 6,000 to 12,000 ft in depth. Units are made in stroke lengths up to 30 ft, running 360 ft per min, and capable of carrying a total load of 35,000 lb. The first pump was a 10-ft stroke unit, and was installed in the Brea Field in 1943.

Axelson Manufacturing Company (now a division of U. S. Industries, Inc.) entered the long-stroke hydraulic pumping field in 1948, based upon developments acquired from the Vernon Oil Tool Company, previously referred to.[260] The present units (Fig. 38) cover both the stripper-well range and the deep, heavy well range. Large units are made for strokes up to 26½ ft and loads up to 32,000 lb, operating at maximum polished-rod speeds of 370 ft per min. The Axelson unit is similar to the Pelton in that it has a hydro-pneumatic counterbalance with the pump and reversing valve between the counterbalance receiver and the wellhead operating cylinder. The Axelson operating unit is a centrifugal pump with a pilot-operated reversing valve controlled by the position of the piston in the operating cylinder.

Consolidated Western Steel Company developed a long-stroke hydraulic unit under invention of P. E. Noll,[273] V. R. Noll,[274] and T. D. Aller and P. E. Noll.[275] In this unit a single ram-type plunger having a head carries two chain sprockets equally spaced from the centerline, with the chain over these having one end attached to the polished rod and the other end anchored to the base of the unit, thus giving a polished-rod stroke double the stroke of the ram. Counterbalancing is accomplished through the operating pump, with a hydraulic-pneumatic system. The power unit is a variable-stroke piston-displacement pump, with the control valve mechanically operated by the ram. Convenient adjustment is provided at the bottom of the stroke to facilitate "spacing" of the bottom-hole pump. Speed control over a wide range is provided with the variable-stroke unit and at good efficiencies over the full range.

Harvey Machine Company also entered the field, producing a hydraulic-pneumatic unit similar in some respects to the Axelson unit, particularly in its use of a centrifugal pump. This development was taken over by Oil Well Supply; and several sizes are currently being offered, with load capacities up to 37,000 lb and stroke lengths to 22 ft 9 in.

Although hydraulic and pneumatic devices lend themselves to long-stroke operation, the patent record shows that various mechanical units have also been developed. To go back to the early developments, S. Lippert[276] in 1907 proposed a direct-operating screw attached to the polished rod and driven through double miter gears, with clutches operating to reverse the motion at each end of the stroke. J. P. Coffman[277] in 1915 designed a self-contained pumping unit with a straight-line motion to the polished rod. Baker Oil Tool Company produced a unit which was reported in 1926[258] as having an 8-ft stroke (Fig. 39). This unit had a double rack and gear stroke multiplier and also produced a straight-line motion. Musser (*op. cit.*) reported on the "wig-wag" unit, in which the pitman of a standard-end unit operated in a horizontal position and was connected to the mid-point of a vertical beam hinged at the

Fig. 39—Baker Long-stroke Unit
(From Musser, 1926)

Fig. 40—Stroke Multiplier
(From Musser, 1926)

bottom. The top end of the beam was attached to a chain, which was oscillated horizontally and was carried to the polished rod over a sprocket mounted on a pipe frame. The other end of the chain operated over a second sprocket and carried the counterweight.

A type of stroke multiplier was also reported by Musser, in which the end of the beam of a standard rig pumping unit carried a sprocket on each side. A double chain connected to the polished-rod hanger passed over these sprockets and was anchored near the bottom of the headache post. Movement of the beam and sprockets imparted a stroke to the polished rod which was double that of the beam movement (Fig. 40).

E. D. Smith et al.[278] in 1930 showed a chain attached to the pitman near the crank end and carried over a sprocket on the beam end to give a long stroke.

Parkersburg Rig and Reel Company produced the first commercial long-stroke beam unit. This unit had a hinged samson post with a linkage to produce a straight-line motion at the polished rod (Fig. 41). The stroke length was 132 in. and the maximum polished-rod load was 35,000 lb. It used a beam counterbalance with the gear box between the samson post and the well, and double pitmans were used in compression. The first installation was made about 1935, which was several years in advance of any other long-stroke beam unit. Since that time a number of other manufacturers have built 10-ft stroke units using horseheads to obtain straight-line motion (Fig. 42).

Within the past 10 years Lacy Oil Tool Company has produced a number of air-balanced long-stroke units, all with horseheads for straight-line motion (Fig. 43). The first was a 120-in. unit, and the first installa-

667

Fig. 41 (above, left)—11-ft Parkersburg
Long-stroke Unit, 1935

Fig. 42 (above, right)—10-ft Stroke
National Unit

Fig. 43 (left)—16-ft Lacy Long-stroke Air-
balanced Unit

tions of record were made in 1947. In 1948 the first 144-in. unit was installed, and in 1955 the first 192-in. unit was installed in Ventura, Calif. Lufkin also built a 192-in. air-balanced unit under license from Lacy.

Engineering Studies of Pumping-equipment Design Problems

The period from around 1928 to 1943 must be considered as the "golden age" of the studies of the literature on beam-pumping systems. It was during this period that petroleum engineers such as Lester C. Uren (Professor Emeritus of Petroleum Engineering of the University of California), C. J. Coberly, Hallan N. Marsh, H. E. Dralle, J. C. Slonneger, Kenneth N. Mills, Emory N. Kemler, F. W. Lake, John F. Kendrick, Paul D. Cornelius, S. B. Sargent, Jr., W. E. Gilbert, D. O. Johnson, and Robert William Rieniets developed theories and performed tests on which our present knowledge of the sucker-rod pumping system is based. Contributions made since 1943 represent, in a majority of cases, an enlargement, elaboration, and refinement of the basic principles set up during the preceding period (an exception is the important contribution made by Arthur Lubinski[101] on the buckling of tubing in rod pumps), although recent developments indicate the beginning of an entirely new phase of the studies of the subject.

Early investigators concerned themselves primarily with static, dynamic, frictional, and shock loads. Later it became apparent that these loads alone were not sufficient to explain certain phenomena of performance of beam installations—repeated breaking of rods at certain specific points of the string or at certain specific operating speeds, or obtaining production under conditions when practically no motion of the subsurface plunger could be expected. This led to revision of the previous thinking on the subject and brought about consideration of behavior of the sucker-rod system as a problem in the longitudinal vibration of bars.

Calculation of Loads

A chart in Fig. 44, copyrighted in 1925 by The National Supply Company, is an example of early work done on determining the pumping loads for design of sucker-rod strings.[205] The chart was developed for determining the unit stress of rods by determining the static and the dynamic loadings. Hallan N. Marsh, in 1928, presented a formula for rod load assuming simple harmonic motion of rods.[197] J. C. Slonneger's formula for peak polished-rod load, recommended in the early API standards for calculation of peak torque, had the advantage of simplicity and agreed fairly well with measured loads, particularly at slow speeds of operation. The formula applies the acceleration factor to the weight of both the fluid and the rod, and neglects the buoyancy and the friction.

In 1939 Kenneth N. Mills introduced his formula for calculation of peak polished-rod load.[279] The basic assumption of the formula was belief that acceleration of fluid contributes little to the peak well load because of the difference in rate of transmission of stresses in the fluid and in the rods and because of comparatively high compressibility of the fluid. Tested on a number of wells, the formula gave results which agreed with actual load measurements with accuracy of 90 to 100 percent in 58 percent of the cases and of 80 to 90 percent in 25 percent.

In the meantime, however, a new concept of loadings within the sucker-rod system was being introduced. In 1937 John F. Kendrick and Paul D. Cornelius presented their analysis of sucker rods as a vibrating system with one degree of freedom, with forced vibration and with viscous damping.[280] In the same year Slonneger developed his chart for speeds of pumping which are synchronous or non-synchronous with natural frequencies of rods for different lengths of rod strings.[281] The chart found wide practical application in analyzing the difficulties of many "problem" wells, by permitting selection of operating speeds at which the two trains of vibration—the natural vibration of rods and the vibratory pumping motion—are not in phase. Slonneger also presented the first authoritative analysis of effect of vibration of rods on the dynamometer cards.

Over 200 tests conducted on a single well equipped with elaborate instrumentation and reported in 1941 and 1942 by H. E. Dralle, E. H.

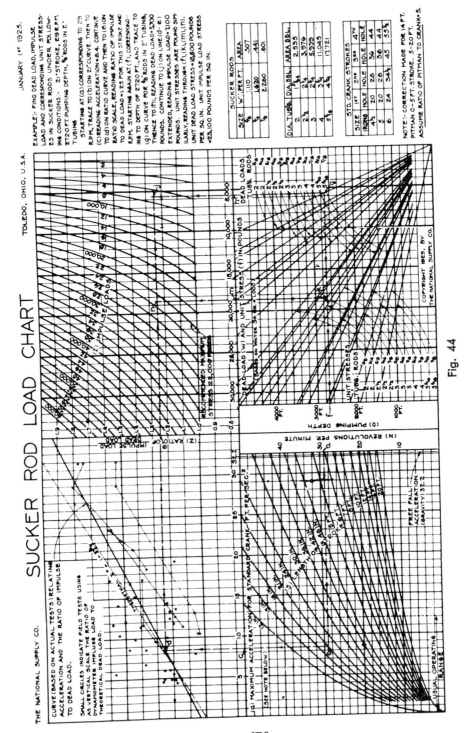

SUCKER ROD LOAD CHART

Fig. 44

Lamberger and B. F. Langer, respectively, furnished a basis for the so-called "Langer formula".[282, 283] This formula, introducing such factors as natural vibration of rods and fluid level, was quite complex. For field use Langer developed a simplified formula in which certain factors were omitted and constants adjusted to compensate for this omission.

Measuring of Loads

Work on theoretical calculation of loads in beam-pumping installations was preceded by the use of actual load measurements, with the dynamometer as the measuring instrument. On April 23, 1921, The National Supply Company acquired the Chatillon dynamometer and adapted it to "well weighing", which represented probably the first application of the dynamometer for determining the well loads.[205] Fig. 45 shows the record of some of the early tests. The Chatillon dynamometer was of the indicating type, a calibrated spring being the measuring element. H. Dave Collins introduced certain modifications in the instrument and used it extensively around 1927.

In the middle 1920's, the Martin-Decker dynamometer of the hydraulic type made its appearance. The pressure-transformer unit of the instrument, installed on the polished rod, converted part of the polished-rod load into pressure transmitted hydraulically to the recording unit, which furnished cards similar to those of the steam-indicator cards. The instrument was widely used in the late 20's and the 30's.

Many other types of dynamometers made their appearance during the 1930's—the Kemler Well Weigher, the Westinghouse Dynagraph, the Slonneger Well-O-Meter, the Carbon Pile Strain Element Dynamometer.[284] In 1948 D. O. Johnson and Leo Fagg introduced their ring-type dynamometer, which is essentially a recording proving ring. Because of its simplicity and accuracy, this instrument gained universal acceptance.

The literature on well dynamometer studies is quite voluminous and it would be extremely difficult to give credit to all who made contributions. Probably the first technical paper presented on the subject was the one given in 1927 by F. W. Lake and H. A. Brett.[285] The paper gave the results of the authors' work with a dynamometer, which was of the recording type, discussed the "ideal card" and the effects of counterbalance, length of stroke, depth, and other factors on operation of the system.

J. C. Slonneger presented in 1937 an extensive analysis of effect of rod vibration on dynamometer cards. Hallan N. Marsh and E. V. Watts offered in 1938 material for practical application of card dynamometer data.[286] In 1939 Eugene Hosford and Emory N. Kemler furnished with their technical paper a large number of dynamometer cards, taken on different wells and under different conditions, which provided valuable reference material for study of the subject.[287] J. C. Slonneger, Hallan N. Marsh, Emory N. Kemler, W. E. Gilbert, Kenneth N. Mills, S. B.

DYNAMOMETER TESTS OF PUMPING WELLS

No.	Well	Operator	Date	Company	Location	Depth	Tubing	Rods	Pump	Oil Bbls.	%	%	Stroke	RPM	Load in Lbs. (Old Method) Running	Maximum	Load in Lbs. (New Method) Up Center	Top	Down Center	Bottom	Dead	Impulse	Impulse Lbs. Sq. In.	Action	Theoret. Dead Load Lbs.	Impulse + Dead / Dead	Impulse + Theoret. / Dead	Remarks
1	OAKES Nº4			STD.		2090	2½		T				30	30	2000-7500	7800							17600	SMOOTH	6580		1.185	NO TROUBLE
2	OAKES Nº5			STD.		2038	2½		T				30	36	1000-7500	7600							17200	VERY SMOOTH	6400		1.185	2 BREAKS IN 3 MOS.
3	SHAW Nº18			STD.		1383	2		H	40			36	32	0-4000	4600							15800	SMOOTH	2850		1.612	NO TROUBLE
4	"			"		"	"		"				"	25	500-4000								13400		2850		1.402	
5	SHAW Nº21			"		2029	2½		H				30	28	2000-7000	7600							17200	LITTLE JERKY	6350		1.198	8-10 BREAKS PER MO.
6	SHAW-PALMER Nº12			"		3024	2		H	148	60		36	24	1000-6000	6500							21200		6250		1.04	
7	SHAW-PALMER Nº13			"		2033	2½		H	134	75		36	23	1300-8200	8400							19000	SMOOTH	6400		1.312	LITTLE TROUBLE
8	MITCHELL Nº1			"		1450	2½		T	220			30	26	800-5400	5600							12700	JERKY-HARD	4525		1.237	MANY BREAKS
9	MITCHELL Nº4			"		"	2		T	168	87		36		700-4400	4500							14700	SMOOTH	3000		1.50	NO TROUBLE
10	LANGSTON PALMER Nº1			"		1267	2½		H	76	0		30	28	1000-6000	6300							14300	JERKY	3980		1.583	20 BREAKS IN 6 MO.
11	Nº17			"		1410	2½		T	380	93		36	42	1200-6500	7800							17700	VERY JERKY	4400		1.772	
12	LANGSTON Nº17			"		1424	2		T	157	0		50	31	1200-3500	3700							12100	SMOOTH-EASY	2975		1.232	NO BREAKS
13	CHATMAN Nº1			GULF		1500	2		M				28	24	700-3300								10800		3100		1.065	
14	"									85	0		"	32	500-4500	4800							15700	LITTLE JERKY	"		1.548	
15													"	36	600-6000	8000							26200				2.58	
16	CHATMAN Nº7			GULF		2080	2½		T	650	85		36	24	1000-9500	10000							22700	FAIR	6525		1.531	
17	CHATMAN Nº9			GULF		2068	2½		T	150	50		36	24	2000-6700	6700							15200	JERKY	6500		1.031	
18	"			"		"	"		"				"	27	7000-6600	6900							15600		"		1.062	
19	"			"		"	"		"				"	40	1750-9200	10000							22700		"		1.53	
20														42	1000-9650	10000											"	
21	CHATMAN Nº10			GULF		2047	2½		T				36	32	1000-8700	8700							19700	VERY JERKY	6400		1.36	
22	"			"		"	"							34	1000-9200								20800		"		1.437	
23	"			"		"								35	800-9700								22000		"		1.515	
24										5.5	85			36	1100-10200	10200							25100				1.595	
25	KING-B Nº5			GULF		2025	2½		T				36	25	1800-7200								16100	HARD JERKY	6350		1.135	
26	"			"		"	"			770	35		36	36	700-10000	10000							22700		"		1.575	
27	"			"		"							"	40	500-11500	11500							26100		"		1.812	
28													"	42	800-10500	11000							25000		"		1.735	
29	S. LUCAS Nº2			PRAIRIE	DRUMRIGHT	2600	2						29	26	2500-9400								21300		6550		1.435	
30	G. BLACK Nº4			PRAIRIE	DRUMRIGHT	2600	2						30	20	1900-6600								21600		5400		1.222	
31	"			"	"	"	"						"	22	2800-6600								21600		"		"	
32	"			"	"	"	"						30	28	2500-7500								24500		"		1.388	
33	"			"	"	"	"						"	34	3200-7500								24500		"		"	
34	G. BLACK Nº1			PRAIRIE	DRUMRIGHT	2600	2						30	18	1800-6800								22200		5400		1.26	
35	"												"	24	1200-8000								26100		"		1.48	
36	G. BLACK Nº33			PRAIRIE	DRUMRIGHT	2600	2						30	20	1800-6800								22200		5400		1.26	
37	"												"	32	1500-7800								25500				1.435	
38	YARHOLA Nº23			PRAIRIE	DRUMRIGHT	2550	2						24	20	2400-6300								20500		5300		1.189	
39	SLOAN Nº2			PENNOK	BRECKENRIDGE	3160	2		J				34	16	3000-7800								25500	VERY SMOOTH	6550		1.18	GAS PRESSURE TO HELP
40	"			"	"	"	"						"	16	2500-8300								27100	" "			1.268	NO GAS PRESSURE
41	"			"	"	"	"						"	28	4000-8000								26300	" "			1.221	GAS PRESSURE TO HELP
42	CONNERS Nº4	M.T.A.	10-21	MAGNOLIA	DRUMRIGHT	2530	3						50	22	500-13000								23600		11000		1.182	MANY BREAKS
43	COKER Nº25	M.T.A.	10-21	MAGNOLIA	DRUMRIGHT	2700	2						30	18	1800-6800								22100		5600		1.213	
44	"												"	24	1800-7700								25200		"		1.375	
45	Nº3 TRACT E.T.	R.N.A.	2-24	OHIO	SALT CREEK	2822	2½		2" AXELSON					13			6050	5050		3150	4800	6600	21500		7650	1.375	.864	
46	"	"	"	"										20			6900	4800		1950	4800	7600	23000		"	1.583	.994	
47	Nº5 TRACT E.T.	R.N.A.	2-24	OHIO	SALT CREEK	2840	2½							13			7500	7000		3050	6300	8950	20300		8500	1.42	1.05	
48	"	"	"	"										20			7900	6400		2150	6300	10050	22700		"	1.535	1.3	
49	Nº13 E½ SEC.12	R.N.A.	2-24	OHIO	SALT CREEK	2340	2		AXELSON					10			4550	4800		2600	4040	5150	16500		4800	1.275	1.072	
50	"	"	"	"		"								20			4630	3600		1500	4050	5650	18500		"	1.395	1.178	
51														30			4150	5050		750	4050	6550	21400		"	1.616	1.365	

Fig. 45

Sargent, Jr., D. O. Johnson, Leo Fagg, and others made a number of contributions to technical literature on the subject of well weighing.

A dynamometer measures the well load at the polished rod, which is a summation of different loads superimposed on each other. Because of this fact, the record furnished by the instrument—the dynamometer card—is quite complex and its interpretation requires considerable skill and experience. To eliminate the factors which distort the contour of the polished-rod dynamometer card, an instrument was developed—the subsurface dynagraph—which, placed in the rod string directly above the subsurface pump, records the actual load on the plunger. Ability to record the direct load on the plunger, particularly in comparison with the polished-rod load, furnished an opportunity for better understanding of the behavior of the subsurface portion of the beam installations. Results of subsurface dynagraph studies were reported first in 1936 by W. E. Gilbert.[288]

The Pumping Unit

Studies of the surface pumping equipment—from the beam hanger to the prime mover—were, of course, primarily within the province of the manufacturers' engineers, as they strove continuously to improve the design of the pumping units. Most of them must remain anonymous because their contributions are not recorded in the technical literature. However, there is still an ample record of the engineering work on the subject.

H. E. Dralle made a study in 1930 of effects of types of prime movers and of counterbalance on stresses in well surface pumping equipment.[289] W. C. Shutts and Bowman Thomas, in 1931, and J. Bayo Hopper, in 1940, reported on field efficiency tests for different arrangements of the geometry of the unit and for different directions of rotation.[290, 291] Kenneth N. Mills, in 1940, offered data on the importance of proper installation of surface pumping machinery.[292] In 1951 Emory N. Kemler and R. J. Howe worked out harmonic analyses of the kinematic performance of the pumping unit.[293] The reducer and the torque conditions of the installation attracted considerable study. Bowman Thomas discussed, in 1932, the surface pumping machinery from the point of view of torque and horsepower rating. P. C. Day in 1933 analyzed the problems of the reducers.[294] In 1938 Kemler presented an analysis showing that a torsional vibration may be set up in gear drives of pumping gear reducers and should be given consideration in design, and that at high speeds of operation use of maximum load in calculating peak torque may result in units larger than necessary.[295] Harold S. Kelly, M. H. Halderson, P. A. Witherspoon, and E. S. Calvert—using data of a large number of tests on one pumping well —in 1948 presented an analysis which led them to conclude that in many cases peak torque could not be calculated with acceptable accuracy and that a more simple and accurate method of calculation was needed.[296]

Proper counterbalance probably contributes more to the satisfactory operation of a beam installation than any other single item of the surface pumping equipment. It is because of this fact that counterbalancing of beam installations attracted the attention of many investigators. Between 1936 and 1951 Emory N. Kemler, Frank Briggs, Kenneth N. Mills, and D. O. Johnson were among those who made the most important contributions.[297-301, incl.] Methods of checking the counterbalance conditions—through the "clutch slipping" method, by special instruments, or through analysis of dynamometer cards—were evolved or reported by Hallan N. Marsh and E. V. Watts, Emory N. Kemler, D. O. Johnson, Frank Briggs, J. L. Laudermilk, and others.[286-305, incl.]

Sucker Rods

As knowledge of the behavior of and load conditions within the sucker-rod strings increased, the question of design of rod strings received increased attention. Emory N. Kemler in 1936 and 1941, S. B. Sargent, Jr. in 1937, and Frank Briggs in 1940 analyzed the problems connected with this design.[306-309, incl.] With the increasing depth of pumping wells, the problem of the weight of rod strings became one of importance. Tapered rod strings—an attempt at a modification, if not a solution of this problem—made their appearance. Two methods of design of rod strings were evolved. The first method assigned to each of the graduated sections of the rod string its maximum stress. The second method consisted of designing the rod string in such a manner that the unit stresses were equal in the top rod of each of the different-size sections.

The questions of rod failures received, of course, early and careful attention from many investigators. The pin failures were met by development of an API joint, and the body failures by improving the metallurgy of rods. The question of corrosion fatigue of rods came into the forefront in the late 20's and early 30's as the sour-crude fields of Kansas and West Texas were developed.

Failure caused by corrosion fatigue occurs in two stages. First, a corrosion pit is formed in the rod, causing concentration of stresses. The second stage of failure then proceeds along the lines of ordinary metal fatigue failure. Blaine B. Wescott was the first to conduct extensive laboratory corrosion-fatigue tests of steels used in the manufacture of sucker rods. In 1931, C. G. Zur Horst and Wescott discussed the causes of sucker-rod failures.[310] In 1933 Wescott and C. Norman Bowers reported on their first corrosion-fatigue tests.[311] In 1935 the same authors furnished tables giving endurance properties of sucker-rod materials for air and sulfide corrosion.[312] *API Code 30: Corrosion Fatigue Testing of Sucker Rod Materials* was approved in 1945. The code, sponsored by API Topical Committee on Materials, provided uniformity in the methods of determining the behavior of sucker-rod steels under repeated stresses in specific corrosive media.

In the meantime, however, field investigations suggested severe limitations of laboratory-test results. D. R. Dale and D. O. Johnson made an elaborate comparison of laboratory tests with field-test results in West Texas.[313] Only a fair degree of correlation was obtained. Other investigations showed wide variation of sulfide-fatigue values of steels. In 1948 it was pointed out that data presented in *Code 30* were being misunderstood, since they were never intended to furnish stress values which could be safely imposed on sucker rods in corrosive service; and decision was made to withdraw *Code 30* and sponsor research on the subject.

In 1949 the project was transferred to the API Committee on Standardization of Pumping Equipment and Engines. Very little has been done on the subject, primarily because of the appearance of efficient corrosion inhibitors. In 1945 Paul Menaul suggested formaldehyde as a hydrogen sulfide corrosion inhibitor, and other successful organic-compound type inhibitors became commercially available several years later. Interest in metallurgy of rods shifted from questions of corrosion resistance to those of mechanical strength. However, during the 1956 API Midyear Standardization Conference a study group was appointed, at the suggestion of Fred J. Radd, to consider again the question of improvement in metallurgy of rods, particularly from the standpoint of corrosion.

The Subsurface Pump

The performance of the subsurface pump in a beam-pumping system quite early attracted the attention of investigators. In 1925 Lester C. Uren and V. J. Collins reported on effects of pump efficiency, of temperature, gas, submergence, plunger velocity, design of valves, and other factors.[314] In the same year, Frank E. O'Neill and T. E. Swigart considered the merits of long-stroke pumping.[315] In 1935 Bruce H. Robinson made a detailed study of the problem of leakage past the plunger.[316] C. J. Coberly offered in 1938 a mathematical formula for plunger size for maximum production for free and anchored tubing, considering stretch of tubing and rods and overtravel of plunger.[317] Using as a starting point the generally accepted formulae for peak polished-rod load, Emory N. Kemler evolved, in 1941, the formula for the size of plunger giving minimum peak polished-rod load for a given set of pumping conditions.[318] D. O. Johnson, S. B. Sargent, Jr., Houston Hoffman, and many others discussed different phases of the subsurface pump performance.[319-321, incl.]

The subsurface pump operation was a subject of several special investigations. E. P. Tallant reported in 1938 on experiments on pump performance sponsored by the California District Subcommittee of the API Topical Committee on Production Practice.[322] The API Mid-Continent District Topical Committee on Production Practice sponsored an experimental research project on pumps at the University of Oklahoma, under the guidance of Glenn M. Stearns. He reported on results of experiments on volumetric efficiency of the pumps in 1943, and on questions of slippage past the plunger in 1944.[323, 324] Of particular interest to the investigators was the question of actual plunger travel, a basic factor determining the pump's displacement. That this travel does not correspond to the polished-rod travel was apparent from the knowledge of the presence of stretch of rods and of tubing as a result of changes in loads during the pumping cycle and the effect of dynamic loads.

C. J. Coberly, in 1931, was first to offer a mathematical expression for overtravel of the plunger under assumption of simple harmonic motion, of no reflected stresses and no time lag in transmitting of stresses through sucker rods.[325] W. E. Gilbert and C. J. Coberly later offered a correction for the constant factor of this formula. As the theories of vibration of rods were applied to determining the loads in the sucker-rod system, they were used also in calculations of plunger travel. S. B. Sargent, Jr. discussed this problem in 1937 in his paper on capacity pumping of oil wells.[308] R. W. Rieniets in the same year derived a formula considering plunger travel as a resulting forced vibration.[326] Charts were offered from which could be determined the two components of the formula —the phase angle, or the angle through which the crank moves before the motion of the plunger begins, and the magnification factor, by which the force at the beam is changed when transferred under conditions of restraint to the lower end of the string. Langer's formula for plunger travel, presented in 1942, takes into consideration—among other factors —the vibration of rods and the differential fluid load.[283] In the simplified form of the Langer's equation, the damping is disregarded and the constants are adjusted to make the calculated results agree more closely with results of actual tests.

Hallan N. Marsh pointed out in 1931 that, under certain conditions, the plunger travel may be determined directly from the dynamometer cards.[327] In 1936 J. C. Slonneger developed a method of graphic determination of plunger travel from dynamometer cards.[328] The method consists of finding, for different positions of the polished rod, instantaneous loadings and instantaneous stretch of rods. This permits plotting instantaneous positions of the lower end of the rods, which gives the plunger travel. In 1941 Emory N. Kemler outlined an approximate method of obtaining the plunger travel from the dynamometer cards, based on determining on the card the points of closing and opening of the pump valves.[329]

Statistical Studies

Statistical studies of artificial lifting of deep wells were undertaken by two API Division of Production study committees—in the Mid-Continent District, J. Zaba, chairman, and the Pacific Coast District, F. T. Lloyd, chairman. The results were presented at the 1952 Mid-Continent District meeting and the 1955 Pacific Coast District meeting.[330, 331]

The reports were based on results of a survey conducted through questionnaires distributed to a large number of operating companies and manufacturers. For the purpose of the survey a "deep" well was defined as one having the working fluid at 7,000 ft or deeper, regardless of size of production, or as one having a working fluid level of 5,000 ft or deeper and producing 500 or more barrels of fluid per day. The survey covered all methods of artificial lifting and furnished a large amount of data for students of the problem of deep-well beam pumping.

Multiple Sucker-rod Pumping

Although at the time the studies of sucker-rod pumping were at their height, the use of central pumping powers was already on the decline and the popularity of back-side pumping was short-lived, the technical literature on the subject is rather large.

Of particular value were the contributions of R. E. Bridges, in 1936, on the subject of installation of rod lines in catenary sags, J. C. Slonneger's analysis in 1938 of back-side pumping installations, and Kenneth N. Mills' several studies of the design and behavior of component equipment of multiple sucker-rod installations.[332-334, incl.] K. C. Sclater, K. B. Nowles, Kenneth N. Mills, Eugene Hosford, Van D. Bennett, Ben Altman, Sylvain J. Pirson, George Weber, and others presented methods of locating and balancing central powers, discussed load and torque conditions of the system, and analyzed the behavior of the equipment involved. [335-342, incl.]

Current Studies

As has been previously stated, the years from 1928 to 1943 have been said to represent the "golden age" of studies of oil-well sucker-rod pumping, but it now appears that we may be on the threshold of an entirely new era of studies of the sucker-rod system—an era which offers a promise of accuracy of design, and of analysis of performance of beam-pumping installations not now possible.

For the last several years voices have been raised pointing out the inadequacy of our present methods and formulae used in designing and analyzing beam installations. The reasoning behind these objections has been about as follows: The formulae and methods used in calculation of beam installations are based on theoretical analysis, on laboratory experiments, or on field tests. In theoretical analysis certain assumptions must be made, which may or may not be correct, and the results are frequently so complex that they are of little practical value. It is difficult, if not impossible, to simulate field conditions in a laboratory. Field tests on one well are of little value because of a wide range of varying well conditions, and field tests on a large number of wells are economically prohibitive. It is true that tens of thousands of installations designed by existing formulae are performing satisfactorily. However, the purpose of engineering is always to arrive at a design which is both the most efficient and the most economical. Perhaps the large safety factors, now built into the pumping equipment to compensate for lack of precise basis for design, are not really necessary.

With the present advance in analyzers, simulators, and computers, a more precise approach to the problem should be possible. Emory N. Kemler reported in 1936 on results of experiments with an electrical model representing an oil well, the use of electrical analogy for study of sucker-rod problems having been suggested to him by Morris Muskat.[343] F. C. Todd and M. H. Halderson were among those who, in the last few years, discussed the possibilities of and the need for simulators for solution of beam-pumping problems.[344, 345]

As a result of the efforts of the Phillips Petroleum Company, Sucker Rod Research, Inc.—a non-profit organization—was formed on January 14, 1954.[346] This organization is composed of a number of oil companies and of manufacturing companies that produce either sucker-rod or associated equipment. The initial objective of the organization is to obtain a general solution of sucker-rod problems. A mechanical simulator for the complete sucker-rod system has been built by the Midwest Research Institute, Kansas City, Mo. The simulator can be operated over a wide range of depth, speed, stroke, pump size, tubing size, and rod-string design. On all tests dynamometer cards will be taken and measurements will be made of prime-mover output, reducer torque, required counterbalance, polished-rod load, plunger stroke, and production rate. From the test data a system of charts will be developed permitting rapid and accurate selection of pumping equipment of proper rating. A catalog of dynamometer cards will be assembled which will permit accurate interpretation of field dynamometer cards.

It is planned to expand this program later to collect factual data on special problems, such as the effect on the efficiency of the system of changes in balance weights, direction of rotation, characteristics of the pumping cycle, and other factors which are involved in the complexities of the pumping system.

Gas Lift

The first use of compressed air to lift fluid is credited to a German mining engineer, Carl Loscher, who in 1797 described laboratory experiments of the application. According to Davis and Weidner,[347] the first practical application of the theory was made by "an American named Cockford who, in 1846, succeeded in pumping petroleum from some wells in Pennsylvania", but the authors do not cite the source of this statement. It may refer to salt-brine wells, several of which are known to have produced some petroleum.

It is conceded by most authorities that the first use of air for lifting petroleum was at Oil Creek in about 1864. J. H. A. Bone[3] reports that the first flowing well—the Empire #1—came in in June 1861, flowed for nearly a year, pumped for a while, and then a "blower" was installed. William Wright[348] confirms this information and indicates that the "blower" installation in the Empire well was made in 1864. Wright also reports on the installation of "blowers" in four other wells—the Sherman, the Noble, the Delameter, and the Ginlet, all in 1864. Wright describes the installation as follows:

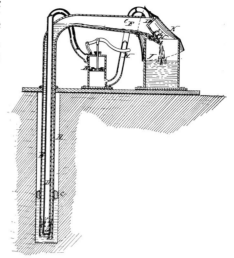

"The blower consists simply of an iron tube, one inch in diameter, which is let down into the well outside of the fixed tube, the lower end of the blower being bent round so as to pass upward into the orifice of the other. A column of air is then forced down the small pipe from which it passes into the larger and the natural action of the gas in forcing up the petroleum."

Fig. 46—T. B. Gunning Gas Lift, 1864

The first air-lift patent, issued to T. B. Gunning[349] in 1864, shows a gas compressor for taking gas from the production and conducting it to the well bottom through an inner string of tubing for assisting the flow of oil (Fig. 46).

Other than these early reports there was little further activity in air lift in the petroleum industry until approximately 1900; but a considerable amount of engineering was being done, as indicated by the patent record. During the period from 1864 to 1900 there were 33 patents issued on various devices relating to air and gas lift. Other than the patents discussed following, most either were similar or were directed to improvements in the foot piece for mixing the oil with gas or the water with air. It has been found in the application of lifting oil that the foot piece does not influence the efficiency enough to be significant.

Dr. Julius G. Pohlé, in a patent issued to him on December 6, 1890,[350] described his invention as being different from previous devices in that the air was not broken up into fine bubbles but rather was introduced in a foot piece and caused the air to form "pipe fitting, piston like layers therein interposed between and entirely separating well defined layers of liquid in the pipe". Dr. Pohlé indicated in a later patent[351] that the ratio of submergence to lift was 3 to 2 and also proposed stage lifts to reduce the maximum pressure required. In this patent he also disclosed introducing air both at the bottom and at a point higher up in the tubing.

In 1865 G. M. Mobray[352] proposed to direct the gas down an inner tube which he raised or lowered until the best results were obtained.

C. N. Royce[353] was issued a broad patent which disclosed setting a packer above the formation with a tail piece to the well bottom with gas supplied to the inner tube, having an eduction nozzle pointing up above the packer. He also proposed parallel tubes packed off at the casing head, one for supplying gas and the other for production, with a packer and means for taking gas from a lower zone to flow an upper zone.

J. E. Bacon[354] in 1895 used an auxiliary valve in the flow string which could be opened from the surface with a rod. W. Moore[355] a year later, and L. Stephens[356] just a week after Moore, proposed tubing valves at intervals which were used for kick-off and were manually closed in succession. S. W. Titus[357] provided similar valves but operated with a single rod outside the flow string.

Also prior to 1900, much attention was given to the theory and engineering of air lift as applied to lifting water, which is similar in many respects to gas-lifting of oil wells but is much simpler in its application. Although this does not strictly come under the heading of the history of petroleum engineering, it is background engineering and a brief reference to this work is of value to the record.

Prof. W. H. Echol developed and presented to the Philosophical Society of the University of Virginia in 1891 the first mathematical analysis of the air lift. Prof. Elmo G. Harris of the University of Missouri published in the *Journal of the Franklin Institute*, in July 1895, a comprehensive analysis of air-lift theory. R. M. Anderson gave a simple static-conditions theory of air lift published by Hudson Engineering Company in 1905; and A. H. Gibson in 1908 extended this to cover dynamic conditions. Dr. H. Lorenz in *Zeitschrift des Vereines Deutscher Ingenieure*, April 1909, gave simple empirical relations; and L. M. Green in *Engineering and Mining Journal*, August 7, 1909, gave a mathematical analysis, air requirements, minimum pressures, and resulting efficiencies. An extensive series of some 1,800 tests made by the Westinghouse Company were reported in *Engineering News*, June 18, 1908.

During the period from 1900 to 1930, 177 patents were issued on methods and apparatus for air and gas lift. The following developments, as given in the patent record, are considered to cover important improvements in gas lift during this period. Many others show variations in the same devices and those discussed following were selected because they were the first to show the development, but not necessarily in the best and most practical form.

A. M. Lockett[358] in 1907 and J. M. McEvoy[359] in 1908 used kickoff valves which were spring-loaded to a normally open position and were closed by gas flow and held closed by pressure differential. These men had the basic conception of kick-off valves which would automatically close in succession until flow from bottom is established, which is the principle of modern flow valves.

In 1908 Conrader[360] clearly disclosed the principle of the gas displacement pump (Fig. 47). This consisted of a bottom-hole chamber with intake and exhaust valves and a gas-input valve. This arrangement of valves admitted the fluid from the well into the chamber, but prevented its entering the gas-drive line from the eduction pipe. A cam-operated valve at the surface admitted gas on a time-cycle basis to the gas-drive line, which was connected to the gas-input valve in the displacement chamber. The application of this gas pressure displaced the fluid from the chamber into the discharge tubing as a slug, followed with gas, and was discharged at the surface. The chamber was then opened to exhaust to permit further entrance of fluid from the well. Multiple-well operation was indicated, with a single fluid motor-actuated valve for controlling the sequence of operation of the displacement chambers by opening and

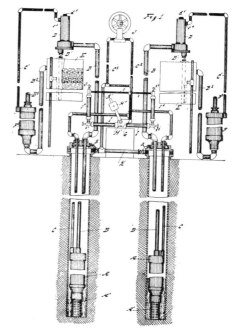

Fig. 47—Conrader Gas-displacement Pump

closing the gas supply and discharge valves provided for each chamber.

The earliest record of an installation of this type appears to be in 1927. W. W. Thayer[361] described the application of a gas displacement pump in which a foot valve was run on the bottom of a chamber carried by the production tubing, and gas was injected through an inside string of tubing to displace the oil from the chamber without exerting a back pressure on the formation (Fig. 48).

A. N. Alten and O. David[362] were the first to control gas valves by rotating the tubing, and W. E. Stuart[363] closed the valves in sequence by raising the tubing with a cylinder at the well head.

W. L. Morrow[364] in 1913 used a packer in the casing with tubing to bottom below the packer, with a standing valve and with a spring-loaded gas valve above the packer, which provided all the elements of an automatic intermitter.

In 1915 J. S. L. Purdy[365] proposed to gas-lift the water from gas wells, using tubing for the flow string, and raising or lowering the tubing to control a valve in the fluid passage, with gas inlets above this valve and at various points higher up in the string.

The use of natural gas for flowing wells in place of air was a much more important development than the actual mechanical devices used in the gas-lift method. The use of gas not only reduced the hazards of the inflammable and explosive mixtures formed when air is used, but

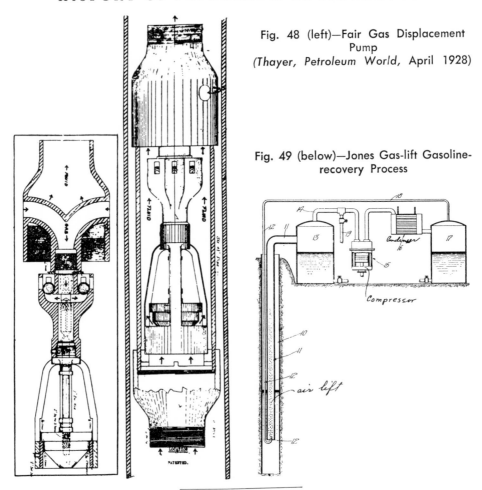

Fig. 48 (left)—Fair Gas Displacement
Pump
(Thayer, Petroleum World, April 1928)

Fig. 49 (below)—Jones Gas-lift Gasoline-
recovery Process

also made it possible to recover large quantities of gasoline and LPG that otherwise would have been wasted.

Philip Jones[366] disclosed the basic idea of gasoline recovery in combination with gas lift, in which he proposed to collect the gas at the well head and recompress this gas, passing it through a condenser to recover the light liquids and returning the dry gas to the well for the gas-lift operation (Fig. 49). This patent was held invalid in 1928 as the result of a suit with Amerada Petroleum Corporation which cited prior use in 1899 and 1903. Gasoline recovered from one operation was marketed as a cleaning fluid under the name of "Energine". W. R. Greenlee[367] was given a broad patent which also shows the recovery of gasoline and re-use of the dry gas, using unloading valves to reduce the kick-off pressure and using single- and multiple-stage chamber gas lift to improve the efficiency. A. E. Chodzko[368] in 1913 disclosed a stage lift with air lift to a number of chambers arranged in series. C. A. Butler[369] provided a chamber for collecting gas from an upper gas sand and directing it into tubing from lower oil sand to lighten the column above the point of injection.

H. B. Halvorsen[370] of the Sullivan Machinery Company described a bottom-hole air or gas valve operated from the surface by a rod connected with an air cylinder and with a timed valve for admitting air to the cylinder. Alexander Boynton[371] in 1923 provided gas lift in which the bottom valve was held closed with a spring, preventing oil from entering the flow string, with a larger tube extending up the casing to prevent the oil from flooding the gas inlets. The bottom gas valve was a velocity-type, which opened at a given differential pressure and was held open by the flow and also controlled the flow of oil into the tubing. This device caused the well to flow by heads without excessive starting pressure, and mixed oil and gas in such proportions as to use a minimum amount of gas.

The E. M. Rogers[372] patent showed a multi-stage lift intended for water with a foot piece for injection of air, a flow tube for the first stage connecting to a separator from which the air was discharged into the casing and the water entered a down pipe for submergence to the second stage, all of which was repeated in a second and third stage.

Alex Boynton[373] showed a flow valve which closed on excess flow and was held closed by pressure differential.

L. J. Black[374] designed a gas valve for bottom-hole intermitting which introduced gas over a standing valve and opened on a predetermined excess of casing pressure over tubing pressure, and stayed open until pressures were equalized.

George Blow[375] showed a stage lift with chambers and gas inlet for each stage. This device was tried in the field in 1927[376] and in 1928.[377] This required three strings of tubing with $\frac{1}{2}$-in. and $\frac{3}{4}$-in. pipe run inside 3-in. tubing with high-pressure and low-pressure displacement chambers. This device apparently was effective in reducing pressures, but was found to be seriously limited in capacity because of the small tubing required in its construction.

H. H. Gracey[378] in 1926 proposed a valve for use as a foot piece in which a piston-type gas valve operated a poppet oil valve. The gas was supplied through an inner string and the flow occurred in the annulus between the two strings. Liquid accumulated in the casing, but was not allowed to enter the tubing until the gas valve was opened by applying a predetermined gas pressure which opened both the gas valve and the oil valve.

M. T. Archer[379] in 1928 described a sleeve-type flow valve controlled by a hollow resilient pressure member filled with gas under selected pressure. Although the action of this valve as shown may be different from later valves, this invention pointed the way to set pressure valves which have been important in improving gas lift.

A. C. Rubel[380] and F. W. Lake[381] in 1929 disclosed methods of initiating natural flow or gas lift in wells filled with dead fluid, which are important to gas-lift operations.

Philip Subkow[382] proposed a novel bottom-hole intermitting valve in which the liquid valve controls the gas valve which had a second velocity-type gas valve in series which closed on excess flow. This interlocked combination provided the desired sequence of valve operation.

The record indicates that scattered use of air lift was reported after 1900, with a generally increasing use in the late 1920's. Of interest is Millikan's statement[383] that intermittent injections were first used successfully in Pennsylvania in 1903, but that there was no subsequent reference to this practice until the late 1920's.

H. C. Miller[348] stated that after 1865 there is no further reference to its application until that reported by A. Beeby Thompson concerning the use of the system in the Baku region of Russia in 1899. There, according to Thompson, a small string of tubing was run inside the production tubing. At first, air was injected down the small tubing, and later there were experiments with injection of air down the annulus with return up the small tubing.

Also, according to Miller, the use of air lift started on the Gulf Coast in 1901 and has been used there continuously ever since. At Spindletop a power company installed a steam-driven compressor plant, which sold compressed air to operators who wished to air-lift wells without installing compressors.

The first use of air lift in California, where it was installed in 1902, was in the Kern River, Cat Canyon, and Midway-Sunset Fields. Miller believes that the first use of natural gas for lifting was in the Cat Canyon Field in 1911. There appears to have been little further application of gas or air lift in California until 1924, when southern California operators began using it in the fields which were being completed. In the Mid-Continent, the first use of gas lift is reported by Cloud to have been in Tonkawa, in 1925.

Without indicating the date of initial use, Miller *(op. cit.)* in 1930 described an experimental multi-stage gas-lift installation which he considered more nearly practical than any of the several others being tried at that time. This installation required the use of four strings of tubing, which were run so as to form a series of chambers in the well. On the surface there were two injection lines and each was connected to alternate chambers. In theory the operator would inject gas down one line and lift fluid in one set of chambers, and then inject gas down the other line and lift fluid in the alternate chambers. This arrangement would reduce both kick-off and operating pressures, but apparently proved too complicated to receive widespread use.

With the revival of interest in gas lift as a medium of artificial lifting, a great deal of experimentation was done in both California and Mid-Continent fields to solve the problems encountered and to improve efficiency of the systems.

In these early applications of gas lift it was found that the problems in the production of oil were much more complex than those of air-lifting water. The properties of both the gas and the liquid varied over a wide range and also the gas was quite highly soluble in the liquid. This was particularly true of the heavy fractions in the gas. The theory that had been developed for air lift, therefore, was found to be inadequate to cover the problems of gas-lifting oil. When the application of gas lift became an important factor in the production of oil in the 1920's, the engineers of the petroleum industry directed their attention to a further study of these problems.

J. Versluys[384] derived a mathematical solution for the flow of oil through vertical tubes of an oil well. L. C. Uren[385] reported on tests on the resistance to flow of gas-oil mixtures in vertical tubing. S. F. Shaw[386] gave both theoretical and practical observations on the gas lift of an oil well. Versluys[387] followed his previous mathematical discussion with some practical factors to be observed in selecting tubing sizes for gas-lift and flowing wells. T. V. Moore and H. D. Wilde, Jr.[388] presented both theoretical and experimental results of slippage in the flow of gas-oil mixtures, which is an important factor in the efficiency of the gas-lift system. J. T. Hayward[389] and R. R. Hawkins[390] presented theoretical and practical limitations of tapered and small-tubing flow strings. J. E. Gosline[391] gave experimental results of vertical flow of gas-oil mixtures through tubing and established the conditions for the annular ring type of flow. E. C. Babson[392] presented a very complete detailed report on the practical range of application of straight gas lift, plunger lift, intermitter, and gas-displacement pumps. A. C. Tutschulte[393] enlarged on Babson's work by giving performance results when using 1½-in. tubing for straight gas lift or intermittent flow. W. E. Gilbert[394] gave the performance of flowing and gas-lift wells with tubing sizes from 1¼-in. to 3-in. and with crude-oil gravities ranging from 25 to 40 API. F. H. Poettmann and Paul G. Carpenter[395] made an important contribution to the theory and practice of flow of oil, gas, and water in vertical flow strings. Prof. C. V. Kirkpatrick[396] in 1953 wrote a complete manual on gas lift, covering both the theory and practical application.

The period from 1930 to the present time shows the greatest advance in gas lift both from the engineering and technical aspects, and from application to the production problems accompanying the increase in well depths.

As a measure of the increased technical activity, the patent record shows that 203 patents were issued during this period which were classed as directly relating to gas lift. In addition, many related patents have been issued under other classifications.

C. C. Carlisle[397] in 1930 was the first to propose a flow valve which was controlled by the density of the fluid in the flow string. He provided a float attached to the operating stem of the gas valve, which opened the valve when the density was high and closed it when the density dropped. The gas pressure applied to the unbalanced areas of the gas valve determined the sensitivity to density change.

F. J. Miller[398] in 1932 provided a bottom-hole velocity valve for increasing the gas flow with increased liquid flow through a venturi nozzle.

Alex Boynton[399] in 1930 obtained several patents which employed the velocity in the flow string to inversely control the amount of gas admitted, giving a desired type of control. B. R. Schabarum[400] in the same year made a similar valve with a balanced sleeve-type gas valve.

M. T. Archer[401] provided an intermitter valve in which the gas and oil valves are interlocked, with the gas valve closed when the oil valve is open and vice versa, and a metallic-bellows unit between the gas supply and the flow tube to initiate the valve action.

Frederick Price[402] in 1931 designed the simplest form of kickoff valve, which has been extensively used, in which a single or 2-way poppet valve is held in its open position with a leaf spring (Fig. 50). Excessive flow in either direction will close the valve and the pressure differential will hold it closed. This valve was known as the "Price-Trawick" valve.

J. W. Taylor[403] in 1931 provided intermittent gas lift with two independent valves—one for liquid and one for gas.

T. E. Bryan[404] in the same year developed a velocity valve for installation inside the flow string to close or control the gas input with change in flow rate.

Surface-controlled intermitting was introduced in the late 1920's and early 1930's. Jordan and Taylor[405] probably were the first with this type of control.

Smallamatic[406] developed bottom-hole chamber-lift devices, followed by Jordan and Taylor,[407] National Automatic, and others.

Starting in the 1920's, H. W. Fletcher developed a free-plunger flow device to reduce the slippage of gas through the oil in slug-type or intermittent flow, either natural or with gas lift. This device was an important development and was marketed, starting in the early 1930's, as the "Hughes Plunger Lift" (Fig 51). A number of patents were issued to Fletcher[408] and N. H. Ricker[409] covering this device. As originally applied in 1932, a specially reamed tubing was required to control slippage. The Hughes plunger lift was purchased by The National Supply

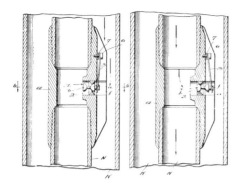

Fig. 50—Frederick Price 2-way Velocity
Valve, 1931

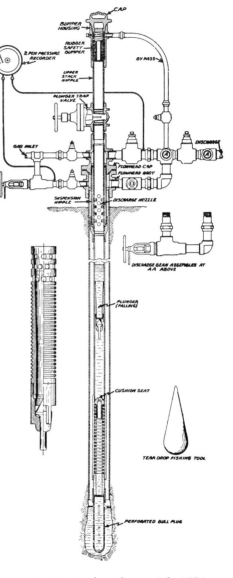

Fig. 51—Hughes Plunger Lift, 1936

Company in 1944, and plunger improvements have been made which give good results in API tubing.

S. H. Grinnell and A. C. Rubel[410] designed wellhead equipment for running or pulling tubing under pressure. Vance, in his chapter in this history on Completion Methods, reports that, in Texas, tubing was being run against oil and gas pressures as early as 1926-27.

F. A. Howard[411] in 1932 proposed a novel system of augmenting production by supplying a combustible mixture from the surface, igniting and burning it in the well bore to both heat the well and to use the products of combustion for gas lift. This method has in recent years been given attention in California heavy-oil fields[412] with considerable success.

Philip Subkow[413] in 1932 was granted a broad patent on the method and apparatus for automatic intermittent gas lift, and on detail improvements in 1934.[414]

Following the early work by Alex Boynton in 1928, J. W. Taylor in 1929, F. Price in 1931, and T. E. Bryan in 1933 on kick-off valves, a very active effort was made by the engineers to extend the use and improve the operation of these valves. G. A. Humason[415] in 1934 designed a

687

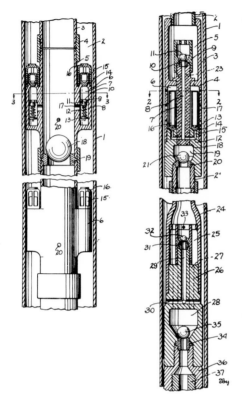

Fig. 52—G. A. Humason Spring-loaded and Float-controlled Gas-lift Valves, 1934

spring-loaded and float-controlled valve (Fig. 52). Alex Boynton[416] in 1934 disclosed a valve with a set-pressure metallic-bellows control. H. C. Otis[417] in 1935 provided a valve controlled by the combination of submergence pressure, flowing pressure, and differential pressure. J. W. Taylor[418] in 1937 made a valve which was weight-controlled and seated in both directions. C. S. Crickmer[419] in 1939 provided a valve which opened on a set pressure differential and throttled the flow to meter the gas. T. E. Bryan[420] in 1939 used a spaced spring-loaded kick-off valve and a bottom-hole intermitting valve with a bellows-controlled set pressure. R. A. Aucoin[421] in 1940 used a spring-loaded valve to control the pressure spread, in combination with a double-seat check valve. M. Bowman Thomas[422] in 1940 designed a valve controlled by the density of the liquid in the flow string compared with a standard applied to opposite sides of a diaphragm-controlled valve.

C. S. Crickmer[423] made a double valve with one valve having a spring-loaded pressure differential valve and a second valve for metering the gas.

Horace M. Stagg[424] designed the first wire-line-operated valves, which unit was later marketed under the name of the "Jones-Stagg Intermitter".

During the 1930's a wire-line-operated gas lift was developed and used quite extensively. This was the J. D. Nixon device, marketed by the Wilson Supply Company. A number of patents were issued to Nixon[425] covering the principle and the details of the device (see Fig. 53). A pointed weight run on a Halliburton line operated spaced kick-off valves in succession as it was lowered into the tubing. Variations of this device were used for intermitting on a time cycle, chamber lift, etc.

R. L. Chenault[426] in 1940 provided a control for continuous gas lift, consisting of a foot valve with the gas controlled by rotating the tubing and the oil controlled by lifting the tubing. T. E. Bryan[427] in 1940 patented the first wire-line-set valve in the form of a bottom-hole intermitting valve. H. U. Garrett[428] in 1941 proposed wire-line-set flow valves,

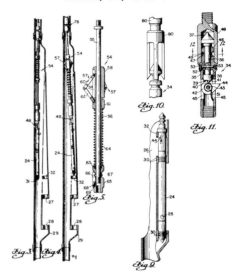

Fig. 53 (left)—Nixon Wire-line-operated Gas-lift System, 1930

Fig. 54 (below)—Retrievable Gas-lift Valve, H. E. McGowen and H. H. Moore, Jr., 1953

and H. C. Otis[429] also in 1940 made a wire-line retrievable gas-lift choke. G. S. Knox[430] in 1942 designed an intermitter valve which operates on a pressure-ratio principle and does not require the tubing pressure to drop to a low value to operate the gas valve. W. R. King[431] provided a timer and injection-rate control for a gas-displacement device using present metallic-bellows valves. R. O. Walton[432] produced a metallic-bellows-operated, pilot-controlled, rubber-sock valve.

C. D. Fletcher[433] in 1953 designed a valve in which the opening and closing pressures are separately adjustable. R. A. Bobo[434] proposed a gas valve with electric solenoid operation. K. C. Howard, H. E. McGowen, and H. H. Moore, Jr.,[435] designed an electric setting tool for valves, in which the valve is screwed into an opening in the bottom of a special internal side pocket coupling with a latch-on, make-up, and latch-off control. A mechanical device for the same purpose (Fig. 54) was designed by H. E. McGowen and H. H. Moore, Jr.,[436] which has been important to retrievable valves.

Another gas-lift device which falls in the same category is the "Ball Pump" (Fig. 55), invented by R. P. Vincent and H. B. Wilder[437] of Stanolind Oil and Gas Company and first used in 1950. Instead of returning the plunger in the flow string—as in the Fletcher lift—the "Ball Pump" uses two parallel tubing strings of equal size connected at the

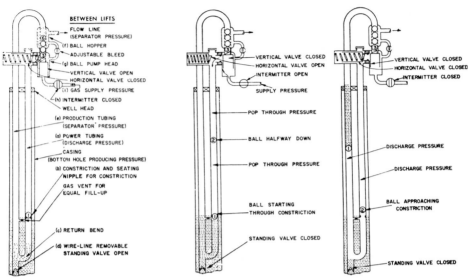

Fig. 55—"Ball Pump", Vincent and Wilder, 1950

bottom with a crossover member having a standing valve, and with a mechanism at the surface for inserting a synthetic-rubber ball into one tubing string where it is carried to the bottom by the flow of gas and crosses over into the flow tubing with a slug of oil above it, depending in length upon the bottom-hole pressure and the residual gas pressure in the tubing. Either single- or multiple-slug flow may be obtained with balls inserted on any time cycle required.

From the patent record, the men who have made the greatest number of improvements in gas-lift equipment and the period of their activity are:

Alex Boynton	1923 to 1941
J. Oliphant	1924 to 1931
H. B. Halvorsen	1924 to 1930
J. W. Taylor	1926 to 1939
T. E. Bryan	1932 to 1956
H. C. Otis	1935 to 1944
C. S. Crickmer	1939 to 1941
J. D. Nixon	1939 to 1946
H. U. Garrett	1941 to 1957

There have been other gas-lift devices with limited application. The Proctor and Miller chamber lift was used in some deep California production in 1935. Another chamber lift operated by lifting the inner string of tubing with a well-headed cylinder was developed by Thompson and Cheska and was known as the "T and C Gas Pump". This was tested extensively in the Kettleman Hills Field with some success.

Gas lift has had a varied and important position in petroleum production. It appears to be in line for considerable activity in extremely deep wells and in offshore production. It also is easily adaptable to two-zone production, which is now a familiar well-completion practice.

Hydraulic Bottom-hole Units

The problem of actuating pumps at the bottom of oil wells through the use of sucker rods was recognized by the operators and engineers in the early days of the oil industry. As wells were drilled to greater depths, the problems became more severe; and it was anticipated that rod systems might reach depth limitations that would necessitate the use of other methods. The essential elements of the hydraulic bottom-hole pump are:

1. A surface power pump for supplying hydraulic fluid under pressure.
2. A control for the quantity of fluid directed to each well.
3. Surface lines conducting the power fluid to the well head.
4. Well tubing for power fluid and production in either parallel or concentric arrangement.
5. A fluid engine directly connected to a bottom-hole pump and discharging its power fluid either into the production tubing or a separate return tube.
6. A means of running the bottom-hole unit into the wells and connecting the tubes to perform the required functions.

In the 1920's sufficient attention was directed to the problem to result in the building and field-testing of hydraulic bottom-hole pumping units. An examination of the history shows that, as with many other developments, the basic concept of this method of pumping oil wells dates back to the early developments of the steam engine. One of the applications of the steam cylinder was to operate pumps by directly connecting the engine piston rod to that of the pump. The Cornish pumping engine of 1798 (Fig. 2) is one of the early records of this type of device. The patent records up to 1900 show 66 patents issued relating to this type of pump.

The application to the pumping of oil was first shown in 1872 by H. W. Faucett,[438] in whose design (Fig. 56) the engine was steam-operated and discharged its steam into the well. As illustrated, it required a dug well or a large-diameter drilled well to accommodate the apparatus. However, the construction shown appears to be operative and contains all the necessary elements, such as a pilot valve controlled by the piston which operated the main valve by the application of steam. It even used the control of the steam by a float-operated valve responding to the fluid level in the well, so that the speed of the unit was regulated to keep the level of the fluid pumped down to the desired point. Faucett also recognized the paraffin problem, and used the heat of the steam to keep the tubing warm and prevent clogging. No record has been found of the field use of the

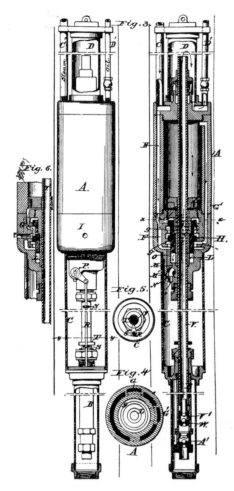

Fig. 56—H. W. Faucett Bottom-hole
Steam Pump, 1878

Faucett device, but it was truly a pioneer patent.

W. C. Wells[439] utilized water pressure to operate twin cylinders in parallel duplex arrangement, with an area ratio between operating and pumping pistons so that water under pressure could serve to raise a part of its volume to a height greater than that of the source of operating fluid. Since much of the fluid must be discharged at a lower pressure level, the construction did not lend itself to oil-well pumping..

C. S. Cox[440] followed Faucett's idea, but used liquid under high pressure, discharging the fluid into the well and using a pump of larger area to obtain a net fluid recovery.

R. H. Russell[441] disclosed a different type of pump in which the valve controlling the engine was located at the surface and two reciprocating columns of fluid communicated with two sides of the engine piston to cause it to reciprocate. A single-acting pump was connected to this engine, which drew liquid from the well and discharged it into a third tube which brought it to the surface (Fig. 57).

F. H. Sibley and H. M. Lasher[442] disclosed a reciprocating-column pump with two columns in **U**-tube arrangement, each having a single-acting piston near the bottom operating single-acting pumps discharging through a third tubing. The pistons were mechanically independent, but were interlocked hydraulically so that as one piston moved down the other moved up. This was an improvement on the Russell device in that work was done on both strokes of the engine, and therefore the possible efficiency was much higher.

Victor H. Palm[443] and W. N. Squires[444] received a number of early patents relating to hydraulic bottom-hole pumps. The Squires' pump was reduced to practice but the operating problems were never sufficiently solved for it to become a commercial device.

692

S. B. Sargent—founder of the Sargent Pump Company—and S. B. Sargent, Jr.[445] disclosed reciprocating-column pumps and were the first to appreciate the possibilities of multiple-well installations operated from a central plant. This device was never operated commercially.

A. G. Gage[446] was probably the first to build a commercially operating pump, and he was truly one of the pioneers of this development. A number of models of the Gage pump were built, based upon one or more of his patents. The first successful field test of record was made with a Gage pump at Santa Fe Springs in June 1924 for General Petroleum Corporation, and at Fruitvale, Calif. on the property of the Western Gulf Oil Company in 1930. Several pumps were later installed for Gulf; and although the wells were not deep, this convincing evidence of successful operation was a real accomplishment. Some seven pumps were installed by Gage, including one which was installed in East Texas by the Shell Oil Company, and he should be credited with being one of the real pioneers of hydraulic pumping.

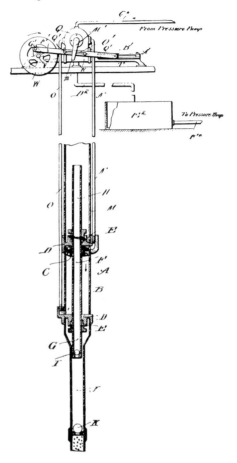

Fig. 57—Oscillating Column Hydraulic Pump of R. H. Russell, 1905

R. R. Crum[447] was the next to obtain a patent on a device that was actually field-tested. The first Crum pump was built by Standard Oil Co. of California in 1922 and was later operated in a well in the Murphy Whittier Field in California.

V. L. Forsyth[448] proposed a reciprocating-column pump which was almost identical to that disclosed in the patent to R. H. Russell.

I. B. Humphreys[449] made important improvements and operated a large-capacity pump in the Mexia Field in 1927. The Humphreys patent was the first to show a complete hydraulic engine and pump in the well with the power oil and production tubing in a concentric arrangement. Crum also used concentric tubes, but was not allowed claims on this feature. The Humphreys and Crum patents were co-pending; but Humphreys filed six months prior to Crum, although the Crum patent was the first to be issued. The concentric-tubing arrangement made it more convenient to run tubing, as the pump was run attached to the production tubing and then the inner tube—usually the power-oil tube—was run afterward and seated into a socket above the pump. The 80 claims allowed in the 2 Humphreys patents completely dominated subsequent developments in this field.

J. H. Suter[450] was the first to show an insert-type pump attached to the inner tube (Fig. 58), which permitted the removal of the complete mechanism by pulling the inner tube only. Prior to the Suter pump, all designs required pulling both strings of tubing to recover the pump. This made the cost of pulling very high and, to a large extent, offset the advantage of pumps of this type over rod pumps.

Another important feature and requirement of the insert type of pump was that of making the bottom-hole unit sufficiently small in diameter to go inside the production tubing. Pumps of the Gage and Humphreys type which were built had an outside diameter of 5 in. to 5½ in. The large-diameter pump unit was much easier to engineer, but it was too large for insert applications and also did not give the greater capacity anticipated by the inventors, since the tubing friction was the most important capacity limitation.

All pumps developed up to Humphreys were single-acting, operated in most cases with a double-acting engine. Many of these had the same engine area in both directions so that the return stroke was made with a great loss of power.

E. B. Galbreath[451] was the first to add the feature of double action to the pump. He went even further and provided an in-line duplex double-acting pump in which the valve for the engine of one pump was controlled by the movement of the piston of the other pump. This construction provided high hydraulic efficiency with a continuous discharge of fluid.

E. S. Grafenstatt[452] also provided a double-acting pump, as did C. Gamer,[453] C. G. Boone,[454] M. A. Clarke,[455] and many later inventors.

Another type of double-acting pump is one in which the suction stroke is single-acting and the discharge stroke is double-acting. The pump built by G. S. Knox[456] is an example of this type. Two field tests were made with the Knox pump, the first in a Shell Oil Company well at Long Beach and the second in a General Petroleum Corp. well at Santa Fe Springs. Both of these tests were successful, and Knox was probably the fourth inventor to demonstrate a commercially operable hydraulic bottom-hole pump.

C. J. Coberly[457] was the first to produce and successfully operate a fully balanced full double-acting pump. This was an insert pump run on 1¼-in. macaroni tubing inside of 2½-in. tubing. The pump was first installed in March 1932 in Standard Oil Company well Baldwin Cienega

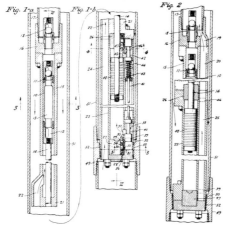

Fig. 58 (upper left)—Suter Insert Hydraulic Pump, 1925

Fig. 59 (lower left)—First Kobe Hydraulic Pump Installation, 1932

Fig. 60 (below)—First Multiple-well Hydraulic Pump Installation, Kobe, 1934

No. 15 at Baldwin Hills (Fig. 59). Several other installations were made in 1932 and 1933 under varying conditions, some as deep as 8,000 ft. Models of a number of other designs were shop-tested between 1926 and 1932 when the first field test was made. This pump was announced to the petroleum industry in 1935 after 8 installations were made—one of which was for 5 wells (Fig. 60)—and operated for sufficient time to prove that this equipment could handle a wide range of conditions. Within a short time a full line of pump sizes was developed, as well as the accessory equipment to apply hydraulic pumping. The original pump design was for a 1:1 engine-to-pump ratio, which was for a maximum lift of 10,000 ft. It was soon found that there was need for ratios other than 1:1 to handle larger quantities of fluid in wells less than 10,000 ft deep, and also ratios less than 1:1 to reduce the capacity for extremely deep wells and to extend the setting depth beyond 10,000 ft—if and when this became a requirement. The capacities were originally based upon a very conservative pump speed. It was later found that these ratings were entirely too conservative, and the rated pump capacities were increased by 50 percent in some cases and 75 percent in others.

The control of the bottom-hole unit is difficult to accomplish from the surface, because of the stored energy in the compressed fluid. This has been found particularly true when the pump is run beyond the capacity of the well or when the fluid contains gas. C. J. Coberly[458] provided an automatic governor which throttles the power oil with the engine valve whenever there is no load on the pump piston. This device functions for fractional strokes and limits the speed for any part of a stroke that is not fully loaded. No limitation is put on the pump speed, however, except under pump-off conditions. This automatic governor improved the life of the pump by reducing the hydraulic shock resulting from its tendency to race when the load was dropped.

An important contribution was made by the introduction of the "free" pump by C. J. Coberly[459] and Gordon Swain,[460] which accomplishes the running and pulling of the pump hydraulically without disturbing the tubing (Fig. 61). The tubing is provided with a standing

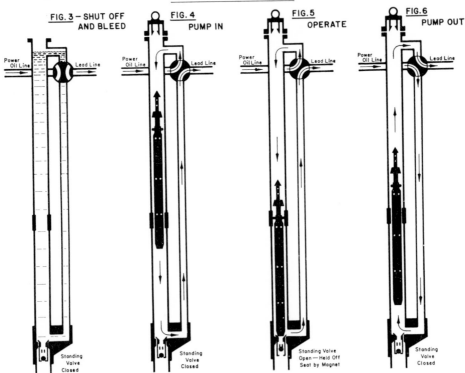

Fig. 61—"Free-pump" Hydraulic System, 1938

696

valve and initially filled with fluid. The pump is then circulated to bottom with power oil, where it enters a sealing collar and seats in the shoe. Power oil is applied to the engine and the unit operates, opening the standing valve and pumping fluid from the well. To retrieve the pump, a 4-way valve at the well head is turned 90 deg to reverse the direction of circulation of power oil, which unseats the pump, seats the standing valve, and raises the pump to the well head where it is held in a catcher until removed by the operator. The time required for this operation depends upon the amount of power fluid available. It normally takes 1 to 1½ hours to retrieve the pump from 6,000 ft. No attention is required except to start the pump out and to remove it when it reaches the well head.

Since the commercial introduction of hydraulic pumping in 1935, other manufacturers have entered the field—O. E. Dempsey[461] and J. B. Woods[462] offered their pump to the industry in 1948. Sargent Engineering Company also developed a single-acting pump which has been tested during the past 10 years and was first offered to the industry in 1953. At the present time (1959) The National Supply Company and Fluid Packed Pump Company are making hydraulic pumps, and other companies are operating experimental pumps but have not offered them for sale.

There have been other patent developments in this field, most of which have been directed to alternate constructions of reciprocating-type bottom-hole units—some single-acting, some double-acting, and others differential double-acting.

C. C. Carlisle[463] made a balanced double-acting engine connected to a full double-acting pump. The displacement differed in the two directions by the rod area, but the forces were fully balanced. The principal feature of the Carlisle pump was a double spring-actuated pilot valve with a toggle linkage to prevent dead-center position.

R. L. Chenault[464] provided a double-acting engine connected to a double-acting pump which was partially balanced, in which the power oil was delivered through a hollow piston rod to an engine valve in the engine piston. A pilot valve in the piston was operated by contact with the ends of the engine cylinder. The engine discharged, through a hollow tubular piston rod connected to the pump, into the space between the engine and pump. The pump discharged into this same space, mixing with the spent power fluid, then passed through holes in the outer tube and into the annulus between the pump and tubing. In a later Chenault patent a double-acting engine was connected to a differential double-acting pump. The pump was sealed into the tubing above the pump barrel to give the well fluid access to the top of the pump piston in order to obtain the differential action. A packed seal was used to obtain a maximum pump diameter.

H. J. Pankratz[465] developed a novel bottom-hole pump, in which the engine valve was operated from the well head by turning the inner tube of the concentric tubing system.

In the period from 1935 to the present there has been considerable Patent Office activity, and at least 165 patents have been issued which were directly concerned with bottom-hole hydraulic units. The greatest activity in the type of unit in which the power fluid is controlled at the bottom of the well was during the period from 1920 to 1940. Reciprocating-column pumps—such as that of Russell[441]—were developed in the early history of hydraulic pumping, but the big activity in this type was in the period from 1930 to 1950. Most of the early disclosures depended upon a reciprocating plunger system on the surface, which transmitted this motion to the bottom of the well through two reciprocating columns or one reciprocating column against a spring or a gas cushion. It was found that this type of device is seriously limited in practical operating depth, as the compressibility of the oil in the two columns corresponds to the stretch in the rod of a sucker-rod pump—the difference being that the pressure in the fluid is less than the stress in the rod, but the bulk modulus of the fluid is only one-hundredth of that of steel. The combination of the stress ratio, the volume of fluid in the tubing, and the difference in modulus makes the compressibility factor using oil columns in this way about 10 times as great as with steel sucker rods. For this reason the reciprocating-column pump was found to have serious limitations and no commercial applications are known to be in operation at this time.

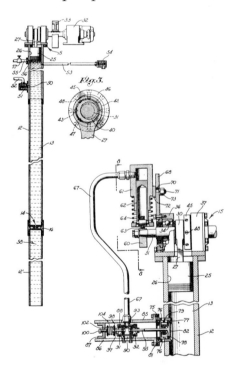

Fig. 62—Bodine Tuned Oscillating Column Pump, 1944

Some inventors recognized this limitation and, instead of slow application of pressure through the reciprocating columns, they applied a pulsating pressure, which was tuned to the natural frequency of the hydraulic system or to a harmonic of this frequency. In this way the loss of efficiency resulting from the compressibility of the oil was avoided. C. G. Holt,[466] R. H. Thompson,[467] J. H. Shimer,[468] R. O. Dulaney,[469] S. E. Ross,[470] J. E. Hall,[471] and other patents all pertain to bottom-hole units operated by pressure-wave action.

A. G. Bodine, Jr.[472] carried the pressure-wave type of operation beyond that of other inventors in producing a pressure surge in the tubing which oscillated over a sufficient range of pressure that the minimum pressure was below that in the well fluid, causing an intake valve to open and take in a certain amount of fluid on each pressure wave (Fig. 62). The device had to be carefully timed to the frequency of the system, and also the amplitude had to be controlled to cause the valve to open. The range of pressure required was later reduced by using a multiplicity of valves spaced at the proper intervals throughout the tubing string. This device was tried in the field in Alexander Well No. 2 at Santa Fe Springs in 1938. One of the problems encountered was that the well fluid is a mixture of oil, gas, and water, and the modulus of the fluid depends upon the percentage of each component in the mixture. Therefore, it was found that, if the mixture changed—which it usually does in an oil well, the natural frequency changed and hence the system would get out of tune.

Bodine avoided this problem[473] by reciprocating the pump tubing, in which case the natural frequency depended upon the modulus of the steel and was only slightly influenced by the modulus of the fluid in the tubing (Fig. 63). This device was first tried in Well No. 25 of South Basin Oil Company at Signal Hill (1943), and is currently being tested in other wells.

Another type of development, made by I. S. Salnikov,[474] depended upon the intermittent application of pressure to a tubing carrying a plunger working in a cylinder anchored to the casing or to a second tubing. The principle was based upon the fact that, when the pressure was applied to this tubing, it elongated; and when the pressure was released it retracted, thus producing a stroke at the bottom end which carried the plunger. As in the case of the reciprocating-column pumps referred to previously, this is an inefficient device when operated under static pressure or

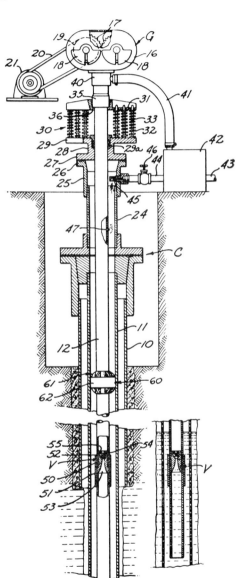

Fig. 63—Bodine Oscillating Tubing Pump, 1955

low speed, and must be operated with a pulsating pressure in phase with the natural frequency to avoid this problem.

Another complete line of hydraulic bottom-hole units has been designed which are based upon a rotary engine and rotary motor, varying from a turbine driving a centrifugal pump to a wobble disc motor driving a reciprocating pump. L. V. Baxter[475] disclosed a gear motor driving a gear pump with the operating fluid returning with the pump fluid.

M. Loewenthal and F. Egersdorfer[476] designed a vane-type motor driving a vane-type pump. The power fluid was transmitted down the inner tube and the production was returned up the tubing annulus, together with the power fluid.

R. V. Grant[477] used a turbine wheel on a horizontal axis driving through a gear reduction to a crank with two throws 180 deg apart operating a duplex single-acting pump.

G. E. Bigelow[478] used a multi-stage hydraulic turbine direct-connected to a multi-stage centrifugal pump, in which the power fluid from the turbine was mixed with the pump fluid from the centrifugal pump and the mixture returned to the surface.

R. J. S. Pigott[479] proposed a multi-stage internal-gear-type motor direct-connected to a pump of the same type, forming a unit. A multiplicity of these units were operated in series to produce the total head required.

F. W. Kennedy[480] developed a closed-system "Imo" motor direct-connected to an "Imo" pump, in which the power oil was supplied through one tubing and was returned through a second tubing in parallel arrangement with the pump fluid discharging into the casing above the packer. H. R. Downs[481] used a vane-type motor direct-connected to a "Moyno"-type pump. This was a gas-operated motor discharging its gas into the production column. It therefore may better be classed as a gas-lift device than a pumping unit, as the pump simply acts as a booster on the bottom end of a gas lift. R. E. Leonard[482] proposed a multi-stage turbine direct-connected to a screw pump which was arranged coaxially with and inside of the hollow shaft of the turbine. So far as is known, none of these rotary-type bottom-hole units has become commercial, although a number have been tested in the field. The Downs pump was tested in West Texas in 1937, and at Kettleman Hills in 1938. Neither of these tests was sufficiently satisfactory to warrant continued operation.

Another rotary-type unit was proposed by E. D. Nothstine,[483] in which a bottom-hole pump was anchored in the tubing against rotation and the production tubing was rotated, operating through mitre gears, to drive two horizontal shafts, with double-throw opposed cranks on each shaft operating opposed pistons in a pair of cylinders. The fluid was introduced through valves in the heads of the lower pistons and discharged through a rotary valve operated by the tubing and timed with the operation of the pistons.

Electric Bottom-hole Pumps

Electrical submersible bottom-hole pumps may be divided into three classes:

1. Rotary electric motors driving rotary pumps.
2. Rotary electric motors driving reciprocating pumps.
3. Reciprocating electric motors driving reciprocating hydraulic pumps.

H. W. Pickett[484] was the first to show an electric-motor type pump (Fig. 64). His device used a rotary motor operating through a "Yankee Screw Driver" device to operate a plunger pump. The "Yankee Screw Driver" consisted of a right and left thread on a shaft, with a pivoted follower which operated in this thread and which transferred from the right-hand to the left-hand thread at each end of the stroke.

R. E. Newcomb[485] proposed a progressive solenoid engine operating a reciprocating plunger pump.

C. C. Scharpenberg[486] proposed an electric motor driving a single-thread screw with a nut attached to the pump plunger (Fig. 65). The plunger entered a dash pot at each end of the stroke, which produced an overload in the motor which was utilized to operate a reversing switch located at the well head. Scharpenberg was Chief Engineer of Standard Oil Co. of California, Production Department, and this pump was built by that company and tried in Well No. 15 at Kern River Field, Calif. in 1926.

L. G. Gates[487] designed an electric motor driving a gear pump with a closed hydraulic system which, in turn, operated through a pilot valve and a main valve to control the application of pressure to a double-acting

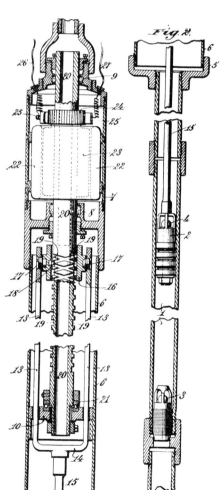

Fig. 64—Pickett Electric Pump, 1894

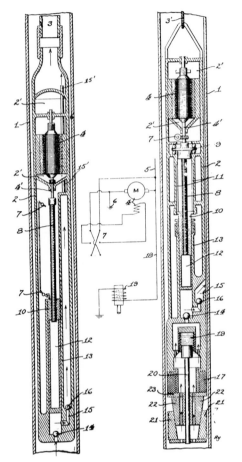

Fig. 65—Scharpenberg Reversing-motor
Electric Pump, 1926

Fig. 66—Reda Submerged-motor Electric
Multistage Centrifugal Pump, 1927

engine direct-connected to a single-acting pump which was packed off from this electric hydraulic unit. Gates was an engineer with Standard Oil Co. of California, and this device was built by A. O. Smith Co. and tested by National Oil Company at Taft, Calif., in 1934.

M. L. Milton[488] designed an electric motor driving through a mitre gear and worm gear connected to a double-throw crankshaft with connecting rods and plungers operating two single-acting pumps.

B. F. Schmidt[489] also provided an electric motor driving a "Yankee Screw Driver" device to produce reciprocating motion. A piston rod extended through packing from this unit and operated a double-acting pump.

E. C. Ekstromer[490] produced a unit with multiple electric motors, each driving a horizontal shaft with single-throw cranks which had connecting rods connected to a common crosshead operating a single reciprocating pump. Another device developed by Ekstromer[491] had an electric motor operating a shaft with a right and left thread having constant mesh right-hand and left-hand nuts on this thread, which were engaged by a pair of clutches to produce the reciprocating motion.

C. J. Coberly[492] proposed a reciprocating polyphase field actuating a plunger carrying single-turn coils forming the secondary of a reciprocating induction motor. Pump plungers were arranged concentric with and inside this plunger.

W. H. Graham[493] proposed an electric motor driving a single screw thread through a direct gear and a reversing gear with clutches operated at ends of the stroke to select the direction of operation, and thus produce a reciprocating action on the screw, which was transmitted to a pump.

J. Penrod[494] used an electric motor driving a wobble disc pump, a rotary 4-way valve driven by the motor through a reduction gear, and a double-acting engine direct-connected to a double-acting pump. This device had a centrifugal governor to bypass part of the power oil if the motor was overloaded and the speed reduced below normal.

E. Freeman[495] proposed a plurality of electric-motor-driven centrifugal pumps, or a plurality of solenoid-operated plunger pumps, arranged in series with a bypass overflow back to the well below each unit which would limit the load handled by each section.

A. Arutunoff was the pioneer of the commercial electric submersible oil-well pump. His work in this field started with the development of an oil-filled and oil-cooled motor[496] (Fig. 66). Other motor patents relating to squirrel-cage induction motors[497] were issued to him. His first submersible-pump patent, issued in 1926,[498] disclosed the principal features which were built and tested and offered to the industry by the Bart Manufacturing Company, organized in 1927. The most important part of this device is a 3-phase, 2-pole induction motor, made up of a long stator and a number of short rotors on a common shaft having bearings between the rotors which are centered in the stator. Two basic-size units were built, limited in outside diameter to $5\frac{3}{8}$-in. and $7\frac{1}{4}$-in., respectively. The $5\frac{3}{8}$-in. unit had rotors $2\frac{1}{2}$ in. in diameter by 15 in. long, delivering $7\frac{1}{2}$ hp at 3,600 rpm, and these were stacked in a stator of the proper length to give the total horsepower desired. The maximum for this size unit was 105 hp, consisting of 14 rotors, making the length of the motor approximately 20 ft.

Attached to the motor and directly above it was a seal unit to prevent the leakage of water into the motor housing. This unit was a greasesealed device in which was provided a grease reservoir with a piston followed by a spring. The grease was directed to a lantern ring between two long packing sections. The grease piston and the top of the packing were both open to well fluid, so that the grease pressure on the lantern ring was greater than the well-fluid pressure by the amount of pressure produced by the force of the spring against the grease piston.

Above the seal was a pump unit, consisting of a multiplicity of centrifugal pump bowls stacked in a housing. Each pump impeller was nearly in hydraulic balance and had its thrust carried by a non-metallic washer between the impeller and the bowl. The design of the pump sections depended upon the amount of fluid to be handled, and the number of stages depended upon the total head. As many as 200 stages were used for pumping against heads of 7,000 ft.

The cable used to supply power to the bottom-hole unit was also developed by Arutunoff[499] and was manufactured by the Simplex Cable Company. Early installations were made for Continental Oil Company and Phillips Petroleum Company in Kansas and Oklahoma in the period from 1927 to 1929. The Phillips Petroleum Company, in addition to testing out a large number of these installations, financially backed the development and later was a stockholder in the Reda Pump Company, which was organized in 1930 to take over the Bart Manufacturing Company.

The big application of Reda pumps at first was to handle large volumes of fluid in fields in Kansas and Oklahoma, such as Seminole, Okla., where the percentage of oil in the fluid could be greatly increased by handling larger total volumes. Also, the practice in establishing allowables in Kansas and Oklahoma was based on a demonstrated potential and the Reda pump was able to handle large volumes for this purpose. An important application of the Reda pump was made in the Oklahoma City Field at a depth of 6,300 ft. Here the Reda pump was able to handle 1,000 bbl per day from bottom, which exceeded the capacity of rod pumps previously used by a factor of 2:1 to 3:1. Many of these installations were handling clean oil, so the operators who were able to take advantage of the use of this pump obtained a very fast payout of their investment. The pumps used for this condition were 90 to 105 hp with 140 stages.

The Reda pump is basically a high-capacity unit, ranging from 5,000 bbl per day at 1,000-ft lift to 1,000 bbl per day at 7,000-ft lift. Pumps were also made for smaller capacities—down to 200 bbl per day, but the centrifugal-type pump is not well-suited to small-capacity operation. For production smaller than this minimum, timers were provided and the pumps were placed on intermittent operation.

Other types of pumps have been developed for use with the Reda motor[500] to handle smaller volumes of fluid under high pressure.

The first of these, invented by Arutunoff, was a gear reduction attached to the motor and driving through a bevelled gear to a horizontal shaft which carried a chain sprocket. An idler sprocket was spaced at a distance from this drive sprocket to give the desired length of stroke. A pitman was connected to the chain—which ran on these two sprockets—and, in turn, was connected to a crosshead and a piston of a single-acting pump which delivered fluid to a surge chamber and to the production tubing.

The second covered a device invented by C. C. Brown and assigned to the Reda Pump Company, which also provided a gear reduction and bevel-gear drive to a horizontal shaft; but in place of the sprocket-and-chain system, this shaft had a double opposed crank with connecting rods, crossheads, and pump plungers making a duplex single-acting pump. The plungers were hollow and took fluid through intake valves in the top of the plungers; and the discharge valves were in the cylinder head in axial alignment with the cylinder, which connected to a passage communicating with the pump tubing.

The third was an invention of Arutunoff which was a single-thread screw driven by the electric motor. In order to obtain a reasonable efficiency with this single-thread screw, Arutunoff developed a ball-bearing nut. To change direction at the end of the stroke, the motor was reversed. This was accomplished by an electrical overload and reversing relay system located at the well head. This pump is almost identical to that patented by C. C. Scharpenberg more than 20 years earlier. This type of pump, however, has not come into extended use in the industry.

In some oil fields of high productivity the fluid levels can be drawn down to a few feet from bottom and still produce large volumes of oil. With the Reda pump of high horsepower, the pump suction is 25 to 30 ft from the bottom of the well, because of the length of the motor and seal. This limitation was overcome by Arutunoff[501] by making a bottom-suction pump, in which the motor was placed at the top of the unit (Fig. 67). Since the motor would be above the fluid level in the well, no cooling would be obtained; and therefore, the discharge of the pump was conducted through a small annular space between the motor and the outer housing. The general features of this type of Reda pump are substantially the same as the standard type, the principal change being that of putting the pump at the bottom of the unit.

Where central-station electric power was not available, Reda pumps were often run by engine-driven 3-phase generators, which were mounted on a skid base and located at any convenient point near the well (Fig. 68).

The electrical losses in the cable were, in some cases, an appreciable factor in the overall performance. To offset these losses without providing a special motor for each different well depth, an autotransformer was provided at the surface, so that the supply voltage—which normally was 440 volts—could be increased to any desired voltage up to 880.

J. G. Keegan[502] proposed a duplex solenoid pump with gravity return of the plungers, in which the pump fluid was produced through the two plungers in series with a valve in each plunger and a standing valve at the bottom of the unit.

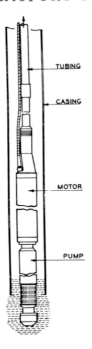

TUBING

CASING

MOTOR

PUMP

Fig. 67 (left)—Reda Bottom-suction Submersible Pump

Fig. 68 (below)—Engine-driven Alternator for Supplying Power to Reda Pumps

F. W. Harris[503] proposed an electric closed-system hydraulic unit, in which an electric motor operated a gear pump, which delivered fluid through a pilot valve and main valve to metallic bellows in place of plungers, and with a pair of intake and discharge valves.

J. W. Chambers[504] proposed a unit which was almost identical to that invented by C. C. Brown, except that the entire unit was placed in an inverted position in the well with the motor on top, whereas Brown had proposed to have the motor on the bottom of the unit.

F. A. Gruetjen[505] designed a unit which was based upon the Gates pump[487] and was simply an improvement in the valve mechanism employed.

E. O. Holmberg[506] proposed an electric motor driving a centrifugal pump which, in turn, operated a multiple-piston engine to utilize the fluid at low pressure, which was connected to a single-acting single-cylinder pump. This also was an attempt to commercialize the Gates pump. This device, as well as that of Gruetjen, was tested by the A. O. Smith Company in a number of Standard Oil Co. wells in California with reasonable success.

Another Gruetjen invention[507] was also an improved patent for the application of the Gates principle. W. Ferris[508] developed a unit—which was assigned to the Oilgear Company—based on the Gates principle and similar in many respects to the improvements made by Gruetjen and Holmberg.

706

J. Lane[509] used an electric motor set on slips in the casing and pulled by the electric cable. Chester Malinowski[510] showed some improvements on the Ekstromer pump, and this is one of the patents that belong to the Electrolift Corporation Limited of San Francisco.

E. J. Weatherby[511] proposed an electric motor driving through a hydraulic coupling to a gear train to reduce the speed and convert the rotary motion to reciprocating motion, which operated a single-acting plunger pump. T. G. Lewis[512] produced a motor-driven unit in which a pair of wobble disc-type pumps were driven.

B. F. Schmidt[513] proposed a motor-driven closed system operating through bellows in place of pistons, similar to that invented by F. W. Harris.[503]

None of the developments in electric bottom-hole pumps other than those made by Arutunoff has become of any commercial importance. It is interesting to note, however, that in the field of water pumping for irrigation and other purposes where centrifugal pumps are well-suited, there have been other submersible motor pumps developed. One of these started about the same time as that of the Reda pump and is now considered a highly successful means of pumping water. This development was made by the Submersible Motor Pump Company of Los Angeles, organized in 1930, which later sold this development to the Byron Jackson Company. In the past few years a number of other electric submersible pumps have been put on the market.

Prime Movers

From before Drake's discovery in 1859 until the mid 1890's, steam was essentially the only form of power available for pumping. Catalogs[8] indicate that there was a limited demand for horsepowers (Fig. 69), both the treadmill type and the walk-around geared to drive a bandwheel, but these were necessarily limited to shallow and intermittent producing operations.

A major change in prime movers for pumping wells came in the latter part of the 1890's when the gas engine was introduced. The first unit was put on the market in about 1894,[514] and by 1900 there was a major swing to the new form of power for pumping. The most popular method of adapting the gas engine to existing installations was the use of a conversion kit, supplied by several manufacturers, which would allow the operator to change out the steam head for a gas-engine head. All of these units were 2-cycle and, with few exceptions, had hot-tube ignition systems. The measure of the swing to gas engines is recorded by one manufacturer,[515] who claims that in the period 1899 to 1901 he sold "over 4,000" gas-engine conversion kits.

Thus, from about 1900 to 1930 it was almost universal practice to drill with steam and then to install a gas or oil engine for pumping.

Fig. 69—Horse-operated Geared Power
(Oil Well Supply Company Catalog,
1884)

Fig. 70—Steam Engine
(Oil Well Supply Company Catalog,
1884)

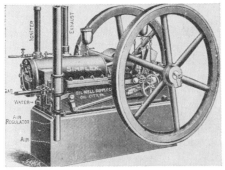

Fig. 71—Early Gas Engine
(Oil Well Supply Company Catalog,
1904)

Fig. 72—Oil Engine
(Oil Well Supply Company Catalog,
1916)

Without exception, these pumping engines were single-cylinder, and the majority of them were of the horizontal type (Fig. 70). Most were in the order of 10-hp to 50-hp rating. There were some, however, that were vertical, with 2-hp to 10-hp rating, suitable for small wells. Oil Well Supply's 1916 catalog describes in detail 3 prime movers apparently comparable to most in service at that time. One is a 4-hp vertical air-cooled gas engine with a choice of hot-tube, spark, or magneto ignition. This unit was particularly designed to fit on a unit pumping jack. Another larger gas engine (Fig. 71), available in 25-hp to 40-hp rating, was horizontal, 4-cycle, and offered choice of magneto, make-and-break or hot-tube ignition, or a combination of the three. The oil engine offered in this catalog (Fig. 72) was available in 11 sizes running from 15 hp to 100 hp. It was described as being able to run on fuel oil, solar oil, crude oil, slops, distillate, kerosene, or gasoline. Most references of the period indicated that oil engines were normally run on crude oil produced in the lease.

These single-cylinder engines, in common with steam engines used previously, ran at speeds in the order of 200 to 300 rpm, and speed reduction to pumping speeds of approximately 20 spm was achieved through the use of the bandwheel. The use of the multi-cylinder engines with

Fig. 73—Multi-cylinder Engine, Waukesha, 1924

higher drive-shaft speeds did not become common until adequate speed reducers were developed in the latter 1920's and early 1930's. According to Zaba,[127] one of the first multi-cylinder engines used for pumping was a Waukesha engine (Fig. 73) installed on a Lufkin unit in 1924. McNeill[516] states that the first multi-cylinder engine for pumping in California was in 1930.

Field[517] states that the first use of electricity for pumping dates back to 1892, when 5 wells in West Virginia were equipped with motors. This conflicts with George,[200] who states that the first use of electricity in pumping was in the Baku Field in 1900; and the first use in the United States—in West Virginia—was in 1906. Other authorities, A. W. Peake and F. O. Prior,[518] reported the first electrified pumping installation in this country as being made by the South Penn Oil Company in 1903 near Folson, West Va. One manufacturer's catalog of 1903[519] lists a unit pumper, and describes it as being suitable for electric drive. All authorities are in agreement, however, that electric power for pumping did not receive general consideration until about 1912. The *Oil and Gas Journal Anniversary Issue* in 1951 states that electric power was used for pumping in the Gulf Coast in 1912, and this is supported by George's statement that in 1913 the use of electric power spread into Texas and Oklahoma.

Most of these motors were slip-ring alternating-current type, and had double ratings to accommodate both pulling and pumping, the higher power being available for the pulling operation (Fig. 74). A measure of acceptance of electrical power was Suman's statement in 1922[520] that there were more than 2,000 electrically operated wells in the United States, and these had been in operation for a period of 1 to 11 years.

709

Fig. 74 (above)—Two-speed Electric
Motor, General Electric, about 1925

Fig. 75 (left)—Modern Electric Drive,
The National Supply Company

In the succeeding years the use of electric power for pumping has
spread considerably. This general acceptance of unit pumpers has made
electric power easier to install and, because of the unit pumper's relative
efficiency, has lowered power consumption. The advent of mobile servicing units has eliminated the use of double-rated motors, which formerly
were used in pulling rods and tubing. Fig. 75 shows a modern electric-
motor-drive pumping unit.

LEASE FACILITIES

Tankage

Like so many of the techniques of early oil production, the arrangements for the storage of oil developed and changed—depending upon

the local need, availability of materials, and the ever-active ingenuity of the industry's people.

It is reported that prior to 1790 Indians were collecting petroleum from the creek waters of Pennsylvania by soaking their blankets, carrying this storage device to the point of use, and delivering by squeezing the oil from the blanket into pots. Better identified[3] is the report that in 1790 Nathaniel Carey was skimming crude oil from springs near Titusville, Pa., filling two small kegs which he carried by horseback, making deliveries directly to customers.

Probably the early practice was to produce crude oil into wooden barrels, which could be easily handled and transported, and provided a measurement of quantity. The first large flowing well, in 1861—the "Empire", with its production of 3,000 bbl per day—quickly overwhelmed the previous storage facilities and filled the hastily built earthen dams. Certainly the earthen storage of the 1860's was an expediency, but economics has since proved it to have a place even in today's oil fields. Many examples of earthen storage are still in use; and it is interesting that at this time (1957) a highly engineered earthen storage pit has been completed in western Venezuela, and successfully tested as a modern answer to long-term, large-volume storage of heavy crude oil.

Aboveground storage was quickly devised and, logically, using the most available and workable material—wood. Apparently the first of these storage vessels were rectangular boxes, immediately followed by round wooden tanks, as noted in the following extract from *The Oil and Gas Journal*, April 4, 1918:

"In 1861, Mr. Akin made one of the first hooped round oil tanks, erected on the Kingsland flats, below Titusville. The size of the tank was an 8 foot diameter bottom with 8 foot high staves.

"In the first days of the oil business all the tanks, aside from the common barrels used at the wells, in which to store crude oil, were made oblong box shaped. These tanks, in size, ranged from 4 feet to 32 feet in length and from 4 to 8 feet wide. In height, they were from 3 feet to 6 feet. Round tanks were first introduced in 1861-1862. In the beginning, round tanks were of small dimensions, holding from 6 to 12 barrels."

The evolution of lease-tank storage developed, and can be dated approximately as follows:

Wood	1861
Riveted iron	1867
Bolted iron and steel	1913
Welded steel	1926

Round wooden tanks quickly became standard after their introduction in 1861, and held their popularity until the 1920's. Since then their general use has decreased greatly, except in certain areas such as parts of West Texas, where the oil and gas contains sulfur compounds that are corrosive to iron and steel.

The early wooden tanks (Fig. 76) were constructed with wooden bottoms and open tops. The side staves were tapered and ranged in width at the bottom from 3 in. to 10 in., depending upon the diameter of the tank. Stave thickness was most generally 2 in., although 2½-in. and 3-in. staves were used. Edge faces of the staves were planed for smoothness and angle to provide a leak-proof joint on assembly. Iron hoops were fashioned using strap ⅛ in. thick and 1½ in. wide, with ends riveted. A series of these hoops of decreasing diameter were placed over the tapered walls and were driven downward with sledge and "hoop set", tightening the edge joints of all staves to provide a seal. As the wood weathered and shrank, the tank could be kept tight by "hoop setting", as required. Understandably, the first improvement was the patent Ware hoop connection, which allowed wrench tightening through a turnbuckle-type connection.

As early tanks were open-top, the effects of wind and rain became intolerable. Floating decks of wood were made as one of the first attempts to seal the top of the tank, but the final solution was to lay a top deck of shiplap with an overhanging eave. This kept out the rain and snow, and also allowed a connection for venting and directing the gas away for better-controlled disposal. The single tank was increased to several to allow emptying a full tank to the buyer without stopping production. It soon became the practice to house in the battery of several tanks to give better weather protection.

Pine was first used for tank construction because of availability; but, due to its sensitivity to weathering and to termites, it was replaced by cypress. However, cypress became scarce and, with the shift of oil-field activity to the central and western states, redwood became the universal tank wood, as it is today.

With the steel-tank competition steadily growing, wood-tank manufacturers have given much attention to improving their product in order to hold the market of West Texas and Kansas, where they have the potential advantage of being better able to meet the corrosion problem. By 1935 the straight-sided design had been replaced by the "head" tank (Fig. 77), which is curved-sided bulging at the middle. This allows a locked-in head at top and bottom, capable of withstanding 16-oz pressure in common sizes. Hoops are curved rods with several tightening lugs at 10-ft intervals on the circumference for better-distributed tightening. These design improvements provided greater durability and reduced maintenance and evaporation.

Fig. 76 (below)—Early Wooden Tank (Oil Well Supply Company Catalog, 1884)

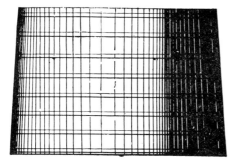

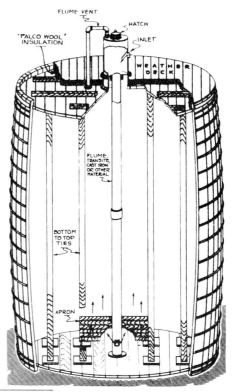

Fig. 77 (right)—Modern Wooden Wash Tank for Sour Crude, 1935

The greatest problem with wooden tanks was the constant coopering necessary to stop joint leaks resulting from the drying out of the wood, and many improvements were devised to overcome this defect. Water-covered decks were provided and arranged with a groove in the edge faces of the deck planking and in the staves, so that within each joint there existed a contained and open passage that could be kept filled with water. Others methods of sealing wood tanks have been the use of tapered tongue-and-groove joints and, more recently, the grooved face joints which are filled with rods of neoprene which become compression gaskets in the assembled tank, and maintain enough resilience and volume to compensate for changes in the stave joint fit. Such a tank gives full protection from weather and reduces gas losses and evaporation from the crude oil to a minimum. Only in durability is it inferior to an iron or steel tank.

Riveted Iron Tanks

The Derrick's Hand Book of Petroleum[7] reports: "In 1863, iron tanks were used to ship oil from the Canada Oil Field by Grand Trunk Railway to Portland, Maine, thence to Liverpool." This same publication reports that, in 1867, Egbert and Brown built the largest iron storage tank in the world—80 ft in diameter by 22 ft 3 in. high—on the Jersey shore at Bellows Island, New York.

Again *The Derrick's Hand Book* reports: "In 1873 there were 800,000 barrels of iron tankage in the course of construction in the oil and gas regions."

Iron tanks were listed in Oil Well catalogs in sizes from 25 bbl to 35,000 bbl, the smallest being 6 ft x 5 ft and the largest 92 ft x 30 ft. The word "iron" was used in all of the early publications and catalogs with reference to metal tanks used in the oil industry, in contrast to wood tanks. We assume the word "iron" referred to "wrought iron", which was more commonly used than steel prior to the 20th century.

The word "steel" was first mentioned in connection with oil-field tanks in the Oil Well catalog, 1892, wherein the statement was made that prices would be furnished on iron or steel tanks upon request.

In all early publications and catalogs the word "riveted" is the only word used to designate the manner in which pieces of iron were fastened together to form a tank. We therefore assume that all iron and steel tanks used in the oil fields prior to the introduction of the bolted steel tank were of riveted construction (Fig. 78).

Bolted Steel Tanks

The first bolted steel lease tanks for the petroleum industry were introduced in 1913, when Gantz Tank Company produced a lease tank of the flanged-bottom and flanged-deck type. The steel of the bottom and top decks was turned at right angles around the periphery high enough to permit straight sides to be bolted to this turned-up flange.

Another type of bolted steel tank with countersunk bolt heads was introduced in approximately 1918 by a man named Walsh of the Superior Tank Company. During the same period H. R. Leland of the Perfection Tank Company produced silos for farm use, known as the "Perfection"

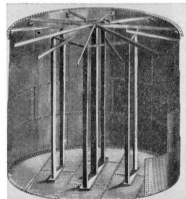

Fig. 78—Riveted Tank
(Oil Well Supply Company Catalog, 1900)

714

or "silo" tank. The low rings of this tank were constructed of sheets of steel approximately 32 in. high and increased in the upper rings to approximately 4 ft. These sheets had all four edges flanged, and were bolted together in rows with rubber gaskets between the joints to form a steel tank of the desired diameter and height. This silo type is used today to a considerable extent for lease tankage in the oil industry.

The American Tank Company, in 1918, produced a steel tank with "staves" or sheets approximately 60 in. wide and 8 ft. high, which was the forerunner of the present API bolted tanks.

Welded Steel Tanks

As fusion welding of steel became more reliable and welded steel vessels were accepted by industry in general, welded tanks for lease storage became increasingly popular. The American Petroleum Institute records show that the first welded-tank committee was appointed in 1928. Since that time *API Std 12F** for shop-welded flat-bottom lease storage tanks has been developed. It lists sizes of tanks from 8 ft in diameter by $7\frac{1}{2}$ ft high with capacity of 65 bbl, to and including 12 ft in diameter by 20 ft high with a capacity of 400 bbl. The most popular steel thickness used for the construction of these welded tanks is all $\frac{1}{4}$-in. or $\frac{1}{4}$-in. bottom with $\frac{3}{16}$-in. sides and $\frac{3}{16}$-in. deck.

In West Texas and parts of New Mexico—where the terrain is practically flat and the roads excellent—heavy trucks and trailers are handling high 500-bbl tanks, 16 ft in diameter by 16 ft high, all of $\frac{1}{4}$-in. steel.

In general the welded or bolted steel tanks have answered most of the problems of wooden tanks except that of corrosion. Inside corrosion is still present and various protective coatings have been tried, ranging from those to be applied in place to shop-built sections incorporating fiberglass plastic covering. Mechanically, corrosion in the most vulnerable section—the tank bottom—has been helped by better-engineered tank grades and foundations to provide better outside drainage, and by the use of the downward-pointing cone bottom which allows complete water drain-off and prevents low-spot accumulation of corrosive water.

Oil and Gas Separators

J. H. A. Bone's 1865 description of early oil-field problems[3] gives the background for the evolution of oil and gas separators. Comments such as the following pretty well set the stage.

"In many of the pumping wells the gas is saved and used either by itself or with coal, as fuel for the engine. To save it, the mingled gas, oil and water . . . is conducted by a pipe from the well tube into a tight barrel."

Specification for Small Welded Production Tanks, American Petroleum Institute, Dallas, Texas, 4th Ed., Aug. 1957.

"... The gas escapes by a small pipe at the top of the barrel and is conducted into the furnace, where it burns with a fierce and steady flame."

W. R. Hamilton of the United States Bureau of Mines describes the first separator introduced to the oil industry in Oil Creek, Pa. in 1865.[521]

"This piece of equipment consisted of a barrel placed on the top of an oilfield lease tank. The oil entered through a bung in one side of the top head of the barrel. The entry nipple extended down inside of the barrel about 2/3 of the barrel height. The oil outlet was in the bottom of one side of the barrel, and through a pipe which extended down into the tank through a 'U' tube which provided an oil-seal and prevented the escape of the gas. The gas produced with the oil into the barrel or top of the tank, had its outlet through a bung in the barrel head opposite the oil and gas inlet line. Thus the gas was conveyed by a line to a desirable and safe outlet point."

A later improvement employing a means of separating the gas from the oil along similar lines consisted of the installation vertically in the lease tank of a piece of large-diameter casing, e.g., 15-in. The bottom end of the casing nipple was held approximately 1 ft above the bottom of the tank. The top end of the casing nipple extended above the tank top approximately 3 ft. The top end of this piece of casing was equipped with a casing cap. The inlet pipe entered the cap at one side and extended downward through the cap a few feet in the gas nipple. The gas outlet was connected to the other side of the casing cap and had a flush inside connection.

The next step in the development of the oil and gas separators was the installation on the outside of the lease tank of a casing nipple similar to the one described in the preceding paragraph, but closed at the bottom except for an oil-outlet line. The produced oil was conveyed from the outside casing separator through a **U** tube, which acted as an oil seal, and then into the lease tank.

The Oil Well catalog of 1884 shows 2 "Iron Gas Tanks". One of these, "Ashton's Patent" (Fig. 79), seems to provide the basic features to be found in later separator improvements—gas-liquid inlet, gas outlet, float-controlled bottom outlet valve for automatic liquid removal (also a chain connection for manual valve control), and a pressure-relief valve. Undoubtedly this equipment was designed to clean the gas *after separation* from the oil for its use as fuel.

The J. S. Bougher patent, issued in 1895 (Fig. 80), applied the principle of the Ashton tank to a device specifically for oil and gas separation with the separator tank mounted on top of the storage tank. It was provided with an extra inlet ("4" on Fig. 80) for casing gas, and a steam heating coil to prevent freezing. Since the early use of such equipment

716

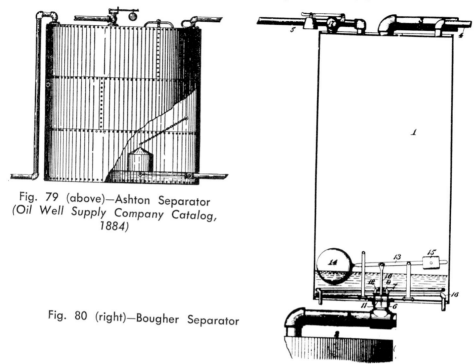

Fig. 79 (above)—Ashton Separator
(Oil Well Supply Company Catalog,
1884)

Fig. 80 (right)—Bougher Separator

was to separate the gas ahead of the stock tanks for disposal or transmission to the nearby pumping engine for fuel, the devices were built for low-pressure conditions.

In time the increase in gas pressures required by longer transmission lines brought higher-pressure separators. The 1904 issue of Oil Well Supply Company's general catalog listed the "OWS Co. High Pressure Oil-Gas Separator". Its test pressure was 150 psi. The separator had no internals, but did have a unique outside-type liquid-level control. Long, curved pipe arms extended from the back side of the separator—one connected high in the gas section and one low in the oil section. One hundred eighty degrees from the connections, the pipes were connected into a big pot at the top and bottom. As the pot filled from the bottom, it became heavy and flexed the pipes downwardly. A valve activator was attached to the side of the pot; and when the activator contacted the stem of a spring-loaded oil valve and depressed the stem, the oil valve opened until the oil level went down. To give some degree of control, the vertical pipes connecting to the pot were fastened to guide posts and a weight-and-lever arrangement could be used to control oil dump level. The aim of this separator was to provide higher gas pressure at the vent and outside controls that could be cleaned and serviced readily.

The 1904 issue of the Oil Well catalog also displayed Wilbur's

717

Automatic Gas Tank" (Fig. 81). The float hung from the top and operated a teeter-totter type arm, one end of which was connected to a float and one end to an outside plug-valve-type oil valve. A gas-vent pipe was used, so the float arm went through a stuffing box of some type. Sizes available were 26-in. x 48-in. and 48-in. x 48-in.

In 1906 A. S. Cooper in California developed a separator which recognized the problem of entrained gas and provided a tangential inlet spreading the fluid along the tank wall to release the gas. This feature, together with the deep-coned bottom for easy sand removal, resulted from local California problems of heavier oil and produced sand. The cone bottom became an identification of California design. As in many of the early designs, inside valving was used to avoid stuffing boxes.

A more extreme answer to the California sand problem in separators was the McLaughlin separator (Fig 82), introduced about 1909. This was designed only for flowing wells and used largely in the Sunset Midway Field. Because of the heavy oil and sand, production was led to settling sumps by troughs instead of pipes. The outlet valve is the seat between the ridge on the oil-inlet pipe and the bottom cone opening of the tank. By proper counterbalancing of the weight of the empty tank system, adjustment can be made so that the weight of a volume of liquid in the tank bears the tank down and keeps the bottom outlet valve open, dumping the oil and sand into the trough to the settling sump. Automatic sand purging and a durable valve arrangement were thus accomplished.

In 1912, The National Supply Company listed a "Washington Trap". It was apparently similar to the Bougher separator of 1895, except that it had no heating coil. The Washington trap was available in the following sizes of riveted construction (no pressures were given): 26-in. x 48-in., 36-in. x 66-in., 36-in. x 72-in., 48-in. x 84-in. and 48-in. x 120-in.

Jarecki Manufacturing Company cataloged the "Jarecki Automatic Gas Tank" in 1914. Its design was almost a duplicate of Wilbur's gas tank, except for an arm extension on the plug-type oil valve to give greater leverage. It was for very low pressure, being offered in size 26-in. x 48-in. and having flat heads.

In 1916 Oil Well Supply Company listed in their Catalog No. 43 a low-pressure gas tank for pressures up to 50 psi. The tank had no internal baffles; and if there was anything new and different about this gas tank, it was the oil-control assembly. An inside float operated an inside rotary port-type valve to release the oil from the tank.

Up to around 1915 separators were generally sold as regular supply-house items. With the construction of gas plants demanding higher supply pressure and an increasing awareness of the importance of oil gravity, companies specializing in designing and making separators began to appear.

The Trumble separator became popular in 1915-16. With the deep

Fig. 81 (right)—Wilbur's Separator
(Oil Well Supply Company Catalog,
1904)

Fig. 82 (below)—McLaughlin Separator,
about 1909

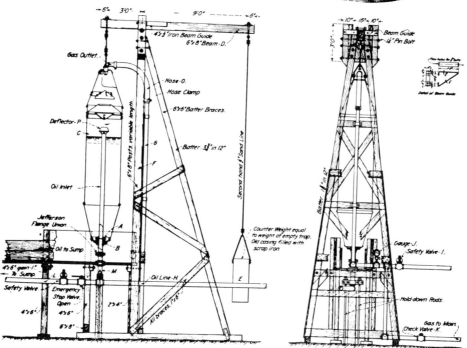

cone bottom marking it as a California design, it seemed to give the first real emphasis to oil scrubbing with its top inlet feeding downwardly over the cone spreader.

The Smith Separator Company supplied many of their units in the Ranger Field, Texas, where the value of gas was beginning to be recognized. In this unit higher-pressure construction was used. The inlet stream was slightly baffled and the gas takeoff pipe was arranged for more convenient piping.

The 1920 patent of A. M. Ballard introduced the dual valve control, in which the float controlled both liquid- and gas-outlet valves. If the liquid level rose, the gas valve was progressively closed to build up gas pressure and provide faster exhaust of the oil. Unfortunately, the inlet line had to be submerged in the liquid to prevent backflow during this operation. Consequently the gas separation at the inlet was completely neglected.

The D. G. Lorraine separator (1921)—Fig. 83—provided the dual valve feature; but in addition, through internal compartments and inlet check valve, allowed separation of gas from the oil at the inlet point. Being of California origin, the internal baffling recognized the sand problem, protecting the valve float, and provided a sand jet nozzle at the bottom cleanout connection.

An interesting early device was described as an oil and gas separator by H. B. Thomson of the California State Mining Bureau as used in the Ventura Field, California.[522] The main problem seemed to be emulsification, because of the necessity for maintaining high back pressures against the well. The purpose was to cause separation prior to back-pressure valving. By providing multiple-orifice takeoffs in the downstream vertical manifold, the gas, oil, and water could be discharged separately. Although the tubular design of this device may have been occasioned by the availability of materials and the high pressures involved, the features of horizontal flow with respect to gravity separation were introduced with this apparatus.

A. M. Ballard's patent of 1923 emphasizes the advantage of imposing some motion favorable to separation on the incoming gas-oil stream through the helical screw baffles in the inlet nipple.

During the 1920's, with crude-oil prices scheduled in increments of API gravity, the importance of better separation became increasingly recognized, and considerable engineering was applied. This was directed toward improving lease facilities to prevent evaporation losses and the resulting reduction in crude-oil gravities.

The J. P. Walker patent of 1928 (Fig. 84) gave much attention to the oil-scrubbing feature. Double tangential inlets provided a spiralling downward flow of the oil and upward of the gas. The baffle arrangement in the gas section was designed to sustain this spiral flow and increase the velocity progressively. Centrifugal force and the prolonged contact of the wet gas with the oil-wetted surfaces provided greater gathering of the oil particles with their subsequent gravity settling to the liquid section. In 1929 M. F. Waters patented his separator, giving similar attention to better liquid separation in the uprising gas section of the tank by slanted baffle plates.

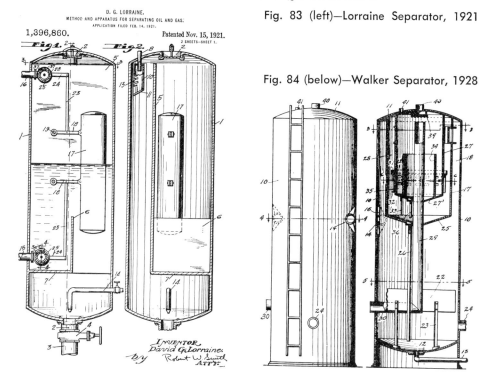

D. G. LORRAINE.
METHOD AND APPARATUS FOR SEPARATING OIL AND GAS.
APPLICATION FILED FEB. 14, 1921.

1,396,860.

Patented Nov. 15, 1921.
2 SHEETS—SHEET 1.

Fig. 83 (left)—Lorraine Separator, 1921

Fig. 84 (below)—Walker Separator, 1928

INVENTOR
David G. Lorraine,
by Robert W. Smith
ATTY.

Previous to the 1930's the main concern in separator design seems to have been in the liquid section with its oil-level control valves and means of sand disposal. Walker and Waters gave greater attention to the separation efficiency of the gas section. With the ever-increasing operating pressures and the continuing emphasis on the value of gas and oil gravity, much work has been done in the 25 years since 1930 to make increasing refinements in this equipment.

In high-pressure operations during the period 1930-1940, stage separation was utilized, adapting equipment of current design to the work. Briefly, stage separation consists of removing all the free gas which can be liberated at various pressure stages one step at a time, thus maintaining the maximum volume and gravity of the liquid oil produced. For example, 4-stage separation consists of well production passing through a 1,000-lb working pressure separator; then the gas removed or liberated at some pressure between 750 and 1,000 lb in that separator is conveyed to gas sales; the oil from that separator is then passed through a 500-lb working pressure unit where gas which is liberated at some pressure between 350 and 500 lb is again piped to sales and the oil is passed through a low-pressure vessel where most of the remaining entrained gas is removed at 45 to 50 lb pressure. Little, if any, gas remains entrained in the oil to be liberated in the last and final pressure drop or stage from the third separator to the stock tank, in which a pressure of only a few ounces and in some cases as much as 1 lb is maintained.

Although separator design seemed to be tied to the vertical tank from the beginning, during the past 20 years there have been many applications of the horizontal settling which give attention to the separation of the oil in the gas section. A current type is illustrated in Fig. 85.

Horizontal design allowing effective use of smaller-diameter but longer tubes for the gas and oil sections lends itself to the higher-pressure problems and portable units. A pair of portable 2-stage high-pressure separation units are illustrated in Fig. 86.

Oil-treating Equipment

J. H. A. Bone, writing in 1865,[3] describes the early problem of treating in these words ". . . for in spite of all precautions some water will come up from nearly every pumping well". He goes on to discuss the answer of the time—"The oil and water fall into the bottom of the barrel [the early gas separator device] and run off by a pipe near the bottom into a huge tank or vat, where another separation is caused by the different gravities of the two fluids, the water sinking to the bottom of the vat." Bone does not mention bottom sediment, possibly because the quantities being produced at that time were small and because he may have considered it as merely an impurity in the oil and therefore of no interest.

In the history of production equipment, the progress made in treating oil to remove gas, water, emulsion, and sand is somewhat difficult to follow in that, although it has always been important, the evolution has been mainly that of techniques rather than specific mechanical devices. In the evolution of gas separator equipment there is noted a continuous

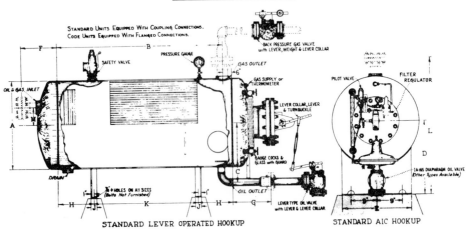

Fig. 85—Modern Horizontal Separator

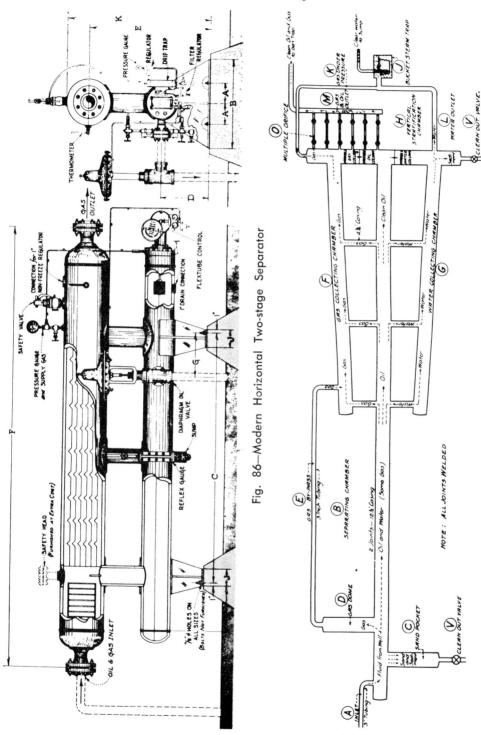

Fig. 86—Modern Horizontal Two-stage Separator

Fig. 87—Allen and Marker Separator

undertone of water and sand separation in the devices. However, the control of the separated gas seems always to have been the most important consideration, because of its fire hazard and its usefulness as fuel. The water and its accompanying sludge were nuisances which were usually disposed of in the nearby streams.

The problem of handling the "free" water in the production varied from place to place, and more or less local answers were devised. Although the main concern was for controlled separation of the gas, it was obvious that in cases of relatively large volumes of free water in the oil production the separator was over-burdened by the need to handle all of the liquid. There is no record of any really early attempt to draw off the free water ahead of the separator. However, as flowing well pressures became greater and the knowledge of the causes of emulsified oil became known, water traps or knockouts were devised to be installed ahead of the flow bean to relieve the separator of the water volume and to prevent the high pressure-drop mixing of the water-oil mixture through the flow bean. The Allen and Marker oil-water-gas separator, Fig. 87, shows one of the more elaborate devices for providing free water separation under pressure.

In the Bureau of Mines *Report of Investigations 3173*, dated May 1932, R. E. Heithecker describes in detail a water trap used in the Hendricks Field in West Texas.[523] Large volumes of free water were produced and this trap was designed for the separation of oil from water under pressure.

More elaborate provisions for water separation were described by Heithecker in showing the "gun-barrel" water-separator tank feeding the secondary water treating in the form of the "hay" tank. This hookup is shown schematically in Fig. 88. In the hay tank, as in the development of the gas-oil separators, the designer recognized the advantage of prolonging the travel of the oil-water mixture through a series of baffles— provided in this case by sections of excelsior—which caused the entrained water to break free from the oil, coalesce, and drop by its weight to the bleeder plates and be drained off.

The bottom sediment which accumulated in the settling vessels, and presented a real problem of disposal (usually by burning), was apparently not generally recognized as an emulsion of water in oil until after 1900. F. G. Cottrell, inventor of the Cottrell process of petroleum dehydration, reported difficulty in 1909 in convincing California operators that an oil-water emulsion formed a large part of the tank bottoms. Another source reported lack of general recognition in Oklahoma as late as 1916, and still later in Pennsylvania. A simple description of the process is that a mixture of the two mutually immiscible liquids—water and oil —is so agitated as to cause the water to be broken up into small droplets, becoming surrounded by a film of the oil. The surface tension of the

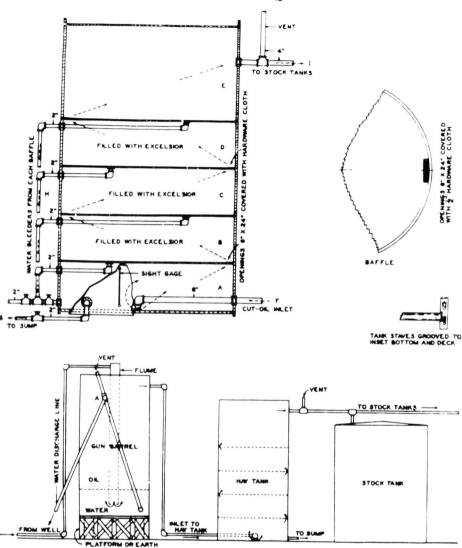

Fig. 88—Hay Tank

oil film is strong enough to keep the water droplet confined. By volume, a great part of an emulsion is water and is, therefore, undesirable for pipe-line acceptance and refinery use.

As the early producers gained experience in producing oil, it was found, for instance, that a pumping well would suddenly produce increasing proportions of unsalable "cut oil". Various theories arose as to the cause, and it is impossible to tell when and how extensively knowledge of the real cause was gained. We now know that emulsion was formed when bottom-hole pump balls and seats became worn or cut, allowing

725

high-velocity leakage to the produced oil and water. Other leaks such as holes in the tubing also caused "cut oil". Local theories developed regarding the effect of sucker-rod agitation in the tubing; and at the time of the introduction of iron sucker rods, there was considerable resistance because of the belief that wooden sucker rods were necessary to prevent the "oil cutting".

With the discovery of higher-pressure flowing wells, it was found that a large pressure drop across the control valve created an emulsion problem. With the advent of gas lift in the 1920's, the liquid-dispersion feature of the process further emphasized the problem.

In the early handling of the emulsion problem it was found that heat was effective in reducing and breaking the surface tension of the emulsion oil film, and the reduced viscosity of the heated oil allowed quicker gravity separation of the water and any contained solids.

The application of heat was merely a technique, and a wide variety of methods and devices was locally improvised without the innovation of any particular equipment. Heat was most crudely applied by means of the "Hot Ditch—a ditch, 20′ or longer—over the axis of which passed the lead line. Crude oil was poured in the ditch and ignited." Converted steam boilers, steam coils, and direct-fired heaters were used.

From these improvisations for heat application have come specifically designed and manufactured equipment with various refinements, but of no distinct change in basic principle. Fig. 89 and 90 show 2 units for applying heat to the wash-tank method of dehydrating.

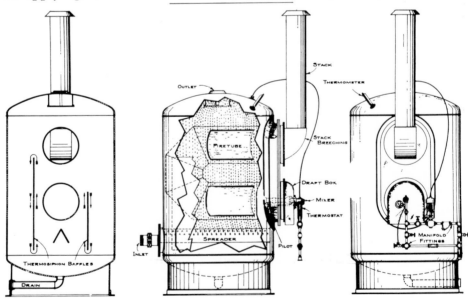

Fig. 89—Vertical Direct-fired Heater

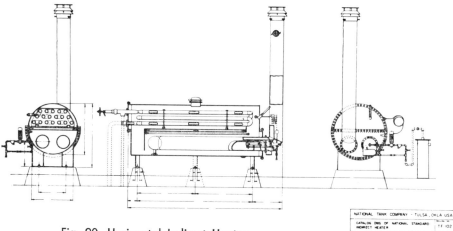

Fig. 90—Horizontal Indirect Heater

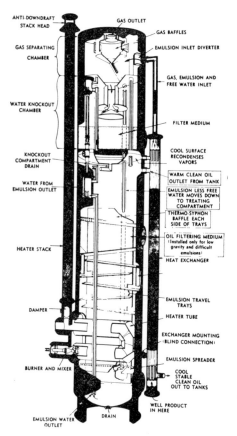

Fig. 91—Flow Treater,
National Tank Co., 1955

As recognition of advantages of conserving the gravity of crude increased, the problems of emulsion-treating equipment were given much attention during the 1920's and 1930's. In 1936, under patents issued to J. P. Walker—No. 2,181,683, No. 2,181,684, No. 2,181,685, No. 2,-181,686, No. 2,181,687, and No. 2,181,688, issued November 1939; No. 2,256,695, issued September 1941—a totally enclosed, unitized, pressure-operated emulsion treater, embodying the generally accepted principles and practices, was introduced to the market. A 1955 version of this treater is shown in Fig. 91.

Chemical Treatment

Deeper wells, higher reservoir pressures, and larger volumes of crude oil being handled were, by the early 1900's, producing such substantial volumes of bottom sediment or emulsion that it began to seem worthwhile to do something about it to find ways and means of recovering the crude oil that was certainly present and was not salable in the form of an emulsion.

William S. Barnickel became interested in this problem, and looked at the troublesome water droplet in its case of oil as a chemical problem. He demonstrated that the oil film could be broken by introduction of chemicals in economically practical quantities. On April 14, 1914, Barnickel was granted Patent No. 1,093,098 relating to this process. With continuing investigation and experience the chemical approach was im-

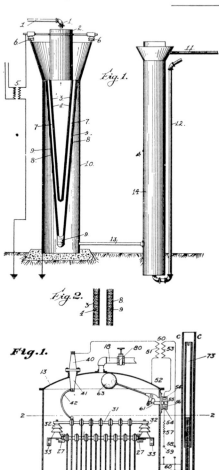

Fig. 92 (upper left)—Cottrell Electric Dehydrator

Fig. 93 (lower left)—Harris Dehydrator, 1922

Fig. 94 (below)—Flow-line Electric Treater, 1934

proved, additional patents were granted, and the process has become universally accepted. Since the action is chemical, the mechanical features of gravity separation provided by the various treating-equipment devices are effective, and the two approaches have been generally combined.

Electrical Treatment

At about the same time that Barnickel was starting his chemical treatment of emulsions, the matter was brought to the attention of F. G. Cottrell of California to see if his electrical system for collecting solid particles from flue gases (Fig. 92) might not be applicable to the treatment of emulsions, large quantities of which were being held in storage in the Coalinga Field of California.[524]

In 1908 an unsuccessful attempt was made, but continued laboratory work made possible the installation, in 1909, of a commercial plant for the Lucele Oil Company at Coalinga. This was an immediate success, reducing the 14-percent emulsified oil to less than 2 percent at a rate of 1,000 bbl per day.

These early devices were necessarily open-tank arrangements, and the largest application was for the recovery of accumulated volumes of waste oil. Attention was given to the value of conserving the lighter volatiles of the oil, and 1918 developments of Ford W. Harris (Fig. 93) were added which provided a closed unit to allow treating under pressure. These units came into general installation in 1922.

The design evolution of equipment depends upon immediate problems. Because the California fields and operations were relatively concentrated geographically, centralized storage and treating facilities were predominant, allowing treating to be a batch operation. Electrical dehydration followed that pattern until 1934, when the "flow-line" treater was introduced (Fig. 94). This design provided continuous flow from the well through the electrical dehydrator and the treated oil directly to "dry" stock storage.

ACKNOWLEDGMENT

The help and cooperation of many individuals are responsible for making it possible to write this chapter. More than 100 people in oil companies and in service and supply companies have contributed information which would not otherwise have been available for inclusion here.

A special acknowledgment should go to Paul H. Jamison of Kobe, Inc., who has been responsible for the planning and most of the detail work on this chapter.

Joseph Zaba wrote the entire section "Engineering Studies of Pumping-equipment Design Problems", in addition to contributing much of the material included in "Beam Units".

S. S. (Pete) Parker of the National Tank Company wrote the section on "Lease Facilities", and D. R. Dale made major contributions to the section on "Sucker Rods".

Kenton Chickering of Oil Well Supply Div., U. S. Steel Corp., loaned rare and valuable catalogs for reproductions and developed important information from old files of his company.

Roy A. Dunbar made his file available to the author and supplied information on and photographs of the Hubbard long-stroke units.

Taylor Milton furnished much of the data on modern gas-lift equipment.

Lester C. Uren provided a number of illustrations and his suggestions were very helpful.

J. R. Mahan and John Spaulding of The National Supply Company supplied important information and photographs for illustrations.

Thanks are also due John Suman, Carl Reistle, D. V. Carter, C. V. Millikan, E. L. Estabrook, and others for their suggestions and corrections.

REFERENCES

[1]Greene, A. M. Jr: *Pumping Machinery,* John Wiley & Sons, Inc., New York.

[2]Eskew, G. L: *Salt, The Fifth Element,* cites well drilled in Paris, France—39 in. in diameter, 1,798 ft deep, completed in 1832.

[3]Giddens, Paul H: *Pennsylvania Petroleum 1750-1872,* Pennsylvania Historical and Museum Commission, 1947.

[4]Henry, J. T: *The Early and Late History of Petroleum,* Jas. B. Rogers Co., Philadelphia, 1873.

[5]Cornelius, Robert: Patent No. 53,117 issued March 13, 1866.

[6]Early, S. H: Patent No. 53,128 issued March 13, 1866.

[7]*The Derrick's Hand Book of Petroleum,* Derrick Publishing Company, Oil City, Pa. Vol. I, period from 1859-1898, published in 1898; Vol. II, period from 1899-1900, published in 1900. (A complete chronological and statistical review of petroleum developments from 1859 to 1900.)

[8]*Oil Well Supply Co. Catalog,* 1884.

[9]*Oil Well Supply Co. Catalog,* 1892.

[10]Chickering, Kenton: Personal communication.

[11]Sands, Louis C: Oil Field Development and Petroleum Production, *A Handbook of the Petroleum Industry,* edited by Dr. David Talbot Day, John Wiley & Sons, Inc., New York, 1922.

[12]Hager, Dorsey: *Oil Field Practice,* McGraw-Hill Book Co., Inc., New York, 1921.

[13]Kraus, Edgar: MER—A History, *API Drilling and Production Practice,* 108 (1947).

[14]Temple, C. V: Personal communication.

[15]Wallace, J. H., Jr: Pumping, *Petroleum Engineering Handbook,* July 15, 1930, 1st Edn.

[16]Price List issued by Eaton & Cole, Oil City, Pa., Nov. 1, 1872.

[17]Lovegrove, T. J: Patent No. 51,602, issued Dec. 19, 1865.

[18]Boeklen, Reinhold: Patent No. 51,007, issued Nov. 21, 1865.

[19]Cornelius, Robert: Patent No. 54,300, issued May 1, 1866.

[20]Crabtree, O. H: Patent No. 2,580,660, issued Jan. 1, 1952.

[21]McGowan, T. J: Patent No. 36,844, issued Nov. 4, 1862.

[22]Davis, J. H: Patent No. 55,626, issued June 19, 1866.

[23]Conrader, Rudolph: Patent No. 1,041,596, issued Oct. 12, 1912.

[24]Ballard, C. D: Patent No. 840,286, issued Jan. 1, 1907.

[25]Nolan, H. L: Patent No. 1,402,950, issued Jan. 10, 1922.

[26]Vroman, J. C: Patent No. 2,394,123, issued Feb. 5, 1946.

[27]Adams, J. Q: Patent No. 182,143, issued Sept. 12, 1876.

[28]Black, W. P: Patent No. 214,751, issued April 29, 1879.

[29]Noyes, W. H: Patent No. 65,419, issued June 4, 1867.

[30]Garbutt, F. A: Patent No. 586,707, issued July 20, 1897.

[31]*Oil Well Supply Co. Catalog*, 1911.

[32]McKissick, W. H: Patent No. 1,372,031, issued March 22, 1921.

[33]Smoot, R. T: Patent No. 2,231,820, issued Feb. 11, 1941.

[34]Camp, Herman: Patent No. 111,316, issued Jan. 31, 1871.

[35]Sparks, John: Patent No. 118,496, issued Aug. 29, 1871.

[36]Perkins, Nelson: Patent No. 374,995, issued Dec. 20, 1887.

[37]Horsley, James: Patent No. 710,778, issued Oct. 7, 1902.

[38]Willard, A. G: Patent No. 885,899, issued April 28, 1908.

[39]Wilson, E. C: Patent No. 1,513,146, issued Oct. 28, 1924.

[40]Hoferer, D. W: Patent No. 2,206,461, issued July 2, 1940.

[41]Snow, W. B: Patent No. 60,586, issued Dec. 18, 1866.

[42]Merrill, G. C. and Ulter, C. C: Patent No. 197,284, issued Nov. 20, 1877.

[43]Branham, R: Patent No. 461,417, issued Oct. 20, 1891.

[44]Thompson, R. D. and Penrod, John: Patent No. 1,479,208, issued Jan. 1, 1924.

[45]*Oil Well Supply Co. Catalog*, 1900.

[46]Burgess, Lysle P: Personal communication.

[47]Daniels, Dan, and Burgess, Lysle P: Patent No. 1,039,496, issued Sept. 24, 1912.

[48]Hahn, John: Patent No. 993,520, issued May 30, 1911.

[49]Hardison, E. A; Gunn, R. W; and Thompson, W. A. S: Patent No. 1,064,071, issued June 10, 1913.

[50]Scharpenberg, C. C. and Gates, L. G: Patent No. 1,504,081, issued Aug. 5, 1924.

[51]Sargent, S. B., Jr: Patent No. 1,702,619, issued Feb. 19, 1929.

[52]Stevenson, E. E: Patent No. 2,787,964, issued April 9, 1957.

[53]Stevenson, E. E: Patent No. 1,992,402, issued Feb. 26, 1935.

[54]McMakin, R. B: Patent No. 867,402, issued Oct. 1, 1907.

[55]Root, J. B: Patent No. 47,224, issued April 11, 1865; Patent No. RE 5,525, issued Aug. 5, 1873.

[56]Mayhen, Theophilus: Patent No. 52,364, issued Jan. 30, 1866.

[57]Devirs, J. H. and Gravatt, Daniel: Patent No. 90,157, issued May 1869.

[58]Carll, J. F: Patent No. 138,477, issued May 6, 1873.

[59]Whipple, J. T: Patent No. 74,738, issued Feb. 18, 1868; Patent No. RE 6,477, issued June 1, 1875.

[60]Wright, W. J: Patent No. 575,498, issued Jan. 19, 1897.

[61]Springer, W. A: Patent No. 618,623, issued Jan. 31, 1899.

[62]Gahagan, A. B: Patent No. 715,253, issued Dec, 9, 1902.

[63]O'Bannon, W. A: Patent No. 1,962,998, issued June 12, 1934.

[64]Warner, W. W: Patent No. 1,466,685, issued Sept. 4, 1923.

[65]Ellis, W. E: Patent No. 1,476,444, issued Dec. 4, 1923.

[66]Ellis, W. E: Patent No. 1,513,699, issued Oct. 28, 1924.

[67]Robb, W. B. and Hunter, Ava: Patent No. 1,516,470, issued Nov. 18, 1924.

[68]O'Bannon, W. A: Patent No. 1,559,766, issued Nov. 3, 1925.

[69]Yerkes, J. A. and Lemmon, R. H: Patent No. 1,877,112, issued Sept. 13, 1932.

[70]O'Bannon, W. A: Patent No. 1,966,994, issued July 17, 1934.

[71]Hoferer, D. W: Patent No. 2,135,076, issued Nov. 1, 1938.

[72]Hoferer, D. W: Patent No. 2,137,403, issued Nov. 22, 1938.

[73]Adams, E. T: Patent No. 1,545,474, and 1,545,475, issued July 14, 1925.

[74]Adams, E. T. and Reilly, J. B: Patent No. 1,549,175, issued Aug. 11, 1925.

[75]Green, H. M: Patent No. 1,546,891, issued July 21, 1925.

[76]Winsor, I. B: Patent No. 1,621,046, issued March 15, 1927.

[77]Patterson, E. W: Patent No. 1,665,473, issued April 10, 1928.

[78]Peters, C. M: Patent No. 2,074,486, issued March 23, 1937.

[79]O'Leary, C. M: Patent No. 2,057,584, issued Oct. 13, 1936.

[80]Nicholson, John: Patent No. 61,447, issued Jan. 22, 1867.

[81]Clark, O. L: Patent No. 739,831, issued Sept. 29, 1903.

[82]Hahn, John: Patent No. 1,045,282, issued Nov. 26, 1912.

[83]Black, W. G. and Segelhorst, A. L: Patent No. 1,219,799, issued March 20, 1917.

[84]Ligon, A. L: Patent No. 1,120,826, issued Dec. 15, 1914.

[85]Gunn, R. W. and Thompson, W. A. S: Patent No. 1,783,615, issued Dec. 2, 1930.

[86]Ostrom, E. W. and Williams, G. H: Patent No. 2,088,971, issued Aug. 3, 1937.

[87]Derby, Earle: Patent No. 1,578,720, issued March 30, 1926.

[88]Neilsen, K. P. and Byers, D. E: Patent No. 1,717,619, issued June 18, 1929.

[89]Kelly, Kork: Patent No. 2,528,833, issued Nov. 7, 1950.

[90]Hall, S. N: Patent No. 780,993, issued Jan. 31, 1905.

[91]Stroup, E. W: Patent No. 818,001, issued April 17, 1906.

[92]Ritchey, R. C: Patent No. 2,690,134, issued Sept. 28, 1954.

[93]Duncan, C. H: Patent No. 89,134, issued April 20, 1869.

[94]Bridwell, C. E: Patent No. 2,304,237, issued March 31, 1942.

[95]Penrod, J. and Thompson, R. D: Patent No. 1,425,276, issued Aug. 8, 1922.

[96]Mullins, E. J: Patent No. 2,669,190, issued Feb. 16, 1954.

[97]Scott, B. H: Patent No. 1,900,588, issued March 7, 1933.

[98]Behnke, G. E: Patent No. 2,039,621, issued May 5, 1936.

[99]Hall, J. E: Patent No. 2,138,002, issued Nov. 29, 1938.

[100]Collins, H. D: Patent No. 2,174, 121, issued Sept. 26, 1939.

[101]Lubinski, Arthur and Blenkarn, K. A: Buckling of Tubing in Pumping Wells, Its Effects and Means for Controlling It, *Trans. Am. Inst. Mining Met. Engrs. (Petroleum Development and Technology)*, **210**, 73 (1957).

[102]Patterson, E. W: Patent No. 1,779,557, issued Oct. 28, 1930.

[103]Mock, T. M: Patent No. 2,615,410, issued Oct. 28, 1952.

[104]Sutton, W. J: Patent No. 2,684,638 and 2,684,639, issued July 27, 1954.

[105]Hall, J. E: Patent No. 2,191,380, issued Feb. 20, 1940.

[106]Morton, M. J: Patent No. 985,052, issued Feb. 21, 1911.

[107]Lotta, M. N: Patent No. 1,309,738, issued July 15, 1919.

[108]Boden, C. S: Patent No. 1,614,865, issued Jan. 18, 1927.

[109]Graser, F. A: Circulating Plunger Pumps, *Summary of Operations, California Oil Fields*, California State Mining Bureau, Report of Oil & Gas Supervisor, **11 [11]**, May (1926).

[110]Upton, C. G. and Barnett, P. B: Patent No. 2,178,822, issued Nov. 7, 1939.

[111]Barnett, P. B. and Upton, C. G: Patent No. 2,180,451, issued Nov. 21, 1939.

[112]Chenault, R. L: Patent No. 2,325,661, issued Aug. 2, 1943.

[113]Schmidt, B. F: Patent No. 2,814,994, issued Dec. 3, 1957.

[114]Brennan, J. R: Patent No. 2,821,933, issued Feb. 4, 1958.

[115]Williams, C. M: Patent No. 2,272,388, issued Feb. 10, 1942; Patent No. RE 22,384, issued Oct. 12, 1942.

[116]Allen, R. N: Patent No. 52,355, issued Jan. 30, 1866.

[117]Parker, H. D: Patent No. 52,793, issued Feb. 20, 1866.

[118]Jones, Daniel: Patent No. 119,232, issued Sept. 26, 1871.

[119]Allison, W. C: Patent No. 240,877, issued May 3, 1881.

[120]Black, R. H: Patent No. 308,233, issued Nov. 18, 1884.

Davidson, J. M: Patent No. 324,922, issued Aug. 25, 1885.

Black, R. H: Patent No. 334,929, issued Jan. 26, 1886.

Whitmore, S. K: Patent No. 338,653, issued March 23, 1886.

[121]Dale, D. R: Personal communication.

[122]Butler, William L: Personal communication.

[123]Salberg, C. O: Patent No. 1,246,329, issued Nov. 13, 1917.

[124]Rigby, C. F: Patent No. 1,357,475, issued Nov. 2, 1920.

[125]Nevins, F. M: Patent No. 1,599,398, issued Sept. 7, 1926.

[126]Watts, E. V: Patent No. 2,198,957, issued April 30, 1940.

[127]Zaba, Joseph: From manuscript.

[128]Dale, D. R: Personal communication.

[129]Wescott, Blaine B. and Bowers, C. N: Economical Selection of Sucker Rods, *Trans. Am. Inst. Mining Met. Engrs. (Petroleum Development and Technology)*, **114,** 177 (1935).

[130]Browne, V. B: Patent No. 1,947,969, issued Feb. 20, 1934.

[131]Rossmann, P. F: Patent No. 2,453,079, issued Nov. 2, 1948.

[132]Tripplehorn, D. R: Patent No. 2,733,768, issued Feb. 7, 1956.

[133]Gunn, R. W. and Thompson, W. A. S: Patent No. 1,326,259, issued Dec. 30, 1919.

Miller, N. O: Patent No. 1,720,049, issued July 9, 1929.

[134]Fitzpatrick, J. J: Patent No. 1,995,095, issued March 19, 1935.

[135]Giles, W. D: Patent No. 1,508,845, issued Sept. 16, 1924.

[136]Bodine, A. G., Jr: Patent No. 2,725,264, issued Nov. 29, 1955.

[137]Loop, Leonard: Patent No. 1,507,972, issued Sept. 9, 1924.

O'Leary, C. M: Patent No. 2,320,646, issued Jan. 1, 1943.

Martin, H. W: Patent No. 2,578,818, issued Dec. 18, 1951.

[138]Leverich, L. B: Patent No. 1,765,279, issued June 17, 1930.

McFarlane, John H: Patent No. 2,400,941, issued May 28, 1946.

[139]Eaton, J. F. and Collins, H. D: Patent No. 2,212,153, issued Aug. 20, 1940.

[140]Korner, T: Patent No. 287,444, issued Oct. 30, 1883.

Black, R. H: Patent No. 308,233, issued Nov. 18, 1884.

Davidson, J. M: Patent No. 324,922, issued Aug. 25, 1885.

[141]Chadwick, Roy: Patent No. 851,118, issued April 23, 1907.

[142]Smith, R. A: Patent No. 2,652,231, issued Sept. 15, 1953.

[143]Nickerson, A. E. and Streeter, L. C: Patent No. RE 6,486, issued June 15, 1875.

[144]Klein, John S: Patent No. 551,537, issued Dec. 25, 1894.

[145]Coffman, J. P: Patent No. 1,146,404, issued July 13, 1915.

[146]Brannon, R: Patent No. 1,601,847, issued Oct. 5, 1926.

[147]Stevenson, E. E: Patent No. 1,703,214, issued Feb. 26, 1929.

[148]Borough, W. L: Patent No. 1,854,290, issued April 19, 1932.

[149]Watson, T. F: Patent No. 1,860,757, issued May 3, 1932.

[150]Stickel, R. E: Patent No. 1,890,135, issued Dec. 6, 1932.

[151]Eurit, Carl: Patent No. 1,903,034, issued March 28, 1933.

[152]Gourley, W. J. and Barney, F. H: Patent No. 2,001,247, issued May 14, 1935.

[153]Porter, A. N: Patent No. 2,054,655, issued Sept. 7, 1937.

Patent No. 2,218,343, issued Oct. 15, 1940.

[154]Hamaker, R. G: Patent No. 1,530,890, issued March 24, 1925.

[155]Ratigan, J. B: Patent No. 1,798,557, issued March 31, 1931.

[156]Trout, W. C: Patent No. 1,834,438, issued Dec. 1, 1931.

[157]Bullum, S: Patent No. 1,994,749, issued March 19, 1935.

[158]Winland, H. A: Patent No. 2,005,283, issued June 18, 1935.

[159]Maier, A. R: Patent No. 2,107,488, issued Feb. 8, 1938.

[160]Athy, C. R: Patent No. 2,175,589, issued Oct. 10, 1939.

[161]Comstock, G. S: Patent No. 2,287,604, issued June 23, 1942.

[162]Clarkson, William, Jr: Patent No. 1,657,150, issued Jan. 24, 1928.

[163]Corey, W. G: Patent No. 1,948,288, issued Feb. 20, 1934.

[164]Jones, W. M: Patent No. 1,951,613, issued March 20, 1934.

[165]Slonneger, J. C: Patent No. 2,023,554, issued Dec. 10, 1935.

[166]Porter, A. N: Patent No. 2,198,348, issued April 23, 1940.

[167]Trout, W. C: Patent No. 1,895,181, issued Jan. 24, 1933.

[168]Maier, A. R: Patent No. 2,153,094, issued April 4, 1939.

[169]Baker, R. C: Patent No. 1,795,922, issued March 10, 1931.

[170]McCrosky, Fred: Patent No. 1,891,552, issued Dec. 20, 1932.

[171]Livingston, C. M: Patent No. 1,979,803, issued Nov. 6, 1934.

[172]Picard, J. B: Patent No. 2,047,490, issued July 14, 1936.

[173]Graham, Fred: Patent No. 2,048,119, issued July 21, 1936.

[174]Humphrey, G. T: Patent No. 2,111,591, issued March 22, 1938.

[175]Porter, A. N: Patent No. 2,113,281, issued April 5, 1938.

[176]Patent No. 2,115,872, issued May 3, 1938.

[177]Hopkins, C. G: Patent No. 2,130,184, issued Sept. 13, 1938.

[178]Porter, A. N: Patent No. 2,157,628, issued May 9, 1939.

[179]Holzer, H. A: Patent No. 2,203,148, issued June 4, 1940.

[180]Willrich, E. G: Patent No. 1,666,227, issued April 17, 1928.

[181]Reschke, W. F: Patent No. 1,782,697, issued Nov. 25, 1930.

[182]Patterson, E. W: Patent No. 2,200,292, issued May 14, 1940.

[183]Wineman, W. H: Patent No. 2,408,014, issued Sept. 24, 1946.

[184]Hall, C. W: Patent No. 2,144,149, issued Jan. 17, 1939.

[185]Crites, W. J: Patent No. 2,268,701, issued Jan. 6, 1942.

[186]Bennett, E. O: Patent No. 2,292,349, issued Aug. 11, 1942.

[187]Hartgering, J. M. and Perkins, Charles M: Patent No. 2,274,601, issued Feb. 24, 1942.

[188]Raulerson, H. H: Patent No 2,274,937, issued March 3, 1942.

[189]Phipps, J. T: Patent No. 2,308,823, issued Jan. 19, 1943.

[190]O'Leary; C. M: Patent No. 2,269,729, issued Jan. 13, 1942.
Patent No. 2,294,093, issued Aug. 25, 1942.
Patent No. 2,325,874, issued Dec. 14, 1943.

[191]Smith, E. D., et al: Patent No. 1,781,347, issued Nov. 11, 1930.

[192]Braly, T. E: Patent No. 1,773,298, issued Aug. 19, 1930.

[193]Kliewer, E. A: Patent No. 2,084,645, issued June 22, 1937.

[194]Whittlesey, R. E: Patent No. 2,170,313, issued Aug. 22, 1939.

[195]Thompson, H. A: Patent No. 2,148,516, issued Feb. 28, 1939.

[196]Lyne, J. A: Patent No. 2,265,379, issued Dec. 9, 1941.

[197]Marsh, Hallan N: Deep-well Pumping in California, *Trans. Am. Inst. Mining Met. Engrs. (Petroleum Development and Technology)*, 75 (1929).

[198]Heeter, C. M: Patent No. 1,240,715, issued Sept. 18, 1917.

[199]Suman, J. R: Patent No. 1,428,866, issued Sept. 12, 1922.

[200]George, H. C: Surface Machinery and Methods for Oil-Well Pumping, *U. S. Bur. Mines Bull. 244* (1925).

[201]Trout, W. W: Personal communication; Lufkin Foundry and Machine Co.
Winfrey, J. W: Personal communication; Humble Oil & Refining Co.

[202]Camden, G. B: Personal communication; Parkersburg Rig and Reel Co.

[203]Ashton, A. A: Personal communication; Emsco Manufacturing Co.

[204]Reid, G. L: Personal communication; Bethlehem Supply Co.

[205]Mahan, J. R: Personal communication; The National Supply Co.

[206]Anderson, C. A: Personal communication; Parkersburg Rig and Reel Co.

[207]Robson, F. W: Personal communication; The Happy Co.

[208]Haury, P. S: Midcontinent Development and Production Practices, *Petroleum Engineering Handbook*, Palmer Publications, 1931, 2nd Edn.

[209]Kirwan, M. J. and Covell, K. A: Pumping Deep Wells in the Seminole Field, Oklahoma, *Trans Am. Inst. Mining Met. Engrs. (Petroleum Development and Technology)*, 50 (1929).

[210]Patterson, E. W: Personal communication; E. W. Patterson Products.

[211]Corey, William G: Personal communication; Lacy Oil Tool Co.

[212]Patterson, E. W: Patent No. 2,169,815, issued Aug. 15, 1939.
Patent No. 2,456,531, issued Dec. 14, 1948.
Patent No. 2,459,334, issued Jan. 18, 1949.

[213]Penick, K. T: Patent No. 2,291,499, issued July 28, 1942.

[214]Saxe, W. E: Patent No. 2,184,436, issued Dec. 26, 1939.

[215]Carter, D. V: Patent No. 2,310,393, issued Feb. 9, 1943.

[216]Thomas, M. Bowman: Selection and Rating of Oil Well Pumping Units, *Proc. Am. Pet. Inst. (Prod. Bul. 210)*, 73 (1932).

[217]Nickerson, A. E. and Streeter, L. C: Patent No. 162,406, issued April 20, 1875.

[218]Yates, E. D: Patent No. 226,948, issued April 27, 1880.

[219]Allen, George: Patent No. 313,907, issued March 17, 1885.

[220]Allen, George: Patent No. 326,008, issued Sept. 8, 1885.

[221]Allen, George: Patent No. 328,099, issued Oct. 13, 1885.

[222]Allen, George: Patent No. 332,318, issued Dec. 15, 1885.

[223]Allen, George, Patent No. 616,206, issued Dec. 3, 1898.

[224]Allen, George, Patent No. 612,184, issued Oct. 11, 1898.

[225]Grimes, G. W: Patent No. 562,602, issued June 23, 1896.

[226]Grimes, G. W: Patent No. 587,525, issued Aug. 3, 1897.

[227]Maher, J. N: Patent No. 575,122, issued Jan. 12, 1897.

[228]Kivis, J. J: Patent No. 591,283, issued Oct. 5, 1897.

[229]Sutton, C. E: Patent No. 627,604, issued June 27, 1899.

[230]Yates, E. D: Patent No. 595,167, issued Dec. 7, 1897.

[231]Yates, E. D: Patent No. 635,630, issued Oct. 24, 1899.

[232]Chickering, Kenton: Patent No. 607,616, issued July 19, 1898.

[233]Corey, W. G: Patent No. 1,495,250, issued May 27, 1924.

[234]Burnham, L. F. et al: Patent No. 1,731,885, issued Oct. 15, 1929.

[235]Anderson, C. M: Patent No. 1,959,806, issued May 22, 1934.

[236]Mahan, J. R. and Picard, J. B: Patent No. 2,003,601, issued June 14, 1935.

[237]Plockrass, W. F: Patent No. 189,955, issued April 1877.

[238]Fell, Thomas: Patent No. 47,289, issued April 18, 1865.

[239]Lytle, M: Patent No. 146,600, issued Jan. 20, 1874.

[240]Barclay, W. P: Patent No. 197,239, issued Nov. 20, 1877.
Patent No. 208,704, issued Oct. 8, 1878.
Patent No. 211,125, issued Jan. 7, 1879.

[241]Thayer, P. J. and Seymour, M. J: Patent No. 245,101, issued Aug. 2, 1881.

[242]Connor, S. B. et al: Patent No. 243,852, issued July 5, 1881.

[243]Worthington, C. C: Patent No. 354,030, issued Dec. 7, 1886.

[244]Klein, John S: Patent No. 551,537, issued Dec. 25, 1894.

[245]Quick, M. W: Patent No. 595,206, issued Dec. 7, 1897.

[246] Quick, M. W: Patent No. 643,156, issued Feb. 13, 1900.

[247]Steiner, J. G: Patent No. 731,241, issued June 16, 1903.

[248]Hoffman, R. J. and Hollingshead, E. H: Patent No. 773,501, issued Oct. 25, 1904.

[249]Davis, Frank W. and King, Albert W: Patent No. 805,267, issued Nov. 21, 1905.

[250]Quick, M. W: Patent No. 828,680, issued Oct. 14, 1906.

[251]Segelhorst, A. L: Patent No. 1,596,630, issued Aug. 17, 1926.

[252]Turman, A. R: Personal communication on early developments of Standard Oil Company of California.

[253]Cook, A. D: and Willers, G. E: Patent No. 460,562, issued Oct. 6, 1891.

[254]Wood, H. L: *Oil Age*, Feb. (1926).

[255]Clapp, W. H: Patent No. 1,607,239, issued Nov. 16, 1926.

[256]Patterson, E. W: Patent No. 1,842,628, issued Jan. 26, 1932.

[257]Musser, E. H: Long-stroke Equipment, *Summary of Operations, California Oil Fields,* **11 [11]** issued by California State Mining Bureau, May 1926.

[258]Musser, E. H: Improved Pumping Equipment for Oil Wells, *Summary of Operations, California Oil Fields*, California State Mining Bureau, Report of Oil & Gas Supervisor, **11 [11],** May (1926).

[259]Hubbard, W. E: Patent No. 1,465,671, issued Aug. 21, 1923.
Patent No. 1,619,474 and 1,619,475, issued March 1, 1927.
Patent No. 1,879,262, issued Sept. 27, 1932.
Patent No. 2,277,761, issued March 31, 1942.

[260]Suter, John H: Patent No. 2,185,448, issued Jan. 2, 1940.

[261]Brett, H. A: *Petroleum World*, March (1932).

[262]Corey, W. G. and Trow, Charles A: Patent No. 1,666,255, issued April 17, 1928.

[263]Salentine, H. M: Patent No. 2,073,809, issued March 16, 1937.
Patent No. 2,147,924 issued Feb. 21, 1939.
Patent No. 2,157,219, issued May 9, 1939.

[264]Vickers: Patent No. 2,367,248, issued Jan. 16, 1945.

[265]Twyman, L. R: Moser, J. R; and Rose, H. E: Patent No. 2,347,301 and 2,347,302, issued April 25, 1944.

[266]Wineman, W. H: Patent No. 2,004,146, issued June 11, 1935.
Patent No. 2,103,308, 2,103,964, and 2,103,965, issued Dec. 28, 1937.
Patent No. 2,156,326, issued May 2, 1939.
Patent No. 2,184,932, issued Dec. 26, 1939.
Patent No. 2,195,206 and 2,195,207, issued March 26, 1940.
Patent No. 2,378,965, issued June 26, 1945.

[267]Cornelius, P. D: Patent No. 2,195,208, issued March 26, 1940.

[268]Covell, K. A: Personal communication.

[269]Kyle, S. C: Patent No. 2,325,138, issued July 27, 1943.
Patent No. 2,470,252, issued May 11, 1949.

[270]White, Morgan: Patent No. 2,562,837, issued July 31, 1951.
Patent No. 2,575,241, issued Nov. 13, 1951.
Patent No. 2,617,256, issued Nov. 11, 1952.

[271]Rued, F. H: Patent No. 2,481,623, issued Sept. 13, 1949.

[272]Billings, E. T. and Garrison, T. E: Patent No. 2,729,942, issued Jan. 10, 1956.

[273]Noll, P. E: Patent No. 2,572,748, issued Oct. 23, 1951.

[274]Noll, V. R: Patent No. 2,574,751, issued Nov. 23, 1951.

[275]Aller, T. D. and Noll, P. E: Patent No. 2,645,899, issued July 21, 1953.

[276]Lippert, S: Patent No. 853,180, issued May 7, 1907.

[277]Coffman, J. P: Patent No. 1,146,404, issued July 13, 1915.

[278]Smith, E. D. et al: Patent No. 1,781,347, issued Nov. 11, 1930.

[279]Mills, Kenneth N: Factors Influencing Well Loads Combined in a New Formula, *Petroleum Engr.*, April (1939).

[280]Kendrick, J. F. and Cornelius, P. D: The Sucker-rod Pump as a Problem in Elasticity, *Trans. Am. Inst. Mining Met. Engrs. (Petroleum Development and Technology)*, **123,** 15 (1937) (reprint, p. 193).

[281]Slonneger, J. C: Vibration Problems in Oil Wells, *API Drilling and Production Practice,* 179 (1937).

[282]Dralle, H. E. and Lamberger, E. H: Oil-well Tests Suggest New Rating Standards, *API Drilling and Production Practice,* 115 (1941).

[283]Langer, B. F. and Lamberger, E. H: Calculation of Load and Stroke in Oil Well Pumping Rods, paper presented at ASME meeting, June (1942).

[284]Johnson, D. O: Personal communication, Johnson-Fagg Engineering Co.

[285]Lake, F. W. and Brett, H. A: Sucker-rod Strains and Stresses, *Petroleum Development and Technology in 1927,* 337, American Institute of Mining and Metallurgical Engineers, Inc., New York, 1928.

[286]Marsh, Hallan N. and Watts, E. V: Practical Dynamometer Tests, *API Drilling and Production Practice,* 162 (1938).

[287]Hosford, Eugene and Kemler, Emory: Typical Dynamometer Cards and Their Application, *API Drilling and Production Practice,* 81 (1939).

[288]Gilbert, W. E: An Oil-well Pump Dynagraph, *API Drilling and Production Practice,* 94 (1936).

[289]Dralle, H. E: The Mechanics of Oil-well Pumping, *Proc. Am. Pet. Inst. (Prod. Bul. 206),* 38 (1930).

[290]Shutts, W. C. and Thomas, M. Bowman: Efficient Operation of Pumping Rigs, *Proc. Am. Pet. Inst. (Prod. Bul. 207),* 30 (1931).

[291]Hopper, J. Bayo: Efficiency and Load Test on Well Pumping Units, *Petroleum Engr.,* Jan. (1940).

[292]Mills, Kenneth N: Proper Installation of Pumping Unit Essential to Satisfactory Operation, *Petroleum Engr.,* Jan. (1940).

[293]Kemler, Emory N: Some Kinematic Aspects of Pumping Unit Mechanisms, paper presented at ASME Petroleum Division, Sept. 1951.

[294]Day, P. C: Capacities and Loads of Gear Units on Pumping Wells, *Oil Weekly,* Sept. (1933).

[295]Kemler, Emory N: Factors Influencing the Application of Pumping Units, *API Drilling and Production Practice,* 183 (1938).

[296]Kelly, Harold S; Halderson, M. H; Witherspoon, P. A; and Calvert, E. S: Factors Affecting the Accuracy of Peak Torque Calculations Using Dynamometer Cards, *API Drilling and Production Practice,* 160 (1948).

[297]Kemler, Emory N: Fundamentals of Counterbalancing, *Petroleum Engr.,* May (1936).

[298]Briggs, Frank: Modern Well Studies, *Oil Weekly,* Oct. 28 (1940).

[299]Kemler, Emory N: Counterbalancing of Oil-well Pumping Machines, *API Drilling and Production Practice,* 87 (1943).

[300]Mills, Kenneth N: Counterbalancing and Determining Peak Torque on Pumping Units, *World Oil,* Nov. (1948).

[301]Johnson, D. O: Counterbalancing of Beam Pumping Units, *API Drilling and Production Practice,* 234 (1951).

[302]Kemler, Emory N: Proper Counterbalancing an Equipment Conservation Measure, *Oil Weekly,* Jan. 11 (1943).

[303]Kemler, Emory N: Calculation of Actual and Effective Counterbalance, *Oil Weekly,* Feb. 13 (1943).

[304]Johnson, D. O: Taking the Pulse of the Pumping Well, *Oil Weekly,* 19, March 25 (1940); *Oil Gas J.,* 46, March 21 (1940); abstracted in *API Drilling and Production Practice,* 258 (1940).

[305]Laudermilk, J. I: Graphical Mechanics of Counterbalancing Individual Well Pumping Units, *Oil Weekly,* Sept. 28 (1942).

[306]Kemler, Emory N: Sucker Rods, Some Problems Involved in Their Application, *International Oil*, Jan. (1941).

[307]Kemler, Emory N: The Design of Sucker Rod Strings from Dynamometer Cards, *Petroleum Engr.*, Jan.-March (1936).

[308]Sargent, S. B., Jr: Capacity Pumping of Oil Wells, *API Drilling and Production Practice*, 148 (1937).

[309]Briggs, Frank: Modern Well Studies, *Oil Weekly*, Oct. 7, (1940).

[310]Zur Horst, C. G. and Wescott, Blaine B: Sucker Rods—Why They Break, *Petroleum Engr.*, Nov. (1931).

[311]Wescott, Blaine B. and Bowers, C. N: Corrosion Fatigue and Sucker-rod Failures, *Proc. Am. Pet. Inst. (Prod. Bul. 212)*, 29 (1933).

[312]*Loc. Cit*: Wescott, Blaine B. and Bowers, C. Norman, ref. 129.

[313]Dale, D. R. and Johnson, D. O: Laboratory and Field Endurance Values of Sucker-rod Materials, *API Drilling and Production Practice*, 209 (1940).

[314]Uren, Lester C: Problems of Pumping Deep Wells, *Petroleum Development and Technology in 1925*, 130, American Institute of Mining and Metallurgical Engineers, Inc., New York, 1926.

[315]Swigart, T. E: Discussion of paper by Frank E. O'Neill, "Improved Production Methods in the California Fields," *Petroleum Development and Technology in 1925*, 77, American Institute of Mining and Metallurigical Engineers, Inc., New York, 1926.

[316]Robinson, Bruce H: Economics of Pumping, *API Drilling and Production Practice*, 91 (1935).

[317]Coberly, C. J: Problems of Deep Well Pumping, paper presented at ASME meeting, March 1938.

[318]Kemler, Emory N: Selection of Pump Size for Optimum Sucker-rod Pumping Conditions, *Oil Weekly*, April 28 (1941).

[319]Johnson, D. O: Analysis of Optimum Sucker Rod Pumping, paper presented at meeting of AIME Petroleum Division, May 1943.

[320]Uren, Lester C. and Sargent, S. B., Jr: The Effect of Submergence on Oil-well Pump Efficiency, *API Production Bulletin 110*.

[321]Hoffman, Houston: Influence of Submergence and Fluid Level on Pumping Wells, *Oil Weekly*, Jan. 20, (1940).

[322]Tallant, E. P: Report on API Pump-performance Experiment, *API Drilling and Production Practice*, 217 (1938).

[323]Stearns, Glenn M: An Experimental Investigation of the Volumetric Efficiency of Sucker-rod Pumps, *API Drilling and Production Practice*, 108 (1943).

[324]Stearns, Glenn M: An Evaluation of the Rate of Slippage of Oil Past Oil-well Pump Plungers, *API Drilling and Production Practice*, 25 (1944).

[325]Coberly, C. J: Discussion of paper by Hallan N. Marsh,"High Volumetric Efficiency of Oil-well Pumping and Its Practical Results," *Proc. Am. Pet. Inst. (Prod. Bul. 207)*, 47 (1931).

[326]Rieniets, Robert William: Plunger Travel of Oil-well Pumps, *API Drilling and Production Practice*, 159 (1937).

[327]Marsh, Hallan N: High Volumetric Efficiency of Oil-well Pumping and Its Practical Results, *Proc. Am. Pet. Inst. (Prod. Bul. 270)*, 47 (1931).

[328]Slonneger, J. C: Graphic Methods of Analyzing Dynamometer Cards, *Petroleum Engr.* Sept. (1936).

[329]Kemler, Emory N: Study of Sucker Rods, *International Oil*, April (1941).

[330]Mid-Continent District Study Committee on Artificial Lifting of Deep Wells: Artificial Lifting of Deep Wells, *API Drilling and Production Practice*, 148 (1952).

[331]Lloyd, F. T. (on behalf of the Pacific Coast District Study Committee on Artificial Lifting of Deep Wells): Artificial Lifting of Deep Wells in California, *API Drilling and Production Practice*, 359 (1955).

[332]Bridges, R. E: Back-side Crank Pumping and Catenary Rod Lines, *API Drilling and Production Practice*, 69 (1936).

[333]Slonneger, J. C: Back-crank Problems and Rod-line Pumping, *API Drilling and Production Practice*, 249 (1938).

[334]Mills, Kenneth N: Selection of Back-side Pumping Equipment, *Oil Weekly*, May (1950); also, A Formula for the Peak Torque Imposed on the Driving System by Back-side Pumping, *Proc. Am. Pet. Inst. (Prod. Bul. 226)*, 207 (1940).

[335]Sclater, K. C: A Method of Installing Catenary Pull-rod Lines, *Petroleum Engr.*, Feb. (1940).

[336]Nowels, K. B: Equipment Loads of Bandwheel Powers, paper presented before the Second Pennsylvania Petroleum and Gas Conference, 1932.

[337]Mills, Kenneth N: Analysis of Stresses in Hookoffs for Wells Pumped by Central Powers, *Petroleum Engr.*, Oct. (1938).

[338]Hosford, Eugene: Determining Torque on a Multiple-well Hookup from Dynamometer Card Data, *Proc. Am. Pet. Inst. (Prod. Bul. 224)*, 270 (1939).

[339]Bennett, Van D: Back-side Crank Pumping in Kansas Fields, *Petroleum Engr.*, May (1935).

[340]Altman, Ben: Locating and Counterbalancing Central Pumping Powers Involves Many Variables, *Oil Weekly*, May (1939).

[341]Pirson, Sylvan J: Locating and Counterbalancing Central Pumping Powers, *Oil Weekly*, April 1, (1940).

[342]Weber, George: Improved Pumping Operations in Central Pumping Powers, *Oil Gas J.*, March 14, (1940).

[343]Kemler, Emory N: An Investigation of Experimental Methods of Determining Sucker-rod Loads, *Trans. Am. Inst. Mining Met. Engrs. (Petroleum Development and Technology)*, **118**, 89 (1936) (reprint, p. 87).

[344]Todd, F. C: Design of an Electrical Analog for Sucker-rod Problems, paper presented at the Spring Meeting of the Southwestern District, API Division of Production, Beaumont, Texas, March 1951.

[345]Halderson, M. H: Artificial Brain is Required to Solve the Sucker-rod Pumping Problem, *API Drilling and Production Practice*, 210 (1953).

[346]Halderson, M. H: Personal communication.

[347]Davis and Weidner: An Investigation of the Air-Lift Pump, *Bull. 667*, Univ. of Wisconsin, (1941).

[348]Miller, H. C: Gas-Lift Method of Flowing Oil Wells, *U. S. Bur. Mines Bull. 323*, (1930).

[349]Gunning, T. B: Patent No. 45,153, issued Nov. 22, 1864.

[350]Pohlé, Julius G: Patent No. 487,639, issued Dec. 6, 1890.

[351]Pohlé, Julius G: Patent No. 532,699, issued Jan. 15, 1895. Patent No. 556,436, issued March 17, 1896.

[352]Mowbray, G. M: Patent No. 45,849, issued Jan. 10, 1865.

[353]Royce, C. N: Patent No. 344,137, issued June 22, 1886.

[354]Bacon, J. E: Patent No. 542,620, issued July 16, 1895.

[355]Moore, W: Patent No. 554,076, issued Feb. 4, 1896.

[356]Stephens, L: Patent No. 554,548, issued Feb. 11, 1896.

[357]Titus, S. W: Patent No. 566,102, issued Aug. 18, 1896.

[358]Lockett, A. M: Patent No. 855,518, issued June 4, 1907.

[359]McEvoy, J. M: Patent No. 906,733, issued Dec. 15, 1908.

[360]Conrader, Rudolph: Patent No. 886,312, issued April 28, 1908.

[361]Thayer, W. W: *Petroleum World*, April (1928).

[362]Alten, A. N. and David, O: Patent No. 999,731, issued Aug. 8, 1911.

[363]Stuart, W. E: Patent No. 1,014,422, issued Jan. 9, 1912.

[364]Morrow, W. L: Patent No. 1,084,843, issued Dec. 9, 1913.

[365]Purdy, J. S. L: Patent No. 1,153,253, issued Sept. 14, 1915.

[366]Jones, Philip: Patent No. 1,102,152, issued June 30, 1914.

[367]Greenlee, W. R: Patent No. 1,310,615, issued July 22, 1919.

[368]Chodzko, A. E: Patent No. 1,071,878, issued Sept. 2, 1913.

[369]Butler, C. A: Patent No. 1,175,599, issued March 14, 1916.

[370]Halvorsen, H. B: Patent No. 1,499,315, issued June 24, 1924.

[371]Boynton, Alexander: Patent No. 1,470,053, issued Oct. 9, 1923.

[372]Rogers, E. M: Patent No. 1,537,264, issued May 12, 1925.

[373]Boynton, Alexander: Patent No. 1,686,262, issued Oct. 2, 1928.

[374]Black, L. J: Patent No. 1,723,992, issued Aug. 13, 1929.

[375]Blow, George: Patent No. 1,737,635, issued Dec. 3, 1929.

[376]Millikan, C. V: Personal communication.

[377]Chenault, R. L: Personal communication.

[378]Gracey, H. H: Patent No. 1,579,606, issued April 6, 1926.

[379]Archer, M. T: Patent No. 1,687,317, issued Oct. 9, 1928.

[380]Rubel, A. C: Patent No. 1,740,039, issued Dec. 17, 1929.

[381]Lake, F. W: Patent No. 1,740,101; 1,740,102; 1,740,103; 1,740,104; and 1,740,105, issued Dec. 17, 1929.

[382]Subkow, Philip: Patent No. 1,740,793, issued Dec. 24, 1929.

[383]Millikan, C. V: Production Engineering in 1929, discussion on "Petroleum Engineering Education," *Trans. Am. Inst. Mining Met. Engrs. (Petroleum Development and Technology)*, **86**, 598 (1930).

[384]Versluys, J: Hydraulics in Flowing Wells—Mathematical Development of the Theory of Flowing Oil Wells, *Trans. Am. Inst. Mining Met. Engrs. (Petroleum Development and Technology)*, **86**, 192 (1930).

[385]Uren, L. C; Gregory, P. P; Hancock, R. A; and Feskov, G. V: Flow Resistance of Gas-oil Mixtures through Vertical Pipes, *Trans. Am. Inst. Mining Met. Engrs. (Petroleum Development and Technology)*, **86**, 209 (1930).

[386]Shaw, S. F: Some Observations on Principles Involved in Flowing Oil Wells, *Trans. Am. Inst. Mining Met. Engrs. (Petroleum Development and Technology)*, **86**, 220 (1930).

[387]Versluys, J: Some Principles Governing the Choice of Length and Diameter of Tubing in Oil Wells, *Trans. Am. Inst. Mining Met. Engrs. (Petroleum Development and Technology)*, **92**, 293 (1931).

[388]Moore, T. V. and Wilde, H. D. Jr: Experimental Measurement of Slippage in Flow through Vertical Pipes, *Trans. Am. Inst. Mining Met. Engrs. (Petroleum Development and Technology)*, **92**, 296 (1931).

[389]Hayward, J. T: Discussion of the Merits of Tapered Flow Columns, *Proc. Am. Pet. Inst. (Prod. Bul. 210)*, 67 (1932).

[390]Hawkins, R. R: Flowing Wells with Small Tubing, *Trans. Am. Inst. Mining Met. Engrs. (Petroleum Development and Technology)*, **98**, 306 (1932).

[391]Gosline, J. E: Experiments on the Vertical Flow of Gas-liquid Mixtures in Glass Pipes, *Trans. Am. Inst. Mining Met. Engrs. (Petroleum Development and Technology)*, **118**, 56 (1936) (reprint, p. 54).

[392]Babson, E. C: The Range of Application of Gas-lift Methods, *API Drilling and Production Practice*, 266 (1939).

[393]Tutschulte, A. C: The Performance of Gas Lift through Small Tubing, *API Drilling and Production Practice*, 9 (1945).

[394]Gilbert, W. E: Flowing and Gas-lift Well Performance, *API Drilling and Production Practice*, 126 (1954).

[395]Poettman, F. H. and Carpenter, Paul G: Multiphase Flow of Gas, Oil, and Water through Vertical Flow Strings with Application to the Design of Gas-lift Installations, *API Drilling and Production Practice*, 257 (1952).

[396]Kirkpatrick, C. V: *The Power of Gas*, published by CAMCO, 1954.

[397]Carlisle, C. C: Patent No. 1,719,589, issued July 2, 1929.
Patent No. 1,744,361, issued Jan. 21, 1930.

[398]Miller, F. J: Patent No. 1,865,873, issued July 5, 1932.

[399]Boynton, Alexander: Patent No. 1,747,570; 1,747,571; and 1,747,572, issued Feb. 18, 1930; Patent No. 1,749,124, issued March 4, 1930.

[400]Schabarum, B. R: Patent No. 1,777,680, issued Oct. 7, 1930.

[401]Archer, M. T: Patent No. 1,780,808, issued Nov. 4, 1930.

[402]Price, Frederick: Patent No. 1,793,193, issued Feb. 17, 1931.

[403]Taylor, J. W: Patent No. 1,807,747, issued June 2, 1931.

[404]Bryan, T. E: Patent No. 1,840,694, issued Jan. 12, 1932.

[405]Jordan and Taylor: Patent No. 1,843,276, issued Feb. 2, 1932.

[406]Smallamatic: Patent No. 1,724,853; 1,724,854; 1,724,855; 1,724,856; 1,724,857; and 1,724,858, issued Aug. 13, 1929.

[407]Jordan and Taylor: Patent No. 1,794,427, issued March 3, 1931.
Patent No. 1,789,855 and 1,789,866, issued Jan. 20, 1931.
Patent No. 1,827,091, issued Oct. 13, 1931.

[408]Fletcher, H. W: Patent No. 2,038,426, issued April 21, 1936.
Patent No. 2,057,425, issued Oct. 13, 1926.

[409]Ricker, N. H: Patent No. 1,833,778, issued Nov. 24, 1931.
Patent No. 1,836,873; 1,836,874; and 1,836,875, issued Dec. 15, 1931.
Patent No. 1,970,917, issued April 21, 1934.
Patent No. 2,001,547, issued May 14, 1935.

[410]Grinnell, S. H. and Rubel, A. C: Patent No. 1,852,716 and 1,852,717, issued April 5, 1932. Patent No. 1,910,762, issued May 23, 1933.

[411]Howard, F. A: Patent No. 1,861,013, issued May 31, 1932.

[412]Kuhn, C. S. and Koch, R. L: In-Situ Combustion, *Oil Gas J.*, **52,** Aug. 10 (1953).

[413]Subkow, Philip: Patent No. 1,856,891, issued May 3, 1932.

[414]Subkow, Philip: Patent No. 1,981,217, issued Dec. 4, 1934.

[415]Humason, G. A: Patent No. 1,964,436, issued June 26, 1934.
Patent No. 1,969,174, issued Aug. 7, 1934.

[416]Boynton, Alexander: Patent No. 1,952,581, issued March 27, 1934.

[417]Otis, H. C: Patent No. 2,002,791, issued May 28, 1935.

[418]Taylor, J. W: Patent No. 2,072,435, issued March 2, 1937.

[419]Crickmer, C. S: Patent No. 2,184,635, issued Dec. 26, 1939.

[420]Bryan, T. E: Patent No. 2,145,918, issued Feb. 7, 1939.

[421]Aucoin, R. A: Patent No. 2,197,064, issued April 16, 1940.

[422]Thomas, M. Bowman: Patent No. 2,216,967, issued Oct. 8, 1940.

[423]Crickmer, C. S: Patent No. 2,144,144, issued Jan. 17, 1939.

[424]Stagg, Horace M: Patent No. 1,683,930, issued Sept. 11, 1928.

[425]Nixon, J. D: Patent No. 2,132,081, issued Oct. 4, 1938.
Patent No. 2,164,469, issued July 4, 1939.
Patent No. 2,171,478; 2,171,479; and 2,171,480, issued Aug. 29, 1939.

Patent No. 2,171,812, issued Sept. 5, 1939.

Patent No. 2,202,462, issued May 28, 1940.

Patent No. 2,204,817, issued June 18, 1940.

Patent No. 2,245,002; 2,245,003; 2,245,004; and 2,245,005, issued June 10, 1941.

[426]Chenault, R. L: Patent No. 2,191,370, issued Feb. 20, 1940.

[427]Bryan, T. E: Patent No. 2,217,305, issued Oct. 8, 1940.

[428]Garrett, H. U: Patent No. 2,230,107, issued Jan. 28, 1941.

[429]Otis, H. C: Patent No. 2,246,811, issued June 24, 1941.

[430]Knox, G. S: Patent No. 2,280,589, issued April 21, 1942.

[431]King, W. R: Patent No. 2,339,487, issued Jan. 18, 1944.

[432]Walton, R. O: Patent No. 2,391,605, issued Dec. 25, 1945.

[433]Fletcher, C. D: Patent No. 2,642,811, issued June 23, 1953.

[434]Bobo, R. A: Patent No. 2,644,404, issued July 7, 1953.

[435]Howard, K. C; McGowen, H. E; and Moore, H. H. Jr: Patent No. 2,664,162, issued Dec. 29, 1953.

[436]McGowen, H. E. and Moore, H. H. Jr: Patent No. 2,679,903, issued June 1, 1954.

[437]Vincent, R. P. and Wilder, H. B: New Gas Lift System, *Petroleum Engr.*, **24 [12]**, Nov. (1952).

[438]Faucett, H. W: Patent No. 132,567, issued Oct. 29, 1872.

Patent No. 204,015, issued May 21, 1878.

[439]Wells, W. C: Patent No. 372,097, issued Oct. 25, 1887.

[440]Cox, C. S: Patent No. 500,856, issued July 4, 1893.

[441]Russell, R. H: Patent No. 784,435, issued March 7, 1905.

[442]Sibley, F. H. and Lasher, H. M: Patent No. 1,330,352, issued Feb. 10, 1920.

[443]Palm, Victor H: Patent No. 1,474,439, issued Nov. 20, 1923.

[444]Squires, W. N: Patent No. 1,488,842, issued April 1, 1924.

Patent No. 1,494,510, issued May 20, 1924.

Patent No. 1,802,790, issued April 28, 1931.

Patent No. 1,805,024; 1,805,025; and 1,805,441, issued May 12, 1931.

Patent No. 1,832,667 and 1,832,668, issued Nov. 17, 1931.

Patent No. 1,961,602, issued June 5, 1934.

[445]Sargent, S. B. Jr: Patent No. 1,503,602, issued Aug. 5, 1924.

[446]Gage, A. G: Patent No. 1,544,898, issued July 7, 1925.

Patent No. 1,597,162, issued Aug. 24, 1926.

Patent No. 1,836,585, issued Dec. 15, 1931.

Patent No. 1,907,947; 1,907,948; and 1,907,951, issued May 9, 1933.

Patent No. 1,933,848, issued Nov. 7, 1933.

Patent No. 2,663,261, issued Dec. 22, 1953.

[447]Crum, R. R: Patent No. 1,562,688, issued Nov. 24, 1925.

[448]Forsyth, V. L: Patent No. 1,568,447, issued Jan. 5, 1926.

[449]Humphreys, I. B: Patent No. 1,577,971, issued March 23, 1926.

Patent No. 1,765,427, issued June 24, 1930.

[450]Suter, J. H: Patent No. 1,557,116, issued Nov. 16, 1926.

[451]Galbreath, E. B: Patent No. 1,623,239, issued April 5, 1927.

[452]Grafenstatt, E. S: Patent No. 1,767,879 and 1,767,880 issued June 24, 1930.

[453]Gamer, C: Patent No. 1,790,982, issued Feb. 3, 1931.

[454]Boone, C. G: Patent No. 1,851,802, issued March 29, 1932.

Patent No. 1,927,734, issued Sept. 19, 1933.

[455]Clarke, M. A: Patent No. 1,867,906, issued July 19, 1932.

[456]Knox, G. S: Patent No. 1,909,493, issued May 16, 1933.

Patent No. 2,005,995, issued June 25, 1935.

[457]Coberly, C. J: Patent No. 2,081,220; 2,081,222; and 2,081,223, issued May 25, 1937. Hydraulic Power Applied to Oil Well Pumping, *Petroleum World*, **32**, Dec. (1935).

[458]Coberly, C. J: Patent No. 2,311,157, issued Feb. 16, 1943.

[459]Coberly, C. J: Patent No. 2,230,830, issued Feb. 4, 1941.

Patent No. 2,338,903, issued Jan. 11, 1944.

Patent No. 2,589,669; 2,589,670; 2,589,671; and 2,589,672, issued March 18, 1952.

[460]Swain, Gordon: Patent No. 2,230,787, issued Feb. 4, 1941.

[461]Dempsey, O. E: Patent No. 2,631,541, issued March 17, 1953.

[462]Dempsey, O. E. and Woods, J. B: Patent No. 2,653,545, issued Sept. 29, 1953.

[463]Carlisle, C. C: Patent No. 2,118,547, issued May 24, 1938.

[464]Chenault, R. L: Patent No. 2,191,369, issued Feb. 20, 1940.

Patent No. 2,679,806, issued June 1, 1954.

[465]Pankratz, H. J: Patent No. 2,329,359, issued Sept. 14, 1953.

[466]Holt, C. G: Patent No. 1,852,242, issued April 5, 1932.

[467]Thompson, R. H: Patent No. 1,867,115, issued July 12, 1932.

[468]Shimer, J. M: Patent No. 1,922,264, issued Aug. 15, 1933.

[469]Dulaney, R. O: Patent No. 1,967,746, issued July 24, 1934.

[470]Ross, S. E: Patent No. 1,981,288, issued Nov. 20, 1934.

[471]Hall, J. E: Patent No. 2,309,897, issued Feb. 2, 1943.

[472]Bodine, A. G. Jr: Patent No. 2,355,618, issued Aug. 15, 1944.

[473]Bodine, A. G. Jr: Patent No. 2,706,450, issued April 19, 1955.

[474]Salnikov, I. S: Patent No. 2,319,749, issued May 18, 1943.

[475]Baxter, L. V: Patent No. 269,167, issued Dec. 19, 1882.

[476]Loewenthal, M. and Egersdorfer, F: Patent No. 1,403,699, issued Jan. 17, 1922.

[477]Grant, R. V: Patent No. 1,775,759, issued Sept. 16, 1930.

[478]Bigelow, G. E: Patent No. 1,894,393, issued Jan. 17, 1935.

[479]Pigott, R. J. S: Patent No. 2,022,781, issued Dec. 3, 1935.

[480]Kennedy, F. W: Patent No. 2,100,560, issued Nov. 30, 1937.

[481]Downs, H. R: Patent No. 2,255,918, issued Sept. 16, 1941.

[482]Leonard, R. E: Patent No. 2,133,213, issued April 5, 1938.

[483]Nothstine, E. D: Patent No. 1,978,595, issued Oct. 30, 1934.

[484]Pickett, H. W: Patent No. 529,804, issued Nov. 27, 1894.

[485]Newcomb, R. E: Patent No. 1,287,078, issued Dec. 10, 1918.

[486]Scharpenberg, C. C: Patent No. 1,428,300, issued Sept. 5, 1922.

[487]Gates, L. G: Patent No. 1,593,820, issued July 27, 1926.

[488]Milton, M. L: Patent No. 1,634,423, issued April 12, 1927.

[489]Schmidt, B. F: Patent No. 1,736,094, issued Nov. 19, 1929.

[490]Ekstromer, E. C: Patent No. 1,772,539.

[491]Ekstromer, E. C: Patent No. 1,799,458, issued April 7, 1931.

[492]Coberly, C. J: Patent No. 1,740,043, issued Dec. 17, 1929.

[493]Graham, W. H: Patent No. 1,834,024, issued Dec. 1, 1931.

[494]Penrod, J: Patent No. 1,845,179, issued Feb. 16, 1932.

[495]Freeman, E: Patent No. 2,006,592, issued June 1935.

[496]Arutunoff, A: Patent No. 1,531,724, issued March 31, 1925.

[497]Arutunoff, A: Patent No. 1,518,952, issued Dec. 9, 1924.

[498]Arutunoff, A: Patent No. 1,610,726, issued Dec. 14, 1926.

[499]Arutunoff, A: Patent No. 1,952,191, issued March 27, 1934.

[500]Arutunoff, A: Patent No. 1,951,919, issued March 20, 1934.

Patent No. 2,073,623, issued March 16, 1937.

Patent No. 2,377,743, issued June 5, 1945.

[501]Arutonoff, A: Patent No. 2,236,887, issued April 1, 1941.

[502]Keegan, J. G: Patent No. 2,090,127, issued Aug. 17, 1937.

[503]Harris, F. W: Patent No. 2,152,802, issued April 4, 1939.

[504]Chambers, J. W: Patent No. 2,187,679, issued Jan. 16, 1940.

[505]Gruetjen, F. A: Patent No. 2,192,402, issued March 5, 1940.

[506]Holmberg, E. O: Patent No. 2,220,334, issued Nov. 5, 1940.

[507]Gruetjen, F. A: Patent No. 2,330,419, issued Sept. 18, 1943.

[508]Ferris, W: Patent No. 2,240,901, issued May 6, 1941.

[509]Lane, J: Patent No. 2,286,365, issued June 16, 1942.

[510]Malinowski, Chester: Patent No. 2,291,972, issued July 1942.

[511]Weatherby, E. J: Patent No. 2,311,893, issued Feb. 1943.

[512]Lewis, T. G: Patent No. 2,431,492, issued Nov. 25, 1947.

[513]Schmidt, B. F: Patent No. 2,489,505, issued Nov. 29, 1949.

[514]*Oil Gas J. Golden Anniversary Issue* (1951).

[515]Bessemer Gas Engine Co. Manual, 1902.

[516]McNeill, James: Operating Costs of Multi-cylinder Gas Engines, *API Drilling and Production Practice,* 257 (1938).

[517]Field, Joe: Pumping Wells with Electric Power, *API Drilling and Production Practice,* 256 (1946).

[518]Peake, A. W. and Prior, F. O: Use of Electricity for Oil-field Operations in Wyoming, *Petroleum Development and Technology in 1927,* 194, American Institute of Mining and Metallurgical Engineers, Inc., New York, 1928.

[519]*Oil Well Supply Co. Catalog,* 1903.

[520]Suman, J. R: *Petroleum Production Methods,* Gulf Publishing Co., Houston, Texas, 1922.

[521]Hamilton, W. R: Traps for Saving Gas at Oil Wells, *U. S. Bur. Mines TP 209* (1919).

[522]Thompson, H. B: A Successful Type of Oil and Gas Separator, *Summary of Operations in California Oil Fields,* **7** [11] (1922).

[523]Heithecker, R. E: Some Methods of Separating Oil and Water in West Texas Fields, *U. S. Bur Mines RI 3173* (1932).

[524]*U. S. Bur. Mines Bull. 417, 74* (1939).

Chapter 11

PRODUCTION TECHNIQUES AND CONTROL

C. E. Beecher and H. C. Fowler

H. C. Fowler was born in California and received an A. B. degree in civil engineering from Stanford University in 1915. After a few years of engineering in California oil fields he moved to Bartlesville, Oklahoma, in 1923 to pioneer in petroleum safety work for the U. S. Bureau of Mines. From 1927 until 1945 he was assistant to the chief engineer, in Washington, D.C., of the Bureau's Petroleum and Natural Gas Division. He returned to Bartlesville as superintendent of the Bureau's Petroleum Experiment Station, and in 1959 was designated research director of the Bartlesville Petroleum Research Center.

Professional and industrial affiliations include AIME and IOCC. He holds the Distinguished Service Award of the Department of the Interior and is the author of numerous articles on petroleum engineering and conservation of natural resources.

H. C. Fowler

C. E. Beecher

C. E. Beecher was born in Los Angeles, California in 1889 and received B. S. (1913) and C. E. (1914) degrees from Stanford University. Three post-college years were spent in highway and building construction and two as a U. S. Army Air Force pilot. After 1918-19 engineering employment by Union Oil Company of California, he was employed for five years by the U. S. Bureau of Mines in supervision of oil and gas operations on Federal lands and in investigation of recovery problems. In 1924 Mr. Beecher joined Cities Service Oil Company for special research on conservation and advanced through the positions of chief petroleum engineer and general superintendent of production to direction of the company's production research and development. He retired in 1958.

Mr. Beecher was chairman of the Petroleum Division of AIME in 1931. His long service in research and Division of Production activities of API has been acknowledged by its *Certificate of Appreciation*. Of his many contributions to the literature his paper with I. P. Parkhurst on effect of dissolved gas upon viscosity and surface tension of crude oil is perhaps the most noted.

11

INTRODUCTION

The pioneer oil producers of the American petroleum industry gave little thought to production techniques, as that term is understood today. They took the best equipment that was at hand, mostly borrowed from the "brine-well" people in pattern and, in fact, made hole and produced oil as best they could. Their initial production methods had little semblance of or relation to applied science, which is the basis of today's production techniques. Their interest in control of any kind was almost completely lacking. This viewpoint was a natural consequence of conditions that for them made a need for the conservation of energy in petroleum reservoirs as remote as were reforestation, protection of wildlife, and soil conservation to the early western emigrants and settlers.

All this was in the lusty days of plentiful resources—of well swabbing, open flow, and the gusher. It was before that era which has been characterized as the "mental-awakening period" of 1914-1919[1] when petroleum engineering as a recognized profession was slowly evolving; when a few men trained not only in geology but also in the techniques of mechanics, strength of materials, hydraulics, electricity, and related engineering subjects were trying to make their voices heard; when "book learning" was laughed at by "practical" oil men.

Actually, it was not until sometime after 1926 that the industry as a whole was awakened to the role played by natural gas in oil production and the energy attributes of a petroleum reservoir because of its contained gas or its natural water drive—each in turn causing specialization in that branch of petroleum engineering now known as reservoir engineering (see Reistle, Chapter 12).

All these and many other factors have had their influence and effect on production techniques and control. In fact, like the intricate crystal candelabra of our forebears, no one facet of this multi-sided subject can be touched without a response from one or several of the interrelated pieces. It might be stated categorically that this chapter should start with conditions after the well has been completed. However, if such an arbitrary boundary marker were set, the question might well be asked, "When is the well completed?"

---

[1]References are at the end of the chapter. Page references within parentheses in the text represent those in the citation and not in this chapter.

This question was answered years ago by H. B. Hill, a pioneer petroleum engineer, who said: "The behavior of a well and its whole production history are greatly influenced by how a well is drilled, completed, and put on production—modified to some extent by surrounding economic conditions". Elkins, in his chapter on petroleum production research herein, and others have pointed out the effects of production research on subsequent practices. Equally important is the fact that no production technique can be applied without the aid of equipment or devices, as described by Coberly in Chapter 10, to accomplish the desired ends. Conversely, no piece of equipment can be placed in a well without influencing the well history from that time forward. These subjects, like others in this volume, must be considered as companion to each other; and later, when reference is given to topics such as conservation, energy concepts, and reservoir engineering, no attempt is made to retell a story that has been treated comprehensively in other chapters. Because of the close interrelationship of one chapter with another some parallelism is necessary. However, an effort has been made to avoid repetition.

With the foregoing viewpoint established, this chapter first describes briefly the more important production methods, some of the vexing problems, and successful as well as some unsuccessful remedial measures and devices that were used in the early days of the industry when production techniques were appraised largely on the basis of initial mistakes. Next, the evolution of technologists having skills in many diversified fields into specialized petroleum engineers is traced. Occasional glances are taken at significant milestone markers to show how the pioneers applied their unprecedented production techniques and methods of control to meet rapidly changing economic, industrial, and national conditions. Finally, the chapter shows how the industry has matured in its engineering approach to many problems. This growth has been the result of recognition of the necessity of applying the results of research through carefully engineered work to bring about the best possible production techniques. These, in turn, have been aimed at increasing the ultimate recovery of oil and gas and at conservation of these natural resources—which is the true objective of control.

At the outset it should be recognized that the word "control" has several connotations. In this chapter, however, linked as the word is with production techniques—which in the last analysis are the result of applied science combined with a requisite quality of art—the meaning is simply *conservation through engineering*. Stated differently, control means the conduct of oil-field operations in accordance with the best-known production techniques so as to utilize the reservoir energy most efficiently and thereby increase the ultimate recovery of oil and gas from the producing strata. The term is not used here to imply legal, price, or other arbitrary controls except as those factors may serve in conjunction with engineering methods to lend support to a rational conservation of natural resources.

Throughout the discussion, the authors have kept in mind the very important fact that economic conditions in the industry and the country have had a marked effect on technologic applications. A few of these affecting elements are high oil prices followed by glutted markets and tumbling prices, the advent of the automobile age which in turn affected supply and demand—particularly for gasoline, the almost simultaneous discovery of large fields competing for market, and the stress of war. Concomitantly, engineering revelations translated into production techniques have had a profound influence on economic trends.

SOME EARLY PRODUCTION TECHNIQUES

No attempt has been made to draw sharp date lines. Invariably there are time lags between the bringing forth of a novel idea resulting from special research and its effective application—whether manifest as a technique or as a "tool" to accomplish a specified desirable end. Many of the techniques that were originated in the earlier periods have been modified and improved from time to time to meet changing conditions. Therefore, the discussion of some ancient items occasionally may lead directly to the mention of modern techniques so as to avoid repetitious references.

However, the first four decades of the industry, roughly marked from Titusville, Pa. to Spindletop, Texas—1859 to 1901—seem to span an era that some have called the days of "Coal Oil Johnnie." Kerosine was the main product, the wells were relatively shallow, dug with the percussion-type drill, and the vigorous pioneers played their hunches. Most of them were adept in applying the rule-of-thumb to their individual conditions. They were indeed rugged, two-fisted individualists.

In general, the early production techniques of that period were concerned primarily with improvements in equipment that would get more oil out of the ground. For example, a better type of inserted working barrel in a plunger-type oil-well pump to replace the pitcher pump meant more oil lifted with fewer costly shutdowns. With the required lifting of more fluid (both oil and water) from greater depths, producers found it necessary to have still better and stronger equipment. This condition led to some design and construction advances that were truly based on engineering. Mechanisms began to appear that would lift these larger quantities of fluid. This first emphasis on equipment was in contrast with a later period when reservoir engineering—with its mathematics, its plotted curves, and its calculations with digital and analog computers—came into the historical picture. The broad engineering concern next became a combination of interest in equipment development and in better knowledge of reservoir characteristics and of the behavior and movement of oil, gas, and water within those confining underground spaces. As has been suggested, one aspect of the broad problem of lifting oil deeply influenced and affected another.

A comprehensive discussion of all of the particulars of early methods of getting oil out of the ground and on its way to market—at first in wooden barrels boomed on the creeks during the spring freshets or hauled by teams over quagmire or dusty, rutted roads—would result in a treatment much too long for this chapter and would be replete with repetition of material covered in other chapters. Accordingly, exemplary items have been selected to show the general trend of slowly evolving engineering thought as the industry spread out generally south and west from its cradlespot on Oil Creek, Pa.

The General Situation

The producing sands along Oil Creek and in other producing areas in Pennsylvania were found at depths from 60 to a few hundred feet. The well-known discovery depth in the Drake well was 69 ft. Strata above the sand were hard, as were the oil sands themselves. This condition made drilling slow with the tools then available, but the competent walls of the hole usually did not cave readily. A short wooden or cast-iron conductor pipe was run in the hole to shut off surface water. Evidence of cast-iron pipe used for this purpose can still be found in some old holes. The well below the conductor usually was open, with no protecting casing.

Wells that came in flowing continued to produce through open hole so long as there was enough pressure in the reservoir rock to force the well fluid to the surface. No effort was made to control the rate of flow. If storage in tanks and barrels was not available, oil was allowed to run into open earthen pits. There was no effort to conserve the gas because nothing could be done with it—except to use it in a limited manner as fuel—even after thought began to be given to its energy attributes. Compared with the flowing gushers that came later as the industry moved southwestward and as drilling depths increased, these wells in Pennsylvania were not large.

The short conductor strings failed at times to shut off surface water, and it was not uncommon for a well to penetrate formations above the oil-producing zone that carried some water. Such water was a constant source of trouble to the producer, especially in pumping wells; in flowing wells also, if present in large volumes. The water had to be shut off if production was to continue; otherwise the well would be drowned out.

The first effective method of water control, and a truly pioneer production technique, was a seed bag attached to the tubing and set above the oil zone. These packers were ingenious contraptions consisting of a specially designed canvas container, usually made at a harness shop, that fastened to and around the tubing. This canvas bag was filled with flaxseed which swelled when wet, making a relatively tight packer in the hole between the wall of the well and tubing. A later section discusses in more detail the techniques of shutoff and control of water— often called the "bane of the oil-producer's life." Some operators observed that wells equipped with tubing and packer would flow longer than those wells producing through the casing. It is doubtful if these producers knew exactly that they were benefiting from a more efficient use of the energy in the reservoir.

Like many of the early improvements in oil-field operations, stopcocking a well to increase the flowing life and to attain greater well efficiency appears to have been discovered accidentally. The advantages of this production technique were applied by the oil operators of Pennsylvania, who "resorted to this method of flowing small wells many years ago."[2] Generally, the wells were shut in at night, allowing the pressure to build up, and then were opened during the daytime to flow off the head of oil that had accumulated.

Despite the early use of this technique on a trial-and-error basis, Swigart and Bopp,[3] when they began their experiments to ascertain the effect of back pressure on the production of oil and gas from pumping wells in Osage County, Okla. in the early part of September 1921, found very few records of the yield of oil wells producing under definitely applied back pressures. Accordingly, their work probably was the first series of systematic engineering tests "to ascertain how far the gas production of an oil well can be curtailed while the sand still contains plenty of gas, which can thus be saved to do work during the later life of the well."

Lovejoy[4] at a meeting in October 1923, referred to the earlier cited work and hesitatingly reported that initial tests in the Brock Field, Carter County, Okla. suggested somewhat different conclusions. The tests on the Amerada Petroleum Corp. wells seemed to show that the holding of straight back pressure on the flowing wells increased their "gas factor". Later this term became known as gas-oil ratio. However, a later report on the technique of stopcocking applied in the Brock Field showed that not only was the daily well production increased appreciably, but the gas factor was cut in half.

Cooperative tests of controlled flowing conditions in wells also were conducted by the Midwest Refining Co. and the U. S. Bureau of Mines in the Salt Creek Field, Wyo. E. L. Estabrook, petroleum production engineer for Midwest Refining Co., presented a written discussion of this work, appended to Lovejoy's paper. This group of petroleum engineers, all of whom were attempting to attain more efficient flow from wells by various means, were of the opinion that each well must be treated individually. Estabrook summed up the situation: "Probably all will agree that a steady stream of oil completely filling the opening through which it flows, and permitting the escape of no undissolved gas, represents the most efficient utilization of the gas of a flowing well." It should be noted, however, that the studies of Swigart and Bopp were concerned with techniques relating to the "efficient handling of wells from the time of their inception" as well as to the rehabilitation of old oil-producing properties.

There is an interesting commentary on this production technique which has been referred to as one of the first "time cycles" to increase production. Whereas Swigart and Bopp manually operated the equipment in their stopcocking tests, Bach of Amerada Petroleum Corp. devised and had built an apparatus which opened and closed the valves automatically at the proper time so that the wells in the Brock Field were operated on a predetermined, continuous flowing cycle. Thus was automation in oil-field operations a practical fact in the early 1920's, although it was not then known by that name.

Automatic devices are now available that will open and shut a well on any desired schedule. By a study of the time-production cycle, it has been possible to reduce gas-oil ratios and increase production. Similar results have been attained by automatic devices to impose a time cycle on pumping wells, resulting in more oil and less gas being produced. Where gas is taken to a gasoline plant, peak loads that overtax the plant facilities have been eliminated by placing the wells on a schedule that delivers approximately the same volume of gas to the plant during the entire 24-hour day.

After many wells had been drilled in a pool, the first ones drilled ceased to flow and new wells did not flow when they were brought in. Operators then found it necessary to devise means of bringing oil to the surface. As the wells were shallow, bailing offered at first a quick and easy way to lift the oil. In the strictest sense, bailing should be classed as a drilling and completion method; but in this earlier period it was resorted to as a production expedient, although the techniques involved were not scientific. Nevertheless, oil was being bailed by horse whims—a special kind of capstan for which a horse was the motive power—in the vicinity of Warren, Pa. as late as 1904 (ref. 2, p. 122). Even when the steam-driven engine used to drill the well was used for power, the bailing method was expensive, required constant attention, and the equipment was not too well-adapted for this purpose. Therefore, other means of lifting oil to the surface were sought by the operators (see chapter herein by Coberly on production equipment).

The transition from bailing to agitating and then to swabbing is not clear as one method led to another quickly, and the method that an individual operator used was controlled by his views and the condition of his well or wells. When the fluid level stood only a few feet from the surface, the wells would start to flow after the fluid column was agitated by the action of the bailer or by running a string of tools through the fluid with slow motion.

During the early 1900's, a special technique of agitating was used in areas of California where large quantities of heavy sand were produced. With the uncemented "oil string hanging in the hole", a smaller "agitating string" was run in and attached to elevators. This made it possible to raise and lower the smaller string through a distance of 50 or 60 ft several times a day. The movement caused the sand-laden oil to flow through the annular space between the agitating string and the oil string. At best, it was an expensive method of combating a special condition.

The questionable production practice of swabbing, which applies almost a total vacuum to a well during the swabbing action, was used extensively in deeper wells in the 1920's and 1930's. This method was used in an effort to obtain oil from wells that produced large quantities of water which threatened to flood the sand face of the wells. Many improvised and some engineered swabbing mechanisms were devised and built that held a plunger tightly against the inside wall of the casing as the swab was moved. From an equipment viewpoint, these efforts to meet a condition had some merit; but, judged in retrospect on the basis of efficient reservoir engineering, swabbing as a continuing production technique must take a very low rating. Later, when the detrimental effects of this method on ultimate production because of water coning and reservoir disturbances were recognized, the general practice was discontinued and operating regulations in some states began to prohibit swabbing.

The transition in pumping methods was gradual from the pitcher pump originally used in water wells, to pumps with modern ball-and-seat-type valves and working barrels through which a plunger operated. However, each equipment improvement, whether in prime mover or in down-the-hole mechanisms, had its marked and lasting effect upon the techniques of oil recovery. Coberly, in the chapter previously cited, has described the efforts of the pioneers to meet their problems of declining production and increasing lifting costs with various types of well equipment.

Probably nowhere, however, has the art of the wheelwright, as practiced 50 or more years ago and now almost forgotten, combined with the craftsmanship of the ancient rig builder been combined to pay a profit to the operator as it was at Volcano, West Va.[5] Here large wooden band-wheels, 15 to 18 ft in diameter with grooved rims, were "stood" in a vertical position and rigged to conduct a moving endless cable over the rough terrain. This steel-line travel was converted by means of other connected vertical wheels and crank shafts into a reciprocating motion that moved the sucker rods in the wells. So far as is known, this is the only place where such a unique method of central-power pumping was practiced with moderate success except in the Yenangyung Field of Upper Burma.

Air-lift methods, described by Coberly and discussed from the view-point of the effect of this method on production techniques and control later in this chapter, were used to a limited extent during the early days of production but proved too expensive for individual well operation. Compressed air piped from a conveniently situated central compressor plant was successfully and commonly used to operate piston-type heads placed on the tops of wells that were in rugged areas not adapted to the use of central powers. Many of these pumping heads were made from used steam-engine cylinders. Rods for pumping the well were attached to the piston, air pressure would lift the piston, then the exhaust port opened and the weight of the rods would cause them to fall. The noise from exhausting air was a familiar sound in many of the wooded and rugged areas of Pennsylvania until the middle 1920's when this equip-ment began to be supplanted by individual motors at the wells.

Thus it is seen from the foregoing thumbnail sketch of a few gen-eral operating practices that the early production techniques in large measure were adaptations from other lines of work in industry devised to increase mechanical advantage to raise the oil to the surface storage facilities. (See Chapter 15 by Swigart.) Virtually all of these efforts were prompted by a reduction of reservoir energy through wasteful use. As wells began to reach the pumping stage or showed signs of early abandonment, stimulative techniques began to be applied.

SELECTED PRODUCTION PRACTICES

Some of the more important specific items of the earlier production practices are described in the following sections, with reference to their imprint on the evolving petroleum engineering profession.

Shooting, Acid Treatment, and Hydraulic Fracturing

The hard, tight oil sands of Pennsylvania produced oil and gas in flowing volumes only for a limited time, especially under conditions of unrestricted flow, and means were sought to keep the wells on produc-tion. One of these means was to shatter the rock surrounding the bottom of a well bore. Vance (Chapter 9 herein) discusses shooting of the pay zone to increase production as a well-completion method— which it is. However, even Carll,[6] who wrote only a decade after the original, first patent of Roberts was granted in 1865 (and during the time when "moonlighters" shot wells at night to circumvent the Roberts patents), recognized this technique as a stimulative procedure. He records that "a tabular statement showing the effects on the first 39 torpedoes exploded" was prepared which showed that of the 6 best wells "increases from 125 to 200 bbl were obtained." Carll noted that shot wells dropped back quickly to their "natural production."

In subsequent years, available records show that a substantial although unknown number of wells were shot, with beneficial results. If a well ceased to flow or a newly drilled well did not flow, a shot of nitroglycerin frequently would produce a flowing well. This shooting became a common practice in the eastern fields and was continued by the oil men in their westward migration.

Kirwan[7] found that shooting methods used in California before 1918 had advanced very little beyond the early Pennsylvania techniques, in which a jack squib consisting of a dynamite cap and fuse in a thin metal container was dropped in a hole to detonate the nitroglycerin or 60-percent dynamite in the hole. However, Illinois operators used electrical firing devices in 1914; and by 1918, solidified nitroglycerin was being molded into torpedoes of different sizes to cope with different well conditions. These shots were detonated by timing delays and electrical fuse devices with comparative safety.

For many years the shooting of wells, both in hard sandstone and limestone formations, was a routine completion and stimulative-production practice. After production had declined, a second or a third shot was not uncommon. It was known that shooting fractured or cracked the formation for a short distance from the face of the well, and the resistance to flow was reduced. Also, the vibration or jarring of the formation resulting from the shot was thought to release gas from solution in the oil.

Wells were shot also to remove the paraffin, asphalt-like material, or chemicals deposited from waters that had formed on the face of the producing formation. The shot would loosen or break these deposits; and after the material and water were agitated with the tools, they were removed from the well by bailing.

Operators found it difficult to adjust the pumping rate to correspond to the rate at which oil entered a small well. However, the shot formed a cavity that would act as a storage space. The well could then be pumped at intervals, and frequently more oil could be produced at less expense by this method. After shooting, it was customary to swab the well vigorously to bring in from the formation any loose material and to stimulate the flow of oil and gas, if possible.

In this earlier period very little, if any, thought was given to the rock physics involved or to an engineering approach to determine the effects of shooting oil wells. There was no expressed interest in whether shooting merely increased production temporarily or caused increased ultimate recovery, or both. It appears that most of the techniques that were applied were borrowed from the explosives manufacturers[8] and the hard-rock miners.[9]

The purpose of this chapter is to record history and not to contrast the relative merits of one method with another. However, it is only fair to state that the results of shooting in some formations were not as successful a stimulative technique as had been hoped, and such practices introduced complications in the later life of wells when secondary-recovery practices were applied.

For example, when water injection became a recognized stimulative technique, particularly in the Mid-Continent area, many problems were introduced by the large shot holes into which 2-in. tubing was run and frequently cemented near the top of the shot-hole. Water-intake rates were difficult to determine by drawdown tests, even with the better types of liquid-level gages. This lack of knowledge of the geometry of well bores, which was necessary to determine rates at which water was entering the formation at different levels in the input wells, led Bureau of Mines engineers, after devising and building a liquid-level gage[10] for use in their water-flooding researches, to devise and build a well caliper that may be run through 2-in. tubing and will measure accurately a shot hole having a cross-sectional dimension of 36 in. for its major axis.[11]

Although the technique of shooting wells was used extensively in the harder types of oil-producing formations, the record is clear that until recently the industry generally has been more interested in the mechanics of placing and detonating the charge than in the rock physics involved around the point of detonation and the ultimate effect of the shot. From an engineering standpoint, it is significant that about 60 years elapsed between the early practices of shooting and the publication of the results of careful engineering analyses of the effects of shooting for increased production.

Such studies were made by Hill[12] in 1925, who used data obtained in the West Red River oil field on the Texas-Oklahoma boundary, and by Rison,[13] who first presented in 1928 specific data on the Papoose oil field and Poteau gas field—both in Oklahoma—and on the Panhandle Field of Texas. Both writers found that rates of production and ultimate recovery of oil were materially increased in individual wells and fields where systematic and careful shooting of wells was practiced. Rison concluded further that, if research were conducted on the characteristics of the rocks as well as methods of shooting and quantity of explosives used, greater benefits would be derived from this general technique of oil production. The techniques of sand tamping, shaped charges, and innovations of detonation with special firing devices have been covered in detail by Rison and others and are described in the previously mentioned chapter by Vance.

Vance, in the same chapter, also has recorded an interesting historical account of the use of acid in wells. The literature on the subject makes frequent reference to the use of uninhibited acid in the lime wells of Ohio as early as 1894. However, it appears that it was not until 1895 that the first treatment of a well with acid, resulting in reported success, was performed by Herman Frasch and J. W. Van Dyke. The Frasch patent (U. S. Patent No. 556,669) was issued about a year later on March 17, 1896. Putnam and Fry[14] succinctly point out that no progress of commercial importance in the art was made "until scientific study of the problems was made in the laboratory." The work that resulted in the practical chemical control of acid in wells began in 1929, and acid treatment entered the scene as an active production technique about 1932. This method soon became highly competitive with shooting in hard limestone strata. Patents were issued to The Pure Oil Company and to Dow Chemical Company in late 1932 covering, respectively, well treatment and the technique of introducing chemicals into wells including corrosion inhibitors, based upon work done in Midland County, Mich. in February 1932.

Heithecker, quick to recognize the efficacy of the technique, studied the results of 134 acid treatments in 113 wells in the Zwolle oil field of Louisiana as of June 1933 and gave an engineering analysis of the data.[15] He also showed that between November 1932, and December 1933, 150 wells in that field produced more than 600,000 bbl of oil attributable to acid treatment of those wells—a gain which probably would not have been accomplished without the acid-treatment technique.

Later, a somewhat similar but more detailed study of the effects of acid treatment was made in fields of Kansas.[16] By the end of 1937, 6,000 wells had been acid-treated in Kansas, with the number of treatments exceeding 8,000. The acid-treatment technique in limestone fields of Kansas not only increased the capacity of many wells to produce but permitted "a specified daily allowable with a higher back pressure on the formation, thus reducing the possibility of water coning." The study showed that operators were able to plug back to upper strata in certain areas and, by acidizing, to produce at a profit from formations that had been passed up in the initial drilling. The response to acid treatment in the Kansas fields generally was favorable, although water-oil ratios increased after treatment in some of the older fields.

With the advent of widespread acid treatment in the limestone areas throughout the country, strong competition between the treating companies and the shooting companies developed. However, when the hydraulic fracturing of sand formations and some limestone formations entered the competitive fields as a producing technique about 1949, the shooting of wells with nitroglycerin began to wane, and in most areas this method has become a relatively small factor in production techniques. It should be recorded, however, that largely due to recommendations of the Secondary Recovery and Pressure Maintenance Committee of the Interstate Oil Compact Commission in the summer of 1949, the Bureau of Mines undertook the task of determining on a scientific basis the rock physics involved when different formations are shot with different kinds and charges of explosives.[17]

When Stanolind Oil and Gas Co. (now Pan-American Petroleum Corp.) perfected and patented a process called "Hydrafrac"[18] for creating fractures in oil- and gas-producing strata and used sand as a propping agent to keep the fractures open, a new era of oil-production technique was initiated in many parts of the world. (See Vance, Chapter 9, for details of the development and use of the fracturing process; also Elkins, Chapter 17.)

The process was made available in 1949 to oil producers by a service company under exclusive license from Pan American Petroleum Corp. This service company developed new equipment or modified equipment already used by it in cementing wells and pumping chemicals into wells to handle the liquid and sand. In 1953, the exclusive license was terminated, and all service companies that desired to sell fracturing service and were capable of supplying it satisfactorily were licensed. In this process the "pay" formation is fractured by forcing oil or other liquid down a well under high pressure. The liquid carries sand into the fractures and these sand grains prop open the man-made fractures and prevent them from closing after pressure is released. After the fracturing liquid is withdrawn from the well, the sand in the fractures creates a porous zone through which oil can flow from the sand body into the well.

Both sand and limestone formations respond to this treatment. However, better results have been obtained in sandstone, probably because of bedding planes that may be lines of weakness which fracture readily. Limestone rocks usually are treated with a thickened acid instead of oil as the fracturing agent. Even water has been used successfully to fracture the reservoir rocks in some wells.

During the few years that the fracturing technique has been available, thousands of wells have been treated. At first, only old wells or those of small production were given this treatment; now the method is applied to many newly completed wells. Accordingly, it may be termed either a method of well completion or a method of stimulation. Regardless of where it is used, the results in many wells have been almost unbelievable with respect to initial flow after treatment.

Studies have been made to determine whether or not this method increases ultimate production.[19] There is no question but what the process as a production technique has made many areas profitable that were considered a lost investment upon initial drilling. Other areas are now being redrilled to sands that were passed up as non-productive when first drilled. One of the most outstanding examples is the Spraberry Trend of West Texas. A treatment using 30,000 gal. of acid and 45,000 lb of sand was reported in 1953.[20]* Fracturing has not given the successful results in Gulf Coast and California fields generally experienced in other areas.

The fracturing process, developed as a production technique by engineers, can be credited with the recovery of several billions of barrels of additional oil that would not have been recovered by other methods in current use.

Vacuum

The faithful and accurate chronicler of early production techniques in Pennsylvania—Carll[21]—described the stimulative effects of "gas pumping," or the application of (partial) vacuum to the casing heads of wells that were producing ever-declining quantities of oil. Operators who applied the method observed that the volumes of both oil and gas were increased for a time, and this method of operation to increase production was in general practice for many years, especially in the Eastern and to a lesser extent in the Mid-Continent fields. However, its use has gradually decreased during the past 20 years; and it is doubtful if a progressive oil producer would start applying vacuum to a lease nowadays, except possibly on isolated small units for special reasons.

Washburne[22] was one of the first scientifically trained persons to recognize publicly the engineering fact that "the vacuum method of pumping is undesirable because it does not create a high enough pressure gradient." He also pointed out the effect of vaporizing the lighter gasoline fractions. This phenomenon of evaporation within the sand body, in his words, "makes the little masses of [residual] oil more viscous and harder to move" through the oil-producing strata.

In 1930, the Bureau of Mines published a comprehensive bulletin giving the results of detailed studies of vacuum operations. Lindsly and Berwald[23] described the general considerations of the application of vacuum and left a permanent record of many properties where vaccum was applied and the results obtained. They pointed out the effects of vaccum application on crude-oil production and on natural-gasoline

---

*Since then a treatment in which 250,000 gal. of water and 200,000 lb of sand were used has been reported; see *Oil Gas J.*, **54** [**65**] 123, July 30 (1956).

extraction. These two major operations were so closely allied that immediate profit from 2 gal. of casinghead gasoline from 1,000 cu ft of gas often masked the ultimate effect on oil production. These studies unmistakably pointed to the fact that, no matter what were the results, they were predicted on a maximum pressure differential of approximately 15 psi; also that pressure restoration usually was more effective in recovering oil than trying to maintain a vacuum on the producing strata.

Gradually operators reached the conclusion that much greater quantities of oil could be obtained by other methods, such as gas or air drive or water flooding, or by methods that would utilize the natural-gas pressure in the formation more efficiently to move oil to the wells. Among these methods were those recommended by Foran,[24] Beecher,[25] and others for controlling pressure in the reservoir from the early stages of development.*

Records show that frequently the effect of vacuum did travel to adjacent wells through highly permeable formations. This was not desirable because the beneficial effects of the vacuum, if any, were lost. Furthermore, air may be drawn into the formations through an open well. On many properties finally converted to more efficient water-flooding projects, the water-input wells when first opened sucked air for days, and sometimes longer, because of a partial vacuum that had been imposed upon the producing zone.

Air in the underground strata, when brought in contact with the casing during the production process, causes serious corrosion. Such conditions were experienced in some wells in the north end of the Oklahoma City Field. There is evidence also that air in contact with the reservoir oil may cause premature oxidation that is detrimental to the recovery of oil.[26]

Today, where extensive gathering systems require a partial vacuum to bring low-pressure gas to natural-gasoline plants, most operators insist that devices be installed that will prevent vacuum from actually being applied to the casing heads of the wells.

Well Cleanout and Related Problems

A routine procedure of early-day operators to keep many wells on production was "clean out, shoot, clean out again." Therefore, the cleaning out of producing wells—made necessary by the caving of shaly material above the producing strata, the sanding up of wells, and the deposition of paraffinic, asphaltic, and carbonaceous materials on the face of the producing formation—may seem so conventional an operation

---

*This subject of the better utilization of reservoir energy is discussed in detail by Reistle herein, and is referred to again in this chapter in the sections "The Function of Natural Gas" and "The Bane of Water and Its Real Function."

that it loses its significance from the viewpoint of petroleum engineering. However, at least a few of the pioneers were applying principles that continue as the basis of present-day cleanout methods. Carll reported production techniques being practiced in Pennsylvania in the late 1870's and early 1880's, such as the flushing action of benzene, the use of a wire brush to clean the face of the sand, and a chemical action set off by an electric spark which he termed the "volcano."

George (ref. 2, p. 208-213), by engineering analysis, in 1931 showed the appreciable increase of ultimate recovery from a well maintained under flowing conditions through cleanout as compared with the general lease operations which did not involve a cleanout program. Parks [27] emphasized this point 8 years later when he said in part:

> "Detailed studies of well histories, their production characteristics as to cumulative values, rates, pressures, and gravity of oil and careful analysis of water conditions has led to discovery of long-neglected productive intervals. In short, a thorough investigation of why one well differs from another rather than ascribing this to chance yields good returns. It may also be true that a decline in rate assumed to have been caused by depletion may be due to reduced permeability about the immediate circumference of the well, or between the sand and casing or more simply to clogged perforations alone. There is a large field for remedial work in this respect, but a solution will require the combined efforts of the mechanical washers, the chemical treatments and perhaps more expensive operations involving reperforating or some other method of opening up a fresh sandface to a well."

Shea[28] in 1943 emphasized that the application of engineering and chemical principles to well-cleaning technology has increased the ultimate recovery of oil from many wells. He also pointed out that in California cleanout work is done by service companies predominantly, and that their representatives and employees are specialists in this kind of work. This likewise is true in the Mid-Continent. In the Eastern fields, cleanout work more likely is handled by the lease maintenance crews as was done in the earlier times.[29]

The large number of devices that have come into being through the years makes it impracticable to trace their historical sequence in this highly competitive part of the industry. Tools and methods are protected by letters patent, so far as possible, in order to give some advantage to the holder of the invention in developing and successfully applying these mechanical, electrical, and chemical means of increasing the production from wells. Methods of removing sand from wells and cleaning the sand face include various cleanout tools ranging from standard bailers and wall scrapers of many designs to devices for hydraulicing the walls of the hole with oil. Attempts to increase production by hydraulicing methods were practiced about 1919 in the old Salt Lake Field, in what is now West Hollywood, Calif., by the Amalgamated Oil Co.

Other tools and methods were developed and patented and many were successful for washing and cleaning perforations, flow strings, and tubing. Other cleanout methods made use of explosives of different types, chemicals that generate heat, electrical heaters, and chemicals that decompose the deposited material, such as acids, caustics, and hot oil and other solvents—some of which were used in Pennsylvania at least 80 years ago.

A unique method of cleaning wells with compressed air was used extensively in the vicinity of Bartlesville, Okla. about 1924 and 1925, with beneficial results in stimulating oil production.[30]

A trend in modern techniques is toward recompletion operations which make use of presently available wire-line methods. These permit many corrective measures in the well—such as squeeze cementing, reperforating, and sand control—without disturbing the original setting of the tubing.

Fine Sand and Gravel Packing

A production problem closely related to cleanout is that of keeping floating or fine sand from entering wells or lodging behind and clogging the well screens or perforations. This problem was especially acute in California* and the Gulf Coast areas of Texas and Louisiana. Flowing wells had to be produced at a controlled rate to avoid sand-cutting of the fittings if the velocity was too great and to prevent deposition of large volumes of sand in the well, thereby shutting off production, if too small. This fine sand was found most difficult to handle with pumping equipment. It would cut working parts of the pump, settle in the tubing so that the rods and pump could not work, and cause many other troubles. One or two types of working barrels were designed and used that handled floating sand slightly better than ordinary barrels, but they were not the answer to the problem. Hollow sucker rods were first used for this purpose about 1916 in several fields in California. When swabbing, bailing, washing down with water, and cleaning out failed, various types of screened or slotted liners with very fine openings opposite the sand were tried. These liners were designed to hold back the particular kind of sand being produced by the individual well, but they would permit oil and gas to enter. Although they made it possible to produce the well for a longer period than otherwise, the liners eventually became plugged and had to be backwashed with specially designed tools. Some-

---

*An early agitating device used in California wells to combat sand has been described in the section "Some Early Production Techniques."

times holes developed in the liners, destroying their effectiveness. Then the liner had to be pulled, if possible, and replaced with a new one—a very costly operation if the liner pulled apart and had to be fished out of the well.

Gravel packing, introduced about 1925,* proved effective in some areas. When a liner is surrounded by gravel, this screening effect for the liner tends to hold back the sand and fine silt.

Current practices of setting and cementing casing through the sand zone, then perforating the casing for production, has eliminated some of these sand problems. If sand comes into the well after being placed on production, it may be partly eliminated by pumping specially graded, small-sized gravel into the well under pressure. This operation is performed by using tubing with a packer set above the perforation. Gravel is forced outside of the casing through the perforations to fill any space caused by sand being produced with the oil. A fine-slotted liner is then run inside the casing through the gravel, and any gravel within the liner is removed. A relatively modern method reported to be successful is based upon pumping finely ground walnut shells coated with plastic into the well in the same manner as that described for gravel. The excess material within the casing is removed, and the well is produced without the requirement of running a liner.

Paraffin and Emulsions

Deposits of heavy paraffin in wells have been a source of trouble from the beginning of the industry in Pennsylvania. As has been suggested earlier, mechanical means, heat, and solvents have long been used to remove paraffin, as well as other deposits, from the sand face. Gasoline, a waste product of refining in the early days, was found useful by the producer as a paraffin solvent. Barrels of gasoline frequently were dumped into a well to dissolve the paraffin that had accumulated there which could then be pumped out of the well with the oil. It was common practice to remove paraffin from lead lines by using steam. Nowadays this operation usually is handled by pumping a rubber ball or other mechanical device through the line at frequent intervals. Paraffin does not collect or deposit readily on plastic surfaces. Therefore, plastic pipe is now used successfully for lead lines in many areas.

Mills[31] made a preliminary report on this subject in 1923, in which he pointed out the causes of "paraffining," methods of prevention, and methods of removal. He described briefly shooting, electric heaters, mechanical scrapers, solvents, other chemicals including acids, and burning. So far as Mills could determine, the Smith-Dunn Company, near Marietta, Ohio, first successfully maintained fire in a well in October 1920. The fire burned for 24 hours, and the rate of production from the well

_____
*See "Completion Methods" herein by Vance, in which he quotes Uren.

was doubled. The Hope Natural Gas Company also "burned" paraffin from the sand face of wells in West Virginia in 1923.[32] More detailed reports on the paraffin problem were made by Reistle[33] in 1928 and 1932.

Although paraffin and "rod wax" problems will always plague operators to some extent, the chemist has come to the help of the engineer in this as in other fields of activity, and company engineers working closely with the chemists of nationally established service-treating companies can now cope with all but the most stubborn "paraffining" problems.

Emulsions are another source of trouble. They have caused engineers and chemists to collaborate in devising ingenious ways of "breaking" these combinations of basic sediment and water (BS&W) and oil into their constituent parts without taking away all of the profits. According to Dow,[34] there were no serious emulsion problems in the early days of the Eastern fields. However, when the industry spread westward beyond the Mississippi River, "cut-oil" problems became important. At first, the operators were mostly concerned with getting rid of the dark material that had the appearance of liver floating on water. When the draining of tank bottoms resulted in the contamination of many streams, states passed laws against this dumping and large sumps and burning pits were built. Long columns of smoke were a familiar sight in the oil fields, and occasionally this evidence of a continuing trouble-spot may still be seen across the prairie country. The only signal it sends out nowadays is that of waste or inability of the operator to meet successfully a difficult and costly emulsion problem.

The chief means of treating oil-field emulsions fall into four groups—chemical, electrical, centrifugal, and the application of heat and later settling. These operations take many forms and use many patented apparatuses. Strangely enough, electrical dehydration seems to have been the first method used and applied on an engineering basis. Electrical dehydration stems from the basic patent of F. G. Cottrell (U. S. Patent No. 987,114, March 21, 1911). Cottrell's precipitator process later became known as the process of the Petroleum Rectifying Company of California. Some early experimental work on this process was carried out in the vicinity of Casmalia, Calif. where the emulsified oil was particularly hard to break.

Chemicals were first used successfully to break emulsions by methods covered in U. S. Patent No. 1,093,098, April 14, 1914, issued to W. C. Barnickel. Operators tried unsuccessfully to evade this and other patents issued to Barnickel by using a washing powder known as "Gold Dust." Later the Barnickel patents were consolidated into the Tret-O-Lite Company, now operating in virtually all parts of the world. Today, many chemicals and other treating methods are readily available to the operator. Greatly improved methods of handling emulsions are described by Shea,[35] who also gives a clear-cut description of the story of emulsion formation in the oil-in-water and the water-in-oil phases.

Blowing Gas Wells for Oil

During the drilling of early anticlinal structures, a common practice was to allow the drill bit to enter the gas cap with an accompanying blow of gas. A belief was prevalent that a gas well could be blown until it became an oil well. As no market existed for the gas, such wells were blown wide open, and sometimes oil would eventually be produced, especially if the gas well was near the gas-oil contact in the productive zone.

Although an operator might profit from what oil the well was made to produce in this way, he actually wasted an enormous amount of gas, as well as the energy represented by the gas under pressure. This gas would have moved oil underground to wells that were drilled into the oil-producing portion of the pay zone if the proper techniques had been used. A gas well that was blown until it produced oil actually recovered only a very small percentage of the oil that moved up-structure. Also, oil from other parts of the structure moved into the dry-gas zone because of the reduced pressure, and this oil usually was a total loss. The facts regarding reservoir behavior and the evil effects of pressure sinks in oil-producing structures were not well-known to the early producers. These faulty production methods that had little or no semblance to applied technology caused the unwarranted early decline of many fields.

The upper producing strata of the Cotton Valley Field in Webster Parish, La. have frequently been cited as a typical, and perhaps horrible, example of poor development techniques that virtually ruined what otherwise might have been an unusually profitable reservoir. Ross[36] reported there was so little regard for the importance of conserving the gas pressure during the early development of the Blossom sand in 1924 that literally "billions of cubic feet of gas were blown to the air in an effort to bring oil into the wells. The beneficial results normally anticipated from a gas reserve, both as a commodity and as a propulsive agent, were lost, largely on account of the competitive methods, and the financial returns from this zone were disappointing." Ross pointed out in the conclusions of his engineering report that the rapid decline of pressure in the Blossom sand shortened the flowing life of the wells and hastened the encroachment of edge water. Apparently, very little oil migrated up-structure into the original gas zone in the central part of the field as the operators had anticipated.

Other examples of gas wasted in the manner described could be cited, but it remained for a later milestone in the era of gas conservation, pressure control, and the application of material-balance and other engineering principles in field operations to save the gas and recover much larger percentages of oil not only from the lower strata of the Cotton Valley Field but also from other contemporary reservoirs in which operators learned the hard way not to despoil nature's gifts of petroleum and associated gas.

An interlocking economic factor hastened the new era of natural-gas conservation and better use. This was the unprecedented growth of the natural-gas industry during the 5 years 1927-1931, when long-distance natural-gas transmission lines were built from the oil and gas fields, predominantly in the Southwest, into urban and manufacturing areas. For many years before the advent of long-distance natural-gas transmission, natural gas had been supplied from low-pressure areas of dry gas supplemented by a few high-pressure areas. By 1935, about 55 percent of all natural gas marketed was coming from oil-gas areas; and instead of blowing the gas to the air with the excuse that it was not worth keeping, some oil operators were beginning to realize that natural gas is a valuable asset serving a twofold purpose—first, to recover more oil, and second, to furnish a source of heat and energy.

This realization did not come quickly nor did it stop the flaring of gas to the air. Nevertheless, a start had been made.

Pumping Oil Wells

The interrelated series of operations required to pump oil from wells falls within the strictest definition of production techniques. This is true despite the fact that virtually every operation of pumping requires some invented mechanism or specially designed and built equipment.*

This situation complicates the tracing of the history of pumping as an engineering evolution because, as the authors have remarked in the section "The General Situation," many of the efforts to maintain production rates as the natural reservoir energy available for lifting the oil to the surface declined were expedients or adaptations from other industries. If a new invention, the revelation of its advantage frequently was withheld until patent protection could be secured—if possible. Nevertheless, the decision when to change from the flowing to the pumping stage was one involving many engineering factors, including costs, if the decision was to be made intelligently. Today, the progressive operator uses virtually every means available within the limits of economics to keep wells in a flowing condition. However, even when the time to place pumping equipment at the wells is based on available engineering knowledge, mistakes sometimes are made.

An example of conditions that changed from those expected was evident in the East Texas Field several years ago. Some operators esti-

*See "Production Equipment," by Coberly.

mated that many wells in the field would have reached the pumping stage within a year or two at most after the wells were drilled. Management of those companies, influenced to some extent by an anticipated increase in the price of machinery, thought it wise to buy and install large units capable of handling the expected volumes of water with the oil. With the formation of the East Texas Salt Water Disposal Co., which returns water down-structure to the Woodbine sand—the producing formation in the East Texas Field, wells continued to flow for years; and some of these units never were used at the wells at which they were first installed. Many were moved to other fields where pumping equipment was required. Thus, ". . . every well is a problem within itself, which requires study and tests to determine the proper method of production." (Ref. 2, p. 125.)

In the earlier decades of the industry, part of the equipment used in drilling the well—such as the boiler, engine, bandwheel, crank, pitman, and walking beam—were left at the wellsite to be used for pumping and pulling operations. Also, the wooden derricks that were used for drilling were left standing over the wells and served their second purpose as a head frame with which to pull the rods and tubing. This action was taken because the operators knew that, whether the well was brought in flowing or had to be shot so as to obtain production, it would not be long before the oil would have to be lifted by some mechanical means.

George[37] stated in 1925 that many of the methods and techniques then in use were virtually the same as those used 25 years earlier. As has been indicated, the pumping methods at the turn of the century were largely on-the-beam operations with steam engines as the prime movers, unless jack plants (central powers) were used. In later years, boilers and steam engines were replaced with gas- or oil-burning engines; and still later, many electric motors were installed as prime powers. Mechanical engineers gave more and more attention to mechanisms that would lift larger quantities of oil with no increase in the expenditure of horsepower. This was brought about because not only were greater quantities of oil needed but, as wells increased in age, more and more water was produced with the oil.

At first, it was relatively simple to change the length of the stroke and the number of strokes per minute. In some wells larger tubing was installed which, in turn, required larger and longer working barrels and heavier rods. Wooden sucker rods and rigs of the first years of the industry would not withstand the shock nor stay together under severe pumping conditions. Counterbalancing by means of weights attached in various ways to the pitman end of the walking beam reduced only part of the shock load and rod breakage. As rod trouble increased, the wooden rods were replaced with steel, and the old drilling derricks of wood gave way to steel pumping derricks.

About this time also, in areas where a considerable amount of gas accompanied the pumped oil, operators had trouble with gas-locking. When the working barrel became filled with gas between the standing valve and the traveling valve, the gas would be compressed on the down-stroke and would expand on the upstroke, thereby preventing oil from entering the working barrel. It was common practice in the early days to "bump the valve" by loosening the rod clamp at the top of the well and permitting the rods to fall until the valve hit. Although this practice would force gas out of the working barrel into the tubing, it was time-consuming and hazardous. It did not take long for some ingenious operator to devise a "gas anchor" consisting of a chamber into which the oil flowed through the openings at the top. A pipe extended from the working barrel into the lower part of the chamber. Through this pipe the oil, now separated from the gas, entered the pump. In fields where solution gas is present in large volume, gas-locking may still occur, but it is less frequent than when free gas has access to the working barrel. Today this is a minor problem in oil-field pumping.

To meet the condition of lifting large volumes of water, especially in the mid-1920's, many mechanical devices were installed at wells in the Mid-Continent area and in California* designed to increase the length of stroke and at the same time reduce strain on the pumping equipment. Some of these devices were mechanical monstrosities. For example, in the vicinity of Florence, Kans. one operator used the head frame and me-chanical-lifting equipment brought from the tipple of a lead and zinc mine in the tri-state district of Oklahoma, Missouri, and Kansas to make a long-stroke pumper of the "Goldberg" type. Others were ingenious and had fairly good engineering design and mechanical efficiency. One such device that seemed to have good mechanical features employed two elliptical gears attached to the crank end of the pitman. These produced a long stroke with a slow reversal. This equipment was put on the market about the time individual pumping units began to be used, and for that reason did not attain wide use. Many of the other long-stroke devices designed for use with standard drilling-rig equipment also were supplanted by individual, electrically operated units.

The advantages of individual pumping units and straightline motion to pump rods were recognized well in advance of the long-stroke pumpers. As early as 1915 a nationally known equipment manufacturer advertised such a unit. The advertisement pointed out how the individual pumping unit equipped with a reciprocating device gave the polished rod an "extra straightline motion."

The long-stroke pumping device associated with Oklahoma City and other fields of the late 1920's, which consisted essentially of a cylin-

---

*According to T. E. Swigart in 1926, there were "15 or 30 different kinds of long-stroke pumps to be found in the fields of Southern California."

der and piston suspended in a rig to which rods were attached and operated either by air or gas pressure, was no innovation of that period but an adaptation of the earlier Pennsylvania practice of using air heads, which have been described. The polished rods were attached to the piston, and strokes of 8 to 12 ft were obtained in the types used in the Oklahoma City Field. However, the efficiency of this equipment was low, although it would produce a good operating motion and pump large volumes of liquid. The cyclic exhaust of these air heads made a noise very similar to the blowout of a high-pressure automobile tire and often startled passing motorists. As it was necessary to run considerable machinery to compress the air, the cost of upkeep and operation of this type of equipment was relatively high. As soon as stronger and more efficient pumping units were designed and built, this method of operation joined the limbo of superseded production techniques.

Other methods of oil lifting include hydraulically operated surface pumps that will handle large volumes of fluid by providing strokes of 20 or more feet. Rod and pump troubles are reported to be reduced appreciably because of the relatively slow movement and easy reversal of stroke. Although a development of the past 12 years, the idea behind pumps of this type is not new. A. R. Segelhorst designed and operated a long-stroke, hydraulic pump on a lease of the Standard Oil Co. of California in the Montebello oil field in 1918.

The hydraulic type down-the-hole pump, which uses oil under pressure as a source of power, has been operated with high mechanical efficiency for many years; but this type of pump will not lift large volumes of fluid. Power oil is pumped down a small string of tubing to actuate the pump which delivers the crude oil from the producing stratum and the power oil to another larger string of tubing that carries both fluids to the surface. Many improvements have been made in this equipment during the past few years.

The submersible electric-driven oil-well pump of the Reda centrifugal type was just coming on the market and making a noticeable change in production techniques, especially in fields producing large volumes of water with the oil, when proration began to take effect in 1926-1927.[38] This enforced cutback in the amount of oil that could be produced in the several states when flowing production was crying for a market caused less emphasis to be placed by industry on mechanical and electrical means of lifting large volumes of oil. Nevertheless, the submersible-type centrifugal pump, both as a lifter of oil and as a means of obtaining much-needed water in water-flooding and other oil-field operations, has in recent years made it possible to produce oil economically in many fields. The greater availability of electrical power throughout the oil fields has had its influence in this direction.

Of historical interest also is the electrically driven subsurface

769

duplex reciprocating pump developed by the Reda Pump Co. The original field tests on this pump were made in the East Texas Field in the winter of 1932. The pump was driven by a motor similar in design to that actuating the submersible centrifugal pump mentioned in the preceding paragraph. A power head with a double reduction gear translated the rotary motion of the motor to the reciprocating motion of the pump plunger and provided the necessary speed reduction. Gear ratios provided either 150 or 200 strokes per minute, and the volume of fluid lifted was about 100 bbl per day from the 3,000-ft wells of the East Texas Field. Although the trial tests were favorable, this unique type of reciprocating pump never was used commercially, and the company turned its whole attention to its centrifugal-type pumps.

Producing Heavy Oils*

The heavy, black, and extremely viscous asphaltic oils with gravities ranging from 14 to 6 API, as found in California, have introduced some special lifting problems. Occasionally some of these wells have enough reservoir energy to flow naturally, but usually some means of artificial lift must be applied to obtain reasonable production rates. Before the advent of modern pumping equipment, gas or air lift was sometimes used, as in the Cat Canyon Field where air-lift operations were in effect as early as 1911. (See following section, "The Gas or Air Lift.")

Today almost all heavy oil is pumped. All types of pumping equipment are used with the exception of those used with rodless hydraulic methods. The greatest difficulty is to get the sucker rods to fall through the heavy oil at the desired rate. Occasionally this is accomplished by adding heat to the well bore. A variety of methods of heating has been tried, such as electrical heating or the use of hot water or steam, as in the Casmalia Field in California about 1918-1919. Most frequently, heat is added by the circulation of hot liquid in a U tube hung in the well bore, or between concentric strings of tubing. Although effective, heating the well bore is not extensively used. Steam lines crawl, and even when half swings and full swings are used on both oil and steam lines to compensate for expansion and contraction, leaks occur at the joints and stuffing boxes, adding to the emulsion problems.

The addition of a diluent oil is the most widely used means of reducing the viscosity of the oil in the well bore. Its popularity depends largely upon the permanent reduction in the viscosity of the oil which benefits the succeeding operations of treatment and transportation.

Usually, even with the addition of a diluent, heavy-oil pumps require long strokes and relatively few strokes per minute. The effective-

---

*Some of the information used in preparing this section was contributed by J. J. McCullough, Union Oil Co. of California.

ness of such pumping methods is attested by the fact that over 550 bbl per day of 7 API gravity oil has been produced from a well by adding enough diluent to obtain a blend of 11.5 API gravity oil which is pumped from the well at 3 strokes per minute with a 10-ft stroke.

THE GAS OR AIR LIFT*

The gas- or air-lift method of bringing oil from the bottoms of wells to the surface of the ground requires certain equipment to perform that operation; but in the last analysis, the lift is a production technique as well as a means of production control. When used unwisely, the method may result in lack of production control. This situation was typically illustrated in the Seminole Field of Oklahoma preceding the days of official proration in that field in 1927.

Carefully authenticated historical reviews of the use of air- and gas-lift methods of flowing oil and water from wells are readily available in the literature and gas-lift devices are described by Coberly, in the chapter herein previously referred to. Therefore, it would be repetitious if this chapter gave more than a few of the highlights of the application of this method.

The *air* lift was used as early as 1864 to raise oil from wells in Pennsylvania, and in 1911 natural gas was used to lift oil of 10.5 API gravity from wells in the Cat Canyon Field, Santa Barbara County, Calif.[39] Although the method was used in the Smackover Field of Arkansas in 1923 and large volumes of oil and water were produced with air lift in fields of Texas, Louisiana, and California before 1925, it was during the period 1925 to 1935 that the gas-air lift played so important a part in production from the Tonkawa, Seminole, and Oklahoma City Fields in Oklahoma, the Hendricks Field in Texas, and in others that contributed to the over-production period with its tumbling price structure.

The Seminole Field focused attention of the whole industry on this method of lifting liquid. According to reports in 1927, for a time a quarter of a million barrels of oil a day were brought to the surface by gas lift in the Seminole Field alone, and production techniques were far over-shadowed by the economic repercussions of this beginning of a flood of oil.

Schwartz, Bopp, and Morris[40] stated that the primary purpose of the operators in applying the lift in the Seminole Pool was to increase daily production. There is no doubt but what that aim was achieved—perhaps beyond all expectations—because of a combination with other circumstances of the industry. There is little doubt, also, that this increased rate of production added to the economic depression then

*Some of the information used in preparing this section was contributed by S. F. Shaw, San Antonio, Texas.

771

sweeping the country. Because the reduced price of crude oil more than offset any gain derived from the immediate increase in production, the lift method in the Seminole Pool was not an economic success; and it is doubtful if the method increased the ultimate recovery from that reservoir. Those engineers concluded:

> "Air-gas lift application, therefore, should have been controlled to decrease the production rate and thereby further conserve the oil and gas in the productive sand."

Nevertheless, the invention and use of improved special valves, plunger lifts, intermitters, and other special devices that were developed through engineering ingenuity combined to keep the gas lift in the foreground as a favored production method in many fields. This condition has been found to be particularly true in fields where the gas-oil ratio increases rapidly during the later flowing life of the wells. At this stage, gas lift may prove to be an economical operation.

As suggested, there are many mechanical means of adapting gas lift to various conditions. Within recent years, although the method generally has been considered a temporary method of production between the flowing and pumping stages, serious study has been given to the techniques and economics of the situation. In fields where ample gas under pressure is available at reasonable cost, a gas lift may be used for the remaining economic life of the wells, thus eliminating the pumping period.

Historically, the gas-air lift method of producing oil had a definite influence on the employment of engineers in the oil fields from 1925 to 1935. More and more young graduates during that decade were coming out of college with degrees in petroleum engineering. The problems of design and installation of gas-air lifting equipment and efficient well operation required technical background. This widespread need was met in large measure by these young men, many of whom soon were to become the industry's reservoir engineers.

Shut-in Production

Many operators believed that a well, after being shut in, could not be made to produce again at the same rate as it did before shut-down. This view was based upon individual experiences and the recognized fact that, if a well is shut in for an appreciable time, it ceases to be a point of reduced pressure; and, therefore, movement of fluid in the formation will be away from that well toward others of lower pressure. This fear of losing production served as the incentive for operators to keep their wells producing at maximum rate. If a well was down for any reason, every effort was exerted to get it back on production as soon as possible.

Naturally, the circumstances have much to do with this production technique. Items to be considered are whether or not the shut down is to be field-wide or applied only to certain wells, whether there is an active water drive (natural or artificial) on the reservoir, the condition of the well equipment, and many other influencing factors—not neglecting those of economic origin.

Shut-in production is not a new device of oil operators to meet an economic condition rapidly growing worse. However, it is doubtful if the producers of Parker's Landing, Pa. in 1872 were motivated by thoughts of conservation when 200 of them "signed a pledge" to stop drilling for a period of 6 months after September 1 of that year. The movement spread, the Oil City Producers' Association followed suit, and by October 5, 1872, the *Oil City Derrick* of that date stated:

> "Reports from all parts of the oil region show that suspension of production continues almost complete. . . ."

As a result of this shut-in of approximately two thirds of the volume of production of the oil region of Pennsylvania at that time, the price of Oil City crude oil per barrel increased from a low of $3.10 on September 18 to $4.60 on November 1, 1872.

The Pennsylvania episode may have been the beginning of over-production of oil with its effect on production techniques, but not the end. It was also an ever-present threat to individual operators before and during the proration days of the late 1920's and early 1930's. Many "knew that their wells would be ruined" if they did not get higher allowables. Some operators in the San Joaquin Valley Field of California requested the U. S. Bureau of Mines to intercede for them.

A problem of shut-in production, manifest in a different way, has become so important in many water-flood areas that the Committee on Secondary Recovery and Pressure Maintenance of the Interstate Oil Compact Commission has had a subcommittee collecting views and data for the last three years to determine, if possible, if there is an engineering approach to an analysis of the effects of curtailed production on ultimate recovery from water-injection projects. Five papers by petroleum engineers qualified by training and experience to discuss this subject understandingly were presented at the summer meeting of the Commission in 1957.[41] The problem continued moot in 1959, showing its complexity.

Spacing Wells

The spacing of wells is not in itself a technique, but it is a production practice that has greatly influenced the history of the whole industry. The 1930 decade, particularly, when the Special Subcommittee on Allocation of Production and Well Spacing of the American Petroleum Institute was actively pursuing this subject, witnessed many and varied discussions before that group as well as in open forums of the AIME, the AAPG, other technical organizations, and in the courts.

Some persons may be of the opinion that close drilling was instituted in such fields as Santa Fe Springs and Signal Hill in California, or perhaps the Oklahoma City Field, where town-lot drilling gained world-wide attention. Actually, a detailed history of well spacing would have to begin with activities along Oil Creek, Pa. However, following the trend of westward oil development, we find that well spacing was a recognized problem of production in the Illinois fields in 1914. Wheeler[42] pointed out that regional drainage rather than actual thickness of sand probably was responsible for the prolific production from some tracts that were studied. In fact, the high recoveries obtained after the line wells were drilled suggested that there was no need for drilling the inside locations because "the line wells will eventually drain the interior of the lease".

Huntley,[43] writing in 1913, pointed out that "town-lot development and the conditions brought about by many operators with small leases fighting for production result in extravagant and wasteful methods of production". The deputy supervisors of the California State Mining Bureau reported too-intensive drilling campaigns and too-close spacing of offset wells in California. Naramore, for example, in his report in 1915, said with reference to a section of land where two companies drilled 4 wells on each 10 acres in a checkerboard tract: "This section affords a splendid example of the uneconomical development in operation of oil land subdivided into small tracts, and especially when neighboring companies fail to establish mutual drilling restrictions. This is merely the culmination of the old-time method of being first to the oil, regardless of the capital investment."

Heated controversy developed out of the well-spacing problem in which Cutler's *Bulletin 228*,[44] published in 1924, was the center. Many excerpts were quoted in the technical press and cited in court actions, frequently with misrepresentation of the context in the light of the time and condition under which Cutler wrote. In view of all this, it is interesting in retrospect to look back to the introductory sentences of a forerunner report of that bulletin. In 1921 Cutler and Clute[45] said:

"It may be desirable to an operator, from an economic standpoint, to produce and market all available oil at the earliest possible time, thus ensuring the early return of expended capital for reinvestment. In small tracts this is often accomplished. There is, of course, a high immediate recovery when a tract is quickly drilled with closely spaced wells in the early life of the field. The wells are relatively large, their initial productions being high due to unimpaired gas pressures. In such a case, with small tracts and townlots, close spacing is practiced.

"Too close spacing is detrimental to the field as a whole, since the gas pressure falls off and its sustained influence is lost to neighboring operators who might otherwise benefit from securing sustained production while their long drilling campaigns were in process. . . .

"Only an agreement between operators regarding the spacing of wells can gain for the field the benefits to be derived from maintaining gas pressures, thereby securing sustained production for all properties concerned."

The whole gamut of the spacing of wells from an engineering standpoint, with its effects upon the production techniques of the 1930's and to the present, cannot be covered in this chapter. The bibliography on the petroleum industry by DeGolyer and Vance[46] contains two and one-half pages of references, in fine type, to the subject of the spacing of wells. Many more technical articles have been written on the subject since the publication of the noteworthy bibliography. Fortunately, most of the acrimonious discussions have ceased; and as shown by Reistle herein, F. G. Miller[47] has pointed the way to an analytical approach which is helping to make a "rigorous quantitative determination" of the optimum spacing of wells more feasible than ever before. Fortunately the preparation of analyses of field data pertaining to well spacing that could be used to prove almost any theory advanced by a proponent has virtually ceased.

INDUSTRY GROWTH AND ACCOMPANYING PRODUCTION PROBLEMS

The discovery of the Seminole Pool in 1926, followed by the rapid development of the Greater Seminole area (20,490 acres of proved productive area in 2 years and 9 months from the date of discovery)[48] closely followed by the Oklahoma City Field in 1928,[49] the prolific fields of southern California at about this same time, and discoveries in other states caused many changes in production techniques. As pointed out in the "Introduction," not only has the innovation of many production techniques caused industry to change its operational structure—usually becoming more complicated—but economic conditions, in turn, have caused production techniques to be changed. For example, the large number of service companies that have become a recognized part of the industry is the direct result of technologic innovations and improvements—electric logging and hydraulic fracturing, to name only two such services. On the other side, curtailment of the output from a field by proration, whether voluntary or enforced, has changed materially its operating program and led to many engineering innovations. The slackening use of pumps and flow devices capable of handling large volumes of fluid during the proration period typifies this condition.

Technical discussions of the years of the 1930 decade reflect many divergent views. Some showed strong support for the principle of *laissez faire;* others were strong proponents of production control and felt that the available energy in a reservoir should be conserved by production methods that would not allow the wastage that was predominant especially in the last half of the 1920 decade, extending into the next.

Curtailment of oil production was not a new device to combat economic conditions in the 1920's. A previous section—"Shut-in Production"—refers to the year 1872, in which a move in that direction was made along Oil Creek and in other early fields of Pennsylvania. Carter[50] calls attention to similar situations in Illinois in 1906-1910, Cushing in 1912, and Healdton in 1914. However, it is likely that proration as known today on a voluntary basis started in the Greater Seminole area in the fall of 1926, with Ray M. Collins as field umpire. The proration plan in this area was implemented by an order of the Corporation Commission of the State of Oklahoma in early August 1927 (ref. 38, p. 12-16). As suggested, curtailment in some fields was voluntary, while in others it was mandatory by order of the respective state conservation agencies. Concerted efforts were made to stabilize a situation that was fast getting out of hand.[51] Many pleas were made to unitize oil reservoirs and place the responsibility of development and production in the hands of one operator who could then use engineering methods directed toward maximum efficient recovery of oil from the reservoir, unhampered by property-line and leasehold requirements. The Van Pool in Texas was an example of orderly and well-engineered development in contrast with contemporary townlot and other uncontrolled drilling and development.

All these and many other evidences pointed to the hard labor pains of a new petroleum engineering profession being born. It did not spring full-grown, vigorous, and resplendent from the forehead of any god. It was delivered into a mundane world—an infant showing signs of many potentialities but, likewise, having many imperfections. The birth of this new profession started before the period of flooded markets and crude oil selling for 10 cents a barrel. Its early years extended through the period of the Federal Oil Conservation Board, the Committee of Eleven, and later, the Gas Conservation Committee of the American Petroleum Institute constituted in 1927.[52]

All this was rigorous discipline for the young profession. However, the publicly stated view at open forums of the API, the AIME, and other technical groups that, given the main engineering facts of a natural petroleum reservoir, the engineers could determine within reasonsonable limits the quantity of extractable oil under known methods of recovery and under a given set of conditions, was strong evidence that reservoir engineers *per se* were coming into their own and that production techniques were improving.

For a better understanding of those conditions and their circumstances, it is helpful to turn the clock back to a significant day in petroleum-engineering history—January 10, 1901. Although that day was almost 13½ years before the first recognized formal degree in petroleum engineering was given at the University of Pittsburgh (see Warner herein), the bringing-in of the Lucas well—drilled with rotary tools into the "Mound of Spindletop"—on that day is an important milestone marker in petroleum-engineering history. From this point, the road of petroleum history rapidly turned in the direction of more and deeper wells (some of them very crooked, as shown in Seminole 25 years later), with a definitely different technique of well completion and resulting operation than had been used before with cable tools. As Brantly has colorfully pointed out in another chapter of this history on rotary drilling, the bore hole of Lucas ushered in the liquid-fuel industry era. Before that, with dependence only on "punched holes" by means of cable tools, the country was truly in the "Coal Oil Johnnie Era."

It was not the innovation of rotary-drilling methods alone that caused the change. Several bright young men, working individually, were finding better and cheaper ways to connect an internal-combustion engine to the chassis and the rear axle of a vehicle. More and more people began to enjoy first the novelty and then the almost necessity of owning and driving automobiles. Roads for this method of conveyance and transportation were improved slowly. Nevertheless, at the time of the 1900 census just before Spindletop, there were nearly 4,200 passenger-carrying automobiles of record. This had come about in 8 short years from the time of Duryea's first American-built gasoline buggy in 1892. By 1920, the number of automobiles had reached 2½ million. With this new skyrocketing market for petroleum products in the form of gasoline, there was small wonder that for a time each new field—including Sunset-Midway in California in 1901 and Glenn Pool in Oklahoma in 1905, as examples of early-1900 discoveries—was a welcome source of new oil.

The rotary-drilling method was not adopted immediately throughout the industry, as there was provincial resistance to the ready exchange of ideas between operators in the Gulf Coast, the Mid-Continent, and the California areas. Nevertheless, the rotary-drilling method soon proved its worth and ultimate economy because of faster drilling time, its ability to go deeper, and eventually its capability of penetrating hard as well as soft formations. These attributes made it possible to explore the deeper high-pressure strata that had not been reached in the earlier operations. All this resulted in new rotary-completion methods which, in turn, called for new and modified production techniques.

The Function of Natural Gas

At about the time industry was on the threshold of a period of over-production, the Federal Government recognized the fact that the nation was destined to consider a petroleum-conservation policy. Waste was a predominant note. In fact, President Coolidge, in his letter constituting the Federal Oil Conservation Board, which carried the date of December 19, 1924, stated in part: "We are not today, however, facing an undersupply of oil. The production of our 300,000 wells is in excess of our immediate requirements. That overproduction in itself encourages cheapness, which in turn leads to wastefulness and disregard of essential values. Oil, of which our resources are limited, is largely taking the place of coal, the supply of which seems to be unlimited, but coal cannot take the place of oil in most of its higher uses, on land or sea or in the air."

Stemming from that letter were the memorable public hearings of the Federal Oil Conservation Board in Washington, D. C., on February 10 and 11, 1926. At that meeting the leaders of industry and Government met to consider waste and what could be done about it. Although a few engineers had suggested that natural gas had much to do with the recovery of oil, it was not until some time following the 1926 public hearings that the industry actually became aware of the function of natural gas in the production of oil.

The members of the Board were the Secretaries of War, Navy, Interior, and Commerce. However, from the viewpoint of the petroleum engineer, the members of the first Board's Technical and Advisory Committee supplied the technical and engineering know-how that set the pattern for the 5 reports with their appendices, issued by the Board from September 1926 to October 1932, and caused the Board's work to attain a high level of technical accomplishment. These reports pointed the way to conservation of the fossil fuels and energy resources of the country. Particularly outstanding was the work of George Otis Smith, committee chairman, then Director of the Geological Survey, and of Harry H. Hill, member, then chief petroleum engineer, Bureau of Mines, then in the Department of Commerce, later returned to the Department of the Interior.

One of the outstanding contributions of that time and occasion was the prepared statement of Henry L. Doherty in which he enunciated his plan of unit operation and directed attention to the enormous waste of natural gas that was taking place under the then-current production methods. He emphasized the necessity for conservation and use of this gas both in the production of oil and at the surface. J. O. Lewis at the same public hearings gave a masterful presentation on the rejuvenation of depleted fields. Lewis previously, as chief petroleum technologist of the Bureau of Mines, had repeatedly pointed to certain phenomena

778

caused by gas being dissolved in oil, based upon simple experiments he had made. However, it remained for Beecher and Parkhurst[53] and Dow and Calkin[54] to bring forcibly to the attention of other engineers—by the results of their respective experiments, conducted independently but concurrently—the effects of gas dissolved in crude oil.

When the Board of Directors of the American Petroleum Institute realized that this subject of gas in solution in oil must be studied on a comprehensive engineering basis, it appointed what was known as the API Gas Conservation Committee, with instructions to collect information, "including the opinion of qualified scientists and engineers regarding the importance of natural gas in the conservation and production of petroleum and the best means for its most efficient utilization." This committee met at Ponca City, Okla. on October 17-19, 1927, under the chairmanship of the late E. W. Marland; and there heard the views and studied opinions of engineers, geologists, scientists, and others from all over the country who were qualified to speak. The information made available at that meeting, together with extensive work done by Bureau of Mines engineers and others, was published as a cooperative report of the American Petroleum Institute and the Bureau of Mines in an epoch-marking volume entitled *Function of Natural Gas in the Production of Oil.*[55]

This volume by Miller was given wide distribution throughout the whole country and had great influence in causing the entire petroleum industry, through its engineers, to become gas conscious. *Function of Natural Gas in the Production of Oil* and the writings of others stimulated an active interest in oil conservation and the more efficient use of gas in the production of oil. A period followed in which emphasis was placed on the energy attributes of petroleum reservoirs and methods of increasing the recovery of both oil and gas through proper conservation practices. The techniques of oil production were radically changed in many respects—with attending improvement—because of this changed attitude regarding natural gas and its function.

Operators seldom had measured gas that was produced with oil; neither did they gage the amount of produced water. Such information as bottom-hole pressures, productivity indexes, buildup rates, and shut-in pressures, the careful measurement of fluid levels, the results of drill-stem tests, the analysis of bottom-hole samples, the determination of the porosity and permeability of well cores, and the taking, interpretation, and correlation of electric logs were not considered—some were not even in the minds of men.

One of the first objectives in the new era was to reduce the amount of gas produced with the oil. The term "gas-oil ratio" (first called "gas factor" and meaning the number of cubic feet of gas produced with each barrel of oil) had been coined but not used extensively. It soon became an important part of the vocabulary of engineers as well as field men and, in fact, the entire producing organization of the industry. The real purpose of a low gas-oil ratio was to obtain more efficient use of the contained energy by reason of the gas pressure to bring oil into the well in addition to lifting it to the surface.

When engineers began to realize the full significance of the relationship of gas to oil in the reservoir and in the flow string, epitomized in the term "gas-oil ratio," the concepts of reservoir behavior came into sharp focus. Although that subject is treated comprehensively in the chapter herein by Reistle, recognition should be given here to the forward steps that have been taken through the years to control reservoir behavior by various production techniques.

The maintaining of pressure has already been referred to in the work of Foran, Beecher, and others.[24,25] Also, this technique is well exemplified in the operation of the Sugarland Field, Texas, where a small experimental plant was built in 1929-1930 to demonstrate the practicability of returning gas to the reservoir to maintain pressure. This pilot operation developed into a field-wide project that has been cited as one of the outstanding examples of what can be done by pressure maintenance in oil fields.

Another forward step to that new era was taken when engineers learned how to prevent gas-cap shrinkage in reservoirs where there is an active water drive. Still another was the technique of cycling to prevent retrograde condensation in fields of the condensate type. Also, but still in the experimental stages, are such methods as miscible-phase displacement or solvent extraction and the injection of gas at high pressures.

Some of these modern developments in techniques and control are difficult, if not impossible, to trace from their inception because they were in the minds of men many years ago. It is well to recognize that "the significance of newly found engineering [and scientific] facts and resulting new departures in economic arrangements cannot be bounded by definite calendar limits."

Each method of production requires devices to make it work. A few of the many that have been used to increase the efficiency of producing oil are mentioned in the following section.

Use of Chokes, Flow Devices, and Other Means of Conserving Gas Energy

Chokes

Surface chokes or "beans" were first placed in the flowline near the Christmas tree in California to control wells that produced large volumes of sand, and later in the Mid-Continent and Gulf Coast areas to restrict oil production especially in prorated fields. An early use to control flowing wells was in the West Coyote Field of California in 1913. Wade[56] has described several of the many unusual devices used in connection with wellhead chokes to prevent sand-cutting of the fittings on wells producing from the Wilcox sand in the Oklahoma City Field during the stormy proration period of the 1930's. As experience in the use of surface chokes developed, operators observed that wells equipped with these devices usually flowed longer with a reduced gas-oil ratio and in the end produced more oil.

It was soon found that bottom-hole chokes placed in the lower end of a string of tubing in a flowing well caused a much better use of the energy of the expanding gas to lift oil; also gas-oil ratios were further reduced in this way. Some companies experimented with these chokes in the 1920's, and many more entered the experimental field in the early 1930's. Some obtained satisfactory results.

Actually, the idea of the bottom-hole bean or down-the-hole choke was not new. Clark[57] reported in 1930 that "a device which in effect was a bottom bean was patented prior to 1890 by John D. Rockefeller." Other sources reveal that down-the-hole chokes were used for some experimental work in the Buena Vista Hills of California in 1914 by J. E. Reynolds. However, very little information on the correct size of orifices was available before 1922 when chokes were installed in the bottom of the flow string in a few wells in the Santa Fe Springs Field, Calif.

Otis[58] in 1931 reported "the recent development and successful demonstration in many of the Midcontinent fields of a removable type of positive bottom-hole choke which is run and pulled under pressure on a steel measuring line and which may be set at any desired level in any string of tubing. . . ." The article shows a picture of the Otis-type flow bean that was used in making the reported experiments. Since that time, adjustable chokes that may be run through a stuffing box on top of the Christmas tree in virtually all types of high-pressure wells have become internationally known and have influenced production techniques applied to flowing wells throughout the world.*

The bottom-hole removable choke has a special use in protecting the high-pressure wells along the Gulf Coast and off shore in the Gulf of Mexico. These devices close and shut off the gas or oil, if and when a predetermined rate of flow is reached. These are referred to as "storm chokes" because they are designed and built to shut the well in if the wellhead connections are broken by a storm or other cause, thus preventing a wild well.

Another example is a bottom-hole choke to control the rate of flow into a pumping well, at the same time holding a pressure on the formation to prevent water encroachment. Where the daily allowable is small —as in the East Texas Field—oil passes through the very small opening in the choke to the interior of the casing, which acts as a reservoir. Once

---

*On October 7, 1957, Herbert C. Otis, Sr., became the first recipient of the John Franklin Carll Award of the Society of Petroleum Engineers, AIME, for his "contributions to petroleum engineering in harnessing reservoir energies for safer and more efficient production of petroleum."

a day, or possibly every few days, the oil is pumped out rapidly without reducing pressure on the formation to any appreciable extent, because of the small opening in the choke.

Flow Devices

The small orifice was found useful in other ways to conserve energy and obtain a greater lifting efficiency. Operators extended the flowing period of their wells by drilling small holes in the tubing at some point above the fluid level in the well. These gas jets permit gas held under pressure between the tubing and casing to enter the tubing and help lift the stream of oil and gas to the surface. The size and number of holes are difficult to estimate.

To overcome this deficiency, J. E. Gosline designed a sliding sleeve that can be moved to change the number of holes without pulling the tubing. The device was first used in a well in Kettleman Hills, Calif. in 1936. If not enough gas is available from the well, it is sometimes feasible to introduce gas under pressure at the casing head. When this is done, flow valves can be attached to the tubing at different intervals and adjusted to open and shut automatically with pressure. Actually, this is an adaptation of gas lift; because if there is enough well gas under pressure between the tubing and casing, gas-lift valves may be used instead of holes drilled in the tubing.

A somewhat similar means of flowing wells with declining gas pressure, devised by I. B. Williams, had the orifices made of commercial gems to prevent enlargement from sand cutting or corrosion. This device, like several other pieces of equipment designed to conserve gas energy, came on the market about 1930 when oil prices were depressed and most operators were more concerned with shutting in production than they were with making wells flow more efficiently.

Tapered Tubing and Tubing Packers

Tapered strings of tubing designed to utilize the expanding gas volume to lift oil and to prolong the flowing life were experimented with extensively in Seminole (ref. 40, p. 30; ref. 48, p. 100) and other fields in the late 1920's and in the 1930's. In theory they were good, and many such strings were designed and installed. They worked satis- factorily until well conditions or production rates were changed— then, like the bottom-hole choke, a new combination of sizes would be required. Frequently, changing tubing in a flowing well was not practical, so tapered flow strings were not extensively used. However, for certain gas-lift operations, tapered tubing was successful.

Another development of that period to get more efficiency from the gas associated with the crude oil was the use of tubing packers. Tub- ing in a flowing well may be free, held with a tubing catcher, or set with a packer making a tight seal between the tubing and casing. Under the first two conditions, gas is held between the tubing and casing under pressure where it may act as in a surge chamber to help maintain uniform flow—provided the rate of flow is not too great. When a packer is used, the fluid between the tubing and casing is dead. Packers are generally considered to be required in deep, high-pressure wells. An operator may or may not use them in shallower wells. A more favorable gas-oil ratio can be obtained by use of packers in some wells, also a longer flowing life.

The Bane of Water and Its Real Function

Water was the bane of the oil producers from the drilling of the earliest wells. It is not recorded that Drake was worried because of water in his well but no doubt he was, even before he bottomed at 69 ft. Most operators fought water as their wells were drilled through the strata above the oil-producing zone and fought it again when bottom or edge water encroached and shut off production. Until methods were devised and techniques learned to seal off and control water, they were more or less at the mercy of the effective hydrostatic head that forced extraneous water into the producing strata. The result was increased lifting costs, at times oil production ceased, and many wells were ruined.

It is not strange, then, that first efforts were to shut off and keep out of oil wells this offending liquid from whatever source it might come. In those early days, there was a lack of understanding of the function of water in reservoirs under hydraulic control in which a great potential energy was available if it could be harnessed and put to work.

In the late 1920's, Herold[59] called attention to the theory of reservoirs being operated under hydraulic control from an energy standpoint; but he left to others the "bridging of the gap," as he expressed it, between theory and practice. It required several years of education to convince operators that water in the oil-producing strata does not necessarily have to be a curse and that reservoirs having a natural water drive can be made to yield higher recoveries than can be obtained from fields with a solution-gas drive.

Some of the earliest concerted work to prevent damage and resulting waste brought about by uncontrolled migration and infiltration of water into the oil-producing strata was done by a small group of engineers employed by the California State Mining Bureau* under the law establishing the Department of Petroleum and Gas of that state bureau which became effective in August 1915 (Calif. Stat. 1915, Chap-

---

*R. P. McLaughlin, State Oil and Gas Supervisor; M. J. Kirwan, Chester Naramore (succeeded by R. N. Ferguson), R. E. Collom, Robert B. Moran, Deputy Supervisors. R. D. Bush and H. B. Bell became deputies later.

ter 718). The letter of transmittal of the first annual report of the State Oil and Gas Supervisor to the Governor of California stated in part: "It is of special importance to note that the details of administering the law have been entirely in the hands of practical men who have had in addition to the experience gained in the oil fields technical training in various universities." The first three annual reports of the State Oil and Gas Supervisor of the California State Mining Bureau show how these pioneers handled water problems on an engineering basis when the profession of petroleum engineering was very young (ref. 1, p. 16-19).

It is noteworthy that although wells are completed today with types of equipment that differ markedly from those used in 1915-1918, the fundamentals shown in 10 original sketches in the second annual report (1916-17) to illustrate possible travel of water from and to strata in and about various types of mechanical equipment in bore holes under different conditions of geologic arrangement of strata are as valuable from an accuracy standpoint now as when they were drawn. Also, the last chapter of the first annual report (1915-16) was the nucleus of what might have been an early petroleum engineers' handbook with particular reference to methods of shutting off water.

Hager and McPherson[60] gave a brief resumé of water problems in the Mid-Continent fields in 1919, and Shidel[61] in that same year summarized results of cementing wells in the Augusta, Kans. field in an effort to exclude bottom water.

Other early contributors to the science and art of controlling water in oil wells were H. B. Hill, who succeeded W. W. Scott in charge of the Dallas, Texas, petroleum field office of the Bureau of Mines, and his associates. This work in fields along the Mexia-Powell (Balcones) fault line began early in January 1924 under the supervision of Scott. For nearly 3½ years the Bureau engineers worked with the companies in an effort to shut off the "big water" in the Powell Field.[62] Because the problems were so pressing in that field of high-gravity oil, which attracted world-wide attention and resulted in a drilling campaign that quickly surpassed all previous records for rapid, intensive development of a productive area, and because of the close spacing of wells and the early and rapid encroachment of water into the Woodbine sand, the Bureau kept a supervising driller in the general area. His purpose was "to keep in close touch with various methods used, to check the results obtained, and to give assistance whenever possible." Frequently W. H. Johnston, who was the last supervising driller of the Bureau of Mines, sat on the "driller's throne"* of a well and ran the tools—

---

*A special kind of platform-ladder used by the driller on cable-tool rigs to operate the temper screw and run the tools.

with the consent of the company—in an effort to find a suitable casing seat and to cement off the bottom water.

The work in Powell and other Texas fields caused the so-called "Cole Committee", when it held hearings in Dallas on H. Res. 441 on November 17, 1934, to call Hill and request his views regarding water problems and related subjects with particular reference to the close spacing of wells in the townlot areas of the East Texas Field. This field, discovered on October 3, 1930, was still running large quantities of "hot oil" at the time of the hearing, despite efforts of the Texas Railroad Commission and Federal Tender Board No. 1, to control production from the field.

Hill's concluding statement to the committee is full of meaning from an historical viewpoint of production techniques. He said: "Although there are many perplexing and controversial questions to be solved, it is believed that the principles of reasonable withdrawal and equity can be maintained if the fields are treated as reservoir systems and operated in accord with the natural laws of fluid and energy and not as 'parcels.' "[63]

The problems of shutting off water no longer present the great obstacles to conservation that they did before the 1920's and 1930's. Cement wagons of the service companies are familiar sights in the oil fields. The bane of water is met today on an engineering basis—but not without many mistakes having been made through the years.

The use of bags filled with flaxseed to shut off water by the early producers has been mentioned in an earlier section. Among the first cement jobs to be recorded are those of Frank Hill in Lompoc, Calif. in 1903, and of G. A. Reynolds, also in California, in 1904. Reynolds is reported to have dumped 20 sacks of cement to the bottom of a hole, raised the $8\frac{5}{8}$-in. casing 30 ft, capped the pipe at the top and lowered the string back to bottom. The success of these early operations is not reported.

Packers made of gunny sacks or burlap and other materials were used at first; later, rubber packers took their place. Special casing shoes designed to obtain a better water shutoff soon became common practice. As pointed out by the technologists of the California State Mining Bureau, many materials were placed back of the casing—such as wheat, oats, cottonseed hulls, and other materials that swell when wet. Later a thick mud was used with fairly good results.

Brantly, in the chapter herein on rotary-drilling systems, has carefully presented the early history of mud-laden fluid in rotary drilling. Fowler (ref. 1, pp. 42-46) reviewed mudding and cementing practices during the years 1914-1919 as means of shutting off water, which is the primary consideration in this chapter on production techniques. How-

785

ever, as brought out by Hill in the introduction, the manner in which a well is drilled influences its whole productive life. Therefore, it is of technical as well as historical interest to call attention here to the fact that Benjamin Andrews, while he and his father were drilling water wells in the vicinity of New Orleans in 1889 or 1890, observed the salutary effect of using muddy Mississippi River water in preventing caving and the sticking of the pipes. In 1896, Andrews made tests with a hydrometer during his water-well drilling operations to determine the difference in specific gravity between clear water and muddy water. It was then that he first realized why "muddy water was so efficacious in preventing the sloughing of the walls of a water well and helping the hole to stand up."*

DeGolyer,[64] in tracing the growth of the rotary method in the oil industry from its inception at Corsicana, Texas, in the 1890's, referred to the use of this method for penetrating soft sands and shales near the surface in the Santa Maria Field of California as early as 1906. However, no reference was made to mud-laden fluid in this connection. On the other hand, Lewis and McMurray[65] discussed the use of mud-laden fluid in oil and gas wells drilled with cable tools. They reported that Harry D. Aggers and others had adapted ideas from rotary-drilling practices and had used successfully in 1906 a circulator with standard (cable) tools in the Coalinga Field of California. Later, as shown in their cited bulletin, this method with modifications was used extensively in the Mid-Continent fields to prevent the waste of natural gas.

Arnold and Garfias[66] made one of the earlier reports on cementing practice in California in 1913; and Tough,[67] writing in 1918, described many technical aspects of shutting off water, with particular reference to the cementing practices of the time. Among the processes and methods which he described are the Baker cement container[68] used under certain conditions when cementing with tubing, and the McDonald process developed to cope with bottom-water conditions in the Illinois fields.[69] Tough also described in detail the two-plug method or Perkins process,[70] later combined with the Halliburton patents now known throughout the industry.

Multiple-stage cementing, as in the North Dome of Kettleman Hills, Calif.,[71] and squeeze cementing, as in the Conroe Field in Texas,[72] came into the technical picture in the early 1930's. These methods improved the techniques not only of well completion (discussed by Vance in the chapter in this history on "Completion Methods" and by others), but also those of production. Squeeze cementing permits doing remedial work where water enters the casing after the well has been on production for some time in a manner only perhaps conjectured by the

---

*From a memorandum written by Andrews to William S. Farish circa 1922; made available through D. V. Carter from the personal notes of the late E. DeGolyer.

early petroleum engineers. Parsons,[73] writing on the subject in 1938, stated: "Squeezing of cement is old, but there have been recent developments in the method, techniques, and cement which are producing remarkable results." He went on to show the improvements in gas-oil ratios and other production techniques resulting from squeeze jobs and referred to the increased use of this method in a very short time from a few experimental jobs to approximately 200 per month—presumably in the Mid-Continent area.

Parsons' reference to the fact that squeeze cementing is old brings to mind that W. A. Williams, first chief petroleum technologist of the Bureau of Mines, speaking before the American Institute of Mining Engineers in 1915 on progressive cementing at the bottom of wells to exclude edge water, said:

"The method of cementing was simple but effective, consisting of placing the necessary cement in the bottom of the well, forcing the cement back into the sand with a pressure equal to a column of water possibly 100 feet above the ground water level."

About the same time that squeeze cementing became an important method of improving production techniques, attention was directed to plastics and other chemical methods for shutting off water in oil and gas wells.[74] Here again the basic idea was not new, as shown by U. S. Patent No. 1,379,657 (1921) by Swann, and U. S. Patent No. 1,421,706 (1922) by Mills. Mills, then a petroleum engineer in the Bureau of Mines, had dedicated his patent, covering the use of sodium silicate and sodium carbonate, to the public through the Department of the Interior; but it was not used extensively by industry at that time.

The advent of plastics with variable and controllable setting times and the specified "jelling" time of some of them that would return to the liquid state and permit their withdrawal after they had served their initial purpose as a bridge or other "assist" broadened appreciably the field of the use of chemicals in wells. By 1944, Miller[75] reported that plastics had recently been developed that permitted control over a wide range of temperatures, that the use of a catalyst made possible the accurate control of the setting time, permitting wide application, that the development of requisite tools made possible the accurate measuring of small amounts of plastic introduced into deep wells, and that plastics could be used in most of the conventional squeeze methods of plugging back and other remedial work.

Recently a mixture of cement and kerosine or cement and diesel oil has been placed in wells under pressure. When the mixture comes in contact with water, the cement sets, and any excess cement and oil can be circulated out of the well. The squeeze pressures used with these oil-cement slurries are relatively low.

The early operators not only had inadequate means for shutting off water but they also had great difficulty in finding the source. As a result, many wells were ruined and large volumes of oil were inevitably trapped. Where the pay zone may be several hundred feet thick, as in some California fields, it is especially important to know the source of water entering the well before undertaking remedial work. Pat Elliott invented a tool (water witch)[76] for this purpose which was first run in a well near Taft, Calif. in 1925.

The operation of this device depends upon "measurements of the electrical conductivity of the fluids in the well." After the well is conditioned with fresh water, the depths of entry of salt water are shown by the greater conductance of electrical current as indicated by the water witch.

Water analysis as a means of finding the source of water entering a well came into use between 1915 and 1920. However, this technique has not been used as extensively as it should. In this connection, the late N. A. C. Smith, former superintendent of the Petroleum Experiment Station of the Bureau of Mines who won recognition as a world authority on the chemistry of crude oils, expressed his view on this subject in the early 1940's about as follows:

"Until petroleum engineers, through their water analysts, learn as much about water associated with crude oil as petroleum chemists have learned about the oil itself, the engineers will be 'working in the dark.'"

Available records fail to show which field was first to have the results of water analyses applied in an engineering manner to its better development and operation. It is well-established, however, that systematic analyses of oil-field waters were being made in the Salt Creek Field of Wyoming in the spring of 1923. Young and Estabrook[77] concluded:

"In spite of the many difficulties as outlined, the water problems presented by the production department are being satisfactorily handled in increasing numbers, and water analysis has become a permanent feature in the operation of the fields."

Today, more and more samples are being collected in various fields throughout the United States, with careful attention being given not only to their analysis but to the actual geologic sources of the water. The Bureau of Mines[78] has been active in this work, as well as several API study groups that are obtaining as many samples as possible from the companies. These analyses help prospective water-flooders who are looking for sources of water to stimulate production (see chapter herein by James A. Lewis). Also, companies obtaining electric logs in old and newly drilled wells alike need to know the resistivity of the oil-field waters in order to interpret their logs correctly.

Other aspects of production techniques are based upon the water content of the sands and its movement in the porous rocks. As early as 1920, Mills[79] gave a masterful presentation, accompanied by photographic records, of the results of his experiments with a pressure vessel having plate-glass windows for sides. With this apparatus he demonstrated "some of the fundamental principles and relationships governing the occurrence and recovery of oil and gas. . ."

As the maximum thickness of the plate glass was ¾ in., the experiments had to be conducted at relatively low pressures of water, gas, and air. They pertained predominantly to the relationships of oil and water in reservoirs of different structure formed of sand having different grain size and porosity. Nevertheless, this was one of the first visual demonstrations to show "that physical and chemical equilibrium in the reservoir rocks are disturbed by the drilling and operation of wells." A large oil company thought so well of these experiments that it had a similar apparatus built, and its engineers performed some of the same experiments as those of Mills, in addition to others, in the 1930's.

Working ahead from the theory propounded by Herold, which has been mentioned, engineers concerned with reservoir behavior began to give more and more attention to the energy effects of water in reservoir rocks, particularly in fields under hydraulic control. This condition is attested by the several technical papers on this broad subject given before engineering groups during the 1930 decade.

Miller and Miller[80] in 1938 gave the American Association of Petroleum Geologists a resumé of the status of engineering knowledge pertaining to edge-water encroachment at that time. Those authors said in part: "In becoming 'reservoir energy conscious' engineers have learned that in many petroleum reservoirs the edge water flanking the oil accumulation constitutes a potential source of energy capable, through proper control, of increasing oil recovery efficiencies materially. No longer is the encroachment of water into the oil and gas filled parts of the reservoir considered as an evil to be combatted by devious ways but rather a natural consequence incident to the withdrawal of oil and gas from the wells and may be used advantageously in lengthening the flowing life of wells and increasing the economic recovery of oil and gas". The text of that report contains 50 footnote references, the majority of which shed light upon the function of water in the production of oil.

In 1937 Schilthuis[81] pinpointed the influence of connate water in oil-production techniques by showing the effect on permeability and recovery values of native water occupying as much as 50 percent of the pore space in some reservoirs. Dunlap,[82] at about the same time, presented other but similar findings, and both writers gave reference to earlier work extending back to 1910. Although this work in the early part of the century was not fully appreciated by the contemporary technologists, certainly the findings seemed to disprove the assumption by many that the interstices of the oil-bearing rocks had "100 percent oil saturation."

One approach of engineers in trying to find means of preventing early and continued water influx into wells is to take advantage of the wetting characteristics of the sands in the oil-bearing and water-bearing zones, and with this knowledge develop methods that will prevent this water entry.[82] Much work remains to be done in developing economical techniques of removing water blocks around oil and gas wells.

Although this section has been treated sketchily, it will serve to show that through long, hard years of expensive and at times disheartening experience, operators and petroleum engineers are moving in the direction hoped for by Smith as paraphrased previously herein (p. 788). First they have had to learn to make water work for them in producing oil—instead of always thinking of water as the evil-omened bane foretelling the early end of the pay; also, they must learn more about its constituents and its behavior when associated with oil and gas. These are such broad subjects, in addition to the requirements of shutting off the waters, that discussion confined solely to production techniques and control is difficult. However, in the last analysis, water must be considered as a source of energy in the same manner as natural gas is considered such a source.

The effectual use of water as an energy source has been demonstrated in many fields. The Midway Field in Arkansas[84] and the New Hope Field in northeastern Texas[85] are among the outstanding examples of what engineers have been able to accomplish in greatly increasing the recovery efficiency of certain reservoirs under hydraulic control by the early injection of water. Lewis, in his chapter elsewhere in this history, calls attention to other examples and cites operations in the Mamou Field in Louisiana in 1948 as "the first high-pressure water-injection project to be initiated at such a depth [11,500 ft]." The Scurry Reef Field in Texas has been found to be amenable to this production technique, and in the East Texas Field a waste-disposal liability has been turned into a reservoir asset by the judicious use of water.[86]

Water in Gas Wells

Although wells that produce gas only are, in general, simple to operate, they too present problems of production techniques and control.* Water may be found initially or appear during the producing life of a gas well and cause a reduction of gas deliverability—even to the extent of shutting off the flow—or result in serious corrosion of equipment in the well and at the well head. If gas is being produced through a string of tubing and the rate of flow is reasonably large, any water present will likely be removed with the gas. However, if the pressure is low and the volume delivered is small, operators may find it necessary to remove the water by "blowing" the well to remove water at regular intervals through the tubing, or through the casing if the well is not tubed.

Such practices result in waste of gas and diminution of the life of the field. One method that has been used successfully to remove water from some gas wells, as well as in the production of oil, is essentially a plunger-type gas lift, developed in the early 1930's by H. W. Fletcher, then chief engineer of the Hughes Tool Company. A cylinder-like apparatus is provided with a packing arrangement that makes a seal with the tubing and the liquid is lifted to the surface as the plunger travels up and down the tubing.

The most common way to dewater gas wells is with a siphon. The term "siphon", as used in the natural-gas industry, is applied to a pipe or tubing installed in a gas well to remove water and is not a true siphon. Its operation depends upon expansion of gas within the eductor pipe and the fact that the rising gas bubbles decrease the density of the column of water in the siphon line.

The Bureau of Mines, recognizing that this method is efficient only when the siphon is designed and built accurately in accordance with engineering principles and maintained methodically, emphasized these requirements in a report published in 1929.[89] However, the problem of shutting out or removing excessive quantities of water from gas wells, both in naturally flowing fields and in gas-storage reservoirs, still remains. Engineers and chemists are working on several approaches. One is the chemical treatment of the sands around well bores to keep the water from entering the producing wells. Another approach is by the use of surface-active agents. In this technique, the water and agent form a foam which is lifted by the gas pressure after the well has be-

---

*The authors have made no attempt to treat this subject broadly as applied to natural gas which is not associated with petroleum in the reservoir. That is a subject unto itself and needs separate treatment. However, the great technical contributions that have been made by petroleum and natural-gas engineers to conservation by eliminating open-flow methods of determining the capacities of gas wells by back-pressure and other more recently devised methods is recognized by citing the pioneer work of Pierce and Rawlins[87] in 1929 and that of Rawlins and Schellhardt[88] in 1936.

come water-logged.* If economical means can be found to cope with the water situation in a single field, such as the Hugoton Field of Texas, Oklahoma, and Kansas, many millions of dollars will be saved to the industry.

OTHER PRODUCTION TECHNIQUES

Improved Equipment and Standardization

As suggested earlier in this chapter, improvements in equipment for conducting and lifting oil and gas to the surface of the ground go hand-in-hand with more efficient production techniques. Engineers, metallurgists, and chemists continually battle with the effect of stress and strain and corrosion of metal goods caused by salt water, hydrogen sulfide, carbon dioxide, and other substances occurring in the ground or associated with the hydrocarbons in the earth's strata—such as the fatty acids. Two problems have continually confronted technologists in this battle between human intelligence and those natural phenomena that eventually cause disintegration of material. First, better mechanical design—such as that applied to rod couplings, casing, tubing and other underground equipment—and better surface equipment; second, stronger metal alloys and heat treatment of steel that will cause them to withstand the loads and reversal of stresses and resist corrosion. A third item might be termed "chemical treatment", as exemplified by the work done in the later 1940's under the sponsorship of the National Association of Corrosion Engineers to control internal corrosion of tubular goods and wellhead equipment by treatment with sodium chromate and other chemicals in the gas-condensate wells of the Gulf Coast.[91]

Engineers, metallurgists, and chemists have worked for years to improve all parts of pumping and other oil-field equipment. As a result, under the able sponsorship of the American Petroleum Institute, the industry now has API specifications recognized all over the world. (See chapter entitled "Standardization" by Scharpenberg.)

Cores and Logs

The unsatisfactory condition resulting from the lack of reliable well records in the earlier years of the 20th century are clearly revealed in the transactions of technical meetings, particularly those of the American Institute of Mining Engineers. In discussing a paper by McLaughlin,[92] A. F. L. Bell, chief engineer of the Associated Oil Company, in 1915 stressed the likelihood of passing up good oil sand with the rotary method of drilling because of the difficulties of log-

---

*This method was reported in 1959 as successfully applied.[90] Water was removed efficiently in the field tests from wells with depths from 650 to 3,900 ft and with various methods of completion. The casing in some wells was as large as 7 in. and the tubing as small as ¾ in. The wellhead pressures were low.

ging. In 1917, M. M. Thompson in discussing a paper by Hager[93] pointed to the unreliability of well records. He reported that often the elevation of the top of the hole was not given, resulting in the erroneous classification of keybeds. Others of that period called attention to the careless and unsystematic manner in which many drilling logs were recorded (see ref. 1, pp. 25-27). However, by 1920 various kinds of cross sections, subsurface contour maps, and peg models in three dimensions were being used extensively in attempts to gain a better understanding of underground conditions.[94]

The first coring was done with cable tools. The core recovery was not good, the sections usually were short, and frequently they were broken into thin pieces like poker chips. Nevertheless, they revealed a considerable amount of information, particularly when studied by geologists and paleontologists. The first core barrels in rotary wells were improvised from sections of pipe. According to R. C. Glover, Baker Tool Co., who used them, the bottom end was cut at a 45-deg bevel, and these "punch barrels" were forced into the formation to obtain a core. Shortly following these initial attempts, a modified barrel was made by cutting teeth in the lower end of the pipe. The teeth would cut into the soft formations as the pipe was rotated and were arranged in such a way that they would crimp and form a basket or core catcher when pressure was applied. The specimen was then removed. With both types of barrels, the cores often were burned by the generated heat.

Jan Koster of the Holland Geological Survey developed a double-barrel core drill for use in loosely consolidated formations, which the Shell Oil Company of California applied in the Santa Fe Springs oil field in 1919. According to Elliott:[95] "The original Elliott core drill as used by The Elliott Core Drilling Company from 1921 to 1924 was somewhat similar in design to the Koster drill but adapted to the taking of cores at considerable depth and with several changes made necessary by California practice in rotary drilling in California formations."

Although coring in itself is a drilling and completion practice, the geologic and reservoir information obtained from cores and the improvement in logs because of scientific core examinations have radically changed the views of petroleum engineers regarding reservoir behavior and has led to changes in production techniques. When the electric log began in the 1930's to be recognized as a very effective oil-field "tool", petroleum engineers for the first time began to "see" a true picture of underground conditions[96]—made still clearer in recent years with radioactivity logging.

The interpretation of electric, gamma-ray, and neutron logs today has become a very specialized type of production technique. The actual logging usually is done by a service company with suitable equipment. If these developments in the past 20 years had not come about, the general use of pressure core barrels, such as those developed by the Bureau of Mines in cooperation with the American Petroleum Institute[97] and by The Carter Oil Co.,[98] might have had more widespread use in determining reservoir characteristics.

As an aid to better interpretation of the results of modern electric logging, engineers are looking more and more to the analyses of oil-field waters, including their resistivities, as discussed in an earlier section dealing with oil-field waters. This is particularly true in fields where the original driller's logs are missing or are faulty in giving authentic information from which correlations can be made with which to apply stimulative methods more effectively to partly depleted strata.

Subsurface Pressures and Temperatures

As the young petroleum engineering profession grew toward manhood, engineers realized more and more that true reservoir conditions could not be determined by using surface data alone. Therefore, they began to devise means of obtaining "bottom-hole"* data in wells in order to determine pressure-volume-temperature (PVT) relationships. At the beginning of their search for means to "look deeper into the reservoirs," they found no data available on bottom-hole pressures except those obtained by estimating the weight of the column of oil and gas in the well and adding it in equivalent pounds per square inch to the surface pressure. As they did not know the fluid level accurately (and frequently the gravity of the oil and the gas in the well were only estimated), they were considerably handicapped in their calculations both in flowing and pumping wells.

One of the earliest attempts to determine a fluid level and compute the corresponding bottom-hole pressure accurately was made by Beecher and Parkhurst in 1925 in a pumping well in Kansas. Only a small quantity of gas was being produced with the oil, and the gravity of the oil was known. In order to determine the fluid level, a tin-float device attached to an ordinary 2-lead, insulated copper wire was lowered into the well with a few dry cells in the circuit. When the top fluid was reached, the float would rise and make contact with a terminal which closed the circuit. This closure caused an electrical doorbell to ring at the surface. This device worked satisfactorily unless it was lowered too rapidly into the liquid causing the pressure to collapse the float.†

---

*The term "bottom hole," of course, is a misnomer.

†Nearly 30 years later, the need for a liquid-level gage caused engineers of the Bureau of Mines to devise and build an accurate gage that would give depth readings at the surface through suitable electrical circuits and a recorder in order that information could be obtained that was necessary in the application of modern techniques of water flooding (see ref. 10).

Other investigators turned to sonic means of determining fluid levels. One device was based upon experimentation by Lehr and Wyatt of Shell Oil Company in 1932. They used the principle of concussion or pressure-wave echo. Walker[99] described and reported on the results obtained with the "Depthograph" in 1936. The principle of its operation is similar to that of Batcheller's invention in 1898 of an "apparatus for locating obstructions in tubes."[100] However, Lehr and Wyatt released compressed gas into the casing to produce the pressure wave instead of firing a gun.

A second commercial method, developed about the same time, employs the principle of a "selected frequency steep-front wave" created by use of a special cartridge. According to Jakosky,[101] who reported on the "Echo-Meter" in 1938, "the component frequencies are filtered so that the frequencies utilized in the measurements include only a relatively narrow band" in order to obtain better resolution.

The sound wave, regardless of source, as it travels toward the bottom of the well is partly reflected at each collar, tubing catcher, wave reflector, or other obstruction. These reflections are recorded at the surface, and the liquid level is indicated by a relatively larger reflection. The depth at which each reflection occurs may be computed from the velocity and time relationships. If there is foam between tubing and casing—resulting from the oil being agitated by gas—or the liquid level is surging, inaccuracies in the measurements may result. Nevertheless, each development has been an engineering contribution to aid in "seeing" more clearly what is going on within the reservoir.

Several farseeing engineers and others were working on devices that could be run into wells on wire lines through casing or tubing to measure the pressure in the bore hole. The first devices were crude affairs constituted primarily of a weighted, pressure-tested "bull plug" or short length of pipe closed at the lower end into which was screwed a gas-tight cap. The cap was provided with a bail, and into an appropriately tapped hole in the cap was screwed a Bourdon gage in an inverted position so that the dial was held in a protected position within the container. The inside face of the gage glass was darkened with candle smoke, and the pin was bent so that it would make a trace on the carbon-coated glass.

This crude device was lowered slowly through the casing by means of a wire line, and a reading of maximum pressure at or near the bottom of the hole was obtained. Sometimes the container carried more than one maximum-reading pressure gage in order to obtain check readings, also a maximum-reading thermometer.*

---

*One of the earliest crude bottom-hole maximum-pressure "bombs", of a size permitting it to be run in 6-in. casing, is in the custody of the Petroleum Experiment Station of the Bureau of Mines at Bartlesville, Okla.

When Bureau of Mines engineers began their quest for more authentic well data in their study of "fluid and energy relations,"[102] which engineers throughout the industry later called "PVT relations," there was no pressure or temperature gage on the market that they could buy to aid them in their studies. Accordingly, Reistle began the design and development of such a device based upon some earlier ideas of Nowels at Laramie, Wyo. Berwald, Buss, and Reistle[103] have given a carefully authenticated account of this development as follows:

"The study of subsurface pressures and temperatures in oil and gas wells begun in 1928 [by the Bureau of Mines] has been continued as a part of a general investigation of fluid and energy relations in producing wells. The development of suitable instruments for measuring subsurface pressures and temperatures has been a major part of this study, and the present satisfactory instruments were the result of the accumulated efforts of several men. K. B. Nowels, supervising engineer of the Bureau's Laramie (Wyo.) field office in 1928, began the work. After the resignation of Nowels from the Bureau in 1930, C. E. Reistle, Jr., was placed in charge and continued the work until August 1933, when he was granted a furlough to do special engineering work in the East Texas field. W. B. Berwald was then placed in charge of the study. Nowels, Reistle, and Berwald all have been largely responsible for the development of methods and instruments for measuring subsurface pressures and temperatures in wells. Three subsurface recording instruments have been constructed, and two are being developed. The first instrument, a recording pressure gage, was developed by Nowels. The second, a combination pressure- and temperature-recording gage, was developed by Reistle, who also deserves most of the credit for the development of the third instrument, a recording pressure gage of new design described in this report. The instruments under development at the present time are a recording pressure gage, built on the same principle as the one described in this report but designed for higher pressures, and a new temperature-recording gage, which employs the same principle as the pressure gages but is actuated by the vapor pressure of a highly volatile liquid confined in the temperature element."

The cited reference states in the introduction: "The work of Sclater and Stephenson[104] in 1928 probably more than any other marked the beginning of accurate subsurface measurements of reservoir conditions." In 1933, Hawthorn[105] gave a clear description of the 10 different kinds of instruments in use at that time, divided into 5 different types.

By that time, the Amerada gage—reported by Millikan and Sidwell[106] in 1931, the Humble gage, the MacDonald gage, and others were available on the market; and all progressive oil companies soon equipped their engineers with one or another of the subsurface instruments in order to obtain pressures and temperatures in wells. Unfortunately, there were times when the number of runs made in a day seemed to be more important to those making the tests than the requirement of stabilized flow in a well and the need for repeated calibration of the instruments to obtain an accuracy of readings commensurate with the time and money spent in obtaining the data.

Probably one of the first field-wide applications of subsurface pressures was in the East Texas Field during the days of proration. Periodic pressure surveys were made in designated key wells and pressure-contour maps were drawn at specified intervals with which to control allowables. Production techniques were influenced accordingly to prevent rapid updip movement of water from the west.

Another area where reservoir pressures were applied to correct a very unsatisfactory condition was in the State of Kansas. Here the desired engineering data were obtained by using liquid-level data. During the days of proration, operators were prone to install large pumping equipment in order to lift a maximum amount of oil during the periods designated for "potential" testing. However, after the test was over, conventional pumping equipment was used. This practice resulted in enormous, unwarranted costs, and many wells were ruined by drawing water into them as a result of the high rate of production from the lime formations during the test period.

Engineers working with the state officials developed a program for taking fluid levels while the wells were being pumped at reasonable rates by the regularly installed pumping equipment. This cooperation led to great saving to the operators, protection to the public against loss of oil underground because of early water intrusion, and an amicable proration arrangement satisfactory to the operators and to the Kansas Corporation Commission. (See ref. 101, p. 80.)

Although the preceding discussion has been mainly on reservoir pressures, corresponding reservoir temperatures are implied. Various subsurface-pressure gages have different means of obtaining and recording the temperatures as the pressure readings are taken. Some depend on maximum-reading thermometers; others, like the Bureau of Mines and Amerada gages, are of the recording type.

Actually, the study of earth temperatures antedates the determination of pressures and temperature in oil and gas wells by many years—in fact, centuries.[107, 108] These early earth-temperature observations in Europe and those made in this country,[109] particularly in deep wells in West Virginia about 1890, were primarily those of geoscientists and geologists in contrast with those made later by petroleum engineers to obtain oil-reservoir data.

Van Orstrand,[110] who became recognized as a pioneer in the science of earth temperatures with particular reference to the geology of oil fields, states that his first attempt to correlate temperature with structure was in Oklahoma in 1919, working in cooperation with Dr. George C. Matson, then chief geologist of the Gypsy Oil Company.

In 1926, the American Petroleum Institute initiated its Fundamental Research Project No. 25, "The Determination of Geothermal Gradients in Oil Fields in Anticlinal Structure." Oklahoma, Texas, and California were chosen for the first work, which was started in the spring of 1927. Heald,[111] reporting on the first three years of work, made special reference to the assistance given by the United States Geological Survey and the cooperation of Van Orstrand, who advised in the selection of apparatus, assisted in training and directing observers, studied the results of work, and made and checked certain critical measurements.

Much of the earlier work on temperature gradients was not appreciated by petroleum engineers because of the predominantly geological application of the data. However, with the expansion of reservoir-engineering concepts, more and more dependence was placed on the accurate knowledge of earth temperatures in oil and gas wells.

In 1936, Leonardon[112] pointed to some of the possible uses of thermal measurements in the drilling and cementing of oil wells and gave the results on a few applications. Later in 1936, Schlumberger, Doll, and Perebinossoff[113] gave a more detailed discussion of temperature measurements in oil wells. They showed that, in addition to helping solve problems relating to mud and cement in wells, thermal data may be used in finding flows of water, oil, and gas in different strata.

Deussen and Guyod[114] extended these researches, and in 1937 described the use of temperature measurements to find cemented zones in wells and the possibilities and limitations of correlation between different wells already cased where other methods in use at that time were not applicable.

A typical application of subsurface-well data (predominantly temperatures) to gas-well operation was made in 1937 and 1938 in the Buffalo Field of Texas. An abnormal decline in shut-in pressure was observed in a well in this field not attributable to a head of liquid in the well. A subsurface leak was suspected, and a series of careful depth-temperature tests were made. From the data obtained, the leak was established to be at a depth indicated by the "kick" in the normal temperature gradient for the wells in that field, and the well was repaired.[115]

Additional anomalies were discussed by Millikan[116] in 1940. He cited examples of wells in which temperature data were used to find the depth of *1*, water sands and gas-producing strata; *2*, casing leaks; *3*, the top of the cement behind the casing; and *4*, where to set packers to reduce gas-oil ratios or to plug back in order to shut off water.

The quest for knowledge is never static, and engineers continue to work on appropriate methods of obtaining and using temperature data for logging purposes in gas wells and other bore holes containing no water-base muds. Kunz and Tixier[117] reported in 1955 on a method applicable to conditions similar to those in the San Juan Basin of New Mexico where gas is used as a drilling fluid in drilling the gas wells. They also found the method helpful in studying the effects of hydraulic fracturing.

Reservoir Samples of Fluid and Related Techniques

Although pressure core barrels did not find extended use, as mentioned, samplers for obtaining fluid under pressure in wells changed many concepts regarding reservoir behavior and, accordingly, led to better production techniques. Sclater and Stephenson (ref. 104, p. 123) had described a "thief" for sampling fluids under pressure in their 1928 paper before the AIME, but it remained for Lindsly[118] to call dramatic attention to the need for thorough and systematic sampling and analysis of subsurface fluid samples in an oil field. This he did in his epoch-marking paper on a study of bottom-hole samples of East Texas crude oils before the American Petroleum Institute, Division of Production, in Tulsa, Okla. on May 19, 1933. This was at a time when not only were conditions in that field uncertain but also the whole industry had a bad case of the "jitters" because of over-production.

Earlier work showed Lindsly[119] that bottom-hole samples were more representative of subsurface mixtures (under the then-known methods of sampling and recombining surface samples) because they were obtained at reservoir temperatures and pressures with no separation of constituents. Having collected his samples underground, he drew upon the experience of refiners and measured gas coming out of solution by the methods of "flash" and "differential" liberation.

The significant part of Lindsly's findings, so far as the operators were concerned in their production techniques, was the fact that the reservoir oil in the East Texas Field was under-saturated with gas and that no gas came out of solution in the oil until the pressure on the oil was reduced to 740 psi at a temperature of 146 F, and that combined liberation and thermal effects caused an overall shrinkage of the reservoir oil of approximately 30 percent by the time it reached the stock tanks.

An interesting commentary on the application of oil compressibility data to the East Texas oil field shows that basic research performed at a much earlier date and in a seemingly unrelated field of activity may have direct and practical application to the researches of the petroleum engineer. When such large factors of compressibility and related phenomena pertaining to the East Texas oil field were observed and were so unexpected, the Bureau of Mines was cautious in approving the release of this information until it was more carefully checked. Some thought that further tests should be made before publication of the results. However, time was of the essence so far as Lindsly's report was concerned; and, as he expressed it, if the compressibility data were held up several weeks for checking, "the color would be taken out of an Oklahoma sunset."

Accordingly, Dr. L. H. Adams, then Director of the Geophysical Laboratory, Carnegie Institution of Washington, was called upon personally for assistance. With little difficulty, he directed attention to the work of Bridgeman,[120] published in 1912, in which Bridgeman experimented with the compressibility of kerosine from 0 to approximately 15,000 psi. Allowing for the relatively small difference in gravity of kerosine and subsurface oil from the East Texas reservoir and recognizing the differences in equipment used by Bridgeman and Lindsly, the compressibility of kerosine as determined by Bridgeman and the compressibility of East Texas oil as determined by Lindsly were considered to be within the limits of experimental error, and "the color was restored to the Oklahoma sunset"—much to Lindsly's gratification and the immediate benefit of the industry.

While many engineers were learning about the taking and analyzing of bottom-hole samples and interpreting the results, and were applying them to the techniques of production in the East Texas and other fields, a few others were observing still other phenomena relating to the behavior of hydrocarbon liquids in deeper producing zones. These discoveries pertained to retrograde condensation and the phase relations of gases and liquids. Knowledge developed about them was to have a profound effect on the techniques of future oil and gas extraction, particularly throughout the Gulf Coast area. No one can properly evaluate their effect scientifically and nationally within the span of a few short years. The fact stands clear that the base stock obtained from reservoirs of the condensate type made possible the aviation gasoline of superior quality and power needed and used by the Allies in World War II.

Foran[121] reported his observations on and thoughts concerning "water-white oil" in the Big Lake oil field, Texas, at the November 1932 annual meeting of the American Petroleum Institute. At that same meeting, W. N. Lacey, commenting on Foran's paper, gave his first pronouncement of a theory that he and his associates, B. H. Sage and others at California Institute of Technology, have proved and expanded upon in an outstanding manner under API Research Project 37.

In the years that followed, engineers—as a part of their work in these deeper zones of high pressures and temperatures and very high gas-liquid content along the Gulf Coast—learned a great deal about taking wellhead samples after the well or wells had been stabilized. Some samples were proportionate to the volume flowing from a well and immediately were processed in special equipment. The apparatus mounted in a mobile laboratory resembled a miniature separating plant with special provisions for measuring the quantity of liquid obtainable from the flowing stream.

Other simultaneous samples of liquid and gas were and are collected at the well head or at the nearby oil and gas separator during a test period when the volumes of liquid and gas and the corresponding flowing pressures and temperatures are carefully measured. These samples of oil and gas are then recombined in special apparatus at pressures and temperatures duplicating conditions in the well bore. From the recombined samples the same kinds of information are obtained regarding reservoir-oil characteristics as may be obtained from samples of well fluid taken in a "thief" under formation conditions.

Regardless of the method of sampling, various calculations and estimates based upon the reservoir-oil data can now be made relating not only to well performance and production techniques in fields of light as well as heavy gravity oil but also to the character of the reservoir, the phase relations in it, and the quality, quantity, and availability of the reserves.[122]

Offshore Operations and New Horizons

As the years have rolled by and the industry has spread from the tree-covered slopes of Oil Creek, Pa. westward over the prairies into the Rocky Mountains and on to the California Coast, and southward to the flat shores and marshlands of the Gulf Coast—eventually extending beyond the historical "three leagues" into the open waters of the Gulf— great changes in production techniques have taken place. Production of oil and gas at high pressures and temperatures, operated and controlled from boats, barges, and hydroplanes, introduces many complications never contemplated by the pioneers who sat on a driller's throne and watched the walking beam go up and down and gave a twist to the temper screw at just the right instant so that the tools would not pound.

This section makes no attempt to describe the many complicated control operations and techniques developed to avoid blowouts, contamination of coastal waters, damage from storms, corrosion of equipment (both above and below the surface of the waves), and all the other factors that make a particularly hazardous venture of sinking a barge to shallow bottom—or building a platform—and drilling several wells from one or the other of these structures. Reference has been made to "storm chokes" that close automatically when there is damage to the well head. Nowhere perhaps is teamwork more essential than on the drilling barge or the offshore platform. Directional drilling is essential in order that one platform or base may serve its most useful purpose. Multiple-well completions are another factor that make the expenditure of several million dollars for one venture worth the risk because of the several separate reservoirs that may be penetrated by the drill. Thus, one well may be made to produce from two or more different pay formations at the same time.*

In the earlier days, such practices were not looked upon favorably and were thought to be non-conducive to obtaining the greatest recovery of oil, but engineers have found a way.

Multiple-completion practices are not confined to offshore operations. With modern means for perforating casing with bullets or by jet methods, new and improved packers, side-door chokes, and other devices, it is now possible to produce oil or gas from two or more formations in the same well and keep each separated from the other. Also, pumping equipment has been designed and is being used to handle two different zones at the same time while keeping the production separated; or one zone can be pumped while the other may flow its production. Gas lift also has been adapted to dual completion with good results.

Thus, the production techniques of the birth years of the petroleum engineer *per se* (the decade of 1914-1924, approximately) are made to shrink to a small stature by comparison with 1957-1958 techniques which include such items as dual completions—which, as now made, are equivalent to completing two separate wells at virtually the cost of one; directional drilling; long-range weather reports; the construction and placing of great man-made structures of steel alloys and concrete that resist corrosion, wind, and water in fair weather and foul in water 20 or more fathoms deep; submerged pipelines with which to conduct the highly volatile well fluids to shore installations where they are processed and sent to market as liquids and gas.

Yet, what was learned in those earlier days makes present-day practices possible and lifts the horizon of thinking to distant vistas. The physical scientists and their engineering partners in the petroleum game are never static. This is a dynamic age in which the human race

---

*Three-zone completion is not common, but the practice is being applied successfully and is growing. Recently (1960), 5-zone completion was announced.

lives vigorously, dangerously, and scientifically. Who can say with surety how far we may go literally in our offshore operations and how far figuratively in our "space travel" in thinking and execution—far beyond our present horizons. The scientists will supply the numbers, and the engineers will show the way.

CONCLUDING STATEMENT

Petroleum engineering as a recognized profession is only about 40 years old, although there were individual petroleum engineers, in fact, a few years earlier. Most of them were called technologists, or were known by their "Founder" Society titles of Civil, Mechanical, Electrical, and Mining Engineer.

As recounted in this chapter, the initial contributions of the engineering profession to the techniques of oil production and control were looked upon with disfavor by the majority of operators. Nevertheless, the advances made—frequently in the face of opposition—have changed a haphazard "drill-and-be-damned" attitude into a consistent, progressive movement of engineering reliability to drill carefully, to complete in accordance with the known attributes of the reservoir, and to produce by means of a well-determined outline based upon techniques applicable to the well and reservoir conditions and a measure of control consistent with economic conditions of the time.

No one can challenge the statement that the oil industry has attained its present position of greatness in large measure because men and women of imagination saw the need for research, performed it, and made engineering application of the results to bring forth better techniques of production and control—ever mindful of the authors' original definition and consistent use of this term, which is to conduct "oil-field operations in accordance with the best-known production techniques so as to utilize the reservoir energy most efficiently and thereby increase the ultimate recovery of oil and gas from the producing strata."

The stimulating challenge to the petroleum engineer is to find new and better ways to recover economically a greater quantity of oil and gas from the strata in which they are found. He has solved many of the problems with the aid of the mathematician, the chemist, the biologist, and others schooled in the scientific field; but so long as another barrel of oil remains in the oil reservoirs for every barrel produced from them, the challenge remains.

This chapter has described the high points of only a few of the great number of production techniques that have evolved during the history of the industry—many of them within the last 4 decades of recognized engineering participation. To make these techniques effective, many types of equipment have been developed to assist in producing and controlling production—many ways of computing and projecting the production of wells, leases, and fields into the future have been evolved. During the same time, improvements in drilling and well-completion techniques have kept pace and have had marked influence on oil-production methods. Likewise, cooperative development, unit operation, proration controls, carefully planned well-spacing programs, and other conservation measures have all had their beneficial effects. However, widely diversified ownership of mineral rights on small tracts of land, which is the American heritage, frequently precludes the application of some of the more efficient production techniques and controls.

Petroleum engineers know how to produce oil more efficiently and to apply controls in better ways with the passing years, but sometimes technology cuts across property lines, existing man-made laws, rules and regulations—even that formidable barrier, public opinion, sometimes based upon misinformation, which requires patience and education to overcome.

This situation could be improved and a greater percentage of oil and gas recovered at less cost if it were possible to develop each pool and produce oil from it as a single unit maintaining the correlative rights of all shareholders. Under such conditions, the petroleum engineer would not have to be bound and restricted by property interest but would be free to apply the best possible techniques of production and control. In conclusion, the word "control" is again used with the meaning maintained throughout this chapter—"conservation through engineering."

REFERENCES*

[1]Fowler, H. C: Developments in the American Petroleum Industry, 1914-19: Exploration, Drilling, Production, and Transportation (A Review and Digest), *U. S. Bur. Mines Information Circ. 7171* (1941).

[2]George, H. C: *Oil Well Completion and Operation, Cooperative Report—United States Bureau of Mines and State of Oklahoma,* University of Oklahoma Press, 1931.

[3]Swigart, T. E. and Bopp, C. R: Experiments in the Use of Back Pressures on Oil Wells, *U. S. Bur. Mines TP 322* (1924); extracted and published under the title "Experiments on Back Pressure on Oil Wells," by T. E. Swigart in *Am. Assoc. Petroleum Geologists Bull.,* **7** [1], 37 Jan.-Feb. (1923).

[4]Lovejoy, J. M: Effect of Back Pressure on Wells in Brock Field, *Trans. Am. Inst. Mining Met. Engrs.,* **70**, 1153 (1924).

[5]*Rig and Reel Magazine:* Pumping with Endless Cables, 1, March (1923).

[6]Carll, John F: *Report of Progress, Second Geological Survey of Pennsylvania, 1875 to 1879,* 325.

[7]Kirwan, M. J: Methods and Reasons for Oil Well Shooting, *Calif. State Mining Bur. Bull. 82,* 82 (1918).

[8]Van Gelder, Arthur, and Schlatter, Hugo: *History of the Explosives Industry in America,* Columbia University Press, New York, 1927.

---

*The authors are indebted to Miss V. Vern Hutchinson, Librarian, Petroleum Experiment Station, U. S. Bureau of Mines, Bartlesville, Okla., for finding and carefully checking many of these references.

[9]Munroe, C. E. and Hall, C: A Primer on Explosives for Metal Miners and Quarrymen, U. S. Bur. Mines Bull. 80, 125 (1915).

[10]Hamontre, H. C; Taliaferro, D. B; McClung, C. F; and Mueller, F. G: Bureau of Mines Liquid Level Gage, U. S. Bur. Mines RI 5060 (1954).

[11]Hamontre, H. C; Armstrong, F. E; and Mueller, F. G: Bureau of Mines Wellbore Caliper, U. S. Bur. Mines RI 5092 (1954).

[12]Hill, H. B: Increasing Production by Shooting, Petroleum Development and Technology in 1925, 101, American Institute of Mining and Metallurgical Engineers, Inc., New York, 1926.

[13]Rison, C. O: Manufacture of Nitroglycerin and Use of High Explosives in Oil and Gas Wells, Trans. Am. Inst. Mining Met. Engrs. (Petroleum Development and Technology) 240 (1928-29).

[14]Putnam, Sherman W. and Fry, William A: Chemically Controlled Acidation of Oil Wells, Ind. Eng. Chem., 26 [9], 921, Sept. (1934).

[15]Heithecker, R. E: Engineering Studies and Results of Acid Treatment of Wells, Zwolle Oil Field, Sabine Parish, La., U. S. Bur. Mines RI 3251, Oct. (1934).

[16]ibid: Effect of Acid Treatment Upon the Ultimate Recovery of Oil from Some Limestone Fields in Kansas, U. S. Bur. Mines RI 3445, April (1939).

[17]Grant, B. F; Duvall, W. I; Obert, L; Rough, R. L; and Atchison, T. C: Use of Explosives in Oil and Gas Wells—1949 Test Results, U. S. Bur. Mines RI 7414, (1950).

Atchison, Thomas C., Jr; Grant, Bruce F; Duvall, Wilbur I: Progress Report on Well Shooting Research, Producers Monthly, 16 [10] 32, Aug. (1952).

Rough, Robert L: Progress Report on Oil-Well-Shooting Research—1954 Tests, U. S. Bur. Mines RI 5345 (1957).

[18]Clark, J. B: A Hydraulic Process for Increasing the Productivity of Wells, Trans. Am. Inst. Mining Met. Engrs. (Petroleum Development and Technology), 186, 1 (1949).

[19]Garland, T. M; Elliott, W. C., Jr; Dolan, Pat; and Dobyns, R. P: Effects of Hydraulic Fracturing Upon Oil Recovery from the Strawn and Cisco Formations in North Texas, U. S. Bur. Mines RI 5371, Nov. (1957).

[20]Elkins, Lincoln F: Reservoir Performance and Well Spacing, Spraberry Trend Area Field of West Texas, Trans. Am. Inst. Mining Met. Engrs. (Petroleum Development and Technology), 198, 177 (1953).

[21]Carll, John F: The Geology of the Oil Regions of Warren, Venango, Clarion, and Butler Counties, Pennsylvania, Second Geological Survey of Pennsylvania, 1875-79, III, 260 (1880).

[22]Washburne, Chester W: The Estimation of Oil Reserves Trends, Trans. Am. Inst. Mining Engrs., LI, 647 (1915).

[23]Lindsly, Ben E. and Berwald, W. B: Effect of Vacuum on Oil Wells, U. S. Bur. Mines Bull. 322 (1930).

[24]Foran, E. V: Effect of Repressuring Producing Sands during the Flush Stage of Production, Petroleum Development and Technology in 1927, 285, American Institute of Mining and Metallurgical Engineers, Inc., New York, 1928.

[25]Beecher, C. E: Repressuring during Early Stages of Development, Trans. Am. Inst. Mining Met. Engrs. (Petroleum Development and Technology), 82, 137 (1929).

[26]Johnson, T. W. and Taylor, S. S: A Study of Oxidation of the Oil in Two Air and Air-Gas Repressuring Projects, U. S. Bur. Mines RI 3325 (1937).

[27]Parks, E. K: Recent Trends in Production Practice, Petrol. World (Los Angeles), Ann. Review, 243 (1939).

[28]Shea, G. B: Some Tools and Methods Used in Cleaning Oil Wells in California, U. S. Bur. Mines RI 3706 (1943).

[29]Taylor, Sam S: Wartime Application of Air-Gas Injection and Oil-Well Reconditioning in the Appalachian Region, U. S. Bur. Mines RI 3777 (1944).

[30]Lewis, James O: Portable Outfit for Cleaning Wells with Air Successfully Used, *National Petrol. News* **16** [**33**] 83, Aug. 13 (1924).

[31]Mills, R. Van A: The Paraffin Problem in Oil Wells, *U. S. Bur. Mines RI 2550* (1923).

[32]*National Petrol. News:* **15** [**34**] 91, Aug. 22 (1923).

[33]Reistle, C. E., Jr: Methods of Dealing with Paraffin Troubles Encountered in Producing Crude Oil, *U. S. Bur. Mines TP 414* (1928).

ibid: Paraffin and Congealing Oil Problems, with a chapter "A Laboratory Study of Rod Waxes" by C. E. Reistle, Jr. and O. C. Blade, *U. S. Bur. Mines Bull. 348* (1932).

[34]Dow, D. B: Oil-Field Emulsions, *U. S. Bur. Mines Bull. 250* (1926).

[35]Shea, G. B: Practices and Methods of Preventing and Treating Crude-Oil Emulsions, *U. S. Bur. Mines Bull. 417* (1939).

[36]Ross, J. S: Engineering Report of Cotton Valley Field, Webster Parish, La., *U. S. Bur. Mines TP 504* (1931).

[37]George, H. C: Surface Machinery and Methods for Oil-Well Pumping, *U. S. Bur. Mines Bull. 224* (1925).

[38]Collins, Ray M: The Mid-Continent Production Situation, *Proc. Am. Pet. Inst. (Prod. Bull. 203)*, 32 (1928).

[39]Miller, H. C: Gas-Lift Method of Flowing Oil Wells (California Practice), *U. S. Bur. Mines Bull. 323* (1930).

[40]Schwartz, F. G; Bopp, C. R; and Morris, W. S: Preliminary Engineering Report on the Seminole Pool, Seminole County, Okla., *U. S. Bur. Mines FR (Field Report)* in cooperation with the State of Oklahoma, July (1928).

[41]*The Oil and Gas Compact Bulletin* (The Interstate Oil Compact Commission) **16** [**1**] June (1957):

Murphy, Bert: Effects of Water Injection and Oil Production Practices on Water-Flood Performance, 51.

Bossler, Robert B: Methods of Curtailing Water-Flood Production, 62.

Hocott, Claude R: Effect of Curtailment on Ultimate Oil Recovery by Secondary Water Flooding, 63.

Buckwalter, John F: A Method for Comparing Water-Flood Results, 77.

Simmons, Arthur C: Water-Flood Curtailment Experiences in the Appalachian Area, 80.

[42]Wheeler, H. A: The Illinois Oil Fields, *Trans. Am. Inst. Mining Engrs.*, **XLVIII**, 533 (1914).

[43]Huntley, L. G: Possible Causes of the Decline of Oil Wells and Suggested Methods of Prolonging Yields, *U. S. Bur. Mines TP 51* (1913).

[44]Cutler, Willard W., Jr: Estimation of Underground Oil Reserves by Oil-Well Production Curves, *U. S. Bur. Mines Bull. 228* (1924).

[45]Cutler, W. W., Jr. and Clute, Walker S: Relation of Drilling Campaign to Income from Oil Properties, *U. S. Bur. Mines RI 2270* (1921).

[46]DeGolyer, E. and Vance, Harold: *Bibliography of the Petroleum Industry, Bulletin of the Agricultural and Mechanical College of Texas, Bull. 83*, 394 (1944).

[47]Miller, F. G: Multiphase-Flow Theory and the Problem of Spacing Oil Wells, *U. S. Bur. Mines Bull. 529* (1954).

[48]Brandenthaler, R. R; Morris, W. S; and Bopp, C. R: Engineering Study of the Seminole Area, Seminole and Pottawatomie Counties, Okla., *U. S. Bur. Mines RI 2997*, May (1930).

[49]Hill, H. B; Rawlins, E. L; and Bopp, C. R: Engineering Report on Oklahoma City Field, Okla., *U. S. Bur. Mines RI 3330*, Nov. (1936).

[50]Carter, D. V: Function and Use of Petroleum Engineering Committees. A paper delivered before a joint meeting of the Illinois Society of Petroleum Engineers and the Illinois Basin Chapter of the American Petroleum Institute, Mt. Vernon, Ill.,

March 1, 1946; published in *Organization and Functioning of Oil-Field Engineering Committees*, Interstate Oil Compact Commission, Oklahoma City, Okla., 5, Sept. (1946).

[51]Oliver, Earl: Stabilizing Influences for the Petroleum Industry, *Trans. Am. Inst. Mining Met. Engrs. (Petroleum Development and Technology)*, **98**, 22 (1932). *ibid.* (and others): Petroleum Stabilization in 1932 (including a symposium on Reservoir Energy led by Joseph B. Umpleby), *Trans. Am. Inst. Mining Met. Engrs. (Petroleum Development and Technology)* **103**, 11 (1933).

[52]Hardwicke, Robert E: *Antitrust Laws, et al., v. Unit Operation of Oil or Gas Pools*, American Institute of Mining and Metallurgical Engineers, Inc., New York, 1948.

[53]Beecher, C. E. and Parkhurst, I. P: Effects of Dissolved Gas upon the Viscosity and Surface Tension of Crude Oil, *Petroleum Development and Technology in 1926*, 51, American Institute of Mining and Metallurgical Engineers, Inc., New York, 1927.

[54]Dow, D. B. and Calkin, L. P: Solubility and Effects of Natural Gas and Air in Crude Oils, *U. S. Bur. Mines RI 2732* (1926).

[55]Miller, H. C: *Function of Natural Gas in the Production of Oil*, A Report of the U. S. Bureau of Mines in cooperation with the Division of Development and Production Engineering of the American Petroleum Institute, 1929.

[56]Wade, Gustav: Mechanical Equipment used in the Drilling and Production of Oil and Gas Wells in the Oklahoma City Field, *U. S. Bur. Mines TP 561*, 67 (1934).

[57]Clark, William A: Bottom-hole Beans—Theory, Methods and Effects of Their Use, *Trans. Am. Inst. Mining Met. Engrs. (Petroleum Development and Technology)* **92,** 206 (1931).

[58]Otis, H. C. and Ross, J. S: Application and Limitation of Bottom-hole Choking, *International Petrol. Technol.*, **8 [10]** 453, Sept. (1931).

[59]Herold, Stanley C: *Analytical Principles of the Production of Oil, Gas, and Water from Wells:* Part II, Reservoirs in Hydraulic Control, Stanford University Press, 107 (1928).

[60]Hager, Dorsey, and McPherson, G. W: Water Troubles in Mid-Continent Oil Fields, and Their Remedies, *Trans. Am. Inst. Mining Met. Engrs.*, **61**, 580 (1919).

[61]Shidel, H. R: Cement Plugging for Exclusion of Bottom Water in Augusta Field, Kansas, *Trans. Am. Inst. Mining Met. Engrs.*, **61**, 598 (1919).

[62]Hill, H. B. and Sutton, C. E: Production and Development Problems in the Powell Oil Field, Navarro County, Texas, *U. S. Bur. Mines Bull. 284* (1928).

[63]Petroleum Investigation: Hearings before a Subcommittee of the Committee on Interstate and Foreign Commerce, House of Representatives, 73rd Congress (Recess) on H. Res. 441, Part 3, 1963 (1934).

[64]DeGolyer, E: Historical Notes on the Development of the Technique of Prospecting for Petroleum, *Science of Petroleum*, Vol. 1, Oxford University Press, pp. 268-275, 1938.

[65]Lewis, James O. and McMurray, William F: The Use of Mud-Laden Fluid in Oil and Gas Wells, *U. S. Bur. Mines Bull. 134*, 6 (1916).

[66]Arnold, Ralph, and Garfias, V. R: The Cementing Process of Excluding Water from Oil Wells as Practiced in California, *U. S. Bur. Mines TP 32* (1913).

[67]Tough, F. B: Methods of Shutting Off Water in Oil and Gas Wells, *U. S. Bur. Mines Bull. 163* (1918).

[68]Baker, R. C: Cement Container, U. S. Patent No. 1,035,674, August 13, 1912.

[69]Kay, F. H: Petroleum in Illinois in 1914 and 1915, *Illinois State Geol. Survey Bull. 33*, 87 (1916).

[70]Perkins, A. A. and Double, Edward: Method of Cementing Oil Wells, U. S. Patent No. 1,011,484, December 12, 1911.

[71]Sawdon, Wallace A: Cementing Off Intervening Water-Bearing Strata in Pay Horizons, *Petroleum Engr.*, **5** [12] 33, Aug. (1934).

[72]Sclater, K. C: Injection Process for Sealing Water Sands, *Petroleum Engr.*, **7** [4] 28, Jan. (1936).

[73]Parsons, C. P: Squeeze Cementing, *The Oil Weekly*, **88** [12] 36, Feb. 28 (1938).

[74]Kennedy, H. T: Chemical Methods for Shutting Off Water in Oil and Gas Wells, *Trans. Am. Inst. Mining Met. Engrs. (Petroleum Development and Technology)*, **118**, 177 (1936) (reprint, p. 175).

[75]Miller, E. B., Jr: Plug-back Work with Plastics, *API Drilling and Production Practice*, 97 (1944).

[76]Garrison, Robert H: Deep Drilling Practice in California, *Petroleum Development and Technology in 1925*, 65, American Institute of Mining and Metallurgical Engineers, Inc., New York, 1926.

[77]Young, H. W. and Estabrook, E. L: Waters of the Salt Creek Field, Wyoming, *Petroleum Development and Technology in 1925*, 255, American Institute of Mining and Metallurgical Engineers, Inc., New York, 1926.

[78]Rall, Cleo G. and Wright, Jack: Analyses of Formation Brines in Kansas, *U. S. Bur. Mines RI 4974* (1953).

Wright, Jack; Pearson, Cynthia; Kurt, Effie T; and Watkins, J. W: Analyses of Brines from Oil-Productive Formations in Oklahoma, *U. S. Bur. Mines RI 5326* (1957).

Ayers, Marion L; Dobyns, Rollie P; and Bussell, Robert Q: Resistivities of Water from Subsurface Formations (North Texas), *Petroleum Engr.* **24** [13] B36, Dec. (1952).

Hawkins, Murphy E: Electrical Resistivities of Oil Field Brines in Northeast Texas, *Petroleum Engr.* **29** [7] B52, July (1957).

[79]Mills, R. Van A: Experimental Studies of Subsurface Relationships in Oil and Gas Fields, *Econ. Geol.*, **XV** [5] 398, July-Aug. (1920).

[80]Miller, F. G. and Miller, H. C: Resumé of Problems Relating to Edge Water Encroachment in Oil Sands, *U. S. Bur. Mines RI 3392* (1938).

[81]Schilthuis, Ralph J: Connate Water in Oil and Gas Sands, *Trans. Am. Inst. Mining Met. Engrs. (Petroleum Development and Technology)*, **127**, 199 (1938) (reprint, p. 259).

[82]Dunlap, Eldon N: Influence of Connate Water on Permeability of Sands to Oil, *Trans. Am. Inst. Mining Met. Engrs. (Petroleum Development and Technology)*, **127**, 215 (1938) (reprint, p. 275).

[83]Stephenson, E. A. and Amstutz, P. T., Jr: Exclusion of Water from Wells, *API Drilling and Production Practice*, 87 (1944). (See U. S. Patent No. 2,377,529 and 2,387,361, "Method of Treating Oil Wells," issued to E. A. Stephenson on June 5 and October 23, 1945, respectively, and assigned to University of Kansas Research Foundation and dedicated to the public.)

[84]Horner, William L: Pressure Maintenance by Water Injection, Midway Field, Arkansas, *API Drilling and Production Practice*, 27 (1945).

[85]Carpenter, Charles B; Anderson, Kenneth F; and Cook, Alton B: Petroleum-Engineering Study of the New Hope Oil Field, Franklin County, Texas, *U. S. Bur. Mines RI 4594*, Sept. (1949).

[86]Morris, W. S: Salt Water Disposal in East Texas, *Petroleum Engr.*, **24** [11] B63, Oct. (1952).

[87]Pierce, H. R. and Rawlins, E. L: The Study of a Fundamental Basis for Controlling and Gaging Natural-Gas Wells, Part 1: Computing the Pressure at the Sand in a Gas Well, *U. S. Bur. Mines RI 2929* (1929); Part 2: A Fundamental Relation for Gaging Gas-Well Capacities, *U. S. Bur. Mines RI 2930* (1929).

[88]Rawlins, E. L. and Schellhardt, M. A: Back-Pressure Data on Natural-Gas Wells and Their Application to Production Practices, *U. S. Bur. Mines Mono. 7* (1936) (revised 1939).

[89]Williams, I. B; Brandenthaler, R. R; and Walker, Morgan; Design and Operation of Gas-Well Siphons, *U. S. Bur. Mines TP 460* (1929).

[90]Dunning, H. N. and Eakin, J. L: Foaming Agents are Low-cost Treatment for Tired Gassers, *Oil Gas J.,* **57 [6]** 108, Feb. 2 (1959).

[91]Eilerts, C. K; Carlson, H. A; Smith, R. V; Archer, F. G; and Barr, V. L: Sodium Chromate as an Inhibitor of Corrosion in Gas-Condensate Wells, *Proc. Nat. Gasoline Assoc. of Am.,* 51 (1946).

Bacon, T. S. and Brown, E. A: Corrosion in Distillate Wells, *Oil Gas J.,* **41[49]** 91, April 15 (1943).

Bacon, Thomas S: High-Pressure Production-Equipment Corrosion, *API Drilling and Production Practice,* 157 (1944).

Menaul, P. L: Causative Agents of Corrosion in Distillate Field, *Oil Gas J.* **43 [27]** 80, Nov. 11 (1944).

[92]McLaughlin, R. P: Protecting California Oil Fields from Damage by Infiltering Water, *Trans. Am. Inst. Mining Engrs.,* **LII,** 225 (1915).

[93]Hager, Dorsey: The Evidence of the Oklahoma Oil Fields on the Anticlinal Theory *Trans. Am. Inst. Mining Engrs.,* **LVI,** 843 (1917).

[94]Ambrose, A. W: Underground Conditions in Oil Fields, *U. S. Bur. Mines Bull. 195* (1921).

[95]Elliott, J. E: The Elliott Core Drills, *Petroleum Development and Technology in 1925,* 58, American Institute of Mining and Metallurgical Engineers, Inc., New York, 1926.

[96]Schlumberger, C. and M. and Leonardon, E. G: Electrical Coring; A Method of Determining Bottom-hole Data by Electrical Measurements, *AIME Tech. Pub. 462,* Feb. (1932).

[97]Taliaferro, D. B. and Heithecker, R. E: Bureau of Mines—API Pressure Core Barrel, *U. S. Bur. Mines RI 3481* (1939).

[98]Sewell, Ben W: The Carter Pressure Core Barrel, *API Drilling and Production Practice,* 69 (1939).

[99]Walker, C. P: Determination of Fluid Level in Oil Wells by the Pressure-wave Echo Method, *Trans. Am. Inst. Mining Met. Engrs. (Petroleum Development and Technology),* **123,** 32 (1937) (reprint, p. 210).

[100]Batcheller, B. C: Apparatus for Locating Obstructions in Tubes, *U. S. Patent No.* 602,422, issued April 19, 1898.

[101]Jakosky J. J: Bottom-hole Measurements in Pumping Wells, *Trans. Am. Inst. Mining Met. Engrs. (Petroleum Development and Technology),* **132,** 62 (1939) (reprint, p. 118).

[102]Cattell, R. A. and Fowler, H. C: Fluid-Energy Relations in the Production of Petroleum and Natural Gas, *U. S. Bur. Mines Minerals Yearbook,* Part III, 707 (1934).

[103]Berwald, W. B; Buss, H. A; and Reistle, C. E., Jr: Bureau of Mines Multiple-Diaphragm Recording Subsurface-Pressure Gage, *U. S. Bur. Mines RI 3291* (1935).

[104]Sclater, K. C. and Stephenson, B. R: Measurements of Original Pressure, Temperature, and Gas-oil Ratio in Oil Sands, *Trans. Am. Inst. Mining Met. Engrs. (Petroleum Development and Technology),* 119 (1928-29).

[105]Hawthorn, D. G: Review of Subsurface Pressure Instruments, *Proc. Am. Pet. Inst., (Prod. Bul. 215),* 11 (1935). See *Oil Gas J.,* **31 [48]** 16-17, 40, April 20 (1933).

[106]Millikan, C. V. and Sidwell, Carroll V: Bottom-hole Pressures in Oil Wells, *Trans. Am. Inst. Mining Met. Engrs. (Petroleum Development and Technology)*, 194 (1931).

[107]Kircheri Athannasii: *Mundus Subterraneus*, vol. II, 184-5, 1678; quoted by Bischof Gustav in *Physical, Chemical and Geological Researches on the Internal Heat of the Globe*, vol. 1, 182, London, 1841.

[108]Prestwich, J: *Collected Papers on Some Controverted Questions of Geology*, 169, Macmillan and Co., 1895.

[109]Darton, N. H: Geothermal Data of the United States, *U.S.G.S. Bull. 701* (1920).

[110]Van Orstrand, C. E: Apparatus for the Measurement of Temperatures in Deep Wells by Means of Maximum Thermometers, *Econ. Geol.*, **XIX [3]** 229, April-May (1924). *ibid:* Some Evidence on the Variation of Temperature with Geologic Structure in California and Wyoming Oil Districts, *Econ. Geol.*, **XXI [2]** 145, March-April (1926).

[111]Heald, K. C: Determination of Geothermal Gradients in Oil Fields on Anticlinal Structure, *Proc. Am. Pet. Inst. (Prod. Bul. 204)*, 102 (1929).

[112]Leonardon, Eugene G: The Economic Utility of Thermometric Measurements in Drill Holes in Connection with Drilling and Cementing Problems, *Geophysics*, **1 [1]** 115, Jan. (1936).

[113]Schlumberger, M; Doll, H. G; and Perebinossoff, A. A: Temperature Measurements in Oil Wells, *J. Inst. Petrol. Technol.* (London), **23**, 1 (1937).

[114]Deussen, Alexander and Guyod, Hubert: Use of Temperature Measurements for Cementation Control and Correlations in Drill Holes, *Am. Assoc. Petroleum Geol. Bull.* **21 [6]** 789, June (1937).

[115]Schellhardt, M. A; Dewees, E. J; and Barlow, W. H: Application of Well-Test Data to the Study of a Specific Gas-Production Problem, *U. S. Bur. Mines RI 3493* (1940); in cooperation with the American Gas Association.

[116]Millikan, C. V: Temperature Surveys in Oil Wells, *Trans. Am. Inst. Mining Met. Engrs. (Petroleum Development and Technology)*, **142**, 15 (1941) (reprint, p. 77).

[117]Kunz, K. S. and Tixier, M. P: Temperature Surveys in Gas Producing Wells, *Trans. Am. Inst. Mining Met. Engrs. (Petroleum Development and Technology)*, **204**, 111 (1955).

[118]Lindsly, Ben E: A Study of "Bottom-Hole" Samples of East Texas Crude Oil, *U. S. Bur. Mines RI 3212*, May (1933).

[119]*ibid:* Preliminary Report on an Investigation of the Bureau of Mines Regarding the Solubility of Natural Gas in Crude Oil, *Trans. Am. Inst. Mining Met. Engrs. (Petroleum Development and Technology)*, 253 (1931).

[120]Bridgeman, P. W: Thermodynamic Properties of Liquid Water to 80° (C) and 12,000 KG M (Kg/CM^2), *Proc. Acad. Arts and Sciences*, **48**, 357 (1912).

[121]Foran, E. V: The Big Lake Oil Field, Reagan County, Texas, *Proc. Am. Pet. Inst.*, *(Prod. Bul. 210)*, 61 (1932).

[122]Eilerts, C. Kenneth, and others: Phase Relations of Gas-Condensate Fluids, *U. S. Bur. Mines Mono. 10*, vol. 1 of 2 vol., (1957); in cooperation with the American Gas Association, published by the Association.

Chapter 12

RESERVOIR ENGINEERING

C. E. Reistle, Jr.

CARL E. REISTLE, JR. was born in Denver, Colorado, in 1901 and graduated from the University of Oklahoma in 1922 with a B.S. degree in chemical engineering. His career in the oil industry began as a roustabout for The Carter Oil Company during summer vacations. Upon graduation he joined the U. S. Bureau of Mines as a junior petroleum chemist. In 1933 Mr. Reistle became chairman of the East Texas Engineering Association and served as such until 1936, when he joined Humble Oil & Refining Company as engineer in charge of the petroleum engineering division. Advancements followed to the positions of chief petroleum engineer, general superintendent of production, and manager of production. He was elected in 1948 to the company directorate; in 1955 to a vice-presidency, and in 1957 to the executive vice-presidency. In 1959 he was elected executive vice-president of the reorganized Humble Oil & Refining Company.

Academic honors include Alpha Chi Sigma, Sigma Tau, Tau Beta Pi, Pi Epsilon Tau, and Sigma Xi. Professional honors include the Anthony F. Lucas medal of AIME, of which society he served as president in 1958. Other affiliations include API — whose *Certificate of Appreciation* he has received, the Mining & Metallurgical Society of America, and councilor status to the scientific and engineering programs of the Universities of Texas and Oklahoma.

Mr. Reistle is the author of over twenty technical papers on a wide range of subjects and the holder of twelve patents. During World War II he was an advisor to the Petroleum Administration for War and later an advisory official on government price administration.

⚜ 12 ⚜

INTRODUCTION

Definition

The history of the principal scientific and engineering fields inevitably recounts the evolution of specialized phases that, in turn, develop into recognized branches of knowledge. Reservoir engineering is such an offspring of petroleum engineering. It may be defined as the applied science concerned with the transfer of fluids to, from, and within natural underground reservoirs. More specifically, it is concerned with the behavior of reservoir fluids and matrix after the reservoir has been pierced by one or more wells and as formation fluids are being removed through these wells.

In the practice of reservoir engineering, the reservoir engineer determines the properties of the reservoir matrix and of its fluids, interprets these data in terms of reservoir-fluid behavior, and recommends the development and production program that will result in the maximum economic recovery of hydrocarbons — spacing of wells, gas-oil and water-oil ratios, rate of production, stimulation procedures, pressure-control program. An important subsidiary function of the reservoir engineer is the prediction of hydrocarbon recovery that can be anticipated under the recommended conditions of development and production. The application of this information to the problems involved in secondary recovery and artificial supplementation of natural energy forces for increasing the recovery of oil and gas provides the reservoir engineer with the opportunity to make his greatest contribution to the industry.

Although the material in this chapter is limited to an historical account of the modern concept of the fluid behavior in producing reservoirs and of the overall development and control of reservoirs, it should be noted that there are other aspects of petroleum technology that are of major importance to the reservoir engineer. The migration of oil and its accumulation in reservoirs are obviously of interest to the thorough reservoir student. Useful qualitative conclusions about reservoir behavior and control can frequently be deduced from geologic and geophysical evidence. Drilling and completion methods, as well as methods of stimulating production from individual wells, are also of concern to the reservoir engineer. Further, even though the reservoir engineer must consider only the most reliable facts and theory available in his evaluation of reservoirs, he must appreciate prevailing economic and legal factors and condition his ultimate recommendations for reservoir development and control to them.

NOTE: The completeness and accuracy of this chapter were facilitated by members of Humble Oil & Refining Company's Production Research and Petroleum Engineering Divisions. This assistance is gratefully acknowledged.

Reservoir Engineering and Conservation

There are two general factors in the evolution of reservoir engineering into its current position as an important petroleum engineering specialty that are of special historic interest. The first is that its development is an excellent example of the tendency of industrial operations to become ever more systematized and increasingly dependent upon organized scientific investigation.

The other is the close parallel and interdependence of the evolution of reservoir engineering and the modern practice of petroleum conservation. In fact, one might logically describe reservoir engineering as the technical son of conservation. Certainly, the political hue and cry raised in the first quarter of this century against "waste of natural resources" in the petroleum industry created a particular impetus for scientific study of behavior and technologic improvement in reservoir control.

Birth of Reservoir Engineering

The need for industrial action became acute when, in 1924, President Coolidge appointed a Cabinet-level Conservation Board to study this alleged waste. He specifically directed the Board to make recommendations concerning the obligation of the Federal Government to regulate the practices of the petroleum industry in order to prevent waste of oil and gas. That the industry recognized this investigation as a challenge to its independence is evidenced by the American Petroleum Institute's initiation of a parallel study shortly after the Federal Conservation Board was established.

The API study apparently convinced the leaders of the industry of the need for organized scientific investigation of oil production, for, at its annual meeting in December 1927, the API Board of Directors authorized the establishment of a Division of Development and Production Engineering. In describing the Board's action, Wallace E. Pratt (a member of the Board) said:

> ". . . One consideration alone moved [the Board] . . . that was that we have the conservation of oil and gas right on top of us. We don't know anything about it, yet we have to find out something that will meet the criticism and answer the charges and suggest the measures that the President's Conservation Board is asking for. Where can we get it if we don't go to the technical men. . .?"

This historic public request for scientific study of oil production and the implied need for industry-wide dissemination of the results of such study may well be termed the birth of reservoir engineering.

Pratt's remarks were presented at an open session of the 1927 API meeting attended by a large number of men who were considered to be the leading academic, government, and industrial experts on production. Some of these men had already made significant contributions to petroleum technology; they and other members of Pratt's audience were subsequently to make notable contributions to the development of reservoir engineering, as well as to other phases of the industry.

Although the general tenor in the discussion at this meeting was apparently one of sober appraisal of deficiencies, there was an underlying current of prophetic optimism indicated in A. C. Rubel's remark that "... we stand on the threshold of a new era in petroleum development and production ... petroleum-engineering methods clearly and unmistakably point the way"; and in that of Max Ball: "This meeting is a starting point for development in production engineering of such extent that we can scarcely conceive."

THE GENERATION OF A SCIENCE (1859-1927)

From Drake to World War I

One of the fundamental facts controlling modern reservoir-engineering practice is that appreciable amounts of gas are dissolved in most crude oils. The presence of this gas in the liquid oil phase lowers its viscosity, specific gravity, and surface tension with a resultant increase in the ease with which it can move through reservoir rock. Furthermore, the expulsive action of this gas as it expands from solution to fill the spaces vacated by produced oil is an important factor in the production from many reservoirs. As early as 1865 Robert Briggs, in a discussion at a Philadelphia meeting of the American Philosophical Society,[1] described petroleum as an intimate mixture of gases and liquids, as did John F. Carll[2] of the Pennsylvania Geological Survey. Edward Orton,[3] State Geologist of Ohio, also emphasized the importance of natural gas in oil production; Orton decried production practices that resulted in the waste of gas. An especially interesting and remarkably accurate hypothesis of the function of hydrostatics and gas expansion in oil production was presented by C. W. Hayes and William Kennedy[4] of the United States Geological Survey in 1903; but many years elapsed before the significance of gas, especially dissolved gas, was appreciated by the industry.

In the latter part of the 19th century, geologists were devoting a great deal of their effort to speculation concerning the origin and accumulation of subterranean fluid reservoirs. As a result of this interest, C. S. Slichter[5,6,7] and F. H. King[8] of the United States Geological Survey undertook detailed studies of the conditions and movements of underground waters. Of special importance was Slichter's use of Darcy's equation to relate pressure and rate of flow of incompressible fluids in porous media. King attempted to define the region of applicability of Darcy's law. He had constructed an

---

[1]References are at the end of the chapter.

apparatus to study the flow properties of cores of water sands. From a study of these data, he concluded that the production of water at a well would affect the pressure in an adjacent well; he also demonstrated that the rate of production is not a linear function of well penetration nor of well diameter.

About this same time several investigators in fields outside of the petroleum industry, notably in soil science, published papers[9,10,11,12] that have proved to be significant in more recent studies of underground flow, especially on the effect of rock geometry on such flow.

Although the studies cited are significant in the light of our present knowledge of reservoir behavior and control, there is no evidence to indicate that they made any appreciable impression upon oil operators of the time. In fact, there is little reason to believe that the practical oil men of the day were devoting much serious thought to the nature and behavior of oil reservoirs. The philosophy of development and production apparently current then was to drill a field rapidly and densely and produce at maximum capacity of natural flow as long as possible. The wells were then placed on pump. A reservoir was considered to be depleted when the pumps were unable to bring up economic amounts of oil or when water production became excessively high. Gas associated with oil was generally regarded as a nuisance except for minor amounts that could be used for fuel in the field or sold to nearby communities and industries. Billions of cubic feet of gas were burned in oil-field flares or simply blown off into the air. Subsurface water was almost universally regarded as a menace to the productivity and life of a field.

However, there were a few voices raised in criticism of certain phases of this philosophy. For example, when Anthony Lucas, the discoverer of Spindletop, returned to Beaumont from a Mexican job in 1904, he was asked by a reporter of the *Beaumont Enterprise* to comment upon the rapid decline in production at Spindletop. He answered that the field had been "punched too full of holes." "The cow was milked too hard," he said, "and moreover she was not milked intelligently." In 1909, David T. Day, who was termed by *Who Was Who In America* as the father of mineral-resources studies in the Federal Government, deplored the rampant waste of gas. As remedial measures he proposed cooperative production by the operators within a field, and legislation to control production rates and to prohibit gas waste.

In actual field operations, several attempts were made to stimulate production beyond that obtainable by natural flow and pumping. Observers had noted an unexpected increase in the rate of production of the Bradford (Pa.) Field within a couple of years after its discovery. An unidentified reporter of the *Oil City (Pa.) Times* reported that "experts . . . have concluded that the increase in production [at Bradford] is due to the entry of surface waters which are pushing more oil to the wells." In

1865, apparently inspired by these observations, operators in the Pithole (Pa.) Field pumped water down several edge wells from which oil production had virtually ceased. According to the *Oil City Times*, ". . . the results are indeed marvelous." Carll *(op. cit.)* stated: "The flooding of an oil district is generally viewed as a great calamity, yet it may be questioned whether a larger amount of oil can be drawn from the rocks in that way than in any other."

Although the function of natural gas in the production of oil was certainly not widely appreciated before the 1920's, there were many early attempts to stimulate recovery by injecting various gaseous fluids, notably air and natural gas, into reservoirs. As was the case for water flooding, the pioneer gas-injection projects were conducted by Appalachian operators. There seems never to have been the prejudice against gas injection that there was against flooding, with the result that more historical data are available.

Among the more successful pioneer gas-injection projects were those conducted by James D. Dinsmoor in Pennsylvania and West Virginia fields beginning about 1890. There is little doubt that Dinsmoor's initial injection program resulted from his observation of the salutory effect of the accidental entry of natural gas from a high-pressure zone into an oil sand of lower pressure in Venango County (Pa.) in 1888. During his career he also tried vacuum methods and, on at least two projects, successfully controlled high gas-oil ratios by applying back pressure.

Shortly after the turn of the century, a competitive gas-injection process which utilized compressed air as the injection fluid was developed by a Marietta, Ohio, operator—I. L. Dunn. The success of Dinsmoor and Dunn resulted in the initiation of many gas-injection projects in various oil provinces of the country. By no means all of these early projects were successful; but, when it is considered that virtually no technical data nor scientific knowledge were available to guide the operators in planning their injection programs, the margin of success is impressive. For example, the Hamilton Corners (Pa.) gas-injection project operated profitably with but little change in procedure and technique for more than 40 years.

Although the stimulation procedures described are of major importance in modern reservoir engineering and their initiators must be credited with major contributions to reservoir control, it should be emphasized that their development was entirely empirical. Most of the early operators were men without technical training and many were prejudiced against geological deductions and engineering studies on oil production.

The United States Bureau of Mines

In 1910 the United States Bureau of Mines was established within the Department of the Interior to study the nation's resources and to recommend programs for their development that would insure a minimum of waste. Four years later a Petroleum Division was established under W. A. Williams. The Petroleum Division of the Bureau of Mines was the first organization in the history of the petroleum industry to make a concerted coordinated effort to understand the mechanics of oil production. From its inception it has emphasized the importance of fundamental understanding of the physicial processes involved in oil production and and of the application of this knowledge to the development and exploitation of reservoirs. With the exception of a few years during which it was charged with the responsibility of supervising production by private lessees from Federal and some Indian lands, the Petroleum Division of the Bureau of Mines has functioned solely as a research agency and technical counselor to government and to the petroleum industry. The importance of the theoretical and laboratory studies of the pioneers in the Bureau of Mines cannot be overemphasized. Similarly the engineering field studies which it pioneered shortly after World War I were forerunners of our modern detailed studies of individual reservoirs.

Perhaps of equal importance with the Bureau's technical contributions to the industry has been its unofficial function as a source of well-trained production engineers and scientists for the petroleum industry. The roster of the application of these principles in order to improve the efficiency and technical leaders of the production industry of the past three decades. It is of interest to note that the majority of the Division's early scientists had earned academic degrees in geology, or civil or mining engineering.

The Exposition of Theory

The first work of the Petroleum Division of the Bureau of Mines was a survey of waste in the oil fields. The earliest reports of such men as A. W. Ambrose, R. Arnold, R. S. Blatchley, C. H. Beal, F. G. Clapp, V. R. Garfias, A. G. Heggem, L. G. Huntley, J. O. Lewis, W. F. McMurray, and J. A. Pollard were largely concerned with losses of oil resulting from premature flooding and surface waste. However, the emphasis was soon changed in such a way as to indicate a growing consciousness of the physical principles involved in oil production and of the importance of the application of these principles in order to improve the efficiency of production. The following statements gleaned from their reports[13] during the first decade of the Division's existence would, without major modification, be appropriate material for a modern text on reservoir engineering:

> "The character and porosity of the oil rock affect . . . drainage, the most favorable material being a sandstone that is coarse and porous, though not loose enough to allow the setting up of sharply defined drainage channels." "The gaseous constituents of petroleum exist chiefly in . . . solution with the oil . . . and as such expand and escape when the pressure is relieved by a well." "Often there is more gas than could be held in solution under the pressures in the oil sand, and . . . the

excess is found in separate bodies." ". . . intrastrata gas pressure is the means of keeping up the continuous movement of fluid to the well." "The physical properties of viscosity, capillarity, and adhesion of an oil . . . tend to oppose expulsion of oil from the sand." "The gas absorbed in the oil . . . is the principal source of energy for expelling the oil from the sand. The flow of oil (may be) assisted by the presence of free undissolved gas which may overlie the oil or by the movements of water. Gravitation is comparatively a weak, slow-acting force."

"In some fields water seems to 'set' the sands, and it is more difficult to get them to produce, once water has been on them." "The flowing period of a well's life is due to the difference in pressure in the sand and in the well. The duration . . . of high production depends on local conditions, such as a porosity and structure of the sand, the extent . . . of the pool, the character of the oil and its associated gas, the rock pressure, the position of the well, the existence of an underlying artesian water supply." "As oil and gas are recovered . . . their places will always be taken by some other medium . . . expanded gas from the same formation . . ., water from the same stratum [or] from the surface [or] from an underlying formation." "That gravitation tends to cause the accumulation of the remnant of oil in some pools is undoubted."

"It has been found that the ultimate flush production from . . . restricted wells has almost invariably been more than the unrestricted flow from neighboring wells." ". . . Probably the only generally feasible methods for recovering more oil from the formations after natural forces have been exhausted involve the forcing of gases (air or natural gas) or liquids (water) through the oil-bearing formation."

"In spacing wells the utilization of the oil in a pool, and the thorough draining of the maximum amount of territory with the minimum number of wells are the two main considerations." ". . . if it were desired so to drill a large area that a certain production would be obtained . . . through a long term, . . . wells would be spaced in accordance with . . . the area that could be drained with comparative efficiency by a single well."

"The maximum usefulness could be derived from a pool of oil or gas by its being controlled by one competent management, as under such conditions it could be developed with the least waste and at the smallest cost. To get the best results the operators should act in unison for the protection of their common sources of supply and for their mutual benefit. To make cooperation among the producers in a field effective, it seems necessary for them to organize with some central authority that can furnish protection against careless, inefficient, or even deliberately negligent acts of individuals."

"By applying pressure to the pool as a whole a greater ultimate production might be obtained . . . and thereby result in an increased profit to individual operators." "In the early life of an oil field while much natural gas is still being produced . . ., it might be profitable to . . . put it (the gas) back into the oil sand, by this means both accelerating and increasing the recovery of the oil."

Although it is freely admitted that irrefutable proof of most of the hypotheses and conclusions quoted did not exist at the time they were published and that an equally impressive compilation could probably be made of invalid quotes from the same publications, recognition must be granted these men as pioneers in production theory. It is regrettable that their work was not studied and evaluated more widely by the petroleum industry of the day.

Two of the men cited—J. O. Lewis and A. W. Ambrose—deserve special mention, not only for their personal contributions to the development of reservoir theory, but especially for the inspirational influence they exerted on their colleagues and their special efforts to encourage the initiation and prosecution of laboratory experiments on recovery phenomena.

Laboratory and Field Studies

Near the end of World War I, field and laboratory studies were initiated by Bureau of Mines engineers and scientists which were the precursors of our modern industrial production-research and reservoir-evaluation programs.

Among the pioneer field studies were those of Cushing by Carl H. Beal,[14] Comanche by T. E. Swigart,[15] and the Rocky Mountains by F. B. Tough.[16] The latter is of special interest because of Tough's enlightened comments upon reservoir mechanics. A few years later, Swigart and C. R. Bopp[17] reported an exhaustive field study that indicated back-pressure could be used to control gas-oil ratios of producing wells.

In 1920 R. Van A. Mills published the first of two publications[18] reporting his studies of fluid relations in a laboratory reservoir model. He proved the existence of "coning," "by-passing," and "entrapment" at high rates of production and demonstrated the importance of sand texture on fluid flow; he also observed a direct qualitative relation between saturation and permeability for water or oil. In 1921 A. F. Melcher,[19] a member of the U.S. Geological Survey described a laboratory method for determining porosity in which he measured bulk and pore volumes of cores. The reports of D. B. Dow and C. E. Reistle, Jr.,[20, 21] in 1924 on laboratory determinations of gas solubilities in oil at various pressures indicated an early appreciation of the importance of properties of reservoir fluids. In 1926, Dow and L. P. Calkin[22] published the results of a later study on gas solubility which had taken place more or less concurrently with that of C. E. Beecher and I. P. Parkhurst.[23] In

1921 the first of an important continuing series of crude analyses was reported by Bureau scientists.[24]

Another important phase of Bureau of Mines studies relating to reservoir behavior was the estimation of reservoir productivity. Certainly the most influential of these studies were the analyses by J. O. Lewis and Carl H. Beal[25] and by W. W. Cutler, Jr.,[26] of production-decline curves as a method of estimation of recoverable oil.

State Technical Activities

In 1915, the California legislature established a Department of Petroleum and Gas under the Board of Mineral Industries "... to so supervise the drilling, operation, maintenance and abandonment of petroleum or gas wells as to prevent damages to the petroleum and gas deposits of the state from infiltrating water and other causes."

Gleanings from the first three *Reports of the State Oil & Gas Supervisor* (1915-1916) indicate that the staff of the Department, which included R. P. McLaughlin (the supervisor), Chester Naramore, M. J. Kirwan, R. B. Moran, and R. E. Collom, had an advanced view of reservoir behavior:

"To economically extract oil from its natural underground reservoirs requires the most complete knowledge possible on two subjects: first, the natural or geological conditions governing the creation and preservation of the reservoirs and, second, the artificial or mechanical conditions created near the reservoir by efforts to drill wells and extract the oil ..."

"The edge water in the Coalinga Field is by no means a menace to the productive life of the field. .... The rate of encroachment is slow, and depends largely on the rate at which oil in the up-slope portion of the reservoir is removed ..."

"It is self-evident that if wells are too closely spaced, some of them are merely a waste of labor and materials."

Although the *Reports* occasionally commend a particular operator for good engineering practice, there is little doubt that the Department took a dim view of the overall technical health of the industry. Witness the statement that:

"... probably no large business is as inefficiently conducted as is that involved in the production of oil in California, notwithstanding the fact that mechanical operations here seem to be more advanced and improved than in any part of the world."

In the first quarter of the 20th century, several other state legislatures — notably Louisiana and Oklahoma — enacted statutes directed principally to the conservation of gas, but the available reports of their administrators were more legalistic than technical. Scientists on several state geological surveys, notably W. L. Russell[27] of South Dakota and

C. R. Fettke[28] of Pennsylvania, developed laboratory methods for determining some useful reservoir properties by core analysis.

Stirrings within Industry

There is no question about the dominant position of the U. S. Bureau of Mines in the scientific study of reservoir behavior and control prior to 1928. However, there were two developments in Oklahoma in the 1920's that presaged the vigorous research program that many production companies were to undertake a few years later.

About 1923 H. L. Doherty, president of H. L. Doherty & Co. which was trustee of the Cities Service Companies, apparently became convinced that the United States would soon be involved in another war. He firmly believed that victory in such a conflict would be dependent upon an adequate supply of petroleum. He was also convinced that the production practices then in general use constituted a profligate waste of this country's potential supply and, therefore, a threat to its security. As a remedy he proposed the enactment of a national law requiring unit operation of oil pools and restriction of production. This proposition was vigorously opposed by most other oil executives, but exerted a tremendous impact on the development of conservation theory and, therefore, on the prosecution of recovery studies.

Doherty had had no formal training in science or engineering, but he was a keen observer and an avid student. Undoubtedly his close contacts with personnel of the Bureau of Mines at the Bartlesville (Okla.) Experiment Station strongly influenced his technical thinking. He employed C. E. Beecher, one of the first three "oil-recovery engineers" hired by the Bureau (in 1919), to undertake laboratory experiments on the relations between reservoir gas and oil. The study, reported by Beecher and Parkhurst *(op. cit.)*, apparently was prosecuted concurrently with that of Dow and Calkin *(op. cit.)* at the Bureau of Mines Experiment Station. It included the measurement of viscosity and surface tension of gas-saturated or bubble-point crude oils. Beecher and Parkhurst concluded that dissolved gas lowers viscosity and surface tension and, therefore, increases the efficiency of oil recovery.

Ponca City, Okla., a few miles across the northern Oklahoma plains from Bartlesville, was the headquarters of another individualistic oil executive, E. W. Marland, who—like Doherty—had no formal training in science or engineering but became interested in recovery technology. There is no indication that Marland himself tried to learn much about petroleum science. Certainly he was not inspired by any crusading zeal such as Doherty's advocacy of compulsory unitization and controlled production — in fact, he actively opposed Doherty's proposals for years. But Marland, probably as a result of the influence of his chief geologist, Irving Perrine, came to realize the importance of scientific investigation of petroleum problems.

In 1925 he hired W. P. Haseman to establish a petroleum-research organization. Early the following year, the laboratories were opened. Among the research personnel were chemists, geologists, engineers, and physicists — men such as W. V. Vietti, E. A. Eckhardt, Ralph Wyckoff, L. F. Athy, and A. F. Melcher. The organization included a special section for production research (under the direction of Dr. Vietti) which immediately began research projects on gas saturation, crude shrinkage, and the measurement of bottom-hole pressure.

During the remaining few years that Marland retained control of the Marland Oil Co., the research organization flourished. However, the management which succeeded Marland did not share his appreciation for research, and the department was liquidated. Several of the staff were to make significant contributions to our knowledge of reservoir behavior and control when in the employ of later research organizations of other institutions.

THE ROAD TO MATURITY (1928-1955)

In retrospect one might ask why the petroleum industry was not immediately inspired to evaluate and extend the pioneer ideas and studies briefly described in the preceding paragraphs. In justification of the industry's failure to have developed the necessary information to "meet the criticisms . . . and suggest the measures" in 1927, it should be noted that the tremendous increase in demand for petroleum products created by the widespread use of the internal-combustion engine was a relatively new factor. Further, the legal climate of the "rule of capture" then prevailing practically demanded that operators place their principal emphasis on rapid recovery rather than maximum recovery. Any experienced operator of the day had recurrently observed prophecies of oil famine drowned in a flood of oil from some newly discovered Seminole.

The oil-production industry may have been slow in undertaking a comprehensive technical study of its operation, but it did not dally after it became convinced of the need for such study. Although the science of reservoir engineering is not complete today, the advances in knowledge of reservoir behavior and control which emanated from the myriad competing companies of the industry between 1927 and World War II constitute a record of brilliant scientific achievement. The increased recovery of oil which has resulted is an excellent example of the progress that can be made by private enterprise operating in a climate of economic freedom. It is worthy of note that this era includes one of the most serious economic depressions in the history of the United States — a condition that might be expected to discourage industrial research.

The Properties of Reservoirs and Their Fluids and Matrices

The first problems in any scientific investigation are the determination of the data that are pertinent and the development of methods of obtaining them. Many of the pioneer petroleum technologists recognized that recovery is affected by the character of the reservoir fluids and of the reservoir matrix — thus, the characterization of fluids and rocks is a basic aspect of reservoir engineering. Since it is patently impossible to make a direct study of a reservoir far below the earth's surface, data must be collected by remote measuring devices in the bores of individual wells or from samples of reservoir rocks and fluids recovered through the wells.

One of the principal limitations of reservoir engineering today is that the conclusions about the reservoir are based upon samples and physical measurements from the small fraction of the reservoir pierced by wells. Needless to say, the validity of conclusions about the reservoir is a direct function of the validity of data extrapolated beyond these relatively widely scattered observation points. Significant changes in reservoir properties may occur within such small areas of a reservoir that their existence is not indicated by data from the meagre sampling possible. Although rigorous quantitative treatment is impossible for such reservoirs, experience has proved that useful qualitative conclusions can be deduced.

Pressure and Temperature

Because of the fugacious nature of reservoir fluids, their behavior and properties are profoundly influenced by both temperature and pressure. These data are important in determining the phase relationships and the viscosity and compressibility of the reservoir fluids needed for the prediction of reservoir behavior. Further, relative pressure data are useful in establishing certain physical characteristics of the reservoir such as homogeneity, communication with surrounding formations, and average permeabilities around the various observation points.

During the 1920's, instruments for measuring maximum pressure in well bores were developed independently by several workers in oil companies as well as in the Bureau of Mines; there is evidence that such measurements were attempted as early as 1918. Among the earlier published papers reporting the measurements and utilization of bottom-hole pressure is that of K. C. Sclater and B. R. Stephenson[29] which disclosed that gas-oil ratios within reservoirs are appreciably different from those measured at the surface. T. V. Moore,[30] and H. R. Pierce and E. L. Rawlins[31] of the Bureau of Mines, reported studies relating potential production and bottom-hole pressures. An interesting application of pressure data was E. V. Foran's demonstration[32] that the initial rapid pressure decline in the East Texas Field was caused by production of oil more rapidly than the driving water could advance, thus effectively changing the producing mechanism from water drive to dissolved-gas drive. Moore, R. J. Schilthuis, and W. Hurst[33] developed a theoretical relation of bottom-hole pressure data, rate of production, and permeability. The usefulness of bottom-hole measurements was appreciably increased by the development of continuously recording instruments such as the pressure gages invented by P. Comins[34] and Geophysical Research Corporation, and reported by C. V. Millikan and C. V. Sidwell.[35] With improved present-day instruments, a precision of plus or minus 1 percent can be obtained.

Temperature variations within a reservoir (either under static or dynamic conditions) are usually not as erratic as pressure changes. Except for the time lag required for thermometers to attain equilibrium at a given depth, satisfactory temperature data for natural reservoir performance studies were more easily obtained than the requisite pressure data.

Among the earliest workers to measure subsurface temperatures was C. E. Van Orstrand, a physicist with the U.S.G.S., who, in 1916, published the first of an impressive series of papers reporting his work on subsurface thermometry and the geologic interpretation of subsurface temperature variations. Within recent years temperature surveys have proved especially useful in studying the progress of fluid-injection projects and the mechanical operation of individual wells.

Sampling and Analysis of Reservoir Fluids

The rate at which oil can be produced is influenced by its viscosity, density and the surface forces existing between it, the matrix, and retained fluids. Information about the physical state and composition of the oil is useful in predicting the volume changes that take place between the reservoir and the collecting lines, and the phase changes that will occur during the productive life of the reservoir. These data can be determined on samples collected in the well bore opposite the producing zone or on samples of the produced fluids recombined at reservoir temperature and pressure. Compositional analysis for reservoir studies is usually limited to a distillation of the produced fluids into fractions boiling in certain ranges; the complete analysis of a crude oil has never been effected.

Sclater and Stephenson *(op. cit.)* were among the first men to attempt to collect samples from the well bore opposite a producing zone. Ben E. Lindsly[36] described an improved Bureau-developed sampler that he used in East Texas in 1932; he also reported techniques for testing the collected sample. An important observation by Lindsly was that the saturation pressure of the reservoir was less than the average bottom-hole pressure. A further result[37] of his East Texas sample studies was an analysis of the effect on reserve and recovery estimations resulting from shrinkage on production. Shortly thereafter, L. A. Pym[38] and R. J. Schilthuis[39] also described independently developed instruments and testing procedures for subsurface samples and discussed the significance of the data obtained from subsurface surveys.

As mentioned earlier, Beecher and Parkhurst, and Dow and Calkin measured viscosity and density of crude oil containing dissolved gas in the middle 1920's. Ten years later, B. H. Sage, J. E. Sherborne, and W. N. Lacey[40] made further studies of oil viscosities as functions of temperature and pressure. In 1938 Sage and Lacey[41] reported experimental data relating viscosity and composition. The viscosity of gaseous reservoir fluids was measured by D. L. Katz and L. B. Bicher[42] in 1944.

In 1943 D. T. Jones[43] reported measurements of the surface tension of crude oil under reservoir conditions. About four years later C. R. Hocott[44] published data on the interfacial tension between reservoir samples of oil and water at reservoir temperature and pressure. Although surface tension undoubtedly is important in the mechanics of oil production, its influence cannot yet be quantitatively evaluated.

Core Studies

Most of the properties of oil-bearing formations which are pertinent to oil production (porosity, permeability, fluid content, the salinity of the formation water, productive capacity, residual oil and gas, mineral composition, texture, stratification) can be determined by the analysis of cored samples of reservoir rock. Obviously, it is desirable that the condition of such cores be substantially the same when analyzed as in the reservoir.

The fluid system within the pores of the rock almost always consists of at least two phases, gas or oil and water; all three may be present. Some, or all, of the water phase will not be produced with the oil and/or gas. Similarly, in natural flow, there is never complete recovery of the reservoir hydrocarbons. Thus, to calculate the hydrocarbons in place in a reservoir, one must know the pore volume, or porosity, and the relative amounts of the fluid components. In order to determine the recoverable oil, he must also determine the irreducible saturations of these components, i.e., the portions that are unrecoverable under a given driving mechanism. The volume of unrecoverable fluid is controlled by surface forces existing among rock, water, oil and gas, the continuity of paths, and the relative permeability of the rock to the produced fluid(s) and to the displacing fluid(s). The latter factor is important because as one fluid (oil) is displaced from a unit volume, the relative volume (or saturation) of the displacing fluid (water or gas) is increased. Permeability to a particular fluid is a direct function of the saturation of the fluid. Therefore, as production of oil takes place, the permeability to oil decreases and that of the displacing fluid(s) increases.

The degree of salinity of the connate water is also useful in reservoir studies because the ratio of the resistivity of the water-saturated rock and that of the connate water is proportional to saturation (and, therefore, productivity).

Melcher (*op. cit.*), who published methods for porosity and permeability determinations on oil sands in 1921, was the most notable pioneer core analyst of the petroleum industry. However, it should be re-emphasized that technologists in other fields had long before measured and studied porosity and permeability. A significant advance in the knowledge of the influence of rock properties on production was the work of G. H. Fancher, J. A. Lewis, and K. B. Barnes[45] which demonstrated a difference between permeability to air and to water; these investigators attributed this to hydration of intergranular clay particles. Also in 1933, R. D. Wyckoff, H. G. Botset, M. Muskat, and D. W. Reed[46] defined the unit of permeability (the darcy) and demonstrated a relationship between permeability and productive capacity.

The two reports cited inspired a great deal of investigative work to obtain data on the flow of multi-phase systems. In 1936, G. L. Hassler, R. R. Rice, and E. H. Leeman[47] described a technique for studying gas flow as a function of oil saturation in porous rocks. Later that year Wykoff and Botset[48] introduced the term "relative permeability," their data for flow through unconsolidated sands of varied permeabilities having indicated that relative permeability to oil did not vary appreciably with the viscosity of the oil. Several years later M. C. Leverett and W. B. Lewis[49] reported a study of three-phase flow.

In 1926, Fettke *(op. cit.)* reported the presence of appreciable amounts of water in oil cores; his observations were questioned by many who believed that oil and water in a reservoir were separated by a well-defined phase boundary. Several years later, N. T. Lindtrop and V. M. Nicolaef[50] concluded that virgin oil sands contain appreciable (20 to 30 percent) volumes of water; experiments indicated this range to be reasonable after oil is forced through a water-saturated sand. J. Versluys[51] concluded that "connate" water must exist in oil sands because the surface forces between water and sand are greater than those between oil and water and thus preclude complete displacement of the original interstitial water by accumulating oil. In 1935, A. D. Garrison[52] published a theoretical analysis of capillary effects which agreed with the conclusions previously cited. He also postulated that, at low rates of flow, the ease with which the sand can be flooded is an inverse function of the average diameter of a pore. Dissenters to the concept of in-situ water in oil reservoirs expressed the opinion that the water observed in cores resulted from filtration of water into the rock from the mud fluid used in drilling. However, in 1937, Schilthuis[53] reported that appreciable quantities of water were found in cores collected from wells drilled with oil-base muds. His data also indicated that a correlation exists between connate-water saturation and permeability. Schilthuis concluded that relative fluid saturations and physical properties of rocks and fluids are the principal factors controlling the fractions of the various reservoir fluids that are contained in the produced liquid.

The determinations of fluid content and irreducible water saturation have been appreciably facilitated by the development and improvement of methods for measuring capillary pressure — the pressure discontinuity across the interface between two fluid phases — on cores. Among the first reported capillary-pressure measurements were those of Hassler.[54] Later publications which report the development and improvement of capillary-pressure measurements and data interpretation are those of Leverett,[55] J. J. McCullough, F. A. Albaugh and P. H. Jones,[56] Hassler, E. Brunner, and T. J. Deahl,[57] O. F. Thornton and L. D. Marshall,[58] and W. R. Purcell.[59] These studies relating capillary forces among the fluid phases in a rock with the corresponding fluid saturations not only provided further proof of the intermingling of the fluid phases in reservoirs, but also a practical means of gaging the effect of surface forces on production.

Logging

Shortly before capillary-pressure measurements were described by Hassler, G. E. Archie[60] in 1942 opened another avenue to the determination of reservoir data when he discovered a relationship between electrical resistivity and formation-water saturation. A variety of resistivity and potential measurements can be made by continuous down-the-hole surveys; these are much less expensive and tedious than coring and core analysis. Archie's work inspired an intensive investigation of the data obtainable from the logs of subsurface surveys and of their possible relation to fundamental reservoir properties. Such studies have definitely established electric and radioactive logging as valuable aids of the reservoir engineer in determining (at least qualitatively) porosity, permeability, and saturation, and in defining the limits of a reservoir. The art has not developed sufficiently that the log data can routinely be substituted for the more difficultly obtained data from core analysis. It is recognized that, in some instances, electric logs may be used safely to extend core analyses where sufficient core coverage is not available. However, some core analyses are always necessary to calibrate the logs for a particular field.

Phase Relationships and Production Mechanisms

Pure fluid hydrocarbons generally behave in accordance with expected functional pressure-volume-temperature (PVT) relationships. Oil deposits are complex mixtures which usually include some hydrocarbons that would be in the liquid state if they were the only hydrocarbons present, others that would be in a gaseous state, and possibly some that would be in the solid state. The latter are not believed to exert an important influence on flow within most reservoirs. In a natural untapped reservoir the hydrocarbons are believed to be at equilibrium. They may exist in a single liquid phase (neglecting the small amounts that may be dissolved in associated water), the gaseous components being in solution at their bubble-point pressures (or higher if the reservoir is undersaturated). Reservoirs of this type are described as "dissolved-gas" reservoirs. Another possibility is that a single gaseous phase exists at a temperature and pressure higher than the critical conditions defining the mixture; reservoirs whose fluid contents are in this condition are identified as "condensate" or "distillate" fields. In other reservoirs, both liquid and gaseous hydrocarbon phases may exist (in this case, the liquid is at its bubble-point pressure). Reservoirs of this type are called "gas-cap" reservoirs. An artesian water supply or a vast expansible body of water may be directly associated with any of these reservoirs; if the advancing or expanding water is the dominant producing force, the reservoir is termed a "water-drive" reservoir.

When the reservoir is opened to production, the fluid equilibrium within the reservoir is disturbed. If an artesian or large expansible water deposit is associated with the oil and gas reservoir and if the rate of production of hydrocarbons does not exceed the rate of advance of this water, there may be little change in the hydrocarbon phase distribution. However, if these conditions do not prevail, significant changes in the hydrocarbon phase relationships may occur that will affect both the rate of recovery and the ultimate yield.

In condensate reservoirs, flow is maintained largely by expansion of gas in which oil is dissolved. As production takes place, the pressure within the reservoir decreases, depending upon the effectiveness of the "water drive" that may exist, and the liquid phase may condense. Such condensation usually results in decreased ultimate recovery. Therefore, in such cases it may be desirable to inject produced gas back into the formation, i.e., to "recycle" the gas.

In a dissolved-gas reservoir without an associated water drive, the pressure drops as production takes place and gas escapes from solution with a resultant shrinkage of the remaining oil. Excluding the effect of gravity, natural flow is dependent upon the expansion of this escaped gas. Complicating factors associated with this type of production are that the viscosity of the remaining oil increases and the relative permeability to oil decreases as gas escapes from solution. Initial production from a gas-cap reservoir is the result of the expansion of the separate gas phase; but, at some stage in the productive life of the reservoir, gas will begin to escape from solution and the conditions described for "dissolved-gas" reservoirs will prevail. In either of these types of reservoirs, it is obviously desirable to retain as much gas as possible in the liquid phase.

Some reservoirs have been discovered whose original gas content was so low that, in the absence of an active water drive, gravity drainage has been the dominant natural recovery mechanism.

From a consideration of the production processes described in the preceding paragraphs, it is evident that the reservoir engineer must determine the fluid phases that exist, their compositions, and the changes that would normally take place during natural flow under the drive available in order to predict the behavior and recommend the control of a given reservoir.

Among the first men to realize the importance of fundamental studies of the phase behavior and thermodynamics of complex hydrocarbon mixtures were Sage and Lacey. Since 1933[61] they, with the assistance of a number of graduate students at the California Institute of Technology, have published a long series of papers reporting the results of important continuing research in this field. Among their more significant contributions was the recognition and characterization of condensate reservoirs.[62] Most of their research work has been conducted with the support of Project 37 of the American Petroleum Institute, one of the first research projects sponsored by the Institute directed principally to the study of production phenomena.

D. L. Katz of the University of Michigan initiated a series of research projects in the early 1930's which have been especially important in determining the volumetric effects of phase changes.[63] In 1937 Katz[64] and S. E. Buckley[65] published research results on the effect of surface-separator pressure on the properties and relative amounts of produced fluids.

Reservoir Equations

One of the principal distinguishing features of a bona fide engineering doctrine is that the behavior of a system within the scope of the doctrine can be more or less completely described by mathematical equations relating several measurable properties of the system. Practical application comes in the use of such equations to predict the behavior of a real system under various anticipated conditions. Ultimately, of course, there must be a sound theoretical basis for all such equations; but, in the actual development of most engineering laws, useful relations are discovered empirically and applied successfully for years before their theoretical significance and justification are exposed and/or understood.

In the case of reservoir engineering, the basic equations are those which can be used to predict the rate of production and the ultimate recovery of each of the fluids from a given reservoir under natural or artificially imposed conditions. The engineering significance of the various investigations described heretofore and in the following paragraphs is largely determined by the extent to which they have contributed to the development, application, and interpretation of such equations.

Flow Equations

A fundamental mathematical challenge to reservoir scientists is the derivation of the equations that describe the flow of reservoir fluid systems and the development of practical solutions for such equations. The problem is complicated because of the transient nature of production from most reservoirs. As soon as production begins, reservoir pressures are reduced, the reservoir fluids comprising gas, oil, and connate water expand, phase equilibria are disturbed, and alterations in the physical properties of the fluid phases occur in varying degree throughout the reservoir. Such disturbances and changes continue with further withdrawal of fluids. Difficult second-order partial differential equations are required to describe correctly this transient, or unsteady-state flow of expansible fluids.

Logically enough, early studies directed to the solution of this challenge, such as that of Versluys,[66] treated the relatively simple case of the linear steady-state flow of an incompressible fluid in porous media in much the same manner that Slichter and King studied underground-water movements. In 1931 Morris Muskat, with his colleague H. G. Botset, published the first[67] of a brilliant series of papers on fluid flow that has been instrumental in advancing the knowledge of reservoir dynamics to its present state; this first paper was concerned with the linear flow of gas through a porous medium. In connection with their study of reservoir drainage and well spacing published in 1932, H. D. Wilde and Moore[68] reported the development of equations for the flow of homogeneous fluids. It is probable that the men cited, as well as other students of the day, realized that steady-state flow does not ordinarily occur in reservoirs.

The first public presentation of an unsteady-state radial flow equation for expansible reservoir fluids was in the 1933 permeability paper by Moore, Schilthuis, and Hurst cited previously in this chapter. They reported the development of a linear second-order equation similar to the classical heat-flow equation that adequately described the flow of a single-phase compressible (or expansible) liquid in a reservoir. In 1934, Schilthuis and Hurst[69] published the application of this equation to the calculation of reservoir-pressure changes in the East Texas Field and to the prediction of the effect thereon of changes in production rates. Of especial interest was their explanation and quantitative description of the importance of the natural water drive operating on the field. They recognized that it resulted from the slight expansion, occurring upon reduction of reservoir pressure, of the tremendous body of connate water and associated fluids existing in the Woodbine basin in contact with and surrounding the field to the west. Later papers by Hurst,[70] Muskat,[71] and Hurst and A. F. van Everdingen,[72] confirmed the validity of the equation and described solutions for linear and radial flow under various conditions.

The flow equation for gases, as developed by Muskat,[73] is a non-linear second-order equation. Approximate solutions of this complex equation based on several simplifying assumptions were presented by C. R. Heatherington, D. T. MacRoberts, and R. L. Huntington,[74] and van Everdingen and Hurst *(op. cit.)*. G. H. Bruce, D. W. Peaceman, H. H. Rachford, Jr., and J. D. Rice,[75] and J. S. Aronofsky and R. Jenkins[76] published numerical procedures based on appropriate difference equations. Bruce et al. made use of a digital computer to perform the laborious numerical integration required.

Many other worthwhile studies of flow equations for various conditions have been published in the past 20 years. Muskat[77] has presented a masterful critical review of the work on fluid flow, as well as on many other theoretical phases of reservoir engineering. The reader is referred to this classic text for more comprehensive coverage of such phenomena than is possible in this chapter.

Material-balance Equations

To determine reserves efficiently, the reservoir engineer must be able to inventory the reservoir fluids in place at any given stage of depletion. Material, or volumetric, balance equations are valuable tools in effecting such inventories. These equations, which are mathematical statements of the law of conservation of mass, present a balance among the original fluid volumes of the reservoir, the produced volumes, the remaining volumes, and any volumes of fluids that may have migrated into the reservoir. Comprehensive production and pressure-decline data, as well as knowledge of the geometry of the reservoir and of the physical properties of the initial reservoir fluids, are required for successful utilization of material-balance equations.

As early as 1929, Coleman, H. D. Wilde, Jr., and T. W. Moore [78] described a material-balance method of analysis. In 1935, Katz[79] proposed a tabular method of obtaining a material balance for closed reservoir. Also in 1935, Schilthuis[80] published a material-balance equation that included the same terms of fluid volumes and volume changes with time as Katz's method. The application of Katz's method required the experimental determination of phase equilibria data; the Schilthuis method represented a simplification in that the requisite terms were reduced to simpler expressions.

Schilthuis recognized the importance of determining the cumulative water encroachment and its rate of influx; the method he suggested for determining the rate of water influx required accurate production-history data. Several years later Hurst[81] introduced a method of determining rate of water influx that was independent of the material-balance equation and production history; only data on pressure history and rock and fluid properties were required. Later he and van Everdingen (*op. cit.*) extended the usefulness of material-balance equations by demonstrating their applicability to reservoirs enclosed by an aquifer of limited extent as well as to those enclosed by the infinite aquifer assumed in previous applications.

Displacement-efficiency Equation

The two displacement-efficiency, or frontal-advance rate, equations constitute another powerful tool of reservoir engineering. One equation describes the fraction of immiscible displacing fluid flowing with the oil through a unit rock volume; the other describes the rate of advance of a particular degree of saturation in the displacing fluid that exists in that volume. Present theory permits their use in the calculation of recovery by any immiscible displacing fluid, natural or induced. Because the equations are based on a fractional-flow formula, they can be used to predict the effects of relative viscosity, relative permeability, volumetric rate, formation dip, differential fluid density, wetting, pressure gradient, etc., on recovery under specified conditions.

These valuable equations were proposed by Buckley and Leverett in 1940[82] in conjunction with a theoretical analysis of the mechanisms involved in the displacement of immiscible fluids. Several laboratory investigations, such as those by R. C. Earlougher,[83] R. A. Morse and S. T. Yuster,[84] J. N. Breston and R. V. Hughes,[85] C. R. Holmgren and Morse,[68] have since been reported which have confirmed the validity of these equations.

Morse, P. L. Terwilliger, L. Wilsey, H. N. Hall, and P. M. Bridges[87] have recently shown that the transient saturation distribution of a system in which gravity is the principal producing force can be accurately predicted from relative-permeability and static capillary-pressure data. Another study by Morse and his colleagues T. M. Geffen, D. R. Parrish, and G. W. Haynes,[88] considered the effect of an immovable (i.e., trapped) gas phase in a reservoir under active water drive. The investigators concluded that undue importance may have been placed on maintaining pressure above the bubble point in water-drive reservoirs.

L. R. Kern[89] has recently presented useful simplified forms of the frontal-drive equations that are particularly valuable in the calculation of the effect on recovery of forcing gas into solution in the reservoir oil.

Computing Machines

Because detailed solutions of the simplest reservoir problems require an enormous number of computations, the reservoir engineer who is dependent upon manual and desk-calculator computations must over-simplify, or even avoid, many problems of reservoir behavior.

Within recent years automatic analog and digital computing devices have been developed which can compute at rates hundreds of times those possible with a desk calculator. The use of these machines has enabled the reservoir engineer to effect more complete (and, therefore, more reliable) solutions of the simpler problems and has encouraged him to develop solutions of problems previously considered insoluble because of the magnitude of the computation work involved.

The operation of analog computers is dependent upon the existence of a valid mathematical analogy between the problem to be studied and a measurable physical phenomenon (most commonly electric current, resistance, capacitance, and/or voltage). The accuracy of the results obtained from an analog computer is limited by the ability to measure the analogous physical property. In 1932 Wyckoff, Botset, and Muskat[90] reported the use of an electrolytic model to study a water-flood problem. Ten years later W. A. Bruce[91] described a more elaborate analog computer that was successfully used to predict the behavior of water-drive pools. Among other reported analog computers is that developed by F. W. Bubb, R. G. Nisle, and P. G. Carpenter[92] to study mass spectrograms and to solve vaporization equilibrium problems for multi-component hydrocarbon mixtures.

The basic operation of digital computers is similar to that of the ordinary desk calculator. However, their rate of operation is infinitely more rapid, and they can automatically sequence millions of operations. Although large-capacity, high-speed digital computers have only been used in reservoir studies for a very few years, their usefulness has been established as indicated by the application to flow studies reported by G. H. Bruce, Peaceman, Rachford, and Rice *(op. cit.)*. There is no reason to believe that W. A. Bruce's estimate[93] of their potential importance in reservoir analysis is over-optimistic.

The Development and Productivity of Reservoirs

The preceding sections of this chapter have been largely devoted to the evolution of the modern theory of reservoir behavior and to the development of means of data collection and interpretation. It is only by intelligent interpretation of these data in accordance with the theoretical principles of behavior that the reservoir engineer can recommend the optimum development program for a given reservoir. Needless to say, the final selection of the development program will be conditioned to an important extent by economic considerations; but it is evident that economic evaluations are useless if the technical appraisal is incorrect.

Well Spacing

Representative of the important relation between reservoir engineering practice and knowledge is well spacing. In essence, the well-spacing problem is the selection of the proper location of the minimum number of wells that are required to produce efficiently the maximum practical volume of hydrocarbons trapped in a given reservoir. It is recognized today that quantitative evaluation of proper well spacing for a given reservoir can only be made after the characteristics of that particular reservoir are established. The geometric and stratigraphic configurations of the reservoir and the nature of the producing mechanism are the controlling factors. When wells are spaced with due regard for these factors, the ultimate oil recovery from the reservoir is essentially independent of well spacing. Once the physical controlling factors are recognized the relationship of ultimate oil recovery and well spacing is, of course, tempered by economic limitations of well investment, operating incoming, and net profit variations.[94]

Well spacing was one of the first technical aspects of production given general consideration within the industry. Controversy between the adherents of close and wide spacing flared intermittently for years — it has not completely disappeared today. However, the area of agreement that does exist is directly attributable to the fundamental advances which have been made in the understanding of reservoir behavior.

For many years, the conclusions of W. W. Cutler, Jr., of the Bureau of Mines dominated the well-spacing controversy. His *Bulletin 228*, published in 1924, has been cited in connection with the early use of production-decline curves in estimating recoverable oil. In a section of that same bulletin captioned "Spacing of Wells," Cutler presented data to show the effect of spacing on ultimate production for shallow wells drilled to the Bartlesville sand in several fields of northeastern Oklahoma; also for wells in the Hewitt district and the Glenn Pool, both in Oklahoma, in the Speechly Pool of Pennsylvania, and in the Buena Vista Hills Field of California. Cutler deduced from these early observations of recoveries from tracts developed to different well densities in the same field ". . . that the ultimate production for wells of equal size in the same pool where there is interference (shown by a difference in the production-decline curves for different spacing) seem approximately to vary directly as the square roots of the areas drained by the wells." He assumed that radial flow in a reservoir was analogous to linear flow through a pipe and that sufficient reservoir energy was required for lateral movement of oil to make the overall productive capacity of a given tract directly proportional to the square root of the number of wells. A report was prepared by H. C. Miller and R. V. Higgins[95] of the Bureau of Mines to point out the meaning and possible limitations of Cutler's rule more definitely than was done in Cutler's bulletin and to show wherein increased understanding of oil-reservoir mechanics and technical progress, in a measure, nullified some of the earlier conclusions of Cutler based upon data then available to him. As the authors so aptly stated, "This rule has been misquoted frequently, often interpreted incorrectly, and apparently is not understood by all who have attempted to apply it to practice." R. C. Craze and J. W. Glanville[96] as well as Muskat joined these authors in observing that variations in actual recoveries with well density between different leases in the same field can be attributed to regional migration and that fluid drainage through porous media over long distances has occurred and does occur.

In the ensuing years, the theoretical and experimental fluid-flow studies of Muskat, Schilthuis, Hurst, and others have proved that Cutler's rule more definitely than was done in Cutler's bulletin and to show experimental and theoretical evidence that ultimate recovery is not appreciably affected by well spacing. Analytical field studies, such as those of R. C. Craze and Buckley[97] and L. F. Elkins[98] have provided further evidence of the independence of recovery from well spacing.

Although a careful reservoir study can be used with a rather good degree of confidence to select a reasonable well spacing, a rigorous quantitative determination of the optimum spacing is not yet possible. However, F. G. Miller[99] has suggested an analytical approach which may make such treatment possible. He believes that solution of the complex equations involved will be possible with the improved knowledge of reservoir behavior that can be expected within the reasonable future and with the aid of digital computing machines.

Rate of Production

Another important function of the reservoir engineer is to recommend the rate at which oil should be produced from a given reservoir under the available or chosen recovery mechanism. It is generally accepted by technologists within the industry that there is a characteristic maximum rate of production for each reservoir operating under the displacement mechanisms and under the influence of gravity and for each well in the reservoir that cannot be exceeded without a decrease in ultimate recovery. This limiting rate, termed the maximum efficient rate of production (MER), is dependent primarily upon the type of drive available and upon the physical nature of the reservoir, it surroundings, and its contained fluids. In a dissolved-gas-drive reservoir that has no free gas cap and no potential water drive and that has physical conditions that prevent any segregation of fluids by gravity, "It has not been conclusively demonstrated that reduction in the rate of production can bring about any improvement in the recovery efficiency. . ." "It is doubtful that a pool of this sort has any natural M.E.R."[100]

Rate of production and recovery are related because of the influence of rate on pressure and pressure gradients. The effect on pressure is especially important in open reservoirs in which the rate of advance of the driving water is proportional to the reduction of reservoir pressure; the higher the rate of production from the reservoir, the lower the reservoir pressure must be to maintain displacement primarily by water. In such reservoirs the MER is, in effect, the maximum rate at which the displacing water can uniformly advance. At higher rates of withdrawal, displacement may take place primarily by gas released from solution in the oil.

In any reservoir, reduction of reservoir pressure may cause shrinkage of the reservoir oil and an increase of its viscosity, both of which reduce recovery. In many reservoirs, regular and effective displacement is dependent upon the equalizing effect of capillary forces upon the exchange of fluids among adjacent elements of the reservoir. Excessively high production rates may not allow sufficient time for this exchange process to take place efficiently.

Obviously, the determination of the MER for a given reservoir or well is a highly technical problem that requires careful evaluation and interpretation of all available information about the reservoir. It should also be evident that MER's must be re-evaluated periodically because of the inevitable changes in reservoir behavior associated with development and depletion. Although economic and legal factors do not enter into the determination of MER, they may dictate an actual appreciably lower production rate.

The history of industry practice and thinking on controlled production is an excellent example of the close relation among economics, conservation, and reservoir engineering.

As stated before, the early philosophy of the industry was to produce as much oil as quickly as possible from a field. From the discovery of the Drake well until the late 1920's, there were occasional periods of over-production that worked hardships on individual producers. However, in the late 1920's a series of major discoveries — Seminole, Oklahoma, Hendricks and Yates, Texas, Oklahoma City, Oklahoma, Hobbs, New Mexico, deep sands at Santa Fe Springs and Long Beach, California, and finally East Texas in 1931 — resulted in tremendous over-production. There were so many restricted or shut-in wells and fields that the whole industry was seriously affected. At first, pipeline or market outlet determined each operator's opportunity to dispose of his oil. Then came pipeline proration, and finally state-regulated proration. It was soon recognized that restricted production under proration was affecting reservoirs in various ways. It was to understand these effects better and their ultimate economic inferences that many of the studies described earlier on controlling drives, pressure behavior, and residual saturation were undertaken.

These fundamental studies, of course, provide the technical background which should be dominant in any consideration of reservoir engineering. However, from the historical viewpoint it should be noted that various published technical reviews of allocation, production rate, and well spacing have exerted a greater direct influence on the industry than have the publications of original engineering and scientific data and principles on which the reviews were based. Among the more important of these reviews are: *The Function of Natural Gas in the Production of Oil*, by H. C. Miller, a report of the U. S. Bureau of Mines prepared in cooperation with the American Petroleum Institute (API, New York, 1929); *Handbook on Unitization of Oil Pools* (Mid-Continent Oil and Gas Association, 1930); *Essential Engineering Factors in the Allocation of Production*, a Report of the Topical Committee on Allocation of Production and Well Spacing of the Central Committee on Drilling and Production Practice (API, 1933, 1934); Progress Reports of American Petroleum Institute Committee on Well Spacing (API, 1938); Progress Report on the Study of Standards for the Allocation of Oil Production Among States, Areas and Pools (API, 1941); *Standards of Allocation of Oil Production Within Pools and Among Pools*, a joint report from both the legal and engineering viewpoints (API, 1942); Joint Progress Report on Reservoir Efficiency and Well Spacing by the Committee on Reservoir

Development and Operation of the Standard Oil Company (New Jersey) Affiliated Companies, and the Humble Oil & Refining Company (1943); Engineering Rules Governing the Establishment of Pool Classifications, Maximum Efficient Rates, Monthly MER Decline Rates, and Intra-Pool Distribution Schedules by the Conservation Committee of California Oil Producers (1946); and various publications of the Interstate Oil Compact Commission.

Field Reservoir-engineering Studies

The practical proof of the importance and utility of the fundamental studies described heretofore, and of numerous other worthwhile published investigations which have not been cited because of space limitations, is their acceptance and application by petroleum producers and interested regulatory bodies. Textbooks by authors such as J. C. Calhoun, Jr., S. J. Pirson, and L. C. Uren[101] have influenced the instruction of reservoir engineering at various universities. Undoubtedly the files of various oil companies and regulatory bodies contain many excellent reservoir-engineering studies that have not been published in the technical periodic literature. However, the number of thorough, published field studies embodying the application of fundamentals is large.

Many of the outstanding published reservoir-engineering studies that have appeared are concerned with the East Texas Field. This field is important not only because of its huge size but also because it is an excellent example of water-drive performance. Among the first studies of the field from the reservoir-engineering viewpoint was that of Reistle and G. L. Nye[102] on pressure-production relationships. They recognized the importance of the powerful, but relatively slow, water drive and recommended sufficient production curtailment to realize its full producing effect. In the ensuing years, important reservoir-engineering studies were reported by Schilthuis and Hurst (*op. cit.*), Buckley,[103] R. C. Rumble, H. H. Spain, and H. E. Stamm, III.[104] Such studies as these predicted the pressure history of the field as a function of time, withdrawal rates, and pressure transients throughout the driving Woodbine aquifer. They led to a most constructive conservation program in the largest known oil field in the United States and set a pattern for analyzing water-drive fields.

The Schuler Field in Arkansas is another reservoir about which several excellent reservoir studies, such as those of R. E. Old,[105] H. H. Kaveler,[106] Jack Tarner, W. R. Evans, and Kaveler,[107] have been published. Gas was injected early in the field's life to restrict pressure decline, maintain production, and create a partial gas-cap drive. As a result of the aforementioned studies, an end-to-end water flood was begun to augment recovery while pressures remained relatively high. An unusually high recovery efficiency will apparently result from this program.

The detailed study of the Pettit lime reservoir of the Haynesville (La.) Field conducted by an engineering committee representing the operators led to the adoption of a relatively wide spacing (80 acres) and a combined gas and high-pressure water-injection program. This study was ably reported by D. W. Akins, Jr.,[108] a member of the engineering committee.

Another example of effective reservoir study by an engineering committee is that published by M. G. Miller and M. R. Lents[109] on the condensate reservoir of the Cotton Valley (La.) Field. The gas-cycling program that resulted has been a model for increasing recovery from such reservoirs.

Elkins' recent account[110] of a detailed engineering study of the Spraberry (Tex.) Field is an outstanding example of the invaluable information that such studies can produce. The method of computing a composite physical oil property for crude oil in the Scurry Reef (Tex.) Field where the physical properties vary with elevation was another excellent study recently reported by A. B. Cook, G. B. Spencer, F. P. Bobrowski, and T. Chin.[111] Although the science of reservoir engineering is far from complete, reports such as these cited certainly justify the conclusion that sound reservoir-engineering study and practice have properly become the cornerstone of the modern oil-production industry.

REFERENCES

[1]Briggs, Robert: *Proc. Amer. Phil. Soc.*, 10, 126 (1865).

[2]Carll, John F: *The Geology of the Oil Regions of Warren, Venango, Clarion, and Butler Counties, Pennsylvania*, Second Geological Survey of Pennsylvania, 1875-79, **III** (1880).

[3]Orton, Edward: *Bull. N. Y. State Mus.*, **6**, 483, Nov. (1899).

[4]Hayes, C. W. and Kennedy, William: Oil Fields of the Texas-Louisiana Gulf Coastal Plain, *U. S. G. S. Bull. 212*, 154 (1903).

[5]Slichter, C. S: Theoretical Investigation of the Motion of Ground Waters, U. S. Geol. Survey, 295 (1899).

[6]Slichter, C. S: The Motions of Underground Water, U. S. Geol. Survey, 13 (1902).

[7]Slichter, C. S: Field Measurement of the Rate of Movement of Underground Water, U. S. Geol. Survey water-supply paper, 9 (1905).

[8]King, F. H: Conditions and Movements of Underground Waters, *U. S. G. S. 19th Ann. Report*, 2 (1899).

[9]Briggs, L. J: The Mechanics of Soil Moisture, U. S. Dept. Agr. Div. of Soils, 10 (1897).

[10]Baldwin-Wiseman: The Flow of Underground Water, *Inst. Civil Eng. Proc.,***165**, 309 (1906).

[11]Bartell, F. E: Permeability of Porcelain and Copper Ferrocyanide Membranes, *J. Phys. Chem.*, **15**, 659 (1911).

[12]Greene, W. H. and Ampt, G. A: Studies on Soil Physics, Flow of Air and Water through Soils, *J. Agr. Sci.*, 4 (1911).

[13]Arnold, Ralph, and Clapp, F. G: Wastes in the Production and Utilization of Natural Gas and Methods for Their Prevention, *U. S. Bur. Mines TP 38* (1913).
Arnold, Ralph, and Garfias, V. R: The Prevention of Waste of Oil and Gas from Flowing Wells in California, with a Discussion of Special Methods Used, *U. S. Bur. Mines TP 42* (1913).

839

Huntley, L. G: Possible Causes of the Decline of Oil Wells, and Suggested Methods of Prolonging Yields, *U. S. Bur. Mines TP 51* (1913).

Pollard, J. A. and Heggem, A. G: Mud-laden Fluid Applied to Well Drilling, *U. S. Bur. Mines TP 66* (1914).

Blatchley, R. S: Waste of Oil and Gas in the Mid-Continent Fields, *U. S. Bur. Mines TP 45* (1914)

Arnold, Ralph, and Garfias, V. R: Methods of Oil Recovery in California, *U. S. Bur. Mines TP 70* (1914)

Lewis, J. O. and McMurray, W. F: The Use of Mud-Laden Fluid in Oil and Gas Wells, *U. S. Bur. Mines Bull. 134* (1916).

McMurray, W. F. and Lewis, J. O: Underground Wastes in Oil and Gas Fields and Methods of Prevention, *U. S. Bur. Mines TP 130* (1916).

Lewis, J. O: Methods for Increasing the Recovery from Oil Sands, *U. S. Bur. Mines Bull. 148* (1917).

Ambrose, A. W: Underground Conditions in Oil Fields, *U. S. Bur. Mines Bull. 195* (1921).

Beal, Carl H. and Lewis, J. O: Some Principles Governing the Production of Oil Wells, *U. S. Bur. Mines Bull. 194* (1921).

[14]Beal, Carl H: Geologic Structure in the Cushing Oil and Gas Field, Oklahoma, and Its Relation to the Oil, Gas and Water, *U. S. Bur. Mines Bull. 658* (1917).

[15]Swigart, T. E: Underground Problems in the Comanche Oil and Gas Field, Stevens County, Oklahoma, *State of Oklahoma Pub.* (1919).

[16]Tough, F. B: Cooperative Petroleum Work in the Rocky Mountain Fields, *U. S. Bur. Mines RI 2105* (1920).

[17]Swigart, T. E. and Bopp, C. R: Experiments in the Use of Back Pressure on Oil Wells, *U. S. Bur. Mines TP 322* (1924).

[18]Mills, R. Van A: Experimental Studies of Subsurface Relationships in Oil and Gas Fields, *Econ. Geology,* **15 [5]** 398 (1920); Relations of Texture and Bedding to the Movements of Oil and Water through Sand, *Econ. Geology,* **16,** 124 (1921).

[19]Melcher, A. F: Determination of Pore Space of Oil and Gas Sands, *Trans. Am. Inst. Mining Met. Engrs.,* **65,** 469 (1921).

[20]Dow, D. B. and Reistle, C. E., Jr: Absorption of Natural Gas and Air in Crude Petroleum, *Mining and Metallurgy,* **5[5]** 336 (1924).

[21]Dow, D. B. and Reistle, C. E., Jr: The Physical Chemistry of Oil-Field Emulsion, *U. S. Bur. Mines RI 2683, 2692* (1925).

[22]Dow, D. B. and Calkin, L. P: Solubility and Effects of Natural Gas and Air in Crude Oils, *U. S. Bur. Mines RI 2732* (1926).

[23]Beecher, C. E. and Parkhurst, I. P: Effect of Dissolved Gas on the Viscosity and Surface Tension of Crude Oil, *Petroleum Development and Technology in 1926,* 51, American Institute of Mining and Metallurgical Engineers, Inc., New York, 1927.

[24]Dean, E. W: Properties of Typical Crude Oils from Eastern Producing Fields of the United States, *U. S. Bur. Mines RI 2202* (1921).

Dean, E. W; Hill, H. H; Smith, N. A. C; and Jacobs, W. A: The Analytical Distillation of Petroleum and Its Products, *U. S. Bur. Mines Bull. 207* (1922).

[25]Lewis, J. O. and Beal, Carl H: Some New Methods for Estimating the Future Production of Oil Wells, *Trans. Am. Inst. Mining Met. Engrs.,* **59,** 492 (1918).

[26]Cutler, W. W: Estimation of Underground Reserves by Oil-Well Production Curves, *U. S. Bur. Mines Bull. 228* (1924).

[27]Russell, W. L: A Quick Method for Determining Porosity, *Am. Assoc. Petroleum Geologists Bull.,* **10,** 931 (1926).

[28]Fettke, C. R: Core Studies of the Second Sand of the Venango Group from Oil City, Pennsylvania, *Trans. Am. Inst. Mining Met. Engrs.,* 219 (1927).

[29]Sclater, K. C. and Stephenson, B. R: Measurements of Original Pressure, Temperature, and Gas-Oil Ratio in Oil Sands, *Trans. Am. Inst. Mining Met. Engrs.*, **82**, 119 (1928-29).

[30]Moore, T. V: Determination of Potential Production of Wells without Open-flow Test, *Proc. Am. Pet. Inst. (Prod. Bul. 206)* 27 (1930).

[31]Pierce, H. R. and Rawlins, E. L: The Study of a Fundamental Basis for Controlling and Gauging Natural Gas Wells, *U. S. Bur. Mines RI 2929 and 2930* (1929).

[32]Foran, E. V: Interpretation of Bottom-hole Pressures in East Texas Oil Field, *Am. Assoc. Petroleum Geologists Bull.*, **16**, 907 (1932).

[33]Moore, T. V; Schilthuis, R. J; and Hurst, W: The Determination of Permeability from Field Data, *Proc. Am. Pet. Inst. (Prod. Bul. 211)* 4 (1933).

[34]Comins, P: Gas Saturation Pressure of Crude under Reservoir Conditions, *Proc. World Petr. Congress*, **1**, 458 (1934).

[35]Millikan, C. V. and Sidwell, C. V.: Bottom-hole Pressures in Oil Wells, *Trans. Am. Inst. Mining Met. Engrs. (Petroleum Development and Technology)*, **92**, 194 (1931).

[36]Lindsly, Ben E: A Study of Bottom-Hole Samples of East Texas Crude Oil, *U. S. Bur. Mines RI 3212* (1933).

[37]Lindsly, Ben E: Effect of Gas Withdrawal upon Reservoir Fluids, *Trans. Am. Inst. Mining Met. Engrs. (Petroleum Development and Technology)* **107**, 94 (1934).

[38]Pym, L. A: The Measurement of Gas-Oil Ratios and Saturation Pressures and Their Interpretation, *Proc. World Petr. Congress*, **1**, 452 (1934).

[39]Schilthuis, R. J: Technique of Securing and Examining Subsurface Samples of Oil and Gas, *API Drilling and Production Practice*, 120 (1935).

[40]Sage, B. H; Sherborne, J. E; and Lacey, W. N: Viscosity of Hydrocarbon Solutions—Solutions of Ethane and *n*-Butane in Crystal Oil, *Proc. Am. Pet. Inst. (Prod. Bul. 216)* 40 (1935).

[41]Sage, B. H. and Lacey, W. N: Effect of Pressure upon Viscosity of Methane and Two Natural Gases, *Trans. Am. Inst. Mining Met. Engrs. (Petroleum Development and Technology)* **127**, 118 (1938) (reprint, p. 178).

[42]Katz, D. L. and Bicher, L. B: Viscosity of Natural Gases, *Trans. Am. Inst. Mining Met. Engrs. (Petroleum Development and Technology)* **155**, 246 (1944) (reprint p. 244).

[43]Jones D. T: The Surface Tension and Specific Gravity of Crude Oil under Reservoir Conditions, *Proc. World Petr. Congress*, **1**, 467 (1934).

[44]Hocott C. R: Interfacial Tension between Water and Oil under Reservoir Conditions, *Trans. Am. Inst. Mining Met. Engrs. (Petroleum Development and Technology)* **132**, 184 (1939) (reprint, p. 416).

[45]Fancher, G. H; Lewis, J. A; and Barnes, K. B: Some Physical Characteristics of Oil Sands, *Pennsylvania State College Mineral Industries Experiment Station Bulletin No. 12*, 65 (1933).

[46]Wyckoff, R. D; Botset, H. G; Muskat, M; and Reed, D. W: The Measurement of the Permeability of Porous Media for Homogeneous Fluids, *Review of Scientific Instruments*, **4**, 394, (1933); also *Am. Assoc. Petroleum Geologists Bull.*, **18** [2] 161, Feb. (1934).

[47]Hassler, G. L; Rice, R. B; and Leeman, E. H: Investigations on the Recovery of Oil from Sandstones by Gas Drive, *Trans. Am. Inst. Mining Met. Engrs. (Petroleum Development and Technology)* **118**, 116 (1936) (reprint, p. 114).

[48]Wyckoff, R. D. and Botset, H. G: The Flow of Gas-Liquid Mixture through Unconsolidated Sands, *Physics*, **7** [9] 325, Sept. (1936).

[49]Leverett, M. C. and Lewis, W. B: Steady Flow of Gas-Oil-Water Mixtures through Unconsolidated Sands, *Am. Inst. Mining Met. Engrs. TP 1206* (1940).

[50]Lindtrop, N. T. and Nicolaef, V. M: Oil and Water Content of Oil Sands; Grozny, Russia, *Am. Assoc. Petroleum Geologists Bull.*, **16**, 924 (1932).

[51]Versluys, J: Can Absence of Edge-Water Encroachment in Certain Oil Fields Be Ascribed to Capillarity? *Am. Assoc. Petroleum Geologists Bull.*, **15**, 197 (1931); and Factors Involved in Segregation of Oil and Gas from Subterranean Water, *Am. Assoc. Petroleum Geologists Bull.*, **16**, 924 (1932).

[52]Garrison, A. D: Selective Wetting of Reservoir Rocks and Its Relation to Oil Production, *API Drilling and Production Practice*, 130 (1935).

[53]Schilthuis, R. J: Connate Water in Oil and Gas Sands, *Trans. Am. Inst. Mining Met. Engrs. (Petroleum Development and Technology)* **127,** 199 (1938) (reprint, p. 259).

[54]Hassler, G. L: The Role of Capillarity in Oil Production, *Am. Inst. Mining Met. Engrs. TP 1623* (1943).

[55]Leverett, M. C: U. S. Patent No. 2,330,721, Sept. 28, 1943.

[56]McCullough, J. J; Albaugh, F. A; and Jones, P. H: Determination of the Interstitial Water Content of Oil and Gas Sand by Laboratory Tests of Core Samples, *API Drilling and Production Practice*, 180 (1944).

[57]Hassler, G. L; Brunner, E; and Deahl, T. J: The Role of Capillarity in Oil Production, *Trans. Am. Inst. Mining Met. Engrs. (Petroleum Development and Technology)* **155,** 155 (1944) (reprint, p. 153).

[58]Thornton, O. F. and Marshall, D. L: Estimating Interstitial Water by the Capillary Pressure Method, *Trans. Am. Inst. Mining Met. Engrs. (Petroleum Development and Technology)* **170,** 69 (1947).

[59]Purcell, W. R: Capillary Pressures—Their Measurement Using Mercury and the Calculation of Permeability Therefrom, *Trans. Am. Inst. Mining Met. Engrs. (Petroleum Development and Technology)* **186,** 39 (1949).

[60]Archie, G. E: The Electrical Resistivity Log as an Aid in Determining Some Reservoir Characteristics, *Trans. Am. Inst. Mining Met. Engrs. (Petroleum Development and Technology)* **146,** 54 (1942).

[61]Sage, B. H; Lacey, W. N; and Schaafsma, J. G: Behavior of Hydrocarbon Mixtures Illustrated by a Simple Case, *Proc. Am. Pet. Inst. (Prod. Bul. 212)* 119 (1933).

[62]Sage, B. H. and Lacey, W. N: Formation Volumes and Energy Characteristics of Gascap Material from Kettleman Hills Field, *API Drilling and Production Practice*, 158 (1936).

[63]Katz, D. L. (with Brown, G. G.): Vapor Pressure and Vaporization of Petroleum Fractions, *Ind. and Eng. Chemistry*, **25**, 1373 (1933); (with Hachmuth, K. H.): Vaporization Equilibrium Constants in a Crude Oil-Natural Gas System, *Ind. and Eng. Chemistry*, **29**, 1072 (1937); etc.

[64]Katz, D. L: Application of Vaporization Equilibrium Constants to Production Engineering Problems, *Trans. Am. Inst. Mining Met. Engrs. (Petroleum Development and Technology)* **127**, 159 (1938) (reprint, p. 219).

[65]Buckley, S. E: Calculation of Equilibria in Hydrocarbon Mixtures, *Trans. Am. Inst. Mining Met. Engrs. (Petroleum Development and Technology)* **127,** 178 (1938) (reprint, p. 238).

[66]Versluys, J: The Equation of Flow of Oil and Gas to a Well after Dynamic Equilibrium Has Been Established, *Proc. Royal Acad. Sci.*, **33,** 578 (Amsterdam 1930).

[67]Muskat, M. and Botset, H. G: Flow of Gas Through Porous Media, *Physics*, **1,** 1 (1931).

[68]Wilde, H. D. and Moore, T. V: Hydrodynamics of Reservoir Drainage and Its Relation to Well Spacing, *Proc. Am. Pet. Inst. (Prod. Bul. 210)* 83 (1932).

[69]Schilthuis, R. J. and Hurst, W: Variations in Reservoir Pressure in the East Texas Field, *Trans. Am. Inst. Mining Met. Engrs. (Petroleum Development and Technology)* **114,** 164 (1935).

[70]Hurst, W: Unsteady Flow of Fluids in Oil Reservoirs, *Physics,* **5,** 20 (1934).

[71]Muskat, M: The Flow of Compressible Fluids through Porous Media and Some Problems in Heat Conduction, *Physics,* **5,** 71 (1934).

[72]Hurst, W. and van Everdingen, A. F: The Application of the La Place Transformation to Flow Problems in Reservoirs, *Trans. Am. Inst. Mining Met. Engrs. (Petroleum Development and Technology)* **186,** 305 (1949).

[73]Muskat, M: *The Flow of Homogeneous Fluids through Porous Media,* McGraw-Hill Book Co., Inc., New York, 1937.

[74]Hetherington, C. R; MacRoberts, D. T; and Huntington, R. L: Unsteady Flow of Gas through Porous Media, *Trans. Am. Inst. Mining Met. Engrs. (Petroleum Development and Technology)* **146,** 166 (1942) (reprint, p. 208).

[75]Bruce, G. H; Peaceman, D. W; Rachford, H. H., Jr; and Rice, J. D: Calculation of Unsteady-State Gas Flow through Porous Media, *Trans. Am. Inst. Mining Met. Engrs. (Petroleum Development and Technology)* **198,** 79 (1953).

[76]Aronofsky, J. S. and Jenkins, R: Unsteady Flow of Gas through Porous Media—One-Dimensional Case, *Proc. U. S. Congress of Applied Mechanics,* Edwards Bros. (Ann Arbor 1952).

[77]Muskat, M: *Physical Principles of Oil Production,* McGraw-Hill Book Co., Inc., New York, 1949.

[78]Coleman, S; Wilde, H. D, Jr; and Moore, T. W: Quantitative Effect of Gas-Oil Ratios on Decline of Average Rock Pressure, *Trans. Am. Inst. Mining Met. Engrs.,* **86,** 174 (1930).

[79]Katz, D. L: A Method of Estimating Oil and Gas Reserves, *Trans. Am. Inst. Mining Met. Engrs. (Petroleum Development and Technology)* **118,** 18 (1936) (reprint, p. 16).

[80]Schilthuis, R. J: Active Oil and Reservoir Energy, *Trans. Am. Inst. Mining Met. Engrs. (Petroleum Development and Technology)* **118,** 33 (1936) (reprint, p. 31).

[81]Hurst, W: Water Influx into a Reservoir and Its Application to the Equation of Volumetric Balance, *Trans. Am. Inst. Mining Met. Engrs. (Petroleum Development and Technology)* **151,** 57 (1943) (reprint, p. 263).

[82]Buckley, S. E. and Leverett, M. C: Mechanism of Fluid Displacement in Sands, *Trans. Am. Inst. Mining Met. Engrs. (Petroleum Development and Technology)* **146,** 107 (1941) (reprint, p. 149).

[83]Earlougher, R. C: Relationship between Velocity, Oil Saturation and Flooding Efficiency, *Trans. Am. Inst. Mining Met. Engrs. (Petroleum Development and Technology)* **151,** 125 (1943) (reprint, p. 331).

[84]Morse, R. A. and Yuster, S. T: Water Flood Tests in Long Cores, *Producers Monthly,* Dec. (1946).

[85]Breston, J. N. and Hughes, R. V: Relation between Pressure and Recovery in Long Core Water Floods, *Trans. Am. Inst. Mining Met. Engrs. (Petroleum Development and Technology)* **186,** 100 (1949).

[86]Holmgren, C. R. and Morse, R. A: Effect of Free Gas Saturation on Oil Recovery by Water Flooding, *Trans. Am. Inst. Mining Met. Engrs. (Petroleum Development and Technology)* **192,** 135 (1951).

[87]Terwilliger, P. L; Wilsey, L. W; Hall, H. N; and Bridges, P. M: An Experimental and Theoretical Investigation of Gravity Drainage Performance, *Trans. Am. Inst. Mining Met. Engrs. (Petroleum Development and Technology)* **192,** 285 (1951).

[88]Morse, R. A; Geffen, T. M; Parrish, D. R; and Haynes, G. W: Efficiency of Gas Displacement from Porous Media by Liquid Flooding, *Trans. Am. Inst. Mining Met. Engrs. (Petroleum Development and Technology)* **195,** 29 (1952).

[89]Kern, L. R: Displacement Mechanism in Multi-Well Systems, *Trans. Am. Inst. Mining Met. Engrs. (Petroleum Development and Technology)* **195,** 39 (1952).

843

[90]Wyckoff, R. D; Botset, H. G; and Muskat, M: The Mechanics of Porous Flow Applied to Water-Flooding Problems, *Trans. Am. Inst. Mining Met. Engrs. (Petroleum Development and Technology)* **103**, 219 (1933).

[91]Bruce, W. A: An Electrical Device for Analyzing Oil-Reservoir Behavior, *Trans. Am. Inst. Mining Met. Engrs. (Petroleum Development and Technology)* **151**, 112 (1943) (reprint, p. 318).

[92]Bubb, F. W; Nisle, R. G; and Carpenter, P. G: An Electronic Analog Computer for Solving the Flash Vaporization Equilibrium Equation, *Trans. Am. Inst. Mining Met. Engrs. (Petroleum Development and Technology)* **189**, 43 (1950).

[93]Bruce, W. A: Use of High-speed Computing Machines for Oil-production Problems, *API Drilling and Production Practice*, 373 (1952).

[94]Muskat, Morris: *Physical Principles of Oil Production*, 810, McGraw-Hill Book Co., Inc., New York, 1949.

[95]Miller, H. C. and Higgins, R. V: Review of Cutler's Rule of Well Spacing, *U. S. Bur. Mines RI 3479* (1939).

[96]Craze, R. C. and Glanville, J. W: *Well Spacing*, Humble Oil & Refining Company, Houston (1955).

[97]Craze, R. C. and Buckley, S. E: A Factual Analysis of the Effect of Well Spacing on Oil Recovery, *API Drilling and Production Practice*, 144 (1945).

[98]Elkins, Lincoln F: Reservoir Performance and Well Spacing—Silica Arbuckle Pool, *API Drilling and Production Practice*, 109 (1946).

[99]Miller, F. G: Multiphase-Flow Theory and the Problem of Spacing Wells, *U. S. Bur. Mines Bull. 529* (1954).

[100]Buckley, S. E: *Petroleum Conservation*, American Institute of Mining and Metallurgical Engineers, Inc., New York, 1951.

[101]Calhoun, J. C, Jr: *Fundamentals of Reservoir Engineering*, University of Oklahoma Press, 1953.
Pirson, S. J: *Elements of Oil Reservoir Engineering*, McGraw-Hill Book Co., Inc., New York, 1950.
Uren, L. C: *Petroleum Production Engineering—Oil Field Exploitation*, McGraw-Hill Book Co., Inc., New York, 1939.

[102]Reistle, C. E. and Nye, G. L: Recent Changes in Reservoir Pressure Conditions in the East Texas Field, *Trans. Am. Inst. Mining Met. Engrs. (Petroleum Development and Technology)* **107**, 77 (1934).

[103]Buckley, S. E: The Pressure-Production Relationship in the East Texas Field, *API Drilling and Production Practice*, 140 (1938).

[104]Rumble, R. C; Spain, H. H; and Stamm, H. E., III: A Reservoir Analyzer Study of the Woodbine Basin, *Trans. Am. Inst. Mining Met. Engrs. (Petroleum Development and Technology)* **192**, 331 (1951).

[105]Old, R. E: Analysis of Reservoir Performance, *Trans. Am. Inst. Mining Met. Engrs. (Petroleum Development and Technology)* **151**, 86 (1943) (reprint, p. 292).

[106]Kaveler, H. H: Engineering Features of the Schuler Field Unit Operation, *Trans. Am. Inst. Mining Met. Engrs. (Petroleum Development and Technology)* **155**, 58 (1944) (reprint, p. 56).

[107]Tarner, Jack; Evans, W. R; and Kaveler, H. H: The Schuler-Jones Sand Pool; Nine Years of Unitized Pressure-Maintenance Operations, *Trans. Am. Inst. Mining Met. Engrs. (Petroleum Development and Technology)* **192**, 121 (1951).

[108]Akins, D. W., Jr: Primary High-Pressure Water Flooding in the Pettit Lime, Haynesville Field, *Trans. Am. Inst. Mining Met. Engrs. (Petroleum Development and Technology)* **192**, 239 (1951).

[109]Miller, M. G. and Lents, M. R: Performance of the Bodcaw Reservoir, Cotton Valley Field Cycling Project; New Methods of Predicting Gas-Condensate Reservoir Performance under Cycling Operations Compared to Field Data, *API Drilling and Production Practice*, 128 (1946).

[110]Elkins, L. F: Reservoir Performance and Well Spacing, Spraberry Trend Area Field of West Texas, *Trans. Am. Inst. Mining Met. Engrs. (Petroleum Development and Technology)* **198**, 177 (1953).

[111]Cook, A. B; Spencer, G. B; Bobrowski, F. P; and Chin T: A New Method of Determining Variations in Physical Properties of Oil in a Reservoir, with Application to the Scurry Reef Field, Scurry County, Texas, *U. S. Bur. Mines RI 5106* (1955).

Chapter 13

FLUID INJECTION

James A. Lewis

James A. Lewis was born in Kansas City, Missouri, in 1908 and received his higher education at Southwestern College, University of Oklahoma (B.S., 1931), and Pennsylvania State University (M.S. in P.E., 1932). He was employed as research assistant at Pennsylvania State and worked for an oil-producing company in Bradford, Pennsylvania, until late 1935 when he became directing officer and manager of Core Laboratories, Incorporated, and established the corporation's first office in Dallas, Texas. He continued as president of this firm until September 1, 1947, resigning then to establish the Dallas-based engineering firm which bears his name.

Academic and professional honors and affiliations include Sigma Gamma Epsilon, Sigma Tau, Tau Beta Pi, Sigma Xi, AAPG, API, and SPE of AIME. His early work on the determination of the permeability coefficient of porous media has been utilized extensively by the industry in conjunction with the broader principles of petroleum engineering. Mr. Lewis has directed and participated in the preparation of numerous comprehensive engineering and economic studies of major oil and gas fields, in the valuation of oil-producing companies, and has been responsible for or instrumental in the design, installation, and operation of fluid-injection programs in many fields throughout the United States, Canada, and Mexico.

Fluid injection is a method of recovery of oil, gas, and/or related hydrocarbons in which part of the energy effective in moving these hydrocarbons through a reservoir is applied from extraneous sources by injection of liquids or gases into the reservoir.

Primary pressure maintenance or *pressure regulation* is an application of fluid injection early in the producing life of a reservoir when there has been little or no loss of natural reservoir energy.

Secondary recovery is an application of fluid injection when a reservoir is approaching or has reached economic production limits.

The withdrawal of oil, solution gas, free gas, and water from an oil and gas accumulation causes a decline in the pressure under which the fluids existed at time of discovery. In all cases the contained fluids expand upon reduction in pressure, while extraneous water encroaches into the reservoir as fluids are withdrawn, tending to restore equilibrium conditions. However, this replenishment generally does not occur as rapidly as depletion, so there is a decline in pressure until a balance is established between rate of expansion and encroachment and rate of production. The reduction in reservoir pressure causes a decline in well productivity which has been recognized as an inherent characteristic of the industry since soon after completion of the Drake well for production of oil. Fluid injection into the hydrocarbon reservoir is used to reduce voidage and decline in pressure. The procedure assists in sustaining oil and gas-producing rates and increases ultimate recovery of hydrocarbons.

Operators first applied gas (vacuum) pumps about 10 years after completion of the first well. The practice established an increased pressure differential between reservoir and well bore, increased the rate of fluid production slightly, and extended the period of profitable operation. This and the more-important practices of injecting gas and water have been used in the ensuing 90 years in an increasingly effective manner to achieve the objective of increasing economic recovery. New procedures are being investigated in research laboratories and in field operations. Some of these new methods show promise of further improvement in recovery efficiency. However, only the established practices of injecting air, gas, or water—or a combination of gas and water —into a hydrocarbon reservoir, and the earliest project of each type, will be discussed in this chapter.

The natural growth in understanding and the economics of secondary-recovery operations, as compared to fluid injection of the pressure-regulation category, leads to the conclusion that from this time hence there will be fewer secondary operations *per se* and that there will be an increasing number of pressure-regulation projects. The majority of oil fields will be operated in such a manner as to permit maximum economic recovery of oil with minimum change in reservoir pressure. Fluids of predetermined and controlled composition will be injected into selected wells soon after definition of the reservoir at near discovery pressure to achieve recovery efficiencies hitherto unknown in the industry.

Early Observations

John F. Carll[1] reported in 1880 that the head of water from shallow sands in a hole retarded the appearance of oil in the well bore until the pressure exerted by the column of water was relieved by bailing; that prior to the initial use of casing in 1875, the seed bags which formerly were run on tubing to exclude water frequently would fail or had to be removed to repair the pump, thus permitting water to stand on the oil sand. If such a condition was not corrected, it would be reflected by an increase in oil-production rates in surrounding wells which ultimately would be taken over by water. He concluded further that the movement of water through the sands was beneficial in increasing the recovery of oil. However, until the movement was closely controlled, it was entirely possible for the practice to be detrimental to some of the operators in a common reservoir. Nevertheless, he reached sound conclusions for the movement of fluids within a reservoir and set forth the basic principles for predetermination of the probable effects of introduction of water into any particular oil district. It is apparent from Carll's discussion—*op. cit.*, Section 483, p. 268—that accidental and perhaps intentional water flooding of the oil-producing zone occurred in the Pithole City area in 1865.

Similarly, Torrey[2] states that James D. Dinsmoor reportedly observed in 1888 that when gas from one formation in a well bore was permitted to enter an oil-bearing sand in the same well, the offset wells were affected by increased rates of oil production which continued until the source of gas was cased off.

The astute observations by Carll and Dinsmoor, of the result of accidental intercommunication of natural forces under favorable circumstances, provided the background for the intentional injection of air, gas, and water, under controlled conditions, to increase the recovery of hydrocarbons.

It is generally concluded that accidental flooding of the Third Bradford sand started to occur around 1905, as evidenced by the increasing rate of oil production from the field as a whole. James O. Lewis[3] reported in 1917 that flooding had been occurring in the Brad-

[1]References are at the end of the chapter.

ford Field, Pennsylvania, for a period of 15 years which would place these operations as having been instituted around 1900. The upward trend of the Bradford oil-production curve after 1906 and the acknowledged fact that circle floods were dispersed throughout many acres of the field, lead to the conclusion that, although not legalized at the time, flooding operations were increasing in number between 1906 and the early 1920's.

In 1913, Huntley[4] referred to a flood taking place in the Oil Springs Pool, in Lambton County, Ontario. In this instance surface water, which accumulated in a swamp, found entry through drilled holes situated in this swamp to a downdip water-bearing position in the Corniferous limestone. Lewis *(op. cit.)* makes further reference to early flooding in the Kern River Field, California.

The proper application of fluid-injection methods to depleted and flush fields is no longer dependent upon trial-and-error evaluation, but upon adequate engineering and geological analysis and understanding of the producing mechanism of the reservoir. The developments contributed by engineers of the United States Bureau of Mines, the engineering and research departments of the oil companies, and educational and research institutions have provided the fundamental laws of fluid flow and fluid behavior in porous media upon which present analyses are based. The historical progress of this work, as well as the development of the in-hole instruments and laboratory equipment and techniques, are presented elsewhere in this volume.

Growth of Fluid-injection Projects

It is reported by Sweeney[5] (Table 1) that on January 1, 1955 fluid-injection operations in the United States were known to affect a minimum of 1,439,028 acres of oil-productive territory. These operations—which included air, but principally gas and water injection—showed an increased application on 1,033,663 acres in the period January 1, 1947 to January 1, 1955—an increase of 431,914 acres for gas and 601,749 acres for water injection. The States of Pennsylvania and New York rely principally on secondary-recovery operations for the production of oil. Such practice was very important in West Virginia and Ohio; of significant importance in Oklahoma, Kansas, Indiana, Illinois, Kentucky, and Arkansas; of minor but increasing importance in Colorado, Louisiana, Montana, New Mexico, Texas, Wyoming, and California; and was of practically no importance in Michigan, Mississippi, and the remaining oil-producing states as of 1955. Substantial expansion of fluid-injection operations has occurred since 1955, and will continue to increase in the unending efforts to recover a higher percentage of the original hydrocarbon content of known reservoirs, as will be shown later in this chapter.

Table 1

Status of Fluid-injection Operations in the United States*

January 1, 1955

Gas-injection Projects

State	Number of Fields	Number of Projects	Area, Acres	Number of Producing Wells	Number of Injection Wells	Daily Average Production, Barrels†	Secondary Recovery to 1-1-55 Thousands of Barrels
Arkansas	2	2	4,644	59	6	7,720	10,000
California	25	38	85,280	2,973	163	214,100	———
Colorado	3	3	23,340	453	14	68,100	———
Illinois	4	20	2,470	408	74	450	1,500
Kansas	4	4	1,837	79	14	270	3,500
Louisiana	17	23	96,904	598	81	44,000	———
Michigan	3	3	9,320	15	236	2,310	———
Montana	2	2	420	24	4	100	———
New Mexico	2	2	8,320	206	36	4,320	7,500
Ohio	5	21	1,384	75	18	55	1,500
Oklahoma	30	42	38,500	3,405	651	46,275	95,000
Pennsylvania	29	106	26,961	7,740	2,185	2,690	17,000
Texas	115	169	307,653	6,866	712	161,875	47,760
West Virginia	36	46	32,850	1,825	327	1,500	3,500
Wyoming	6	7	30,557	1,328	65	31,900	———
Total	283	488	670,440	26,054	4,580	585,665	211,260‡

Table 1 (Cont'd)

Water-injection Projects

State	Number of Fields	Number of Projects	Area, Acres	Number of Producing Wells	Number of Injection Wells	Daily Average Production, Barrels†	Secondary Recovery to 1-1-55 Thousands of Barrels
Arkansas	13	15	15,618	392	82	26,905	24,000
California	30	37	2,500	428	92	13,899	———
Illinois	69	255	75,000	6,906	3,788	68,500	107,735
Indiana	22	36	4,975	421	205	4,520	17,000
Kansas	78	168	34,650	5,773	4,325	41,650	141,075
Kentucky	26	45	5,990	1,393	1,309	2,980	5,392
Louisiana	19	22	48,100	598	117	16,375	39,450
Michigan	1	1	360	30	2	1,775	———
Montana	1	1	640	26	4	200	———
New Mexico	6	7	3,130	51	25	1,375	623
New York	2	200	27,000	13,500	11,350	8,400	114,000
Ohio	7	42	1,315	573	430	440	3,500
Oklahoma	148	449	119,750	15,102	10,455	74,380	107,500
Pennsylvania	16	599	61,020	5,362	23,545	23,550	300,308
Texas	130	389	359,630	30,720	3,756	466,759	96,058
West Virginia	11	13	2,300	195	115	3,200	4,000
Wyoming	2	2	6,610	45	7	830	4,000
Total	581	2,280	768,588	101,513	59,607	755,738	960,641‡

*From: A Survey of Secondary Recovery Operations and Methods Employed in the United States, Interstate Oil Compact Commission by Albert E. Sweeney, Jr., before Illinois Oil and Gas Association, April 11, 1957.

†For latter part of 1954.

‡Estimates from incomplete data.

Capacity Production

The unrestricted production of oil from fields discovered early in the life of the industry caused a rapid decline in reservoir pressure and in the productive capacities of the wells. The decline in producing rate due to natural causes and associated mechanical problems in connection with production resulted in numerous patents being issued, starting in 1864, claiming the application of unique techniques primarily to recondition wells from the standpoint of cleaning the well bores. One patent, however, relates to fluid injection.

Quoting from Torrey:[2] "In the Richards Patent No. 308,522, issued in 1884, the invention claimed relates to a method of extracting oil and increasing the productivity of oil wells. Attention is called to the use of explosives for the purpose of shattering the oil-bearing rock to release oil and gas and to improve the flow. It is stated that explosives are dangerous and often are the cause of damage to the well and its equipment and, as a substitute, Richards states that similar results may be obtained by supplying the oil rock with compressed air, gas, or fluids to force the oil from such rock to an upward position within the wells from which it is to be drawn, as an efficient substitution for the gas which has already escaped. To effect his purpose, he provides for the insertion in one of a series of wells (preferably the one nearest the center of a group) of a tube through which, by means of a force pump, compressed air, gas, or other suitable fluid, at a pressure of 1,000 psi, is forced down into the oil-bearing rock. By maintaining pressure of the formation the oil will be forced to the adjoining wells, where it can be recovered."

It is evident from these early patents in the field of oil production that considerable attention was being given to improvement in oil-production techniques within the early days of the oil industry.

Air and Gas Injection

The early history of the effects of the entrance of gas into a depleted oil sand is ably set forth by Torrey *(op. cit.)* as follows: "In 1888 James D. Dinsmoor was working as a roustabout on the William Hill property in Venango County, Pennsylvania, which produced oil from the Third Venango sand. On an adjoining property the Oil Supply Company deepened one of its Third sand oil wells to the underlying Speechley sand to obtain a gas supply for lease purposes. A substantial quantity of gas was found in the Speechley; but, inasmuch as the operator did not have a string of pipe and a packer available immediately, the well was shut in temporarily to save the gas. An immediate improvement in oil production was observed in three nearby Third Venango sand oil wells, which was maintained until the Oil Supply Company was able to obtain a string of casing and run it with a packer through the Third Venango sand. When this was done, the oil production from the adjoining wells returned to the previous normal level. This accidental repressuring operation represents the first known application of secondary methods in the United States."

Dinsmoor recognized the beneficial effects resulting from the introduction of gas into a depleted oil reservoir and pursued the idea by further application of the method in 1890 or 1891, followed by a combination of repressuring and a vacuum on a lease in 1895. Subsequent acquisitions by Dinsmoor and associates in 1903 further expanded the application of the method. It is well-known that Dinsmoor continued, throughout his active life, to acquire shallow oil-producing leases throughout the Eastern portion of the United States as well as in Illinois and Texas. He pursued the application diligently, always confining his activity to the injection of air and gas in combination with vacuum on producing wells.

James O. Lewis *(op. cit.)* in 1917 stated:

"The present successful practice of stimulating the production from oil wells by forcing air through the oil sand was started on the Wood farm of the Cumberland Oil Company near Chesterhill, Ohio, by I. L. Dunn, in August, 1911. However valid the claims of others for priority in idea and application may be, the fact remains that the now extensive use of this method can be traced back to this first successful demonstration. With the aid of Orton C. Dunn and Harvey E. Smith, the details of practical operation were worked out and demonstrated to other oil producers. Because Messrs. Smith and Dunn have been credited with bringing the method into successful public use, the process became known as the Smith-Dunn process, though it is also called the Marietta process because of its first extensive use near Marietta, Ohio.

"Mr. I. L. Dunn states that this idea originated when operating in the Macksburg pool Ohio in 1903, when gas at a pressure of 45 pounds was forced into an oil well producing from the 500-foot sand. After ten days the gas pressure was released and the well began to pump much oil, which continued until the gas had worked out again. In 1911 the experiments on the Wood farm were started. About 150,000 cubic feet of free air was compressed and forced into one well daily, at a pressure of 40 pounds, and within a week production of the surrounding wells had increased, after which the use of the compressed air was extended to other parts of the property."

At the time of Lewis' investigation, it was estimated that the injection of air or gas had been used on over 90 projects involving some 4,000 wells and that 80 percent of the installations had been successful. A large

855

number of the projects were located in the Appalachian fields in south-eastern Ohio and northwestern West Virginia. He reported that most of the plants were less than 3 years old and that probably half of the total number of plants were installed during the year 1916. Lewis summarized operating data from 42 projects, ranging in depth from 80 to 2,500 ft in Pennsylvania, West Virginia, Ohio, and Oklahoma. Production curves were included for 14 representative properties.

As a general rule, the proper application of air repressuring resulted in a 3½- to 4-fold increase in production rate. That the process was economic is evidenced by the increasing number of installations following 1916 and extending to include many of the depleted fields throughout the shallow sand areas of the United States.

About the time of Lewis' work, it was stated that the first intensive repressuring project, where an entire field was included in the operation, was started in the Hamilton Corners Field, near Oil City, Venango County, Pennsylvania in June 1916. Fettke[6] reported on the essential features of this project after it had been in operation for 10 years. Starting with a few widely dispersed injection wells, the facilities were expanded; and a total of 21 air-injection wells were used to sustain the producing rate of the 76 producing wells which had been completed in the 300-acre field. The operation caused the average production rate to increase from 0.1 bbl per well per day to 0.4 bbl per day, which yielded 102,373 bbl of oil from June 1916 to March 1927. Torrey[2] reported that the project was continuing to show an operating profit in the late 1940's.

J. E. Roth[7] reported that prior to the spring of 1924, when the Elliott plant was built, there were no successful air plants operating in Oklahoma. The process at that date had not been tried in Texas, and there were only five successful plants in Kansas. Recorded also were 12 failures of the method in the Chanute, Kans. area. The Elliott Pool of Nowata County, comprising 650 productive acres, obtained production from the Bartlesville sand at a depth of approximately 450 ft upon which 111 wells had been drilled with an average initial potential of 250 bbl of oil per day. Vacuum had been applied in 1913 and was continued until July 22, 1924, when injected air broke through the producing sand and caused the vacuum pumps to go down. The pool—which had been discovered in October 1909—had declined in oil rate until, at the start of air injection in 1924, 18 producing wells were averaging 0.53 bbl of oil per day. Within a month after starting the air injection the oil rate started to increase through the remaining months of 1924, and continued to increase during the entire year of 1925 until there was a sustained level of production amounting to three or four times the level prior to application of the process. Roth further stated that by 1926, 2 years after the Elliott plant was started, 80 projects were operating or building within the State of Oklahoma. In Kansas, at the same time, there were 22 successful plants in operation and 7 that had been classified as failures, other than those previously mentioned in the Chanute area. Texas at this time is reported to have had 10 operating plants.

At about the same time (1924) that the air-injection program was initiated in the Elliott Pool, Nickerson[8] stated that Honolulu Oil Corporation had been injecting dry gas in a volume of 200,000 to 280,000 cu ft per day under a maximum injection pressure of 200 psi into the oil measures of the Buena Vista Hills area. The producing sand occurred between depths of 3,000 and 4,000 ft, and individual wells were yielding 20 to 80 bbl of oil per day at the time the injection program was initiated.

In the middle 1920's, with increased recognition being given by the technical men of the industry and the United States Bureau of Mines to the function of natural gas in the production of oil, little effort had been made to conserve this valuable source of a naturally occurring hydrocarbon. Among the early projects, if not the first involving the return of produced gas on a broad scale, was that instituted in the Cook Ranch Field, Shackelford County, Texas, which was discovered February 19, 1926 with the completion of the Roeser and Pendelton, Inc.—Marland Oil Co., W. I. Cook "A" No. 1 well. This well was completed at a total depth of 1,242 ft for an initial flowing production of 1,000 bbl per day of 39 API gravity oil after penetrating only 1 ft of Cook sand. Wilson[9] reports that the development of the field was rapid, and by the end of 1929 a total of 213 producing wells had been completed. Peak oil production was reached in December 1926, when a total monthly oil production of 264,785 bbl was obtained from 112 wells. Soon after reaching peak production, portable compressors were installed in the gasoline plant for compressing fractionator vapors and residue gas at pressures up to 400 psi in order to return this gas to the formation. This operation was started on July 15, 1927, at which time the field was producing at a rate of 4,000 bbl per day. At this time, when only about one-half of the ultimate number of wells had been completed, the operators set out on a program of returning a substantial amount of produced gas to the formation for conservation purposes and to increase ultimate recovery of oil. The detail of this comprehensive field operation is reported by Wilson *(op. cit.)* and shows the advantages to be gained by proper application of full-scale reinjection of produced gas to a formation that was particularly susceptible to the method of operation. This Cook Ranch Field, being one of the first to undergo full-scale gas-injection application, has produced in excess of 1,000 bbl of oil per acre-foot of productive sand. This high yield is undoubtedly the result of significant gravity drainage combined with the effective injection program.

The earliest injection project involving a higher level of injection pressure (1,160 psi) was instituted by Marland Oil Company in the

Seal Beach Field of California in the fall of 1927. This operation was continued until the spring of 1928, at which time it was indicated that oil was moving away from the area of injection to leases and wells of other operators. Although the operation was successful in increasing the rate of production from Bixby zone wells, it was discontinued for the reasons cited; and, at a later date—starting in February 1929—was instituted in the Selover zone which was producing oil from a 200-ft oil-bearing zone occurring between 4,625 ft and 4,825 ft. Gas was injected through a 2½-in. upset tubing string set on a packer at 4,445 ft, with 150 ft of tubing below the packer. Injection volume ranged between 1 and 2½ MMcf per day; and it is stated by Bell and Webb,[10] reporting on the results of this project, that the most noticeable tendency was for the gas to short-cut to up-structure wells while the downdip wells would have large increases in oil-production rates without significant change in gas-oil ratios. They concluded that the ideal location for gas-injection wells would be at the highest structural position; and that by following such practices, where correlative rights were protected, it would be possible to maintain reservoir pressure to the point that the necessity of gas-lift and artificial-production methods would be eliminated and the wells could be made to flow again.

Early in 1928 E. O. Bennett[11] called attention to the increased use of natural gas for injection into oil reservoirs to aid in the recovery process.

Dwyer[12] reported in September 1928 that 17 wells were being used for the introduction of gas into the oil sand of the Burbank Field, Osage County, Oklahoma. This project, initiated by Gypsy Oil Company, Sinclair Oil & Gas Company, Phillips Petroleum Company, and The Carter Oil Company, was expanded to a program of major proportion in the following years. Dwyer states that lean gas was being used, as well as propane and butane which was recovered during the stabilization process for manufacture of gasoline. At about this same date, in discussion of a paper by C. E. Beecher[13] advocating early injection of gas, J. F. Dodge mentioned that Union Oil Co. of California was injecting propane with dry gas into the Dominguez Field of California.

The foregoing operations indicate the trend of thinking toward the conservation of natural resources to increase the recovery of oil from oil-bearing formations. By 1928 it had been fairly well-established, as stated by Beecher, that gas-injection operations would result in an increase in oil recovery amounting to 30 to 60 percent over the primary yield. It is in this paper that Beecher stresses the importance of repressuring during the early stages of development.

A noteworthy investigation and operation was instituted by Humble Oil & Refining Company in the Olney Field, Archer County, Texas in 1929.[14] An entire oil-productive Swastika sand lens that had produced 349,140 bbl of oil from discovery in 1925 to August 1929 was acquired; the oil rate had declined to 60 bbl per day under primary methods of operation. By eliminating withdrawals and by injecting 170,136,000 cu ft of purchased gas during a 10-month period, reservoir pressure was restored almost to its original value. The field was then shut in for a period of 12 months, during which time the reservoir pressure declined from 416 psi to 354 psi on November 21, 1929. At this date, oil production was resumed by flowing and continued gas injection added another 2,000,000 cu ft to the reservoir during the next 27 months.

Wells continued to flow until the period September 1936-January 1937, when pumps were installed. The reservoir produced about 205,-000 bbl of oil from November 21, 1929, after pressure had been restored, until the operation was discontinued on or about November 1, 1938. Primary recovery from the reservoir has been estimated at 25 percent of the oil in place, and the second phase accounts for an increase of 14.7 percent to give a total yield of 39.7 percent of original oil in place.

Although the principles of gas injection initially were developed in the Eastern United States, the rapid increase in number of projects and annual production resulting from applications in Oklahoma—starting in 1925—soon placed that state in the position of leader in the application of secondary-recovery methods. Sweeney[15] in a chart reproduced herein as Fig. 1—with extensions from Sweeney[5]—shows that the annual production resulting from gas-injection projects in the United States reached a peak about 1935, maintained a relatively constant level until 1945, and increased rapidly to 1952. The recent increases are ascribed to projects started in Texas and in states other than Oklahoma and Illinois. Annual production from gas-injection projects is estimated to have reached 212,000,000 bbl in 1955.

Recovery Efficiency

The production of oil which results solely from the expansion of a gas-oil mixture contained in a porous-sandstone reservoir generally will not exceed 20 percent of the original stock-tank oil content. The substantial quantity of oil which remains to be recovered has provided the incentive for improved recovery methods utilizing fluid-injection procedures. With few exceptions, the return of produced or extraneous gas under low-pressure operation has resulted in increases in recovery falling in the range of 10 to 30 percent of the primary yield. In instances, as previously cited, where the force of gravity aided by the formation of secondary gas caps has been utilized in the production mechanism, the recovery has accumulated to a much higher proportion of the original content.

859

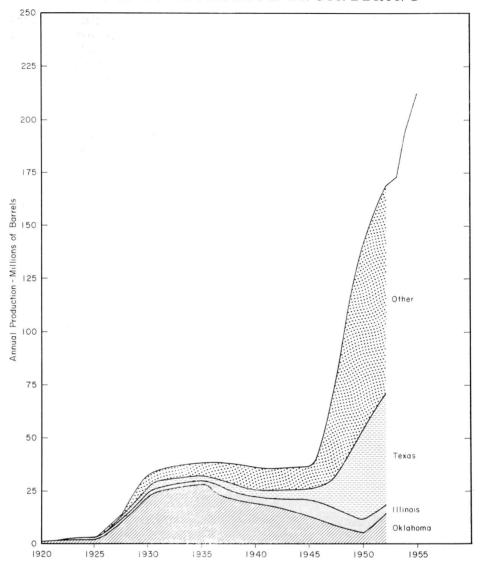

Fig.1—Production from Gas-injection Fields[15]
Extensions for 1954 and 1955 from Sweeney.[5]

Pressure Maintenance

As engineers in the industry developed better working knowledge of the mechanical problems to be met in gas-injection operations and became aware of the substantial increases in recovery achieved by the application of the method to depleted reservoirs, there developed the application of gas injection to reservoirs early in their productive life while a substantial level of native reservoir pressure existed in the formation.

The Sugarland Field, Fort Bend County, Texas—discovered on March 27, 1928 by the completion of Humble Oil & Refining Company's Sugarland Industry's No. 1 from the Marginulina zone of Middle Oligocene formation at 3,561 ft—has been operating under a combination gas-injection program into the cap region in conjunction with primary water encroachment since the gas-injection program was started on April 2, 1930. McCarter and O'Bannon[16] describe the reservoir as occurring in the arched super-cap sedimentary beds overlying a moderately deep-seated salt dome. The oil reservoir rocks are composed of a zone of sandy shales and sands interspersed with impervious shale members. The oil-bearing section includes 300 ft of interval which incorporates 4 sands that are continuous over a large portion of the field. The average thickness of the clean oil sand included in the productive interval is 90 ft.

An original free gas cap of significant volume was defined; and, after observing the performance of the reservoir and the pattern of natural water encroachment, it was concluded that the injection of gas into the free-gas zone would be beneficial in controlling edgewater encroachment and reservoir pressure. The original reservoir pressure in the oil zone was estimated at 1,550 psi, which had declined to 1,280 psi at the time gas injection was started on April 2, 1930. Since that date, as reported by Sterne,[17] reservoir pressure was increased 100 psi by October 1937, at which time the gas-injection program was discontinued. Injection was resumed in March 1938 and continued until November 1941. Increased production rates in 1943 caused pressure to decline rapidly and gas injection was resumed in November of that year at an average reservoir pressure of 1,282 psi, and has been maintained at this approximate level for the period 1945 through January 1952. It is significant that there has been essentially no change in reservoir pressure in the past 25 years of production from this field as a result of the balance maintained between production and injection and encroachment.

Since the inception of the Sugarland project and the general recognition that the maintenance of reservoir pressure at a high level was beneficial in increasing the recovery of oil, there have been an increasing number of injection programs which have utilized the injection of gas into free gas caps, into secondary gas caps, and into oil zones to retard the rate of decline of reservoir pressure or to fully maintain it at or near its discovery level.

During the late 1930's, when the economics of the producing industry returned to a firmer position, the petroleum engineer had opportunity to evaluate and to install those methods of operation that would increase producing performance and ultimate oil recovery.

For further examples, the reader is referred to the numerous references starting at p. 777 of *Secondary Recovery of Oil in the United*

States (2nd Ed.), published by the American Petroleum Institute in 1950.

Recycling

William N. Lacey[18] in November 1932, in his discussion of the paper by E. V. Foran on The Big Lake Field, stated: ". . . at high pressures, liquids have higher vapor pressures than is ordinarily the case. At considerably higher pressures, such as 3,000 to 4,000 lbs., . . . that effect is quite marked. Liquids which ordinarily have fairly low vapor pressures have relatively high ones under these conditions . . . that under these conditions, about 185 degrees temperature and 3,000 to 4,000 lb pressure, the upper zone (Big Lake Field) with its white oil is existent in the formation in the gas phase entirely." This new concept of the behavior of hydrocarbon mixtures provided the basis for the production, processing to remove liquid products, and return of dry gas to the formation to maintain pressure, which operation became known as "recycling."

The first commercial cycling plant to obtain operating permission from the Texas Railroad Commission was an outgrowth of Vaughn's[19] experimental work in the Cayuga Field of Central Texas. This plant, installed by Tide Water Associated Oil Company and Seaboard Oil Company of Delaware, started operation in March 1938 by processing 11 MMcf of gas.

Simultaneously with the design and construction of the Cayuga plant, it is reported by Foran and Dixon[20] that preparations were being made for construction of a distillate-recycling plant in the Agua Dulce Field, Nueces County, Texas. The early background which led to actual operation in January 1939 is presented in the *Cycler.*[21] On the first 24-hour run, the plant processed 40 MMcf of gas and recovered 800 bbl of distillate. Separator pressure was 1,200 psi and discharge pressure into the return injection well (No. 7) was 2,765 psi. The capacity of the plant soon was increased to 60 to 65 MMcf daily capacity.

The economic success of the process, when applied under proper conditions supplemented by encouragement of conservation bodies, led to an increase in the number of applications in following years which has continued to this writing. The procedure also permitted producers to obtain return on investments which theretofore had been of low income-producing value.

Gas Vaporization

Work in the research department of The Atlantic Refining Company led to the finding reported by Whorton and Kieschnick[22] that, at reservoir pressures in excess of 3,000 psi, certain types of under-saturated liquid hydrocarbons responded to substantial increase in volume when in association with an excess of gas-phase material. The procedure

862

develops a miscible front between the injected fluid and the fluid being displaced, thus creating and perpetuating a solvent-extraction operation which achieves a high-percentage recovery of oil in place in the paths of travel. The method has been instituted by The Atlantic Refining Company in Block 31 Field, Crane County, Texas. From the date of inception in mid-1949, the reservoir has responded satisfactorily to the program; and, with appropriate levels of gas injection, full reservoir pressure has been maintained. Performance, as reported by Fancher,[23] indicates that the mechanism is performing as expected and substantial increases in recovery will be achieved through the operation.

Patterns of Flow

High recovery efficiency of a gas-cycling or vaporization operation is dependent upon achieving high sweep efficiency in the areal plan between injection and producing wells. Engineers[24, 25] in the industry have contributed materially to a better understanding of the effects of injection and production rates by utilizing electrolytic and potentiometric models wherein the flow of electrical current, in proportion to injection and production rates, is studied to determine potential distribution and infer flow patterns between injection and production locations. These studies have been utilized extensively in improving operating practices.

Water Injection

John F. Carll,[1] in the investigation conducted between 1875 and 1880, developed an outstanding knowledge of fluid flow within and from an oil sand. At an early date in the history of the industry, he recognized the beneficial as well as the detrimental effects resulting from the invasion of water into an oil sand. He published an analysis of the various factors to be considered in judging the *probable effects* of movement of water through an oil sand. His work has been quoted by numerous petroleum engineers interested in reservoir mechanics and in water flooding. It is timely to repeat here the following excerpts from his chapter entitled "Flooded Territory."

"*In judging of the probable effects of the introduction of water* into any particular oil district several things are to be considered:

"1. *The time for flooding* whether early in the progress of development while yet a large percentage of oil remains unexhausted, or at a later period after the supply has suffered from long, continued depletion.

"2. *The structure of the rock* whether regular and homogeneous throughout, or composed of fine sand interbedding connected and irregular layers of gravel, sometimes lying near the top and at others near the bottom.

"3. *The shape of the area being flooded.*

"4. The position of *the point at which water is admitted* in relation to the surrounding wells still pumping oil.

"5. *The height (which governs the pressure) of the column of water* obtaining admission.

"6. *The duration of the water supply.*"

Fluid injection into an oil reservoir, to increase not only the rate of production but the ultimate recovery, was clearly set forth by Carll in the reference cited. The industry is indebted to him for an accurate analysis, at an early date in its history, of the basic concepts involved in the production and recovery of oil from reservoir rocks. His work has served as the basis for further progress in this field toward maximum recovery of an important natural resource.

Although the beneficial effects of the movement of water into an oil reservoir had been recognized by Carll, from the standpoint of ultimate recovery from the field as a whole it is understandable why operators feared the appearance of water in their producing wells, for it marked the inevitable beginning of the end of their salable product. In view of the competitive nature of the industry, the absence of unitization programs, and the experience of producers, it is understandable why operators always have tried to exclude water from their oil-producing horizons. The haphazard and uncontrolled admission of water into an oil sand might be beneficial to an operator in certain cases but, at the same time, might be detrimental to offset operators. Statutes in most oil-producing states provide that the admission of water is unlawful and that appropriate steps be taken to plug wells and exclude such inter-communication between water horizons and the oil zone. The high displacement efficiency and the pronounced response in oil rate to an invading region of water undoubtedly caused the concern of offset operators. However, when gas-injection programs later became more widespread, offset operators frequently would not oppose such programs because, first, of the beneficial effects that resulted in their own wells and, second, of the fact that entry of gas into their producing wells did not in all cases preclude the future production of oil. The widespread application of gas injection generally was not associated with cooperative or unitized operations, but was accomplished by balanced cross-line programs.

Despite applicable regulations, there are many instances recorded in the literature where water gained entry into the oil measures. James O. Lewis[26] reported that there were intentional water-injection operations in Bradford in the early 1890's, and from Carll's work it is to be surmised that similar conditions existed in the middle district of Pennsylvania prior to 1875. That flooding had attained sizable proportions in the Bradford Field is reflected by the production curve of this area,

Fig. 2. After discovery in 1871, the field reached a peak producing rate of 23,000,000 bbl per year in 1881 and declined to 2,000,000 bbl per year in 1906. Thereafter, a gradual increase in the total field rate from the 83,000 productive acres occurred until water flooding was legalized by the Legislature of Pennsylvania in 1921, after which time a sharp increase was noted starting in 1926 as a result of the adoption of more intensive injection patterns.

The early method of water flooding, which developed from the improper abandonment of a well, became known as the "circle flood." The growth of the water-invaded zone increased until adjacent wells were watered out, at which time they also were utilized as injectors to extend the area of influence. The rate of advance of the water, diminishing with time and cumulative injection, prompted Forest Oil Corporation[27] to convert a series of wells at one time to form a line drive, which practice increased in acceptance as benefits from the program became recognized. These methods, utilized in Bradford prior to 1924, were responsible for the increased oil rates which started in 1907.

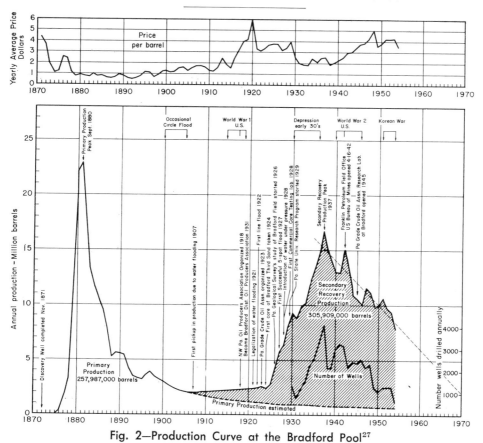

Fig. 2—Production Curve at the Bradford Pool[27]

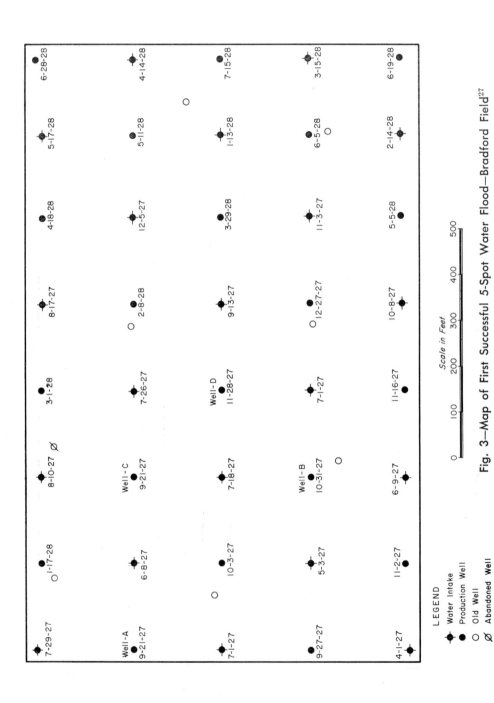

Fig. 3—Map of First Successful 5-Spot Water Flood—Bradford Field[27]

The Legislature of the State of New York passed appropriate measures to permit legal injection of water into oil reservoirs in 1919. Soon thereafter, in 1921, the Pennsylvania Legislature passed similar laws; and within the following 5 years there occurred a substantial increase in the number of applications of more intensive water-injection operations utilizing the circle and line-type drives. These injection methods, limited by the nature of the Bradford sand to accept water, resulted in only nominal increases of oil-production rates in surrounding wells.

The first 5-spot pattern was attempted by Associated Producers Company (Tide Water Associated Oil Company) on a property in the southern part of the Bradford Field in 1924. The idea is credited by Fettke[27] to Frank Haskell. The distance between like wells—500 ft— proved too great to obtain quick response. The first increase in oil rate from a 5-spot development is credited, therefore, to Arthur E. Yahn's[27] 190-ft 5-spot development at the head of Oil Valley in the northeastern part of the Bradford Field. Water-injection wells were completed between April 1927 and May 1928; and the producing wells were completed prior to July 1928, as shown in Fig. 3. At first only surface water entered the wells; but later, in November 1929, a pressure plant was installed and utilized to increase rate of injection. The peak oil-producing rate had been developed, however, prior to use of the pressure plant. The complete history of this project is reported by Fettke *(op. cit.)*, with monthly oil and water production as recorded in Fig. 4 and Table 2. Prior to installation of the pressure plant at Yahn's flood in November 1929, Paul D. Torrey* reports that he recommended utilization of such a plant on Messer Petroleum Corporation's Shaner property, Allegany County, New York, in early 1928 which was subsequently put into operation before the end of the year.

Early applications of the 5-spot plan for water flooding required re-development of shallow fields to achieve replacement of prior withdrawals in reasonable time under conditions that would confine the injected fluid in the oil-saturated sand members. Wider spacing of like wells has been possible for formations more permeable than the Bradford sand, and existing uniformly spaced wells have been utilized for flooding of fields drilled since 1935. The utilization of available wells has permitted the recovery of substantial quantities of oil from reservoirs which otherwise would have remained unflooded under prevailing price structures.

The intensive 5-spot pressure method of flooding depleted fields gained widespread acceptance throughout the Bradford area as reflected in the total oil-production rate for the field (Fig. 2), which increased to reach a peak of about 16,500,000 bbl in 1937. It is to be noted that

---

*Personal communication.

this rate of oil production approached the primary peak of 23,000,000 bbl which was established in 1881. Fettke *(op. cit.)* states that 54 percent (305,909,000 bbl) of total production (563,896,000 bbl) from the Bradford Field through 1954 had been obtained by water flooding. To this date primary recovery accounted for a yield of 2,750 bbl per acre and water flooding 3,250 bbl per acre. An estimate of future oil production should add another 850 bbl per acre to the yield by water flooding.

It first was believed that the uniform character of the Bradford sand made it particularly susceptible to the application of the water-flooding principle. That it possesses the normal irregularities in character found in the average sand subsequently was proved by the analysis of cores to determine variation in porosity and permeability.

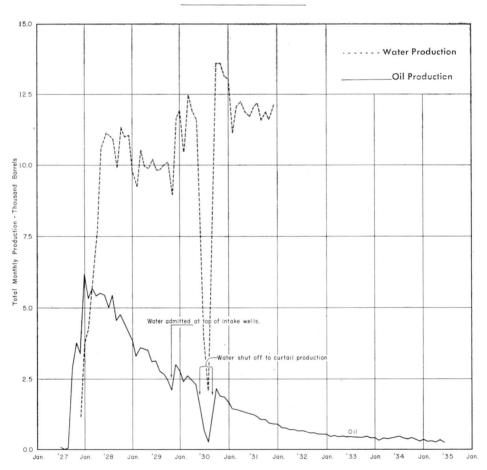

Fig. 4—Curves Showing Total Monthly Oil and Water Production of First Successful 5-Spot Water Flood[27]

Table 2[27]

Total Monthly and Cumulative Oil and Water
Production of First Successful Five-spot Water Flood
Bradford Oil Field

Date	Oil Production		Water Production	
	Monthly	Cumulative	Monthly	Cumulative
1927				
July	87	87		
August				
September	82	169		
October	2,885	3,045		
November	3,823	6,877		
December	3,411	10,288	1,205	1,205
1928				
January	6,194	16,482	3,695	4,900
February	5,356	21,838	4,290	9,190
March	5,717	27,555	5,693	14,883
April	5,446	33,001	7,491	22,374
May	5,537	38,538	10,623	32,997
June	5,490	44,028	11,114	44,111
July	5,028	49,056	11,083	55,194
August	5,463	54,519	10,924	66,118
September	4,561	59,080	9,872	75,990
October	4,794	63,874	11,343	87,333
November	4,513	68,387	11,030	98,363
December	4,210	72,597	11,066	109,429
1929				
January	3,893	76,490	9,808	119,237
February	3,331	79,821	9,240	128,277
March	3,625	83,446	10,594	138,871
April	3,576	87,022	9,947	148,818
May	3,544	90,566	9,880	158,698
June	3,136	93,702	10,246	168,941
July	3,178	96,880	9,854	178,798
August	2,805	99,685	9,846	188,644
September	2,710	102,395	10,034	198,678
October	2,516	104,911	10,149	208,827
November	2,159	107,090	8,981	217,808
December	3,046	110,116	11,660	229,468
1930				
January	2,839	112,955	11,965	241,433
February	2,418	115,373	10,422	251,855
March	2,657	118,030	12,531	264,386
April	2,499	120,529	11,947	276,333
May	2,334	122,863	11,630	287,963
June	1,522	124,385	8,424	296,387
July	686	125,071	3,978	300,365
August	285	125,356	2,100	302,465

(Continued on following page)

Table 2 (Cont'd)

Date	Oil Production Monthly	Oil Production Cumulative	Water Production Monthly	Water Production Cumulative
September	1,307	126,663	9,204	311,669
October	2,231	128,894	13,625	325,294
November	1,940	130,834	13,633	338,927
December	1,901	132,735	13,160	352,087
1931				
January	1,762	134,497	13,073	365,160
February	1,498	135,995	11,109	376,269
March	1,473	137,468	12,098	388,367
April	1,435	138,903	12,270	400,637
May	1,398	140,301	11,906	421,543
June	1,313	141,614	11,761	424,304
July	1,285	142,899	12,028	436,332
August	1,228	144,127	12,261	448,593
September	1,107	145,234	11,588	460,181
October	1,103	146,337	11,902	472,083
November	987	147,324	11,628	483,711
December	960	148,284	12,116	495,827
1932				
January	950	149,234		
February	814	150,048		
March	806	150,854		
April	742	151,596		
May	740	152,336		
June	701	153,037		
July	700	153,737		
August	672	154,409		
September	630	155,039		
October	621	155,660		
November	576	156,236		
December	564	156,800		
1933				
January	570	157,370		
February	492	157,862		
March	524	158,386		
April	497	158,883		
May	504	159,387		
June	480	159,867		
July	478	160,345		
August	470	160,815		
September	454	161,269		
October	451	161,720		
November	499	162,219		
December	428	162,647		
1934				
January	432	163,079		
February	348	163,427		
March	414	163,841		

Table 2 (Cont'd)

Date	Oil Production Monthly	Oil Production Cumulative	Water Production Monthly	Water Production Cumulative
April	402	164,243		
May	429	164,672		
June	448	165,120		
July	475	165,595		
August	423	166,018		
September	381	166,399		
October	431	166,830		
November	373	167,203		
December	314	167,517		
1935				
January	364	167,881		
February	304	168,185		
March	320	168,505		
April	275	168,780		
May	372	169,152		
June	284	169,436		

Summary

Oil Production and Yearly Percent Recovery of First Five-spot Water Flood

Year	Oil Production, Bbl	Percent of Total	Year	Oil Production, Bbl	Percent of Total
1	44,028	26.0	5	11,423	6.7
2	49,674	29.3	6	6,830	4.3
3	30,683	18.1	7	5,728	3.3
4	17,229	10.1	8	3,841	2.2

The principal features of the Bradford Field which have made it particularly outstanding in water-flooding history are the large productive area and the absence of primary water encroachment. There was, however, an area containing a free-gas zone which complicated the application of water flooding in that portion of the field.

Operators, faced with existing economic conditions in the early 1930's, were slow to extend the water-flooding procedures developed at Bradford to areas outside the field. The middle district of Pennsylvania was under investigation but did not appear suitable for application of the procedures. In 1931, however, The Carter Oil Company initiated their Collins pilot water flood in the shallow Bartlesville sand of Nowata County, Oklahoma. The results were not encouraging and the project was abandoned. Within 3 to 4 years following, however, Forest Oil Corporation, after preliminary investigation, instituted a somewhat larger pilot water flood on the Allen lease in the Coody's Bluff area of Nowata County to develop the Bartlesville sand at a depth of approximately 450 ft. The favorable results, reported recently by Earlougher,[28] encouraged further development in the area which has been expanded substantially by Forest and other operators to include most of the favorable Bartlesville areas in northeastern Oklahoma. During the course of its development in this area, water flooding was extended into shallow sand areas of eastern Kansas.

The first pilot water-flood operation in the State of Texas is credited to The Texas Company[29] in the Fry Pool of Brown County, which was started in January 1936 and continued for 2 years then abandoned because of production of excessive amounts of water in wells adjacent to the water-injection wells. The water-flooding method, however, was utilized by Peterson and McCarty[30] on their Hardin lease, Burkburnett Field, Wichita County, Texas, in June 1936; 1,300 bbl of oil per acre were recovered before the project was abandoned in May 1942. Many other water-injection projects were initiated in the shallow sand area of North Texas following the first application in 1936. However, it was not until Magnolia Petroleum Company initiated the West Burkburnett flood in 1944 that an outstandingly successful operation was achieved. Typical of secondary-recovery projects, Magnolia drilled, cored, and analyzed new wells to establish the potential of the area. Elsewhere in West Burkburnett, a 20-acre 5-spot program was adopted to flood the Gunsight sand of Pennsylvanian age which occurred at 1,750 ft. Pilot operations on the 160-acre J. G. Goins lease increased production from 40 to 755 bbl per day. The project ultimately included 2,560 affected acres which produced a maximum of 7,000 bbl per day in August 1953, as reported by Whitney.[31] The Goins pilot operation has recovered 1.7 times primary production. The entire project has recovered 9 million barrels by water flooding, or 1.4 times that recovered by primary methods. Ultimate production should be in excess of 50 percent of the stock-tank oil originally in place in the reservoir.

The initial field-wide 5-spot water-flood program in Illinois was conducted by Adams Oil and Gas Company—Felmont Corporation in the Patoka Field, Marion County, when salt water was started into 9 injection wells in September 1943. The application of the method, about 5½ years after reaching peak rate under primary production, resulted in a much more rapid response in oil rate than previously had been observed and prompted the operators to expand development to include the entire productive area. This field, which had produced 2,800,000 bbl by primary production to date of starting the water flood, has produced an additional 6,400,000 bbl of water-flood oil to August 1, 1960. The outstanding success of the Patoka project, a broader acceptance of the principles of water flooding, and the improvement in price of crude oil—which started in 1947—have encouraged further expansion of flood developments in Illinois which have extended to other projects in Oklahoma, Texas, and other states.

The details of operations carried forward in Oklahoma, Kansas, and Illinois are adequately covered in U.S. Bureau of Mines *Reports of Investigations* on these activities.[32, 33, 34] The oil production resulting from these and other applications of the method are summarized by Sweeney[5, 15] and presented on Fig. 5. The rapid growth in rate, starting in 1949, is attributed to expanding development in Ward County, Texas, and operations in Oklahoma—in counties outside the northeast area—including the outstanding Olympic Pool flood of Buffalo Oil Company, Hughes and Okfuskee Counties.

Pressure Regulation by Water Injection

During the expansion of water-flooding operations of depleted oil reservoirs, petroleum engineers became cognizant of the advantages to be gained by application of the principles to the production of flush reservoirs. Over and above the advantages to be gained by pressure control was the advantage of disposing of produced water in natural water-drive fields. The earliest application of the method occurred in the East Texas Field on an experimental basis in 1936 as reported by Morris.[35, 36] Earlier analytical studies of this reservoir by Schilthuis and Hurst[37] led to the conclusion that, as reservoir pressure declined, salt water contained in the aquifer of the Woodbine sand expanded and encroached into the oil reservoir and, depending upon the rate of production, sustained an equilibrium level of reservoir pressure which was interdependent with rate of production. After observing the performance of the field for a number of years, the water-disposal program—instituted in 1936—was expanded in 1938 and more substantially in 1942 when the East Texas Salt Water Disposal Company was formed. The return of produced water to assist in maintaining reservoir pressure has been accomplished with outstanding success.

Phillips Petroleum Company initiated the return of produced water to the Wilcox zone of the Billings Field, Noble County, Oklahoma, in January 1940 to supplement gas injection started in October 1938, 2 years after discovery of the field. The reduction in rate of reservoir voidage, accomplished by the supplemental injection of water to the aquifer at a downdip location, permitted better pressure regulation in the reservoir. The simultaneous injection of gas and water has continued throughout the producing history of the reservoir.

The utilization of extraneous water to maintain pressure in oil reservoirs, producing under partially effective natural encroachment, was recommended in October 1940, by James A. Lewis[38] who stated:

"Field results have shown and recent research on the flow of gas, oil and water mixtures through sand has confirmed, the presence of an equilibrium residual oil saturation after water drive. By adjusting production rates in potentially natural water drive

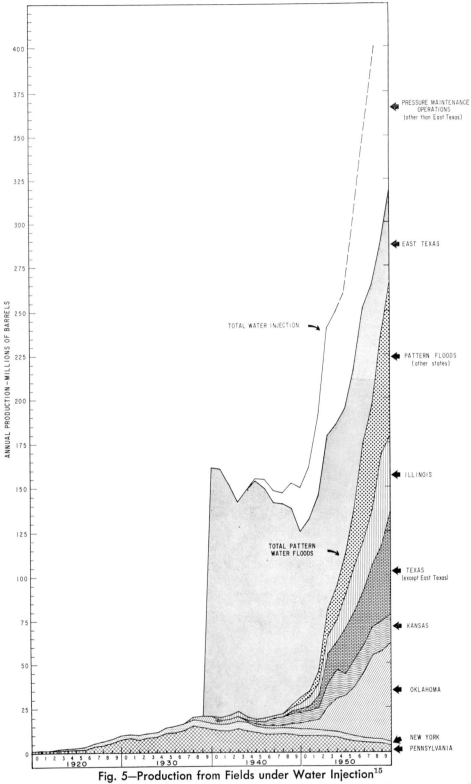

Fig. 5—Production from Fields under Water Injection[15]
(From Ref. 5 and subsequent data from A. E. Sweeney, Jr. by personal communication)

fields so that a minimum drop in reservoir pressure results, or by artifically supplementing this water drive by injection of extraneous water to maintain reservoir pressure and obtain profitable rates of production, it will be feasible to economically recover a larger portion of the original oil content. . . . Such a method of artificial maintenance of reservoir pressure will result in an even higher recovery than would be possible by later application of water drive after the reservoir pressure had fallen to a low value."

Soon after the Billings project, Barnsdall Oil Company (Sunray Mid-Continent)[39] began injection of extraneous water, in April 1943, into the Reynolds "oolitic" zone of the Smackover limestone oil reservoir of the Midway Field, Lafayette County, Arkansas, to maintain and increase ultimate recovery. Pressure has been maintained above the saturation pressure of 2,528 psi during the entire productive life of the field. Recovery has exceeded estimated primary yield and a restricted rate of 5,703 bbl of oil per day was being maintained in 1959, as shown on Fig. 6.

Extraneous fresh-water injection into the Hill sand reservoir, New Hope Field, Franklin County, Texas[40] was started in September 1945, thus marking the initiation of pressure-maintenance operation of reservoirs producing without benefit of primary water encroachment. Prior unitization of operating and royalty interests permitted Tide Water Associated Oil Company and Seaboard Oil Company to institute the program in the multiple-pay field early in its productive life, soon after determination of type of reservoir control. The other oil zones— including the Hill sand—which exhibited an effective degree of natural water encroachment, soon were added to the operation and are continuing to produce in efficient manner.

The highly permeable Hogg sand of the Wesson Field, Ouachita County, Arkansas, discovered in March 1946, exhibited a rapid decline in reservoir pressure during the early months of production because of the highly under-saturated nature of the reservoir crude. Studies performed by petroleum engineers before 1 percent of original oil content had been produced indicated the feasibility of injecting extraneous water to improve recovery efficiency. The field was unitized and injection started before 3 percent of original content was recovered. Continuation of the program in the ensuing years has confirmed the original estimates of expected performance and recovery. To January 1, 1961, 86.7 percent of anticipated ultimate recovery of 50 percent of original oil in place has been produced. The producing wells have sustained an average restricted oil rate of 3,250 bbl per day during the year 1960; prior data on Fig. 7.

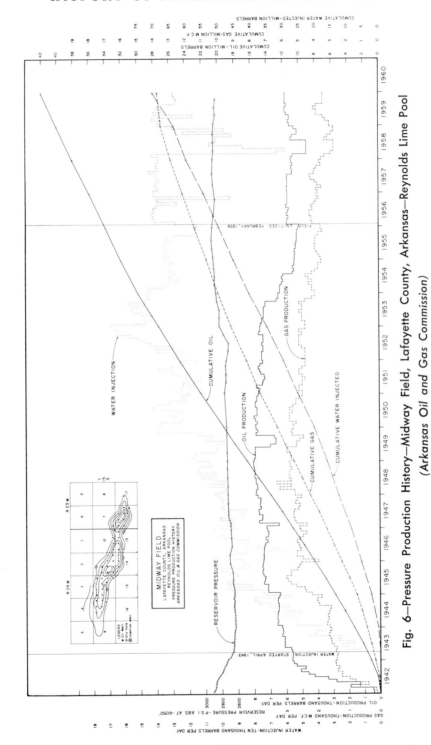

Fig. 6—Pressure Production History—Midway Field, Lafayette County, Arkansas—Reynolds Lime Pool
(Arkansas Oil and Gas Commission)

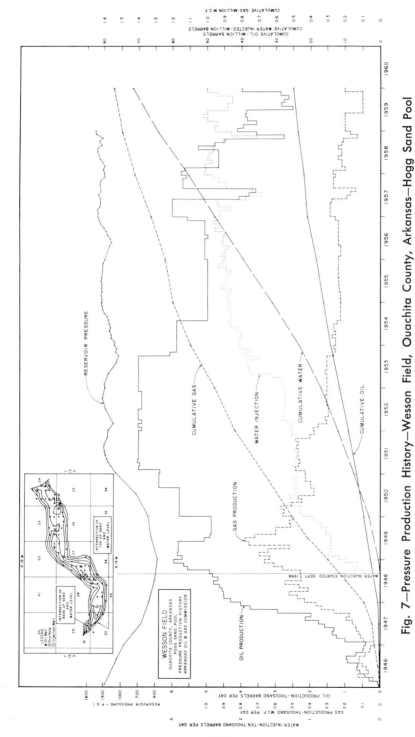

Fig. 7—Pressure Production History—Wesson Field, Ouachita County, Arkansas—Hogg Sand Pool
(Arkansas Oil and Gas Commission)

The Mamou Field in Evangeline Parish, Louisiana, discovered by Magnolia Petroleum Company in December 1945, produces from the Wilcox formation at a depth of approximately 11,500 ft. Approximately three years after discovery, the royalty interests were unitized by Magnolia and water injection was started on the flanks of the reservoir to maintain reservoir pressure. This was the first high-pressure water-injection project to be initiated at such a depth. It was estimated that the recovery of oil would have been abnormally low had the reservoir been produced to depletion by natural methods. Maintenance of reservoir pressure above the saturation pressure of 4,540 psig was particularly critical in the reservoir as the oil contained in excess of 4,000 cu ft of gas in solution per barrel, and had a formation volume factor of approximately 3.0 bbl per barrel of stock-tank oil. Water injection was initiated on the north flank and later a second injection well was added on the southwest flank of the reservoir. Injection over the life of the project varied. However, it has averaged approximately 2,000 bbl per day at a surface pressure of 3,200 psi. Water from a water-supply well and produced water have been combined for water injection. A progress report giving detailed reservoir and performance data for the project was published by Crego and Henagan[41] in 1951. Performance of the reservoir has been as predicted under pressure-maintenance operations, and a substantial increase in recovery has been obtained.

The foregoing programs, constituting the early field applications of a new method for control of reservoir pressure, all have continued in operation in excess of eight years—each project has been an economic success and has fulfilled expectations for performance. Numerous other similar applications have been made and are continuing to expand to include a broad scope of producing conditions.

The further extension of water-injection procedures to new fields by utilizing split-line and peripheral-type programs permits the application, under pressure maintenance concepts, to all reservoirs almost regardless of depth. The wide variation in pattern of injection and producing wells dictates the need for a proper understanding of the reservoir characteristics and behavior of the contained fluids before adopting a program which deviates from the conventional 5-spot plan. Early application of injection procedures permits broader latitude in pattern and spacing of injection wells with respect to their producing counterparts.

Operational Considerations

Many factors not common with the return of gas to an oil reservoir are encountered in the injection of water. Since the reservoir rock generally consists of minute pore openings of variable size, shape, and continuity, it is of prime importance to introduce water free of suspended solids, chemically stable, and of proper composition to hold at a minimum any detrimental reaction which might occur with the reservoir rock and the fluids contained therein. The water must be injected under pressure conditions that will not cause fracturing of the sedimentary strata, and the flow must be continuous without major interruption. These and other factors prerequisite to successful water-injection projects are discussed in great detail in *Secondary Recovery of Oil in the United States (op. cit.)*, which will justify close study by one interested in the process for secondary application or in conjunction with pressure regulation during primary production.

Improvement in Techniques

Soon after the broad-scale initiation of water flooding in the Bradford Field, petroleum engineers attempted to reduce the residual-oil saturation that remains after passage of water through the reservoir rock, by the addition of chemicals to the water, to improve recovery efficiency. These efforts thus far have not been successful in discovering an additive that can be economically used in field operations to accomplish a substantial reduction in residual-oil content. However, the intensified attention being given this subject should yield indicative results in the future. Holmgren and Morse,[42] Calhoun,[43] and Dyes[44] have reported that oil recovery can be increased if a gas phase is present when the oil is displaced by water. The residual reserve, which varies from 15 percent to as high as 80 percent of the original oil content for light and heavy crudes, respectively, should provide sufficient incentive to justify substantial dedication of research funds to accomplish the objective. Further investigation of surfactants, carbon dioxide, miscible phase displacement using propane and butane in advance of gas and water injection, and in-situ burning may bring forth the solution. Recent field trials of in-situ burning,[45, 46] originally suggested by Lindsly in 1928,[47] offer promise. The economics of the operation will be improved with expanded field trials and with a higher market price for crude oil.

REFERENCES

[1]Carll, John F: *The Geology of the Oil Regions of Warren, Venango, Clarion, and Butler Counties, Pennsylvania*, Second Geological Survey of Pennsylvania, 1875-79, **III** (1880).

[2]Torrey, Paul D: A Review of Secondary Recovery of Oil in the United States, *Secondary Recovery of Oil in the United States*, Chapt. 1, 3, American Petroleum Institute, New York, 1950, 2nd Ed.

[3]Lewis, James O: Methods for Increasing the Recovery from Oil Sands, *U. S. Bur. Mines Bull. 148*, 128 (1917).

[4]Huntley, L. G: Possible Causes of the Decline of Oil Wells and Methods of Prolonging Yield, *U. S. Bur. Mines TP 51*, 19 (1913).

[5]Sweeney, Albert E., Jr: A Survey of Secondary-Recovery Operations and Methods Employed in the United States, Interstate Oil Compact Commission, presented at Illinois Oil and Gas Association, April 11, 1957.

[6]Fettke, C. R: Ten Years' Application of Compressed Air at Hamilton Corners, Pennsylvania, with Core Studies of the Producing Sand, *Petroleum Development and*

Technology in 1927, 303, American Institute of Mining and Metallurgical Engineers, Inc., New York, 1928.

[7]Roth, J. E: Application of Pressure to Elliott Pool, Nowata County, Oklahoma, *Petroleum Development and Technology in 1926*, 195, American Institute of Mining and Metallurgical Engineers, Inc., New York, 1927. Also *Oil Weekly*, **43** [5] 49, Oct. 22 (1926); *National Petroleum News* (title: Large Production Gain Results from First Major Air Drive in Oklahoma) **18** [42] 68, Oct. 20 (1926).

[8]Nickerson, C. M: Repressuring in Depleted Oil Zones, *Petroleum Development and Technology in 1929*, 246, American Institute of Mining and Metallurgical Engineers, Inc., New York, 1930. Also *National Petroleum News*, **21** [41] 48, Oct. 9 (1929); *Oil Weekly*, **55** [4] 44, Oct. 11 (1929); *Oil Gas J.*, **28** [20] 184, Oct. 3 (1929); *Petroleum World and Oil Age* (title: How Repressuring Can Make Small Producing Wells Pay a Profit) 81, Dec. (1929).

[9]Wilson, Wallace W: Engineering Study of the Cook Ranch Field, Shackelford County, Texas, *Trans. Am. Inst. Mining Met. Engrs. (Petroleum Development and Technology)*, **195**, 77 (1952).

[10]Bell, A. Hamilton, and Webb, E. H: Repressuring in the Selover Zone at Seal Beach and the Effect of Proration, *Petroleum Development and Technology in 1929*, 240, American Institute of Mining and Metallurgical Engineers, Inc., New York, 1930.

[11]Bennett, E. O: Increase in Use of Gas for Oil Recovery, *Oil Gas J.*, **26** [51] 41, May 19 (1928). Also *Natural Gas*, **9** [7] 7, July (1928): *Oil Bulletin* (title: Oil Recovery through the Use of Natural Gas: Increase in Use of Natural Gas for Oil Recovery and Its Economic Effect on the Natural-Gas Industry), **14** [8] 826, Aug. (1928).

[12]Dwyer, J. L: Burbank Field is Being Repressured, *Oil Gas J.*, **27** [18] 41 (1928).

[13]Beecher, C. E: Repressuring during Early Stages of Development, *Petroleum Development and Technology in 1928*, 137, American Institute of Mining and Metallurgical Engineers, Inc., New York, 1929.

[14]Gouldy, Roland, and Dobyns, Rollie P: Gas Repressuring in Texas, *Secondary Recovery of Oil in the United States*, Chap. 47, 594, American Petroleum Institute, New York, 1950, 2nd Ed.

[15]Sweeney, A. E: *The Oil and Gas Compact Bulletin*, **XIV** [1] June (1955).

[16]McCarter, W. B. and O'Bannon, P. H: Sugarland Oil Field, Fort Ben County, Texas, *Gulf Coast Oil Fields*, 707, American Association of Petroleum Geologists, Tulsa, 1936.

[17]Sterne, W. P: *Oil Gas J.*, 105, Nov. (1953).

[18]Lacey, W. N: Discussion of "The Big Lake Oil Field, Reagan County, Texas," by E. V. Foran, *Proc. Am. Pet. Inst.*, *(Prod. Bul. 210)* 65 (1932).

[19]Hanlon Award Goes to Vaughn, *Oil Gas J.*, **54** [50] 135, April 16 (1956).

[20]Foran, E. V. and Dixon, P. C: Condensate Wells — Completion and Recycling Operations, *API Drilling and Production Practice*, 340 (1939). (Includes bibliography on this subject by E. A. Stephenson, University of Kansas.)

[21]*Cycler*, 1 [1] Jan.-Feb. (1954), The Chicago Corporation.

[22]Whorton, L. P. and Kieschnick, W. F., Jr: A Preliminary Report on Oil Recovery by High-pressure Gas Injection, *API Drilling and Production Practice*, 247 (1950).

[23]Fancher, George H: Some Outstanding Fluid Injection Projects in Texas, *The Oil and Gas Compact Bulletin*, **XIV** [1] 81, June (1955).

[24]Wyckoff, R. D. and Botset, H. G: An Experimental Study of the Motion of Particles in Systems of Complex Potential Distribution, *Physics*, **5**, June (1934).

[25]Hurst, William, and McCarty, G. M: The Application of Electrical Models to the Study of Recycling Operations in Gas-distillate Fields, *API Drilling and Production Practice*, 228 (1941).

[26]Lewis, James O: Methods for Increasing the Recovery from Oil Sands, *U. S. Bur. Mines Bull. 148,* 109 (1917).

[27]Fettke, C. R: Bradford Oil Field, Pennsylvania and New York, *Pennsylvania Geological Survey, 4th Series,* **M-21** (1938).

[28]*The Oil and Gas Compact Bulletin,* **XIV** [1] 65, June (1955).

[29]*U. S. Bur. Mines RI 3906,* 42, July (1946).

[30]*ibid:* 71, July (1946).

[31]Whitney, J. W. W: West Burkburnett Water Flood, *Oil Gas J.,* **53** [33] 93, Dec. 20 (1954).

[32]*U. S. Bur. Mines RI 3728* (1943).

[33]*U. S. Bur. Mines RI 3761* (1944).

[34]*U. S. Bur. Mines RI 3778* (1944).

[35]Morris, W. S: East Texas Field Has Record of Outstanding Results from Its Four-year Program of Salt-water Disposal, *Oil Gas J.,* **45** [17] 92, Aug. 31 (1946). Also, *J. Inst. of Petroleum* (abstract) **32** [276] 419A, Dec. (1946); *J. Inst. of Petroleum* (abstract, title: Salt Water Disposal) **33** [279] 93A, March (1947).

[36]Morris, W. S: Results of Water Injection in the East Texas Field, *Proc. Am. Pet. Inst. (Prod. Bul. 233)* 36 (1947). Reprinted as Chapt. 46, 582, *Secondary Recovery of Oil in the United States,* American Petroleum Institute, New York, 1950, 2nd Ed.

[37]Schilthuis, Ralph J. and Hurst, William: Variation in Reservoir Pressure in the East Texas Field, *Trans. Am. Inst. Mining Met. Engrs. (Petroleum Development and Technology)* **114,** 164 (1935).

[38]Lewis, James A: Core Analysis—An Aid to Increasing the Recovery of Oil, *Trans Am. Inst. Mining Met. Engrs. (Petroleum Development and Technology)* **146,** 68 (1942) (reprint, p. 68).

[39]Horner, W. L. and Snow, D. R: A New Application of Water Injection for Maintaining Reservoir Pressure and Increasing Natural Water Drive, *API Drilling and Production Practice,* 28 (1943). Also *Oil Weekly,* **111** [12] 17, Nov. 22 (1943); *Oil Gas J.* (title: A New Application of Water Injection for Maintaining Reservoir Pressure and Increasing Natural Drive) **42** [27] 226, Nov. 11 (1943); *Petroleum Engr.,* **15** [10] 120, Reference Annual (1944).

[40]Carpenter, Charles B; Anderson, Kenneth F; and Cook, Alton B: Petroleum Engineering Study of the New Hope Oil Field, Franklin County, Texas, *U. S. Bur. Mines RI 4594* (1949).

[41]Crego, William O. and Henagan, James N: Report on the Mamou Field Pressure Maintenance Project, *Trans. Am. Inst. Mining Met. Engrs. (Petroleum Development and Technology)* **192,** 263 (1951).

[42]Holmgren, C. R. and Morse, R. A: Effect of Free Gas Saturation on Oil Recovery by Water Flooding, *Trans. Am. Inst. Mining Met. Engrs. (Petroleum Development and Technology)* **192,** 135 (1951).

[43]Calhoun, John C., Jr: The Injection of Gas as an Aid in Water Flooding. Interstate Oil Compact Commission (1952).

[44]Dyes, A. B: Production of Water Drive Reservoirs Below Their Bubble Point, *AIME J. Petr. Tech.,* **6** [10] Oct. (1954).

[45]Kuhn, C. S. and Koch, R. L: In-situ Combustion—Newest Method of Increasing Oil Recovery, *Oil Gas J.,* **52,** 92, Aug. 10 (1952).

[46]Grant, Bruce F. and Szasz, Stefan E: Development of an Underground Heat Wave for Oil Recovery, *AIME J. Petr. Tech.,* 23, May (1954).

[47]Lindsly, B. E: Oil Recovery by Use of Heated Gas, *Oil Gas J.,* **27,** 27, Dec. 20 (1928).

Chapter 14

THERMAL, SOLVENT AND IMPROVED GAS-DRIVE OIL-RECOVERY METHODS

L. E. ELKINS

883

LLOYD EDWIN ELKINS was born in 1912 near Golden, Colorado, and received the degree of P.P.E. from Colorado School of Mines in 1934. His service with Pan American Petroleum Corporation (and its predecessor, Stanolind Oil and Gas Company) dates from graduation from C.S.M. and includes progression through the positions of apprentice engineer, field engineer, senior petroleum engineer, chief production engineer and chief engineer, producing department. In 1949 he became production research director.

Academic, professional and industrial honors include Tau Beta Pi, Sigma Gamma Epsilon, Pi Epsilon Tau; the chairmanship in 1949-1950 of the Petroleum Branch of AIME; the Mid-Continent District chairmanship of API Division of Production (1948-49); and presidency of the Tulsa Engineers Club (1950). He will assume the presidency of the American Institute of Mining, Metallurgical and Petroleum Engineers in 1962. He has made numerous contributions to petroleum engineering literature.

~ 14 ~

INTRODUCTION

Other chapters of this volume, covering a century of history, were written over a period of 10 years ending in 1960. During the time they were being written, research was being emphasized and engineering studies were being made concerning the recovery methods to be described in this chaper. Some of these methods may be referred to briefly in other chapters, but it is the purpose here to develop historical aspects in more detail and order.

Concepts of the recovery methods to be described are still evolving. Laboratory studies and field tests are under way which will result in more precise definition of conditions under which these recovery methods are operable and economical. A history written 10 or 20 years hence would record and bring into clear focus a number of those factors which are now recognized as important, but are still not well-defined.

In the years immediately following World War II, several situations developed which led to the study and application of new types of recovery methods. The continuing increase in demand for crude oil and recognition that cost of discovering new reserves in North America was increasing, together focused the attention of management on increasing recovery of known oil in place. It became apparent that improved recovery methods in the future would play a very significant role in adding reserves and productivity. The industry's engineers and scientists were aware of the limitations of conventional gas and water injection for improved recovery. Conventional fluid-injection methods added much, but they also left much to be desired.

Management recognized that new methods should be considered. In the post-war era scientific and engineering manpower became available, and research programs in many of the oil-producing companies were sharply accelerated.

In this atmosphere of urgency, old concepts were studied and some new ones were brought forth. Laboratory tests and field pilot tests were made to evaluate various new fluid-injection methods. The highlights relating to these developments are listed in this chapter. A comprehensive list of references and bibliography is included which will direct the reader to source material which embraces details too voluminous and too technical in nature to be discussed in this review.

DEFINITIONS

The recovery methods to be described are divided into two broad classes, viz.: *1,* thermal, and *2,* solvent and improved gas drives.

Thermal Recovery Methods

A thermal recovery method is defined as one in which heat is applied in a reservoir to raise the temperature significantly above ambient with the purpose of increasing hydrocarbon-displacement efficiency by: improving viscosity ratios, taking advantage of steam distillation, hydrocarbon cracking, and materially altering capillary restrictive forces at the displacement front.

Two types (hot-fluid injection and in-situ combustion) will be reviewed from an historical standpoint.

Solvent and Improved Gas-drive Recovery Methods

Interfacial forces between water, gas, oil, and rock surfaces combine to cause varying percentages of oil to be bypassed by water or gas used as displacing fluids. In solvent flooding and improved gas drives, a displacement fluid is used that exhibits little or no interfacial tension with the reservoir oil. This minimizes bypassing of oil in the area swept by the miscible or partially miscible displacement fluids. This displacement fluid is also usually driven by another ("scavenging") fluid which is, in turn, miscible or partially miscible with it.

There are three types of processes to be reviewed from an historical standpoint. These are: *1,* solvent flooding; *2,* enriched gas drive; *3,* high-pressure gas drive.

HISTORY OF METHODS

Four published papers set forth in excellent detail the history of recovery methods to be described in this chapter. The references and bibliography are taken essentially from these four papers, and this author will draw heavily upon them in highlighting the historical developments. These four papers are listed here to give them special recognition.

1. "Preliminary Report on Oil Recovery by High-pressure gas Injection", by L. P. Whorton and W. F. Kieschnick, Jr., The Atlantic Refining Company, Dallas, Texas; published in *Oil and Gas Journal,* April 5, 1950, and also in *API Drilling and Production Practice,* 1950.[1]

2. "Past, Present, and Future Development in Oil Recovery by Thermal Methods", by T. W. Nelson, Socony Mobil Oil Company, Inc., New York, and J. S. McNiel, Jr., Magnolia Petroleum Company, Dallas; published in *Petroleum Engineer,* February and March 1959.[2]

---

[1]References are at the end of the chapter.

3. "A Review of the Enriched Gas Drive Process", by D. M. Kehn, Humble Oil & Refining Company, Houston; published in *Producer's Monthly*, February 1960.[3]

4. "Miscible Slug Flooding — A Review", by F. F. Craig, Jr. and W. W. Owens, Pan American Petroleum Corporation, Tulsa; published in *AIME Journal of Petroleum Technology*, April 1960.[4]

Thermal Recovery Methods

There are two different types which are to be considered. One involves introducing heat generated at the surface, as hot water, steam, or perhaps superheated steam. The other method deals with generating the heat in the formation and causing a hot zone or bank to move through the formation. The first is referred to as "hot-fluid injection" and the second as "in-situ combustion."

Hot-fluid Injection

All of the following quoted material is taken directly from Nelson and McNiel *(op. cit.)*.

"A method of thermal recovery more closely akin to conventional techniques than others that will be discussed is the direct injection of a hot fluid (water, gas, or steam) with the objective of taking advantage of . . . [viscosity reduction, steam distillation, etc.]

"The idea of flooding with heated water has been with us almost as long as the conventional water flooding, but useful field information has not yet been made available to the general public.

"Documented field applications on the use of steam or hot injection water include those of Barton[5]* of Forest Oil Company; Stovall[6] of Houston Oil Co. of Texas; and Breston and Pearman[7] for the Penn Grade Crude Oil Association. A case of steam injection in a shallow sand of the Bellevue Pool, Louisiana, in 1936, was mentioned by Tucker,[8] who also stated that steam injection had been tried many times before this date. More recently, at least three operators are known to have field tested steam injection as a recovery technique, but information has not been released on the results of these experiments.

"Barton's work was initiated not for the purpose of increasing production, but in an effort to improve injectivity of water into tight Bradford sands . . ."

---

*Reference numbers shown in quoted material are those of this chapter.

By surface heating the water, injection rates into the Bradford sands were increased severalfold over those before heating; and even after cessation of heating, rates remained as much as 100 percent greater than prior to heating.

"Breston and Pearman reported much less improvement of injectivity (a maximum increase of 35 percent) with a 24-kw electric heater positioned opposite the sand face. The possibilities of hot waterflooding for the purpose of improving injectivity were recently revived by the proposal of James A. Lewis Engineering[9] to use warm injection water in a Pembina Field waterflood.

"Stovall's work in West Texas represents the only successful steam injection test reported in detail . . ."

The injection of hot water or steam, with the heat generated at the surface, intended to carry the heat back down the well and through the formation, poses some problem with relation to heat loss.

"The amount of heat lost compared to the amount generated will undoubtedly be a major factor in a full-scale recovery program, and this depends upon depth, formation thickness, and temperature level of the injected fluids. Depth is of particular importance when heat is applied at the surface, rather than being generated downhole by some process such as combustion or electrical resistance heating."

A number of investigators have shed some light on this problem of heat loss and the degree of recovery that might be expected with temperature increase in the reservoir. They are: Schaller and Bjornsson,[10] Van Heiningen and Schwarz,[11] Croes and Schwarz,[12] Lauwerier,[13] and Nelson and McNiel (*op. cit.*).

A paper by Willman, Valleroy, Runberg, Cornelius, and Powers,[14] of Jersey Production Research Company, presented at the 1960 fall meeting of the Society of Petroleum Engineers of AIME at Denver, Colo., points up a number of advantages that can be obtained by passing a hot fluid bank through the reservoir and making use of steam distillation as a major contributing factor toward increasing oil recovery.

"The use of non-condensable gases heated externally or in the well bore to provide a thermal drive was proposed by Lindsly[15] in 1928, and hot-air injection was tried by Hartman[16] in 1942. However, the low heat-carrying capacity of gases renders these techniques of doubtful utility because of the resulting long periods between initiation of a gas-driven thermal wave and the appearance of a temperature rise at a production well. It is interesting to note that a review of Hartman's test indicates that he may have actually ignited the formation inadvertently, initiating a different type of recovery process — in-situ combustion."

Although heat-loss problems are important, it is indicated at the close of 1960 that hot-fluid injection of one type or another may find application.

In-situ Combustion

In-situ combustion is a type of thermal oil recovery in which the energy required for moving crude oil through the reservoir and eventually into the production well is provided by injecting air or another oxygen-bearing gas into the reservoir and burning a portion of the crude oil therein. The process can be visualized as a slowly moving and narrow burning zone which advances between an air-injection well and a production well, moving oil ahead of it. There are several variations of this basic process which are described by Nelson and McNiel *(op. cit.)*.

"1. The 'heat' wave process which involves the formation of a large heat wave to be propelled by gases of limited oxygen content to control the rate of advance of the burning front,

"2. Halting combustion part way between the injection well and the production well and propelling the heat wave toward the production well by cycling the produced gases, and

"3. Use of a 'reverse combustion' technique where the combustion is halted part way between the injection well and the production well and air flow is reversed by injecting air into the production well and turning the original air-injection well into a production well."

In the in-situ combustion method, sometimes called "forward combustion," Nelson and McNiel recognize four types of displacing processes taking place. The oil which has not yet been contacted by the actual combustion front is subjected to: *1*, a condensing steam drive; *2*, a gas drive; *3*, a miscible drive; and *4*, a thermal drive which vaporizes part of the oil, leaving a heavy residuum which is fuel for combustion.

Roberts and Walker[17] explained a principal difference between reverse combustion and forward combustion. In reverse combustion, all of the products that are displaced from the burning front move through a hot portion of the reservoir and likely stay in the vapor phase. Some oil is burned and coke is often left on rock surfaces. Also in reverse combustion, more heat is generated in the reservoir because after the front has passed through a reservoir, the tendency is for the entire contacted reservoir to remain hot. In forward combustion, all the products removed from the combustion front pass into a cold zone and the cold air or gas coming up to the front continuously transfers heat toward the combustion front. Heat tends to concentrate in a narrow bank. In forward combustion, less heat has to be generated, so less air injection is required. Each method has its preferred application. The reverse method is particularly adapted to recovery of heavy oils or tars which would present greater operating problems to forward combustion.

Development History

"The idea of recovering petroleum by an in-situ combustion process was first disclosed publicly 35 years ago in patents issued to Edson Wolcott[18] and Frank Howard.[19] The first known attempts to apply an in-situ combustion process in the field in the United States were in 1952 when Magnolia and Sinclair engineers, each group working independently only 300 miles apart in Oklahoma, initiated movements of combustion fronts in pattern-type experiments after several years of laboratory tests."[2]

Since then, some 25 to 30 field tests have been conducted or are being conducted. Table 1 (p. 893-94), listing some of the recent field tests of in-situ combustion, is presented to show the field-trial history of the modern in-situ combustion method and to indicate the variety of conditions and some of the methods being tried by different operators. This information is essentially that prepared by Nelson and McNiel *(op. cit.)*, but has been brought up to date with the addition of some information not available at the time their work was published.

The history of underground combustion developments in the oil industry starts in Russia. The trade literature[20] reported that in the period 1933 to 1935 the Russians conducted an underground combustion operation in a pressure-depleted reservoir containing 36 API gravity oil. A small but significant amount of oil was recovered by this operation.

Following World War II, when production research received increased emphasis, unknown numbers of research investigators were developing new methods for recovering oil. In August 1953, Magnolia[21] reported some laboratory and field-test information and described in the literature a concept of forward combustion. At about the same time that Magnolia was conducting their field experiment in West Loco Field, Oklahoma, Sinclair—who had also done research on various underground combustion methods—was conducting a little larger-scale field test in the Delaware-Childers Field in Oklahoma. The Sinclair work was first made public at the AIME meeting in New York, February 1954.[22]

The report of these two field tests and the description of the process envisioned by earlier laboratory studies were probably the impetus for an accelerated research pace in many laboratories. The next important report on combustion was made by H. Walter[23] at the fall meeting of the Petroleum Branch of AIME in October 1956. His technical paper was published in *Journal of Petroleum Technology* in February 1957. News items had appeared in the trade journals and news media several months earlier covering this Worthington Corporation and Forest Oil Company test. Walter described this field test in Illinois in which surface-generated steam and hot gases, carrying some oxygen, were injected into an oil sand. This was, therefore, a combination of heat-injection and in-situ combustion.

During the first year or two following the publication of the Magnolia and Sinclair field-test results, General Petroleum Corp.— with assistance from Magnolia—was planning a cooperative field test in the South Belridge Field in California. This test, supported by 10 oil companies, but principally under the direction of General Petroleum and Magnolia, was first described at the meeting of the Society of Petroleum Engineers of AIME in Los Angeles, October 16-17, 1958.[24] While the South Belridge test was under way, it was known generally that many of the oil-industry research laboratories were aggressively evaluating some of the limiting factors that would control various types of combustion methods in underground oil reservoirs.

Referring specifically to the type of combustion methods tried in the field and reported in the literature, viz., forward combustion of one type or another, Nelson and McNiel *(op. cit.)* offer the following: "In summary, in-situ combustion is a promising new method of oil recovery that has the unique ability of recovering a high percentage of the oil in a reservoir in a relatively short period of time. The economics of the process already appear reasonably attractive under field conditions that exist in a number of areas in the U. S. today. Further development of the process promises to extend its application appreciably to the point at which it could become a significant factor in oil production in many areas."

Another type of in-situ recovery method which is being evaluated in the laboratory and in field tests will be briefly mentioned.

Public hearings held by the Conservation Board of Alberta, Canada,[25] indicate that Shell and Pan American et al. are conducting underground combustion operations of one type or another in an attempt to recover in-place liquid hydrocarbons from the tar-sand deposits in the Athabasca region. The news reports from the Conservation Board hearings indicate that Shell is conducting a thermal project that may heavily

891

involve the use of steam. No details are described and this could still be a very limited indication of the composite nature of the process being tested. Similarly, the news reports indicate that Pan American et al. are conducting a field test relating to reverse combustion of some type. It is rumored that other underground combustion tests are being considered for application in tar sands.

Other Thermal Methods

Quoting from Nelson and McNiel *(op. cit.)*:

"Interest has arisen during the past year in the potential use of thermonuclear energy release as a means of producing oil not recoverable by conventional techniques. The explosion of a 1.7 kiloton atomic bomb 900 ft under the top of a Nevada mesa (Operation Plumbbob) in September of last year,[26] plans to detonate a 10 kiloton bomb in New Mexico salt beds,[27] and some speculation[28] on the use of an H-bomb to recover oil from thick shale beds, such as those in the Piceance Creek Basin, Colorado, represent some of the events which ignited and fueled this interest.

"Most encouraging aspect of Operation Plumbbob was the apparent trapping of fission products in fused rock with little likelihood of contamination of ground waters. Less encouraging, from the thermal-energy standpoint, was the rapid dissipation of high temperature apparently caused by vaporization of formation water. Three months after the explosion no elevation of temperature was noted beyond the crushed zone (a sphere of 130-ft radius), and the highest temperature observed at that time was only 70 F above the original temperature of the rock. On the basis of information now available, one must come to the perhaps surprising conclusion that the useful mechanical effects of an A-bomb explosion underground are likely to extend to a greater distance than the useful thermal effects.

"Other possible methods of heating an oil-bearing formation, such as the process of 'electrocarbonization', or 'electro-linking' tested in recent years for coal gasification[29, 30] may become of future economic importance, depending on the cost of energy from various sources. One can visualize, for the distant future, the possibilities of distilling petroleum directly from reservoirs by solar or electrical heating. A similar process is now under commercial development for application to oil shales in Sweden.[31] The very high energy consumption observed in this process (some 900 kwh per bbl of oil produced) may not appear exorbitant in the liquid fuel markets of this country in 2000 A.D."

Table 1
Some Field Tests of In-Situ Combustion

		Location				Reservoir Properties						Test Characteristics		
Date[1]	Operator	Field	County	State	Formation	Depth, Ft.	Thickness, Ft.	Porosity, Percent	Oil Saturation, Percent	Oil Gravity, Deg API	Well Pattern	Pattern Size, Acres	Ignition Method	Injected Gas
1933	Russia	Shirvanui	Baku Peninsula	U.S.S.R.	"E" Maikop	264	59	42	15	36	3-well (in-line)	(69 ft)	Hot charcoal	Air
1952	Sinclair	Delaware-Childers	Nowata	Oklahoma	Bartlesville Sandstone	600	26	21	44	36	7-well (inverted)	5.2	Downhole burner	Air product gas, natural gas
1952	Magnolia	West Loco	Jefferson	Oklahoma	Pontotoc Sand	180	20	29	60	18	3-well (in-line)	(40 ft)	Electrical	Air
1953	Magnolia	West Loco	Jefferson	Oklahoma	Pontotoc Sand	180	20	29	60	18	5-well (inverted)	0.07	Electrical	Air
1953	Worthington-Forest Oil	Parker	Clark	Illinois	Pennsylvanian Sand	275	35	21	42	26	5-well	00.28	Injection gases heated at surface	Steam, air, combustion gas
1954	California Research California Co.	Irvine-Furnace	Estill	Kentucky	Corniferous	70 to 1,200*	0.61*	——	——	30-36*	——	——	——	——
1955	Sinclair[2]	Spraberry	——	Texas	——	8,000*	10-165*	12-18*	——	32-42*	——	——	——	——
1956	Sinclair	Humboldt-Chanute	Allen	Kansas	Bartlesville Sandstone	600	14	20	——	25	3:1 line drive	(3)	Downhole gas burner	Air
1956	General Petroleum[4]	South Belridge	Kern	California	Tulare Sand	700	30	37	60	13	5-well (inverted)	2.5	Spontaneous	Air
1956	California Research	Midway-Sunset	Kern	California	——	2,000	——	——	——	——	4-well (inverted)	1.2	Downhole gas burner	Air
1956	Richfield	Sisar-Silver-thread	Ventura	California	Miocene Sandstone	1,000*	——	——	——	11-30*	——	——	——	Gas and air
1957	Tejas	Camp Hill	Anderson	Texas	Carrizo Sand	420	32	35	——	19	——	——	Injection gases heated at surface	Heated air
1957	Teikoku	Niitsu	——	Japan	Koguchi	590	33	——	5.1 (wt. %)	18	Irregular (injection)	(56 ft)	Downhole gas burner	——
1958	Pan American-Midwest	Shannon Salt Creek	Natrona	Wyoming	Shannon	950	33	23.3	60	24.6	9-well (irregular)	5	Downhole gas burner	Air
1958	Shell	Tia Juana	——	Venezuela	——	——	——	——	——	——	——	——	——	——
1958	Kendall Refining Bradford Prod.	Alleghany	Alleghany	New York	——	1,120	49	15.8	35.1	43	Irregular	——	Electrical[5]	——
1959	Continental	N. Tisdale	Johnson	Wyoming	——	——	——	——	——	——	——	——	——	Air

(See following page for footnotes)

Table 1 (Cont'd)

Date[1]	Operator	Field	County	State	Formation	Depth, Ft.	Thickness, Ft.	Porosity, Percent	Oil Saturation, Percent	Oil Gravity, Deg API	Well Pattern	Pattern Size, Acres	Ignition Method	Injected Gas
			Location			Reservoir Properties						Test Characteristics		
1959	Continental	Cook Ranch	Shackleford	Texas	Cisco	----	----	----	----	----	5-spot (inverted)	4	----	----
1959	Mene Grande Creole	Melones		Venezuela	"T" Sand	----	----	----	----	----	----	----	----	----
1959	Standard of California	Huntington Beach	Orange	California		4,000	----	----	----	20	----	----	----	----
1959	Lamret	Regular	Brown	Texas	Amerada	100	15	23	----	28	6-well (2 inj.)	25 Total	----	Air
1959	Pan American[6,7]	Athabasca Tar Sands	Alberta	Canada	McMurray	1,000	----	----	----	5	2-well	----	----	Air
1960	Texaco	Charco-Redondo	Zapata	Texas	Cole	160	15	32	----	17.5	5-spots (2, inverted)	5	----	Air
1960	Conka Prod. Co.	Brown Co. Regular	Brown	Texas	Strawn	1,250	----	12	----	----		----	----	Air
1960	Shell	Cabimas		Venezuela		----	----	----	----	----	----	----	----	Air and recycle gases
1960	Tejas	Loco	Stephens	Oklahoma	Pontotoc Sand	420	----	----	----	----	----	----	----	Air
1960	Thermal Oil Producers	Seay	Jefferson	Oklahoma	Cisco	850	34	28.5	----	24	4-well (inverted)	7½	----	Air
1960	Mobil	Midway-Sunset	Kern	California	Moco	2,100	490	----	----	14.3	18 wells (irregular)	80 Total (30 ft)	----	----
1960	Shell	Athabasca Tar Sands	Alberta	Canada	McMurray	150	----	----	----	----	3-well (in-line)	----	Electrical	Steam/air
1961	Sinclair	Delaware-Childers	Nowata	Oklahoma	Bartlesville Sandstone	650	----	----	----	----	5-spot (inverted)	20	Downhole gas burner	Air
Proposed	U.S. Bureau of Mines	Appalachian Region				----	----	----	----	----	----	----	----	----
Proposed	British Petroleum	Formby	Lancashire	England		----	----	----	----	----	5-spot (4inj.; 1 prod.)	----	----	Air

*Specific data not released; values given are from published field data.

[1]Date of initiation of specific test, where available; otherwise date of publication.

[2]Failed to initiate a moving combustion front.

[3]Two or more rows of input wells about 150 ft apart, spaced 400-450 ft from rows of production wells.

[4]Participating companies: Continental, Esso Research and Engineering, Gulf, Honolulu, Ohio, Shell Development, Sunray Mid-Continent, Union, Chanslor-Western.

[5]Well-bore explosion terminated test.

[6]Participating companies: British Petroleum, Cities Service, Hudson's Bay, Mobil, Standard (Jersey), Sun.

[7]Reverse combustion.

Solvent and Improved Gas-drive Recovery Methods

It is interesting to recall some early oil-field experiences during which time operators were conducting operations that, in retrospect, followed some of the principles incorporated in the recovery methods to be reported in this section. As early as 1931, Union Oil Co. of California[32] was injecting some high-gravity oils into some of the heavy viscous oil reservoirs in California, primarily for storage. The movement of this light oil into the heavy-oil sands and its later recovery might have suggested some of the displacement phenomena now employed in miscible flooding. Also as early as 1927,[33] the Midwest Refining Company was injecting surplus liquefied gas products into the secondary gas cap area of the Salt Creek First and Second Wall Creek reservoirs. While they planned to improve gas-drive operations, they were not aware of the enriched-gas-drive mechanism now being used.

Furthermore, in about 1936 or 1937, Bennett[34] injected alcohol (substantially miscible with oil and with water) in oil wells to displace capillary-held water away from the well bore where it offered the most severe restriction to oil flow. When oil was again produced from the well it was expected to remove the alcohol surrounding the well bore, with resultant increase in oil productivity. Injection of either gasoline or oil would have left the water, just as oil being produced leaves connate water in place as it flows past. This experiment is recalled to illustrate how some of the principles that might be later included, with others, in a reservoir displacement process may have actually been tried in a different sequence and for a different reason in some early oil-field operations.

A broad description of the various types of solvent flood and improved gas-drive processes reported in the literature is as follows:

1. The solvent-flood or miscible-slug method involves the injection of a slug of solvent, miscible with the reservoir oil. This slug is then followed by the injection of a displacing fluid miscible with the solvent, but which can be much cheaper than the solvent. In this way the injection of a displacing fluid to recover oil, which normally is an immiscible process, is converted to a miscible displacement process by the interposition of solvent between the oil and displacing fluid. The injected displacing fluid moves the solvent through the reservoir. The solvent in turn removes the oil from the portion of the reservoir through which it passes. Some of the engineering problems in designing the volume of solvent required in a miscible-slug process involve the degree of mixing of the solvent with oil and displacing fluid with solvent as these fluids move through the reservoir. Hydrocarbon solvents which have been tested and incorporated into some floods of this type are propane and butane, and mixtures of these with or without methane. When these

hydrocarbon solvents are used, the displacing fluid is usually natural gas under sufficient pressure (above about 1,100 psi) so that single-phase conditions exist and there is no interface between the displacing gas and the solvent. When water is the displacing fluid, some alcohols which have a high degree of solubility with both oil and water have been suggested.

2. In the enriched-gas-drive method, gas enriched typically with propane and butane is injected into the formation. As this enriched gas contacts the reservoir oil, some of the constituents condense into the oil, swelling it, reducing its viscosity, and changing its phase-behavior properties. The rest of the gas travels on to producing wells. Under favorable conditions of gas enrichment, reservoir-oil composition, and pressure, contacted oil becomes enriched by the condensing constituents to the point where it is miscible with the injected gas. Further gas injection displaces this miscible zone which displaces the reservoir oil ahead of it. Some time after miscibility is achieved, dry gas (non-enriched) can be injected for the remainder of the project. The production behavior progresses from what appears to be a conventional gas drive with increased gas-oil ratio in the beginning to declining, then stabilized gas-oil ratios as in a miscible-slug drive. If the gas enrichment is not sufficient to form a miscible zone, dry gas following the enriched gas vaporizes the light hydrocarbon constituents from the enriched reservoir oil and carries these forward to oil of lower enrichment. In this way a bank of oil enriched with propane and butane moves through the reservoir. Some increased oil recovery is realized through oil swelling and viscosity reduction. However, maximum displacement of the oil is not obtained unless a miscible zone is formed.

3. In the high-pressure gas-drive process, natural gas is injected at pressures (above about 3,000 psi) substantially above the gas saturation pressure of the reservoir oil. Transfer of hydrocarbon components between the injected gas and reservoir oil takes place until, under certain conditions of pressure and reservoir-oil composition, the gas becomes sufficiently enriched to be miscible with the reservoir oil. This miscible zone, which is formed using constituents already in the reservoir oil, results in substantially complete displacement of the reservoir oil in the part of the formation swept by the injected gas.

Development History

It is interesting to recall some of the advances in petroleum technology which subsequently resulted in formulating the concepts of the described processes. Perhaps the continuous efforts of Sage and Lacey[35] at California Institute of Technology on API Project 37 supplied the basic foundation upon which some of these concepts were built. Huntington and Mertz,[36] and Huntington and Hendrix,[37] in 1941 reported on studies of gas mixing in porous media. This work must have been very helpful to some later investigators as they started to grapple with the displacement processes eventually developed. Also, perhaps the work of Fowler and Brown[38] on the studies of mixing in pipe for turbulent and laminar flow regimes—reported in the *Transactions,* American Institute of Chemical Engineers in 1943—supplied some insight for later investigators. In 1949 Everett, Gooch, and Calhoun[39] reported on some work done at Pennsylvania State College on liquid-liquid displacement in porous media as affected by the liquid-liquid viscosity ratio and liquid-liquid miscibility. This was reported at the 1949 AIME Petroleum Branch fall meeting. Very likely this work triggered a number of laboratory investigations which later led to the development of parts of the oil-recovery methods described previously in this chapter.

In 1950 Whorton and Kieschnick[1] made a preliminary report to the oil industry on oil recovery by high-pressure gas injection. They reported that, based upon experimental results, high-pressure gas injection will recover at reasonably low gas-oil ratios appreciably more oil than can be recovered with conventional low-pressure gas drive and, in many cases, significantly more than with water flooding. They set forth certain prerequisites, viz., that generally pressures would have to be greater than 3,000 psi; that one would need a large volume of gas to fill the reservoir which was being depleted; that there should be little channeling; and that there should be a sufficient concentration of intermediate hydrocarbons in the reservoir oil.

In June 1951 Stanolind Oil and Gas Company initiated a solvent-flood pilot test in the South Leonard Pool, Wagoner County, Okla., although this was not publicized until March 1958.[40] This is the first known field application of the solvent-flooding process where a bank of LPG was driven through an oil reservoir by natural gas. As later reported, the experiment in the field was not carried to its ultimate objective because of the loss of the LPG bank from the reservoir through which is was intended to move. About the same time, International Petroleum Company, Ltd. was injecting a mixture of approximately 20 percent propane and 80 percent butane in the San Pedro Block D in Peru.[41]

The first publication relating to the specific solvent-flood process appeared in a German patent issued to R. A. Morse[42] and assigned to Stanolind Oil and Gas Company, in July 1952. Later, in September 1953, a British patent[43] was issued to Morse on this process. From 1952 until 1955 a review of the literature indicates that there was activity in various research organizations—considering various aspects of the solvent-flood, enriched-gas-drive, and high-pressure gas-drive methods. Typical of these reports in the literature are those listed in the supplemental bibliography.

In 1955 Stone and Crump[44] presented a paper describing recovery of oil by "condensing gas drives". This paper reported on laboratory studies relating to what has later been included in the "enriched-gas-drive" process.

In a review of the enriched-gas-drive process, Kehn[45] recalled that in 1953 an enriched-gas-drive pilot injection project was initiated in the Haynesville Field, Claiborne Parish, Louisiana. Performance of this pilot demonstrated that an oil bank enriched with ethane and propane was arriving at producing wells adjacent to the injection area. This was evidenced by a decrease in gas-oil ratio and an increase in the gravity of produced stock-tank oil.

Also in 1955, Enright[46] reported on an LPG flooding test in Texas in which the Shamrock Oil Company had injected LPG in the Panhandle Field in Moore County, Texas.

A technical session on miscible fluid displacement at the 1956 AIME Petroleum Branch fall meeting in Los Angeles probably was a turning point in the history of the technological development, after which these various methods were given more widespread attention. At this meeting, Hall and Geffen[47] of Pan American Petroleum Corp., and Koch and Slobod[48] of The Atlantic Refining Co., presented papers dealing with laboratory studies of the solvent-flooding, or miscible-slug, process. At the same meeting, Jenks, Campbell, and Binder[49] of The Carter Oil Co. presented their paper on a field test of a gas-driven liquid propane method of oil recovery. In the next two years there was great activity by research departments and operators in testing various methods and evaluating some of the problems associated with various types of the miscible fluid displacement. In March 1958, at a meeting sponsored by the Mid-Continent Section, Society of Petroleum Engineers of AIME, in Tulsa, an entire session was directed toward solvent flooding and improved gas drives. Reports were given of pilot testing of the solvent-flood process in Bisti by Sunray Mid-Continent,[50] of the Pan American South Leonard pilot test previously mentioned, of a solvent-flood pilot test in the Panhandle Field by Cities Service,[51] of Humble's enriched-gas-drive test at Seeligson,[52] a review of some operating problems in Atlantic's successful high-pressure gas drive in Block 31,[53] an up-to-date review of Carter's[54] gas-driven liquid propane field test, and—perhaps most noteworthy at that time—Magnolia's[55] field-wide solvent flood initiated in the Parks-Pennsylvanian Field in West Texas. It is interesting to note that very much of the technology specific to the processes being tested around 1958 had been introduced in one way or another in the literature of the previous 3 or 4 years. It is also interesting to note that Magnolia committed themselves to a major field application (Parks-Pennsylvanian) of the solvent-flood process without previously conducting a pilot test.

By this time, some problems in operational control were evident. It was recognized that in a miscible displacement operation an unfavorable contrast in mobility can exist between the reservoir oil and the final displacement fluid, such as gas. If it does, then volumetric sweep efficiency can be poor with resultant low oil recovery. In miscible flooding the importance of this increases with higher reservoir oil viscosity, particularly in reservoirs with extreme variation in permeability. A way to remedy this undesirable effect was proposed by Caudle and Dyes[56] of Atlantic, in a 1958 paper. Their method was to inject gas and water rather than gas alone to move an LPG slug. This procedure would provide for an adjusted contrast in mobility and result in higher volumetric sweep and oil recovery. This supplemental step in the engineering of the solvent-flood process could very well lead to a higher success ratio in application. A number of other investigators made reports in 1958-59, primarily aimed at improving the engineering of bank size and mode of introduction to accomplish a minimum of mixing between the oil and the LPG solvent slug. Much effort was directed toward reconciling some of the methods used in laboratories for determining slug requirements, etc. Highlighting some of these investigations are the literature references listed in the supplemental bibliography. In March 1959, the *Oil and Gas Journal*[57] published the results of its survey, which listed 39 miscible drives in progress or planned. These results, augmented by information becoming available through 1960, are presented in Table 2. This list may be incomplete but illustrates interest and growth in these methods.

Perhaps the next important milestone reflected in the literature was the report by Mobil Oil Company[58] on its Pembina solvent-flood pilot test and the analysis of its performance. This was presented at the meeting of the Society of Petroleum Engineers of AIME in the fall of 1959, at Dallas, Texas. Solvent flooding has since been initiated in an area of about 5,000 acres in Pembina by Mobil.

At the fall meeting of the Society of Petroleum Engineers in Denver in 1960, an observer could listen to both pessimistic and optimistic reports on the ultimate importance and practicability of solvent flooding. Haberman[59] of Union Oil Co. of California, and Lacey, Faris, and Brinkmann[60] of Jersey Production Research Co., because of their prediction of slug requirements—based on laboratory studies—would tend to be discouraging; whereas Marrs of Mobil,[61] based upon field experience in the Parks-Pennsylvanian flood, and Block and Donovan[62] of Standard Oil Co. of California, with their San Joaquin Valley field experience would add a note of optimism.

Table 2

Some Field Tests of Solvent Flooding and Improved Gas Drive

Year	Operator	Field	County or Parish	State	Formation	Oil Gravity, Deg API	Type
1949*	Atlantic	Block 31	Crane	Tex.	Devonian Lime	43.8	HPGD
1951	Pan American	So. Leonard	Wagoner	Okla.	Dutcher Sand (Penn.)	36.0	SF
1951	International Petroleum	San Pedro Block D		Peru	Parinas	38.7	SF
1952	Shamrock	Panhandle (Brumley Lease)	Moore	Tex.	Pennsylvanian	38.0	SF
1953	Haynesville Operators' Committee	Haynesville (SW Lower Pettit)	Claiborne	La.	Pettit Lime	42.0	EGD
1953	Humble	Seminole City (C-2 Block)	Seminole	Okla.	Booch Sand (Penn.)	39.0	SF
1954	Frank Buttram	Camp Hill	Anderson	Tex.	Carrizo-Wilcox	41.0	SF
1955	Shamrock	Panhandle (Hight Lease)	Moore	Tex.	Pennsylvanian	38.0	SF
1955	Phillips	Spraberry Trend (Pembrook Area)	Upton	Tex.	Spraberry Sand	34-41	SF
1956	Atlantic	Neale	Beauregard	La.	Wilcox Sand	47.1	HPGD
1956	Pan American	Elk Basin Frontier	Park	Wyo.	Frontier Sand	42.0	EGD
1956	Sun	Millican	Coke	Tex.	Strawn Lime	45.0	SF
1956	Wherry and Green	Taylor-Ina	Medina	Tex.	Navarro Sand	18.0	SF
1956	Petrocel	Killam	Webb	Tex.	Mirando Sand	22.0	SF, w/S
1957*	Humble	Bronte	Coke	Tex.	Goen and Cambrian Sand	51.0	EGD
1957	Humble	Seeligson (Zone 20B)	Kleberg	Tex.	Frio Sand	43.0	EGD
1957	Ohio	So. Coles Levee	Kern	Calif.	Stevens	37.0	SF
1957	Continental	Meadow Creek	Johnson	Wyo.	Lakota Sand	40.6	SF
1957*	Mobil	Parks-Pennsylvanian	Midland	Tex.	Bend Lime	44.2	SF
1957	Winthrop	Chincon Lake	Medina	Tex.	Olmost Sand	20.0	SF
1957	Cities Service	Panhandle (Hughey B)	Gray	Tex.	Permian Dolomite	41.0	SF
1957	Southern Minerals	Stratton	Nueces	Tex.	Wardner Sand	43.0	EGD
1957	Sun	North Sun	Starr	Tex.	Frio Sand	45.0	SF
1957	Continental	W. Short Junction	Cleveland	Okla.	Bois D'arc Lime	40.0	SF
1957	Sunray	Bisti	San Juan	N. Mex.	Lower Gallup	40.0	SF (pilot)
1957	Cities Service	Columbus	Colorado	Tex.	7C Zone, Wilcox	45.8	HPGD
1957	Sunray	Eram	Okmulgee	Okla.	Booch Sand	40.0	SF (after WF)
1957	Sunray	Newhall-Potrero	Los Angeles	Calif.	Upper Miocene	34.0	SF w/storage

900

Table 2 (Cont'd)

Year	Operator	Field	County or Parish	State	Formation	Oil Deg API Gravity,	Type
1957	Pan American	Three Bar	Andrews	Tex.	Devonian Lime	41.9	SF
1957	Texaco	Tijerina-Canales (Blucher)	Jim Wells	Tex.	Frio Sand (Zone 3)	40.0	SF
1957	Cities Service	Wilbarger (Regular)	Wilbarger	Tex.	"1,100-ft" Sand	26.0	SF
1957	Mobil	Pembina		Alberta	Cardium Sand	38.0	SF (pilot)
1957	Texas Gulf	Headlee	Ector	Tex.	Devonian Lime	—	HPGD
1957	Canadian Bishop	Pembina		Alberta	Cardium Sand	38.0	SF
1957	Humble	Katy Unit	Waller	Tex.	Yegua Sand	44.0	SF, w/S
1958	Standard of California	Midway Sunset (29 D Pool)	Kern	Calif.	Miocene Sand	31.0	SF
1958*	Atlantic	Slaughter (Boyd)	Cochran	Tex.	San Andres	32.0	SF
1958	Mobil	Sand Creek	Washakie	Wyo.	Frontier Sand	47.0	SF
1958	Ohio	Johnson	Cheyenne	Nebr.	Muddy "J" Sand	37.0	SF
1958	Continental	Rincon	Starr	Tex.	Frio H-4 Sand	40.0	SF
1958	Phillips	Burkett	Greenwood	Kan.	Bartlesville (Sand)	—	SF (after WF)
1958	McColl Frontenac	Pembina		Alberta	Cardium Sand	38.0	SF
1958	Western Gulf	Paloma	Kern	Calif.		41.0	SF
1959	Union Oil	Guijarral Hills	Fresno	Calif.	Gatchell Sand	30.0	SF
1959*	Sunray	Bisti (Central Bisti Unit)	San Juan	N. Mex.	Lower Gallup	40.0	SF
1959*	Shell	Wasson	Yoakum	Tex.	San Andres	32.0	SF
1959*	Mobil	Pembina (No. Pembina Unit)		Alberta	Cardium Sand	37.2	SF
1959	Dome Petroleum	Pembina		Alberta	Cardium Sand	38.0	SF
1960*	Pan American	Midland Farms (Wolfcamp)	Andrews	Tex.	Wolfcamp Lime	41.0	EGD
1960	Atlantic	University (Block 9)	Andrews	Tex.	Wolfcamp Lime	35.5	SF, HPGD
1960	Humble	Neches	Anderson } Cherokee }	Tex.	Sub-Clarkesville (Sand)	—	EGS

* = large-scale commercial application.

SF = solvent flood.

EGD = enriched-gas drive.

HPGD = high-pressure gas drive.

S = storage

WF = water flood.

In this field of recovery most of the literature has been directed toward the use of LPG in the solvent-flood and improved gas-drive methods. However, there is one other process of the solvent type which has been described in the literature and is under field test. This relates to the use of an alcohol slug which is substantially miscible with the oil being driven and with water used as the driving agent. U.S. Patent No. 2,742,089, issued April 12, 1956 to Morse et al., assigned to Pan American Petroleum Corp., describes a closely related process. Laboratory studies have been fairly extensively reported by Slobod and Gatlin,[63] and by Taber, Kamath, and Reed of Gulf Oil Corp.[64] Although most investigators have been concerned with the economic limitations of this particular solvent-flooding method, primarily because of the relatively high cost of alcohol, South Penn Oil Co. et al.[65] have reported the initiation of a field test to explore both positive and negative factors in ultimate application. Results are not known as this book goes to press.

At the end of 1960 all reported laboratory studies do not agree on the amount of solvent needed to conduct a solvent flood or an improved gas drive. The confusion centers around the interpretation of laboratory data as to which factors in experiments are meaningful in terms of what happens in reservoirs. There is general agreement that miscible flooding inherently is associated with poorer sweep than that associated with, for example, water flooding. Remedies for this have been proposed and more ideas should be forthcoming.

Field results have been encouraging to some people; others have expressed disappointment. It is still too early to definitely know the part solvent flooding and improved gas drives will contribute to the total oil-recovery picture. There are widespread expressions that more attention will have to be given to the gross nature of reservoirs when selecting this type of recovery process. Since more of the limitations of these recovery methods are becoming known, it is expected that more corrective procedures will be developed in the future. In the meantime, there are several large-scale commercial applications of miscible recovery methods under way (noted by * in Table 2). Atlantic's Block 31 Field, Crane County, Texas, is the oldest active operation, having been started in 1949.

Calculated economics of solvent and improved gas drives based on discounting future income can imply that, in many cases, water flooding is more desirable. This situation is a result of the usually higher capital investment needed and the limited present worth of the greater oil recovery that could be realized. The income from the incremental oil recovery is not recognized until after a recovery amounting to that expected by, for example, water flooding has been obtained. This delay in time between investment and income can be a strong influence in choosing between a solvent flood or improved gas drive and a water flood for a specific field application.

REFERENCES

(Principally Highlighting Historical Development)

[1]Whorton, L. P. and Kieschnick, W. F., Jr: Preliminary Report on Oil Recovery by High-pressure Gas Injection, *API Drilling and Production Practice*, 247(1950); also *Oil Gas J.*, **48 [48]** 78, April 6 (1950).

[2]Nelson, T. W. and McNiel, J. S., Jr: Past, Present, and Future Development in Oil Recovery by Thermal Methods, *Petroleum Engr.*, (in 2 parts): Part 1, **31 [2]** B-27, Feb. (1959); Part 2, **31 [3]** B-75, Mar. (1959).

[3]Kehn, D. M: A Review of the Enriched Gas Drive Process, *Producers Monthly*, **24[4]** 28, Feb. (1960).

[4]Craig, F. F., Jr. and Owens, W. W: Miscible Slug Flooding—A Review, *AIME J. Petr. Tech.*, **XII [4]** 11, April (1960)

[5]Breston, J. N. and Pearman, B. R: Hot-water Injection Treatment of Wells to Increase Water-intake Rates, *Producers Monthly*, **18 [1]** 15, Nov. (1953).

[6]Stovall, S. L: Recovery of Oil from Depleted Sands by Means of Dry Steam, *Oil Weekly*, **74 [9]** 17, Aug. 13 (1934).

[7]*Loc. cit:* Breston, J. N. and Pearman, B. R., ref. 5.

[8]Tucker, M: Secondary-recovery Methods Used to Revive Bellevue Pool, *Oil Gas J.*, **35 [37]** 172, Jan. 28 (1937).

[9]Anon: Warm-water Drive May Bring Big Payoff, *Oil Gas J.*, **54 [58]** 80, June 11 (1956).

[10]Schaller, Alwin, and Bjornsson, C. A: Influence of Heat upon the Recovery of Oil by Water Displacement, *National Petroleum News*, **15 [45]** 53, Nov. 7 (1923).

[11]Van Heiningen, J. and Schwarz, N: Recovery Increase by Thermal Drive, *Proceedings of the Fourth World Petroleum Congress, Section II*, 299, Rome, Italy, June 5-16, 1955; Carlo Colombo, Rome, Italy (1955); also *World Oil*, **141 [5]** 230, Oct. (1955).

[12]Croes, A. G. and Schwarz, N: Dimensionally Scaled Experiments and Theories on the Water-drive Process, *Trans. Am. Inst. Mining Met. Engrs. (Petroleum Development and Technology)* **204,** 35 (1955).

[13]Lauwerier, H. A: The Transport of Heat in an Oil Layer Caused by the Injection of Hot Fluid, *Applied Scientific Research, Sec. A*, **5,** 2-3, 145 (1955).

[14]Willman, B. T; Valleroy, V. V; Runberg, G. W; Cornelius, A. J; and Powers, L. W: Laboratory Studies of the Steam Recovery Process, *Trans. Am. Inst. Mining Met. Engrs. (Petroleum Development and Technology)* **219** (1960) (in press).

[15]Lindsly, B. W: Oil Recovery by Use of Heated Gas, *Oil Gas J.*, **26 [32]** 27, Dec. 20 (1928).

[16]Gibbon, A: Thermal Principle Applied to Secondary Oil Recovery, *Oil Weekly*, **115 [10]** 170, Nov. 6 (1944).

[17]Roberts, George, Jr. and Walker, Scott W: Fluid Injection for Increased Oil Recovery, *Proceedings of the Fifth World Petroleum Congress, Section II*, 253, New York, N. Y., June 1-5, 1959.

[18]Wolcott, Edson: Method of Increasing the Yield of Oil Wells, U. S. Patent No. 1,457,479, June 5, 1923.

[19]Howard, F. A: Method of Operating Oil Wells, U. S. Patent No. 1,473,348, Nov. 6, 1923.

[20]Sheinman, A. B; Dubrovai, K. K; Sorokin, N. A; Charugin, M. M; Zaks, S. L; and Zinchencho, K. E: Gasification of Crude Oil in Reservoir Sands, *Neftyanoe Khozyaistro*, **28 [4]** April (1935).

[21]Kuhn, C. S. and Koch, R. L: In-situ Combustion, Newest Method of Oil Recovery, *Oil Gas J.*, **52 [14]** 92, Aug. 10 (1953).

[22]Grant, B. F. and Szasz, S. E: Development of an Underground Heat Wave for Oil

Recovery, *Trans. Am. Inst. Mining Met. Engrs. (Petroleum Development and Technology)* **201**, 108 (1954).

[23]Walter, H: Application of Heat for Recovery of Oil: Field Test Results and Possibility of Profitable Operation, *Trans Am. Inst. Mining Met. Engrs. (Petroleum Development and Technology)* **210**, 16 (1957).

[24]Gates, C. F. and Ramey, H. L., Jr: Field Results of South Belridge Thermal Recovery Experiment, *Trans. Am. Inst. Mining Met. Engrs. (Petroleum Development and Technology)* **213**, 236 (1958).

[25]Order No. Misc. 5921, The Province of Alberta, The Oil and Gas Conservation Act, Oil and Gas Conservation Board, August 21, 1959; also Approval No. 358, Sept. 30, 1960.

[26]Johnson, G. W; Pelsor, G. T; and Preston, R. G: The Underground Nuclear Detonation of September 19, 1957, Ranier Operation of Plumbbob, University of California Radiation Laboratory Report UCRL-5124, February 4, 1958.

[27]Anon: *Nucleonics*, **16** [9] 156, Sept. (1958).

[28]Anon: *Time Magazine*, **72** [11] 70, Sept. 15 (1958).

[29]Anon: Electrocarbonization of Coal, *Chem. Eng. News*, **28** [3] 180, Jan. 16 (1950).

[30]Anon: Unmined Coal Gasified by Electric Power, *Coal Age*, **55** [12] 103, Dec. (1950).

[31]Odell, W. W. and Baldeschwielen, E. L: European Shale-treating Practice, *U. S. Bur. Mines Information Circ. 7348* (1946).

[32]Rubel, A. C. (Union Oil Co. of California): Private communication.

[33]Private communication.

[34]Private communication.

[35]Sage, Bruce H. and Lacey, Wm. N: *Some Properties of the Light Hydrocarbons, Hydrogen Sulfide, and Carbon Dioxide*, Monograph on API Research Project 37, American Petroleum Institute, New York, N. Y., 1955.

[36]Mertz, R. V. and Huntington, R. L: Gas Mixing in Porous Media, *Oil Weekly*, **103** [1] 26, Sept. 8 (1941).

[37]Hendrix, V. V. and Huntington, R. L: The Effect of Velocity on the Mixing of Liquid in Porous Media, *Petroleum Engr.*, **12** [1] 48, Oct. (1941).

[38]Fowler, F. C. and Brown, G. G: Contamination by Successive Flow in Pipe Lines, *Trans. Am. Inst. Chem. Eng.*, **39**, 491 (1943).

[39]Everett, J. P; Gooch, F. W; and Calhoun, J. C: Liquid-Liquid Displacement in Porous Media as Affected by the Liquid-Liquid Viscosity Ratio and Liquid-Liquid Miscibility, *Trans. Am. Inst. Mining Met. Engrs. (Petroleum Development and Technology)* **189**, 215 (1950).

[40]Elkins, L. E: Miscible Fluid Displacement in South Leonard Pool, Wagoner County, Oklahoma, presented at meeting of Mid-Continent Section, Society of Petroleum Engineers of AIME, March 20-21, 1958, Tulsa, Okla.

[41]Moscrip, Robert: Secondary Recovery by Butane Injection in San Pedro Block D, *Petroleum Engr.*, **30** [10] B-19, Sept. (1958).

[42]Morse, R. A: Recovery of Oil from Reservoirs, German Patent No. 849534, July 1952.

[43]Morse, R. A: British Patent Specification No. 649,524, Sept. 2, 1953.

[44]Stone, H. L. and Crump, J. S: The Effect of Gas Composition upon Oil Recovery by Gas Drive, *Trans. Am. Inst. Mining Met. Engrs. (Petroleum Development and Technology)* **207**, 105 (1956).

[45]*Loc. cit*: Kehn, D. M., ref. 3.

[46]Enright, R. J: LPG Flooding Tested in Texas, *Oil Gas J.*, **53** [47] 92, March 28 (1955).

[47]Hall, H. N. and Geffen, T. M: A Laboratory Study of Solvent Flooding, *Trans. Am. Inst. Mining Met. Engrs. (Petroleum Development and Technology)* **210**, 48 (1957).

[48]Koch, H. A. and Slobod, R. L: Miscible Slug Process, *Trans. Am. Inst. Mining Met. Engrs. (Petroleum Development and Technology)* **210**, 40 (1957).

[49]Jenks, L. H; Campbell, John B; and Binder, G. G., Jr: A Field Test of the Gas-driven Liquid Propane Method of Oil Recovery, *Trans. Am. Inst. Mining Met. Engrs. (Petroleum Development and Technology)* **210,** 34 (1957).

[50]Brooks, R. E: Miscible Displacement in Bisti Pool, San Juan County, New Mexico, presented at meeting of Mid-Continent Section, Society of Petroleum Engineers of AIME, March 20-21, 1958, Tulsa, Okla.*

[51]Relph, J. L: LPG Injection in Panhandle Field, Gray County, Texas, presented at meeting of Mid-Continent Section, Society of Petroleum Engineers of AIME, March 20-21, 1958, Tulsa, Okla.*

[52]Wright, H. T., Jr. and Die, R. R: Enriched Gas Drive Project, Zone 20-B, Seeligson Field, presented at meeting of Mid-Continent Section, Society of Petroleum Engineers of AIME, March 20-21, 1958, Tulsa, Okla.*

[53]Kern, L. R; Kimbler, O. K; and Watson, R: Detection of Injected Gas Losses in a Miscible Displacement Field Operation, presented at meeting of Mid-Continent Section, Society of Petroleum Engineers of AIME, March 20-21, 1958, Tulsa, Okla.*

[54]Walker, Richard E; Engle, James D; and Jenks, L. H: Performance of a Gas-driven Liquid Propane Field Test, presented at meeting of Mid-Continent Section, Society of Petroleum Engineers of AIME, March 20-21, 1958, Tulsa, Okla.*

[55]Marrs, Doyle G: Field-wide Miscible Displacement Project, Parks Field Unit, Midland County, Texas, presented at meeting of Mid-Continent Section, Society of Petroleum Engineers of AIME, March 20-21, 1958, Tulsa, Okla.*

[56]Caudle, B. H. and Dyes, A. B: Improving Miscible Displacement by Gas-water Injection, *Trans. Am. Inst. Mining Met. Engrs. (Petroleum Development and Technology)* **213,** 281 (1958).

[57]Anon: Miscible Drives: A Growing Tool for Oil Recovery, *Oil Gas J.,* **57** [**13**] 64, March 23 (1959).

[58]Justen, J. J; Hoenmans, P. J; Groeneveld, H; Connally, C. A; and Mason, W. L: The Pembina Miscible Displacement Pilot and Analyses of Its Performance, *Trans. Am. Inst. Mining Met. Engrs. (Petroleum Development and Technology)* **219,** 38 (1960).

[59]Habermann, Ben: The Efficiency of Miscible Displacement as a Function of Mobility Ratio, *Trans. Am. Inst. Mining Met. Engrs. (Petroleum Development and Technology)* **219,** 264 (1960).

[60]Lacey, J. W; Faris, J. E; and Brinkmann, F. H: Effect of Bank Size on Oil Recovery in the High-pressure Gas-driven LPG-Bank Process, *TP 1619G,* presented at fall meeting, Society of Petroleum Engineers of AIME, Oct. 2-5, 1960, Denver, Colo.

[61]Marrs, D. G: Field Results of Miscible Displacement Program Using Liquid Propane Driven by Gas, Parks Field Unit, Midland County, Texas, *Trans. Am. Inst. Mining Met. Engrs. (Petroleum Development and Technology)* **219** (1960) (in press).

[62]Block, W. E. and Donovan, R. W: An Economically Successful Miscible-phase Displacement Project—San Joaquin Valley, California, *AIME J. Petr. Tech.,* 35, Jan. (1961).

[63]Gatlin, Carl, and Slobod, R. L: The Alcohol Slug Process for Increasing Oil Recovery, *Trans. Am. Inst. Mining Met. Engrs. (Petroleum Development and Technology)* **219,** 46 (1960).

[64]Taber, J. J; Kamath, I. S. K; and Reed, Ronald L: The Secondary and Tertiary Recovery of Oil from Consolidated Sandstone by Alcohol-Water Flooding, *Trans. Am. Inst. Mining Met. Engrs. (Petroleum Development and Technology)* **219** (1960) (in press).

[65]Breston, J. N: Alcohol Slug Miscible Phase Flood in Bradford Field, *Producers Monthly,* **24** [**11**] 22, Sept. (1960).

*Published under slightly different titles in *Journal of Petroleum Technology,* **10** [**5**] May (1958).

BIBLIOGRAPHY

Anon: Miscible Test Shows Improved Recovery, *Petroleum Week,* 24, July 11 (1958).

Benham, A. L; Dowden, W. E; and Kunzman, W. J: Miscible Fluid Displacement—Prediction of Miscibility, *Trans. Am. Inst. Mining Met. Engrs. (Petroleum Development and Technology)* **219**, 229 (1960).

Binder, G. G., Jr: U. S. Patent No. 2,718,262, Sept. 20, 1955.

Blackwell, R. J; Terry, W. M; and Rayne, J. R: Factors Influencing the Efficiency of Miscible Displacement, *Trans. Am. Inst. Mining Met. Engrs. (Petroleum Development and Technology)* **216,** 1 (1959).

Blackwell, R. J; Terry, W. M; Rayne, J. R; Lindley, D. C; and Henderson, J. R: Recovery of Oil by Displacement with Water-Solvent Mixtures, *Trans. Am. Inst. Mining Met. Engrs. (Petroleum Development and Technology)* **219**, 293 (1960).

Brownscombe, E. R: Atlantic's High-pressure Gas Process Being Used in West Texas Block 31 Field, *Oil Gas J.,* **53 [6]** 133, June 14 (1954).

Clark, N. J; Schultz, W. P; and Shearin, H. M: New Injection Affords Total Oil Recovery, *Petroleum Engr.,* **28 [11]** B-45, Oct. (1956).

Henderson, J. H; Gove, N. B; Ledbetter, H. J; and Griffith, J. D: A Laboratory Investigation of Oil Displacement from Porous Media by a Liquefied Petroleum Gas, *Trans. Am. Inst. Mining Met. Engrs. (Petroleum Development and Technology)* **198,** 33 (1953).

Lacey, J. W; Draper, A. L; and Binder, G. G., Jr: Miscible Fluid Displacement in Porous Media, *Trans. Am. Inst. Mining Met. Engrs. (Petroleum Development and Technology)* **213**, 76 (1958).

Morse, R. A; Ireland, J. D; and Terwilliger, P. L: U. S. Patent No. 2,742,089, April 17, 1956.

Offeringa, J. and van der Poel, C: Displacement of Oil from Porous Media by Miscible Fluids, *Trans. Am. Inst. Mining Met. Engrs. (Petroleum Development and Technology)* **201**, 310 (1954); also *AIME J. Petr. Tech.,* **6 [12]** 37, Dec. 1954.

Sievert, J. A; Dew, J. N; and Conley, F. R: The Deterioration of Miscible Zones in Porous Media, *Trans. Am. Inst. Mining Met. Engrs. (Petroleum Development and Technology)* **213,** 228 (1958).

Slobod, R. L. and Koch, H. A., Jr: High-pressure Gas Injection—Mechanism for Recovery Increase, *API Drilling and Production Practice,* 82 (1953).

Talash, A. W. and Crawford, P. B: Oil Recovery by Miscible Displacement after Water Flooding, *Petroleum Engr.,* **24 [10]** B-27, Sept. (1957).

von Rosenberg, D. U: Mechanics of Steady-state Single-phase Fluid Displacement from Porous Media, *J. Am. Inst. Chem. Eng.,* **2 [1]** 55, March (1956).

Weinaug, C. F. and Ling, D: U. S. Patent No. 2,867,277, Jan. 6, 1959.

Whorton, L. P. and Brownscombe, E. R: U. S. Patent No. 2,724,437 and 2,724,438, Nov. 22, 1955.

Chapter 15

HANDLING OIL AND GAS
IN THE FIELD

Theodore E. Swigart

THEODORE E. SWIGART received an A.B. degree (1917) and an engineering degree (1918) from Stanford University. After five years with the United States Bureau of Mines, and seven months as consulting petroleum engineer in India and Burma, he joined Shell Company of California as production engineer in 1924. With this company he rose through the positions of assistant general field superintendent in California and vice-president for exploration and production in the southwestern states to the presidency of Shell Pipe Line Corporation, from which position he retired in October 1954. Among his accomplishments with Shell was the preparation in 1942 of the technical report justifying the Big Inch Pipe Line. Post-retirement responsibilities include a petroleum advisorship to Morgan Stanley & Co., investment bankers; the board chairmanship of North Central Oil Corporation, and directorships in the Texas Fund and Peruvian Oils & Minerals, Ltd.

Mr. Swigart was chairman for 17 years of the API Committee on Standardization of Pumping Equipment and Engines, and also served as chairman of the Drilling and Production Practice and District Activities Committees. In 1949 and 1950 he was the Institute's Vice President for Transportation. His API service has been acknowledged by its *Certificate of Appreciation.*

Professional and industrial affiliations include SPE of AIME, AAPG, the Texas Mid-Continent Oil & Gas Association, and the 25-Year Club of the petroleum industry. He is the author of numerous Bureau of Mines and other technical publications.

∝15∝

INTRODUCTION

From the beginning of the petroleum industry, the producer has been confronted with a variety of problems in the handling of oil and gas after they have been reduced to possession.

Oil, upon leaving the well head, generally passes through an oil and gas separator and a dehydrating unit before reaching the stock tanks where it is measured and sampled for quality preparatory to sale. Gas passes through a heater, a separator, a dehydrator, and an orifice meter, thence to the purchaser's pipeline.

For the past 30 years or more petroleum engineers have concerned themselves with surface problems incident to these operations. The prevention of waste of natural gas and light products, the separation of oil and water, the disposal of salt water, and the establishment of standard methods for measuring, sampling, and testing crude oil, natural gas, and natural gasoline have all occupied their attention.

Engineers have also been interested in developing economic methods for measuring the production of wells because well data are essential for solving lifting and workover problems, conducting programs for recovering maximum amounts of oil and gas from their underground reservoirs, complying with state proration laws and regulations, and—finally—for estimating reserves.

In recent years, revolutionary advances in the handling of oil and gas aboveground have been made under the broad heading of "automation". Here, the petroleum engineer, the pipeline engineer, and the oil and gas accountant meet with a common purpose—to improve accuracy, minimize losses, increase overall efficiency, and reduce operating expense.

This chapter attempts to trace the development of these various activities, including the adaptation of onshore methods and equipment to isolated offshore locations, over the industry's 100 years of history.

Not included are accounts of the technological improvements that have been made in storing oil in tank farms and transporting it in trunk pipelines. Those problems are recognized as belonging to the pipeline industry, which has developed its own engineers and technology. Likewise, with the exception of underground gas storage, the petroleum engineer has had little to do with problems of gas transmission and they are not discussed here.

EARLY HISTORY

The industry's first product—oil—has always been measured volumetrically in America. In the beginning oil was run from wells into all kinds of liquid containers—barrels, tanks, barges, and even dams and sumps. The operator's interest in measurement was twofold, viz., how much was he delivering for sale and how were his wells and leases holding up in production. Little effort was made to use production data scientifically.

In the very early days the operator even showed little concern over the methods and equipment for measuring crude oil because oil was cheap and, by custom, purchasers supplied their own containers or barrels. As related in *The Lamp*,[1] "Prices were set by the barrel—and just about any size and kind of barrel qualified, as long as it was ample enough to suit the buyer, yet not too commodious in the eyes of the seller . . . Such an arrangement was bound to cause not only confusion, but friction. Tempers quickened as prices rose and fell, and before long it was apparent to everyone that a realistic measure would have to be established and held to."

In 1866, Dr. M. C. Egbert and some 30 or more of the leading producers at Oil Creek, Pa., posted the following notice:[2]

"Whereas, It is conceded by all producers of crude petroleum on Oil Creek that the present system of selling crude oil by the barrel, without regard to the size, is injurious to the oil trade, alike to the buyer and seller, as buyers with an ordinary sized barrel cannot compete with those with large ones. We, therefore, mutually agree and bind ourselves that from this date we will sell no crude by the barrel or package, but by the gallon only. An allowance of two gallons will be made on the gauge of each and every 40 gallons in favor of the buyer."

This virtually established 42 gallons as the standard measurement for crude oil. The 42-gal. barrel was adopted by the Petroleum Producers Association in 1872, and has been used by the petroleum industry ever since. The U. S. Geological Survey began reporting petroleum production in barrels in 1882—the date of its first statistics—and other governmental agencies, such as the U. S. Bureau of Mines, Bureau of Standards, and Bureau of Foreign and Domestic Commerce, followed as the years went on.

History records that the Drake well was first produced into an 8-bbl fish-oil container. This was soon replaced, however, with a wooden tank and for a long time virtually all field tanks were the old cone-shaped wooden tanks. By driving down the staves, the operator could tighten them and reduce leakage.[3] But such tanks often leaked anyway; and gagers, in measuring oil sold from the lease, made arbitrary deduc-

---

[1]References are at the end of the chapter.

tions—depending upon the tank's size and condition—for leakage, frothiness of the oil, the time it had stood or settled, and the time required to run it to the pipeline.

Gas separators were unknown and the only means of separating water was by settling. Such matters as disposal of waste water, prevention of the waste of gas, and reduction of losses by evaporation were not recognized problems.

First gages or measurements of crude oil in field tanks were taken with a pine slat which was marked off in feet, inches, and fractions of an inch. This crude piece of equipment was later replaced by the gage pole. At the turn of the century the steel tape, which had been developed by the logging industry about 1890, was brought into the oil fields and was equipped with a plumb bob, snap, and frame.[4] The metal tape is still standard equipment for manual gaging as well as for some remote-reading liquid-level gages.

These early crude methods of handling oil on the lease have, over the years, been gradually refined with the advent of better tanks and with improved devices and methods for saving gas and light fractions of the oil and for separating water. A further improvement has come with the development of standard procedures for measuring oil, gas, and natural gasoline and accounting for them—and now, with automation.

NATURAL GAS AND ITS PRODUCTS

Prevention of Waste of Natural Gas

The usefulness of natural gas, whether as a propelling medium in oil reservoirs or as a commodity in industry, is so widely accepted today that it is difficult to recall the low regard in which gas was once held. But from the early days of their profession, petroleum engineers have concerned themselves with the use of gas in recovering oil from underground reservoirs, and this subject is dealt with in other chapters of this book. The history of the prevention of waste of gas aboveground is an equally fascinating story.

For several decades following the discovery of the Drake Well, natural gas and volatile fractions of petroleum were considered troublesome by-products of oil production. They were of no use and had no market value except when burned as fuel in or near the field where they were produced. Thus, there was little inducement for their conservation and operators' practices of flowing their oil wells into open tanks or pits, as pictured in Fig. 1 and 2, encouraged immediate gas separation and waste. Gulf Coast operators developed the flow box which was set in an open pit, Fig. 3. This box largely prevented the physical loss of oil by spraying and splattering, but the flume with which it was equipped

Fig. 1—Flow Tank Showing Loss of Gas and Volatile Products Circa 1920

provided a convenient and intended outlet for the gas to the air. Hazards from fire were great but had to be accepted as part of the business.

Eventually operators adopted the practice of installing gas traps or separators connected to vent lines with stand pipes at the top of which gas was burned as a measure of protection to life and property. This practice gave rise to the term "flare gas". Oil fields were dotted with flares and instead of these being viewed as evidences of waste, they were often admired as characteristic symbols of oil fields.

In the early part of the century the rapid growth of the automotive industry began to place new values on the "light ends" of petroleum. Also, the demand for natural gas as a fuel began to be evident in a few localities. Operators in oil fields favored with markets for gas developed equipment for separating it for delivery to domestic and industrial customers. But even after potential markets were available, the old "law of capture", which was the accepted principle of production and made oil and gas the property of the person who reduced them to possession, continued to contribute to great surface wastes of gas produced with oil. New oil fields were developed as rapidly as possible in order to drain the other fellow—or at least prevent him from draining you—with the result that fields reached their peak productions soon after discovery. When the gas pressure in a new field had blown off, as it soon did, production declined rapidly.

Fig. 2—Oil Flowing into Open Sump—Smackover Field, Arkansas

Fig. 3—Flow Boxes in the West Columbia Field, Texas, in 1921

Gas-transmission companies, knowing that flush production would be high and of short duration, could not hope to develop markets for the gas produced with the oil during these periods and they, therefore, seldom laid lines to collect it. As a result, except in California where there were practically no gas wells and where many flush oil fields happened to be near consuming centers, gas companies built their businesses around the stable and controllable supplies of gas from dry-gas fields. Gas associated with oil was allowed to waste.

Proration, which began to take hold in the late 1920's, had a number of beneficial effects. With it came gradual acceptance of a new concept of ownership which petroleum engineers called the "law of correlative rights". This set off a chain reaction. Regulatory bodies recognized the right of every operator to recover the oil and gas originally under his land and began to devise proration formulas with this end in view. Losses of oil and gas reserves by migration and drainage were reduced, making it possible for operators to institute slower and more orderly programs of development and production. Wider well spacing was adopted, and production methods were designed to obtain maximum recoveries of oil and gas from their underground reservoirs. Finally, producing rates were established that were commensurate with market demands for oil.

This transformation in the technique of oil-field exploitation did not always solve, however, the problem of saving and utilizing the natural gas produced with oil. Although proration tended to level out and maintain gas production over longer periods, which encouraged gas companies to buy it, production rates were geared to meet oil market demand. It is not surprising that the supply of gas from this source did not match gas market demand because oil demand—and, therefore, oil and gas production—was highest in summer when gas demand was lowest. This anomalous situation has gradually changed over the years as a result of the rapid growth in demand for burning oils. Now the total demand for petroleum is much higher in winter than in summer, with a resultant effect on the production of gas from oil wells.

In passing it should be mentioned that gas from gas fields has never posed an important waste problem because gas wells can be flowed at various rates—as long as the rates are not too high—or can even be closed in without damage. Gas-field production, therefore, can be regulated to meet market demand.

Over the past 25 years the greatest single factor in eliminating the waste of natural gas produced with oil has been the opening of enormous new markets by gas-transmission companies. These concerns can now buy all of the gas produced with oil that can be economically gathered. Because such gas constitutes only a small part of the total supply, it can be taken continuously into the systems at the rates at which it is produced and fluctuations in gas demand can be met by varying purchases from gas wells. This has brought much-needed relief to oil producers who, in the past, were faced with wasting large volumes of gas in the field.

At one period in the industry's history the processing of gas for the recovery of liquid products was considered to be an acceptable measure of use even though there was no market for the residue gas and it had to be flared. As additional natural-gasoline plants were built, more and more gas was treated. But large amounts of gas still had to be flared at tank batteries because many oil fields were not large enough to support a gasoline plant.

As time went on, natural-gasoline plant operators began to find it possible to contract the sale of residue gas to transmission companies. This not only added greatly to the profitability of the plants but led to a further change in the industry's concept of waste. The flaring of dry gas at gasoline plants or even the burning of residue gas for carbon black were beginning to be looked upon as wasteful practices.

State regulatory bodies exerted an important influence on gas conservation. The Railroad Commission of Texas, representing the nation's largest producing state, has been particularly diligent in pressing measures to prevent gas waste—aboveground as well as underground. Texas' basic conservation law was passed in 1919,[5] and by 1928 the Commission began to exercise control of production rates of oil and gas in the interests of conservation.

In 1947, the Railroad Commission of Texas entered an order which prohibited operators in the Seeligson Field from producing oil and gas unless the gas was used for: 1, light or fuel; 2, chemical manufacture (other than carbon black); 3, reinjection to the formations to increase oil recovery; or 4, natural-gasoline extraction—but this only when the residue gas was disposed of as in 1, 2, or 3.

This order brought a storm of protest and a court attack; and although the Texas Supreme Court upheld the Commission's right to prevent waste, it struck down this particular order. However, the operators soon completed plants and arranged to sell residue gas and thus placed themselves in compliance with the original order. In 1948, the Commission entered similar orders in 16 other fields and again there were court attacks, but the ultimate effect of these actions was to increase the industry's consciousness of waste and to bring about the conservation of gas. Regulatory bodies everywhere are still attacking gas waste, as witness the action of the United States Department of the Interior as recently as November 1958, in shutting down about 300 wells in the Aneth Field of Utah because gas was being blown to the air.

By this time the tremendous growth of the gas industry has brought markets to almost every oil and gas field of importance—not only in Texas but throughout the United States. The profit to be earned from gas sales, together with the relentless campaign of the industry and regulatory bodies, has largely eliminated surface gas waste.

Gas Storage

For many years both oil operators and gas companies were conscious of the need for some method of storing gas. Steel gas holders of the bellows-type, which were familiar sights in most cities, were only useful in balancing minute-to-minute or at the best, hour-to-hour fluctuations in demand. They were much too small to meet seasonal variations.

In the summer of 1915 gas was stored experimentally in an oil reservoir in Welland County, Ontario. That winter it was successfully withdrawn to supplement normal supply. Similar experiments were made in the Zoar Field, New York, in 1916, and in the Menifee Field, Kentucky, in 1919.

About 1927, Union Oil Co. of California, Shell Oil Company, and Southern California Gas Company undertook a cooperative program of injecting dry gas into the oil sands of Dominguez Field, California. Substantial volumes of dry gas—as much as 25 MMcf per day—supplied by the gas company were injected in the summer or on warm days, into high gas-oil ratio oil wells to be withdrawn when needed to help meet the gas company's peak demands in winter. This was a major gas-storage project and was entirely successful. The situation was recognized as being unusually favorable in that gas from oil wells constituted the main source of supply for Los Angeles and its environs, and Dominguez was located in the very heart of that large gas-consuming area. The field, in effect, was a huge gas tank that materially aided the gas company in saving gas that it was contracted to buy in summer and in meeting consumer demand in winter.

The storage of gas underground is now accepted practice of most large gas-transmission companies.[6] It did not gain impetus until the 1940's when gas companies concluded that such projects not only were feasible but, if developed near large consuming centers, would be extremely useful in helping to meet fluctuations in demand resulting from warm spells or cold snaps, or even changing seasons. Gas companies began to look for depleted oil and gas reservoirs, preferably near cities, and even for nonproducing geologic structures with suitable reservoir formations in which to store gas.

As of December 31, 1959, there were 209 storage pools in operation in 20 states of the United States with an estimated ultimate reservoir capacity of 2 trillion 521 billion cubic feet. Over 1 trillion 902 billion cubic feet of gas were in storage. These pools were capable of delivering as much as 11.3 billion cubic feet per day.[7] Thus, they have made unnecessary the building of 11.3 billion cubic feet per day of gas trunkline capacity merely to meet peak demands.

As approximately 2 trillion cubic feet of gas-storage capacity is in, or reasonably close to, major consuming areas, transmission companies having such storage are able to operate their lines at high load factors throughout the year, and thereby lower the unit cost of gas delivered. The largest reservoirs are in Pennsylvania, Ohio, West Virginia, Michigan, and New York, in the order mentioned.

An interesting recent development in the natural-gas industry is the transportation of liquefied natural gas in specially insulated tank ships. The first shipment was made in February 1959, from a refrigerating plant in Lake Charles, Louisiana, to London, England. Although experimental, the project was a technical success. Operators and government officials in certain foreign oil and gas-producing countries are envisioning large-scale liquefied gas movements to areas of high-cost fuels, such as English Channel ports. Conceivably, cheap foreign gas, shipped in liquefied state, might even supply some of the fuel demand of New England.

Another application of this process is liquefaction of "summer gas" delivered by pipeline for storage at points of consumption. Liquefaction, together with underground storage, may provide the means of preserving high pipeline load factors and low unit costs which are necessary to protect gas against the loss of markets to competitive fuels.

Recovery of Natural-gas Liquids

The value of natural-gas liquids was recognized and steps were taken to recover them long before there was a concerted movement to save and market natural gas. Wet gas suitable for treating generally was that produced from oil wells and was known as "casinghead" gas. There is a record of recovery of liquids from gas mains at Titusville, Pennsylvania, as early as 1904.[8] This led to the development of gasoline extraction by compression and chilling. Between 1905 and 1909 "one-product" extraction was effected by single-stage compression.[9] This was soon improved, however, by two-stage compression, the less volatile products being recovered in the low-pressure stage and the "wild" products, which were used for increasing the volatility of refinery gasoline, in the high stage.

The absorption process for natural-gasoline extraction is believed to have been first applied in Hastings, West Virginia, in 1913.[10] It rapidly gained favor and before many years largely replaced the compression method.

Natural-gasoline manufacture is not within the scope of this chapter and suffice it to say that the years have brought great technical advances—particularly in the field of fractional distillation. The product of the modern gasoline plant is seldom the single one which used to be known as casinghead gasoline and, later, as natural gasoline. Today it often includes a number of separate products, such as ethane, propane, butane, isobutane, pentane, isopentane, and even heavier components. These products are finding a variety of uses ranging from blends for motor fuels to chemical feed stocks and fuels for household cooking and heating.

Liquefied Petroleum Gas

One class of natural-gas liquids comprised chiefly of propane and butane, and known as liquefied petroleum gas (LPG), has found its own special markets and has developed into an important by-product for the petroleum industry. In the early days there was no demand for propane and butane, which are gases under normal pressures and temperatures but will liquefy under comparatively low pressures. Natural-gasoline plants and refineries—their sources of supply—did not try to recover them, and they were left as part of the fuel-gas stream. However, the fact that these products could be transported and stored as liquids and yet be easily converted to gas made it inevitable that they would find a market.

Mixtures of propane and butane were first sold as "bottled gas" for cooking and water heating, principally in resort areas, but their use soon spread to farms and towns not served with natural gas. As their utility became apparent, larger containers were installed by users into which LPG could be delivered in bulk from tank trucks—at much lower costs.

Now thriving businesses have been built in LPG distribution, and it is not unusual to see entire towns dotted with the conventional spherical or cylindrical tanks (usually coated with aluminum paint) which contain LPG for use both in cooking and in space heating of homes and business houses.

Coincident with this growth of demand for LPG for household purposes, other uses for butane have developed which have made it a premium product. Refiners find it a desirable blending agent for increasing the volatility of motor fuel for winter use, and the synthetic rubber industry and certain other chemical operations require it as a basic raw material.

917

Propane, because of its low boiling point, has the advantage over butane of being a gas even on the coldest winter days. Consequently, there is a strong trend toward supplying only propane for space heating.

The early engineering problems in handling LPG related to the development of pressure containers, regulators, fittings, and appliances for handling bottled gas. But today, the most important engineering problems are those in connection with the transportation and storage of LPG in bulk form.

Until recently the principal means of transportation have been truck, rail tank car, inland barge, and ocean-going barge. One tank ship specially built to transport LPG under pressure plies between Gulf and East Coast ports. For some years operators have mixed LPG with crude oil in the field and transported it to refineries through crude pipelines. More recently, a few products pipelines have begun to batch propane and butane and this practice is increasing.

Butane demand has a strong seasonal aspect because refiners require it in large quantites in the period extending from about August to February when they are building their supplies of winter gasoline. Propane is in greatest demand in the cold months of winter. Thus an efficient and cheap method of storing large quantities is needed.

Steel storage tanks, capable of holding the pressures necessary to contain propane and butane in liquid form at normal temperatures, cost upwards of $20 per barrel. Consequently, engineers looked for cheaper methods and found that underground storage was feasible.

Two general types of underground storage reservoirs are in use. The first is a large pear-shaped cavity which is dissolved or leeched out of the salt in a piercement-type dome or a thick salt bed by pumping fresh water down a well and continuously replacing the resultant brine with fresh water. The other is a cave or cavern mined in solid rock.

Obviously, salt-dome type reservoirs are limited to areas where such domes occur, viz., the Gulf Coast areas of Texas and Louisiana, the East Texas Basin, and Michigan. Salt beds, however, occur in adequate thicknesses and at sufficiently shallow depths in a number of other parts of the United States to permit the washing of reservoirs. These cavities, or "jugs" as they are called, range in size from 100,000 bbl to 500,000 bbl. Some now being washed are planned for capacities of 1,000,000 bbl. The cost of this type of storage reservoir ranges from $2 per barrel for small jugs to as little as 50 cents per barrel for large jugs.

Storage caverns are developed in areas where thick impervious strata of chalk, shale, limestone, or granite (preferred in that order), occur at reasonable depths. A shaft is sunk and the cavern is actually mined in the rock. These man-made cavities are generally constructed at depths of from 300 to 500 ft below the surface and at costs of from $3 to

$10 per barrel, depending upon depth and nature of the formation excavated and capacity of the reservoir.

Approximately 270 salt jugs and 19 mined caverns with a total capacity of 34,958,000 bbl are in existence at the present time (1959). Both types of underground storage have proved satisfactory and new projects are constantly being planned and developed.

Although propanes and butanes may be batched as single products through products pipelines, or may be transported together as a single batch, fractional distillation of the contaminated ends of the batches—or of the mixed streams, as the case may be—is necessary to separate them and to remove any residues (including moisture) picked up from the pipe walls. Thus, underground storage and fractional distillation equipment at delivery points are becoming recognized as being necessary when LPG's are transported in products pipelines.

Production and use of LPG has risen rapidly, climbing from 5,013 bbl per day in 1935, to 498,200 bbl per day in 1958, and further increases are expected.

Gas-condensate Production

The development of gas-condensate fields, beginning in the 1930's, resulted in a new type of producing operation. Unlike wells in dry-gas fields, gas-condensate wells produce substantial amounts of liquid hydrocarbons with the gas. Liquid reserves sometimes may be as valuable as the gas reserves. In contrast to natural gasoline, these new liquids, although including some light fractions, are comprised chiefly of the stable components of motor fuels and burning oils. Removal of these liquids from natural gas may be effected in field-type separating units which are discussed in the following section, or in absorption plants.

Cycling, which is a comparatively new process, is a product of the gas-condensate field. Operators have found it profitable to gather gas under high pressure from gas-condensate wells, strip it in high-pressure absorption towers, and then boost the residue with compressors to pressures necessary to reinject it to the producing formations where it picks up another load of products.

The economic importance of the liquid products recovered from natural gas is great. Both the U. S. Bureau of Mines and the American Petroleum Institute collect statistics and report the productions of crude oil and natural gasoline, but unfortunately they do not report separately the liquid products from gas-condensate fields. When these liquids are separated on the lease in lease separators, they are reported as crude oil production. When recovered by absorption and cycling plants, they are reported as natural gasoline.

In 1959 natural-gasoline production (including cycling products) averaged 876,000 bbl per day as against crude production of 7,045,000 bbl per day. Thus, reported liquid products from natural gas amounted to considerably more than 10 percent of the total liquid production of oil wells in the United States. These statistics, imperfect though they are, give some idea of the economic importance of natural-gas liquids now being produced by the industry.

Gas Separation

The need to separate gas from oil probably arose originally from the operator's desire to recover gas for field fuel. But separation in a trap ahead of the stock tank also assisted him in disposing of gas with the least hazard to life and property and in meeting the oil purchaser's requirement that he deliver only "solid oil".

Early devices to separate gas were known as "gas traps". Now they are commonly called "separators". Almost all traps use the same principle, viz., directing the mixture of oil and gas from a well through a chamber large enough to cause an important reduction in the velocity of flow. Separation takes place because of the difference in specific gravities of the fluids. In all separators gas is drawn off at the top and oil from a lower point.

One of the earliest gas traps on record was installed in Oil Creek, Pennsylvania, about 1865[11]—probably to recover gas for use as fuel under boilers. It consisted of a barrel placed on top of a tank. Oil and

gas entered the top of the barrel through one hole, the gas was led off at the top through another, and the oil was drained off at the bottom through a **U** tube which provided an oil seal and prevented the downward escape of gas. This early trap, although primitive, embodied the basic principles of gas-trap construction.

Another early trap familiar to operators (Fig. 4) consisted of a joint of large casing set vertically in a tank with its lower end open. The flow line or lines projected well down into the pipe through the cap.[12] Separation took place in the casing, the oil in the tank providing the seal. Gas was drawn off through a line screwed into another hole in the cap.

Fig. 4—Prairie Oil & Gas Company Trap Used in the Mid-Continent for Pumping Wells in the Early Part of the Century

The vertical casing trap set alongside the derrick at a flowing well was still another form. It was designed to deliver gas above atmospheric pressure. In this trap the oil seal was provided by a gooseneck of 2-in. pipe which led from the bottom of the casing trap upward some 30 ft or more. The back pressure such a trap would hold was determined by the height of the gooseneck and the weight of the column of oil in it.

These very early traps were constructed of material at hand and were not suitable for wells of large productions and high flowing pressures. Later oil and gas separators were pressure vessels provided with automatic controls to regulate fluid levels in them and to separate oil and gas over a wide range of operating pressures.

In 1919, the U. S. Bureau of Mines published a paper by W. R. Hamilton,[13] a well-known petroleum engineer, giving the results of his field investigations of gas traps. This paper was the most complete coverage of the subject at the time and presented information on various traps that were in use or had been used, including those capable of delivering gas at high pressures. Famous gas traps of that day were the Tico, Fuqua, Baker, Washington, Starke, Trumble, Bell, Scharpenberg, and McLaughlin—all named for well-known engineers and operators who had designed them.

Early installations provided for single-stage separation; but during the 1920's, high-pressure flowing wells in California, which produced comparatively large volumes of oil and gas, led to multistage separation.[14] Flow from a high-pressure well entered the high-pressure separator which trapped most of the gas. From there, the oil was led to the second or low-pressure separator where much of the entrained gas was removed. This system reduced the volume of liquid products carried over into the high-pressure gas stream. Multistage separation soon spread and is still in common use.

About 1926, there was renewed interest in the "air lift" in some areas because of its adaptation to lifting large volumes of fluid from oil wells. Actually, producers used the gas lift instead of the air lift—partly because of the explosive hazards of mixtures of natural gas and air and partly because natural gas was frequently available at pressures above atmospheric, which resulted in much lower compression costs than for air. This brought a further innovation in trapping.

The gas lift is an artificial-lifting method adapted to wells that will no longer flow but will yield large volumes of fluids. By its very principle it imposes some back pressure on the oil sand and this tends to reduce the rate of flow of oil and gas from the reservoir into the well. To reduce bottom-hole flowing pressures to a minimum and thus secure maximum production, operators frequently streamlined flow lines and elevated traps at the well head or tank battery so that the separated oil would flow by gravity from the elevated traps to the tanks. The reduction in pressure over conventional installations in which oil and gas flowed through flow lines to separators at ground level, and from which the oil had to be forced up to the top of tank batteries by well pressure, often amounted to as much as 20 psi. Even greater savings in pressure could be realized if flow lines were small or long, or if water and emulsion were present.

Today, three forms of separators are available—the conventional vertical cylinder, the horizontal cylinder, and the spherical vessel. All use the original basic principle, viz., reduced velocity of flow and gravity separation. However, the interior arrangements of baffling, mist-arresting screens, floats, and other mechanical features vary greatly.

Many operators still prefer the vertical cylinder-type separator for low gas-oil ratio wells because of its large fluid capacity. Others choose the horizontal type—particularly for high gas-oil ratio flows—because mist tends to drop out of the horizontal flowing gas stream and run down the baffles to the shell and then to the bottom of the cylinder. In the vertical type mist has to fall back through the upward flow of gas.

Because of its form, it was thought that the spherical separator could be designed for a given pressure with thinner walls and, therefore, with less steel and at lower cost than the cylindrical separator. However, there is some question as to this advantage because the form of the vessel constricts the gas space and increases the gas velocity toward the outlet. Comparison of spherical and cylindrical separators suggests that a larger diameter is required in the spherical type to provide the same capacity, with the end result that about the same amount of steel may be used.

In late years high-pressure separation has received further impetus with the advent of gas-condensate fields in the Gulf Coast areas of Texas and Louisiana (see "Gas-condensate Production"). Engineers have made intensive studies of the behavior of hydrocarbon mixtures under the various conditions of pressure and temperature in which they occur in underground reservoirs and have developed techniques for obtaining maximum recoveries of liquid products—both from the reservoirs and from the gas at the surface.

Most efficient recoveries on the surface can be obtained in high-pressure absorption plants, and such plants are installed when gas-condensate reserves and production are large enough to support them. But many times the operator is faced with the need to strip gas from a single well or from a few wells, and this has raised the need for efficient field-type separators.

The first installations for this service comprised settings of conventional high and low-pressure separators, together with gas-dehydrating equipment. Operation with such an arrangement is commonly referred to as "stage separation".

In recent years a new form of separator, known as the "low-temperature unit",[15] has been developed. It uses the phenomenon of low temperatures caused by expansion of gas from well head to delivery pressure to remove liquids from the gas. Under suitable operating conditions this unit will recover 15 or 20 percent more of the liquid hydrocarbons than stage separators.

Fig. 5 is a schematic drawing of a typical unit. Gas from a high-pressure well, with condensate and water vapor, is preheated in heater A, and passes through coil B in low-temperature separator C, thence through knockout D where some free water and hydrocarbons separate, the latter fluids being led back to separator C. The high-pressure gas next passes through heat exchanger E which, by utilizing part of the cold sales gas (the amount regulated by the temperature-controlled 3-way valve G), delivers the high-pressure stream to choke (a) at such temperature that water vapor in the gas will not freeze in the choke when expansion takes place. Upon expanding into separator C, the gas reaches low temperatures and the hydrocarbons and water in it (in the form of crystals) separate and fall to the bottom of the separator. Hot gas in coil B furnishes heat to melt the water crystals. Sales gas passes off at the top through line F and condensate and water are drawn off at the bottom through float-operated valves H and I. A fine balance of temperatures is required for efficient separation with this unit.

All natural gas, when produced from underground reservoirs, carries some water, the amount being that of complete saturation at the pressures and temperatures of the reservoir. Even dry gas injected into underground reservoirs—whether for cycling or storage—will pick up

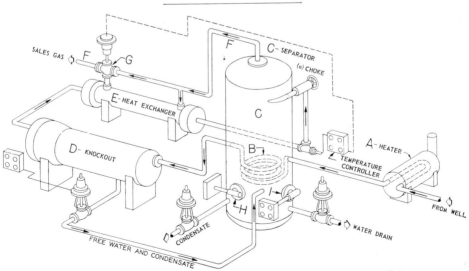

Fig. 5—Schematic Drawing of Low-temperature Separating Unit

water vapor if there is a downdip water level in the gas sand or other reservoir formation. As most gas companies limit the water content of gas they purchase to a maximum of 7 lb per MMcf, gas usually has to be dehydrated. The low-temperature unit will dehydrate gas to this specification as long as there is enough differential between wellhead and delivery pressures to achieve the necessary level of (low) temperature. And even when the flowing pressures decline below this point, the low-temperature unit may be used for a time by adding glycol to the gas stream to prevent freezing in the choke.

Eventually, however, the differential between well and line pressures will become too small to provide the low temperature required for dehydration. At that time the low-temperature unit may be provided with a separate dehydrator and used as a stage separator or, alternatively, may be replaced with conventional high and low-pressure separators which also require a separate dehydrator.

Another field-type separator in common use is the dry-bed adsorption unit.[16] Originally this was designed as a dehydrator. Gas passed alternately through two towers packed with a solid desiccant—such as alumina gel or silica gel—which has a natural affinity for water. The unit operated on long cycles—several hours each—one tower adsorbing water as the other was purged with hot gas. Eventually it became apparent that, although the gels have a preferred affinity for water, they are also effective in adsorbing hydrocarbons, provided the adsorbing cycles are shortened enough that the desiccant does not become oversaturated.

This led to the short-cycle unit shown in Fig. 6. It has four vessels including a scrubber on the flow line. The first vessel (scrubber) is both a high-pressure separator and liquid (i.e., hydrocarbons and water) accumulator, and the other three are adsorption towers packed

Fig. 6—Short-cycle Dry-bed Adsorption Unit Showing (left to right) Stabilizer, High-pressure Separator, Three Adsorbing Towers, and Heater

with the desiccant. The unit operates in cycles of about 15 min. While one tower is functioning as an adsorber, the second is being purged with hot gas to regenerate the desiccant, and the third is cooling preparatory to the next adsorbing cycle.

The adsorbed hydrocarbons and water are vaporized by hot gas during the purging cycle and are led through an atmospheric condenser where they are converted to liquids. They are then led back to the separator and drawn off as distillate and water.

These units have the advantage of recovering liquid hydrocarbons and dehydrating gas throughout the life of a field—down to depletion pressures.

For dehydrating only, the glycol dehydrator is commonly used. It introduces the chemical glycol, which also has an affinity for water, at the top of a small tower. In passing downward counter-current to the upward flowing gas stream, the glycol absorbs water vapor from the gas. The glycol with absorbed water is then pumped to a second tower known as a "reconcentrator", where it is heated. Water is driven off at the top in the form of vapor, the glycol being returned to the absorption tower for re-use.

These modern field separating units—whether stage separators with dehydrators, low-temperature units, or dry-bed adsorption units — approach absorption plants in complexity of design and operation, but are smaller and cheaper and can be attended by field personnel. On the other hand, they are considerably less efficient in removing liquid hydrocarbons, and as soon as the volumes of gas and liquid hydrocarbons justify an absorption plant, operators almost always install one.

Gas traps, or oil and gas separators as they are now called, including the complex form of units for separating liquid hydrocarbons and water from gas streams just described, have become so widely used that they are almost taken for granted and there is little appreciation of the slow and arduous course of development through which this class of equipment has passed. Whereas early gas traps were many times the invention of the field man, later innovations, beginning with the high-pressure separator and including the modern separating units of today, are without exception the product of the engineer.

SEPARATION OF OIL, WATER, AND EMULSIONS

Most oil fields produce water with the oil, and the problems of separating water and oil have been with the producer since the beginning of the industry.

Water is produced by oil wells in three forms: As "free" water which because of differences in the gravities of oil and water, promptly settles out in a receiving vessel and presents no problem other than that of disposal; as water in suspension which will settle out with time or the application of heat or chemicals; and as emulsion which requires intensive heating, chemical treatment, electrical treatment, or combinations of these.

Water in suspension is in the form of drops which are held in the oil largely because of the oil's viscous character. Given time, or a lowering of the oil's viscosity by heating, such water will usually drop out because of its higher specific gravity.

Oil-field emulsions consist of drops of water of microscopic size which are encased in films of oil. They are often stubborn to treat and, in fact, cannot be broken unless the oil films are ruptured so that the fine drops of water join to form larger ones. Oil-water emulsions have been studied by chemists for more than 50 years and many technical papers dealing with them are on record.

Refiners have always objected to the presence of water in oils they purchase, and therefore operators, from the early days, have had to take steps to clean their crudes in the field. One of the first methods of removing water and emulsions was to allow the "dirty oil" to settle in a tank. If it stood long enough, most of the water settled to the bottom and the emulsion separated to form a layer between the clean oil above and the water below. The clean oil could then be recovered. This method did not break the emulsion, however, and it had to be burned in sumps or otherwise disposed of with the result that the oil in it was lost.

Another early scheme was to run dirty oil into large ponds and expose it to the heat of the sun. Given time, this process of "sunning" caused water to settle out and it even broke down some of the emulsion, but it resulted in large losses by evaporation.

From these crude methods the steaming plant was developed. It generally consisted of a tank or a battery of tanks with steam coils, in which emulsified oil was heated. Sometimes oil was run through heat exchangers of horizontal pipe with a steam line inside. High temperatures, together with time, tended to break the emulsions; but the process was slow and only partially effective, and the heating distilled off much of the gasoline.

Heavy viscous crudes generally have a greater tendency to emulsify than light crudes. Many California fields, as well as certain ones in Arkansas and Texas, produce oils of this character and, therefore, much early work in water separation was done in those areas.

The hay tank was a contrivance that was placed in the flow line to break emulsions and separate oil and water. It depended upon the packing—usually excelsior—to rupture the oil films surrounding the small drops of water. These drops of water would then coalesce into large drops which would settle out. Interestingly enough, many modern separators, including the heater-treater, have compartments with excelsior or filtering materials and thus use the hay-tank principle.

Horizontal water traps came into use in certain fields of California, Texas, and Arkansas 40 years or more ago. They varied in design but essentially consisted of an inclined gas leg, an oil leg, and a water leg, made of 10- or 12-in. casing and connected by risers. Gas could find its way to the top leg from which it was bled through a choke, oil was drawn off the middle leg, and water and other impurities from the bottom leg. In the days of these separators, fluid levels were maintained manually—sometimes with the aid of gage glasses.

Traps of this class depended entirely upon the principle of reducing the velocity of flow enough that the differences in specific gravities of the fluids caused them to separate. They were adapted to flowing wells and were installed in flow lines ahead of the chokes so that gas, oil, and water would separate under flowing pressures, thus preventing or reducing the emulsifying action of high-velocity flows of the mixtures through the chokes.

The modern version of these separating devices is the widely used "free-water knockout". Like the old-time water trap, the free-water knockout is designed to allow the well stream to slow down for a long-enough period of time that free water or water in suspension will settle out. The typical knockout is a horizontal cylindrical vessel which receives the well stream through a diverter or arrester. Water in the slow-moving stream settles to the bottom and a layer of oil collects on top. The oil-water level is maintained by drawing off the water through a valve actuated by a liquid-level control pilot, and skimming off the oil over a weir. The principle of operation is the same as that of the three-phase separator discussed later in this chapter, and shown in Fig. 11.

These knockouts fall into two classes—high and low-pressure. The high-pressure type, used ahead of the choke, has the advantage of preventing or reducing the formation of emulsion, but is much heavier and more costly than the low-pressure knockout and may not be adapted to handling the well stream over the life of a well. If a low-pressure knockout can be used, its original cost is lower and, moreover, it may not have to be replaced during the well's life as it will operate satisfactorily over a wide range of changing well conditions—such as declining pressures and increasing water production.

The wash tank in California and the gun barrel in the Mid-Continent came into use many years ago for separating oil-water mixtures. Both are vertical cylindrical tanks which are usually taller than the stock tanks (so oil will flow by gravity to the stock tanks) and are placed in the system just ahead of the tank battery. No absolute formula is used in their selection, but in California, where stubborn emulsions have to be broken, a rule-of-thumb requirement is a wash tank of enough capacity to provide a turnover of, say, 24 hours of production. Gun barrels seldom have such capacities because the service they are called on to render—the cleaning of lighter, less viscous crudes —is less difficult.

The wash tank or gun barrel receives the oil-water part of the well stream from the separator or, in the case of small pumping wells when a separator is not used, the full well stream direct. The flow line may enter at the bottom but usually enters at the top where entrained gas escapes. The liquids are led to the bottom through a flume or down-pipe fitted with a spreader. The oil then rises through a column of water, which is purposely maintained, and collects on top where it spills off through the discharge line to the stock tanks. Water is drawn off from the bottom through a water leg of such height as will maintain the desired oil-water contact.

The wash tank or gun barrel enables the operator to establish the necessary conditions for separation. Combinations of such factors as velocity of flow, time, degree of heat treatment, and amount and kind of chemicals can be selected after experimentation and just about any kind of dirty oil can be cleaned.

The gun barrel has been used for many years and is in general use today, which testifies to its effectiveness.

Early efforts to separate water and break emulsions in the field included attempts to apply the principles of filtration, distillation, centrifugal action, and, finally, electrical and chemical treatment.

Although a few plants were installed in the early part of the century to filter oil and others to break oil-water mixtures by the combined effect of heating and distilling, these did not come into common use. The centrifuge was utilized to a limited extent and the names De Laval and Sharples became known to the industry. But these methods soon gave way to others that were cheaper and better adapted to solving the actual problems.

The use of electricity for dehydration of crude oil was an outgrowth of pioneer work of Frederick G. Cottrell, a well-known engineer and one-time director of the U. S. Bureau of Mines. Cottrell was granted a patent on his principle on March 21, 1911.[17]

The standard Cottrell apparatus consists essentially of an electric treater and a settling or trap tank.[18] The treater is a vertical tank with a revolving electrode. A potential of 11,000 volts alternating current is maintained between the electrode and the tank shell. Emulsified oil is fed continuously to the treater and passes through the electric field which breaks down the emulsion.

The first commercial application of electrical dehydration of which there is record was on the property of the Lucile Oil Company in the

Coalinga Field, California, in 1909.[19] One of the later and improved installations is shown in Fig. 7. Eventually, many plants were installed in American and foreign fields by the Petroleum Rectifying Company, owner of the Cottrell patent. This company also developed the National-type dehydrator for use in fields of the Gulf Coast of Texas and Louisiana, and about 1925 it brought out the H. F. or horizontal-flow dehydrator.

Experiments by J. L. Sherrick and G. W. Jones, in May 1917,[20] served as a starting point for the patenting of the Siebert and Brady electric treater.[21] This treater differed from others in mechanical design, but more particularly in its use of low-voltage direct current instead of high-voltage alternating current.

Because of their size and cost of installation, electrical dehydrators are generally situated at central gathering points or even at refineries where large volumes of dirty oil can be fed to them. Electrical treaters found their greatest application in California. By 1921, it was estimated that 92 percent of the dirty oil produced in California was treated in Cottrell units,[22] and some are still in use there.

The pioneer inventor in the field of chemical demulsification was William S. Barnickel. He went to Oklahoma in 1907 and became interested in the problem of saving waste oil in the Glenn Pool where large quantities of emulsified oil were being burned or allowed to flow down creeks because it was considered worthless.

By 1910 Barnickel found that certain chemicals would convert emulsified oil into merchantable crude oil, and in 1914 he received the first of many patents on chemical demulsifiers.[23]

In 1916, a small manufacturing plant with a capacity of 5 drums per month was installed in St. Louis, Missouri; and by 1922 more than 5,000 drums of Tret-O-Lite—the trade name given this chemical—were sold, with which more than 36,000,000 bbl of marketable oil were recovered.[24] Tret-O-Lite became the most widely used chemical for treating dirty oil because of its low cost and effectiveness. As years have gone on, chemicals have been used in various ways—sometimes being mixed with dirty oil in the gun barrel or flow tank, but often in the flow

Fig. 7—Battery of Cottrell Electric Dehydrators in the Casmalia Field, California

or lead line. Occasionally they are even injected into the well so that mixing takes place in the tubing, although this method is not in general use.

Methods and equipment for injecting emulsion-breaking chemicals have changed with the years. In the beginning, chemicals were introduced into low-pressure lead lines from pumping wells by lubrication and to high-pressure flow lines or to tanks by means of small duplex pumps operated by steam or natural gas. Eventually the modern injector was developed. It is essentially a small pump actuated by gas under well or separator pressure, or by electricity or by mechanical linkage to the pumping unit, depending upon the most convenient source of power.

Chemical treatment, because of cost and adaptability to lease operations, has gained acceptance in most oil fields of the United States. In fact, it is almost universally used by producers in all fields including California where it has largely replaced the electrical process.

The modern heater-treater, which is shown schematically in Fig. 8, was developed in the 1930's. It is, in effect, a gas-oil separator, gun barrel, and heater combined in a single unit. It separates gas as well as water from oil, and with chemicals it is effective in breaking emulsions. These units have a water space (A) at the bottom, a filter section (B) at midpoint, an oil space (C) above, and a gas compartment (D) at the top. Flow from the well generally passes through a heat exchanger (a) and enters the treater near the top where initial gas separation takes place. From there the stream is led through a "downcomer" pipe (b), entering the bottom compartment of the treater through a "spreader" (c). Fluids are heated in the bottom compartment by gas fire box (d), and the oil rises through the hot water and filter section where emulsion is broken. Clean (hot) oil is drawn off near the top (e) and flows downward through the heat exchanger and on to the stock tanks. All the gas is removed from the top (f) and water is drawn off at the bottom (g).

Modern heater-treaters are made in various designs and sizes and are truly engineered equipment. Large units have capacities up to 3,000 or 4,000 bbl per day of fluid and 10 to 15 MMcf per day of gas.

Various combinations of gas separators, heater-treaters, and gun barrels are in use. High-pressure flowing wells may require separators ahead of heater-treaters for high-

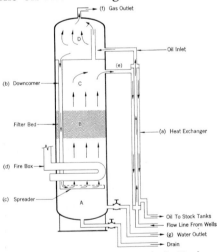

Fig. 8—Schematic Drawing of Modern Heater-treater

pressure separation, but the heater-treater can often be substituted for a separator and gun barrel unless volumes of water are unusually large or for some special reason separation is not complete in the heater-treater. In such unusual cases both a heater-treater and gun barrel may be used. Heater-treaters are now in general use where heat is an essential part of the treating process.

Over the years many engineers and chemists have worked on the emulsion problem and numerous technical papers have been published. In 1926, the U. S. Bureau of Mines issued *Bulletin 250: Oil Field Emulsions,* by D. B. Dow, and in 1928, *Bulletin 417: Practices and Methods of Preventing and Treating Crude Oil Emulsions,* by G. B. Shea. Dow's bulletin was a comprehensive treatise on oil-field emulsions. It discussed physiochemical characteristics of emulsions, the effects of operating practices on the formation of emulsions, and finally, practical methods of dehydration. Shea set out methods of preventing the formation of emulsions in oil-producing operations, and he also described practices and methods of economically dehydrating oil-water mixtures and breaking emulsions. The works of Dow and Shea were the most complete documents of their time; but, as may be expected, much has been done since in the direction of improved equipment and techniques.

Disposal of Salt Water

The disposal of oil-field salt water, or "waste water" as it is called in California, is another problem that has always been with the oil producer. The volume of salt water produced with oil in the United States is at least equal to the volume of oil itself, and some have estimated it to be as much as 2 bbl of water to one of oil. Many fields in their late stages of depletion produce several times as much salt water as oil.

For a long time following the Drake well, salt water was allowed to run into creeks and rivers, or water courses leading into them. Often it was trapped in sumps, or in draws from which it soaked away into surface sands and soils—or, aided by the sun and winds, evaporated leaving the salt behind. In the early days, and even in the 1930's in the East Texas Field, some operators burned waste gas over sumps to speed evaporation. Heavy rains frequently provided much needed relief by washing out dams and clearing away the salt water. Fortunately, at such times streams and rivers would be so swollen that they would dilute the salt water and thus minimize damage.

However, as oil fields were found in agricultural areas and fruit belts, strong opposition arose to the practice of permitting salt water to soak into the soil. Also, states passed pollution laws to protect fish and game and the oil producer often found himself confronted with volumes of salt water that would not evaporate and could neither be allowed to seep into the soil nor run into streams.

In the Los Angeles Basin in the 1920's, operators joined in forming nonprofit waste-water disposal companies. Most of these installed pipelines to carry the water to the sea. Similar companies were formed in other areas.

Subsurface disposal of salt water by returning it to the water-bearing parts of the reservoir formations, or to other porous and permeable formations, suggested itself to operators as early as 1916. In that year, salt water was injected into porous caprock above salt domes in two fields in the Gulf Coast. But it was not until subsurface disposal was successfully demonstrated in the East Texas Field in the late 1930's that operators began to adopt the technique of injecting salt water into porous underground formations on a wide scale. This has now become the most satisfactory method of disposal except in fields close to tidewater, where it can be economically piped to the sea.

The East Texas salt-water disposal system is an outstanding disposal and conservation project. A few years after the discovery of the field, the volume of salt-water production had become so great that its surface disposal was practically impossible. In 1939, the Attorney General of Texas brought suit against certain East Texas operators to prevent pollution of the Neches-Angelina watershed. This signaled the end of haphazard salt-water disposal and prompted the formation of the East Texas Salt Water Disposal Company.

By the end of 1958, this company had extended its gathering system to serve 206 different operators and 714 leases. Water is treated and injected through 60 wells into the downdip, water-bearing portions of the Woodbine sand. Parallel with this operation, a number of oil companies operate their own injection systems.

Petroleum engineers realized that, apart from the necessity of disposing of extremely large volumes of salt water, injection of this water into the producing sands could be expected to be very beneficial by maintaining reservoir pressures and increasing ultimate oil recovery. This has been borne out by results. From the beginning of the East Texas disposal company's operations in 1942, to the end of 1958, 2,092,055,000 bbl of oil and (equivalent volumes of) gas had been withdrawn from the Woodbine reservoir, together with approximately 2,863,014,230 bbl of salt water. Some 2,558,708,503 bbl of salt water had been injected, resulting in a net fluid withdrawal of 2,396,360,727 bbl. Estimated average reservoir pressure in the field in 1942 was 1,020.71 psi; and in the ensuing 16 years, it has only varied a few pounds either way, being 1,048.67 psi on December 31, 1958.

In addition to the successful disposal of tremendous volumes of salt water, this program has actually caused many pumping wells to resume natural flow with resultant saving in operating expense. The number of pumping wells reached a high of 9,783 in January 1950, but by December

31, 1958, declined to 8,946. All in all, this operation promises to increase total ultimate oil recovery in the East Texas Field by an estimated 600 million barrels.

Over the years other disposal projects, too numerous to mention, have been undertaken by operators throughout the United States. Perhaps of latest historical interest is a novel plan devised by the State of Arkansas to assist producers in meeting the disposal problem in that state. In 1958, the Arkansas Water Pollution Control Commission ruled that producers should discontinue dumping salt water into the Ouachita River. The state commission eased the effect of the order by permitting operators successively to reduce the amount of salt water discharged into streams by 20 percent per year with the aim that within 5 years the problem would be met. However, as many of the state's fields had reached the stripper stage, it was foreseen that the financial burden imposed on producers for developing underground disposal would, in many cases, be greater than the value of the remaining oil reserves. Early in 1959, the legislature passed a new law permitting severance tax relief to operators who install salt-water injection systems by giving them tax credit to the extent of the entire cost of those installations.

The technical aspects of oil-field waters and their disposal and utilization have long interested engineers, and this subject has recently been discussed in considerable detail by Henry Lewelling and Monte Kaplan of The Atlantic Refining Company.[25] Practically all oil-field waters contain mineral salts in solution, the content of sodium chloride greatly exceeding that of other minerals. But calcium, potassium, and magnesium in the form of chlorides, carbonates, and sulfates are also often found. These salts, upon being exposed to the air or subjected to changes in temperature and pressure, may precipitate to form scale. Scale may form in the equipment in producing wells, in surface lines and pumps, and also in water-disposal wells, seriously impairing their usefulness.

Carbonate scales are susceptible to acid treatment, but sulfate scales are difficult to remove by chemicals. Hence, the operator seeks to prevent their deposition. Inhibitors are frequently used to prevent the formation and deposition of sulfate scales. Alternatively, chemicals may be added to cause their precipitation on the surface—as in pits.

Oil-field waters sometimes carry suspended matter, such as sand and silt, bacterial or organic material, iron compounds, and of course, some oil and oil-water emulsions. Unsaturated iron compounds—such as ferrous oxide—frequently occur in solution and, upon exposure to the air, convert to ferric oxide (rust) which is not soluble. Such solids must be precipitated or filtered out if water is to be injected into underground formations, as they will soon plug the formations and destroy the usefulness of disposal wells.

933

The corrosion problem is one of the most troublesome in handling oil-field waters. So-called "acid gases", such as hydrogen sulfide and carbon dioxide, combine with water to form weak but corrosive acids. Galvanic action also frequently occurs in the steel systems comprising wells, lines, pumps, and vessels. Engineers and chemists have pretty generally adopted noncorrosive materials for surface equipment—particularly for gathering lines and disposal lines. Cement-lined pipe, asbestos-cement pipe, and even plastic pipe or plastic-coated pipe and vessels are commonly used. But coatings cannot be applied to the casing, tubing, sucker rods, and pumps in producing wells nor to the water-injection pumps on the surface wells. Chemical inhibitors are used to neutralize acids and sacrificial anodes (cathodic protection) to overcome galvanic action.

Algae may form in open-type disposal systems and tend to plug the formations of injection wells. Living organisms may also be present in the reservoir formations or may thrive in the steel well or surface equipment of closed systems. The behavior of these latter sulfate-reducing bacteria is not always understood, but it is known that they may cause hydrogen sulfide to form. This results in corrosion of pipes and vessels and plugging of formations by scales.

Research on this problem is taking the direction of developing better separating and dissolving agents and more effective inhibitors to reduce corrosion and scale deposits. Bacteria and ways to combat them are also being studied. Practical methods for extracting chemicals from oil-field waters and converting such waters into fresh water would furnish the ideal solution; but while much work has been done along this line, so far as is known, no economic methods have been developed.

Salt water will always be with the oil producer, and its economic aspect is important as it involves extra costs for lifting as well as for treating and disposal. Unfortunately, these costs are frequently highest in the late life of an oil field when the operator can least afford them; and, in fact, these costs can very well determine the economic limits of production.

Evaporation is the cheapest method of disposal but, by and large, fails to solve the disposal problem. Dumping into the sea after eliminating oil, or injecting into wells, involves capital costs for skimming and treating and for pumping equipment, pipelines, and disposal wells. Operating costs for power, labor, chemicals, and maintenance of plant are incurred in these operations.

When widespread consideration was first given to subsurface disposal of salt water, it was believed that the water had to be conditioned almost as carefully as a municipal water supply, and this was costly. Eventually operators realized that many times only limited measures had to be taken in order to return the water to the formations with a heavy load of chemicals and in pretty much its original form. Handling in closed systems to prevent aeration, use of precipitants or inhibitors, or filtering may or may not be necessary and it is desirable, of course, to restrict treatment to those measures that are necessary.

As illustrated by the East Texas system, salt water may be used to great advantage in oil-field flooding operations, as fresh water is often in short supply; and when this can be done, an otherwise expensive and bothersome operation may be turned to good account.

Because salt-water disposal is expensive at best, and can become extremely burdensome to those who have small holdings, there has been a definite trend toward cooperative efforts by groups of operators. By this time, operators accept water disposal as a matter of course and, excepting in fields near the coast, injection in underground formations is the method commonly used.

MEASUREMENT OF WELL PRODUCTION

Producers have always measured oil that is sold and run from each lease, both to ascertain amounts due them and to account to their royalty owners. Practically every producing lease has two or more tanks so that wells can produce into one while oil is being run to the pipeline from another. If natural gas is sold from a lease—other than temporary sales to drilling rigs—it is usually measured by an orifice meter.

The sales of oil from a lease in any given month, however, may not accurately reflect production because of variations in the amount of oil on hand at the month's end. Gas sales are a true measure of gas production of a lease if the lease is connected to a gas system; but as gas is still flared in many fields, either because it cannot be profitably gathered or no outlet is available, these figures are frequently incomplete. Finally, lease produc-

Fig. 9—Arrangement for Individual Well Gaging of Small Wells, Bartlesville Pool about 1910

Notice swing pipe for maintaining oil-water level.

935

tion statistics do not provide information on individual well behavior except on the occasional lease with only one well.

Before the advent of petroleum engineering, the main value in individual well gages was to the production foreman, and many years ago he adopted the test-tank idea. Fig. 9 illustrates the crude early methods devised by the industry. As the foreman was responsible for obtaining the maximum production from every well every day, he wanted to know how much oil, gas, and water his wells were producing. Abnormal changes in oil or gas production or flowing pressures, or increases in water production might warn of the end of the flowing period of a flowing well or early exhaustion of the oil and gas reservoir; or they might reflect failure of the water shutoff* or a leak in the casing, the correction of which would require a redrilling job or "workover". Individual well gages found their most common use, however, in signalling the need for repair or replacement of the pumping equipment in a pumping well.

Beginning in the "teens", individual well gages of oil, gas, and water gained new importance. Such problems as diagnosing trouble and planning well repair work, designing efficient lifting methods, developing methods for securing maximum primary recoveries of oil and gas from reservoirs, applying secondary-recovery programs and estimating reserves, all became the recognized responsibility of the petroleum engineer and their solutions required accurate knowledge of individual well behavior. In the late 1920's, when proration was introduced, state regulatory bodies began to issue orders in terms of allowable well productions. This made it necessary to adopt measures for obtaining individual well production data.

In such fields as Long Beach, Santa Fe Springs, Dominguez, Ventura, and others with great sand thicknesses which promised long lives and high ultimate recoveries, California operators found it economically possible to install a separator, a gas meter, and two gage tanks for each well. Similar systems were also used in some Gulf Coast fields, such as Sugarland, and even in the East Texas Field in the early days. These installations provided accurate data and were highly desirable from the petroleum engineer's point of view but, generally speaking, were too expensive for fields of the Mid-Continent and Southwest which produced from smaller reservoirs and besides in recent years have produced under rigid proration.

For a long time it has been common practice to install an extra or test separator at a battery of lease tanks for testing individual wells. By manifolding the flow lines, each well periodically can be turned into the test separator and a separate tank, and its production of oil, gas, and water measured. A typical installation of the 1940's is shown in Fig. 10, and

---

*A term used years ago to describe the shutting off of waters above the oil and gas sand with casing, whether by formation shutoff or cementing.

Fig. 10—Typical Lease Battery Showing Flow Lines, Manifolds, Dirty Oil, Clean Oil, and Test Separators, Gun Barrel, Lease Storage Tanks, and Gas Vent Lines—Friendswood Field, Texas, about 1940

is in great contrast to the early gage tank pictured in Fig. 9. Here, oil and gas from 21 wells flow through individual flow lines to the manifolds to make up the bulk streams. Actually, clean (so-called pipeline) oil and dirty oil are segregated at the manifolds, clean oil going directly through the "clean" separator (center) to the stock tanks, and dirty oil through the "dirty" separator (left) and the gun barrel to the stock tanks. The complete system of manifolding makes it possible for the switcher to divert any well to the test separator (right) for individual measurements of gas and oil production—as often as, and for as long as the switcher considers necessary. Switching, sampling, temperature reading, tank gaging, and changing of gas meter charts are manual operations.

Fig. 10 illustrates other points of interest in handling oil on a typical lease. Some wells require artificial lift and the small manifold in the foreground enables the switcher to admit and regulate gas under pressure for gas lifting of certain wells. Also, the drum and pump for chemicals used in treating dirty oil appear in the right foreground. Finally, the system of gas vent lines connecting the domes of all tanks is clearly visible.

The importance of well production data has prompted both operators and manufacturers to devise special equipment for obtaining them— always with the limitations of cost in mind. One development of recent years employing the manifold system is the horizontal gas-oil-water trap. The single-barrel form is shown schematically in Fig. 11, but a double-barrel type is also available. Such traps are suited to small flowing or pumping wells. The flow from the well to be gaged is diverted by the manifold to this separator, entering at (A). Differences in specific gravities cause the fluids to separate. A float-operated liquid-level control pilot (B) operates the water draw-off valve (F) and this, together with an oil discharge pipe of predetermined height, maintains a constant oil-water level. A pressure-regulating valve on the gas discharge line (C)

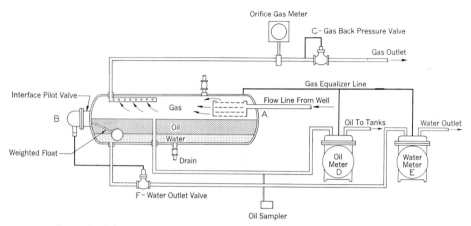

Fig. 11—Schematic Drawing of 3-phase Separator for Small Wells

holds enough pressure in the separator to force the oil and water through their respective meters (D) and (E), and the oil to the stock tank. Displacement meters are generally used to measure the liquids and even the gas, but if the gas volume is large enough, an orifice meter is substituted.

Fig. 12 illustrates a different scheme for measuring production. Here an elaborate battery of separators with automatic dump-type fluid meters and orifice-type gas meters was installed to measure the oil and gas production of flowing and gas-lift wells. This installation was erected in the Conroe Townsite, Texas, where each well is on a different lease and has to be

Fig. 12—Separators, Dump-type Fluid Meters, and Orifice Gas Meters for Individual Wells—Conroe Field, Texas

measured separately. Metering makes possible the handling of production of 35 wells in 5 tanks instead of 70.

In the Big Foot Field, Texas, Shell Oil Company has installed a battery of homemade low-cost displacement or dump-type meters for small pumping wells which use the same principle as the meters shown in Fig. 12. These meters have two compartments and float-actuated valves which cause one compartment to fill while the other dumps. The volume of fluid produced by a well is measured by means of calibration and a counter. These meters gage total fluid, the oil and water production being determined by a shakeout.

Metering separators first became available about 1935. The simplest is the two-phase type which separates

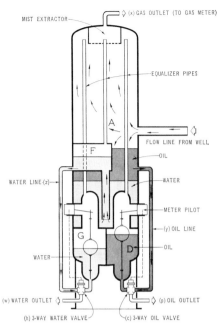

Fig. 13—Schematic Drawing of Modern Metering Separator

and measures gas and liquids; but an improved type—known as the three-phase metering separator—separates gas, oil, and free water and measures all three. The three-phase unit, shown schematically in Fig. 13, consists essentially of a separating chamber and two liquid dump-type meters built into a single shell. The flow from the well enters the separator section (A) where gas separates and is led off through a mist extractor and line (x) to an orifice-type gas meter. Free water drops to the lower part of the separator section (A), oil and any emulsion collecting on top of the water. The float-controlled three-way valve (c) allows oil to flow from (A) through line (y) to the oil meter chamber (D) which, when full, dumps through the three-way valve and line (p), the oil volume being measured by the number of dumps. While the meter chamber is dumping, valve (c) remains closed against line (y) and the oil builds up in separator section (A). As soon as meter chamber (D) is empty, the three-way valve (c) closes against line (p) and opens to line (y) to permit oil again to flow from the separator, thus starting the next measuring cycle.

The water cycle operates similarly. A separate chamber, or water box, (F) collects water (the oil and water levels in (A) and (F) being controlled by their respective differences in specific gravity), and the cycle of emptying through line (z) into meter chamber (G) and measuring proceeds in the same way as in the oil meter.

The metering separator is particularly adaptable to well testing although if the oil is of such character as to emulsify badly, the accuracy of the meter is impaired. Average or composite samples must be taken and the volumes of oil and water adjusted after a shakeout. The metering separator is finding favor on offshore platforms where space is at a premium.

In summary, because of the cost, neither individual separators and gage tanks nor modern metering devices are commonly installed for each well, no matter how much the petroleum engineer and production man may need the data they make available. On the other hand, test separators at each tank battery with manifolds on the flow lines are in general use; and if the field staff is properly trained to take systematic and frequent individual well tests, and such tests are correlated with lease production, the operator can closely estimate the daily productions of his wells.

The subject of measurement of production of wells is a live one at the present time and is a part of the general program of automation which is discussed later in this chapter.

PREVENTION OF EVAPORATION LOSSES

Early Studies

The U. S. Bureau of Mines is generally credited with focusing the attention of the petroleum industry on the enormous losses in dollars and irrecoverable products from evaporation. As early as 1915, or within the first year of establishment of the Petroleum and Natural Gas Division of the Bureau, its technologists were thinking about evaporation losses and means for their prevention.

In his annual report for the fiscal year ended June 30, 1915, the Bureau's director mentioned that A. G. Heggem, a petroleum engineer, was beginning a study of precautions to be taken to prevent and methods to extinguish fires at wells and tanks in Oklahoma, Texas, and Louisiana. He further stated that Heggem's report would include discussions of the design and construction of tanks and the losses of oil by evaporation during storage.

In 1916, the Bureau reported that C. P. Bowie—another of its petroleum engineers—had begun an investigation of various methods of storing petroleum, and that his report would contain data on losses of oil in storage caused both by evaporation and seepage. Bowie's *Bulletin 155: Oil Storage Tanks and Reservoirs,* was published in January 1918, and referred to the large quantities of hydrocarbon products that "vanish into thin air" in a single year from wells, transportation systems, storage farms, and refineries. He presented estimates of losses from wooden roofed tanks in different parts of the Mid-Continent area, and compared the losses from "standing storage" consisting of wood-roofed tanks with losses from steel-roofed tanks at Port Arthur, Texas, and in other terminals. Bowie also discussed various devices for lessening evaporation losses, such as water-sealed roofs, sprinkling systems, gasometers for collecting light gases from batteries of gasoline tanks (anticipating the "breather" and vapor-recovery systems to follow), and various types of tank coverings including tile and concrete.

Others were also interested in this subject. In 1917, Gardener[26] published results of tests on the heat-reflecting properties of colors applied to oil and gas storage tanks. His initial laboratory tests showed that aluminum paint gave the least rise in temperature when subjected to the rays of a carbon arc. In 1921,[27] he reported that the lighter the paint color used, the lower the temperature rise and the less the loss by volatilization in small tanks exposed to the sun.

In 1918, Bradley[28] discussed the losses by evaporation that took place during the period of flush production in the Cushing Field, Oklahoma. Because storage space was at a premium, water in the oil, which would settle, was promptly drawn off at the bottom to create additional storage space. This space was utilized by refilling the tanks to the very top with fresh oil (called "topping out"). Throughout these operations, absorbed gas in the oil was allowed to escape. In 1924 the same kind of emergencies brought on similar practices in the Long Beach Field, California, and doubtless this was common practice in the early or flush days of most large oil fields before proration became effective.

Until some time in the 1930's, it was common practice to allow oil to stand in well or lease tanks long enough to "weather" or "settle" before making a "run" to the pipeline. Settling, weathering, topping out, and similar practices were indisputable evidence of the industry's acceptance of the loss of light products to the air, even at that late date.

About 1919 the Bureau of Mines announced its intention to make a systematic effort to obtain all possible data regarding evaporation losses from oil in storage. J. H. Wiggins, then an assistant petroleum engineer, was assigned to begin studies in the Mid-Continent area. He was to attempt to determine as accurately as possible what losses were taking place by evaporation from the well to the refinery and what practical measures could be applied to reduce or eliminate them.

Wiggins, who was soon to be recognized as a leading authority on the subject, interviewed many engineers, superintendents, and managers of producing, pipeline, refining, and natural-gasoline companies. He learned that, although many of them were aware of the problem, few had any clear ideas of the physical principles involved or of the monetary losses from evaporation. The effects of temperature changes, vapor pressures, and other factors which caused the lighter hydrocarbons to escape from crude oil were largely unknown or not recognized. Some stated that the oil "settles" or that the gas "gets out of the oil" in some manner. However, almost everyone was anxious for the Bureau to evolve a standard method for determining the amount of these losses, and many were far-sighted enough to hope that the Bureau would find ways and means of reducing or preventing them.

The first paper by Wiggins was *Bureau of Mines Report of Investigations 2118* of May 1920. In it he pointed out the effects of filling tanks with overshot connections as against those with bottom connections. He also compared evaporation losses from small, unprotected tanks on leases with those from small tanks having protection such as shading or air-tight jackets. Finally, he presented data showing the effects of storing in what were then considered large tanks, (i.e., 55,000-bbl) with and without so-called gas-tight roofs.

Wiggins' second paper, *Report of Investigations 2236*, in April 1921, compared the losses from a test battery of "open" lease tanks having customary sheet-steel roofs equipped with two 8-in. gage holes on opposite sides of the roof and an 18-in. open manhole in the center, with those from a tank having only one 4-in. vent and with those from a third tank having only "pinhole" vents. The results were so revealing that operators and manufacturers alike began to give serious thought to the use of gas-tight tank roofs.

Probably Wiggins' *Bureau of Mines Bulletin 200: Evaporation Losses of Petroleum in the Mid-Continent Field*, which was published in February 1922, was the medium that did most to alert the industry to the real seriousness of the problem. In the meantime, Ludwig Schmidt, assistant to Wiggins, wrote an article that was published in the Mid-Continent Oil and Gas Association *Yearbook* for 1922, entitled "The Use of Vapor-Tight Tankage in Oil Fields".[29]

Later Schmidt, in a formal bulletin, presented a simple exposition of the theory of evaporation and the principles that govern its rate.[30] Evaporation was defined as the change by which any petroleum fraction is converted from the liquid or solid phase to the vapor phase. Applying the molecular theory, Schmidt explained that petroleum—like all liquids —is composed of molecules in ceaseless motion. These are constantly colliding with one another, and some are flying off the liquid into the space above it. Because increased temperature increases the activity of molecules, it increases the evaporation rate. Therefore, heat from the sun on tanks causes increased evaporation. Increased pressure decreases evaporation. Renewal of unsaturated air or gas over the surface of the liquid increases evaporation. But containment of saturated air or gas by vapor-tight tank roofs capable of withstanding some pressure tends to cause a balance to be reached between flying molecules leaving the liquid and those leaving the vapor and re-entering the liquid and thus reduces evaporation. These principles, of couse, had long been recognized by physicists and engineers.

942

Meanwhile, oil companies had begun investigative work of their own. In 1923, Standard Oil Company (New Jersey) established a committee to study evaporation losses. It found that losses of gasoline stored in large, dark-colored tanks were 4 percent higher than in tanks painted in light colors. About the same time The Pure Oil Company, after studies and tests by its engineers, concluded that aluminum paint was the most efficient type for reducing evaporation losses and the company adopted this type of paint as a standard for its crude oil, refined products, and even its bulk-station storage.[31] These early findings led to widespread use of aluminum paint for tanks in all branches of the petroleum industry, which use continues to this day.

Others were studying the effects of tank colors, water-seal roofs, and gas-tight roofs to reduce the flow of unsaturated air over the oil surface; and tank builders began to offer tanks capable of withstanding some pressure.

Evaluation of Evaporation Losses

During these early days, investigators were seeking methods of quantitatively evaluating losses by evaporation. Volumetric measurement was the obvious one because traditionally the oil industry measured its products in that manner. However, volumetric measurements involved the difficulties and inaccuracies of tank strapping, effects of uneven and progressive settling of tanks on their foundations, expansion and contraction of tank steel, and temperature corrections for the oil itself. Even a temperature correction had to be made for the change in length of the steel gage tape. An error of 1/16 in. in a gage reading in a 55,000-bbl tank caused an error of 10 bbl. An error of 1 deg in oil temperature amounted to 25 bbl. Thus was emphasized the problem of determining the true average temperature of the oil in a tank.

Engineers also turned to measurements of physical characteristics of the oil before and after evaporation as a means of measuring losses. Calculation of the loss from changes in gravity was one method. Specific-gravity determinations of average samples could be made at 60 F, and thus avoid the errors of temperature corrections; but the method depended upon securing true average samples, and this was difficult. Besides, laboratory equipment had to be used to minimize errors.

Fractional distillation of average samples taken at the beginning and end of the test period was another method. By plotting distillation curves, the losses were revealed. But again, this method had the disadvantages of requiring laboratory equipment and, of course, of obtaining true average samples.

Finally, measurements of the change in vapor pressure of average samples, taken at the beginning and end of a test period, were proposed by the Bureau of Mines, which stated that such measurements were of

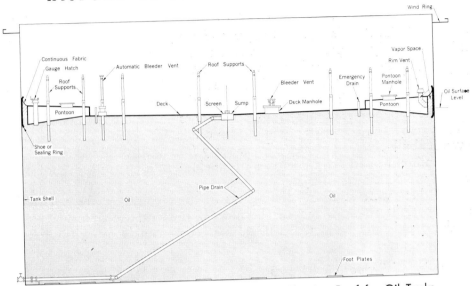

Fig. 14—Schematic Drawing of Pontoon-type Floating Roof for Oil Tanks

the very characteristic that caused the oil to evaporate. Stauffer, Roberts, and Whitman[32] developed a dependable method about 1930; but again, laboratory technique was needed, and the old question of the average sample had to be met.

No method of loss determination was foolproof, but the several methods developed in the 1920's were accurate enough to give investigators a good idea of the order of magnitude of the losses, and they knew they were justified in prosecuting their studies.

In the survey of 1919, Wiggins had reported that the average loss from crude in flow tanks, lease tanks, and gathering systems was $4\frac{1}{2}$ percent; and by the time the crude oil had stood in tanks at pipeline tank farms and was delivered to the refinery, the loss totaled $6\frac{1}{2}$ percent. Schmidt estimated that by 1931 the industry had reduced evaporation losses of crude oil from wells to refineries to 3 percent. A test on operating leases showed a reduction of evaporation losses from more than $3\frac{1}{2}$ percent to less than 1 percent by the use of vapor-tight tanks. Schmidt thought that the average loss from large storage tanks had probably been reduced to one-half the former figure. Even so, the annual volumetric loss of light fractions continued to be enormous.

Methods of Preventing Evaporation Losses

While Wiggins and his associates were studying the subject of evaporation losses, he was evolving a novel idea as a remedy. This was the "floating roof" shown in Fig. 14—a roof that actually floats on the surface of the oil as its level rises and lowers in a tank. By eliminating the vapor space—and therefore the opportunity for air to come into contact with the oil, emptying and filling—wind-drift and temperature-change losses are largely eliminated.

The Chicago Bridge and Iron Works took over fabrication and marketing of the floating roof in the early 1920's, and thousands of floating-roof tanks have since been installed throughout the world. In fact, this type of roof is in general use on large tanks although it is seldom installed on small lease tanks because of the high cost per barrel of storage space.[33]

By the late 1920's producers began to develop equipment and operating practices of their own to reduce evaporation losses. Some deliberately passed dry gas through the vapor space of flow tanks and recovered the gasoline which it absorbed in their field gasoline plants. Others pulled a "vacuum" on separators to extract gasoline from the crude oil, recovering it in natural-gasoline plants. About 1926 the Shell Company of California installed in some of its newly discovered fields in California, the first complete oil-field vapor-recovery systems of which there is record. It was the company's practice to equip each of its large flowing wells with high- and low-pressure separators and two 250-bbl well (gage) tanks. Both high-pressure and vacuum gas-gathering lines took gas from the separators to nearby natural-gasoline extraction plants. To prevent evaporation losses, Shell manifolded all of its vapor-tight well tanks in a battery and connected the manifold, through pressure-regulating valves, to the vacuum gas-gathering system as well as to the field fuel-gas system. When tanks were filling, saturated gas in the vapor space was expelled to the vacuum line, which took it to the field natural-gasoline plant. When tanks were emptying, dry gas from the fuel system was admitted to prevent pulling in the tanks. This dry gas would become saturated with light vapors and later would carry them to the gasoline plant.

This system was highly satisfactory from the point of view of conservation and for furnishing daily measurements of oil, gas, and water from each well, but was too expensive to be adopted by the industry in areas where margins of profit were lower than in California.

Over the intervening years many operators have used adaptations of this system, including vapor-tight tanks and headers—with breather valves—which connect all tanks in a battery. The vapor driven from the tanks during the interval of filling partly fills the vapor space created in tanks being run to the pipeline.

Wiggins worked on two other innovations which he hoped would be less complicated—viz., the diaphragm roof[34] and the so-called steel balloon.[35] The diaphragm roof was a steel roof for large tanks constructed with "slack" in it so the roof would raise and lower to change the volume of the vapor space and thus prevent breathing losses. It was intended for

945

large tanks and standing storage, and as it would not accommodate the changes in volume of vapor resulting from filling and emptying, it had no application on the producing lease.

The steel balloon was a bellows-like affair, both the top and bottom of which moved freely as vapors entered or were expelled. A balloon was installed on a battery of tanks at a refinery in West Tulsa, Oklahoma, in 1930. The system was vapor-tight at all times and, within limits, provided gas storage for the tank battery. But the balloon found no application on the lease.

By the early 1930's, oil companies were installing various vapor-saving devices—mostly in tank farms and at refineries. There is a record of a vapor-recovery system at the Beacon Oil Company refinery, Everett, Massachusetts, as early as 1922, and another at the Cosden Refinery at Tulsa in 1925. Similar systems were installed in 1933 at the plant of the Globe Refining Company, McPherson, Kansas, and at the tank farm of the Reagan County Crude Oil Purchasing Company in Big Lake, Texas.[36]

Over the years, other ideas have been advanced for decreasing evaporation. A floating foam known as "Sealite" was developed by Frank A. Howard, Clarence I. Robertson, and James M. Jennings of the Standard Oil Company (New Jersey) in 1922.[37] Sealite was a "gaseous emulsion" that was poured on the surface of oil in a tank in quantities large enough to make a covering about 1 in. thick. Although Sealite was effective in reducing evaporation losses, it would last only about one year if not disturbed. It appears that difficulties were experienced in making this water-soluble foam stand up, probably because it was broken by agitation during filling. Besides, it was difficult to keep it out of lines, pumps, valves, and other parts of a pipeline. It never gained widespread acceptance in the industry and, moreover, was not suited to the daily filling and emptying of lease tanks.

A recent invention by the staff of Standard Oil Company of Ohio was described in a paper presented at the annual meeting of the American Petroleum Institute on November 9, 1953.[38] The authors pointed out that millions of dollars worth of crude oil were still being lost annually through evaporation despite the use of many vapor-tight tanks, floating-roof tanks, and other installations. They proposed to float a layer of tiny hollow plastic spheres called "microballoons" on the surface of the oil to form a kind of foam. They reported that microballoons had been found effective in reducing the rate of evaporation in crude-oil tanks and that they did not damage pumping equipment, meters, or other mechanical apparatus. If they were drawn into the pump and pipeline, they were crushed and finally became a part of the "bottom sediment" in a tank. Microballoons have not been accepted for lease tanks.

Unfortunately, on the producing lease where fresh or volatile crude is handled and all conditions are conducive to evaporation, operators usually cannot afford to install complete loss-prevention equipment because of the limited volumes being handled. Consequently, over the years, they have gradually developed practices which they can afford and which, though not perfect, go a long way toward preventing losses. It has become common practice to install vapor-tight tanks in lease batteries and very often all such tanks are connected into a vapor header provided with pressure and vacuum relief valves. Aluminum paint is used almost exclusively.

Perhaps the latest development in evaporation-loss prevention is a new type floating roof made of material such as nylon, dacron, or other fabrics coated with a polyester resin, which has recently been announced by the Esso Standard Oil Company. The roof is a doughnut-shaped ring with a center membrane. The ring, which is inflated with air, is fitted with a wiper to provide a snug contact with the tank wall. The material itself has characteristics which cause it to resist wear and tear and is not adversely affected by contact with oils and gases. Because of their low costs, these floating roofs, if further testing proves their practicability, would be suited for use on lease tanks.

The attack on the evaporation-loss problem has been one of the industry's most conspicuously successful conservation efforts. In recent years these studies have been coordinated through the API Evaporation Loss Committee, and various companies, including Atlantic, British-American, Humble, Imperial, Shell, and Mobil, have established their own groups to develop practical tools and methods for crude oil and products conservation. Their pipeline engineers, refinery engineers, and even marketing engineers have all played important roles; but the first and greatest losses were recognized at producing leases and here petroleum engineers have long applied their talents.

The ultimate solution of the evaporation-loss problem in the field will probably come with complete automation, as this will involve the separation of oil, gas, and water and their measurement and delivery in completely closed systems.

MEASURING, SAMPLING, AND TESTING

The volume of crude oil and natural-gas liquids produced in the United States each day and measured by American standards is of the order of 7 million barrels. Even in the simplest chain of ownership changes this oil is measured at least twice between the well and the refinery, and part of it is measured three or four times. The volume of crude oil imported into the United States averages about 950,000 bbl per day. Thus, the total volumes that have to be measured probably amount to 20 million barrels per day and the values, not including taxes, to at least 55 million dollars. Products measured by American standards greatly increase these figures.

Over 30 billion cubic feet of natural gas are sold daily, and this is measured at least 3 or 4 times between the well and the consumer as ownership changes. These figures emphasize the importance to the industry and to the public of standard and accurate methods of measuring oil and natural gas and their products.

The science of measuring oil has gradually improved over the years. Until very recently, all oil has been measured in tanks by taking a high gage before running a tank (to the pipeline) and a low gage after taking it off the line, and converting these linear gages to barrels. It is necessary not only to know the capacity of every tank but also its capacity for each foot, inch, and fraction of an inch of height. Tanks are not perfect cylinders and, besides, may not be level. Some are even spherical in shape and some cylindrical tanks are set in horizontal position. Many have appurtenances in them such as roof supports, coils, pipes, spreaders, and so on. Consequently, engineers have always had to measure or "strap" individually every tank used for oil measurement—taking into account the variations which affect volumes. Because of the factors mentioned, strapping is a tedious and imperfect science and in late years the industry has begun to use the liquid-calibration method by which volumes of fluid are metered and recorded against linear gages as a tank is filled or emptied. Tank strappings or volumetric measurements are translated into tank tables to which field linear gages can be applied to determine volumes.

Gas has been measured mostly by orifice meters although, where small volumes are involved, displacement meters have sometimes been used.

With advances in the field of automation, the trend is in the direction of metering oil, gas, and water.

Refiners make deductions for any water in the crude oils they purchase. Besides, as they cannot handle more than small quantities of water in their plants, they place a limit on the amount of basic sediment and water in the crudes they will receive. Usually this is of the order of 1 or 2 percent, although in California it may sometimes be as high as 3 percent when the purchaser runs the oil into his privately owned pipeline. In any event, accurate determination of the amount of sediment, water, and emulsion in oil being sold is a matter of first importance.

Deductions for basic sediment and water have always been made by determining the percentage of basic

Fig. 15—Snap Thief and Running Thief

sediment and water in an average or composite sample and applying that percentage to the tank of oil being run. Any error resulting from failure to obtain a true average sample is magnified when applied to a tank of oil. Early methods of sampling consisted of taking small amounts of oil from nail holes in the shells of wooden tanks and allowing the samples to settle out in glass bottles. Later, petcocks in the shells of steel tanks served a similar purpose.

Soon "thiefs" were developed. The "snap thief", shown in Fig. 15, was designed by the Robinson brothers in 1867.[39] The valve at the bottom was tripped by a line or a chain and the thief, therefore, could be used to obtain fluid samples at any desired level in a tank. A number of samples so taken were combined to form a composite sample.

The "running thief", also shown in Fig. 15, came later. It was made with a restricted opening which caused it to fill continuously as it was lowered through the oil to the level of the pipeline outlet and raised again to the surface. Another type thief consisted of a pipe with a valve in the bottom. It was lowered through the oil and, when lifted, the valve closed and the thief recovered a complete column of fluid from top to bottom.

In late years various types of line samplers have come into use. In principle they are devices which steal a small amount of oil from the stream as it passes through a pipeline.

Various methods have been used for determining the amount of basic sediment and water in a sample.[40] They are: *1*, the early gravity-settling method—with or without artificial heat; *2*, centrifuging—with or without heat; and *3*, water by distillation.

The gravity-settling method is no longer used but centrifuging finds wide application. The oil-field centrifuge stems from De Laval's original patent of 1887,[41] covering the device for separating milk. The hand-operated centrifuge is in general use in the field today. API specifications require the operator to maintain a speed of 1,500 rpm for a period of from 3 to 10 min, depending upon the character of the sample, then to read the percentage of impurities and rotate the sample again before taking the final reading. Because of these requirements and greater capacity, the power-driven machine is favored by pipeline companies and oil refiners.

Distillation has always been recognized as the most accurate method for determining the water content of oil, but of necessity has always been a laboratory method. A further test, known as "sediment by extraction" in which a solvent or demulsifier is added to the oil sample to precipitate solids, is frequently used in conjunction with water by distillation.

As oil expands or contracts with changes in temperature, corrections of volumes of oil being bought and sold are necessary. Early procedures were crude and cumbersome. Before the 60 F standard temperature was adopted, volumes of oil were corrected to "cold" or "normal" temperature. Purchasing companies would even set aside a battery of tanks filled with crude oil for the express purpose of determining cold temperature. The volume of any oil measured at a temperature above that recognized as the cold or normal tank temperature was reduced by one-tenth of one percent for each degree Fahrenheit of temperature difference.

The average temperature of oil in a tank has always been a troublesome factor because, as with the average sample, it is not susceptible of exact determination. Oil temperatures not only vary throughout the day and night with changes in the outside air temperature and as a result of radiation from the sun's rays, but they also vary from top to bottom and from tank shell to center. Methods of taking temperatures have differed over the years, some operators taking one reading and others multiple readings. But an average temperature—by one method or another—must be determined and recorded at the time a tank is gaged preparatory to running the oil to the pipeline, and again at the end of the run. With automation, continuous temperature readings are recorded throughout the run.

Thermometers used today are improved versions of those built centuries ago. All thermometers used in the oil field are the mercury type and are graduated in the Fahrenheit scale. Conventional thermometers have been adapted to field service by mounting them in frames for protection. They usually have a cup at the bottom for retention of a small quantity of oil in which the bulb is immersed. This guards against changes in recorded temperature while the thermometer is being withdrawn and read. In late years other temperature-recording devices, such as those using bimetallic and electrical resistance elements, have come into use.

Gravity (i.e., weight relative to water) has long been accepted as a general measure of the quality and value of crude oil in the field. There are records of price quotations based on gravity as early as February 1, 1868, 9 years after the discovery of the Drake well.[4] For example, it was reported that on that day, oil at Pioneer, Titusville, Petroleum Center, and Miller Farm was quoted at $2 to $2.15 per barrel for 40- to 49-deg gravity delivered on tank cars.*

Most purchasers now determine the values of crude oils on the basis of refinery realizations, but they still quote field prices on gravity schedules. Hydrometers and gravity-correction tables are therefore important to buyer and seller alike.

As reported to the API Symposium on Measuring, Sampling, and Testing Crude Oil and Petroleum Products in 1954,[42] "The principle of hydrometers was known in the time of Archimedes, 250 B.C. He had

---

*Tank cars of that time were flat cars with vertical tub-like wooden tanks mounted on them. Horizontal cylinder-type cars came into use about 1871.

discovered that a floating body sinks until the weight of the liquid it displaces is equal to its own weight. The first information on hydrometers was published by Robert Boyle of England in 1675." ***

"In 1768 Antoine Baumé, a French scientist, designed the Baumé linear hydrometer scales for liquids both lighter and heavier than water. The United States Petroleum Association in 1864 approved and standardized on the Jarvis Arnaboldi-C. J. Tagliabue Baumé-type hydrometers due to their uniformity and accuracy."[43]

The National Academy of Sciences, in 1881, reported differences in the moduli of Baumé hydrometers of different manufacturers, varying from 145.98 to 139.94. In 1904 the Bureau of Standards found the modulus 140 for light liquids in common use, but it was not until 1916 that it recommended this modulus and urged that all nonstandard hydrometers be discarded.[44]

In December 1921 the American Petroleum Institute, working with the Bureau of Mines and the Bureau of Standards, recommended that only the scale based on the modulus 141.5 be used in the petroleum industry, and that it be known as the "API Scale". From that time on, instead of expressing gravities of oil in degrees Baumé, the official and standard designation has been in degrees API.[45]

Observed gravities have to be corrected for temperature just as do volumes. The correction of specific gravity and volume to 60 F apparently dates back to 1764 when George Gilpin[46] of England developed tables on temperatures and specific gravities of alcohol solutions.

In 1916, the Bureau of Standards published *Circular No. 77*, which was based on experimental data from Bearce and Peffer on thermal expansion of American petroleum oils.[47] These tables listed volume-correction factors and true specific and Baumé gravities at 60 F for oils having measured volumes and observed gravities at other temperatures.

In 1924 the Bureau of Standards compiled and published *Circular No. 154*, which listed volume corrections for oil measured at various temperatures between 0 and 99 F in increments of 1 deg. This circular was refined and reissued in 1936 as *Circular C-410*. The tables in both circulars were believed to be more detailed than necessary for oil industry purposes and it became common practice to use abridged tables. In 1954, Tables 6 and 7 of the *ASTM-IP Petroleum Measurement Tables (ASTM D 1250) (IP 200)* replaced Bureau of Standards *Circular C-410*.

Recognizing the petroleum industry's intense interest in the subject of measuring petroleum, the American Petroleum Institute, in September 1928, sponsored a movement to standardize procedures for measuring, sampling, and testing crude oil and petroleum products. President E. W. Clark appointed W. S. Farish chairman of a committee which eventually developed the well-known *Code 25*. Work on the code was

951

divided into two parts, the first, "Tank Measurements and Gage Tables", which was prepared by a subcommittee under the chairmanship of C. A. Young, and the second, "Measuring, Sampling and Testing Crude Oil" by a subcommittee under the guidance of R. P. Anderson.[48]

The first edition of *API Code 25: Tank Strapping and Gage Tables*, was published in April 1929. The second edition was published in January 1931 and included, as Part II, "Gaging, Sampling and Testing Crude Oil". In all, seven editions of *Code 25* were published. The Institute's activities were then reorganized on a broader scale, with the result that a more comprehensive and expanded code was published as *API Std 2500: Measuring, Sampling, and Testing Crude Oil*, 1st Edition, January 1955.

Over the years the American Petroleum Institute has sponsored and developed a number of codes, standards, and bulletins pertaining to the measuring, sampling, and testing of crude oil and petroleum products, and natural gas, the latest editions of these being:

API Std 2500: Measuring, Sampling, and Testing Crude Oil (Supersedes Parts 2 and 3, *API Code 25*, 7th Ed., June 1948), 2nd Ed., March 1961.

API RP 50A: Recommended Practice for Measuring, Sampling, and Testing Natural Gas, 4th Ed., June 1957.

API RP 50B: Recommended Practice for Measuring, Sampling, and Testing Natural Gasoline and Other Light Liquid Petroleum Hydrocarbons, 4th Ed., June 1957.

API Std 1101: Measurement of Petroleum Liquid Hydrocarbons by Positive Displacement Meter, 1st Ed., Aug. 1960 (supersedes 1952 edition of *API Code 1101*).

API Bulletin 1103: Bulletin on Recommended Practices in the Setting, Connecting, Maintenance, and Operation of Lease Tanks (Tentative), 3rd Ed., September 1952.

API Std 2501: Crude-oil Tank Measurement and Calibration (supersedes Part I, *API Code 25*, 7th Ed., June 1948), 2nd Ed., 1961.

API Bulletin 2509A: Bulletin on Lease Automatic Custody Transfer, August 1956.

The industry has made great progress in developing methods and procedures for measuring, sampling, and testing natural gas, crude oil, and petroleum products but it is now working on revolutionary new methods, some of which are mentioned in the following section.

AUTOMATION

The oil industry's theoretical objective in handling its product is to provide a continuous and uninterrupted flow of oil from the well to the refinery and on to the consumer—eliminating all tankage excepting possibly that needed to service the customer. Every time flow is arrested, extra expense is incurred—in the form of capital for facilities to contain the oil, as interest on a dead asset (oil and products) which has been expensive to reduce to possession and to process, and from losses by evaporation.

Rapid strides are being made in this direction by the application of automation in the field, as well as in other branches of the industry. For many years automatic and semiautomatic devices have been used to an increasing extent in operating oil and gas wells. More recently, engineers have developed automatic equipment to measure oil and determine its qualities in the process of changing ownership—an operation now known as custody transfer. In short, as in many other industries, "automation" in the oil-producing industry may be said to be a subject of the hour.

The ideal system is one in which well production and scheduling would be controlled automatically; individual wells would be selected and tested in desired sequence by automatic equipment with the results being transmitted by wire or microwave to a central office where they would be recorded and made immediately available to supervisory personnel and petroleum engineers. The system would also include automatic measurement of volumes of oil and gas sold from a lease, determination of quality and corrections for temperatures and impurities, and transmittal of the data by wire or microwave to machines in a central accounting office which, after applying prices, would furnish amounts owed producers and royalty owners. Suitable equipment to give alarm in the event of malfunctioning would necessarily have to be included.

Engineers already can design equipment that will perform practically all of these functions. But chiefly because of costs and indicated long payouts of some components of automatic systems, today's installations have not encompassed all of the concepts of the ideal or fully automatic operation. However, the science of automation is advancing so rapidly that a development today (1959) may be obsolete tomorrow and, in the long run, it may be expected that many completely automatic systems will come into use.

History

At the time of writing, many devices for automatic well testing are in operation and more than 200 automatic custody-transfer systems are in use or being installed. Some 15 producing and 29 pipeline companies are involved and over 170,000 bbl of oil per day are being handled in these systems—a small amount, to be sure, in comparison with the national production, but a large amount considering the science is only a few years old.

The first experiments in automatic custody transfer of which there is record were made by Shell Oil Company in the Antelope Field, Clay County, Texas, in 1948.[49] Others soon became interested and in November 1955, Imperial Oil Company of Canada installed an automatic system in the Red Water Field of Alberta which had the distinction of being the first to receive governmental approval. Gulf Oil Corporation followed in the Bloomer Field, Kansas, in December 1955, with the first approved automatic custody-transfer system in the United States.

In 1953, Shell began the installation of an automatic system for custody transfer in the Wasson Field, Texas. In January 1957, it added microwave transmission of data to a central office. This installation approached the ideal system, but it also demonstrated some of the weaknesses and excessive costs which have prevented its general adoption. The telemetering parts of the Wasson installation were eventually dismantled as uneconomical, but the installation operates as an unattended system and it has been followed with some 15 installations by Shell and Pan American in the same field.

Meanwhile, Shell was also turning its attention to automatic systems for well control and well testing in fields in Oklahoma, Louisiana, California, and Canada and this phase of oil-field operation soon began to interest others as well.

In 1956, Phillips and Texaco placed automatic custody-transfer units in regular operation. By the present time, it is reported that probably one-third of both Pan American's and Carter's production is being handled through such units.

The American Petroleum Institute, which for 30 years has been a leading force in the standardization of oil-field equipment and methods for measuring, sampling, and testing petroleum and its products, became interested in the new movement about 1952. In 1956, its Committee on Crude-oil Measurements issued *Bulletin 2509A*[50] which, as an informational circular, summarized much of the knowledge on automatic equipment and methods then available on automatic custody transfer. The Institute also sponsored three papers on lease automatic custody transfer that were presented at the annual meeting in 1956,[51] directed primarily to the management and policy aspects of the problem.

In the following pages, oil-field automation is discussed under two general headings—the automatic control of producing wells, including individual well testing; and the automatic measuring of quantity and quality of oil and gas as they leave the lease, and the recording and accounting for them.

954

Automatic Control and Testing of Wells

Engineers have long worked on automatic devices to control producing wells. Chokes—originally the positive type and later adjustable forms, but both manually operated—have been used for 50 years or more to control the producing rates of flowing oil wells. Before the advent of proration, pumping and gas-lift wells were controlled manually with the single objective of obtaining the highest possible production.

Since the 1930's, time clocks have been used for scheduling on-and-off periods for pumping and gas-lift wells with the view of obtaining their maximum productions or their allowable productions (under proration orders) with the least use of power and minimum wear and tear of lifting equipment.

In recent years the time-clock type of control, with motor-operated valves at the well head, has also been applied to flowing wells for meeting proration schedules. This method is used extensively in the East Texas Field where flowing wells may be turned on and off without harm or impairment of their abilities to flow. In Wasson Field, similar controls are used to regulate production or to shut in wells in the event of trouble. So far as is known, there has been no effort to regulate the flowing rates of oil wells, subject to proration, by the use of variable chokes or intermittent flow devices that are controlled by totalizing meters. This operation would be somewhat complicated, and would require the separation and continuous measurement of the flow of oil, gas, and water from every well—control being exercised by the oil meter.

The positive-displacement gas meter is frequently used in well-testing installations and, because of its rangeability, is particularly well-adapted to measuring the relatively small but sometime widely fluctuating gas productions of pumping wells or gas-lift wells controlled by intermitters. This meter actually measures volumes and not differential pressures, as does the orifice meter; and it will measure accurately over a volume range from mere whispers of gas to flows that equal its capacity.

Gas wells which may be regulated by manual changing of chokes or automatically by volume-control regulators usually flow at uniform rates for protracted periods. For many years orifice meters with continuous recording charts have been used to record their rates of flow. The orifice meter is generally less accurate than the positive-displacement meter, but it has greater flexibility because, by changing orifice plates, the same metering installation can be used to measure small flows of gas or, conversely, large flows. Positive-displacement meters to measure large flows are very heavy and expensive and, besides, are not built to measure gas at high pressures such as 1,000 psi or more.

The operators' interest in individual oil-well gaging—or well testing, as it is now called—has been emphasized in an earlier part of this chapter. Shell was probably the first operator to devise automatic well-testing equipment, having begun experiments in 1952. Other operators soon became interested and the technique has advanced to the point that many producers now make unattended well tests.

Basically, automatic well testing employs the now accepted method of bringing the flow lines of a group of wells into a manifold at a tank battery and providing a test separator and meter in addition to the main or bulk separator and meter. Wells are diverted to the test equipment one at a time and their respective productions measured over a test period. The automatic equipment to do this includes a sequencing device or programmer which actuates pneumatic diaphragm or electrically operated valves on the flow line manifold. This sequencing device can be set automatically to select a well for testing and divert its flow to the test separator and meter as often and for as long a test period as desired. Likewise, any desired sequence of testing can be established.

The measuring device for oil may be a positive-displacement meter, a dump tank or dump meter, or a metering separator. Gas is measured by a conventional orifice meter, a totalizing orifice meter, or even a displacement gas meter if volumes are low. Temperature correction of oil volumes is a refinement usually dispensed with in well testing, but water content of the fluid is almost always determined so that well productions can be reported in barrels of clean oil and total water.

Methods of determining the percentage of water in a well's flow vary from a manual "shakeout" of a representative sample—generally obtained by an automatic line sampler—to some form of automatic device for determining water content.

The capacitance cut recorder,[52] in Fig. 16, is such a device. It employs the principle of measuring the dielectric constants of oil-water mixtures. Preferably the probe of this instrument is installed in a vertical segment of the oil line leaving the separator, although in many installations the probe is placed in a horizontal

Fig. 16—Capacitance Cut Recorder (right foreground) with Dump-type Fluid Meter and Spherical Separator (background)

segment of the flow line. The capacitance cut recorder will measure with considerable accuracy the percentage of water in oil-water mixtures up to 65 percent water. In some cases these instruments have been installed in conjunction with meters, the data from the capacitance recorder and the meter being fed back through an integrating computer which records barrels of gross oil (i.e., total oil and water) and clean oil.

Another form of recording device is the differential cut recorder which operates on the principle of measuring the differences in weight of two columns of fluid of equal height; one the actual oil-water stream filling the dump tank, and the other clean oil obtained by filtering a part of the stream to remove the water. The differential gives a direct comparison of the oil in its clean and dirty forms and makes it possible to compute the volume of clean oil passing through the dump meter.

Data from unattended well tests may be recorded on a simple counter on the meter, on a counter on a field panel, or on a ticket or a strip chart. They can also be transmitted to the field office by wire or microwave if cost permits. In any event, as well data are needed at once by the production foreman who has the responsibility of keeping wells on production, they must be readily available for his use. They must also be recorded in a convenient form for use by petroleum engineers.

Actual installations vary from field to field and even from lease to lease, and the one shown in Fig. 17, though not necessarily representative of all types, is one of the most advanced well-testing installations in use today.

Although the economies of some of the advancements in well testing are recognized as being borderline, operators are pushing ahead with experimental and developmental work. The rewards of automatic well testing come from the following:

1. Greater accuracy in measurements.
2. Round-the-clock testing (i.e., continuous use of facilities and more frequent testing of each well).
3. Elimination of human error.
4. Savings in manpower.
5. Reduction or elimination of evaporation losses.
6. Greater safety as to fire, explosion, and asphyxiation.
7. Savings in capital costs through reductions in tankage.

Oil and gas wells are not susceptible to complete automatic handling throughout their lives, and it would seem safe to say that some superintendence will always be required. The need to undertake special work—such as changing worn chokes, changing pump depths, pulling, cleaning out, or redrilling—must still be determined by petroleum

Fig. 17—Automatic Well-testing Installation, Brea Canyon Field, California, Showing (left to right) Spherical Separators, Fluid Meters, Manifolds, Flow Lines, Orifice Gas Meters, and Field Panel Station

engineers or production foremen; and the work itself must be done by maintenance personnel acting under necessary authorities of the management. Automation, however, can furnish the complete and accurate records which will signal such needs.

Automatic Custody Transfer

The movement of oil and gas from the lease to pipelines or other forms of carriers usually involves change in ownership, change in custody, or both. This operation, which is now commonly referred to as custody transfer, requires accurate volumetric measurement, determination of quality and price, and finally, exact accounting in terms of volumes and dollars.

Since the beginning of the industry, tank strapping, high and low gaging, placing a tank on the line, sampling, deducting basic sediment and water, determining gravity and temperature, correcting volumes and gravity to 60 F, pricing, and computing working interests and royalties have all been manual operations—lightened only by the occasional remote liquid-level gage and, of course, the business machine. Today, engineers of a number of companies are developing various assemblies of automatic devices for the performance of many of these functions.

As may be expected of this rapidly developing technique, there is no unanimity of opinion regarding automatic custody-transfer installations. Moveover, excepting experimental units, custody-transfer installations have not reached the point of complete automation. Operators point out that as a lease will always have to be visited occasionally by supervisory personnel, the latter can pick up composite samples and can also collect meter tickets or charts more cheaply than the data can be transmitted by wire or microwave.

Measurements of oil and gas for custody transfer involve some of the same problems met in well testing, but in custody transfer accuracy is the first requirement. This extends not only to volumes, but to corrections of volumes for water content and temperature and to determinations of true gravity. Automatic custody-transfer installations, at the present state of development, have the following essential components:

1. Meters or dump tanks for measuring volumes of oil and gas.
2. Monitor to protect the pipeline against excessive water content of oil being delivered.
3. Composite sampler.
4. Gas eliminator (when needed).
5. Automatically controlled motor-operated valve to shut down the system if there is malfunctioning of equipment or if it "runs out of oil".
6. Alarm or telewarning devices.

Fig. 18 is a schematic flow chart of an automatic custody-transfer system which is being used with success. In this system—as indeed with all others—the flow from the wells passes through one of the usual arrangements of separators, heaters, and gun barrels (not shown) which removes gas and water, and delivers oil in merchantable condition (i.e., basic sediment and water content of less than 1 percent) to the float or surge tanks (A). From the surge tanks the oil is pumped through a line containing a capacitance cut monitor probe (3). The capacitance instrument monitors the stream for basic sediment and water by the

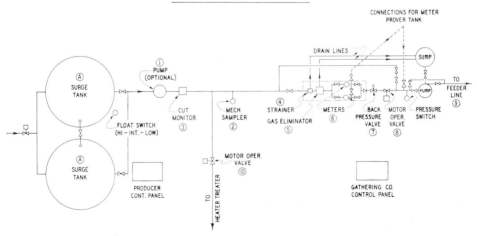

Fig. 18—Schematic Layout of Automatic Custody-transfer Installation

Fig. 19—Lease Automatic Custody-transfer Unit in the Four Corners Area, Utah, Showing (left to right): 1, Booster Pump; 2, Sampler; 3, Monitor in Background; 4, Strainer; 5, Gas Eliminator; 6, Meters; 7, Back-pressure Valve; 8, Motor-operated Valve; and 9, Pipeline

dielectric method. If the basic sediment and water content is below 1 percent, the cut monitor maintains valve (8) in the open position so that deliveries are made to the pipeline (9), through the strainer (4), gas eliminator (5), and temperature-compensated meters (with ticket printers) (6). If the basic sediment and water content reaches or exceeds 1 percent, the cut monitor closes the motor-operated valve (8), and opens valve (10), causing the stream to recirculate through the heater and gun barrel for the purpose of reducing the basic sediment and water content to the required level. The mechanical sampler (2) is designed to collect a true average sample over the period of the run.

Fig. 19 is a photograph of an automatic custody-transfer system which delivers oil from a lease in the Paradox Basin of Utah to the Four Corners pipeline. With one slight difference the systems depicted in Fig. 18 and 19 are alike. Experience has led to the elimination of the recirculating system (shown in Fig. 18) because, if the oil-cleaning facilities do not reduce the basic sediment and water content to less than 1 percent, recirculating will overload the gun barrel or heater-treater and they may not be expected to deliver pipeline oil to the custody-transfer unit. The monitor (3) is retained in these systems, however; and if the cut reaches 1 percent, it will close the motor-operated valve (8), shutting off deliveries and lighting a warning light. Necessary corrections in oil-treating facilities are then made by the field personnel, the oil from the wells accumulating in the surge tanks meanwhile.

Thirty or more installations of the type just described are in operation in various fields of the United States.

Experience has shown that, up to the present time, all automatic custody-transfer systems require some kind of tankage to level out surges and insure a constant stream to the meters or measuring tanks and to hold incoming oil for a time if anything goes wrong. Frequently, some of the existing tanks on a lease are converted to this use.

Temperature-compensated positive-displacement meters are preferred by most engineers for oil measurements. Such meters may have ticket printers or only counters. They must be checked periodically for accuracy by some form of calibration or test unit. Other engineers prefer the dump tank for volumetric measurement, an actual installation of which is shown in Fig. 20. This device operates on the principle of filling one calibrated vessel while a second is emptying, the cycle being controlled by floats. A temperature recorder is always used with the dump tank. A refinement of the ordinary dump tank is the "dump meter" (Fig. 21) which uses a temperature compensator and eliminates the need for recording temperatures and subsequently calculating the temperature correction. The dump meter uses a small measuring vessel and has a cost advantage over dump tanks.

An essential component of lease automatic custody-transfer systems is the meter prover which, as its name implies, is a device for making periodic checks and calibrations of the meters. Volumetric meter provers are small tanks which are calibrated with great accuracy. The volume of oil recorded by the meter is compared with the true volume as established by the prover and the meter correction factor is calculated. The gravimetric prover actually weighs a volume of oil which has been metered. By applying the specific gravity measured by certified hydrometers, the true volume is calculated. This type of prover is used in areas where paraffin or other substances may be deposited on the walls of a tank-type prover and thus affect its accuracy.

Fig. 20—Dump-tank Installation for Automatic Custody Transfer

Fig. 21—Dump Meters with Temperature Compensators

Accepted practice is to provide a meter prover capable of receiving the normal throughput of the line for a period of at least one and preferably two minutes. However, as provers must be portable, their capacities are limited and this, in turn, tends to limit the size of meters used in the system. Actually, the 2½-in., 240 gal. per min positive-displacement meter, which will measure up to 8,230 bbl per day of throughput, is about the largest now in use. If, on the occasional lease, more capacity is needed, the operator usually installs dual meters which can be checked by his prover and which have the added advantage of providing partial capacity in the event of meter disorder.

Some operators are giving consideration to the use of master meters which are portable and can be readily connected in series with working meters for checking their accuracy. A master meter must be calibrated with a portable or fixed tank-type prover.

A late development in the oil meter field is the turbine-type flow meter which uses a rotating vane actuated by the flow and is calibrated to reflect volumes in barrels. This meter had hardly passed the experimental stage at the time of writing (1959).

Proration is now an accepted practice in the oil industry and state regulatory bodies are strict in its enforcement. Therefore, a trend has developed in automatic custody transfer toward installing totalizing equipment on oil meters which will shut down lease deliveries when they reach the "allowable".

The capacitance cut recorder or the differential cut recorder are accepted as being accurate enough to protect the pipeline against oil with more than 1 percent water, but until now have not been used for custody transfer. Most operators still collect composite samples with an approved form of line sampler and rely on the usual shakeout for basic sediment and water determinations. It is reasonable to expect that cut recorders will eventually be developed which, in conjunction with temperature-compensated meters, will record barrels of net oil at 60 F. This will eliminate sampling, manual tests for basic sediment and water, and manual temperature readings and corrections which, with volumes, are essential elements of a transaction involving a transfer of ownership of oil.

Automatic gravity recorders are available, and some are in use but they are delicate and expensive. Their use, so far, is largely confined to making batch (tender) switches in pipelines. Most operators still rely on manual gravity readings of composite samples for custody-transfer accounting, but here again, gravity recording instruments will doubtless be perfected and eventually will be accepted in custody-transfer operations.

As the producer has customarily provided necessary tankage for the delivery of his oil to the pipeline and as the first savings from automatic custody-transfer equipment are from reductions in storage and lease facilities, automatic equipment is generally installed at the producer's expense. However, automatic custody transfer has already progressed to the point that some pipeline companies have developed policies in connection with their installation and operation. For example, one pipeline company offers to provide portable meter-prover equipment and to make periodic calibrations of meters, also to check automatic controls and instruments or equipment used to determine properties of the oil. It further has declared its willingness to maintain and service these facilities, if requested by the producers—all at the producer's expense.

In automatic custody-transfer operations, gas from conventional separators is still measured almost exclusively by orifice meters with two pen charts which require planimeter readings. There is some trend, however, toward the improved-type meter which, by automatic integration, totals the amount of gas that has passed in a given interval.

Development work has been under way for some time on a gas meter of entirely different principle than the orifice meter. In this new meter, passing fluid (gas) is rotated and the mass flow rate is determined by measuring the resultant torque on a stationary member. Another form of gas meter is the turbine meter which employs the simple principle of a propeller in the gas line.

The positive-displacement gas meter is not in general use for custody transfer of gas, although it will measure accurately up to its capacity and may be obtained with totalizing equipment. The relative adaptabilities of positive-displacement meters and orifice meters have already been discussed.

Necessary adjuncts to unattended well-testing installations, as well as to automatic custody-transfer equipment, are suitable alarm systems. As the name implies, these devices sound an alarm or light warning lights whenever there is improper functioning of the equipment. In the interests of economy, alarm signals frequently are given at control panels in the field but they may be transmitted by wire or radio to the office. The latter is desirable because there they are most likely to be seen or heard by supervisory personnel.

As mentioned before, data from unattended custody-transfer systems are still gathered manually in most cases, because meter readings, for example, are not needed more often than once a week or once a month; and these infrequent requirements will not support the cost of expensive wire or microwave transmission systems just for that purpose.

Data on volumes, cuts, temperatures, gravities, and prices are usually fed to computing machines on punched cards in about the same manner as before the advent of automatic custody-transfer systems.

Regulatory bodies charged with jurisdiction of oil and gas measurements have been slow in permitting the use of these new techniques and have adopted the policy of requiring them to be proved as to accuracy and dependability before approving them. But by now, certain automatic custody-transfer units have been approved by regulatory bodies in Alberta and Saskatchewan, Canada, as well as by commissions in Kansas, Illinois, Louisiana, Montana, New Mexico, Oklahoma, and Texas. Likewise, the Department of the Interior of the United States Government has approved certain installations. Units operating in California and Utah do not require state approval.

The reduced expense, improved accuracy in measurement, and savings from evaporation, which automatic well-control and custody-transfer systems promise, are leading to their adoption by many companies, although it is recognized that they may not be justified in fields in late stages of depletion. Some of their advantages even apply in foreign operations despite cheap labor, and most of their advantages would seem to apply offshore where operating costs are high because of expensive transportation and the need to maintain personnel at sea.

Petroleum engineers, pipeline technologists, and oil and gas accountants have all contributed to automation and results to date testify as to the success of their efforts.

HANDLING PRODUCTION OFFSHORE

General Statement

The first offshore oil-field operations in the United States were at Summerland, Santa Barbara County, California. This field was discovered in 1886 by a well drilled on a cliff 250 ft above the Pacific Ocean.[53] Some time later, in the period 1890-94, development spread to the beach and into the ocean where the drilling rigs were supported by wharves of light piling. The longest wharf extended 1,230 ft from shore. By 1906, there were 200 shallow producing wells at Summerland but even the comparatively mild storms of the Pacific played havoc with the wharves, and high costs coupled with low production discouraged further development.

Some time later, fields in coastal waters in Texas and Louisiana, such as Goose Creek, though not offshore by today's definitions, gave operators some insight into offshore production problems.

Beginning in the late 1920's, California operators again drilled wells in the Pacific Ocean from piers in the Rincon and Elwood Fields. In 1932, one well at Rincon was drilled from the first offshore pile-supported platform of which there is record. The most impressive operations, however, came in the 1930's at Huntington Beach and Wilmington, where major development campaigns were conducted by directional drilling under the ocean from shore locations.

British American, Pure, and Superior drilled two wells off Cameron Parish, Louisiana, in the late 1930's, but the real beginning of offshore operations as presently understood began in 1948. By then, oil men began to realize that submerged lands in the Gulf of Mexico and off the California Coast offered virgin hunting grounds and they naturally turned to them as the incidence of discovery on land—as well as the depth and size of discovered reserves—became less favorable.

Over the past 12 years about 2,700 wells have been drilled in the offshore areas of Louisiana and Texas,* of which 1,800 were producers. Daily production rose from nothing to 169,000 bbl of oil and almost 800 MMcf of gas in the same interval. Expenditures for offshore exploration and development, including lease bonuses, are estimated to have exceeded $2,000,000,000. This remarkable growth has taken place despite such unfavorable factors as extremely high costs, rigid proration of production, and obstacles to leasing and development resulting from a running controversy between the states and the Federal Government as to ownership of minerals underlying coastal waters.

The basic requirements of separating and measuring oil, gas, and water in offshore fields are the same as onshore. Offshore operations, however, have created a whole new series of problems heretofore unmet by the oil operator—onshore or even in inland waters. In contrast to the land operator, who can easily set a test separator and tanks for a production test of a wildcat well, the offshore operator must find space on the drilling platform for the test equipment and then barge the oil to shore. If a new well is drilled with a mobile unit, no platform is available and even the testing of a well becomes difficult and expensive. Finally, if a wildcat well indicates commercial production, the operator cannot simply tie into an oil or gas pipeline and begin to sell his production for only in a few areas have marine lines been laid.

Space for separators, dehydrating equipment, manifolds, meters, storage tanks, and other producing equipment is necessarily limited in area and of high cost. Special facilities must be rigged to dispose of gas because of the dangers of fire and asphyxiation on platforms.

Operating and supervisory personnel cannot "drive" over the property with usual speed and facility, but must depend upon surface vessels and aircraft for transportation—both for themselves and for material. Even the safe transfer of personnel between boats and structures—particularly in rough weather—presents a problem unmet on land. Workmen cannot live in the nearest town and walk or drive to work each day; but because of time and expense in reaching the job, must be accommo-

---

*Statistics as of January 1, 1959. Figures do not include California where practically all offshore production has been from near-shore areas and recovered from wells directionally drilled from shore locations and wells drilled and serviced from piers.

dated in living quarters that have to be created at sea. Usually crews have to remain at sea for days at a time.

In the beginning, operators naturally turned to barging as a means of transporting produced oil, just as land operators resort to trucking when no pipeline is within reach. This method is still used to move oil from single wells, such as successful wildcats, and from fields where pipelines to shore have not been or cannot economically be built. But bad weather and high seas reduce effective barge time to an average of about 20 or 25 days per month in the Gulf of Mexico and this encourages the laying of pipelines as soon as the reserves and volumes of daily production will justify them. Gas, of course, cannot be moved at all except through marine pipelines leading to shore.

Thus, waves, weather—including tropical storms, working space, limited storage, transportation, communications, living arrangements, fresh-water supply, corrosion, safety of personnel and equipment from fire and explosion, pollution, insurance, and resultant high costs all raise special problems in handling offshore production.

Types of Offshore Installations for Production

The type of installation used for drilling has an important bearing on subsequent production operations. Offshore wells have been drilled from four kinds of supports: The drilling platform supplemented by tender, the latter carrying pipe, mud tanks, auxiliaries including electric generating equipment and crews' quarters; the self-contained platform which is large enough to support the drilling rig, auxiliary equipment, material storage, and crews' living quarters; the mobile unit which carries the drilling equipment, pipe storage, mud tanks, auxiliary equipment, and crews' quarters, but which is floated and towed to a new location once drilling is completed; and the floating drilling barge which is now coming into use.

In the early years of offshore operations, the drilling platform and tender were often preferred for exploratory wells because, unless a mobile unit could be found to drill by contract, the first cost of this arrangement was lowest. If a wildcat well came into production, the operator installed a separator and one or more small tanks on the drilling platform, and emptied the oil from the tanks into barges by means of a hose and gravity flow. Gas associated with oil was flared at a safe distance, but gas wells had to be shut in to await a pipeline. Many of these platforms are in use, the one shown in Fig. 22 being equipped to handle the production of 2 wells that were drilled from it.

The self-contained platform, which is much larger and more costly than the drilling platform, is sometimes installed for wildcat drilling but finds its greatest use in proved fields. An operator may drill 5 or 10 directional holes from one platform. Frequently, these are dual, triple, or even quadruple completions and one platform, therefore, may serve as many

Fig. 22—Tender Platform with Production Equipment and Tanks and Well Heads of Two Flowing Wells—West Delta Block 20 Field, Louisiana

as 20 to 40 "wells". These platforms are large and manifolds, separators, gas meters, well-testing equipment, and oil storage tanks of limited size may be erected on them. As illustrated in Fig. 23, it is not unusual to conduct producing operations on these platforms while drilling is still in progress.

Fire walls are frequently installed on self-contained platforms to protect personnel and property from fire and explosion. However, the practice of producing, separating, and measuring oil and gas, storing oil, drilling new wells, and housing men—all on the same platform and all at the same time—is recognized as involving great risks and present trends are towards erecting a separate platform for the crews' quarters.

A platform is not required for drilling with a mobile unit or floating drilling barge and this raises some very special problems. If production is found, the well is usually tested by temporarily setting up a separator and tank on the pipe racks of the mobile drilling unit. Owners of mobile units discourage this practice, however, because of the fire hazard; and operators themselves are inclined to limit such tests to a few hours because of the high cost of "rig time". Sometimes the operator will bring a barge alongside the mobile unit and flow a well into it—the separator

967

Fig. 23 (left)—Aerial View of Self-contained Platform in Grand Isle Block 47 Field, Louisiana, on which Producing Operations Were Being Carried out While Drilling Was Still in Progress. Later converted to a production platform.

Fig. 24 (below) Conventional Well Jacket with Foghorns and Lights

being on the mobile drilling unit, but this is also a costly procedure as the drilling unit is tied up for the test period.

Following the test of a successful wildcat, the mobile drilling unit is moved off and the operator drives a pile cluster or, more often, installs a prefabricated steel structure known as a "well jacket" (Fig. 24) or a caisson to protect the well head and to carry navigation warning devices. These structures are too small to carry separators and tanks and a producing well must be shut in after its initial test to await additional producers and the establishment of large enough reserves to justify a production platform.

The operator's decision as to whether to continue development of his new field with mobile units or by directional drilling from a self-contained platform has an important bearing on the methods employed in handling production. The mobile-unit plan generally leads to the installation of "satellite" platforms, such as the one shown in Fig. 25, where separating and well testing are done, and a "mother" or production platform where bulk streams are separated and measured and from which oil shipments are made. Recently, elevated well jackets (Fig. 26) have been designed to carry a separator and meters, or a metering separator for well testing, and a helicopter deck. Such well-jacket installations may

Fig. 25 (left)—Block Station or Satellite Platform in Block 27, South Pass Area, Louisiana

Fig. 26 (right)—Elevated Well Jacket with Helicopter Landing Deck and Section Carrying
Low-temperature Separation Unit and Navigation Warning Devices
West Cameron Block 192 Field, Louisiana

eliminate the need for satellite platforms, but they must be used with some kind of mother platform because they cannot support storage tanks for accumulating barge lots of oil, or pumps and compressors for shipping oil and gas ashore through pipelines.

If, following the completion of a wildcat well with a mobile unit, the operator elects to install a large platform for drilling development wells, deck space is created for manifolds, separators, tanks, and meters and the problem of handling production immediately becomes much simpler.

The separate production platform, despite its cost, is growing in popularity. Such platforms vary in type and design from small tender platforms which may carry separators, well-testing equipment, and limited storage for one or two wells (Fig. 22) to the elaborate installations shown later in Fig. 28 and 29. There is no such thing as a cheap platform and the owner of an offshore discovery well drilled with a mobile unit or floating barge is always confronted with the difficult problem of deciding when a large investment for a production platform is justified.

Barge Operations

As mentioned earlier, the very nature of offshore operations results in extremely high capital costs which, in turn, restrict working space, limit field storage, and retard the installation of pipelines. Consequently, operators attempt to use barges as a transporting method unless a pipeline is within reach.

969

The most elementary use of the barge is to flow a well which has no platform directly into the barge, the separator being set on the barge deck. This is attempted from time to time when the operator is faced with the necessity of producing some oil to "save" a lease or fulfill a contractual obligation, or possibly to confirm the productivity of a well before making an additional large expenditure. But experience has shown that this use of a barge can only be made in periods of calm seas which virtually restricts it to protected waters. Lost producing time and the narrow field of usefulness render it impractical as a regular operating method.

Early in offshore operations barges were used to transport oil from wells which had separators on their platforms but little or no storage. The barge would be moored to the platform and the well produced directly into it through a hose from the separator. When full, a tug would bring an empty barge alongside and tow away the full barge. Sometimes the full barge would be turned loose while the new barge was being secured, the full barge later being "chased down" by the tug. Such operations also can be carried out only in relatively calm seas and are pretty much restricted to protected waters.

The most common use of barges is to transport oil from a well which has platform storage, or from a field which has a central production platform with storage. Arrangements are made for a tug and barge to come by at regular intervals to pick up the oil. Barges are held in place during filling by the tug, aided by a mooring line to dolphins or to the platform. Because platform storage is necessarily small, the time required to empty such storage is short and the tug can afford to stand by, then move the barge to the next location. Again, weather is the chief deterrent to these operations and when seas are too rough for loading barges, the operator may be confronted with full storage and the necessity of shutting in his wells.

One arrangement which has been devised to overcome the need for platform storage is the so-called "carousel buoy" and accompanying production barge. Flow lines from producing wells are laid on the ocean floor to the buoy which is well anchored. The production barge is moored to the buoy. A hose connection between the carousel buoy and the production barge is made through a swivel on the buoy which permits the production barge to swing with the winds and tides through a full 360-deg arc. As weather permits, the transporting agency brings an oil barge alongside the production barge and makes a hose connection. Oil is pumped from the production barge to the carrier's barge with pumps mounted on the production barge. A small back pressure is usually held on the production barge so that malfunctions, such as line or hose breaks, will cause automatic equipment to shut in the wells and prevent serious oil losses and pollution.

Oil delivered to barges is generally measured and netted for custody transfer from tanks at offshore locations. Barge operators, who are often contract carriers, may check such deliveries by gaging their barges. Official volumes are allocated back to wells on the basis of well tests.

By and large, barge operations inevitably lead to interruptions of producing schedules of wells in open waters. These are reduced if the operator has several days storage at sea—which he seldom does. Most operators would be glad to discontinue barging if a pipeline to shore could be justified or if a connection to an existing marine pipeline could be arranged.

Operations in Offshore Fields Served by Gathering Systems and by Pipelines

As time has gone on certain fields and groups of fields have justified the laying of marine oil and gas lines. Also, several fields in Louisiana and in California have been found near shore, and there the cost of pipelines is low enough that separate gas and oil lines have been laid to shore.

In remote offshore fields marine lines frequently perform a more varied service than the usual gas or oil line. For example, in gas-distillate producing areas, it is common practice to separate the gas and distillate at the well or production platform, dehydrate the gas, measure the gas and distillate with meters, recombine the streams, and transport them ashore in the marine gas line. At the shore terminal the gas-distillate mixture is again separated and, depending upon contractual arrangements, the gas may or may not be measured again. The distillate, however, is gaged in tanks or metered for delivery to purchasers who, in turn, transport it by pipeline, tank-truck, or barge.

Similarly, pipelines from oil-producing fields far offshore may be used to transport oil or oil-water mixtures or mixtures of oil and gas. In the latter operations, oil and gas are usually separated offshore for measurement, then recombined and flowed ashore under separator pressure (i.e., well pressure). Eventually, as wells decline, it becomes necessary to pump the oil into the line and compress the gas from the separator pressure to the necessary line injection pressure.

There are many variations in these practices and operators adapt their methods to the facilities available, taking into account the respective volumes of oil, gas, and water to be handled. But by and large, the custom is to separate and measure oil and gas offshore, recombine, transport, and separate and measure again for sale on shore—allocating the net amounts back to wells and fields on the basis of well tests.

All of these operations—whether delivering to barge or pipeline—require day-by-day attendance by field personnel, and have sharpened the operator's interest in automatic devices which can switch tanks, test wells, and shut in wells in case of full storage or failure of equipment. Completely automatic field operations are not common offshore but rapid strides in that direction are now being made.

Miscellaneous Offshore Problems

Aids to Navigation

The offshore operator is faced with an unusual problem that has never bothered the onshore producer, viz., meeting the requirement of the United States Coast Guard to maintain lights and foghorns on offshore structures.

If a structure is manned, the lights can be turned out by day and the horns blown only during periods of low visibility, such as those caused by fog, mist, or rain.

On unmanned structures, warning lights—which are run off special batteries that last for months—can be set to burn only at night or during the dark periods of storms as their switches are actuated by light intensity. However, foghorns, which are generally powered by diesel engines, must operate continuously.

Transportation and Communication

Materials and equipment for offshore operations must be transported by boat and personnel by boat or helicopter.

Several types of craft are in use. The slower and less-expensive lugger-type boat is used by switchers and roustabouts engaged in field operations. Crew boats of from 35 to 80 ft in length and with speeds of 15 to 25 knots are used for transporting crews to and from shore. These boats also handle light cargo such as bits, drums of oil, commissary supplies, and so on. Heavy equipment must be transported in cargo boats which are up to 140 ft in length and cruise at speeds of 8 or 9 knots. These craft are designed with maximum deck space for pipe and heavy equipment and with tanks in their holds for diesel fuel, fresh water, and drilling water.

Oil operators occasionally own some boats, but by and large they contract for marine transportation.

Transportation for offshore drilling operations is much more expensive than for land operations, running as much as $1,000 per day per drilling well. Marine transportation to service producing operations is also expensive because the producer must provide transportation to and from shore and operate boats in the field—both to transport personnel and material and to stand by in case of accident or other emergency. If a large field is being operated, these costs are not excessive when considered on a unit basis, but boat hire for a single well or small field can be extremely burdensome.

Helicopters have come into great favor in recent years and are credited with important reductions in manpower requirements and expense. Moreover, their usefulness in times of emergency is appreciated by men working at sea. Their initial cost and operating costs are relatively high, however.

Satisfactory means of communication must be maintained for off-shore operations. Almost never can an offshore field be connected to a wire (telephone) system. The FM radio has been almost universally adopted as it has been found to be economical and reliable. Platforms, boats, shore stations, and even automobiles and city offices of offshore operators are usually equipped with radio and ready communication is accepted as a part of the overall operation.

Radio channels are fairly crowded and the oil industry, some years ago, set up the National Petroleum Frequency Coordinating Association to receive applications for new channels. After studying local conditions, with the view of minimizing interference, the Association makes recommendations to the Federal Communications Commission, and its recommendations are generally accepted.

Microwave is used only to a limited extent at the present time, but as it provides multiple circuits, including remote-control circuits for automatic field operations, it may be expected to find wider application in the future.

Corrosion

Corrosion, sometimes called the cancer of American industry, is an extremely important factor in offshore operations. Salt water, humid atmosphere, salt-water spray, and alternate immersion and exposure at tide levels are conditions conducive to rapid corrosion. Corrosion is much more of a problem in permanent steel structures used during the producing life of a field than in drilling structures which are moved after the completion of a well. This subject, therefore, is of great concern to the offshore producer.

Submerged structures and pipelines, including those below the mud line, are susceptible to cathodic protection. Both sacrificial anodes and rectifiers are used with some success. Structures, lines, and equipment above splash levels or essentially in atmospheric areas, are protected by the usual methods—sand blasting, protective coatings, and, last but not least, constant maintenance.

The tidal levels of offshore structures are subject to greatest attack and are perhaps the most difficult to protect. Double plating (i.e., extra layers of steel) and sheathing with monel metal are measures most commonly used. Wrought iron and concrete have also been used to some advantage.[54] Double plating has the disadvantages of high original cost and excess weight. Monel is expensive and is subject to mechanical damage, but it is light and will withstand the corrosive action of sea waters.

It is not feasible to estimate the effect of corrosion on costs offshore as compared with costs onshore; but, excepting those occasional shore fields with highly corrosive waters and gases, the offshore operator again finds himself at a pronounced disadvantage.

This problem is under constant study by engineers and advancements in protection may be expected.

Offshore Allowables

All domestic operators in recent years have felt the pinch of restricted production caused by world oversupply, and the offshore operator has been no exception. In fact, because of the high costs of drilling and producing offshore, the hardships of proration are magnified.

At least two regulatory bodies have recognized that special consideration must be given to offshore producers in order to make them competitive. Louisiana, the state with the most important offshore fields, permits shallow offshore wells to produce at rates about twice those of onshore wells of comparable depth. Part of this advantage is lost in deeper wells as the ratio declines to about 1.7 to 1 at 10,000 ft, and 1.5 to 1 at 15,000 ft.* The Federal Government usually adopts the rules of the state commission.

A "spell of weather" which is frequently encountered offshore, can shut down a field for hours or days. This almost never happens onshore. As early as 1948, the Louisiana Department of Conservation recognized this problem and since then has permitted operators to make up production lost for "reasons peculiar to offshore operations", over a succeeding 30-day period with the limitation that no well produce at a rate higher than 125 percent of its allowable. Recently, the department further relaxed this rule by permitting up to 150 percent of the daily well rate and a makeup period extending over the entire succeeding quarter. Depending upon the time of lost production, this allows producers from 3 to 5 months to make up production.

Examples of Offshore Producing Operations

The following pages present discussions and photographs of several different types of offshore facilities for handling and measuring oil and gas production. These examples bring out some of the operating practices that have been developed by various producers and emphasize the ingenuity that has been shown in using every physical installation to the best advantage.

Block 126, Eugene Island Area, Louisiana[55]

The field, which is owned by Mobil Oil, Continental, and Newmont, is a piercement-type salt dome some 30 miles offshore and in about 40 ft of water. It has been developed from 12 self-contained and tender-type platforms shown schematically in Fig. 27. As many as seven holes have

---

*Approximate ratios in mid-1959. Subject to monthly change.

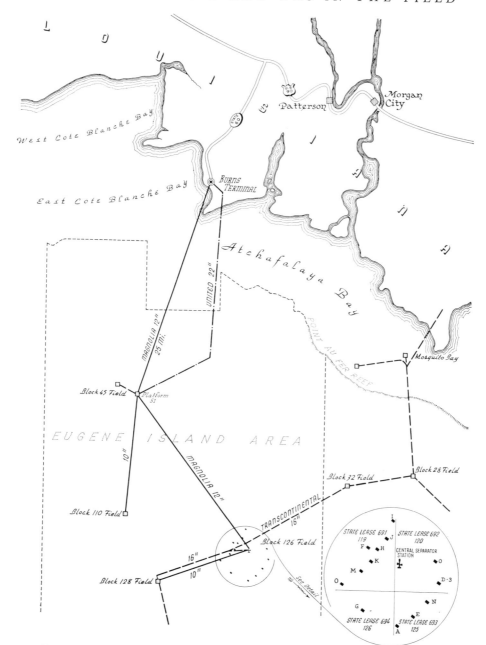

Fig. 27—Map of Eugene Island Area, Offshore St. Mary Parish, Louisiana

been drilled from a single platform and many wells are multiple completions. At the end of 1958, daily production from 78 completions (53
holes) was averaging about 9,500 bbl of oil and 6,300,000 cu ft of gas.

975

The 12 well platforms carry free-water knockouts and sand traps for wells that need them and provide working space for well pulling, cleaning out, and workover operations. Practically all wells have their own 3-in. flow lines to the central separator platform upon which are located chokes, manifolds, separators, and meters. Exceptions are a few wells that produce sand or water in troublesome amounts; these are choked on the well platforms. Thus the control of producing operations, including well testing, and the separation and measurement of oil, gas, and water is on the central separating and measuring platform and not on the well platforms. This concentration of well-control activities greatly reduces the switcher and boat requirements and, therefore, operating costs.

The central separating and measuring unit, which is pictured in Fig. 28, comprises the separator platform mentioned; a second platform with two 5,000-bbl working-storage tanks; a third with pipeline pumps, compressors, and electric generating units; and a fourth with living quarters. All are connected by a series of bridges which serve as walkways and pipe supports.

Fig. 28—Central Production Unit, Block 126 Field, Eugene Island Area, Louisiana
Left foreground—5,000-bbl storage tanks; left background—separating and measuring platform; right foreground—pump, compressor, and generating platform; right background—crews' quarters

The large number of separators—some 32 in all—and the complete system of manifolding enables the operator to direct each well's flow through a bulk production separator or a test separator and meter. Separators operate at pressures of 1,000, 600, 300, and 30 psi. Wells with enough pressure are directed to the 1,000-lb separator and others to the highest pressure separators into which they will flow. As wells decline in flowing pressure, they are diverted to the next lower pressure separator. Oil from high-pressure wells can pass through as many as four stages of separation, thus minimizing the loss of natural-gas liquids.

After separation the oil flows through meters to the 5,000-bbl tanks from which it is pumped into a 12-in. line to a shore terminal (see Fig. 27).

Originally, the absence of a market for the gas resulted in its being flared. In November 1959, a gas purchaser's transmission line was extended to Block 126 and now gas from the high-pressure separators is directed through glycol dehydrators and delivered for sale. Gas from separators operating below transmission-line pressure must be boosted. The operator also plans to compress part of the low-pressure gas for use in gas-injection projects in the field.

As it was intended originally to transport both oil and gas through the pipeline to the shore terminal, the multistage separation plan was devised—not to increase the efficiency of separation, as the gas and oil flows were to be commingled in the pipeline after measurement, but to reduce the horsepower required for gas compression. Now the emphasis is on efficiency of separation and the multistage separators are of great advantage.

The test separators are set to operate at the separator pressures at which the wells on test flow, day by day. As oil from wells flowing into 1,000-lb separators will carry over much more gas than oil from low-pressure separators, the positive-displacement test meters must be calibrated—using one of the test tanks which can be seen in Fig. 28—for mechanical errors and for vaporization which occurs when the pressure on the oil is reduced from the separator pressure to atmospheric pressure. Wells are tested from 1 to 4 times a month, over periods of from 4 to 24 hours unless they are observed to be changing in producing characteristics, in which event they are tested more often.

Although some wells produce water with the oil, the use of free-water knockouts on the well platforms ahead of the chokes largely prevents the formation of emulsions. Later, if water and emulsion should become a major problem, chemicals will be injected into the flow lines or dehydrating facilities will be installed on the separator platform. Paraffin formation in the flow lines is sometimes bothersome and necessitates cleaning with a solvent when pressure drops become excessive.

Safety to life and property in the event of fire, explosion, or mal-functioning of equipment, has received greatest possible attention in this installation. Some of the safeguards are: *1,* dual relief valves on the separators and relief valves on the flow-line headers, which discharge gas to the vent line in case of excess pressure; *2,* "high liquid-level controllers" in the separators and storage tanks, any one of which will actuate control valves on the headers and on the oil lines to the storage tanks, backing up oil in the system and closing down the entire platform—and even the wells; and *3,* low-pressure shut-down valves on the oil line to shore which close in the event of a line break and minimize the loss of oil into the sea.

In addition, 11 quick-opening valves are located at convenient points on the separator platform and walkways, the manual operation of any one of which—by an escaping attendant, for example—will release the instrument air pressure, thereby closing the diaphragm-operated valves (air-opened, spring-closed) between the headers and separators, thus shutting down the entire platform.

High-low pressure valves have also been installed in the flow lines at the well heads of gas wells and high-pressure oil wells to shut in those wells if a flow line should break. Storm chokes, which close when the differential pressure across them becomes too high, have been set in the tubing strings of most wells. Although these tend to cut out with sand, or even to sand up, they are used as an added precaution unless experience in individual wells proves that it is impractical to maintain them.

Carbon dioxide extinguishers and a sea-water system comprise the fire-fighting equipment.

The costliness of this operation is apparent, but it is further evidenced by the necessity of maintaining commissary and living quarters at sea for 20 to 30 men. The complement includes a foreman, switchers, roustabouts, pump and compressor operators, utility men, a welder, a mechanic, boat crews, and a galley crew of six. In this field, men generally are on duty six days and off six days. Two stand-by boats with crews are maintained for transportation from the central separator platform to well platforms and for emergencies.

It should be noted that even with this elaborate installation, only 10,000 bbl of platform storage, or slightly more than one day's production, is available. If the operator had to depend upon barge transportation there would be many shut-down days for the wells.

It is clear from the foregoing description that the problems of operating this one 53-well offshore oil field are many times those of a similar field on land and, as may be expected, the costs are much higher.

Other Fields in Eugene Island Area

Mobil, Continental, and Newmont also own wells in Blocks 128, 110, and 45 (Fig. 27) in the Eugene Island area, and have connected them in such manner as to make full use of the 12-in. oil line to shore.

Twenty-one wells in Block 128, some 10 miles southwest of Block 126, flow through sand traps and water knockouts into 2 production and 4 test separators on a central production platform in that field. Oil and gas are separated and measured and the streams are recombined for movement through a 10-in. 2-phase line leading to the Block 126 central separator platform. There the combined streams are again separated, the gas being dehydrated and delivered to the gas-transmission line and the oil being pumped ashore through the 12-in. oil line.

Blocks 110 and 45 are approximately 15 miles and 22 miles, respectively, northwest of Block 126. The owners have connected wells in these blocks to a platform at Block 51 which is served by the 12-in. line (Fig. 27). Production from these fields is separated, metered, and recombined on the respective field platforms, then delivered to Block 51 where the gas is again separated and sold to a transmission company and the oil is injected into the 12-in. line.

Oil from all of these fields, including Block 126, is measured and reduced to net oil at 60 F at the shore terminal, and volume distribution is made to the several fields on the basis of field meter readings and well tests.

Block 129-A, Eugene Island Area, Louisiana

This block is operated by Ocean Drilling & Exploration Company and comprises six oil wells (nine completions) on three platforms. Each well platform is connected to the central production unit, shown in Fig. 29, by a 6-in. bulk flow line, a 3-in. test flow line, and an electric cable which provides power and control circuits.

Well-control valves, dual chokes, chemical (for emulsion breaking) pumps, and manifolds are on the well platforms; but separators, well-testing equipment, and measuring devices are at the central unit. Oil is transported to shore by barge and gas is sold to a gas-transmission company.

The central production unit, consisting of a separator and storage platform, a quarters-control platform, and a third small structure to carry the gas-vent lines, is perhaps more unusual in design than in operation. The main platform is comprised of three horizontal cylindrical tanks set on steel piling, and they serve both as oil storage tanks and as structural members in the platform. The deck across the top of the tanks carries the manifolding, separators, and well-testing equipment, as well as fresh-water storage and a crane.

Fig. 29—Central Production Unit, Block 129-A Field, Eugene Island Area, Louisiana

The second platform carries the crews' quarters, the control equipment, and the machinery room in which are located the electric generating units.

Great savings were achieved by fabricating, rigging up, piping, and wiring these units onshore and setting them with a single lift on their pile foundations—already prepared at sea. Platforms are set 50 ft above mean Gulf level and are designed to withstand 45-ft waves and 125-mile winds—specifications that are commonly accepted for Gulf installations.

Day-to-day operations on the well platforms are performed remotely from the control house on the quarters-control platform. These include opening up or shutting in wells, switching chokes, switching wells to the test flow lines, starting or stopping chemical pumps, and controlling navigation warning devices. All separating and measuring operations, however, whether bulk or test, are conducted on the separator and storage platform and barges are likewise loaded there.

Block 24-27 Field, South Pass Area, Louisiana

This field, owned by Shell, though near shore, is large enough and its mode of operation distinct enough to warrant discussion.

All of its 355 oil wells have been drilled by mobile units—either of the inland-barge or mobile drilling platform type—and all wells are protected by pile clusters or well jackets. Originally flow lines were laid to manifolds on block stations (Fig. 25) where gas and oil were separated and measured and individual wells were tested. Gas was vented and the oil, both clean and dirty, was directed to a central production platform. Oil was pumped ashore through a pipeline and shipped from a shore terminal up the Mississippi River by barge.

As development progressed, an oil trunk line and a gas-transmission line were laid to the field, and important changes were made in oil and gas-handling facilities. Today production flows as before to the block stations through individual flow lines. The block stations, although relatively small in area, are elaborate enough to justify Shell's present designation of "production platforms". The lower deck, which is 5 ft above mean Gulf level, is used for boat landings and manifolds (see Fig. 25). The second deck—some 30 to 40 ft above water level—carries electric generating equipment and a production office; and the top deck, at 50 ft above mean Gulf level, carries the separators, test equipment, and oil and gas meters.

Horizontal gas-oil separators are commonly used and a platform may have as many as four separators, viz., high-pressure, intermediate-pressure, low-pressure, and test. Gas from the high-pressure separators, except that used for gas lifting of wells, is taken ashore and delivered to a gas-transmission company's line under well pressure. Gas from the other stages of separation is taken ashore and compressed for delivery. All gas to be sold is dehydrated ashore just before delivery but it is not processed for gasoline because of its low liquid content.

The operator has installed facilities on some platforms for segregating clean and dirty oil. These grades are taken ashore in separate clean and dirty-oil gathering lines, the dirty oil being led to heater-treaters where chemicals are added when needed. So-called "pipeline oil" is delivered to the line from storage tanks that were erected in the days of barge loading.

Royalty accounting to the state government and Federal Government for oil sold is made on the basis of volumes determined by conventional tank gages at the shore terminal, corrected for cut and temperature. Gas accounting is on the basis of conventional orifice meter readings at the shore delivery point. Reports to the Louisiana Conservation Commission are compiled by allocating the net oil and gas sold back to the wells on the basis of well tests.

Today's methods of handling production have largely eliminated the need for the central production platform which was erected some years ago, but it is understandable that the field's large production and its nearness to shore could have brought this about.

Grand Isle Block 47, Louisiana

Continental, Atlantic, Tidewater, and Cities Service (known as the CATC Group), have converted a self-contained platform with nine wells—some of which are dual and triple completions—into a production platform. This platform is also the gathering point for wells on four surrounding self-contained platforms. A fire wall separates the well heads and the oil-handling facilities. The platform is pictured in Fig. 23, before the completion of drilling.

Well testing is carried out on the outlying platforms by means of metering separators and orifice gas meters. Wells are automatically programed on each platform and the results are recorded on charts. All well platforms have their own electric power generators to furnish power for the automatic equipment and for operating aids to navigation.

This installation does not provide separate flow lines from individual wells to the central platform but instead, a single 6- or 8-in. line carries the combined streams of gas, oil, and water from all of the wells on each outlying platform (including those on test) to the central platform. Eleven large metering separators with counters and 11 orifice gas meters on the central platform measure the oil and gas from the outlying platforms and from the producing wells on the central platform. After separation and measurement, the streams are recombined and transported ashore by pipeline.

Crews live on the central platform and this is an example of housing men on a platform which carries well heads and production-handling installations.

There are no longer any tanks on the central platform except those used for meter calibration.

Treating (in heater-treaters), final separation, and measuring is done at the shore terminal and net oil and gas production is allocated back to the wells on the basis of well tests.

West Delta Block 30, Louisiana

This field is of unusual interest as it provides an example of cooperative action by three companies which are using automatic measuring in the field and automatic custody transfer ashore for determining their shares of oil and gas produced and sold. This operation signals future trends in oil and gas handling.

Three operators, Continental (for CATC Group), Humble, and Humble-Shell (joint ownership) own and operate wells in this field, the arrangement of platforms being shown schematically in Fig. 30. The CATC Group has six production platforms (A to F, inclusive, Blocks 44-45), the combined bulk streams from each of them being led to a central production platform (G), as in Grand Isle, Block 47. Well testing is done on the individual platforms by metering separators. The bulk

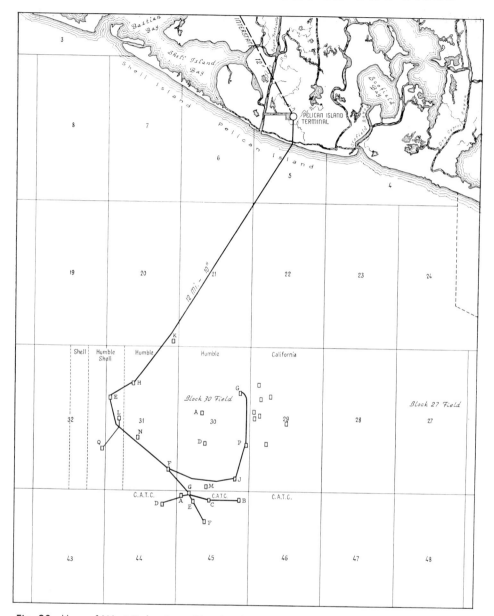

Fig. 30—Map of West Delta Area Showing Locations of Platforms, Gathering Pipelines, and Pelican Island Terminal

streams are sampled and measured by metering separators and orifice meters on the central platform and then recombined and delivered into a gathering pipeline.

Humble, with four platforms on which measuring equipment is

983

installed, and Humble-Shell with three, test their wells and measure their bulk streams in much the same manner.

As Humble owned the gathering system serving its platforms and extending to a shore terminal on Pelican Island, the CATC Group and Shell arranged through purchase of an interest in the system, for their production to be transported ashore through the line. This gathering line carries a common stream of oil and gas in two-phase flow. At the terminal oil and gas are separated, the oil being delivered by automatic custody transfer to purchasers and the gas being sold to a gas-transmission company.

This arrangement has raised some unusual problems that have been met by a business agreement among the three operators. As mentioned, all of the oil delivered to the gathering system is measured at the respective platforms under pressure by metering separators or automatic positive volume measuring tanks. The gas is measured by orifice meters.

The volumes of oil delivered by the oil pipeline at the shore terminal are allocated back to each operator on the basis of his deliveries from the platforms after adjusting for solution gas and water. Finally, because the gravities of oil vary, accounting is made to each operator in dollars. Despite the somewhat complex nature of the operation and the accounting, the economies fully justify the arrangement.

The history of Block 30 Field includes a disastrous fire in late 1958, on the CATC Group's E platform. At that time, the E platform was serving both as a drilling and production platform. In addition to the production handling equipment and an active drilling rig which was undertaking a quadruple completion, the E platform carried the well heads of 7 single, dual, triple, and quadruple completions, or a total of about 20 wells. Flow lines from four outlying platforms converged on the E platform where they connected directly to the line leading to shore.

This fire, the cause of which has never been fully determined, was the most costly in offshore history and probably one of the worst in American oil-field history. It was finally brought under control by drilling several wells to the producing zones being drained and killing the flows of the burning wells by pumping in water, mud and cement.

Losses included the drilling rig and other equipment, crews' quarters, costs of repairing the platform, costs of relief wells, and costs of reworking the producing wells. Moreover, production from all other CATC Group platforms was lost for several weeks, because, as mentioned, their flow lines converged on the E platform and the other platforms had to be shut down. Interestingly enough, all of the producing wells were saved by reworking, although at great expense.

Gas-distillate Operations, East and West Cameron Areas, Louisiana

The CATC Group owns several gas-distillate fields in these areas, each of which has been developed by wells directionally drilled from a single tender platform. An exception is the Block 192 Field which is large enough that 4 drilling platforms have been used.

Shell also has holdings in Block 192, 8 holes with 10 gas-distillate completions having been drilled from a self-contained platform, and 5 wells having been drilled with mobile units.

All gas-distillate wells in this area were shut in until late 1958, when Tennessee Gas Transmission Company completed its 26-in. marine line to a central point in Block 47, East Cameron area, together with gathering lines to the several outlying platforms.

In general, CATC's procedure is pretty much the same in all of its fields. Well heads and producing facilities are installed on the platforms used for drilling (Fig. 31), and at each of these platforms the operator produces gas-distillate, separates, knocks out water, dehydrates the gas, measures the dry gas for sale, and recombines the gas and distillate

Fig. 31—Gas Separating and Dehydrating Equipment on CATC Group Tender Platform in the Block 192 Gas-distillate Field, West Cameron Parish, Louisiana
Well heads are visible between separators.

streams for transportation ashore. Water from the knockouts and from the gas dehydrators is disposed of at the platforms.

One interesting development is illustrated here. To make greatest use of the one expensive pipeline into the area, the operators have included requirements in their gas contracts that the gas-purchasing company transport the distillate ashore in its line. At the shore terminal the gas and distillate are again separated, the gas company retaining the dry-gas stream and the operators taking possession of the distillate. In this operation, the gas, which has been dehydrated in the field, is measured and sold to the gas company in the field (i.e., offshore). Distillate is not measured in the field but only at the shore station after final separation. It is allocated back to wells—and therefore, to fields—on the basis of well tests.

Shell has a somewhat different arrangement of equipment in Block 192. A separate platform was installed adjacent to its well platform (see Fig. 32) for gas processing and dry-desiccant dehydrating equipment. The flow lines from the 7 wells (10 completions) on the original drilling platform, which also carries the crews' quarters, lead to the heaters and processing equipment on the new platform. Chokes are installed on the downstream side of the heaters to prevent freezing.

Other Shell wells, which have been drilled with mobile units, are equipped with well jackets that have elevated deck sections to support low-temperature separating units, as shown in Fig. 26. Gas and distillate are separated and the gas is dehydrated in the low-temperature units,

Fig. 32—Shell Platforms, Block 192 Field, West Cameron Area, Louisiana
Left: Self-contained platform with crews' quarters and helicopter landing deck, electric generating equipment, fire-fighting equipment, etc. on top deck and well heads on second deck (not visible). Right: Platform carrying gas-processing equipment.

the water being dumped into the sea. The dry gas and distillate are metered, recombined, and led to the processing platform shown in Fig. 32. At this platform the combined gas-distillate streams from these individual wells become a part of the bulk stream and, as such, are again separated, dehydrated, and metered before recombining for transportation ashore in the gas-transmission company's line. The first separation and dehydration at the individual wells are to prevent freezing in the flow lines, and the measurements of the separated streams are to provide individual-well production data. Separation and measurement a second time at the processing platform are to enable the company to measure its bulk stream from the field by master meters.

As with the CATC Group, Shell sells dry gas in the field to a gas company, and requires the gas company to transport the distillate ashore where it is again separated from the gas, measured, and allocated back to the wells in the field on the basis of well tests.

Block 10 Field, High Island, Texas

This field is of interest in that it furnishes an example of completely unattended offshore field operations. Production and gathering of gas and liquid hydrocarbons from the field are controlled by microwave from a station onshore some 26 miles distant. There are seven gas-distillate wells in this field, all owned and operated by Mobil Oil Company and located on one platform. This platform also carries the production and control equipment.

Each well stream is individually measured at wellhead pressure by a full-stream orifice meter. Flow lines are so manifolded that any or all wells may flow through a high-pressure header or a low-pressure header, thence through volume-control regulators and a gas heater into a production separator or a test separator. From the separators, the gas stream is directed through a glycol-type dehydrator and a master orifice meter into the pipeline leading ashore. Water and distillate are drawn off the bottom of the separators and passed through a skimmer tank from which the water is metered before disposal. The distillate is returned to the separator, from which it is pumped into the pipeline and recombined with the gas for transportation to the shore terminal. This follows the now established practice in the Gulf of Mexico of gathering both gas and liquids through the gas purchaser's system.

At the onshore separation and microwave control station, the streams are again separated, the distillate being metered and delivered to a products pipeline leading to the operator's refinery at Beaumont and the gas being metered and delivered into the gas purchaser's transmission line.

At the microwave control panel in the onshore separation station, the operator, by means of push buttons, can:

1. Open or close in any or all wells.
2. Change setting of volume-control regulators and thus increase or decrease the flow rates of the wells in each of the production headers as a group.
3. Shut down or switch generators used to supply electrical power on the platform. (If one generator stops, the other starts automatically.)
4. Start or stop either of the glycol pumps.
5. Shut down all equipment on platform and vent all vessels and lines.

In addition to control functions, the microwave control panel provides the following information:

6. Which wells are producing and which are shut in.
7. Individual flow rates from every well.
8. Pressure on each production header.
9. Low heater temperature (i.e., warning if temperature of gas leaving heater is below pre-set point).
10. High or low level in production separator.
11. Which glycol pump is in operation.
12. Water content of gas delivered into pipeline.
13. Open or closed position of valve on emergency flare line.
14. Operation of distillate skimmer transfer pump.

Manual controls are also provided on the platform and the usual overriding automatic safety devices are used on the wells and equipment.

The onshore measurements of gas and distillate are used for accounting and royalty payments. Platform measurements, including well tests for gas-oil ratios, provide the basis for allocating gas and distillate production to individual wells. The flow rates of individual wells (item 7), which are transmitted to the shore station by microwave, are used for well-control purposes only, such control being exercised by microwave settings of the volume-control regulators (item 2).

This use of microwave control enables the owner to operate this field without personnel, except for a weekly trip by two men—one to change charts and inspect equipment and the other to handle the boat and provide a factor of safety. Conventional operation would require multiple crews on the platform together with living quarters, commissary arrangements, stand-by boat, and crew boat or helicopter for transportation of personnel—all at greatly increased cost.

California Offshore Operations

The ocean floor drops off rapidly along the California Coast in contrast to the gentle slope of the Gulf floor adjacent to Texas and Louisiana. As a result, until recently all wells except one, penetrating

Fig. 33—M o n t e r e y-Texaco Island, Offshore Seal Beach, California

Bulk separator (large), surge tank, and test separators (small) on a pile-supported structure seen in the lower left of the photo.

oil reservoirs under the Pacific Ocean have been drilled directionally from shore locations or from platforms at the ends of piers. At Elwood and Rincon such offshore locations are less than a mile from shore. Actually, in both areas certain wells located on land have been directionally drilled to oil-sand targets farther out than well locations at the ends of the piers.

Drilling and producing operations are serviced by trucks. Separators, meters, and well-testing equipment have either been placed on the piers near the wells or on shore. Lines to shore are laid on the piers and are short and relatively inexpensive. In general, operators have not been faced with the many and difficult problems of the offshore operator in the Gulf of Mexico.

Recently, two oil wells have been completed from a steel drilling platform a short distance offshore from Carpenteria. Drilling is proceeding, but already oil and gas lines have been laid ashore where production facilities will be located. These wells must be serviced by boat and helicopter but are near enough to shore that crews are brought to the platforms every tour. No men live on these platforms.

Offshore from Seal Beach, Monterey Oil Company and Texaco Inc. have completed 30 directionally drilled oil wells from a man-made island, 8,100 ft offshore from Seal Beach (see Fig. 33). In addition conductor pipe has been installed for 40 additional wells on this island.

The island—75 ft in diameter—is in 42 ft of water but the level

989

on which the well heads and production facilities are located is only 18 ft above mean low water. This compares with structures in offshore Louisiana fields 45 ft or more above mean low Gulf. The Pacific at this locality is not subject to the threat of violent hurricanes like those in the Gulf, and only four or five times during the past five years have seas been too high for the crews to come ashore at the end of their regular tours.

This island is capped with a reinforced concrete structure divided into 14 compartments, 10 of which enclose from 2 to 4 well heads each. Steel fire doors (heat-actuated), close automatically in case of fire—or can be closed manually—to isolate all compartments. Besides, a "sniffer" continuously samples and tests the air in the several compartments in rotation and sounds an alarm if the hydrocarbon content reaches 5 or 6 percent.

At the time of writing, production from this field was averaging about 3,000 bbl per day of oil and 2,500,000 cu ft of gas. The general plan for handling production provides for the separation of all oil and gas on the island. Both the bulk stream and the well-test streams of oil and gas are measured there and then taken ashore in pipelines where they are measured again in tanks and with orifice meters for accounting purposes.

As shown in Fig. 33, several vertical separators have been installed on the island. One small separator is used as the first stage and the large separator as the second stage in two-stage separation of the bulk stream. The other separators are used for well testing. All wells are tested regularly, gas being measured by orifice meters on the island and total fluid by dump-type meters. Automatic samplers catch samples from the dump meters and the clean oil and water productions of the wells on test are calculated from shakeouts.

As some wells require artificial lift, gas from the bulk separator at a pressure of about 100 psi is boosted to 1,000 lb by a compressor on the island and used for gas lifting. A generating unit on the island provides electricity.

Four pipelines connect the island and the shore terminal, one 8-in. for gas, two 3-in. lines for oil, and one 3-in. line for fresh water from shore to the island. The island is also connected to shore by a cable which provides three telephone circuits.

All in all, this island is an outstanding example of engineering efficiency. The concentration of so many well heads in one space is recognized by the operator as creating a potential hazard from fire and explosion and every precaution is taken to safeguard against them.

Offshore Problems of the Future

Although many innovations and advances in offshore operating methods have been mentioned, it has not been possible—nor is it the purpose of this chapter—to present a treatise on this most interesting subject. The study, however, has brought to light certain areas in which major advances may occur in the future.

Automation has not received the full acceptance that might be expected. Although operators are beginning to install some automatic devices, such as metering separators, it would seem that the isolation of offshore fields, the difficulties in transportation and communications, the high cost of maintaining supervisory and operating personnel at sea, and the unusual hazards from weather, fire, and explosion would encourage the acceptance of automatic field operation—almost to the ideal defined earlier in this chapter.

High costs have emphasized the need for some relaxation of control of producing operations by regulatory bodies and, indeed, this has already occurred in the matter of allowables and rules permitting makeup allowables in Louisiana. Automatic custody transfer and well testing are already established methods on land and their acceptance by regulatory bodies for offshore operations is wholly justified.

Cheaper and therefore greater storage capacity at sea has long been desired by operators as it would lessen the impacts of weather. But so far, storage has required platform support and this is one of the most expensive factors in offshore operations. Submerged storage placed on the ocean floor has been envisioned by some producers and, as this is written, at least two installations of this kind are being tested in the Gulf of Mexico. One scheme that has occupied the attention of operators, and the U.S. Geological Survey as well, is the possibility of leaching out storage cavities in shallow salt domes in the same manner as mentioned previously (p. 918). With large storage available a field might be produced at its maximum efficient rate and the oil withdrawn from storage for market in accordance with fair proration schedules.

Coupled with storage is another dream—the creation of deep-sea tanker terminals to receive oil directly from offshore wells or production platforms and to load it directly onto tankers to avoid the cost of transshipping ashore by barge or pipeline. This, too, has not been realized but conceivably could become a reality in areas with high concentrations of reserves.

Still another hope is for the construction of one or more large-scale offshore gathering systems, which might be owned by a pipeline carrier and would pick up the production of various companies. As the accepted offshore procedure is to separate, measure, and recombine at sea, and transport and separate and measure again on shore, such a system would probably be designed to carry oil and gas in two-phase flow. Experience at West Delta Block 30 illustrates the practicability of the measuring and accounting for oil and gas carried in such a system.

It is recognized that gas "fills up" a line very quickly and separate gathering systems, therefore, would be needed for large gas-distillate producing areas.

Weather, particularly wind and wave action, will always be an important factor in offshore operations. Forecasters can now warn of hurricanes hours or days in advance and can define squall areas as much as 12 hours ahead. They can also predict wave heights with considerable success. Most offshore operators subscribe to weather-forecasting services and plan their operations accordingly.

Weather forecasts, however, lose accuracy as they extend further into the future. Thirty-day predictions may tell the operator that he may expect generally fair or stormy weather conditions, but they cannot resolve such matters as wind velocities and wave heights on given days. Seasonal or annual predictions are probably still of doubtful accuracy.

This subject has much broader implications to the petroleum industry than just aid to offshore operators; and in 1954 the American Petroleum Institute appointed the Advisory Committee on Fundamental Research on Weather Forecasting to work with the United States Weather Bureau, the Navy, Air Force, and private agencies. Both short- and long-range forecasting are being studied and it may be expected that ultimately this science will be greatly advanced to the benefit of the oil industry.

It may seem visionary to expect man to control the weather but even this may eventually be achieved.

The development and operation of oil fields in deep waters have challenged the imagination of many people in the industry. Already core and stratigraphic drilling have been successfully carried out with floating units and eventually this type of equipment may be applied to full-scale wildcat and development drilling. It seems likely that herein lies the solution to the problem of drilling in waters several hundred feet deep.

Operators have given much thought to completion and workover methods in deep waters, their ideas ranging from abovewater completions protected by well jackets, to well heads on the ocean floor—possibly encased in water-tight chambers—with flow lines leading to production platforms in shallow water or to shore installations where separating, treating, and measuring would be done. Until now, actual planning has not gone much beyond that for operations in water depths of 150 ft which are about the maximum in which divers can work. But the promise of large reserves in still deeper waters will spur oil men in their search for methods to recover them.

Today, oil and gas-field operations in deep waters must be considered as being still in the realm of speculation, but as drilling methods advance to the point of completing wells in, say, 500 ft of water, suitable means will undoubtedly be found for handling the production.

Finally, experience has shown that near-shore knowledge gained from the design of piers, breakwaters, and so on, cannot always be extrapolated for use in deep water. This lends importance to the research efforts of the meteorologist, the oceanographer, and the soil mechanic. Studies of the atmosphere and its variations in temperature and winds, of waves, tides, and currents which erode or deposit material, and of ocean-floor materials themselves could be of untold importance in designing economical structures and in meeting some of the unusual problems encountered in operating at sea.

CLOSING STATEMENT

As the last pages in this chapter are being written, the petroleum industry finds itself in its one-hundredth year. Surely few industries have experienced the romance, the progress, and the opportunities for public service of this one. It is essentially an engineering industry. Petroleum engineering has always been a part of it, although petroleum engineering as such has only been recognized for about 40 years.

Over this period the petroleum engineer has become a man-of-all-work and has extended his field of activity from drilling and production to the conservation of oil and gas, studies of reservoir conditions, methods for increasing recoveries, appraisals, cost reductions, and many other subjects. Few oil-field operating problems have been more varied or more interesting than those on the surface which have been discussed in this chapter, for that is where oil and gas are reduced to possession, are first seen, and are processed and measured for sale.

The petroleum engineer's contributions to the revolutionary advancements in handling oil and gas aboveground have been many, although they have often been matched by the efforts and ideas of field men and equipment manufacturers, to whom full credit is given.

ACKNOWLEDGMENTS

This chapter could not have been prepared without the assistance of a great many individuals and companies engaged in the oil and gas and allied industries. Kenneth Cooley of Shell Pipe Line Corporation collected the basic material for the first part of the chapter, while S. F. Bowlby, Fremont Schmieder, and Paul Lehr of Shell Oil Company, C. E. Beecher of Cities Service Oil Company, R. A. Cattell and H. C. Fowler of the United States Bureau of Mines, Olin Culberson of the Railroad Commission of Texas, Douglas Ragland, C. E. Reistle, Jr., and Ralph J. Schilthuis of Humble Oil & Refining Company, and C. Arliss Watts of North Central Oil Corporation, all supplied information and assisted with general reviews. In addition, a number of members of the Editorial

Board, including D. V. Carter and E. L. Estabrook, chairman and advisory editor respectively, read and criticized the manuscript.

Special assistance on the sections dealing with natural gas and its products was given by Harold Burrow of Tennessee Gas Transmission Company, Ed DeMouche of Houston Natural Gas Company, Millard Neptune of Texas Eastern Transmission Company, George F. Tennison of Shell Oil Company, and R. C. Buchan of Humble Oil & Refining Company. Fred Hubler of the Petrolite Corporation furnished some of the history on separating water and emulsions, and D. B. Dow reviewed that part of the manuscript.

W. S. Morris of the East Texas Salt Water Disposal Company supplied valuable information and reviewed the section on waste-water disposal, and Henry Lewelling of The Atlantic Refining Company furnished the data on chemical treatment of waters.

The writer is indebted to James E. Moss of the American Petroleum Institute and H. C. Packard of Shell Oil Company for their help with the section on measuring, sampling, and testing.

Adin H. Hall of Shell Pipe Line Corporation, Howard Shatto of Shell Oil Company, and the petroleum engineering staffs of several oil companies furnished information and reviewed the section on automation.

A number of industry engineers assisted in the preparation of the section on the handling of production offshore. Among them are R. L. Adams, Rex Alford, and Walter Poimboeuf of Continental Oil Company; Lee B. Agers, Leonard Franklin, Alex Massad, and C. V. Templeton of Mobil Oil Company; R. C. Buchan of Humble Oil & Refining Company; Eugene L. Davis and Albert W. Gentry of Monterey Oil Company; J. E. Gallagher of Shell Oil Company; J. F. Hendrickson of Phillips Petroleum Company; and Alden J. Laborde of Ocean Drilling & Exploration Company.

Thanks are due the following oil and gas companies and associated industries for the continued assistance provided by various members of their staffs throughout the preparation of this chapter: Cities Service Oil Company; Continental Oil Company; Humble Oil & Refining Company; Mobil Oil Company; Monterey Oil Company; National Tank Company; *Offshore Magazine; The Oil and Gas Journal;* Parkersburg Rig & Reel Company; Phillips Petroleum Company; Shell Oil Company; Shell Pipe Line Corporation; Tennessee Gas Transmission Company; and Transcontinental Gas Pipe Line Company.

Kibby Allen, Paul Coons, and Guy Drew of Shell Pipe Line Corporation prepared all of the drawings.

Space does not permit the listing of the many others who assisted by supplying information for this chapter but the writer gratefully acknowledges their help.

Finally, the writer is indebted to Betty Prettyman who for more than five years acted in the capacity of editorial assistant and without whose help this chapter could not have been prepared.

REFERENCES

[1]*The Lamp*, 75th Anniversary Issue, Standard Oil Company (New Jersey), 1957.

[2]*The Derrick's Hand Book of Petroleum*, 77, Derrick Publishing Company, Oil City, Pa., 1898.

[3]Whiteshot, Charles A: *The Oil Well Driller—History of the Oil Industry of the World*, 895, The Acme Publishing Company, Mannington, West Virginia, 1905.

[4]The Petroleum Industry, 1895-1934, *Oil Gas J.* and *The Oil City Derrick* (Diamond Jubilee Issue) (1934).

[5]Acts 1919, 36th Texas Legislature, Regular Session, Chapter 155, approved March 31, 1919.

[6]Bizal, Robert B: Gas Storage: Big Business, Big Future, *Oil Gas J.*, **55** [21] 88, May 27 (1957).

[7]*American Gas Association Monthly*, 10, May (1959).

[8]Allen, Irving C. and Burrel, George A: Liquefied Products from Natural Gas, *U. S. Bur. Mines TP 10* (1912).

[9]Dykema, W. P: Recovery of Gasoline from Natural Gas by the Compression Method, *U. S. Bur. Mines. Bull. 151* (1918).

[10]Burrel, George A; Biddison, P.M; and Oberfell, G. G: Extraction of Gasoline from Natural Gas by Absorption Methods, *U. S. Bur. Mines Bull. 12* (1917).

[11]Whiteshot, Charles A: *Op. cit.*

[12]Morris, A. B: Evolution of the Oil and Gas Separator, *National Petroleum News*, **19**, 235, Sept. 21 (1957).

[13]Hamilton, W. R: Traps for Saving Gas at Oil Wells, *U. S. Bur. Mines TP 209*, 34, Feb. (1919).

[14]Stage Separation of Oil and Gas Mixtures Increases Profits, *Oil Gas J.*, **42**, 75, Feb. 10 (1944).

[15]Gravis, C. K; Davis, T. O; and Fields, R. E: Practical Application of Low-temperature Separation and Stabilization, *API Drilling and Production Practice*, 226 (1955).

[16]Parks, A. S. and Dow, W. M: Development of Dry-desiccant Wellhead Absorption Units, *API Drilling and Production Practice*, 399 (1956).

[17]Cottrell, F. G: Breaking Emulsions, U. S. Patent No. 987,114, March 21, 1911.

[18]Mahone, F. D: The Electrical Dehydration of Cut Oil, report before the American Institute of Mining and Metallurgical Engineers, Tulsa, Okla., October 1923.

[19]Dow, D. B: Oil Field Emulsions, *U. S. Bur. Mines Bull. 250*, 112 (1926).

[20]Sherrick, J. L: Oil Field Emulsions, *Ind. Eng. Chem.*, **12**, 133, Feb. (1920).

[21]Siebert, F. M. and Brady, J. G: Breaking up Emulsions of Oil and Water, U. S. Patent No. 1,290,369.

[22]Eddy, W. G. and Eddy, H. C: Discussion of Electrical Dehydration of Crude Oil, *Ind. Eng. Chem.*, **13**, 1016, Nov. (1921).

[23]Barnickel, W. S: Coppers for Dehydration, U. S. Patent No. 1,093,098, April 14, 1914; Separating Naturally Emulsified Brine from Crude Petroleum, U. S. Patent No. 1,223,659, April 24, 1917; Sulphanates for Dehydration, U. S. Patent No. 1,467,831, Sept. 11, 1923.

[24]Dow, D. B: *Op. cit.*

[25]Lewelling, Henry, and Kaplan, Monte: What to do About Salt Water, unpublished manuscript delivered as a lecture to petroleum engineering class at the University of Texas, November 1958.

[26]Gardener, J. A: The Heat Reflecting Properties of Colors Applied to Oil and Gas Storage Tanks, Paint Mfg. Assoc., *U. S. Circular 44* (1917).

[27]Gardener, J. A: Paints for Light Oil Storage Tanks and a Note on Spray Equipment, Paint Mfg. Assoc., *U. S. Circular 131* (1921).

[28]Bradley, O. U: Losses of Crude Oil in Steel and Earthen Storage, Am. Inst. of Mining, **139**, 135, July (1918).

[29]Schmidt, Ludwig: The Use of Vapor-Tight Tankage in the Oil Fields, *Mid-Continent Oil and Gas Association Yearbook*, 1922. Also published as *U. S. Bur. Mines TP 2442* and incorporated in *U. S. Bur. Mines Bull. 279*.

[30]Schmidt, Ludwig: Applied Methods and Equipment for Reducing Evaporation Losses of Petroleum and Gasoline, *U. S. Bur. Mines Bull. 379*, 160 (1934).

[31]Tests Show Cutting Crude Losses Possible by Using Proper Tank Paint, Editorial, *National Petroleum News*, **17**, 36, April 8 (1925).

[32]Stauffer, J. C; Roberts, J. K; and Whitman, W. G: Determination of the Vapor Pressures of Naphthas, *Ind. Eng. Chem.*, **2** [1] Jan. 15 (1930).

[33]Schmidt, Ludwig: A Floating Roof for Oil Tanks, *U. S. Bur. Mines RI 2547* (1923).

[34]Schmidt, Ludwig: A Diaphragm or "Breather" Roof for Oil-Storage Tanks, *U. S. Bur. Mines RI 2984*, 9, Jan. (1930).

[35]Bignell, L. G. E: Vapor Gathering Systems with Steel Balloon Reduce Evaporation and Corrosion Losses, *Oil Gas J.*, **32**, 8, Oct. 12 (1934).

[36]Bignell, L. G. E: Evaporation and Corrosion Practically Eliminated in Oil-Field Pipeline Gathering Equipment, *Oil Gas J.*, **32**, 13, April 19 (1934).

[37]Truesdell, P: Durable Foam Seal Stops Evaporation and Reduces Fire Risk, *National Petroleum News*, **14**, 43, July 12 (1922).

[38]Ellerbrake, E. G. and Veatch, F: Microballoons and Their Use in Reducing Evaporation Losses of Crude Oil, *Proc. Am. Pet. Inst., Sect. VI (Interdivisional)*, 193 (1953).

[39]Symposium on Measuring, Sampling, and Testing Crude Oil and Petroleum Products, Part I: 95 Years of Bulk-oil Measurement, *Proc. Am. Pet. Inst., Sect. VI (Interdivisional)*, 175 (1954).

[40]*API Std 2500: Measuring, Sampling, and Testing Crude Oil* (Supersedes Parts 2 and 3, *API Code 25*, June 1948, 7th Ed.), March 1961, 2nd Ed.

[41]Centrifuge, *Encyclopedia Britannica*, **V**, 145, Encyclopedia Britannica, Inc., London, 14th Edn.

[42]Symposium on Measuring, Sampling, and Testing Crude Oil and Petroleum Products, Part I: *Op. cit.* ref. 39; Part II: Present Methods of Bulk-oil Measurement and Desired Improvements; Part III: A Glance into Bulk-oil Measurement of the Future; Part IV: Management Looks at Bulk-oil Measurement, *Proc. Am. Pet. Inst., Sect. VI (Interdivisional)* 171 (1954).

[43]Tagliabue, C. J: Specific Gravity of Coal Oils and How the Test May be Applied, *Am. Mining Gazette*, **1**, 166 (1864).

[44]United States Standard Baumé Hydrometer Scales, *National Bur. Standards Circular No. 59* (1916).

[45]National Standard Petroleum Oil Tables, *National Bur. Standards Circular No. 154*, 1, May 29 (1924).

[46]Gilpin, George A: Tables for Reducing Quantities by Weights in Any Mixture of Pure Spirits and Water, *Philosophical Trans. of the Royal Society of London*, **82**, 439 (1792).

[47]Bearce, H. W. and Peffer, E. L: Density and Thermal Expansion of American Petroleum Oils, *National Bur. Standards Technological Paper No. 77* (1916).

[48]*Proc. Am. Pet. Inst.* (1928).

[49]Shatto, H. L. and Hall, A. H: The Growth of Automatic Custody Transfer, presented at the annual pipeline conference, American Petroleum Institute, New Orleans, La., March 31-April 2, 1958.

[50]*API Bull. 2509A: Lease Automatic Custody Transfer,* American Petroleum Institute, New York, Aug. 1956, 1st Edn.

[51]Automatic Custody Transfer of Crude Oil, Part 1: General Considerations, H. C. Packard; Part 2: From the Producer's Viewpoint, Harold S. Kelly; Part 3: From the Pipeliner's Viewpoint, A. H. Newberg, *Proc. Am. Pet. Inst. (Prod. Bul. 242),* 15 (1956).

[52]Carlson, B. C. and Schmidt, T. R: Progress in Oil-field Automation, *API Drilling and Production Practice,* 323 (1956).

Kuntz, L. E: New LACT Instrumentation, *Oil Gas J.,* 177, Oct. 12 (1959).

[53]Petroleum in Southern California, *Bulletin 63,* California State Mining Bureau, 408 (1913)

[54]Grosz, O. L: Corrosion Control in Offshore Operations, *Offshore* (in 2 parts), Part I: **8 [4]** 39, June (1958); Part II: **8 [5]** 41, July (1958).

Wrought Iron Beats Corrosion Offshore, *Offshore,* **8 [4]** 43, June (1958).

[55]Illingworth, R. H; Montgomery, W. L; Aldridge, Clyde; and Temple, C. V: Proposed Offshore Production and Gathering Facilities, Eugene Island Area, Louisiana Gulf of Mexico, *Proc. Am. Pet. Inst. (Prod. Bul. 241)* 74 (1955).

Massad, A. H. and Pela, E. C: Facilities Used in Gathering and Handling Hydrocarbon Production in the Eugene Island, Block 126 Field, Louisiana, Gulf of Mexico, Preprint Paper No. 675-G, Society of Petroleum Engineers, AIME.

Chapter 16

EVALUATION

Harold Vance

Mr. Vance's photo and biography appear
on page 580.

INTRODUCTION

Many persons contributed to our present knowledge of evaluation. It is believed most people responsible for the literature have been recognized in this chapter. The literature on the subject was practically non-existent until about 1905, with the exception of publications of the Geological Survey of Pennsylvania. Such books as *The Derrick's Hand Book of Petroleum— 1859-1900;*[1] *Sketches in Crude-Oil*, by John J. McLaurin, 1896;[2] and *The Oil Well Driller*, by Charles A. Whiteshot, 1905,[3] are of historical interest but contribute very little to the subject of evaluation.

Although the problem of determining the value of an oil property confronted the early operator, values based on how much oil a property would produce had no place in the early reports. When engineers and geologists demonstrated that oil occupied the pore spaces in rocks, estimates of the amount of oil in place were calculated by using the porosity of the producing rock. The amount in place to be recovered was sometimes estimated by comparison with recoveries from depleted fields. Later a study of the oil-production-decline curves showed that, under certain conditions, an extension of these curves into the future would give a reliable estimate of the rate and total amount of future production.

The Revenue Act of 1918[4] provided a real incentive to place a value on new discoveries by permitting the operator to value these discoveries as of 30 days after discovery, and to use this value as a basis for determining the depletion allowance instead of the cost method.

Proration of oil production, which started in 1928, made a restudy of reservoir conditions necessary because the decline-curve method of estimating future production was not applicable in prorated fields. The material-balance concept applied to an oil and gas reservoir was an important contribution at this time.

In about 1930, banks started making loans to producers for development purposes and for the purchase of properties. A valuation of the properties which were to serve as security for the loan was essential.

Merger of oil companies and the sale of stock of a new oil company to the public made a valuation of the properties of these companies necessary.

As gas-transmission lines provided a market for shut-in gas, the valuation procedure developed for oil properties was modified and applied to gas properties.

---

[1]References are at the end of the chapter.

EARLY RESERVOIR CONCEPTS

Some oil producers[5] believed in the 1870's that 1,000 to 3,000 bbl per day wells were possible only if the oil occurred underground in fractures and the drilled hole intersected these fractures. It was inconceivable that oil could be produced at such high rates from porous sandstone.

Experiments made on oil rock in about 1871 *(op. cit.)* proved that the rock was absorbing and holding 1/15 to 1/10 of its own bulk of water or oil. Assuming the area of the interspaces in the oil rock amount in proportion to its whole bulk and that only 1/17 of the volume was occupied by the interspaces, then for every inch of 5½-in. hole drilled in oil sand, 17.28 sq in. of its surface are laid bare, not including the bottom of the hole. Thus, there would be 1 sq in. of space through which oil could flow into the hole for every 1 in. of penetration into the oil rock. Where there are 5 to 10 ft of this oil rock to be drilled, it is easy to see that a flow of 3,000 to 4,000 bbl per day could be possible, considering friction as a retarding factor and the high pressure as a compensating factor. Thus, a crevice in the oil rock is not essential for a large producer.

Another group of operators *(op. cit.)* imagined the oil to be present in underground caverns. They thought in terms of lakes of oil interconnected with streams. It was inconceivable to this group that large quantities of oil could be contained within the pore spaces of the oil rock. On Oil Creek there were two producing sands—the Third sand was 30 to 50 ft thick, and the Stray sand 15 to 30 ft thick. On the basis that 1/10 to 1/8 of the bulk volume of the oil rock was full of oil and that only 15 ft were good-bearing "pebble", then there would be a producing capacity of 15,000 bbl per acre or 9,600,000 bbl per square mile.

The idea *(op. cit.)* that not all the oil originally in the oil rock was recoverable does not seem to have been considered as early as 1874-79. It has been noted, however, that the early wells in a field were the most productive and that there was interference between wells in the same pool.

John F. Carll *(op. cit.)* compared a petroleum reservoir to a barrel of beer. "The barrel is placed in the cellar and a bar pump inserted . . . at first the liquid flows freely through the tube without using the pump, but presently the gas weakens and the pump is called into use, and finally the gas pressure in the barrel becomes so weak that a venthole must be made to admit atmospheric pressure before the barrel can be completely emptied by a pump." The foregoing statement leads one to believe Carll thought in terms of a petroleum reservoir in which all the gas was in solution and that, as the pressure dropped, a gas cap was formed until finally the gas was all exhausted and the oil reached the hole through, principally, gravity drainage and had to be pumped to the surface. The idea of a partial water-drive reservoir does not seem to have been considered at the time of Carll's study.

ESTIMATING RECOVERABLE OIL AND GAS

The first published estimates of recoverable oil were the volumetric estimates of the Third Bradford sand, by John F. Carll,[5] which appeared in the Second Pennsylvania Geological Survey in 1879.

Period from 1909 to 1917

By 1909, 4 years after Ralph Arnold's initial work[6] in land classification, more had been learned about the porosity of sands and its effect on production. In February of that year, the U. S. Geological Survey published *Bulletin No. 394*,[7] in which there is a discussion concerning the productive rate of Pennsylvania's hard and compact sandstone—which had an initial production of 50 to 500 bbl of oil in the first 24 hours and which settled down to the comparatively steady production of 1/10 this amount—as compared with the productive rate of the other extreme represented by the very loose unconsolidated sands of the Spindletop area of Jefferson County, Texas, in which wells produced thousands of barrels in the first 24 hours and then declined rapidly and were abandoned within 6 months to 4 years from the time they were completed. It was also stated in the *Bulletin* that 7 years was the fair average life of a well in Pennsylvania. Tables were included to show the number of active wells which contributed to each year's production from 1859 to 1907, using the 7-year average for the Appalachian, Lima-Indiana, Illinois, and the Mid-Continent fields, 4 years for the fields of Texas, 6 years for California fields, and 7 years for the other minor petroleum fields.

David T. Day[7] stated, also in February 1909, that it was customary to consider 10 percent as the average porosity of the pay streaks but that these pay streaks varied from zero to 30 percent in the more porous strata. The principal effect of these variations in porosity had to do more with the rate at which petroleum could be obtained from the pool than upon the total amount obtainable. Thus, Day recognized permeability, but he did not use that term in connection with his description of the pay strata—or pay sands. Using 10 percent for the average porosity, 1 cu ft of pay sand "would yield approximately one gallon of petroleum" or 5,000 bbl per acre would be recovered from a similar sand having an average thickness of 5 ft. The estimated recovery for New York and Pennsylvania was around 800 bbl per acre. In California, according to measurements made by Arnold, there were some 8½ billion barrels of petroleum stored in the rocks of that state but perhaps only 5 billion barrels would be produced.

Day *(op. cit.)* presented a production-decline curve for the states of Pennsylvania and New York (see Fig. 1) and commented as follows: ". . . The decline has become regular, and, logically extended, will render the production negligible in ten years."

This is the earliest production-decline curve found in the literature in which an attempt had been made to estimate the future rate of production by extending the curve into the future.

L. G. Huntley,[8] in 1913, stated that he believed the well-known physical laws offer a possible solution for all underground problems, but that the data are so scarce that care should be taken not to make general deductions based on such a small amount of data. Under ideal producing conditions, decline of production from oil wells depended upon the quantity of oil available, the rock pressure, and the character and porosity of the sand.

M. E. Lombardi[9] stated that a fair estimate of the percentage of voids in well-washed sand is from 30 to 35 percent, with an estimated recovery from these voids of from 10 to 50 percent of the volume of voids, or from 3 to 17½ percent of the volume of the container. Records were available to indicate production recoveries from 1 to 15 percent of the total volume of the reservoir rock. The method of estimating recoveries of oil based on thickness and saturation of sand was probably going out of vogue, but Lombardi believed it was a useful method of checking on the probable recovery from the field or property.

In 1915, Chester W. Washburne[10] stated that the porosity of the stratum is the measure of maximum reservoir capacity for liquids and gases, and gave the following estimate of recovery in which he assumed the producing sand was 12 ft thick, the porosity of the sand was 15 percent, and the relative saturation was 75 percent, and multiplied, $12 \times 0.15 \times 0.75 \times 7,758 = 10,473$ bbl per acre in place. Then, if the extraction factor is assumed to be 60 percent, each acre would produce 6,284 bbl.

Washburne made the interesting statement in the same article that the relative saturation depends mainly upon the volumes of free gas and of water which are occluded in the oil or entangled in the oil-bearing layers. This is one of the first references mentioning that the oil sand itself contains some water.

Roswell H. Johnson, in a discussion of Washburne's paper *(op. cit.)*, stated there are two kinds of pores in an oil sand—those which are entirely enclosed so that they do not belong to a system of communicating pores, and those which are connected to a communicating system.

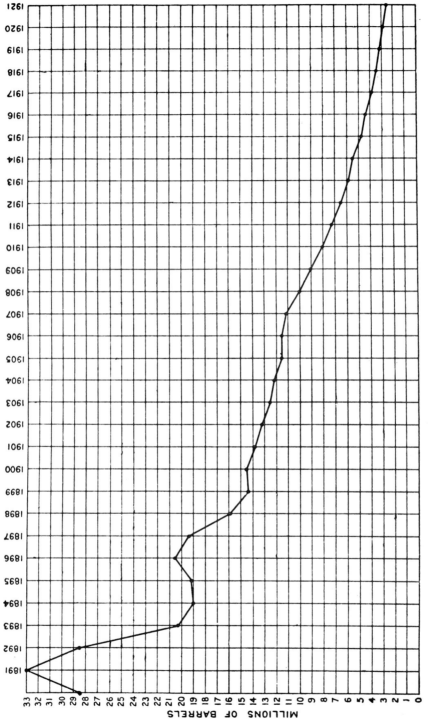

Fig. 1—Decline in Production of the New York and Pennsylvania Oil Fields and Its Probable Rate in the Future[7]

He proposed the term "effective porosity" for those pores which are interconnected and stated that this was the only porosity determination of any value from the standpoint of oil recovery.

Johnson[11] raised the question, "What becomes of the water which must have filled the oil and gas sands at the time of deposition . . . .?" and stated he believed that as the gas, oil, and water pass through a body of larger pores, the gas, owing to its lack of capillary attraction, stays in the large pores; and that the water, having a high capillarity, fills the finer pores. In this way a greater part of the oil and gas is found in the large pore spaces and a greater part of the water in the smaller pore spaces. Johnson was speaking of the accumulation of oil and gas in a sand which contains its original connate waters. These connate waters must be pushed out of the way during the process of accumulating oil and gas to make space available for them. Thus, the water is retained in the smaller pore spaces and fills part of the void which also contains oil and gas. This is believed to be one of the earlier references as to the existence of water in the oil sand, a fact which was not generally recognized until a later date.

Carl H. Beal and J. O. Lewis,[12] in 1921, indicated that they recognized the existence of something comparable to what is now known as "permeability" but did not use the word, as evidenced by the following statement:

"So different in porosity are the members of some sandstone beds that in many oil fields most of the production comes from a 'pay' or 'pay streak' that forms only a small portion of the total thickness of sand."

Porosity determines the possible oil content, but a careful distinction must be made relative to the productive capacity *(op. cit.)*. In sands of high porosity the grains may be so minute that the oil will not be produced at a commercial rate. In contrast to this, a sandstone highly cemented and of low porosity may be very productive.

". . .The productivity of an oil sand, for reasons given hereafter, is not solely dependent upon porosity or capacity."

Beal and Lewis further stated that all parts of the sand are saturated, but the question is whether the sand is saturated with oil and gas dissolved in the oil, or partly filled with water and free gas.

Robert W. Pack,[13] in August 1917, stated that there are two general methods of estimating the quantity of oil and gas in the ground and also the amount to be recovered. He mentioned first the saturation method, and second the production-curve method. In using the saturation method an extraction factor must be used to determine the amount of oil and gas believed to be recoverable, but the production-decline-curve method gives the amount of recoverable oil direct.

Carl H. Beal,[14] in 1918, mentioned three general methods commonly used for estimating future oil output, as follows:

"1. The saturation method based on a calculation of the oil content of the productive sand.

"2. A production curve method which consists of determining from the decline in production of a well in the past, the amount of oil that would probably be produced in the future.

"3. The production per acre method which estimates the future output like comparing actual recoveries per acre from similar properties in the same district or in one where the conditions are comparable."

Beal gives credit to J. O. Lewis for many of the ideas which he presented.

Production-decline Curve

Certain production-decline data *(op. cit.)* plotted on logarithmic coordinate paper fall into a straight line, which straight line can be extended into the future. Fig. 2 is an example of curves plotted by Beal on logarithmic paper for the purpose of showing the differences in the rate of decline for large and small wells. When plotted on such paper, an equation of the form Y equals cx to the nth power will be represented by a straight line whose slope is n.

Lewis and Beal,[15] again in 1918, mentioned the use of logarithmic coordinate paper as the type on which to plot percentage-decline curves, and that in a number of instances the line connecting these various percentage figures gives a straight line. The writers made the following statement:

". . . it will eventually prove to be very useful in studying production-curve problems. The purpose here is only to suggest the use of logarithmic paper and to point out a few of its advantages."

It will be noted that Lewis and Beal are here using the percentage-decline curve, Fig. 3, which they later discarded in favor of the actual production-decline curve described in the *Manual for the Oil and Gas Industry Under the Revenue Act of 1918, Revised August 1921.*[16]

It was found[4] that if decline curves were anywhere near symmetrical, the curve was approximately the shape of a hyperbola. Much interesting work was done in connection with investigating this feature of extrapolating decline curves. If a true decline curve is hyperbolic in form, it becomes a straight line when plotted on logarithmic coordinate paper; and the unknown factor in the mathematical equation, the slope of the line, is definitely fixed in the earlier periods of production. And quoting: "This method of extrapolation of decline curves is worthy of consideration, but until better understood it must be used with extreme caution."

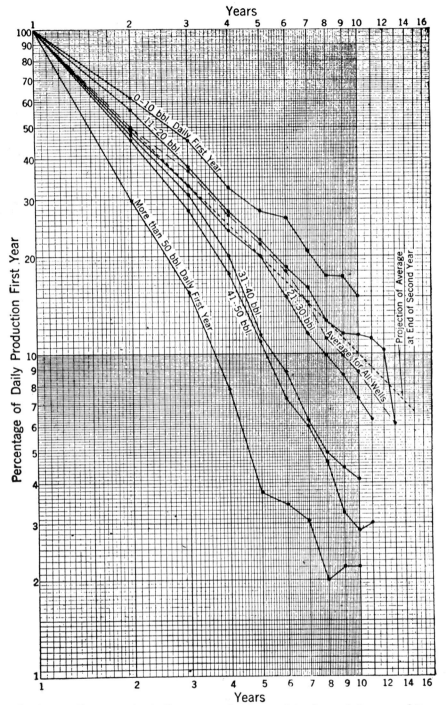

Fig. 2—Curves Showing the Difference in the Rate of Decline of Groups of Properties in the Bartlesville Field, Okla., on which the Initial Yearly Output Was Different[14]

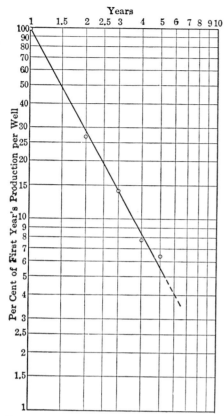

Years

Fig. 3—Average Production-decline
Curve for Wells on 34 Properties in a
West Virginia Field, Plotted on Logarith-
mic Coordinate Paper[15]

In the revised edition of the
Manual for the Oil and Gas Industry
(op. cit.) there appears to be much
more certainty regarding the
methods proposed than had existed
in the earlier edition, as evidenced by
the following statement:

"The simplest and safest
basis upon which to form estimates of future production of
wells or properties is by the projection of the record of past
production of the wells or properties themselves."

In plotting production-decline
curves on logarithmic coordinate
paper, it was noted that "If the
curve is plotted anywhere on the
paper except in a certain position, it
retains the form of a curve." The
procedure for shifting the curve
to obtain a straight line was described and is illustrated by Fig. 4.

"The use of logarithmic
paper also forms a convenient
method of recording production-decline curves. The co-
ordinates of two points of a curve as recorded by a straight line on
logarithmic paper definitely established the smooth-out curve. Thus
in figure (4) the following record establishes the curve:

$$x_1 = 5, \quad y_1 = 2,400$$
$$x_2 = 12, \quad y_2 = 250$$

"The coordinates of curves for hundreds of properties may be
written on a few sheets of paper and can be reproduced readily by
plotting the two points on logarithmic paper and connecting them
by a straight line. Points representing yearly production may then be
read on the curve extended to the economic limit, and an estimate
of future production obtained."

In the revised *Manual (op. cit.)*, tables were published showing the
X and Y coordinates from the logarithmic curve which could be used
to produce the production-decline curve as worked out in a number of
fields. Table 1 is a copy of one of the tables published in the *Manual*.

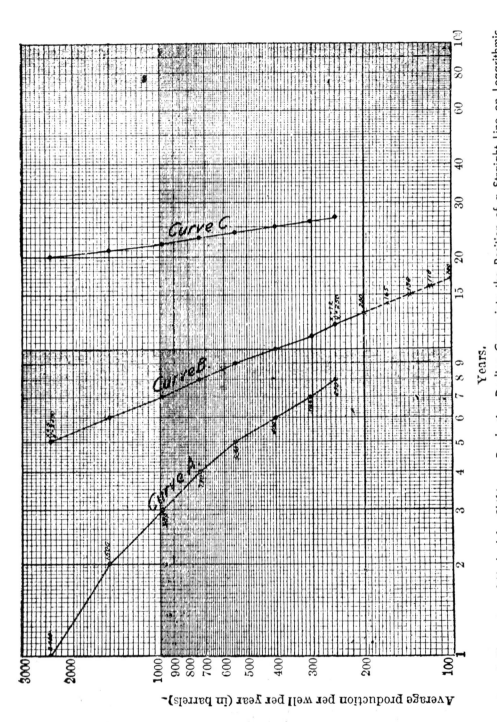

Fig. 4—Illustration of Method for Shifting a Production Decline Curve into the Position of a Straight Line on Logarithmic Paper[16]

In the position of "A", the curve is too far to the left; move all points to the right 4 spaces or year units. In the position of "C", the curve is too far to the right; move all points to the left 15 spaces or year units. In the position of "B," the curve falls approximately into a straight line which has been extended from the point representing a production of 250 bbl downward to indicate the future production for five years as shown by the broken extension of the line. The number at each dot

Table 1

Table Showing X and Y Values for Various Pools and Districts[16]

County	Pool or District	Sand or Formation to which Curve is Applicable	X_1	Y_1	X_2	Y_2	Remarks
OHIO:							
Allen	Lima district	Trenton limestone	5	920	20	35	
Belmont, Jefferson, and Monroe:	Several pools	Berea	9	700	23	40	
Jefferson, Monroe, and Belmont.	do	do	9	700	23	40	
Hancock	Lima district	Trenton limestone	9	940	30	35	
Hocking and Perry	Gore pool	Clinton	2	6,300	10	200	
Lucas and Ottawa	Lima district	Trenton limestone	3	730	21	35	
Mercer	do	do	3	640	20	35	
Monroe, Belmont, and Jefferson.	Several pools	Berea	9	700	23	40	
Monroe	Jackson Ridge pool	Keener	10	1,500	28	102	
Ottawa and Lucas	Lima district	Trenton limestone	3	730	21	35	
Perry and Hocking	Gore pool	Clinton	2	6,300	10	200	
Sandusky	Lima district	Trenton limestone	2	4,200	14	110	
Seneca	do	do	21	780	35	35	
Van Wert	do	do	3	690	20	35	
Washington	St. Marys pool	Keener	10	1,120	18	100	
Wayne	Several pools	Clinton	9	7,500	15	200	
Wood	Lima district	Trenton limestone	3	8,600	17	100	
OKLAHOMA:							
Carter	Healdton district	Healdton or deeper sand	40	53,000	49	1,000	Quarterly production curve
Do	Hewitt pool	Upper Hewitt sand	15	58,000	20	1,550	
Creek	Cushing pool	Bartlesville sand	3	100,000	9	1,200	
Do	do	Layton sand	2	22,500	6	1,025	
Do	do	Tucker sand	2	100,000	7	2,000	
Do	do	Wheeler sand	11	41,000	15	1,100	
Creek and Tulsa	Glenn pool	Glenn sand	10	54,000	18	1,100	
Do	do	Red Fork sand	2	9,300	17	103	
Do	do	Taneha sand	10	9,700	21	100	
Garfield	Garber pool	Any of a number of sands	3	75,000	6	1,000	
Kay	Blackwell district	Any of several deep sands	2	8,900	9	103	
Muskogee	Muskogee-Boynton district	Any of a number of sands	5	5,600	12	105	
Nowata	Adair pool	Bartlesville sand	2	3,000	10	110	
Nowata and Rogers	Nowata district	do	4	4,550	13	140	
Okmulgee	Okmulgee district	Any of a number of sands	3	40,000	9	1,080	
Osage and Washington	Avant-Ramona district	Bartlesville sand	11	60,000	20	1,250	
Osage	Hominy district	Either Peru, Oswego, or Bartlesville sand	8	85,000	16	1,250	
Do	Okesa district	Bartlesville sand	5	9,000	26	120	
Do	Pawhuska-Wynona district	Either Peru or Bartlesville sand	5	82,000	13	1,150	
Osage and Tulsa	Bird Creek-Skiatook district	Bartlesville sand	9	9,800	23	150	
Pawnee	Cleveland district	Cleveland, Bartlesville, or Tucker sand	6	9,100	21	200	

Appraisal Curve

Lewis and Beal, in the previously cited article published in 1918, mentioned the "appraisal curve". The purpose of this curve was to determine what an average well would ultimately produce based upon the amount of its initial production. Its basis was the so-called "law of equal expectation", which was as follows:

"If two wells under similar conditions produce equal amounts during any given year, the amount they will produce thereafter on the average will be approximately equal, regardless of their relative ages."

The law applied particularly to the output of wells that had become "settled".

Fig. 5 *(op. cit.)* was the means by which Lewis and Beal demonstrated that the future production of wells of equal output, on the average, was approximately the same regardless of the ages of the wells. In this curve, the ordinate is in percent cumulative and runs from 200 to 1,000. The abscissa is in years and goes from 1 to 6. The curve was constructed by plotting wells averaging 2 to 7 bbl daily against their total cumulative percentages along vertical lines representing their ages. Thus the cumulative percentages of wells from 2 to 7 bbl daily during their initial year are plotted along the first line, and the cumulative percentages of wells 2 to 7 bbl 2 years old along the second line, and so on. It will be noticed that the dots representing the different wells form in bunches not far from the average line, which is approximately horizontal. The fact that the average line — i.e., the dotted line — is nearly horizontal indicates that the future production of wells making 2 to 7 bbl daily is practically the same, regardless of the ages of the wells. If one were to eliminate the first year's production, the line would actually be horizontal. This type of demonstration was continued to wells of other sizes and the authors considered the results obtained sufficient to prove the "law of equal expectations" mentioned previously.

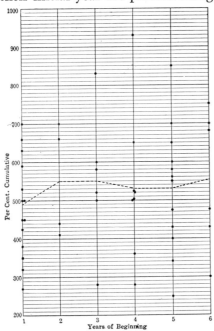

Fig. 5—Method of demonstrating that the future production of wells of equal output, on the average, is approximately the same regardless of the ages of the wells.[15]

Fig. 6 *(op. cit.)* illustrates the method of computing the percentage decline and cumulative percentage curves.

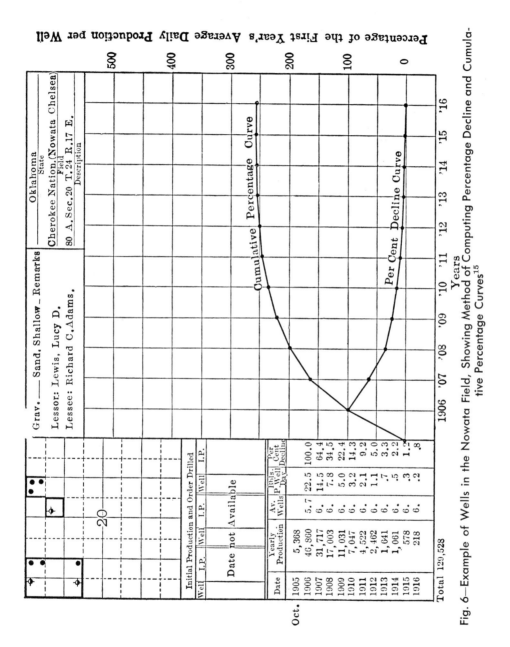

Fig. 6—Example of Wells in the Nowata Field, Showing Method of Computing Percentage Decline and Cumulative Percentage Curves[15]

Fig. 7 (*op. cit.*) represents the total cumulative percentage for a property with a certain average daily production per well the first year. After all the properties were represented, the numerical average of the dots between each set of vertical lines was obtained. These average points were then connected by lines which made a regular curve, representing the average total cumulative percentages for the well data shown on the curve. The maximum and minimum percentage curves were then drawn in, their locations being determined by the outermost dots. The maximum average and minimum total production curves were derived from these three curves. From these curves, with the first year's production of a well or group of wells given, it is possible to determine the minimum amount of oil that in all probability will be produced, the maximum that one may expect, and the amount that the average well of corresponding initial yield will ultimately produce. For example, a well in the Osage Indian Reservation of Oklahoma producing 110 bbl daily, or about 40,000 bbl during its first year, according to Fig. 7 has an estimated total (or ultimate) production of 87,000 bbl and, hence, a future of 47,000 bbl. Reversing the process, and reading from 47,000 bbl on the right margin of this figure to the left where the average total production curve is intersected, we find that a well with a future production of 47,000 bbl must the first year produce, on the average, about 15,300 bbl. This amount deducted from the 47,000 bbl leaves a

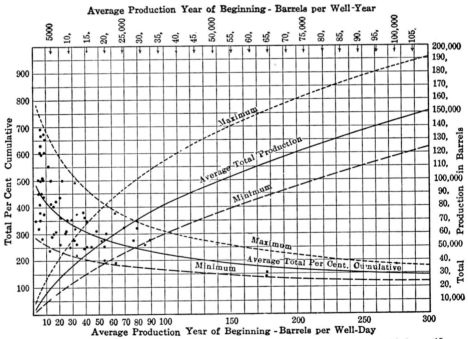

Fig. 7—Appraisal Curve for Wells in the Osage Indian Reservation, Oklahoma[15]

1014

future of 31,700 bbl which, in turn, is the ultimate production of a well producing about 8,800 bbl the first year, and so on. These calculations may be continued until the original 87,000 bbl are extinguished, which should occur at the time the estimated production has declined to 1 bbl per well-day, which is the assumed minimum daily production to which Osage wells can be profitably pumped. The yearly production of the generalized production curve thus derived reads 40,000, 15,300, and 8,800 bbl for the first 3 years, respectively.

"The appraisal curve,[4] illustrated by figure (8), is based on the relation that exists between the production of wells for their first year, and the quantities of oil they will produce ultimately. This particular figure was drawn from the production records of 209 properties in an Oklahoma field. As the average property in that field contains 10 producing wells, the figure may be said to represent about 2,000 wells. The records of each property were taken and each year's average daily production per well was computed and curves plotted from them. Only records where practically the full production had been obtained or where the future could be estimated with confidence were used. From these curves the future production of each property was estimated as explained . . . The future production of each property was added to past production to determine the ultimate production for each property. The next step was to plot for each property the average production per well during the first year or second year against the ultimate production of the well. Each dot, therefore, on figure (8), shows the average production per well the first year on a property and the estimated average ultimate production per well.

"The method illustrated in figure (8) makes use of the first year's production, but the most recent year's production may be used with equal assurance, and the total production, beginning with the production of the well for the past year can be worked out in the same manner. This fact is based on a conclusion for which there seems to be abundant statistical proof. This is as follows:

"*If two wells under similar conditions produce equal amounts during any given year the amounts they will produce thereafter, on the average, will be approximately equal, regardless of their relative ages.* That is, if two groups of wells in the same pool have averaged, say, 5 barrels per day during the past year, they will on the average produce the same amount of oil in the future, even though the wells of one group may be only two years old, whereas the wells of the other group may be five years old. The writers were at first skeptical, but finally were forced to this conclusion because of the preponderance of evidence disclosed by the records of many thousands of wells in many different fields."

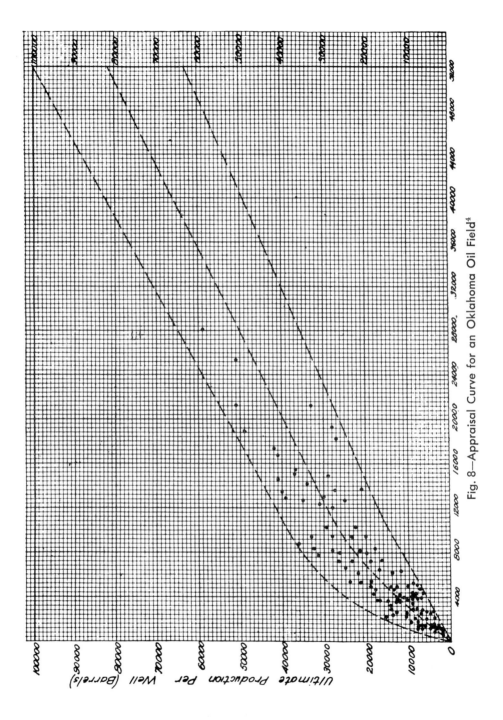

Fig. 8—Appraisal Curve for an Oklahoma Oil Field[4]

Table 2
Estimated Future Production Table — Bradford Sand[4]

Average Production per Well during Taxable Year, Barrels	Estimated Average Future Production per Well, Barrels	Average Production per Well during Taxable Year, Barrels	Estimated Average Future Production per Well, Barrels	Average Production per Well during Taxable Year, Barrels	Estimated Average Future Production per Well, Barrels	Average Production per Well during Taxable Year, Barrels	Estimated Average Future Production per Well, Barrels
30	0	200	1,800	500	3,400	900	5,050
50	250	250	2,150	600	3,850	1,000	5,400
100	850	300	2,450	700	4,300	1,250	6,100
150	1,400	400	2,950	800	4,700	1,500	6,600

In the first edition of the *Manual for the Oil and Gas Industry (op. cit.)*, a number of average future production curves and tables were published — including Table 2 and Fig. 9 shown herein — and comments concerning the Bradford sand made, viz:

"Bradford Sand, Cattaraugus and Allegany Counties, N.Y., and M'Kean County, Pa.

"The Bradford sand is one of the longest lived producers of the Appalachian district. It is of Upper Devonian age and is encountered at depths ranging from 1,300 to 1,700 feet. The pay is unusually thick, averaging about 35 feet, and is commonly fine grained and homogeneous. Porosity averages 18 per cent by volume. The production for the entire field is a quarter of a barrel per well per day and many wells yield only one-tenth of a barrel per day. The curve shows estimated average future production without reference to flooding. The recent introduction of the so-called 'water drive' or flooding method of rejuvenating old properties is accomplishing some remarkable results, but records do not go back far enough to warrant prediction as to ultimate production."

Composite Production-decline Curve

It is possible to combine the decline curves of wells from the same pool and same sand. Only wells exhibiting similar decline characteristics should be used, and the term "composite production-decline curve", as well as "family curve", has been applied to curves made by combining production data. Beal[16,17] proposed that wells be classified according to size. Then, with the law of equal expectation as a basis, one could predict the future production of a well by comparing the production-decline curve of one well with the production-decline curve of another well. There are two common methods of constructing these curves— one is the graphical method and the other the mathematical method.[18,19]

Table 3 shows the production data used in preparing such a curve by the graphical method; and description follows of the procedure to be followed in preparing production-decline curves by the graphical method illustrated in Fig. 10.

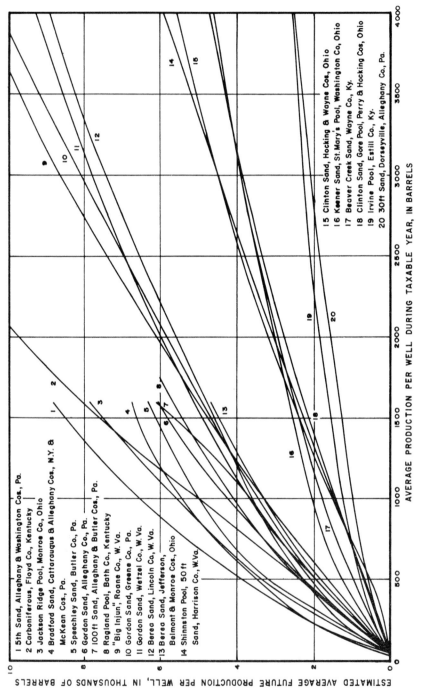

Fig. 9—Estimated Average Future Production Curves, Appalachian Field[‡]

ESTIMATED AVERAGE FUTURE PRODUCTION PER WELL, IN THOUSANDS OF BARRELS

AVERAGE PRODUCTION PER WELL DURING TAXABLE YEAR, IN BARRELS

1 5th Sand, Alleghany & Washington Cos., Pa.
2 Carboniferous, Floyd Co., Kentucky
3 Jackson Ridge Pool, Monroe Co., Ohio
4 Bradford Sand, Cattaraugus & Alleghany Cos., N.Y. & McKean Cos., Pa.
5 Speechley Sand, Butler Co., Pa.
6 Gordon Sand, Alleghany Co., Pa.
7 100ft Sand, Alleghany & Butler Cos., Pa.
8 Ragland Pool, Bath Co., Kentucky
9 "Big Injun", Roane Co., W. Va.
10 Gordon Sand, Greene Co., Pa.
11 Gordon Sand, Wetzel Co., W. Va.
12 Berea Sand, Lincoln Co., W. Va.
13 Berea Sand, Jefferson, Belmont & Monroe Cos., Ohio
14 Shinnston Pool, 50 ft Sand, Harrison Co., W. Va.

15 Clinton Sand, Hocking & Wayne Cos., Ohio
16 Keener Sand, St. Mary's Pool, Washington Co., Ohio
17 Beaver Creek Sand, Wayne Co., Ky.
18 Clinton Sand, Gore Pool, Perry & Hocking Cos., Ohio
19 Irvine Pool, Estill Co., Ky.
20 30ft Sand, Dorseyville, Alleghany Co., Pa.

Table 3

Illustration of Graphic Method[18]

	1915	1916	1917	1918	1919	1920
Calendar Year						
Tract No. 1:						
Total yearly tract production				92,760	43,000	15,200
Number of producing wells				10	10	10
Average yearly production per well				9,276	4,300	1,520
Tract No. 2:						
Total yearly tract production				63,532	54,180	42,960
Number of producing wells				7	9	8
Average yearly production per well				9,076	6,020	5,370
Tract No. 3:						
Total yearly tract production	82,200	74,800	51,850	34,952	29,200	19,890
Number of producing wells	10	17	17	17	16	13
Average yearly production per well	8,220	4,400	3,050	2,056	1,825	1,530
Tract No. 4:						
Total yearly tract production		7,650	13,545	12,625	10,200	7,250
Number of producing wells		1	3	5	5	5
Average yearly production per well		7,650	4,515	2,525	2,040	1,450
Tract No. 5:						
Total yearly tract production		15,060	37,750	14,900	13,100	8,250
Number of producing wells		3	5	5	5	5
Average yearly production per well		5,020	7,550	2,980	2,620	1,650
Tract No. 6:						
Total yearly tract production		16,250	17,400	7,840	7,760	5,880
Number of producing wells		5	8	8	8	7
Average yearly production per well		3,250	2,175	980	970	840
Tract No. 7:						
Total yearly tract production				9,700	8,500	3,650
Number of producing wells				5	5	5
Average yearly production per well				1,940	1,700	730

The curve is started by plotting the entire production history for the average well which had the highest first-year production, regardless of the age of the wells. In this case, the curve was started with the production history of the average well on Tract No. 1. The curve for the second highest average well production (Tract No. 2) is started on the first curve at its proper place. At some point below the point of the tie-in of these two curves an average of the two curves is determined; and this average point is connected with the point of tie-in between the first and second curve, forming an average curve for these two curves. The curve for the third highest average well production (Tract No. 3) is then started on this average curve and a new average curve is determined. This same procedure is continued until all the production-decline data have been used and an average well curve for the several tracts is obtained.

W. W. Cutler, in 1920,[19] discussed a mathematical method of constructing average oil-well production-decline curves. He stated the method was equally applicable to the compilation of curves from both

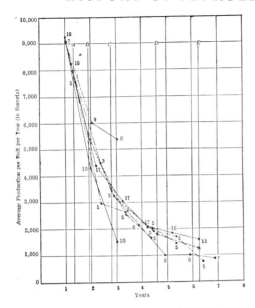

Fig. 10—Family-curve Method of Constructing an Average Production-decline Curve from Production Records of Separate Tracts

(Dashed line, heavier than the broken line, represents the average production-decline curve obtained. The figures along the basic curves represent the number of wells involved.) (From the *Manual for the Oil and Gas Industry*[18])

individual wells and properties. Using the records of tract production as illustrated in Table 4, each year's production for the several tracts was divided by the number of wells producing during the year, thus furnishing the successive yearly productions for the average well of each tract. The tract whose average well showed the highest production for the initial year was used to start the curve.

In 1945, William E. Schoeneck[20] presented a series of hyperbolic curves which were prepared by varying the value of a in the equation for a rectangular hyperbola, $XY = a^2/2$; *wherein:* $X =$ the distance on the abscissa, $Y =$ the distance on the ordinate, and $a =$ the distance from the origin to a point where $X = Y$. A majority of the curves formed by plotting periodic production vs. time on plain coordinate paper will take the form of a hyperbola. Some of these will conform to one of the group of rectangular hyperbolas shown in Fig. 11, and may be extrapolated accordingly.

Fig. 11—Family of Rectangular Hyperbola Curves[20]

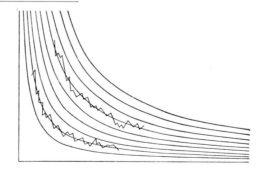

Table 4

Illustration of Cutler's Method[18]

Tract No.	Column 1 A	Column 1 B	Column 2 A	Column 2 B	Column 3 A	Column 3 B	Column 4 A	Column 4 B	Column 5 A	Column 5 B	Column 6 A	Column 6 B
1	84,910 (3)	254,730	52,800 (3)	158,400	------	------	------	------	------	------	------	------
2	83,200 (5)	416,000	53,500 (8)	428,000	40,500 (10)	405,000	32,900 (10)	329,000	24,400 (10)	244,000	17,000 (8)	136,000
3	77,991 (1)	77,991	60,700 (2)	121,400	16,460 (2)	32,920	------	------	------	------	------	------
4	75,500 (6)	453,000	61,500 (8)	492,000	57,600 (8)	460,800	44,300 (11)	487,300	28,650 (14)	401,100	------	------
5	------	------	59,400 (1)	59,400	54,400 (2)	108,800	35,400 (2)	70,800	26,900 (3)	80,700	12,600 (3)	37,800
6	------	------	------	------	43,300 (5)	216,500	36,600 (5)	183,000	28,060 (5)	140,300	17,380 (5)	86,900
7	------	------	------	------	47,800 (6)	286,800	37,800 (6)	226,800	31,600 (6)	189,600	------	------
Dividing to obtain average yearly productions	(15) 1,201,721	80,114	(22) 1,259,200	57,236	(33) 1,510,820	45,782	(34) 1,296,900	38,144	(38) 1,055,700	27,781	(16) 260,700	16,293

A—Yearly production of average well of tract.   ( )—Number of wells producing in tract.   B—Total yearly tract production.

Yearly Production of Average Well Obtained from Above Illustration

Year	Production, barrels
First	80,114
Second	57,236
Third	45,782
Fourth	38,144
Fifth	27,781
Sixth	16,293

Determining Rate of Production from Yearly Production-decline Curves

In October 1921, W. W. Cutler[21] devised a method of determining the rate of production at a particular time by using the yearly production-decline curve. The determination of the rate of production at a particular time in the past would be of considerable value in appraising a piece of property if one were using the Pennsylvania method. However, there are other methods, even at the present time, of arriving at the rate of production if only the yearly production-decline curve is available; and Cutler's method of arriving at the rate of production is presented herewith not only from the historical standpoint, but also with the thought that it might be of use under present conditions. This procedure divides the yearly sector of a production-decline curve into 10 equal time segments and averages the rates of the segments to obtain the yearly average production rate.

In a later publication, in 1924, Cutler[22] mentioned 4 methods which were used to determine or estimate the future production before the development of the production-decline-curve method. These methods were: *1*, the barrels-per-acre method; *2*, the saturation method; *3*, the constant percentage-decline method; and *4*, the percentage-decline method. He believes the barrels-per-acre method and the saturation method are still useful for making preliminary or rough estimates in undrilled areas and also for checking the results obtained by the production-decline-curve method.

Percentage Production-decline Curve

Cutler *(op. cit.)* stated that, if the production of the wells declines at a constant yearly percentage, then this data plotted on semi-logarithmic paper will be a straight line which may be extended into the future. He further stated that very few pools in the United States showed a constant yearly percentage decline under the methods of operation in 1924, and that the constant percentage decline or the percentage-decline-curve method should not be used unless production data indicate this method should be used.

The "law of equal expectations" *(op. cit.)* had been supported by much additional evidence since the time it was first proposed, and in 1924 it was accepted generally. However, the law did not apply to wells producing under hydrostatic pressure, such as wells in the Tampico-Tuxpan district in Mexico. Wells in this area produce under a pressure that is almost constant, and the rate of production is constant until they are drowned out by water.

Material-balance Method of Determining Amount of Oil and Gas in the Reservoir

In Ocober 1929, Stewart Coleman, H. D. Wilde, Jr., and Thomas W. Moore[23] stated that they had developed a series of equations by which, with sufficient data, one could determine the volume of oil contained in a given reservoir. Their equations for the determination of the volume of oil originally in place included the use of factors such as mean rock pressure, amount of dissolved gas, coefficient of volume expansion of gas and oil, fraction of gas wasted, and ratio of volume of gas to oil in the reservoir.

In describing the practical use that could be made of their equation, Coleman, Wilde, and Moore stated:

".... By averaging a number of such calculations made from data taken at various periods in the life of the field, a fairly reliable estimate can be made.

"The lack of essential data is the principal obstacle in applying the derived equation in this paper to most of the existing fields. The initial rock pressures were not recorded, the volumes of gas wasted during flush production were not measured, and the relative volumes of free gas and liquid in the reservoir at the start were not determined. The present trend is toward measuring and recording all pertinent data from the beginning. The usefulness of this equation emphasizes the need of gathering these data."

This is the first reference found in the literature to formation-volume factor which was actually measured later by Ben F. Lindsly and others.

O. L. Brace[24] stated, in 1934, that with the coming of proration, the method of estimating future production from oil wells by the decline-curve method became of little value in connection with fields which were actually prorated, because there was no decline in production during this proration period. Thus, the industry was confronted with going back to the old "volume-content method" of determining the volume of oil in a reservoir and assuming a recovery factor for the oil in the reservoir. These circumstances necessitated a more detailed and accurate appraisal of the reservoir itself and the reservoir rock.

Brace *(op. cit.)* emphasized the correction to be made for stock-tank oil as compared to reservoir oil and recognized the work done by Ben F. Lindsly of the Bureau of Mines in determining the reduction in the volume of reservoir oil due to liberation of the gas from the oil and the necessity for such a correction mentioned by Coleman, Wilde, and Moore *(op. cit.).* According to Brace *(op. cit.)* reporting on work done by Lindsly, it took 327 million barrels of reservoir oil to produce 262 million barrels of stock-tank oil in the East Texas Field.

Ralph J. Schilthuis[25] derived certain formulas patterned after those contained in the Coleman, Wilde, and Moore paper *(op. cit.);* and stated that the formula which he presented took care of the relationships which actually existed between pressure and volume on actual samples

1023

Table 5

Calculation of Initial Oil and Gas Content in Oklahoma City Wilcox Zone [27]

Col. No.		Units	Calculations Made from Reservoir Conditions as of Various Dates					
			7-1-32	1-1-33	7-1-33	1-1-34	7-1-34	1-1-35
1	Crude oil produced	Million bbl	50.0	65.3	87.5	119.2	144.0	167.0
2	Gas produced	Billion cu ft	110.0	163.0	260.0	393.0	480.0	545.0
3	Bottom-hole pressure	Lb per sq in.	1990.0	1740.0	1360.0	790.0	545.0	393.0
4	Gas dissolved in crude	Cu ft per bbl	568.0	509.0	420.0	282.0	225.0	188.0
5	Gas evolved	Cu ft per bbl	147.0	206.0	295.0	433.0	490.0	527.0
6	Correction factor for deviation from ideal gases	No units	0.83	0.84	0.87	0.92	0.95	0.97
7	Dissolved gas in produced crude oil	Billion cu ft	35.7	46.7	62.5	85.2	103.0	119.0
8	Excess gas produced	Billion cu ft	74.3	116.3	197.5	307.8	377.0	426.0
9	Vol. of 1 std cu ft of gas at reservoir conditions	Cu ft	0.00699	0.00809	0.0107	0.0195	0.0292	0.0413
10	Vol. produced oil and dissolved gas at reservoir conditions	Million cu ft	380.0	496.0	665.0	906.0	1093.0	1270.0
11	Vol. occupied by excess gas when dissolved in reservoir crude.	Million cu ft	170.0	266.0	451.0	704.0	861.0	975.0
12	Reservoir volume of total oil and gas produced	Million cu ft	550.0	762.0	1116.0	1610.0	1954.0	2245.0
13	Vol. of gas in the gas cap	Billion cu ft	117.7	131.3	132.7	83.5	72.6	57.5
14	Crude necessary to produce gas-cap gas	Million bbl	801.0	637.0	449.0	193.0	147.0	109.0
15	Crude necessary to produce excess gas	Million bbl	505.0	564.0	669.0	710.0	769.0	808.0
16	Total crude (residual) initially present	Million bbl	1365.0	1266.0	1205.0	1022.0	1060.0	1084.0
17	Initial volume of gas when dissolved in crude	Million bbl	477.0	446.0	425.0	360.0	374.0	384.0
18	Initial fluid present in reservoir	Million bbl	1833.0	1712.0	1630.0	1382.0	1434.0	1468.0

Cubic feet of gas per cubic foot of liquid when dissolved in reservoir crude = 437.0.

Cubic feet of gas vaporized when vaporizing initial crude from 2600 to 14.7 lb = 715 cu ft per barrel.

Percentage of shrinkage based on residual crude when vaporizing initial crude from 2600 to 14.7 lb = 35.4; i.e., residual = 100 per cent.

Residual crude = crude at 60° F. that has been vaporized down to 14.7 lb and 132° F.

of oil and gas, whereas the formulas presented heretofore assumed that the oil and gas behaved as perfect gases and perfect solutions. He stated the formula presented might be valuable in estimating reserves, but that much additional data were necessary in order to determine how valuable a tool the method was for this purpose.

Donald L. Katz[26] was asked in December 1933 if he could estimate the quantity of oil in the Oklahoma City-Wilcox Field, based on the solubility and shrinkage data which Lindsly had obtained. Katz stated that he developed the material-balance procedure which was later described in an AIME publication in 1936, without the benefit of the work done by Coleman, Wilde, and Moore published in 1930 *(op. cit.)*; and that his method of estimating the initial quantity of oil and gas present was based on the premise that the volume occupied by the oil and gas in the reservoir was constant, and that the oil and gas would behave in the reservoir as it did in the laboratory under similar conditions of temperature and pressure. Katz[27] stated:

"In order to apply the method, the data on the oil and gas production, bottom-hole pressures and properties of the crude oil-gas mixtures are obtained. (1) The crude oil produced gives one portion of the initial crude present. The gas produced in excess to the gas dissolved in the crude at the initial reservoir conditions comes from crude in the reservoir and at a definite number of cubic feet per barrel, as shown by solubility data and reservoir-pressure changes. (2) Thus this excess gas accounts for a second portion of crude that was present in the reservoir. When the crude and gas are produced from the reservoir, a space is left, which is occupied by gas vaporizing from the crude in the reservoir with a corresponding drop in reservoir pressure. The volume of this space can be calculated as containing a definite quantity of gas that was evolved from the crude at a definite number of cubic feet per barrel. The cubic feet of gas in the gas phase in the reservoir divided by the gas evolved per barrel of oil gives the barrels of crude that must be present to have maintained the reservoir pressure. (3) This third quantity of crude when added to the other two portions gives the total quantity of crude oil that was present initially. The gas present is then calculated from solubility data and the crude-oil quantity."

Table 5 shows the results of six material-balance calculations made by Katz, who concludes:

"In using the initial quantity of oil present in the reservoir to predict reserves, a recovery factor similar to the one used in sand-volume method is the best way known at present."

The Electric Analyzer

The complete mathematical approach[28] to reservoir-energy analysis has been handicapped by the lack of sufficient information. Therefore, efforts have been directed toward the development of analyzers based upon the analogy between the flow of fluids through porous media and the flow of electric current through conductive media. The data required for an analyzer analysis are the same as required for a material-balance study of the past reservoir performance, viz., the original hydrocarbon-in-place values, the stock-tank oil, water and gas production, the PVT characteristics of the reservoir fluids, and the reservoir pressures. The analyzer and all other methods used in predicting reservoir performance have limitations due to the highly complex nature of the problem which involves three-dimensional movement of non-homogeneous fluids in an irregularly shaped non-homogeneous reservoir.

Determining the Recoverable Oil and Gas by Use of the Physical Properties of the Reservoir

The discovery of the Seminole fields in 1926, and the Oklahoma City Field in 1928, both in Oklahoma, and the following great oil fields in Texas—Yates in 1926, Hendricks in 1926, Van in 1929, East Texas in 1930, Conroe in 1931, Hastings in 1935—brought into existence so much potential oil production that it was necessary to prorate the production from these fields.

The oil-production-decline curve, upon which so much dependency had been placed to estimate the future recovery of oil, ceased to be of any value in prorated fields. In these fields, the production was less than the ability of the wells to produce; thus there was no decline in production during this period. This compelled the industry to go back to the old volume-content or saturation method of estimating the amount of oil in place and assuming a recovery factor for this oil.

The bottom-hole pressure bomb perfected by C. V. Millikan[29] made it possible to determine the reservoir pressure in these new fields. The reservoir-pressure data plotted against accumulative oil production at intervals resulted in a curve which could be extended to any assumed abandoned pressure. The information obtained from this curve, when used with reservoir volume-content data, proved valuable in determining the ultimate production from some oil fields.

In order to determine the amount of oil and gas in place and how much will be recovered, the following data are needed on the reservoir rock: *1*, the porosity; *2*, the fluid saturation; *3*, the permeability; and *4*, oil-recovery factor. These data, with the exception of the oil-recovery factor, are determined by core analysis.

Porosity

Probably the earliest estimates of the porosity of oil reservoir rocks was made by J. F. Carll in 1880.[5] However, the first publication on porosity of oil reservoir rocks by a technical society appeared in *Bulletin 148*, AIME, published in 1920, and written by A. F. Melcher.

Melcher published a paper in 1921,[30] and this paper, along with one by the same author in 1924,[31] described a technique for the determination of porosity and discussed the significance of reservoir-rock porosity in the production of oil.

Melcher is also believed to have been the first person to determine the porosity of a complete core section in 1925.[32] Charles R. Fettke[33] published the first graphic profile of the porosity of an oil sand in 1926.

In 1926, W. L. Russell[34] described a new method for the determination of porosity.

Fluid Saturation

Paul D. Torrey[35] opened the first commercial core laboratory in Bradford, Pennsylvania, in 1928. Not only did he determine the porosity of the reservoir rock, but also the oil and water saturations. On April 8, 1928, Torrey published probably the first graphic representation of a core analysis on which the percent oil and water saturation was shown. Fig. 12 is a copy of this first core graph. Although Chester W. Washburne,[10] in 1915, recognized the existence of water in the oil sand, Torrey is believed to be the first person to make an actual determination of the quantity of water contained within an oil sand.

Permeability

The first detailed discussion of "permeability", as it refers to the fluid-conveying capacity of oil reservoir rocks, was by A. F. Melcher[36] in 1922.

In 1933, the paper by Wyckoff, Botset, Muskat, and Reed,[37] and another paper by Fancher, Lewis, and Barnes,[38] were extremely important reports on the subject of permeability. The term "darcy" as a unit of permeability was first proposed by Wyckoff, Botset, Muskat, and Reed (*op. cit.*). George H. Fancher (*op. cit.*) was the chairman of a special committee of the API which established in 1935 "a standard procedure for determining permeability of porous media". Fancher, Lewis, and Barnes (*op. cit.*) stated that the first work on permeability of porous rock to come to their attention was a thesis by F. H. Newell presented to the Massachusetts Institute of Technology in 1885. Although Newell did not define permeability as was done by more recent investigators, he did force water, kerosene, and crude oil through small disks cut from oil sands which were so contained in holders that the liquids could flow through them at a constant pressure differential.

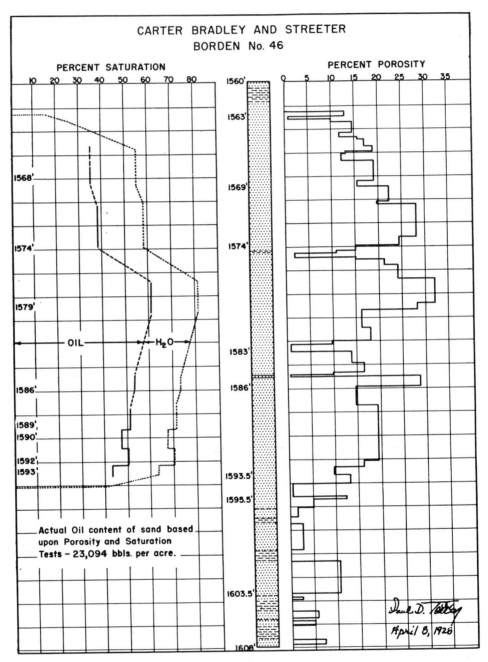

Fig. 12—Copy of First Graphic Representation of a Core Analysis on which the Percent Oil and Water Saturation Was Shown[35]

Volume Content of the Oil and/or Gas Reservoir

In fields that do not show a natural decline in production due either to proration or water encroachment, an accurate determination of the volume of oil and/or gas originally in place is essential in order to arrive at remaining reserves. This is done, first of all, by outlining the areal limits of the reservoir and by constructing an isopachous map of the net effective pay within these limits as determined from electrical logs, micrologs, and core analyses. Calculations based on the results of planimetering the isopachous map provide the gross volume of the reservoir rock. Once this is determined, the amount of oil and/or gas contained therein is calculated through the use of porosity data, oil-, gas-, and water-saturation data, formation-volume-factor data, and, if free gas is present in the reservoir, the compressibility factor for the gas.

During the development of a field, however, there is often a need to determine the amount of oil and/or gas beneath a specific proved lease in order to place a value on the lease. This is usually done in basically the same manner as just discussed, with the areal limits defined by the lease lines and with an average net effective pay beneath the lease as determined from electric logs, micrologs, and core-analysis data.

Park J. Jones[39] developed in 1957 a method of determining the volume of the producing reservoir, provided the reservoir is small, using the data obtained from drawdown tests on the discovery well while it is producing at constant rates.

Oil-recovery Factor

Core Laboratories, Inc.[40] was probably one of the first commercial laboratories to present in their core-analysis report an estimate of the amount of recoverable oil from the cores under gas-drive conditions and under water-drive conditions. James A. Lewis and William L. Horner were primarily responsible for the establishment of this core-analysis service. Many commercial laboratories now furnish the same service and some oil companies handle core-analysis work in their own laboratories.

In 1945, R. C. Craze and S. E. Buckley[41] made a study of 27 fields which appeared to be depletion-type reservoirs. The final gas saturation in these fields showed considerable variation, ranging from 20 to 40 percent of the pore space with the average at 30.4 percent.

The final gas saturation gives a measure of the recoverable oil. If the original gas saturation were zero, then the pore space was occupied by oil and interstitial water. If only the oil were produced from a depletion-type reservoir, the space initially occupied by the oil would be occupied by gas. Thus final gas saturation is a measure of recoverable oil.

In 1956, J. J. Arps[42] stated that, if a sufficient number of accurate oil- and water-saturation data are available from analyses of freshly recovered cores, an approximation of the total free-gas space to be expected may be obtained. In this method it was assumed that the behavior of the core's contents as the core was being removed from the hole would be similar to the behavior of a depletion-type reservoir.

Arps (*op. cit.*) presented an equation for calculating the unit recovery of oil from a depletion-type reservoir in barrels per acre-foot. This equation is:

$$DR = 7,758 \cdot f \cdot [(1-S_w/B_i) - (1-S_w-S_g/B_a)], \text{ bbl per acre-foot} \tag{1}$$

Wherein:

f = porosity, as a fraction.
S_w = interstitial water, as a fraction of total pore space.
S_g = final gas space, as a fraction of total pore space.
B_i = single-phase formation-volume factor for oil under initial conditions.
B_a = single-phase formation-volume factor for oil at abandonment reservoir pressure.

In another approach to the problem, Arps presented Table 6, which shows recoveries in percent of oil in place calculated from the well-known depletion equation for 6 different types of reservoir rock and 12 synthetic crude-oil—solution-gas combinations.[42,43,44] He stated that, where no detailed data are available concerning the reservoir rock or fluid contents, data in Table 6 can be used for estimating the possible range of depletion recoveries.

Table 6

Primary Recovery in Percent of Oil in Place for Depletion-type
Reservoirs[42]

Oil Solution Gas-oil Ratio, Cu ft per Bbl	Oil Gravity, Deg API	Sand or Sandstones			Limestone, Dolomite or Chert		
		Maximum	Average	Minimum	Maximum	Average	Minimum
60	15	12.8	8.6	2.6	28.0	4.0	0.6
	30	21.3	15.2	8.7	32.8	9.9	2.9
	50	34.2	24.8	16.9	39.0	18.6	8.0
200	15	13.3	8.8	3.3	27.5	4.5	0.9
	30	22.2	15.2	8.4	32.3	9.8	2.6
	50	37.4	26.4	17.6	39.8	19.3	7.4
600	15	18.0	11.3	6.0	26.6	6.9	1.9
	30	24.3	15.1	8.4	30.0	9.6	(2.5)
	50	35.6	23.0	13.8	36.1	15.1	(4.3)
1,000	15	------	------	------	------	------	----
	30	34.4	21.2	12.6	32.6	13.2	(4.0)
	50	33.7	20.2	11.6	31.8	12.0	(3.1)
2,000	15	------	------	------	------	------	----
	30	--	------	----	.	------	----
	50	40.7	24.8	15.6	32.8	(14.5)	(5.0)

S. E. Buckley and M. C. Leverett,[45] S. J. Pirson,[46] and H. J. Welge[47] proposed methods for determining the recoverable oil from water-drive reservoirs using laboratory data on relative-permeability relationships for reservoir oil and water combined with viscosity data.

The method[42] most commonly used to determine recoveries from water-drive reservoirs is to consider the oil-saturation data from core analysis as the residual oil remaining in the reservoir rock after complete water flooding. This method assumes that the water from the drilling fluid floods the oil out of the core as it is being cut. The oil recovery calculated by this method does give a measure of the possible recovery from a completely water-flooded core, but one could not use this same figure for an actual water-drive reservoir without correcting for permeability, stratification, and lateral-sweep effects.

Craze and Buckley,[41] in their statistical study of water-drive reservoirs, found the recovery data closely related to the oil viscosity and the reservoir permeability. The residual-oil saturation under reservoir conditions for a formation containing 1 centipoise oil and having an average permeability of 500 millidarcys was estimated at 36.5 percent of the pore space.

R. K. Guthrie and M. H. Greenberger[48] made a study of the statistical data on water-drive fields presented by Craze and Buckley *(op. cit.)* and formulated an equation for the recovery factor which took into consideration the permeability of the formation, the interstitial water saturation, the oil viscosity, the porosity, and the pay thickness. As in the Craze-Buckley correlation, one will obtain from the Guthrie-Greenberg equation an overall recovery factor per acre-foot and not the unit recovery factor obtainable by 100-percent efficient water flooding as is obtained using core-analysis data.

Arps presented the following equation for calculating the unit recovery factor for a water-drive reservoir *(WR)*:[42]

$$WR = 7,758 \times f \times [(1-S_w/B_o)-S_o], \; bbl \; per \; acre\text{-}foot \quad (2)$$

Wherein:

f = porosity, as a fraction.
S_w = interstitial water, as a fraction of the pore space.
S_o = residual - oil saturation under surface conditions, as a fraction of total pore space.
B_o = original oil formation-volume factor.

During the early life of a field, it is important to determine whether a reservoir is producing under a depletion-type drive, an effective water drive, or a combination of both, inasmuch as the oil recovery from a water-drive reservoir is sometimes twice as much as from a similar depletion-type reservoir. The type drive is generally determined through a study of production in conjunction with reservoir pressures. A rapid decline in reservoir pressure with production indicates a depletion-type reservoir, and a slow decline in reservoir pressure indicates a water-drive reservoir. It should be borne in mind, however, that the removal of a relatively small amount of oil from a large depletion-type reservoir will result in a small drop in pressure, which might lead to the erroneous conclusion that a water drive existed.

George R. Elliott, in 1945,[49] with a series of curves showed the relationship between reservoir pressure and accumulative oil production for 10 reservoirs showing varying degrees of water influx. He calculated the water influx (K) in barrels of water encroachment per month per pound of pressure at a given time and the original reservoir pressure. To show the "degree" of water drive when comparing one reservoir with another, he divided the factor K by the acre-feet of oil in the reservoir.

Comparative Oil-recovery Data

Oil recoveries from old fields have always been used as an indication of the recoveries one might expect from a similar new oil field. A recent survey[50] showed the oil recoveries from fields producing from the principal producing formations in the 7 southwestern states through 1954. These recovery figures are on the basis of recovery per acre and per acre-foot.

The following is an example of these data on 3 productive formations in Texas which have been producing from representative fields for 10 years or more.

Formation	No. of Fields	Range of Oil Recovery, Barrels	
		Per Acre	Per Acre-foot
Woodbine—East Texas	22	686-55,724	60-1,095
Frio—Middle Gulf Coast	9	2,549-15,114	86- 541
Ellenburger—West Texas	12	1,268-10,358	6- 116

The annual statistical publications of the American Institute of Mining and Metallurgical Engineers contain oil-recovery data on fields throughout the United States.

Summary of Methods of Estimating Recoverable Oil

Dean H. Sheldon, in February 1953,[51] stated the production-decline method of estimating future recovery of oil permits an estimate of the rate at which the oil would be recovered. No other production-decline relationship offers this advantage. The rate of oil production plotted against accumulative oil production gives a curve which approaches a straight line and may be extended into the future to estimate the future recoverable oil from a depletion-type reservoir. The reservoir-pressure data plotted against accumulative oil-production data gives a curve which is useful in estimating the future production from the same type reservoir.

The material-balance equation method *(op. cit.)* and the volumetric method may be used for the same purpose. However, none of the foregoing methods will give us an estimate as to the rate of production.

Estimating Recovery of Gas from Natural-gas Fields

Ralph E. Davis, in June 1927,[52] stated that gas was commonly measured by the application of Boyle's Law for gases and gave an illustration of the effect of pressure on the volume of gas by the application of this law, as shown in Fig. 13.

This demonstration illustrates a direct relationship between the pressure and the volume of gas. If the pressure on a given quantity of gas is doubled, the illustration shows there is only half as much volume as in the first instance. If the pressure is doubled again, the volume is reduced by half again.

The fact *(op. cit.)* that the escape of gas from a reservoir is accompanied by a proportional reduction in pressures forms the basis for the estimation of gas reserves underground. For example, if a reservoir had an original pressure of 1,000 psi and if, when the pressure dropped to 900 psi, 50 billion cubic feet were withdrawn, the conclusion would be that 1/10 of the total quantity of gas in the reservoir had been produced; thus the total original gas present must have been 500 billion cubic feet.

Fig. 14 is an illustration of how this principle was applied in the appraisal of a West Virginia gas field at the end of 1923. The relation between the rock pressure decline and immediate gas production which accompanied this decline is shown by the two curves *AB* and *CF*, from which it is possible to estimate the ultimate production of the field.

There are two methods[53] of estimating gas reserves: *1*, the porosity-pressure method; and *2*, the rock-pressure—production-decline method.

The equation *(op. cit.)* used in the rock-pressure—production-decline-curve method of estimating recoverable gas or gas in place in a reservoir takes into consideration the deviation from Boyle's Law which would be expected where original reservoir pressure exceeded 500 psi.

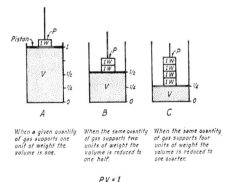

When a given quantity of gas supports one unit of weight the volume is one.

When the same quantity of gas supports two units of weight the volume is reduced to one half.

When the same quantity of gas supports four units of weight the volume is reduced to one quarter.

$$PV = 1$$

Fig. 13—Illustration of Effect of Pressure on Volume of Gas[52]

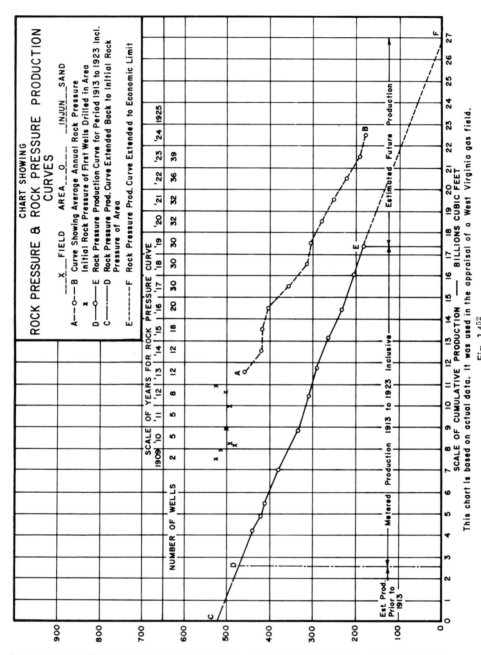

CHART SHOWING
ROCK PRESSURE & ROCK PRESSURE PRODUCTION CURVES

X FIELD AREA O INJUN SAND

A—o—B Curve Showing Average Annual Rock Pressure
x Initial Rock Pressure of First Wells Drilled in Area
D—o—E Rock Pressure Production Curve for Period 1913 to 1923 Incl.
C——D Rock Pressure Prod. Curve Extended Back to Initial Rock Pressure of Area
E———F Rock Pressure Prod. Curve Extended to Economic Limit

Fig. 14[52]

This chart is based on actual data. It was used in the appraisal of a West Virginia gas field.

Production-performance estimates[54] may be made when sufficient production and pressure data are available, and the average pressure plotted against cumulative production on Cartesian coordinate paper will yield substantially a straight line which may be extended to an assumed abandonment pressure in order to measure the total estimated ultimate production.

It may be necessary to compare a new gas field with production characteristics from similar nearby fields, when sufficient data on the newly discovered field are not available.[53] The open-flow capacity of a well, or rather the decline in open-flow capacity of a well, may be plotted and extended into the future provided there are sufficient open-flow test data which have been made over a sufficient period of time to indicate a decline in the open-flow capacity of the individual well.

Compressibility Factor

Joannes D. van der Waals in 1873,[55] recognized the fact that the volume of gas decreased less rapidly with a given increase in pressure than the simple gas laws would call for, if the gas is at high pressure.

van der Waals pointed out that at very high pressures the molecules are crowded together so closely that there is little space between them for further compression. It is the space between the molecules of the gas, rather than the gas molecules, which is decreased when pressure is increased. To take care of this fact and that of intermolecular attraction also, he wrote an equation of gas compressibility.

A number of persons have worked on the theoretical method of calculating the compressibility of natural gas, and another group worked upon the experimental method of determining this compressibility factor using a sample of natural gas.

E. S. Burnett in his paper, "Compressibility Determination without Volume Measurements",[56] developed an apparatus for determining the compressibility without volume measurements. Equipment very similar to that developed by Burnett was constructed by A. B. Stevens[57] and Lee Freidman in 1941, and the compressibility factor was determined on four typical natural gases from two fields in Texas and one in Louisiana.

George Granger Brown in 1940,[58] in an article entitled "Deviations of Natural Gas from Ideal Gas Laws", presented a chart from which the compressibility factor could be determined provided the pseudo-reduced pressure and the pseudo-reduced temperature were available.

Katz, Matthews, and Roland[59] compared the calculated compressibility factor for 29 different natural gases with the experimental compressibility factor for the same gases and found the numerical average error to be 1.19 percent and the algebraic average error to be —0.16 percent.

VALUATION OF OIL PROPERTIES

Values and Valuation Methods

One of the first references in the literature to anything approaching the term "valuation of oil and gas properties" appears in a book entitled *Rock Oil in Pennsylvania and Elsewhere* which was written by Thomas A. Gale[60] of Riceville, Pennsylvania, in 1860. Gale stated that oil was selling for 40 cents per gallon, that it cost up to $2,000 for equipment and land to drill a well, and $5 per day for 2 men and a boy, plus fuel and maintenance. The problem to be considered was whether these costs could be returned out of the sale of the oil to be produced. Since it was believed by many at that time that oil ran underground in great rivers and collected in vast lakes, valuation procedures of the day were, in Gale's words, ". . . in regard to the yield, we pretend to nothing more than to give a guess—the Yankee's privilege."

On May 5, 1867, the *Titusville Herald*[1] carried the following: "The average cost of sinking wells is $3,300 each . . . . The average life of wells is six months. The average profit of a 30 bbl. well, run entirely by gas, with oil at $2 per bbl. is $504 for its whole life."

In a book by John J. McLaurin, published in 1896,[2] we find some statements of which the following are examples: "John McClintock's farm . . . was leased in September of 1859 for one-half the oil . . . One hundred wells rendered the farm extremely productive." Again: ". . . 'I'll give you three hundred thousand dollars for it,' he said to Wade, whom the offer well-nigh paralyzed." The following statement is of interest because this is evidence that bonuses were paid for drill sites: " . . . A half-acre lease on the Holmden farm realized bonuses of twenty-four-thousand dollars before a well was drilled on the property." Also: "Eight rods square on the Heydrick tract leased for five-thousand dollars and fifty per cent of the oil . . ." And then: ". . . The speculative mania . . . ., that swept over the oil regions in 1864-65, deluged the banks with applications for temporary loans to be used in purchasing lands and oil-interests."

Paul Paine, a consultant from Los Angeles, writing in 1954,[61] stated he believed the earliest valuation work was probably done by Colonel E. L. Drake in 1859 because he used some valuation talk in order to "hosstrade" his way out of a bad lease-royalty provision. Paine also stated, "The younger Silliman made many valuation reports in the early '60's for use in the promotion of Scott, Hyde, Alexander, and Green, of the Pennsylvania Railroad [group]. Estimates of the recoverable oil had no place in these reports, but they did contain valuations in the form of statements of anticipated future income. Silliman painted with a big brush the supply of oil was unlimited (in theory) and he relied on his estimates of earnings to convert [the prospective investors]."

According to E. B. Redpath, executive vice president of The Ohio Oil Company until his retirement September 1953,[62] the valuation of oil properties was a very simplified matter in the early 1900's as compared to present-day methods. With nothing more than production by months and an occasional incompletely described driller's log indicating the oil sand, it was common practice to discount any estimates and depend pretty much upon the appraiser's vast experience. The appraiser was, in effect, comparing the production experience from older fields based on the recorded thickness of the sand and applying this reasoning to the new properties being appraised.

Pricing a piece of property on the payout basis, i.e., "money-in-and-money-out", the "per-daily-barrel" of production was used as a measure of value. Sometimes deals *(op. cit.)* were made on a matter of instinct and judgment, or other rule-of-thumb methods which the appraiser might have originated himself. In Redpath's opinion these early methods were more effective and more accurate than one generally concedes.

In 1901, according to M. E. Lombardi,[9] a comparative valuation report was prepared by Arthur F. L. Bell, William Mulholland, and Bernard Benfield, on a group of properties in the Kern River Field, Kern County, California. This report placed no dollar value on any of the properties, but compared the value of a number of properties with the value of a quarter section of oil land near the center of the field. Its value per acre was assumed to be so many thousands of dollars, and the three engineers just mentioned were instructed to express a value of all other properties in terms of this one. These three engineers determined the average thickness of the sands by use of cross sections, conducted certain tests to determine the possible recovery of the oil in place in the reservoir, and assumed all the oil would be recovered from half the oil sand.

Values in Land-classification Work

In 1905, Ralph Arnold[6] undertook the oil work of the United States Geological Survey in California. It was his task to gather ideas as to the values in order to classify government lands. However, even this work was not then identified as being that of a "valuation". Assisted by Robert Anderson and Harry Johnson, a detailed study was made of Santa Maria, Coalinga, and other California fields. The importance of shutting off upper water before drilling into and producing the oil sand was recognized, but the operator was not easily convinced this procedure would increase the oil recovery.

As an arbitrary rule-of-thumb method *(op. cit.)*, it was assumed that a 10-percent fall-off of production each year could be used in order to estimate the life and probable total productivity of any well. This method was soon found to be wrong as no two wells fell off in production at the same rate.

It was no problem to determine the volume of the reservoir rock provided sufficient data were available. It was a problem to determine the volume of the oil in the reservoir rock, because the amount of saturation produced a factor which was considered a sort of practical guessing contest. There were no such things as cores in those days, but sometimes the reservoir rock outcropped and samples from these outcrops were examined as the guessing contest continued. The production indicated by curves seldom checked with the estimates of recovery based on the volume content of the reservoir.

It was found that the future selling price of the oil and the cost of recovering the oil were just as important as the amount of reserve and the rate at which these reserves would be recovered. The future selling price of the oil would be influenced by the relationship between the value of the oil as a fuel and that of coal. The operators' financial ability to carry on a development program would also affect the value of the property.

The public-land situation in some cases entered into the appraisal of the property. Entire properties could be lost for the failure of original owners to take advantage of the protective clauses of the continually changing lease laws. In other words, one might lose title to the property, which would mean that he lost what value the property might have.

The lack of cooperative organizations among the smaller independent operators left them at the mercy of those who provided a market for the oil.[2] This naturally affected the value of their properties. Subsequently, organizations were formed which tended to protect or improve the lot of the independent operator. Similarly, an operator who was unable to protect himself from drainage from offset wells was at a disadvantage and this, also, affected the value of his property.

The infiltration of water from natural causes[6] or by faulty casing jobs had an effect on the value of the property until finally the geologist or engineer was able to predict the rate of movement of water infiltration and also find methods of correcting the entrances of extraneous water into the oil reservoir. Later it was found, in the case of heavy oil, that the infiltration of the edge water was very beneficial in that it helped flush the heavy oil out of the sands and into the well.

Arnold lectured on oil geology and appraisal techniques at the University of Chicago in 1914. In 1915, he lectured on the same subjects at Harvard and at Massachusetts Institute of Technology.

A 1911 Valuation Report[63]

W. W. Orcutt of California, was another pioneer in the valuation of oil and gas properties. Much of the following data concerning a 1911 valuation report comes from unpublished papers in the library of the University of California, which were placed there by Walter Stalder and others.

Orcutt developed a percentage-decline curve which he used in preparing the valuations for the Monte Cristo Oil Company properties in the Maricopa Field, California. The following data were used in preparing this percentage-decline curve.

W. W. Orcutt Percentage-decline Curve

Year	Percent Decline from Previous Year	Percent of Initial Year
1	—	100
2	20	80
3	20	64
4	20	51
5	15	43
6	15	37
7	15	31
8	15	26
9	10	23
10	10	21
11	10	19
?	10	to economic limit

Table 7 is a copy of Orcutt's valuation of the Monte Cristo Oil Company properties. As is shown on the bottom of this original sheet, Stalder stated, "The above figures are from a pencil copy of a valuation made by Mr. W. W. Orcutt of the Union Oil Company of California, in February 1911." Walter Stalder and A. K. P. Harmon III prepared the percentage-decline curve shown in Fig. 15 from the production data used in Orcutt's valuation. This is probably the first use of the production-decline curve data in preparing a valution of an oil property.

Valuation of Illinois Properties—1913

Raymond S. Blatchley, writing about Crawford and Lawrence Counties, Illinois, in 1913,[64] stated that investments in developed oil fields were matters of calculation and judgment. In those days, it was customary for the purchasing company to carry on a 10-day gage of the properties which they were considering purchasing and then offer so much per barrel for settled production. The prices varied at that time between $400 and $500 for each barrel of daily production.

Table 7

Copy of W. W. Orcutt's Valuation of the Monte Cristo Oil Company
Properties in 1911[63]

Monte Cristo Oil Co. (Mariposa Calif.)

No. wells completed 19 (2 now producing)
No. wells to be drilled { 10 line, 5 inside

average thickness of producing sand 85 ft.
Est. Oil Content 80,000 bbl. for ... recoverable 40,000 ..

160 Acres

Year	No. wells producing	Daily av. wells table.	Production av. bbls. net	Price per bbl.	Gross total $	Expenditure developing & op. at 75¢	Expenditure Cumulative Totals	Profit $	Present worth 6% per ant.
1909	15	55	399,091.80	.50					
1910	17	43	266,215.37	.50					
Estimated:									
1911	27	50	492,750	.50	246,375	.25	124,275	122,100	115,140
1912	40	50	730,000	.50	365,000	.23	170,500	194,500	179,105
1913	40	40	594,000	.50	297,000	.08	47,520	249,480	209,563
1914	40	33	474,000	.50	237,000	.09	42,840	195,160	154,566
1915	40	26	380,980	.50	190,490	.10	38,098	152,393	113,836
1916	40	23	323,883	.50	161,916	.10	32,383	129,533	91,321
1917	40	20	276,258	.50	138,129	.11	30,388	107,741	71,648
1918	40	15	234,820	.50	117,410	.11	25,830	91,580	57,421
1919	40	13	199,597	.50	99,798	.12	23,951	75,847	44,901
1920	40	12	177,638	.50	88,819	.12	21,566	68,253	38,085
1921	40	11	161,675	.50	80,887	.13	21,017	59,870	31,551
1922	40	10	145,508	.50	72,754	.13	18,916	53,738	24,708
1923	40	9	130,958	.50	65,474	.14	18,333	47,141	22,109
1924	40	8	116,863	.50	58,431	.15	17,529	40,902	17,079
1925	40	7	104,177	.50	52,083	.16	16,668	35,415	14,768
1926	40	6	93,760	.50	46,880	.17	15,969	30,911	12,179
1927	40	6	84,384	.50	42,192	.18	16,189	27,003	10,018
			4,725,201		2,362,938		680,972	1,681,566	1,204,998

602,499

The above figures were prepared in our office and an estimate made by Wm. W. Orcutt of the Union Oil Company of California about February 9, 1911, and were modified. The accompany of decline curve was made by Walter Stalder and Wm. P. Hanson III therein 1911 by this same principle of the oil company of the proper way the oil field. Report on the present value of the Oil Properties of the Union Oil Company of California by Walter Stalder July 21, 19...

Walter Stalder
July 31, 1942.

S.1911
.s.

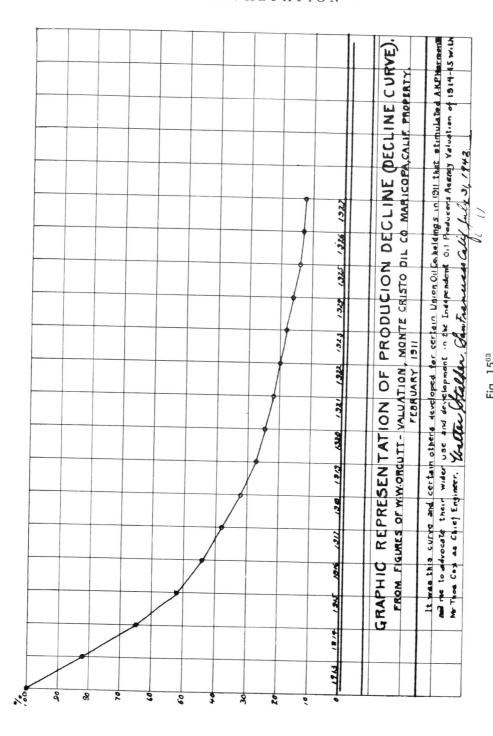

GRAPHIC REPRESENTATION OF PRODUCION DECLINE (DECLINE CURVE).

FROM FIGURES OF W.W.ORCUTT - VALUATION, MONTE CRISTO OIL CO MARICOPA,CALIF. PROPERTY.
FEBRUARY 1911

It was this curve and certain others developed for certain Union Oil Co holdings in 1911 that stimulated A.K.P.harmon
and me to advocate their wider use and development in the Independent Oil Producers Agency Valuation of 1914-15 with
Mr Thos Cox as Chief Engineer. Walter Stalder. SanFrancisco Calif July 31, 1942.

Fig. 15⁶³

For example, for a 40-acre lease producing steadily 500 bbl of oil per day, the purchasing price would be—at $400 per barrel—500 times $400 or $200,000. With a reasonable decline in production, this property should pay itself out within about three years.

Independent Oil Producers Agency of California Valuation Report—1914-15

An important milestone in the development of oil-property valuation occurred in 1914 and 1915 through research made by the Independent Oil Producers Agency of California. Mark L. Requa[65] was the chairman of this committee and the engineering work was done under the direction of Thomas Cox. Their problem or job was to prepare an accurate appraisal of all the properties held under the IOPA.

The purpose of the valuation was to bring about the consolidation of certain oil companies with the idea of improving financial conditions of the operators who were consolidating their properties. The appraisal was completed in September 1915, and Thomas Cox [63] developed in his study what he called the "Cox Formula Equation". This formula presented a method of projecting the future (declining) production of producing oil wells by use of a declining percentage curve.

Cox stated that his formula or equation was not presented as a "mathematical" formula, but it was applicable for individual wells where past production data permitted its use. The basis for the formula was "that the past performance of the well is the indication of the future, provided that the well is kept in good physical condition."

The formula or equation followed, and was:

$$[(log\ a/b)/n—1] = log\ x \qquad (3)$$
$$r = x — 1 \qquad (4)$$

Wherein:

a = highest production for total time period considered.

b = lowest production for total time period considered.

n = number of time periods between high and low production.

r = average time period percent of decrease in decimal form for the total time period considered.

M. L. Requa *(op. cit.)* of San Francisco, California, in February 1918, presented an abstract of the appraisement committee report of the Independent Oil Producers Agency (1914-15), of which he was chairman. The other members of the committee were M. V. McQuigg and R. S. Haseltine. They gave due credit to Thomas Cox, the engineer in charge.

"In valuing the properties of the Independent Oil Producers Agency, the Committee has considered the following facts:

"1. That from each property there will ultimately be produced a certain total quantity of oil.

1042

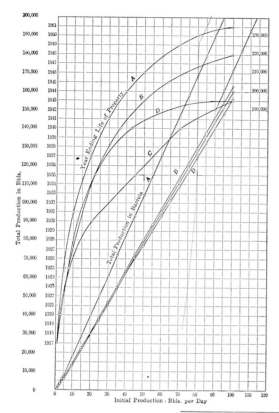

Fig. 16—This shows by direct reading the estimated production of 1 well and the year of ending at the 1 bbl per day[65]

Illustration: New well with initial production of 50 bbl per day first year, read up to intersection of total production line, thence to the left and read 104,000 bbl. Going back to the 50-bbl line and up to the intersection of the curve line, thence to the left, 1946 will be the year ending the production at the 1-bbl-per-day point.

A=Coalinga curve
B=Maricopa curve
C=Santa Maria curve
D=Newlove and Hartwell curve

"2. That in the production of that oil a certain total quantity of money will be expended.

"3. That a certain total amount of money will be received from the oil.

"4. That the total net receipts will be the total gross receipts less the cost of the development and production.

"5. That the present value of the net receipts must be such an amount that when invested by a purchaser it will be returned with 8 percent interest additional during the life of the property."

Requa *(op. cit.)* presented the curve shown in Fig. 16, which was developed for the purpose of estimating the ultimate production to be derived from an individual well having a certain average production for the first year. This curve also showed the year when this well's production declined to 1 bbl per day.

Miscellaneous Views of Valuation Methods—1915-1919

M. E. Lombardi, writing in 1915,[9] described the Pennsylvania method of determining the value of an oil property, as follows: "As applied by some of the largest buyers of oil-land, this method is as follows: An oil-property is priced on the basis of a certain amount per barrel of daily settled production from wells on the property. This price varies with the price of oil, and is usually about $100 a barrel per day for each 10¢ variation in the price of oil. The price for the property must be such that money will be returned in, at most, four years. Undrilled land must be sufficient to hold production for these four years, taking account of the inevitable decline of the old wells. Wells must be six months old before their production is considered settled."

An equation (op. cit.) with two unknown factors could be written and solved by trial, which would theoretically fix the value of oil properties which are near the beginning of their life. At least, by means of such an equation the weight to be given, in the final judgment, to each of the factors in a valuation could be mathematically indicated. For example, Lombardi considered an undeveloped property, consisting of 300 acres, in a partly developed field and arrived at the value of the property in the following equation:

"Known or approximated factors:

A. Yield per well, first year =200 bbl. per day
    (net saleable).
B. Cost of development per well = $30,000.
C. Price received for oil, net = 50¢ per bbl.
D. Cost of production (including drilling to maintain production) = 30¢ per barrel.
E. Rate of interest demanded (profit) = 12%.
F. Amortization fund (10 years)—8%.

"Unknown factors:

X = value of land.
Y = number of initial wells to be drilled and charged to capital account to establish satisfactory income; assumed, in this instance, as 15.

then:

$$(E + F) \ X + (E + F) \ (B \times Y) = A \ (C-D) \times 365 \times Y.$$

substituting:

$$0.20X + 0.20 \ (30,000 \times 15) = 200 \times 0.20 \times 365 \times 15.$$

solving:

$$X = \$645,000, \text{ or } \$2,150 \text{ per acre for the land.}$$"

Roswell H. Johnson and L. G. Huntley stated, in 1915,[66] that the barrel-per-day, or Pennsylvania method, of determining the value of an oil property was essentially unsound in that the decline curve was not a straight line, but one where the rate of decline itself gradually declined. The maintenance was assumed by this method to be a constant per barrel, whereas it gradually increased. In their opinion, an oil property had two values, or value in two different senses. First, it had an exchange value which is an amount for which it could be sold; and second, it had productive value or the amount of present capital which the income could repay with that rate of interest necessary to attract capital to such ventures, including the consideration for risk. The appraiser should ascertain the productive value as his basis, because the property should not sell below this figure.

Also, the appraiser should consider the use for which the valuation is intended *(op. cit.)*. If the purpose of the valuation is for buying or selling, it must be concerned with both exchange and productive values.

Carl H. Beal stated, in 1919,[14] that there were two methods generally used in purchasing oil lands, or determining the amount of the purchase price. First was the settled-production or Pennsylvania method; and the second was an appraisal method in which one determines the amount of money the purchaser can afford to invest in a property under certain conditions.

Beal made a very detailed study of the settled-production or Pennsylvania method, and came to the conclusion that there was no scientific basis for the method. The one purchasing the property by the Pennsylvania method apparently was only concerned or was thinking in terms of what the property would sell for, rather than what earnings one might secure from operating the property. They were placing a value on oil property somewhat as one might value a horse. They were thinking in terms of what the horse could be sold for, not how much money could be made by using the horse in a business venture.

In 1919, Ralph Arnold[67] wrote that one of the best gages of the value of a property was how long it would take to pay out the initial price, or how long it would take to get the investment back. This payback was a valuable thing as it varied with fields and properties. Arnold made the statement that a good rule-of-thumb approximation of the value of the lessor's one-eighth royalty was that it was equal to a quarter interest in the working interest, because there were no expenses attached to the royalty. However, after making such a statement, he gave a number of reasons why it could not be true; and, in other words, indicated that there was no rule-of-thumb approximation which was reliable because of the many factors entering into the values of properties.

Valuation for Income-tax Purposes
First Tax Laws

The Federal income-tax law was responsible for a great expansion of interest in and use of valuations of oil and gas properties. The first income-tax law was styled "Tariff Act of October 3, 1913" and was passed by the 63rd Congress on October 3, 1913. This revenue act provided for a depletion allowance as a tax reduction effective for the year beginning March 1, 1913, and the basis for depletion was the fair market value of the property at March 1, 1913. Cost depletion only was effective for the years 1913 to 1918. The 1918 revenue law, known as the "Revenue Act of 1918",[4] was passed by Congress on February 24, 1919. One of the outstanding tax provisions of the 1918 act was the provision for discovery depletions. It provided for a deduction which, at the time the recoverable mineral content was exhausted, would amount to the value of the property within 30 days after discovery. In other words, it put the discoverer on the same footing as the one who bought the property after its value was demonstrated by discovery. In the Revenue Act of 1924, the discovery depletion was limited to 50 percent of the net income from the property of the taxpayer (before depletion); but by provision of the Revenue Act of 1926, passed by Congress on February 26, 1926, and made effective as of January 1925, discovery depletion was superseded by depletion determined as a percentage of income, and was fixed at $27\frac{1}{2}$ percent of the gross income, limited to 50 percent of the net income from the property. Thus, beginning with the 1926 act, one could use percentage depletion or could use cost depletion. The discovery valuation for the purpose of calculating depletion was not included in the act of 1926. At the present time (1957), the depletion allowance is the same as that provided in the act of 1926.

The Revenue Act of 1918 (op. cit.) provided a reasonable deduction for depletion of natural deposits and for depreciation of improvements which was permitted, based: "(a) Upon cost, if acquired after February 28, 1913; or (b) Upon the fair market value as of March 1, 1913, if acquired prior thereto; or (c) Upon the fair market value within 30 days of discovery in the case of mines, oil and gas wells, discovered by the taxpayer after February 28, 1913, where the fair market value is disproportionate to the cost."

The Manual for the Oil and Gas Industry under the Revenue Act of 1918 (op. cit.) was published in 1919 by the U. S. Treasury, Internal Revenue Department. Those taking part in the collection and compilation of the material on which the manual was based, comprised the following:[68]

"Ralph Arnold, Chief of the Oil and Gas Section; Brokaw, A.D.; Darnell, J. L.; and Donnelly, L. G.

"California Field: Carl H. Beal. Blackmar, C. A.; Hall, L. S.; Johnson, H. R.; Moran, R. B.; Nolan, E. D.; Gibson, E. J.; Arrell, D. B.; White, N. R.; Kingsberry, J. W.; Boyd, H.; Clute, W. S.; Campbell, Harry; Trengrove, S. R.

"Rocky Mountain Field: C. A. Fisher. Lewis, J. W.; Patton, H. B.; Eaton, Arthur; Prommel, H. W.; Comstock, Chas. W.; Prather, R. C.; Olds, Thos. H.

"Mid-Continent Field: J. O. Lewis. Richards, Ralph; Sampson, C. E.; Hance, J. H.; Wrather, W. E.; Hammer, A. A.; Lloyd, E.R.,U.S.G.S.; Goodrich, H. B.; Taylor, C. H.; Moore, C. T.; McKnight, R. J.; St. Clair, Stuart; Blisingame, Wade A.; Caudill, S. J.

"Gulf Field: E. DeGolyer and A. F. Dixon. Hopkins, O. B.; Mattison, M. W.; Prather, W. W.; Garfias, V. R.; Springer, A. R.; Bentley, W. T.; Kupferstein, J. T.

"Illinois and Lima-Indiana: T. E. Savage. Donnelly, L. G.; McConnell, K.; Darnell, J. L.; Henney, T. V.; Franklin, Louis; Lines, E. F.; Dawson, Dan; Barnett, Edw.; Blatchley, R. S.; Kahn, J. B.; White, K. D.; Morgan, D. M.; Herald, F. A.; Campbell, R. M.; Welsh, LeRoy G.; Rasmus, Walter; Cox, Eugene G.; Eskill, Rolf M.; Penngilly, H. E.; Duval, Wm. C.

"Appalachian Field: Geo. B. Richardson. Glenn, L. C.; Stout, W.; Ports, P. L.; Brown, Barnum; Hoeing, J. B.; Melcher, A. F.; Miller, A. M.; McElroy, S. M.; Johnson, R. S. H.; Miller, M. M.; Johnson, F. Arthur; Herzig, J. A., Rev. Agent; Bender, W. J., Rev. Agent; Bernard, G. A., Rev. Agent; Jillson, M. R.; Stephenson, E. A.

"Gas Fields: E. W. Shaw. Clark, F. R.; Moore, R. C.; Wrather, W. E.; Lee, W. T.; Patton, H. B.; Finch, E. H."

Fair Market Value for Tax Purposes

The following statements concerning values appear in the first edition of the *Manual (op. cit.).*

"The value sought should be that established assuming a transfer between a willing seller and a willing buyer as of that particular date.

"No rule or method of determining the fair market value of mineral property is prescribed, but the Commissioner will lend due weight and consideration to any or all factors and evidence having a bearing on the market value, such as (a) cost, (b) actual sales and transfers of similar properties, (c) market value of stock or shares, (d) royalties and rentals, (e) value fixed by the owner for the purposes of the capital-stock tax, (f) valuation local or state taxation, (g) partnership accounting, (h) records of litigation in which the value of the property was in question, (i) the amount at which the property may have been inventoried in probate court, (j) disinterested appraisals by approved methods, and (k) other factors."

In the *Manual for the Oil and Gas Industry under the Revenue Act of 1918, Revised August 1921 (op. cit.),* the present-value method of determining the fair market value was mentioned under the heading "Determination of Fair Market Value of Mineral Property", as follows:

". . . The value sought should be that established assuming a transfer between a willing seller and a willing buyer as of that particular date."

* * * *

"(b) To determine the fair market value of a mineral property by the present value method, the essential factors must be determined for each deposit included in the property. The factors are (1) the total quantity of mineral in terms of the principal or customary unit (or units) paid for in the product marketed, (2) the average quality or grade of the mineral reserves, (3) the expected percentage of extraction or recovery in each process or operation necessary for the preparation of the crude mineral for market, (4) the probable operating life of the deposit in years, (5) the unit operating cost, i.e., cost of production exclusive of depreciation and depletion, (6) expected average selling price per unit during the operating life, and (7) the rate of profit commensurate with the risk for the particular deposit."

* * * *

"The fair market[54] value of a property is the price at which a willing and informed owner would sell to a willing and informed buyer, with full consideration given to their relative tax positions."

Leland E. Fiske,[69] in presenting the viewpoint of the Internal Revenue Service in 1956, said:

"The fair market value is defined in the regulations as the amount which would induce a willing seller to sell and a willing buyer to purchase. This definition has the approval of the courts. Fair market value is then the price for which an oil and gas property could be sold on the open market. Since trading in oil and gas properties is very active, any property which is not completely worthless can find a ready market."

Fiske listed, in the approximate order of the preferential weight, the methods used to determine the fair market value:

"1. An actual sale of the property near the valuation date.
"2. A bona fide offer to sell or purchase the property near the valuation date.
"3. Actual sales of similar properties in the same or nearby oil and gas fields near the valuation date.
"4. Valuations made for purposes other than Federal taxation near the valuation date.
"5. Analytical appraisals.
"6. Opinions of qualified oil and gas operators."

The price per barrel of daily production, the payout of investment, the price per well, and the price for oil or gas in the ground are all methods commonly used for determining the price for which a property is sold or purchased. These methods are recognized by the Internal Revenue Service and are often used to compare values of different properties.

Fiske further stated:

"The regulations state that analytical appraisals will not be used if the value can reasonably be determined by another method. In practice, the Commissioner will consider analytical appraisals along with all other evidence for what they are worth, which is the rule followed by the courts. The courts have considered appraisals in setting the value of oil and gas properties when supported by expert testimony."

The "fair market value"[70] of an oil and gas property has been considered to be the price agreed upon between a willing buyer and a willing seller each in possession of all known facts. The literature is full of definitions similar to the one just stated. However, this definition needs to be revised in light of the present tax situation and the use to which the property will be placed. It now appears that a much better definition for "fair market value" would read somewhat as follows: "Fair market value" of an oil and gas property is the price agreed upon between a willing buyer and a willing seller both being producers of oil and gas, exclusively, each in possession of all known facts and both in the same tax bracket, the property being purchased without the tax advantage of the oil-payment method.

Many properties have such high speculative value from deeper untested formations that one might be justified in paying up to the full present value of the future net income from known producing formations.

Discovery Revaluation for Income-tax Purposes

The Revenue Act of 1918[4] created an incentive to find new oil and gas reserves by providing that property could be revalued as of 30 days after discovery. The depletion allowance per barrel was then determined by dividing the value thus determined by the recoverable oil in barrels. This ruling brought about widespread interest in analytical appraisals, especially among persons making a new discovery, because the costs connected with an individual wildcat discovery are very low compared to the amount of oil discovered; and if this cost were used, then the depletion allowance would be negligible. The act provided and defined the discovery and outlined the procedure for determining the value of the property after discovery.

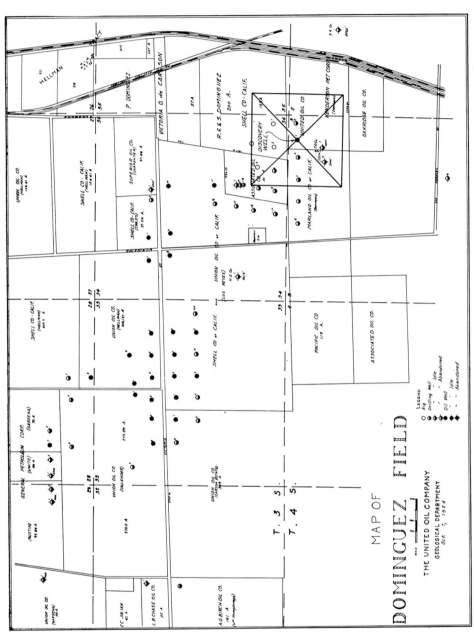

Fig. 17—Showing the 160-acre Area Oct. 7, 1924, Effective Date of Discovery Revaluation[71]

Later, the law[16] provided that a square containing 160 acres, with the new discovery in the center, outlined the area which could be revalued and stated that a depletion allowance based on the revaluation would be acceptable.

In 1924, Harold Vance[71] made a discovery revaluation for The United Oil Company of Los Angeles, California. In order to illustrate the actual procedures used, the following data are presented.

Fig. 17 is a map of the Dominguez Field, Los Angeles County, California, showing the 160-acre area with the discovery well in the center. The discovery well was The United Oil Company-Henderson Petroleum Company-Dominguez #1, completed September 7, 1924; and this map shows the development on the effective date of the discovery revaluation, October 7, 1924.

Fig. 18 shows the method used in determining the future production from the property. In this particular instance, the area revalued was an extension to the regular producing formation in the Dominguez Field. There were a number of wells to the northwest of the discovery area which had produced for as long as 20 months. The production-decline data from these wells were used to prepare a low-average curve and a high-average curve, through which an average curve was drawn; and this average curve was extended into the future using the logarithmic extension method of predicting future production.

Table 8 *(op. cit.)* shows the summary of the present worth and the depletion rates from the discovery revaluation made on the United Oil Company's Dominguez lease.

Table 8[71]

Valuation of the Dominguez Lease of The United Oil Co. for Income-tax Purposes

Summary

Present Worth

Oil	$ 1,301,247
Dry gas	34,837
Gasoline	67,675
Total present worth	$ 1,403,759

Depletion Rates

Oil, per barrel	0.6547
Dry gas, per Mcf	0.0665
Gasoline, per gallon	0.0647

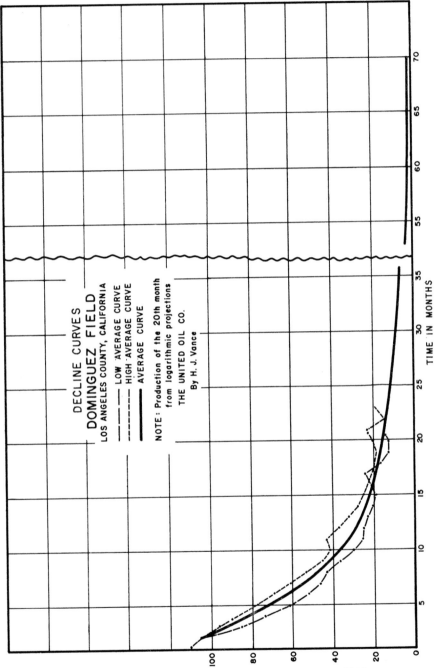

Fig. 18—Decline Curves, Dominguez Field, Los Angeles County, Calif.[71]

Miscellaneous Views on Valuation Methods—1919-22

In 1919, Carl H. Beal[17] listed 6 important factors to be given consideration in the valuation of oil lands, as follows: *1*, the amount of oil the property will produce; *2*, the amount of money this oil will bring (based upon the future price of oil); *3*, development and production costs; *4*, the rate of interest on the investment; *5*, the retirement or amortization of invested capital; and *6*, the salvage or scrap value of the equipment when the property is exhausted.

The rate of interest to be received on the investment had to be high enough to attract capital to an oil investment, which is always speculative to some degree.

Beal stated the basis of value in oil land was net income. The present value of this income must be determined for each future year of the productive life by reducing these future values to present values at a given rate of interest. This is known as discount, which is the reverse of compound interest, and the factors used in the reduction of future values are called discount factors. The present value of each year's income when added together gives the present value of the future net income from the property. The present value of a future income may be defined as that sum which, when placed at interest at a stated percent, will equal the income at the date when it is realized.

Roswell H. Johnson, in 1919,[72] considered the decline curve the most essential tool to one who would appreciate an oil and gas property, or determine its rate of depletion.

Earl Oliver, in his paper entitled "Appraisal of Oil Properties" published in 1920,[73] stated that the value of oil property varied according to the use for which it was intended. The same property would have a different value to the speculator, the fraudulent stock promoter, the refiner and pipeline owner, or the oil producer.

Prior to 1888, the oil industry *(op. cit.)* operated as two distinct divisions: first, the producing division; and, second, the refining division. After that date, the refining interests started purchasing their own producing properties in order to assure themselves of a supply of crude oil.

The relative value of the same oil property as between the producer, transporter, and refiner was discussed by Oliver as follows:

"... Thus, while to the oil producer, as such, an oil property has value only to the extent of the margin of profit between the cost of the oil as produced and his receipts for it as sold in its crude state, to the refiner and transporter it has a double value— one of which is identical with that of the producer, while the second is that it stabilizes and makes secure his more important business of transporting and refining, provided his producing properties are so situated as to make his production available for his facilities. The value of the property for the latter purpose is frequently of much greater importance than for the former."

Oliver divided oil property into developed and undeveloped properties and stated that in the field of undeveloped properties the work of the petroleum engineer was in most need of extension. He also emphasized the importance of the prediction of the future price of crude oil and stated that there certainly was a relation between the law of supply and demand and the market price of crude.

Carl H. Beal, in commenting on Earl Oliver's paper, said that even though the market value of the property might fluctuate due to new discoveries or the prices offered by speculators and fraudulent stock promoters, the actual value reposing in the oil did not change except as the factors influencing such values changed, as, for instance, increase in price, or higher or lower drilling costs. Beal disagreed with Oliver as to the use of the acre-foot recovery figures, and stated that there were not sufficient reliable data as to the actual producing thickness of the sands being produced from to use the acre-foot recovery figure. Beal much preferred to use the acre-recovery figure as a basis of comparing the anticipated recoveries in new fields with actual recoveries from old fields.

R. P. McLaughlin stated, in 1920,[74] that the value of oil land depended upon the prospective profit to be obtained from extracting the oil, and the three most important factors contributing to this profit were the amount of oil available, the cost of extraction, and the market price. He further stated that it was impossible to formulate a rule for accurate prediction as to the purchase price of crude; however, there was a relationship between the price of crude and the amount of stocks of stored oil, and even then it was noted that the prices of crude and the amount of stocks generally moved in opposite directions.

W. W. Cutler, Jr. and Walker S. Clute stated, in 1921,[75] that there was a big advantage in the early drilling of a well insofar as ultimate production was concerned. They also stated that one would expect greater production per well from wide spacing and greater production per acre from close spacing, but indicated that the economics would determine what type of spacing should be used.

In 1922, W. Irwin Moyer[76] described the time-of-payout method in valuing an oil well or property, as follows:

"... For any one field an imaginary well was assumed to have produced a given amount of oil during the first year. Estimating that this well will produce, in the future, an amount of oil corresponding to the decline curve of the field, its value was ascertained, using a fixed price for oil. This value was based on future returnable revenue, the sum of the annual revenues to be derived from sales of oil from the well being the total expected revenue. From this was deducted the original drilling cost and the annual operating expense for as many years as were required for the well to pay out. As soon as the revenue received from the sales of oil from the well equalled the expense of drilling and operating, the well had paid out."

H. J. Smith, commenting on Moyer's paper *(op. cit.)*, stated that from his experience in estimating values, it should be expected that the properties should pay out in not over four years.

Influence of Financing on Methods of Valuation[70, 77, 78]

Bank loans to oil operators were practically unknown prior to about 1930. Before that time the production and prices of crude varied widely, making the income from oil production so erratic that bankers hesitated lending depositors' money to develop more oil production.

During the early life of the East Texas Field, from 1931 to about 1934, such financing called for oil payments which would return to the lender as much as $3 for each $1 advanced to drill a well in proved territory. This type of loan was still not understandable to the average banker, who viewed such financing with much uncertainty.

The stabilization of prices and production rates in the early 1930's brought about by proration made loans to oil producers more acceptable. A knowledge of how long an oil property would produce was still a mystery to bankers until they learned that petroleum engineers and geologists could determine the amount of recoverable oil with reasonable accuracy. Using the engineer's or geologist's figures on proved properties, the value of the security could be determined even more accurately than the security behind the conventional bank loan.

Since the late 1930's, bank loans to operators for the development and purchase of properties have become more common in oil-producing territory. Bankers in the large cities saw the advantage of oil loans and rapidly expanded their bank's loans in the heart of the oil country. Today the bankers located in the oil fields, through their connections with larger banks having oil and gas departments, are able to take care of the financial needs of their customers for the purchase and development of oil and gas properties.

Conventional Oil Loan

The term "oil and gas loan"[78] has a special meaning among bankers, and it is generally defined as a loan secured by a mortgage on a producing property having the ability to produce future net income

Table 9

Determination of Present Value of Future Net Income for Producing Oil Property[78]

Year	Est. Gross Production, Barrels	7/8 Production, Barrels	Est. Future Price of Oil	Gross Income*	Est. Future Operating Expense	Net Income	Present Value Discount Factor 5 Percent	Present Value
1st	40,000	35,000	$ 2.50	$ 87,500	$ 5,000	$ 82,500	0.9756	$ 80,487
2nd	26,400	23,100	2.50	57,750	5,000	52,750	0.9286	48,984
3rd	17,400	15,225	2.50	38,062	5,000	33,062	0.8839	29,224
4th	12,000	10,500	2.50	26,250	5,000	21,250	0.8413	17,878
5th	8,400	7,350	2.50	18,375	5,000	13,375	0.8007	10,709
6th	6,000	5,250	2.50	13,125	5,000	8,125	0.7621	6,192
7th	4,400	3,850	2.50	9,625	5,000	4,625	0.7254	3,355
8th	3,400	2,975	2.50	7,437	5,000	2,437	0.6905	1,683
Totals	118,000	103,250		$258,124	$40,000	$218,124		$198,512

*Value of gas not considered.

The evaluation in Table 9 gives a present value of future net income at $198,512 for the 7/8 working interest. On the basis of a factor of safety of 2, the loan value would be one-half this amount, or $99,256. If the payment were 60 percent of the run to be applied to principal and interest, the loan would pay out in about 30 months.

The following information is also shown in the valuation:

Total ultimate recovery, bbl	118,000
Ultimate recovery to 7/8 W.I., bbl	103,250
Ultimate recovery to 1/8 R.I., bbl	14,750
Gross income to 7/8 working interest	$258,124
Total operating expense	$ 40,000
Total future net income	$218,124
Present value of future net income	$198,512

$$\text{Present value per barrel of recoverable oil} = \frac{\$198,512}{103,250 \text{ bbl}} = \$1.92$$

from the production of oil and/or gas and using this income in whole or in part to pay off the loan.

The objective in any valuation of an oil and/or gas property should be to determine the present value of the future net income from the property. Lending institutions are usually concerned with the present value of the future net income for the first 20 years from the formation presently being produced and do not consider for loan purposes the value of salvageable equipment on the lease. Usually, no value is placed on behind-the-pipe producing formations or possible deeper horizons.

The only value[70] anyone should consider initially is the present value of the recoverable oil within the proved part of the property being valued. When the productive history indicates the property is being affected by drainage, then the property should be revalued.

A number of banks and insurance companies maintain separate oil departments staffed by oil men who specialize in the type of oil loans covered by the foregoing definitions. Valuation of oil and gas property is a specialized phase of petroleum engineering, and it involves fundamentally an estimation of the future rate of production and the determination of the yearly net income to be expected from the property down to the time the property has reached the point where the expense is equal to the income from the property, at which time the property is said to have reached its economic limit. Banks generally lend[77] from 40 to 65 percent of the "present value" of the future net income before income taxes from the property, depending upon the present-value discount factor and the bank policy. The term "present value" in this instance means the present value of the future net income from the property discounted at a certain interest rate. It may be better understood if one says, when the price of property is equal to the present-value figures, then the purchase price plus the selected interest will be returned over the life of the property.

Since no value is placed on sands known to be productive but which are not producing at the time the valuation is made, a bank's valuation for loan purposes is seldom a measure of the market value of the property.

Table 9 is an illustration of a present-value determination. The present value of the future net income is used as a yardstick to determine the amount of the loan because the future net income must be brought back to its value at the time the loan is made.

Table 9 shows that the present value of the expected production from the property is twice the amount of the loan. This means that there is a factor of safety of 2 when the loan was initiated. If this same factor of safety is to be maintained throughout the payout period, at least 50 percent of the gross income should be taken to retire the loan.

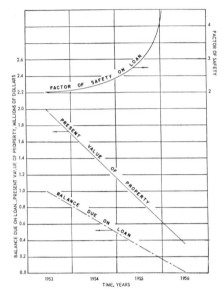

Fig. 19—Illustrates a Loan Starting with a Safety Factor of 2 and Using 61 Percent of the Runs to Retire the Loan[77]

Fig. 19 illustrates a loan starting with a safety factor of 2 and using 61 percent of the runs to retire the loan. It will be noted that the factor of safety towards maturity of the loan increases very rapidly. At this time, the loan could be rearranged and additional funds advanced so that the renewed loan would also start with the factor of safety of 2. Actually, this is often done.

Lyon F. Terry and Kenneth E. Hill, in 1953,[79] stated that from the standpoint of the lender on an oil property, the primary object should be to determine what the property would sell for if it were necessary to foreclose. Their method of valuation is to use a discount factor which, when applied to the present value of the future net income, will result in the fair market value. The property should be able to generate sufficient net cash income, after all expenses including income tax, to pay off the loan within a reasonable time. They also stated that the banker should not be a party to a transaction which was priced so high that it would result in an unprofitable venture from the standpoint of the borrower.

Terry and Hill *(op. cit.)* stated that in their experience the loan should not exceed 60 to 70 percent of the value of the property. They stated further, that another test of the safety of a loan was whether the total estimated future production from the property would be at least twice as great as the production required to pay off the loan.

Although one bank engineering group arrived at a figure which they called the "fair market value" by applying a certain discount factor to the present value of the future net income, it is believed that this method is not being generally used among bank valuation engineers *(op. cit.)*. The more general practice is probably to determine the present value of the future net income to the property and then, with this as a basis of value, apply some lending formula, usually one-half of this amount, without any thought or reference as to the "fair market value" of the property.[70,78]

Some lending agencies will lend no money on a property which has not been on production for, say, 12 to 16 months. This is a commendable safeguard, but such a policy is not too helpful to a man who is just starting operations. The policy of most banks is to lend money on 2 or more wells and not wait until there is 12 to 16 months production from the wells, unless a satisfactory appraisal cannot be prepared without these data.

Production-payment Method

Terry and Hill *(op. cit.)* gave an illustration of determining the value of an oil property and showed the appraised value if it were purchased for cash, again if the same property were purchased for a loan of $2,500,000 and cash outlay of $1,400,000, and, then again, the appraised value of this property if it were purchased by the oil-payment method. Table 10 shows a comparison between these appraised values.

Table 10[79]

Comparison of Valuation of a Property under Various Methods of Financing

	Appraised Value, Thousands of Dollars	Discount or Rate of Return, Percent	Value per Barrel, Dollars per Net Barrel	Loan Ratio, Percent
Purchase for Cash	3,900	8	0.91	—
Purchase with Loan	2,500	4½	—	64
Cash	1,400	11½	—	—
Total	3,900	8	0.91	—
Purchase by Oil Payment	3,500	5½	—	74
Cash	1,200	12¾	—	—
Total	4,700	8	1.09	—

Determination of Value by Oil-payment Method

Value by cash or cash and direct loan	3,900	8
Present worth of tax savings	800	8
Value by oil-payment method	4,700	—8

Table 11 *(op. cit.)* shows the value and payout of the property being considered when financed by a direct loan. It will be noted that the corporate income-tax rate of 52 percent is used.

Table 11

Valuation and Payout of Property "P" Financed by Direct Loan[79]

Estimated Future:	1953	1954	1955	1956	1957	5 Years Total	Thereafter	Grand Total	Dollars per Net Bbl
Net Production:									
Crude Oil, 1,000 Bbl	434	460	461	431	396	2,182	2,118	4,300	----
Natural Gas, MMcf	347	414	461	631	780	2,633	10,634	13,267	----
					Thousand Dollars				
Gross Revenue:a	1,180	1,255	1,261	1,193	1,112	6,001	6,432	12,433	2.89
Deductions:									
Operating expenses	82	89	93	95	100	459	1,176	1,635	0.38
Production and ad valorem taxes	70	76	76	70	67	359	382	741	0.17
General and administrative expenses	24	26	28	30	30	138	300	438	0.10
Intangible development expenditures	150	150	50	60	--	410	125	535	0.13
Depletion and depreciationb	395	419	419	392	360	1,985	1,927	3,912	0.91
Interest at 4½ percent per annum	104	84	63	39	14	304	----	304	0.07
Total	825	844	729	686	571	3,655	3,910	7,565	1.76
Taxable Income:	355	411	532	507	541	2,346	2,522	4,868	1.13
Federal income tax at 52 percent	185	214	277	264	281	1,221	1,311	2,532	0.59
Net Income:	170	197	255	243	260	1,125	1,211	2,336	0.54
Add back: depletion and depreciation	395	419	419	392	360	1,985	1,927	3,912	0.91
Sub-total	565	616	674	635	620	3,110	3,138	6,248	1.45
Less: tangible development expenditure	90	90	30	--	--	210	150	360	0.08
Net Cash Income:	475	526	644	635	620	2,900	2,988	5,888	1.37
Excess over loan requirements	75	76	144	85	20	400	2,988	3,388	0.79
Discount factor at 11½ percent	.90	.80	.72	.65	.58	.75	.37	.41	0.41
Present Worth:	68	61	104	55	12	300	1,106	1,406	0.33
Loan Amortization Schedule:									
Loan at beginning of year	2,500	2,100	1,650	1,150	600	2,500	----		
Less: principal payments	400	450	500	550	600	2,500	----	2,500	0.58
Loan balance at end of year	2,100	1,650	1,150	600	--0--				
							TOTAL VALUE	3,906	0.91

Notes: aCrude oil, including natural gas liquids, at $2.66 barrel; natural gas at 7.5 cents per Mcf.
bAt cost (91 cents per barrel).

Terry and Hill *(op. cit.)* made the following statement regarding the purchase of oil properties by the use of the oil payment:

". . . The use of an oil payment in the purchase of the same property is illustrated by assuming the property is purchased for $1,200,000 cash, subject to an oil payment of $3,500,000, plus interest at 5½ percent, payable out of 70 percent of the production. The oil payment is sold simultaneously to a third party, who borrows the entire cost of his investment, at 4½ per cent, and retains the one percent difference as interest on which he pays income taxes. . . . Hence, if the property be purchased by this procedure, it will be worth more than if purchased for cash or financed by a direct loan. . . . The present worth of the tax savings at eight per cent is $800,000. Adding this increment to the value of $3,900,000 indicates a value of $4,700,000 for the same property if purchased by the oil payment procedure, or 20 per cent more if the property were purchased for cash or by direct loan."

VALUATION OF GAS PROPERTIES

A separate section on valuation of natural gas is considered necessary because gas, unlike oil, cannot be carried to market in a barrel. Transportation through pipelines is the only way gas can reach a market. Gas produced with the oil has been considered, until recent years, a waste product of the oil-producing business. At times in the past, a wildcat gas discovery was considered a greater calamity than a dry hole and many such discoveries were abandoned as dry holes.

In September 1916, Samuel S. Wyer in discussing the "Intrinsic Value of Gas"[80] stated that gas in the ground has little intrinsic value because a service must be performed on it by delivering it to the ultimate consumer. The value of the gas in the field cannot be determined without considering wells and distribution systems. Thus gas differs markedly from oil which, from its discovery, has been delivered in containers to the ultimate consumer or processors, whereas natural gas can be distributed only through a system of pipeline transmissions. However, certain hydrocarbons, which are generally considered as gases, have been liquified and delivered in containers under pressure. Wyer stated that there were so many uncertainties involved in the valuation of gas properties that such a valuation approaches a guess. With this statement, F. G. Clapp[80] was in disagreement and stated, in his discussion of Wyer's paper, that the actual value of natural-gas leaseholds was not largely a matter of opinion.

Even in the *Manual for the Oil and Gas Industry under the Revenue Act of 1918*,[4] there is a separate discussion of natural-gas properties, the first paragraph of which follows:

"On account of the peculiar conditions surrounding the production of natural gas, it is necessary to compute the depletion allowance for gas properties by methods suitable to the particular cases. Usually the depletion should be computed on the basis of decline in closed or rock pressure, taking into account the effects of water encroachment and any other modifying factors. In many fields more or less additional evidence on depletion is to be had from such considerations as (a) details of production and performance records of well or property, (b) decline in open flow capacity, (c) comparison with the life histories of similar wells or properties, particularly those now exhausted, and (d) size of reservoir and pressure of gas."

Eugene Wesley Shaw, in 1919,[81] stated that the true value of a natural-gas property depended upon its earning power. The price of a gas well, particularly one several miles from a pipeline, was commonly just a little more than the cost of the lease and the cost of drilling the well. Because wells were usually drilled for the purpose of finding oil, the seller was apparently satisfied to get his money back plus a small margin of profit.

The gross return *(op. cit.)* from the average square mile of oil territory was from 100 to 400 times that to be expected from the average gas territory. However, due to wide spacing for gas wells, there was considerable saving in development costs, such that in the final analysis the average oil well at the well mouth returned an ultimate net of 25 to 75 times that returned by an average gas well.

Eugene A. Stephenson, in 1933,[53] stated that the buyer and seller of a piece of property were generally thinking in the same terms insofar as the value of the property is concerned; and in this connection they were thinking in terms of the earning power of the property. The seller was already familiar with the earning power, while the buyer was anticipating a profit from the operations of the property based on the prior experience of the seller. Thus, the value of the property was based upon the anticipated earning power of the property.

H. A. Ley wrote, in 1935,[82] that not many years past, the value of a gas well was determined by its ability to produce gas—a sum of dollars for each million cubic feet of daily open-flow capacity. This appeared to have been something like the Pennsylvania method of determining the value of oil property which was made applicable to natural-gas wells.

The yardstick[54] sometimes used, which places the value of $1 per barrel for oil in the ground or 10 cents per Mcf of gas in the ground, is most misleading. This method does not take into consideration the cost of recovering the oil or gas or the time to recover. Oil in the ground might be worth anywhere from 50 cents to $1.50 per barrel and gas might be worth from 5 cents to 15 cents per Mcf.

The gas contract *(op. cit.)* has great bearing on the value of the property. It may provide for a minimum take and for an increase in the price of gas at specific times, or at a time when there has been a general increase in the area; and further, it may provide that these price increases are all subject to government regulations which may make the price increases cited in the contract ineffective.

As the property is produced *(op. cit.)*, the reservoir pressure declines and it may become necessary either to drill additional wells or to install compressors or both to provide the amount of gas contracted for.

The value *(op. cit.)* of a property is related to payout time. Therefore, a property which will return its cost in 5 years would be worth much more than a property which would return its cost in 10 years, even though the reserve is in both cases the same. Further, a purchaser would wish not only the return of his capital but a substantial income after the return of capital.

Ralph E. Davis and J. Milton Wege[83] stated that a gas property will sell for more money when financial conditions of the country and the industry are good. Also, it will sell for more money when the conditions are such as to expect an increasing demand for the product but no serious threat of a cheaper competitive fuel; and, further, it will sell for more money if the political atmosphere is favorable. Naturally, the property would be less desirable if threatened with regulation and price fixing by governmental agencies.

Davis and Wege *(op. cit.)* presented an evaluation on a gas property which showed a total cash generated, based on 20-cent gas, of $6,-149,094 in 22 years, where the term "cash generated" means net earnings after income taxes plus amounts set aside for depletion and depreciation. The following tabulation shows the present value of the total cash generated at different discount interest rates.

Percent Interest Discount Factor	Present Value of the $6,149,094
6	$4,619,000
8	4,266,500
10	3,965,400
12	3,706,300

After taking out the depreciable capital sum of $1,300,600, then the range of values of the gas reserve is from $2,405,700 to $3,318,400.

Table 12 *(op. cit.)* shows a comparison between payout time and cash income for several assumed selling prices for this property. The

Table 12

Selected Gas Property Comparison of Payout Time and Cash Income for a Proved Developed Gas Property[83]

1. Assumed sales price of property	$3,500,000	$3,750,000	$4,000,000	$4,250,000	$4,500,000
2. Value of fixed assets to be depreciated	1,300,600	1,300,600	1,300,600	1,300,600	1,300,600
3. Assumed value of gas in ground to be depleted	$2,199,400	$2,449,400	$2,699,400	$2,949,400	$3,199,400
4. Assumed value of gas in ground, cents per Mcf[a]	2.60	2.90	3.20	3.49	3.79
5. Net operating income before depreciation, depletion, and income tax[b]	$7,948,050	$7,948,050	$7,948,050	$7,948,050	$7,948,050
6. Allowable depreciation	1,300,600	1,300,600	1,300,600	1,300,600	1,300,600
7. Allowable depletion	3,187,919[c]	3,187,919[c]	3,187,919[c]	3,187,919[c]	3,199,400[d]
8. Taxable income	$3,459,531	$3,459,531	$3,459,531	$3,459,531	$3,448,050
9. Income tax at 52-percent rate	1,798,956	1,798,956	1,798,956	1,798,956	1,792,986
10. Total cash generated[e]	$6,149,094	$6,149,094	$6,149,094	$6,149,094	$6,155,064
11. Payout time, years to return investment and pay income taxes during period	4.98	5.53	6.09	6.74	7.46
12. Remaining cash income after payout	$2,649,094	$2,399,094	$2,149,094	$1,899,094	$1,655,064

Notes: [a]Based on reserves of 84,450 MMcf.
[b]From Schedule A.
[c]Depletion based on earnings.
[d]Depletion based on costs.
[e]Equals net operating income before depreciation, depletion, and income tax, less income tax.

authors concluded that a sales price of $4,000,000 was in line, but point out at this price the value of the gas in the ground was 3.2 cents per Mcf for gas selling at the well head for 20 cents. It will also be noted in Table 12 that the Federal government took almost as much out of the business, at no risk, as did the purchaser.

Davis and Wege *(op. cit.)* also presented a similar analysis of the same gas property at a time when it was only partially developed.

SALES PRICE VS. PRESENT VALUE OF FUTURE NET INCOME

The fair market value of an oil and gas property for tax purposes has already been discussed and a number of definitions of the "fair market value" have been cited. There have been a number of attempts to relate the present value of the future net income of an oil and/or gas property to the sale price of the property. For example:

W. W. Orcutt, in 1911,[63] indicated the justifiable purchase price of an oil property was 50 percent of the present value of the future net income, discounted at 6 percent.

E. L. DeGolyer stated in 1949,[84] that he was familiar with cases in which the trading figure was approximately one-half the future net revenue before depreciation and Federal taxes, discounted at 4 percent. He further stated that this figure was very close to the future net revenue before depreciation and Federal taxes, discounted at 10½ percent per year.

The formula proposed by the Committee on Valuation of Securities of the National Association of Insurance Commissioners,[85] in 1951, stated that the value of the oil, gas, and condensate in the ground shall be one-half of the present worth of the future net revenue discounted at an interest equal to the interest rate on the loan.

H. J. Gruy, in 1952,[86] considered that the fair market value was about two-thirds of the future net cash earnings before depreciation and Federal taxes, discounted at 5 percent.

It has already been cited that Terry and Hill,[79] in 1953, considered that the present worth of the future net receipts discounted at 8 percent was considered to be approximately the value of the property and that this figure had been indicated by sales of similar properties.

In 1956, Harold Vance[70,78] stated it had been found that properties have sold for 60 to 80 percent of the future net income, discounted at 5 percent.

Leland E. Fiske stated, in 1956, "In many cases a reasonable value can be obtained by taking fifty percent of the expected future net income, thus giving a return on the investment of two for one, which is the basis of trading in many actual sales."[69]

Ralph E. Davis and J. Milton Wege, in 1956,[83] stated that a sales price of $4,000,000 was in line for a gas property which they evaluated where the total cash generated was $6,149,094 in 22 years. In this case, the suggested price was equal to the present value of the total cash generated using a 10-percent interest discount factor.

J. J. Arps, in 1957,[87] presented a chart which indicated that properties had traded at a price which would yield an average annual rate of return before taxes of somewhere between 10 to 20 percent per year. However, in long-lived fields, like the East Texas Field, a number of trades were made which would yield less than 10 percent per year before Federal taxes.

VALUE OF UNDRILLED ACREAGE

Jack A. Crichton[88] defined undrilled acreage as "any land which has not been tested for the possibilities of petroleum, by having a hole drilled on it." He listed a number of factors which affect the value of this undrilled acreage, as follows: the nearness to production from which petroleum is or has been produced; the value per acre of producing petroleum property in the area; the evidence and data on hand to substantiate the possibility of petroleum existing under the acreage considered; whether one may expect drilling activity in the vicinity of the acreage being considered; the cost of drilling such a well in the area; the going price of similar acreage in the area; the trading ability of sellers in the area; the competitive situation, generally; the psychological factors which are whether one considers Woodbine production better than Spraberry production; the size of ownership in the area; and, of course, general business conditions.

One of the most valuable services a valuation engineer can perform for an employer is to determine whether a proved undrilled location should be drilled or farmed out.[70] The following is an illustration of how one determines the value of a proved undrilled location.

Assuming the present value of the future net oil income *(op. cit.)* to be recovered from a proved location is $198,512, and the cost of a well to produce the income indicated is $50,000 and the net value of the equipment recoverable at the time of abandonment is $10,000, then the value of this location is as follows:

Present value future net oil income $198,512
Less—cost of well to produce income 50,000

$148,512

Plus—present value of salvageable
  equipment—$10,000 $\times$ 0.6736* 6,736

Value of the location $155,248

---

*5-percent value factor on total income to be received at the end of 8 years.

The foregoing illustration indicates that it would be profitable to drill this location. However, if one assumed the well cost $250,000 instead of $50,000, then the owner of the location would find it profitable to make some kind of a farm-out deal.

VALUE OF OIL STOCKS USING VALUATION METHODS

Edwin L. Kennedy, in 1953,[89] discussed the appraisal figures on oil properties as compared to stock prices and offered some interesting comments. He stated that, as of February 1953, the oil stocks on the New York Stock Exchange were selling for from 30 to 150 percent of the appraised values of the stock. One reason given for this variation was that an appraisal is an estimate of value based on the assumption of liquidation, and that the investor prices the stock on the basis that the company is going to continue to be a going concern—will continue to acquire new properties and is not going to be liquidated.

Management *(op. cit.)* is of such great importance that an investor tries to place some value on the managerial policies of the company in which he is investing his money. Further, appraisals carry into the future many of the factors which exist at the time the appraisal is made, while the investor is looking for changes in the future which will influence the value of the stock. In the case of a sellout, the appraisal becomes the controlling factor in security prices.

A valuation report *(op. cit.)* properly prepared and correctly used can be of great assistance to the investor. With this background he can study managerial policies and the effectiveness of management, which, taken together, will let him place a value on the stock he intends to purchase.

THE VALUATION REPORT

Dean H. Sheldon stated as follows:[51]

"The analytical engineering appraisal gives expression to the engineer's estimate of the earning power of an oil producing property. It serves as a means of comparing estimates of market value with actual transactions in oil properties. Its presentation should distinguish clearly between facts and the engineer's opinions developed from those facts."

C. E. Reistle, Jr.[90] emphasizes the importance and the reliance placed by management on proper valuations. He stated there was one factor which should not be included in the valuation report and that is "the safety factor". Further, "the valuation should be based upon the best available facts, and no attempt made to distort or select data to present either a conservative or optimistic picture. Uncertainties in the basic data should be pointed out, but they should not be compensated by a unilateral correction." He stated, "that without such a report, management would have no place from which to start in making a decision as to what type of investment should be considered by management."

J. Ed Warren[91] stated, concerning valuation reports, if it were the bank policy to review and check consultant's findings, it was necessary that this report be prepared in sufficient detail to contain all the information, assumptions, judgments, and methods employed in its preparation. He further stated that the report should present all pertinent data organized and appraised in logical sequence before final conclusions are stated. He even suggested that, in view of the fact there was such a wide difference in the information contained in various consultants' reports, he thought there might well be a study made to determine what information should be made a part of these reports which are frequently used by oil companies and financial institutions.

The value[70] arrived at should never be on the conservative nor optimistic side, because neither of these factors has anything to do with the preparation of a proper report. The evaluator should arrive at a figure which is indicated by the facts and should never present a greater or lesser figure. If he does so, he is misleading the people who have employed him in the first instance. If the one using these values cannot depend on them to be as indicated, there is no foundation or starting point with which to make negotiations—whether these negotiations be for the purpose of making a loan or for the purchase or sale of a piece of property.

The evaluation, if properly prepared, will determine the present value of future net income to be expected from the property.

Data Used in Preparing a Valuation Report

The purpose of the usual valuation report is to determine the present value of the future net income from an oil and/or gas property. The following data are needed: an estimate of the annual rate of production of oil and/or gas, the estimated future price of oil and/or gas, the estimated future operating expense, and the present-value interest discount to be used. The methods of estimating the future oil and/or gas production have already been discussed.

Future Price of Oil and Gas

Accurate forecasts as to the future price of oil and gas are as essential to the valuation of oil and gas properties as the estimate of the ultimate production and future rate of production. The law of supply and demand generally controls prices of everything unless the law is made inoperative by governmental regulations. If fuel prices are allowed to fluctuate, the price of both oil and gas will find a level competitive with other fuels in the area where the fuels are being consumed.

In 1911, W. W. Orcutt[63] in preparing a valuation report assumed the future price of oil would be the same as the present price which was 50 cents per barrel. The future period covered was from 1911 to 1927. In 1924, the price of oil produced in the Dominguez Field in California was $1.25 per barrel. This same price was used as the future price of oil in a discovery revaluation report[71] made at that time.

It is common practice to use the present price of oil as the expected future price in valuations, unless there has been a recent radical price change. There have been times when the present price was so out of line with the average price for the past 20 years that the average price was used. This condition existed in the early 1930's when East Texas crude sold for 10 cents per barrel, but even then one major purchaser paid 25 cents per barrel.

Dean H. Sheldon, in 1953,[51] stated that in estimating future income for an analytical appraisal, the current commodity price should be used, taking into consideration existing contractual agreements concerning prices, and the costs should be forecast in most cases on a well-month or well-year basis.

Excess capacity to produce oil in this country brought government restrictions on domestic production and world-wide productive capacity at this time makes a continuation of production regulation inevitable.

The ability to produce oil from our enormous shale-oil deposits at a price almost competitive with our present crude prices appears to place a ceiling on the future price of crude oil produced from wells.

Unless Federal price regulations are removed, natural gas, although not in excess supply, will not be permitted to reach its competitive price level.

Future Cost of Production

The present costs of production are easily ascertainable. If the property has already been produced, past production costs are available. In the case of new properties, the cost of producing similar properties will serve as a guide for the property being evaluated.

The future cost of production depends upon many factors, but during an inflationary period the costs will continue to increase as they have in the past. A well-qualified individual owner-operator has been able to produce oil and/or gas at less cost than a similarly qualified corporate operator.

It is common practice to assume that the future cost of production will remain constant, although the cost benefits from future anticipated technological advances appear to be the only justifiable reason for such practice.

A fixed cost of production per month, or year, is most commonly used instead of a cost-per-barrel figure. The cost of production per barrel definitely increases with declining production.

Interest Discount Factor

The present-value interest discount factor is used to reduce income to be received in the future to its value today.

There are a number of viewpoints to the use to be made of this method of discontinuing future income and the interest rate to use. In some cases it seems desirable to apply an interest discount factor of 5 percent, because 5 percent is the interest rate being charged by lending institutions; or if one already had the money, it could be lent out at this interest rate without any business risk.

Some use an interest discount for the purpose of arriving at a figure believed to represent the fair market value [79] of the property. In this case, some interest rate in excess of 5 percent would be used.

The relatively small importance of income [84] to be received in the distant future was illustrated by an example wherein an income of $1,000 per month for 20 years was discounted at $10\frac{1}{2}$ percent per year compounded monthly and the present value of this income amounted to $102,000, whereas 5 additional years' income increased the present value to $105,000 or just 3 percent.

The rate of producing the same total amount of income from oil production affects the present value of this income. For example, [70] a property produced under conditions of declining production, as compared with the same property produced at a constant rate, had a present value of $198,000 as compared to $180,000 for the same property produced at a constant rate when a 5-percent present-value discount factor was used.

MEASURING WORTH OF INVESTMENT

There is a general relationship between the return on an investment and the risk involved. James W. Glanville, in 1957, [92] presented a method of determining the interest rate which discounts the future earnings of a project down to a present value equal to the project cost. This interest rate is the rate of return on the investment.

J. J. Arps [87] presented a series of curves which could be used to determine the price one could pay for a producing property, in terms of percent of future net income, to yield a specific average annual rate of return on the invested capital. One of the charts given shows the percent of future net income one can afford to pay when the average 5-percent discount factor for a given income projection is known, and also shows the corresponding years of constant-rate production. The curves from this chart have been replotted showing the number of

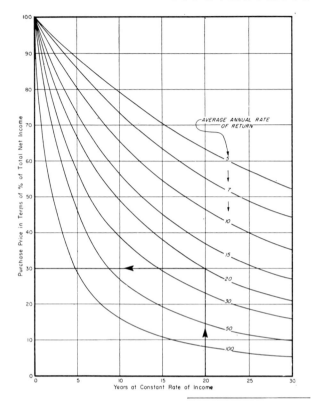

Fig. 20—Curves Showing Relationship between Purchase Price in Terms of Future Net Income at Constant Rate in Years for Various Returns on Investment[87]

years of constant rate of production as the abscissa and the percent of future net income as the ordinate. The family of curves (Fig. 20) represent the average annual rates of return on invested money from 5 percent to 100 percent. Thus, if one wanted to know what should be paid for a property which will produce at a constant rate for 20 years and yield a return of 20 percent, then, using the proper curve, it can be read from this chart that 30 percent of the future net income can be paid for the property.

VALUE OF OIL AND GAS PROPERTIES AS AFFECTED BY GOVERNMENT REGULATION AND TAXES

In some areas the continual decrease in allowable production has brought about a decrease in the value of oil properties by increasing the overall cost, including interest, of producing a given reserve of oil.

The same property may have a different value to each of two individuals, depending upon their relative income-tax positions.

The same individual who conducts his oil business as a corporation even finds himself placing two different values on the same property he plans on purchasing. The income from the property would be subject to the corporate tax, and the earnings of the property distributed to the owner as dividends would again be taxed at the individual's income-tax rate; whereas if the individual owned the property direct, the income would be subject only to the individual income tax.

E. L. DeGolyer[84] stated that an individual owner of an oil property who is paying 70 to 90 percent of the income from a property to the government as income tax, might be better off to sell his property at a comparatively low figure and use the provisions of the capital-gains tax.

Terry and Hill[79] showed that the appraised value of the same property was $800,000 more if the property could be purchased by the oil-payment method, than if it were purchased for cash—this $800,000 being the present worth of the tax saving at 8 percent interest. Thus, the measure of worth of any oil property is the amount it will return to the purchaser after taxes. In the instance just cited, the present value of the income returned due to the tax saving of the oil payment was $800,000.

Davis and Stephenson[54] have already stated that a property owned by an institution which was not taxed could be worth two or three times as much to the institution as it would be to an individual in a high tax bracket.

A corporation, having its income-tax rate fixed by law—generally 52 percent—will go into business ventures which will let them keep the most money after taxes. It is this cash-keep after taxes which is the deciding factor in comparing one investment with another when one has funds to invest. The income-tax rate is so high that the amount of money one can keep after taxes is usually the deciding factor in any investment. Term of payout as a basis of value is often misunderstood as to whether this is payout before or after income taxes. Some people think in terms of payout before income taxes, and for these people many purchases turn out to be a loss because the cash-keep after taxes is the determining factor. An example was given[70] which indicates that, if the term "payout" were used on the basis of gross income from a royalty interest, the purchase price would be returned in four years. However, if the income were subject to a 60-percent income tax, the payout based on the cash-keep after taxes would amount to almost 9 years provided the property was purchased without benefit of the oil-payment method.

In this same example, it was assumed one could purchase a producing oil royalty interest which was paying $10,000 per year for $40,000. Reserve estimates indicated the same income should continue for 15 years. If the property were purchased without the tax advantage of the production-payment method and the income were subject to 60 percent income tax, the present value of the money the purchaser could keep after taxes would be $58,600; but, if the income were taxed at

90 percent, the present value of the money the purchaser could keep after taxes would be $36,475, or $3,525 less than the purchase price.

CONCLUSION

The valuation of oil and gas properties grew with the industry. The owner in valuing his own property, especially if he were selling his property, had great visions for the future. The early appraiser was thinking in terms of what the property could be sold for and not what it would yield by producing the oil from the property. The early records of dry holes and short-lived wells, due in a measure to close spacing, made the business so speculative there appeared to be no reasonable method of valuation other than what the property might be sold for.

The public land classification work was responsible for the beginning of a wider interest in valuations. The Federal income tax was responsible for the development of most of the basic principles now used in valuation work. There are many reasons now for making valuations of oil properties, some of which are: *1*, for the purchase and sale of oil properties; *2*, for the dissolution or merger of corporations; *3*, for the creation or change in capitalization of a corporation; *4*, for the unitization of petroleum properties; *5*, to help determine the fair market value of an estate for inheritance-tax purposes; and *6*, to provide management with the value of its reserves of oil and gas.[84]

At the present time, some 10 to 20 percent of the petroleum engineers in large companies are engaged in some phase of valuation work. Probably 50 percent of the work done by consultants is valuation work.

There has been continual progress in the methods of estimating the recoverable oil and gas. The time-honored methods are not always adequate when used to determine recoveries from fields which are producing at less than capacity. The records indicate as of the end of 1957,[93] that 57 percent of the oil reserves in the United States are in some 204 oil fields. If the production from these 204 oil fields is restricted by proration and the approximately 11,650 remaining oil fields are producing at their maximum capacity, then a production curve of some type could be used to estimate the future production and future rate of production from 98 percent of the oil fields in the United States.

Income taxes and governmental regulations have so influenced the value of oil and gas properties that without considering these factors a proper valuation cannot be prepared.

REFERENCES

[1] *The Derrick's Hand Book of Petroleum*, Derrick Publishing Company, Oil City, Pa. Vol. I, period from 1859-1898, published in 1898; Vol. II, period from 1899-1900, published in 1900.

[2] McLaurin, John J: *Sketches in Crude-Oil*, published by author at Harrisburg, Pa., 1896.

[3] Whiteshot, Charles A: *The Oil Well Driller—History of the Oil Industry of the World*, The Acme Publishing Co., Mannington, West Virginia, 1905.

[4] U. S. Treasury Dept. Internal Revenue Service: *Manual for the Oil and Gas Industry Under the Revenue Act of 1918*, published in 1919.

[5] Carll, John F: *The Geology of the Oil Regions of Warren, Venango, Clarion, and Butler Counties, Pennsylvania*, Second Geological Survey of Pennsylvania, 1875-79, **III** (1880).

[6] Arnold, Ralph: Letter to Harold Vance dated Sept. 20, 1954.

[7] Day, David T: The Petroleum Resources of the U. S., *U.S.G.S. Bull. 394*, National Conservation Commission, Feb. (1909).

[8] Huntley, L. G: Possible Causes of the Decline of Oil Wells and Suggested Methods of Prolonging Yield, *U. S. Bur. Mines TP 51* (1913).

[9] Lombardi, M. E: The Valuation of Oil Lands and Properties, *Western Engineer*, **6**, Oct. (1915).

[10] Washburne, Chester W: The Estimation of Oil Reserves, *AIME Bull. 98*, Feb. (1915).

[11] Johnson, Roswell H: The Role and Fate of the Connate Water in Oil and Gas Sands, *AIME Bull. 98*, Feb. (1915).

[12] Beal, Carl H. and Lewis, J. O: Some Principles Governing the Production of Oil Wells, *U. S. Bur. Mines Bull. 194* (1921).

[13] Pack, Robert W: The Estimation of Petroleum Reserves, *AIME Bull. 128*, Aug. (1917).

[14] Beal, Carl H: The Decline and Ultimate Production of Oil Wells, *U. S. Bur. Mines Bull. 177, Petroleum Technology 51* (1919).

[15] Lewis, J. O. and Beal, Carl H: Some New Methods of Estimating the Future Production of Oil Wells, *AIME Bull. 134*, 477, Feb. (1918).

[16] U. S. Treasury Dept. Internal Revenue Service: *Manual for the Oil and Gas Industry Under the Revenue Act of 1918, Revised August 1921.*

[17] Beal, Carl H: Essential Factors in Valuation of Oil Properties, *AIME Bull. 153*, Sept. (1919).

[18] Brown, Robert Wesley: *Valuation of Oil and Gas Lands*, McGraw-Hill Book Company, Inc., New York, 1924.

[19] Cutler, W. W., Jr: A Mathematical Method of Constructing Average Oil Well Production Curves, *U. S. Bur. Mines RI 2148* (1920).

[20] Schoeneck, William E: The Engineering of Oil-well Abandonments, *Trans. Am. Inst. Mining Met. Engrs. (Petroleum Development and Technology)* **165**, 147 (1946).

[21] Cutler, W. W., Jr: Rate-of-production Curve and Its Application to the Valuation of Oil Properties, *U. S. Bur. Mines RI 2285* Oct. (1921).

[22] Cutler, Willard W., Jr: Estimation of Underground Oil Reserves by Oil-well Production Curves, *U. S. Bur. Mines Bull. 228*, Aug. (1924).

[23] Coleman, Stewart; Wilde, H. D., Jr; and Moore, Thomas W: Quantitative Effect of Gas-oil Ratios on Decline of Average Rock Pressure, *Trans. Am. Inst. Mining Met. Engrs. (Petroleum Development and Technology)* 174 (1930).

[24] Brace, O. L: Factors Governing Estimation of Recoverable Oil Reserves in Sand Fields, *Am. Assoc. Petroleum Geologists Bull.*, **18**, March (1934).

[25] Schilthuis, Ralph J: Active Oil and Reservoir Energy, *Trans Am. Inst. Mining Met. Engrs. (Petroleum Development and Technology)* **118**, 33 (1936) (reprint, p. 31).

[26]Katz, Donald L: Letter to Harold Vance, dated January 3, 1955, regarding material balance, etc.

[27]Katz, D. L: A Method of Estimating Oil and Gas Reserves, *Trans. Am. Inst. Mining Met. Engrs. (Petroleum Development and Technology)* **118,** 52 (1936) (reprint, p. 50).

[28]Montague, K. E; Noble, M. D; and Buchanan, F. E: Application of Engineering Effort Through Use of Reservoir Analyzers, *AIME J. Petr. Tech.*, 12, Dec. (1956).

[29]Millikan, C. V. and Sidwell, Carroll V: Bottom-hole Pressures in Oil Wells, *Trans. Am. Inst. Mining Met. Engrs. (Petroleum Development and Technology)* 194 (1931).

[30]Melcher, A. F: Determination of Pore Space of Oil and Gas Sands, *Trans. Am. Inst. Mining Met. Engrs.* **65,** 469 (1921).

[31]Melcher, A. F: Texture of Oil Sands with Relation to the Production of Oil, *Am. Assoc. Petroleum Geologists Bull.*, **8,** 716 (1924).

[32]Melcher, A. F: Porosity of the Bradford Sand Near Custer City, Pennsylvania and Its Relation to the Production of Oil, *U.S.G.S. Memorandum for the Press No. 1008.*

[33]Fettke, Charles R: Core Studies of the Second Sand of the Venango Group, from Oil City, Pennsylvania, *Petroleum Development and Technology in 1926*, 219, American Institute of Mining and Metallurgical Engineers, Inc., New York, 1927.

[34]Russell, W. L: A Quick Method for Determining Porosity, *Am. Assoc. Petroleum Geologists Bull.*, **10,** 931, Oct. (1926).

[35]Torrey, Paul D: Some Early Contributions to Petroleum Technology from Fluid Injection Operations, *More Oil for America, The Oil and Gas Compact Bulletin*, **XIV [1]** June (1955).

[36]Melcher A. F: Investigations on Permeability and Absorption of "Sands" for Oil, Water, and Gas, with Reference to Their Normal and Possible Yield, *Am. Assoc. Petroleum Geologists Bull.* **6,** 143, (1922).

[37]Wyckoff, R. D; Botset, H. G; Muskat, M; and Reed, D. W: Measurement of Permeability of Porous Media, *Am. Assoc. Petroleum Geologists Bull.*, **18 [2]** 161, Feb. (1934).

[38]Fancher, George H; Lewis, James A; and Barnes, K. B: Some Physical Characteristics of Oil Sands, *The Pennsylvania State College School of Mineral Industries Bull. No. 12, 65* (1933).

[39]Jones, Park J: Drawdown Exploration Reservoir Limit, Well and Formation Evaluation, Permian Basin Oil Recovery Conference, Midland, Texas, April 1957, sponsored by Permian Basin Section AIME and Texas Petroleum Research Committee.

[40]Core Laboratories, Inc: Recovery Factor—letter to Harold Vance dated March 1, 1957, and one dated April 4, 1957, from T. L. Kennerly, Manager, Reservoir Data Department (1936).

[41]Craze, R. C. and Buckley, S. E: A Factual Analysis of the Effect of Well Spacing on Oil Recovery, *API Drilling and Production Practice*, 144 (1945).

[42]Arps, J. J: Estimation of Primary Oil Reserves, presented at AIME Petroleum Conference on Economics and Valuation, Dallas, Texas, March 29-30, 1956.

[43]Arps, J. J. and Roberts, T. G: The Effect of the Relative Permeability Ratio, the Oil Gravity, and the Solution Gas-Oil Ratio on the Primary Recovery from a Depletion-Type Reservoir, *Trans. Am. Inst. Mining Met. Engrs. (Petroleum Development and Technology)* **204,** 120 (1955).

[44]Arps, J. J. and Roberts, T. G: Letter Symbols for Reservoir Engineering, *AIME J. Petr. Tech.*, 37, Jan. (1955).

[45]Buckley, S. E. and Leverett, M. C: Mechanism of Fluid Displacement in Sands, *Trans. Am. Inst. Mining Met. Engrs. (Petroleum Development and Technology)* **146,** 107 (1942) (reprint, p. 149).

[46]Pirson, S. J: *Elements of Oil Reservoir Engineering*, 285, McGraw-Hill Book Company, Inc., New York, 1950.

[47]Welge, H. J: A Simplified Method for Computing Oil Recovery by Gas or Water Drive, *Trans. Am. Inst. Mining Met. Engrs. (Petroleum Development and Technology)* **195**, 91 (1952).

[48]Guthrie, R. K. and Greenberger, M. H: The Use of Multiple-correlation Analyses for Interpreting Petroleum-engineering Data, *API Drilling and Production Practice*, 130 (1955).

[49]Elliott, George R: Behavior and Control of Natural Water-drive Reservoirs, *Trans. Am. Inst. Mining Met. Engrs. (Petroleum Development and Technology)* **165**, 210 (1946).

[50]Vance, Harold: *Oil Production History of the Southwest*, Bank of the Southwest, Houston, Texas, June 28, 1956.

[51]Sheldon, Dean H: Valuation of Oil Properties, presented at the Annual Meeting of Petroleum Branch, AIME, Los Angeles, Calif., Feb. 1953.

[52]Davis, Ralph: Estimation of Natural Gas Reserves, *Oil Gas J.*, June 16 (1927).

[53]Stephenson, Eugene A: Valuation of Natural Gas Properties, *Geology of Natural Gas—A Symposium*, Am. Assoc. Petroleum Geologists (1933).

[54]Davis, Ralph E. and Stephenson, Eugene A: The Valuation of Natural Gas Properties, presented at the Annual Meeting of Petroleum Branch, AIME, Los Angeles, Calif., Feb. 1953.

[55]van der Waals, Joannes D: Equation developed in his doctor's dissertation at the University of Leyden, 1873. van der Waals was Professor of Physics at the University of Amsterdam. *Physical Chemistry*, by Louis J. Bircher, Prentice-Hall, Inc., New York, 1942.

[56]Burnett, E. S: Compressibility Determination without Volume Measurements, published by permission of the Director, U. S. Bureau of Mines, in *J. Applied Mechanics*, **3 [4]** Dec. (1936).

[57]Stevens, A. B. and Vance, Harold: Experimental Determinations of the Compressibility Factors of Several Natural Gases and the Application of These Data to Simple Gas Computations, *Oil Weekly*, June 8 (1942).

[58]Brown, George Granger: Deviations of Natural Gas from Ideal Gas Laws, *Oil Weekly*, Dec. 30 (1940).

[59]Katz, Donald, L; Matthews, T. A; and Roland, C. H: High-Pressure Gas Measurement, *Petroleum Engr.* (in 3 parts) Sept., Oct., Dec. (1942).

[60]Gale, Thomas A: *Rock Oil in Pennsylvania and Elsewhere*, Sloan & Griffeth, Erie, Pa. (1860).

[61]Paine, Paul: Letter to Harold Vance dated May 12, 1954.

[62]Redpath, E. V: Letter to Harold Vance dated August 6, 1954.

[63]Cox, Thomas; Stadler, Walter; and Orcutt, W. W: Determining Future Production by Decline Curve Method, a report written and filed in 1947 in Bancroft Library, University of California at Berkley.

[64]Blatchley, Raymond S: The Oil Fields of Crawford and Lawrence Counties, Illinois, Economic Features of the Illinois Fields, published in *Ill. State Geological Survey Bull.*, 22 (1913).

[65]Requa, M. L: Methods of Valuing Oil Lands, *Trans. Am. Inst. Mining Met. Engrs.*, 526 (1918).

[66]Johnson, Roswell H. and Huntley, L. G: *Principles of Oil and Gas Production*, John Wiley & Sons, Inc., New York, 1916.

[67]Arnold, Ralph: Problems of Oil Lease Valuation, *Am. Assoc. Petroleum Geologists Bull.* **3**, 389 (1919).

[68]Arnold, Ralph; Darnell, J. L; and others: *Manual for the Oil and Gas Industry under the Revenue Act of 1918*, John Wiley & Sons, Inc., New York; Chapman & Hall Limited, London, 1920.

[69]Fiske, Leland E: The Valuation of Oil and Gas Properties in Estates and Trusts, *Second Annual Edition, Rocky Mountain Mineral Law Institute* (1956).

[70]Vance, Harold: *Appraisal of Oil and Gas Properties from the Viewpoint of a Banker and an Oil Man*, Bank of the Southwest, Houston, Texas, March 1957.

[71]Vance, Harold: Valuation of the Dominguez Lease for The United Oil Company for Income Tax Purposes, October 7, 1924, prepared for The United Oil Company of California.

[72]Johnson, Roswell H: Decline Curve Methods, *Am. Assoc. Petroleum Geologists Bull.*, **3**, 421 (1919).

[73]Oliver, Earl: Appraisal of Oil Properties, *Trans. Am. Inst. Mining Met. Engrs.*, 353 (1920).

[74]McLaughlin, R. P: *Oil Land Development and Valuation*, McGraw-Hill Book Company, Inc., New York, 1921.

[75]Cutler, W. W., Jr. and Clute, Walker S: Relation of Drilling Campaign to Income from Oil Properties, *U. S. Bur. Mines RI 2270*, Aug. (1921).

[76]Moyer, W. Irwin: Time to Pay Out as a Basis for Valuation of Oil Properties, *Trans. Am. Inst. Mining Met. Engrs.*, 1121 (1922).

[77]Vance, Harold: Bank Loans on Oil and Gas Production, *Petroleum Engr.*, Oct. (1954).

[78]Vance, Harold: Oil Loans from the Viewpoint of a Banker and an Oil Man, presented before the Technical Day Meeting, West Central Texas Oil & Gas Association, Abilene, Texas, November 8, 1956.

[79]Terry, Lyon F. and Hill, Kenneth E: Valuation of Oil and Gas Producing Properties for Loan Purposes, presented at the Annual Meeting of Petroleum Branch, AIME, Los Angeles, Calif., Feb. 1953.

[80]Wyer, Samuel S: Principles of Natural Gas Leasehold Valuation, *Trans. Am. Inst. Mining Met. Engrs.*, 782 (1917).

[81]Shaw, Eugene Wesley: Principles of Natural Gas Land Valuation, *Am. Assoc. Petroleum Geologists Bull.*, **3**, 378 (1919).

[82]Biddison, R. McDonald: Estimation of Natural Gas Reserves, introduction by H. A. Ley, *Geology of Natural Gas—A Symposium*, Am. Assoc. Petroleum Geologists, 1935.

[83]Davis, Ralph E. and Wege, J. Milton: Valuation of Gas Reserves, presented at AIME Petroleum Conference on Economics and Valuation, Dallas, Texas, March 29-30, 1956.

[84]DeGolyer, E. L: Valuation—Engineering Aspects, presented at the first Oil and Gas Institute, Dallas, Texas, March 23-26, 1949, published in *First Annual Institute on Oil and Gas Law, by Southwest Legal Foundation, Dallas, Texas*, Matthew Bender & Co., New York.

[85]Anon: Report and Proposals with Respect to the Principles of Valuation of the Committee on Valuation of Securities of the National Association of Insurance Commissioners (Oil and Gas Production Loans), 30, June 15, 1951.

[86]Gruy, H. J: Talk before Petroleum Engineers Club of Dallas, October 17, 1952.

[87]Arps, J. J: Profitability Analysis of Proposed Capital Expenditures for Development Drilling and Appraisal of Producing Properties, paper presented at Annual Meeting of the Society of Petroleum Engineers, AIME, Dallas, Texas, October 6-9, 1957.

[88]Crichton, Jack A: Factors Affecting Value of Undrilled Properties, Paper No. 625-G, presented at AIME Petroleum Conference on Economics and Valuation, Dallas, Texas, March 29-30, 1956.

[89]Kennedy, Edwin L: Vaulation Reports and Security Analysis, presented at the Annual Meeting of the Petroleum Branch, AIME, Los Angeles, Calif., Feb. 1953.

[90]Reistle, C. E., Jr: Applications of Engineering Valuations in Management, presented at AIME Petroleum Conference on Economics and Valuation, Dallas, Texas, March 29-30, 1956.

[91]Warren, J. Ed: Considerations Concerning Bank Financing of Oil and Gas Properties, presented at AIME Petroleum Conference on Economics and Valuation, Dallas, Texas, March 29-30, 1956.

[92]Glanville, James W: Rate of Return Calculations as a Measure of Investment Opportunities, *AIME J. Petr. Tech.*, June (1957).

[93]Anon: Liquid Reserves Gain Despite Drilling Loss, *Oil Gas J. (Annual Review-Forecast)* **56** [4] 160, Jan. 27 (1958).

BIBLIOGRAPHY

Barb, Clark F: Porosity-Permeability Relations in Appalachian Oil Sands, *The Pennsylvania State College School of Mineral Industries Bull. No. 9*, 47 (1930).

Bean, H. S: An Apparatus and Method for Determining the Compressibility of a Gas and the Correction for Super-compressibility, *U.S. Bur. Standards J. of Research, RP 170*, **4**, 645 (1930).

Bean, H. S: Determining Compressibility of a Gas, *Oil Gas J.*, 42, Jan. 16, (1930).

Beckman, Philip E: A Simplified Apparatus for Determining the Deviation of Gas from Boyle's Law, *Am. Gas J.*, 20, March (1932).

Bell, H. W: *The Monroe Gas Field*, Department of Conservation of Louisiana, Bull. No. 9, July 1921.

Bowers, E. H. and Rountree, R. H: *Economics for Engineers*, McGraw-Hill Book Company, Inc., New York, 1931.

Bradley, Oliver U: Valuation Factors of Casinghead Gas Industry, *Trans. Am. Inst. Mining Met. Engrs.* 395, Sept. (1920).

Brandenthaler, R. R: Problems of Estimating Gas Reserves, *Oil Gas J.*, June 30, (1927).

Brown, George Granger; Katz, Donald Laverne; Oberfell, George G; and Alden, Richard C: *Natural Gasoline and The Volatile Hydrocarbons*, sponsored by the Natural Gasoline Association of America, Tulsa, Oklahoma, Mid-West Printing Co., Tulsa, Okla. December, 1947.

Brown, George Granger: The Compressibility of Gases, *Petroleum Engr.*, Jan. (1940).

Bruin, J. and Hudson, H. E. Jr: *Selected Methods for Pumping Test Analysis*, State Water Survey Division, Urbana, Illinois, 1955.

Burrell, G. A. and Robertson, I. W: The Compressibility of Natural Gas at High Pressures, *U. S. Bur. Mines TP 131* (1916).

Burrell, G. A. and Jones, G. W: Pressure-Volume Deviation of Methane, Ethane, Propane, and Carbon Dioxide at Elevated Pressures, *U. S. Bur. Mines RI 2276*, 6 (1921).

Burrell, G. A. and Robertson, I. W: Compressibility of Natural Gas and Its Constituents, with Analyses of Natural Gas from 31 Cities in U. S., *U. S. Bur. Mines TP 158* (1917).

Carter, D. V: Application of Reserve Estimates of Hydrocarbon Fluids (Crude Oil, Gas and Condensate), *Am. Assoc. Petroleum Geologists Bull.*, **XXVIII**, Part 1, 630 (1944).

Davis, Ralph E: General Geologic Description of Natural Gas Properties Classification of Acreage, and Estimated Gas Reserves, as of December 1923, United Fuel Gas Company. Hearings before the Public Service Commission of West Virginia, Part 1, 1924.

DeGolyer, E. and Vance, Harold: *Bibliography on the Petroleum Industry, Bull. 83, Texas Engineering Experiment Station,* Texas A & M College, College Station, Texas, Sept. 1, 1944.

Diehl: *Natural Gas Handbook,* 1927 Edition.

Earhart, R. F. and Wyer, S. S: *Deviation of Natural Gas from Boyle's Law,* American Society of Mechanical Engineers, New York, 1916.

Eilerts, Kenneth, and Smith, R. Vincent: Specific Volumes and Phase-Boundary Properties of Separator-Gas and Liquid-Hydrocarbon Mixtures, *U. S. Bur. Mines RI 3642,* April (1942).

Elfrink, E. B; Sandberg, C. R; and Pollard, T. A: A New Compressibility Correlation for Natural Gases and Its Application to Estimates of Gas-in-Place, *Trans. Am. Inst. Mining Met. Engrs. (Petroleum Development and Technology),* **186,** 219 (1949).

Anon: Estimation of Natural Gas Reserves, *Oil Gas J.,* June 16 (1927).

Fettke, Charles R: Core Studies of the Bradford Sand from the Bradford Field, Pennsylvania, *Petroleum Development and Technology in 1928,* American Institute of Mining and Metallurgical Engineers, Inc., New York, 1929.

Fettke, Charles R: *National Petroleum News,* July 23 (1930).

Garrison, Allen D: Selective Wetting of Reservoir Rock and Its Relation to Oil Production, *API Drilling and Production Practice,* 130 (1935).

Gruy, H. J. and Crichton, J. A: A Critical Review of Methods Used in the Estimation of Natural Gas Reserves, *AIME J. Petr. Tech.,* July (1948).

Highsmith, J. H: *Appraisal of Oil Production,* published by J. H. Highsmith, Lawrenceville, Lawrence County, Ill., 1921.

Horner, William L: Control and Prediction of Secondary Recovery, *API Secondary Recovery of Oil in the United States,* American Petroleum Institute, New York, Chapt. 10, 140, 1950, 2nd Ed.

Johnson, R. H. and Morgan, L. C: A Critical Examination of the Equal Pound Loss Method of Estimating Gas Reserves, *Am. Assoc. Petroleum Geologists Bull.,* **10 [9]** Sept. (1926).

Johnson, T. W. and Berwald, W. B: Deviation of Natural Gas from Boyle's Law, *U. S. Bur. Mines TP 539* (1932).

Katz, Donald L. and Standing, M. B: Density of Natural Gases, *Trans. Am. Inst. Mining Met. Engrs. (Petroleum Development and Technology)* **142,** 140 (1942) (reprint, p. 182)

Kay, W. B: Density of Hydrocarbon Gases and Vapors at High Temperatures and Pressure, *Ind. Eng. Chem.,* **28,** 1014 (1936).

Kvalness, H. M. and Gaddy, V. L: The Compressibility Isotherms of Methane at Pressures to 1,000 Atmospheres and at Temperatures from —70 to 200°, *J. Am. Chem. Soc.,* **53,** 394 (1931).

Leith, C. K: *Mineral Valuations of the Future, AIME Series,* published for the Seeley W. Mudd Fund by AIME in 1938.

Lombardi, M. E: Letter to Harold Vance dated March 15, 1957.

Melcher, A. F: Apparatus for Determining the Absorption and the Permeability of Oil and Gas Sands for Certain Liquids and Gases Under Pressure, *Am. Assoc. Petroleum Geologists Bull.,* **9,** 442 (1925).

Miller, H. C. and Higgins, R. V: Review of Cutler's Rule of Well Spacing, *U. S. Bur. Mines RI 3479,* Nov. (1939).

Munn, Malcolm J: The Anticlinal and Hydraulic Theories of Oil and Gas Accumulation, *Economic Geology,* **IV,** Sept.-Oct. (1909).

Paine, Paul M. and Stroud, B. K: *Oil Production Methods,* Western Engineering Publishing Company, San Francisco, Calif., 1913.

Paine, Paul: *Oil Property Valuation,* John Wiley & Sons, Inc., New York; Chapman & Hall Limited, London, 1942.

Parsons, C. R: Accurate Estimates of Gas Reserves, *Oil Gas J.,* May 10 (1928).

Pierce, H. R. and Rawlins, E. L: The Study of a Fundamental Basis for Controlling and Gauging Natural Gas Wells; Part 1: Computing the Pressure at the Sand in a Gas Well, *U. S. Bur. Mines RI 2929,* May (1929).

Roland, C. H; Smith, D. E; and Kaveler, H. H: Equilibrium Constants for a Gas-distillate System, *Oil Gas J.,* March 27 (1941).

Sage, B. H. and Lacey, W. N: Series of publications in *Ind. Eng. Chem.,* and by American Petroleum Institute, 1933 to date (about 1948).

Sage, B. H. and Lacey, W. N: Partial Volumetric Behavior of the Lighter Paraffin Hydrocarbons in the Gas Phase, *API Drilling and Production Practice,* 641 (1939).

Sage, B. H. and Reamer, H. H: Volumetric Behavior of Oil and Gas from the Rio Bravo Field, *Tans. Am. Inst. Mining Met. Engrs. (Petroleum Development and Technology)* **142,** 176 (1942) (reprint, p. 368).

Sage, B. H. and Olds, R. H: Volumetric Behavior of Oil and Gas from Several San Joaquin Valley Fields, *Trans. Am. Inst. Mining Met. Engrs. (Petroleum Development and Technology)* **170,** 156 (1947).

Schilthuis, Ralph J: Connate Water in Oil and Gas Sands, *Trans. Am. Inst. Mining Met. Engrs. (Petroleum Development and Technology)* **127,** 199 (1938) (reprint, p. 259).

Shaw, E. W: Natural Gas Resources of Parts of North Texas—Gas in the Area of Fort Worth and Dallas, *U.S.G.S. Bull.* 629 (1916).

Silcox, D. E: *Mechanical Engineer,* 897, Nov. (1925).

Stephenson, Eugene A: Problems in Proration on the Basis of Gas Energy, *Petroleum Development and Technology in 1930,* American Institute of Mining and Metallurgical Engineers, Inc., New York, 1931.

Smith, R. L. and Watson, K. M: Boiling Points and Critical Properties of Hydrocarbon Mixtures, *Ind. Eng. Chem.,* **29,** 1408 (1937).

Spoor, H. C., Jr: Estimation of Gas Reserves, report of composite study group papers, Texas Gulf Coast, Houston Geological Society, 1946.

Torrey, Paul D: Significance of Fluid Injection Operations in the U. S., *More Oil for America, The Oil and Gas Compact Bulletin,* **XIV [1]** June (1955).

Vance, Harold: *Petroleum Subsurface Engineering,* Educational Publishers, Inc., St. Louis, Mo., 1950.

Vance, Harold: So You Want to Drill Your Own Oil and Gas Production, *Oil Gas J.,* Sept. 26 (1955).

Vance, Harold: Financing the Oil Well Drilling Contractor, *The Drilling Contractor,* Oct. (1955).

Vance, Harold: Financing Oil Production, presented before Petroleum Engineering 270, University of Texas, Austin, Texas, February 25, 1957; *Producers Monthly,* June (1957).

Versluys, J: An Investigation of the Problems of the Estimation of Gas Reserves, *Am. Assoc. Petroleum Geologists Bull.,* **12 [11]** Nov. (1928).

Williams, I. B; Brandenthaler, R. R; and Walker, Morgan: Design and Operation of Gas-Well Siphons, *U. S. Bur. Mines TP 460* (1929).

Ziegler, Victor: *Popular Oil Geology,* John Wiley & Sons, Inc., New York, 1918.

Chapter 17

RESEARCH

L. E. ELKINS

Mr. Elkins' photograph and biography appear on
page 884.

INTRODUCTION

In this chapter we shall review briefly the growth of research organizations and trace the development of some of the results. Considering research broadly as work resulting in an increase of knowledge, there has been research in the production of oil ever since it was first produced; that is, men faced with the immediate problems of drilling, completing, and producing wells have solved them in ingenious new ways that represented an advance in technology. Such additions to existing knowledge have come from drilling rig, lease, machine shop, and drawing board as well as from university laboratories and highly developed research organizations of today.

Inasmuch as this chapter is concerned essentially with organized industry research, no attempt has been made to present the history of numerous important contributions by many pioneer scientists, engineers, and oil-field workers to the knowledge of petroleum production.

The early research in petroleum production was primarily work of immediate utility. There was little organized fundamental research before about 1927. Progress in the mechanical arts, in improvement of drilling and pumping equipment, had been relatively rapid as compared with progress in understanding the behavior of oil, gas, and water in the reservoir and at the surface. It was not until there had been some accumulation of knowledge from fundamental research that there began to emerge a science of reservoir engineering.

BEGINNING OF ORGANIZED RESEARCH

Possibly the first organized research in petroleum production was that done by the Pennsylvania Geological Survey which employed John F. Carll from 1875 to 1890. Carll was a pioneer in laying the foundations of reservoir behavior and also designed a number of oil-well tools. Near the end of the 19th century, the United States Geological Survey conducted investigations of the conditions and movements of underground waters having a direct bearing on reservoir engineering. Particularly important was the work of C. S. Slichter[1,2,3] and F. H. King.[4]

The United States Bureau of Mines, soon after its establishment in 1910, began studying means of preventing waste of oil and gas, and methods of increasing the recovery of oil. Their investigations of oil-well cementing, drilling mud, and the physical properties of hydrocarbons were followed by petroleum-engineering studies of specific fields. The Bureau took the lead in advocating uniform casing programs and restriction of production to rates that would result in less waste and greater recovery.

---

[1]References are at the end of the chapter.

A. W. Ambrose, H. C. Miller, and several other pioneer workers at the Bureau made important contributions in petroleum research.

In 1917 the Bureau of Mines published J. O. Lewis' "Methods for Increasing the Recovery from Oil Sands," in which he recognized the importance of the gas dissolved in oil, and the effect of the forces of capillarity, viscosity, and adhesion on oil recovery. This pioneer work also considered the effect on the flow of liquids and gases of such factors as the porosity, cementation, grain size, mineral composition, and texture of the reservoir rocks. Lewis reported experiments to determine the amount of oil left in drained sands, and gave an extensive discussion of secondary recovery by compressed-air drive and by water flooding.

In 1920 the Bureau began experiments on underground flow of oil and water. These were followed by a wide range of studies continuing to the present, including development of bottom-hole pressure bombs and samplers, determination of the physical properties of hydrocarbons, estimation of reserves, correlation of oil-field brines, secondary-recovery experiments, and fluid-flow research.

ENDOWMENT OF FUNDAMENTAL RESEARCH

In 1925 John D. Rockefeller, and in 1926 Universal Oil Products Company, each agreed to give $50,000 a year for 5 years to support fundamental research in the petroleum industry under the sponsorship and technical guidance of the American Petroleum Institute. During the 5 years of these grants, 41 fundamental-research projects were carried on at 25 institutions in the United States. The gifts ended in the depression year of 1931, but the API continued the program on a somewhat reduced scale, concentrating on the more important projects for the next 5 years and expanding its support since then. Petroleum-production research projects under these various grants have included *Project 37—Physical Properties of Hydrocarbons, Project 27—Surface and Interfacial Phenomena in Production of Oil from Reservoirs,* and *Project 47—Mechanism of the Displacement of Oil from Porous Materials.* Geological research projects have included *Project 4 — Origin and Environment of Source Sediments of Petroleum, Project 43 — Transformation of Organic Materials into Petroleum, Project 49 — Clay Mineral Standards, and Project 51 — Near-shore Recent Sediments.*

Project 37, which has turned out valuable data for 27 years, was initiated in 1927 at California Institute of Technology as "The Fundamentals of the Retention of Oil by Sand". The early work determined the solubility of gas at various temperatures and pressures, the rate of solution of the gas, and the effect of dissolved gas on the volume, gravity, and viscosity of oil. The project has concentrated on accurate studies of the physical properties of hydrocarbons over a wide range of temperatures and pressures. The data are of great value in understanding and operating oil and gas reservoirs, in high-pressure separation of oil and gas, in natural-gasoline production, and in refinery engineering. The data, which are recorded in more than 100 technical papers, make it possible to calculate the volumetric and phase behavior of many hydrocarbon systems.

INCREASE IN RESEARCH EFFORT

Many factors led producing companies to employ technical personnel and to begin research investigations. From 1920 to 1940 the total number of research employees in the entire petroleum industry is estimated by an unpublished company report to have increased from 145 people to 7,176.[5] Managements of the more aggressive companies realized that progress in the industry was based on technology, that this technology came from research, and that, with the increasing complexity of problems and of knowledge, research demanded a team of specialists in several fields rather than a single man.

By 1930 research by the Bureau of Mines, the API projects, universities, service and supply companies, and by individuals in producing companies was resulting in improved efficiency in mechanical accomplishments and in the beginning of a knowledge of the behavior of oil and gas reservoirs. Methods were being developed for determining porosity, permeability, and saturation of cores; and experimental work with the bottom-hole pressure gage began to supply data on reservoir producing mechanisms.

A wide range of subjects was covered in these production-research activities, some of the more important being drilling (including drilling equipment and drilling technology), drilling fluids, oil-well cementing, well completion, acidizing, production equipment (control of corrosion, handling of well fluids, i.e., separation and storage systems, pumping and gas-lift equipment, well-logging equipment and other special instruments for determining bore-hole and formational characteristics), processing and utilization of natural gas, and elementary reservoir engineering.

In the last years of the great economic depression, the term "reservoir engineering" had not yet been coined and knowledge of this subject was meager and relatively undeveloped. Since then, particularly in the last two decades, much research has been done on three basic aspects of reservoir engineering, viz., petrophysics (the study of physical properties of rocks and their relationship to the contained fluids), physics of reservoir fluids, and basic reservoir-performance equations.

SCOPE OF PRESENT PETROLEUM PRODUCTION RESEARCH

Fundamental and applied research, theoretical and experimental investigations, are under way at present on a wide range of problems—from drilling to reservoir engineering. Major oil-producing companies have set up separate research departments or subsidiaries, and since 1945 have expanded facilities and personnel severalfold. The U. S. Bureau of Mines has experimental stations in five states engaged in production research ranging from thermodynamics to water flooding. The American Petroleum Institute is continuing and expanding its support of fundamental research. Several of the states are also doing research. The Pennsylvania State University, in cooperation with the Pennsylvania Grade Crude Oil Association, studied secondary recovery, core analysis, flow problems, and reservoir engineering. The Texas Petroleum Research Committee is doing research primarily on increasing oil and gas recovery. This is a joint project of the University of Texas, Texas Agricultural and Mechanical College, and the Railroad Commission of Texas. Other major research institutions, a part of whose work is in petroleum production, include Battelle Memorial Institute at Columbus, Ohio; Midwest Research Institute, Kansas City, Missouri; Arthur D. Little Company, Boston; and the Armour Institute at Chicago. One relatively young institution in Texas doing research in oil production is the Southwest Research Institute. This institution is available to the small producer for aid in the solution of his research problems. Several universities have established research organizations to accept approved projects of many types, including petroleum production.

Drilling Research, Incorporated, is an organization set up by a number of companies to study drilling problems and to investigate fundamentally new methods of drilling wells. Similarly, Sucker Rod Pumping Research, Incorporated, has been formed to study well-pumping mechanics.

Extensive research is being conducted by service and supply companies such as those specializing in drilling and production equipment and in cementing, perforating, acidizing, hydraulic fracturing, core analysis, electric logging, and well surveying. An important amount of fundamental research is conducted under fellowships and grants made by oil companies to universities. E. G. Gaylord[6] estimated in 1948 that all branches of the industry provide at least 300 grants and fellowships for research work in universities costing over $500,000 per year.

EXPENDITURES FOR RESEARCH

The entire oil industry was spending in 1948 an estimated 70 to 75 million dollars a year in its own research laboratories, employing 10,000 people *(op. cit.)*. Two 1950 estimates indicate some 100 million dollars per year;[7] and a 1952 estimate indicates 120 million dollars per year was spent on research for oil.[8] During 1955 this rate of expenditure rose to 161 million dollars. It is not known what part of this effort is devoted to petroleum-production research, but probably less than 10 percent (possibly 8 to 10 million dollars) was spent in 1952. Gaylord *(op. cit.)* estimated that 15 percent of the total research budget of the oil industry was being spent for production and exploration research in 1948, amounting to some 11 million dollars for these two activities; and further estimated that expansion was such that in 1949 this total would be from 15 to 20 million dollars. In 1955 this total reached 30 million dollars; probably 40 to 50 percent was spent on production. These figures do not include research conducted by supply and service companies and this is a significant amount.

The growth of research for all industries between 1937 and 1947 is estimated[6] to be, for the entire United States (government, industry, universities, others), from 238 to 1,385 million dollars per year, or about a sixfold increase. Industrial organizations themselves increased their research expenditures during this period about fivefold. These figures check with the data given by Elkins[9] on the sixfold growth 1937-1952 of the professional personnel in 7 major oil companies who were doing research on drilling and production problems. During 1955 total research expenditures in the United States for all categories amounted to 4 billion dollars.

INFLUENCE OF RESEARCH DEVELOPMENTS

Effects of this research program can be seen in every phase of the business of producing oil. In drilling, advances in equipment, technique, metallurgy, and drilling fluids now make it possible to drill to depths below 20,000 ft, and currently at least one well is producing at these depths. Wells and fields that 10 or 20 years ago might have been either passed up without detection or considered to be only marginally productive are now yielding commercial quantities of oil through improved well-logging techniques, new types of drilling fluid, better methods of well completion, and hydraulic fracturing. Through better understanding of the reservoir behavior, improved recovery methods make it possible in some areas to produce up to twice the amount that would have been obtained without the knowledge gained by research.

RESULTS OF PRODUCTION RESEARCH

This review should be prefaced with the recognition that very seldom does a research idea become translated into practice without the aid and full cooperation of operating people, and there is no intent in this review to imply that these developments have been possible only because of research and development. Often the original research ideas are significantly improved or enormously enhanced in scope of application through the subsequent contributions of others than research men, and sometimes the initial idea may have been contributed by people not in research and development.

DRILLING AND PRODUCTION PRACTICES RESEARCH

Drilling Methods

In drilling, the impact of research has been felt in improved metal-lurgy and design of equipment, in the development of drilling fluids, in the technique of perforating, cementing, well surveying, and well completion. Stronger bits and bearings have been developed to carry the load of heavier weights on bit imposed by up to 20 or more drill collars. Jet bits[10,11] utilizing optimum fluid velocities for efficient cutting removal allow penetration rates in soft formations of more than twice those possible 10 years ago. For hard formations, such as chert, special insert bits have been developed to drill efficiently through formations that only a few years ago would have been prohibitively expensive to penetrate. Coring bits—including wire-line retrievable core barrels for continuous coring, diamond bits, and open-hole side-wall sampling bits have been highly developed. Controlled directional drilling to inaccessible locations, and for reaching the bottom of blown-out wells and stopping their flow or drilling from marine platforms;[12] the fast-developing technique of drilling and completing wells in the open Gulf; improvement of efficiency in every phase of drilling methods and equipment—all have benefited in some degree from the results of research developments. In the last 10 years, drilling speed has increased about 50 percent. Much of the research effort behind these developments is outside the bounds of organized research in the oil industry proper. Quite often, however, research in the oil industry has pointed up problems and improvements which encouraged efforts by service and supply companies.

Drilling Fluids

The development of drilling fluids has followed an evolutionary path in which the contributions of the research laboratory have become meaningly important.[13,14] As wells became deeper, the properties of the simple clay-water mixtures were found increasingly inadequate to meet drilling requirements. Clay-water mixtures of sufficient density to control high-pressure sands were too viscous to be handled, and about 1921[15] muds were developed utilizing heavy weighting materials which increased weight without greatly affecting viscosity. Later, chemical agents were used to control the viscosity, particularly tannates and phosphates.[16] In the middle 1930's the significance of low-filtrate-loss properties in preventing development of thick mud cakes on the walls of the hole was realized,[17] and the practice of controlling the filtrate loss of mud came rapidly into use thereafter. Bentonite was an early additive used to control filtrate loss; and later on starch and various gums, natural and synthetic, were utilized.

Subsequently, study of cores and of producing formations showed that some sands were plugged by the action of water or by the filtrate from water-base drilling mud or from cement filtrate, and that for maximum productivity it was necessary to complete wells in these formations with an oil-base instead of a water-base mud. Oil-emulsion muds, lime-base muds,[18] and other specialized muds have been developed—even air and gas are being used as drilling fluids. Improved additives have also been developed to control loss of circulation,[19] viscosity, and other properties.[20] Other basic research on the problem of lost circulation[21,22] has led to suggestions of preventive measures that have been widely adopted in the industry.

Cementing

Research in the physics and chemistry of oil-well cements[23] has determined the influence of temperature, pressure, and composition on setting time and strength. Laboratory studies showed that the pressure and temperature conditions in cementing the deeper wells resulted in a sharp reduction in setting time. This led to changing of field rules to allow drilling out the cement plug one to two days earlier than had been customary, with savings to the industry of several million dollars a year.[24] Research into the mechanics of cementing showed that mud contamination was the primary cause of bad cementing jobs, and that wiper plugs and wall scratchers were necessary to remove the mud and to secure a better bond to the formation.[25,26] Modern high-pressure consistometers can analyze the behavior of cement for deep, hot wells so that the operator can select a cement providing a safe margin of pumping time.

Well Completion

In the field of well completions, the development of the bullet casing perforator in the 1930's represented a great advance in efficiency, economy, and certainty over the old mechanical methods of perforating; and together with advances in electric logging of formations, has resulted in obtaining increased oil production and in decreasing water and gas intrusion. After World War II, the bazooka was applied to the business of perforating,[27] and the use of these shaped charges made more deeply penetrating holes than were obtainable by previous methods, giving more certainty of penetrating through casing, cement sheath, and 6 in. or more of the adjacent formation. The need for better uses of perforating techniques became evident following the introduction of improved cementing methods.[28] Here again much credit is due the service companies with assists from organized research in the oil industry.

Well-stimulation methods have included the early use of explosives[29,30] for formation shattering and the use of acids.[31] Acid was first used in wells in 1895, but interest in this method declined until the early

1930's. Research resulted in the introduction of chemical additives and methods which extended the use of acidizing to dolomites and other more complex formations and minimized corrosion of equipment.[32] The hydraulic fracturing of formations[33] has developed into the treatment of some 4,000 wells per month. In some low-permeability fields, fracturing is the only known method of obtaining commercial production;[34] and in many other fields it has prolonged the economic life of the wells. Research developments in hydraulic fracturing include methods of selective fracture placement at desired depths, better propping agents, processes to create multiple fractures,[35] combined fracturing and acidizing, large-volume fracturing, additives to reduce fluid loss in fracturing fluids,[36] and some methods that might assist in making the fractures either horizontal or vertical.[37]

Completion and reworking of wells without using heavy rigs to kill the well, and pull and rerun tubing, have become practical by use of the "permanent-type well completion".[38]

Production Equipment

The need for corrosion control became evident early in the history of petroleum production, and research on various aspects of this problem was conducted by oil companies and other organizations.[39-43, incl.] This work led to improved practices to control corrosion. The huge losses ascribable to oil-field corrosion have stimulated continuous research in the selection of better materials, development of corrosion inhibitors,[44-47, incl.] and development of methods of stopping corrosion caused by electric currents.[48] This research, in addition to effecting substantial reductions in operating costs, has encouraged the chemical and service companies to develop still better inhibitors and other corrosion-control methods.

Advances in metallurgy and design have made possible the safe handling of wells with pressures of several thousand pounds per square inch. Accurate knowledge of the properties of hydrocarbons has furnished data for design of multistage separation systems for better conservation of lighter components. Tankage has evolved from wooden and earthen tanks to modern steel tanks, pressure tanks for high-pressure mixtures, and the recently developed underground storage in salt cavities and other excavations.[49] Tank stations are in operation that automatically fill and switch tanks and close in wells according to predetermined sequence. The ancient lineage of pumps has, under the stimulus of research, been extended to include fluid-actuated bottom-hole pumps,[50] hydraulic long-stroke rod pumps, electrically operated bottom-hole pumps, gas-lift plungers, and pumps which use rubber balls and gas pressure.[51] A hydraulically balanced rod string, with a hydraulic booster at depth, increases the potential depth for rod pumping.

RESERVOIR RESEARCH

Phase Behavior

One of the many outstanding results of the program of fundamental research directed toward new information and better understanding rather than toward immediate application was the discovery that retrograde condensation phenomena were taking place in producing reservoirs. In the experimental work done by API Project 37 to determine accurately the physical properties of hydrocarbons over a wide range of temperature and pressure, it was observed that at high pressures and temperatures some normally liquid hydrocarbons went into the gaseous phase. This behavior was fundamentally different from the ordinary concept and diametrically opposed to the customary behavior of hydrocarbons—that of going from gas to liquid with increased pressure.

Production conditions in the Big Lake Field in Texas had been puzzling to the petroleum engineers, in that from a vertically continuous permeable stratum, the upper part of the pay produced a light, water-white oil and the bottom part a heavy, brown oil. No theory was available to explain how two oils could exist through geologic time in contact with each other without mixing. Puzzling too was the fact that water was produced from the upper portion, above any known water table, and the fact that the gas-oil ratio remained constant regardless of how fast the well was produced or from what level in the upper section the well was producing.

Dr. W. N. Lacey, who was directing API Research Project 37, heard the presentation of a paper describing the Big Lake Field[52] and saw that there were not two oils, but one oil and one vapor, thus explaining the lack of mixing, the constancy of the gas-oil ratio, and the production of water. The white oil and the water existed in the formation in the gas phase entirely; and when the pressure was relieved at the surface, the oil condensed into liquid. Although retrograde condensation had previously been known to the physical chemists, this is believed to have been the first published recognition of the fact that high-pressure petroleum reservoirs sometimes show retrograde condensation.

Research Project 37 went on to make further investigation of condensate production, which also had been found at Kettleman Hills Dome in California and was later discovered in many fields on the Texas-Louisiana Gulf Coast; and experiments at high pressures with methane-propane mixtures and with Kettleman Hills light oil and natural gas confirmed the existence of retrograde condensation under reservoir conditions.[53] Considerable subsequent work has been done along the same lines by the Bureau of Mines and by several producing companies; and experimental technique and apparatus have been developed so that it is possible, with sufficiently careful sampling and experimenting, to start with the reservoir fluid and determine for any given pressure or temperature the quantity and the composition of the fluid that will be condensed. Such information makes it possible to arrive at an economic balance for the condensate reservoir between the additional liquid hydrocarbons to be gained by maintaining pressure at a given level and the costs of injection. It also makes it possible to design surface separators for maximum recovery of condensate, especially the more volatile fractions.

The discovery of retrograde condensation as a recognizable condition in many oil reservoirs has resulted in the establishment of a new branch of the petroleum industry. The modern gasoline-plant recycling project strips the reservoir gas of its normally liquid fractions plus the liquefied petroleum gases, and maintains the reservoir pressure by reinjecting the stripped gas while pushing the rich gas towards the producing wells.

Measurement of Rock Properties

Melcher[54] pioneered core analysis in the petroleum industry, publishing methods for porosity and permeability determinations in oil sands in 1921. The earliest estimation of the porosity of oil-producing formations was probably that made by Carll.[55] Apparently the first publication on the porosity of oil reservoirs by a technical society was that made by an AIME committee.[56]

In 1933, Fancher, Lewis, and Barnes published the results of 3 years of research conducted at Pennsylvania State College on measurement of porosity and permeability.[57] This important work marks the beginning of the modern era in core analysis. In the same year the Darcy unit of permeability was given its present definition,[58] and in 1935 there was adopted *API Code 27: Standard Procedure for Determining Permeability of Porous Media.* Soon laboratories of major oil companies and a number of service companies were set up to provide core-analysis information, and both groups have continued research to improve techniques.

The next significant development in this field was the realization that these standardized procedures, although yielding valuable results, still gave incomplete information inasmuch as the permeability measured was that to a single fluid. It became generally realized that reservoirs contained interstitial water even in pays producing water-free oil, and that there existed simultaneous flow of oil and water, gas and water, and of all three. Early work on this problem was confined to the relatively simple case of the linear steady-state flow of an incompressible fluid in porous media.[59] In 1931 Muskat and Botset[60] published the first of a series of papers that has provided a good part of the foundation for today's science of reservoir engineering. This first paper dealt with the linear flow of gas through a porous medium.

About 1936 several investigators established the fact that the permeability of a rock to a given fluid was not the same as the "dry" permeability, but was a function of the saturation of the flowing fluid and of other fluids in the pores. In 1936, Hassler, Rice, and Leeman,[61] studying the flow of gas as a function of oil saturation, used the term "relative permeability" to indicate the ratio of the permeability to a given fluid under stated saturation conditions to the permeability at 100-percent saturation of that fluid. Later in the same year Wyckoff and Botset made the first complete studies of this nature, showing relative-permeability curves for both liquid and gas and for varying grain sizes, packings, oil viscosities, and permeabilities.[62] They showed that the permeability was independent of the viscosities of the oil used, and was a function of saturation. These and following experiments and especially the manner of presenting the curves of percentage specific permeability against percentage liquid saturation, resulted in a marked acceleration and clarification of information concerning flow of fluids in oil and gas reservoirs. The curves typically show an almost complete single-fluid permeability to gas even with 10 to 20 percent of liquid in the pores; they show a sharp drop in liquid permeability and a very slow rise in gas permeability for small percentages of gas saturation; the curves are also interpreted to give the gas-oil ratio throughout the system tested.[63] The fact that the sum of the gas and the liquid permeabilities did not equal the single-fluid permeability had important implications for theoretical analysis of flow, as did the fact that gas-oil mixtures with low gas-oil ratios tend to attain equilibrium conditions by the accumulation of free gas in the sand.

With the general increase in knowledge of the physical properties of rocks, there eventually came the realization that the electrical resistance of a formation, and the difference in potential between various beds might be measured and interpreted so as to correlate formations and give information as to their fluid content and properties. The first electric log, comprising only a resistivity curve, was publicized in 1929.[64] This log, as proved by correlation with core analysis, was useful in providing a sharp correlation between wells. In 1931, the self-potential log was added, making it possible to determine the boundaries of permeable beds, at least in unconsolidated formations. Continued research resulted in qualitative interpretation of these logs; and in 1942, Archie published the first paper[65] on quantitative interpretation. Since that time there has been a rapid and intensive development of well logging, and there have been developed detail logs for shallow investigation (microlog); focused logs for deep investigation behind the mud invasion (laterolog, induction log, guarded electrode log); the gamma-ray or radioactivity log introduced in 1940, which measures the natural radioactivity of the formations, and can be used in both open hole and cased hole; and the neutron log, introduced in

1942. At present it is possible to determine, from an adequate combination of well logs, the porosity, water saturation, approximate permeability, and net pay. Other important well-logging developments of recent years include directional surveys to measure both inclination and direction of the bore hole, caliper logs, dipmeter surveys which determine the direction and angle of formation dip, water- and gas-entry surveys, and side-wall coring surveys, introduced in the late 1930's. Much research has been conducted in logging by service companies, with some important contributions from oil-company research departments.

Occurrence of Water in the Producing Reservoir

Although geologists had long recognized that since most oil and gas reservoirs had been deposited in the sea, they would contain water, and that, in addition, migration of oil took place in the presence of water; still the concept of a definite water table or plane of sudden vertical change from total water saturation at the base of the pay to zero water saturation in the pay continued to persist up into the 1930's. This erroneous concept influenced the thinking about estimates of oil and gas reserves, secondary-recovery practices, well-log interpretation, and completion of wells. Evidence of the existence of connate water in the Bradford sand was reported by Fettke[66] in 1929. By about 1938, however, several investigators[67,68,69] proved that in most reservoirs water is present in varying amounts throughout the producing formation, and that even in the portions of the reservoir producing water-free oil, water would exist, generally as a film between the oil and the rock. These findings corroborated previously developed theories of capillarity,[70,71] which indicated that there would be a gradual change from 100-percent water saturation at the base of a producing formation to a lower saturation higher in the sand body, and that the water occurred as a network of capillaries above the zone of 100-percent water saturation. This explanation was harmonious with the fact that the connate brine of the formations was later partially displaced by the oil migrating into the structure.

The fact that in water-wet reservoirs the water tends to occupy the smaller pores and capillary connections and the oil tends to flow through the larger pores and more open channels, explained why a fine-grained, silty sand could have a water saturation of over 50 percent and still produce water-free oil for a part of the reservoir life. Quantitative measurements of the amount of interstitial water in oil-producing reservoirs led to important changes in estimating reserves, in estimating recovery efficiency, and in studying the flow of oil and gas. More importance was given to careful coring and core analysis; oil-base fluid was used in coring to obtain reliable water saturations. Flow tests on cores were redesigned to include the effect of water.

Schilthuis[67] showed that higher water saturation (therefore lower oil saturation) generally correlated with lower permeability. Therefore, recovery figures based on experience in the older, shallow fields with higher permeabilities would be too high for less-permeable fields. The recognition of interstitial water saturation was especially important to secondary-recovery projects because a higher water saturation after primary recovery would mean less oil left for secondary recovery. It also led to a more careful study and re-evaluation of electric logs for horizons whose oil and gas content had been hidden in silty sands by the presence of high concentrations of conductive brines. The high concentrations of conductive brine obscure the electrical resistance of the oil and gas, resulting in an electric log of low resistance normally associated with non-productive strata. As explained previously, silty sands may have a high water content and still produce water-free oil.

Function of Gas in the Production of Oil

In the earlier days of the oil industry, where cable-tool drilling was used exclusively, a gas sand or a gas cap above the oil pay was regarded as a nuisance to be blown off into the air as fast as possible. As early as 1909 the USGS pointed out the waste of natural gas, and estimated the loss at about a billion cubic feet per day.[72] In the Glenn Field of Oklahoma it was reported in 1913[73] that the loss of gas was such that before the field was 3 years old it was without sufficient gas for its own uses. Although thoughtful men had long realized the importance of gas energy in expelling oil from the reservoir rocks, only a few appear to have suspected that blowing off gas had an effect upon the oil remaining in the producing sand. It was not until the engineers of the U. S. Bureau of Mines, in 1913, began to publish the results of their early investigations of gas wastage, and of the rapid decline in the production of oil wells, that it became clear that withdrawals of free gas from an oil sand, which reduced the reservoir pressure, took out not only the free gas but also some gas which had been dissolved in the crude petroleum and was being progressively released as the rock pressure declined.[74]

The first extensive experimental investigation of the effects of dissolved gas on the properties of oil was an AIME contribution by Beecher and Parkhurst in 1926.[75] They showed that the viscosity of some oils was reduced in half by saturation with gas at 500 lb and that surface tension was reduced by about 20 percent. The USBM was making similar studies at about the same time which culminated in H. C. Miller's book, *Function of Natural Gas in the Production of Oil*, published in 1929.[76]

Theoretical and Experimental Investigations into Reservoir Behavior

With the change from open flow to prorated production, the problem of estimating underground reserves became more difficult, since for fields producing under greatly restricted rates, the decline-curve method is no longer satisfactory. To meet this need, mathematical methods of analysis were developed using material-balance equations, and based on variation of reservoir pressure with production, analyses of bottom-hole samples of the reservoir fluid, gas cap, amount of water influx in the reservoir, and other information. As early as 1930, Coleman, Wilde, and Moore[77] described a material-balance method of analysis. Improved methods were proposed by Schilthuis and Katz[78] in 1936. Hurst,[79] Van Everdingen and Hurst,[80] and others extended the applicability of this method of analysis.

The following is quoted from a paper by Elkins and Pirson:[81]

"Method for the calculation of the displacement efficiency of water encroachment or of an expanding gas cap have their origin in a momentous contribution of Buckley and Leverett[82] on the mechanism by which any fluid non-miscible with oil is able to displace oil from a porous rock. In effect these authors propose two-point equations, one governing the fraction of the displacing fluid flowing with the oil through an infinitesimal rock volume element and the other the rate of advance of a particular degree of saturation in the displacing fluid that exists in that element. It may be said that these equations are all-inclusive of the rock and fluid properties as well as of the rate of displacement and the direction of flow. It therefore became possible to gage in a water drive, in a gas drive, or in a gas-cap injection program, the effect of oil viscosity, relative permeability ratio, rate, degree of formation dip, capillary pressure gradient, differential fluid density, etc. That these equations could be reliably used in practical problems is being realized rather slowly by the industry. Some objection is being made on the applicability of steady-state relative permeability curves and static capillary pressure measurements obtained in the laboratory to the actual transient state. These fears should have been dispelled by a conribution of Terwilliger, Wilsey, Hall, Bridges, and Morse,[83] which showed that the transient saturation distribution obtained in gravity drainage could be predicted with great accuracy from steady-state relative permeability and static capillary pressure curves. The practical use of the Buckley-Leverett equations in actual reservoir calculations has not yet received the generalization that they deserve, perhaps because of the inaccuracy with which reservoir rock properties are known, owing to the meager sampling provided by core analysis as well as to difficulties in restoring reservoir conditions in the laboratory. A laboratory demonstration of the significance of these fundamental equations was reported by Holmgren and Morse[84] and further elaborated on by Geffen, Parrish, Haynes, and Morse[85] when they specifically studied the significance of a trapped and immovable gas phase in reservoirs where water is the displacing fluid. This pointed to a possible reversal in thinking concerning the importance of maintaining pressure above the bubble point in water drive reservoirs and also suggested an approach for increasing recovery in waterflood operations."

Model Studies of Reservoirs

In 1932, Wyckoff, Botset, and Muskat reported the use of an electrolytic model to study a gas-cylinder problem. Later Bruce[86] described a more elaborate analog computer that was developed to predict the pressure fluid withdrawal performance of water-drive reservoirs. This analog computer uses electricity to study fluid flow. Also, in order to study pattern sweep efficiencies in reservoirs, the potentiometric model was developed.[87]

It was recognized that many reservoir problems could not readily be solved with existing mathematical tools. The complexity of reservoirs imposed this limitation. To provide answers to otherwise very complex problems, a technique for scaling models was developed. In substance, many physical factors, such as thickness and area of a reservoir (which cannot be duplicated in the laboratory), can be properly weighted into laboratory measurements. Leverett et al., in 1942, first publicized this concept.[88] At present, many investigators feel confident in their ability to specify the factors which must be scaled in a model and this approach is becoming more popular.

The fundamental developments in reservoir engineering and comparisons of developed theory with field performance have fortified today's reservoir engineer with growing confidence in ability to control and alter forces to achieve a more perfect degree of oil and gas recovery. The various types of reservoir drive have been categorized (depletion, water, gravity, and gas-cap) and the factors governing production in these drives have been recognized. Water-flooding and gas-drive recovery methods have been systematically developed. The fundamental information is finding increasing usefulness in recommendations concerning well spacing and maximum efficient rates of production (MER).

Unconventional Recovery Methods

Several concepts for new recovery methods have evolved out of the storehouse of fundamental knowledge available to researchers.

Studies in phase behavior led to the suggestion that gas injection at pressures substantially above the natural bubble-point pressure of oil in a reservoir could result in relatively high oil-displacement efficiency.[89] It was also suggested that gas, with composition relatively heavy in ethane and propane, could lower the pressure required to achieve the same objective. An investigation of oil displacement from porous media by a liquefied petroleum gas (*iso*butane) was reported in 1953.[90]

Research on cores and reservoir models observed the capillary imbibition of water into natural Spraberry virgin-state cores. This led to the suggestion of a pilot to evaluate this phenomenon as a field recovery method in the vast Spraberry area of west Texas.[91] Various means of applying heat to increase oil recovery from underground reservoirs have been suggested by many in patent literature and a type of combustion-in-place was reportedly tried by the Russians as early as 1935. At least two major research organizations have reported the results of field pilots designed to further prove up laboratory concepts of oil recovery by in-situ combustion.[92,93]

A number of other new ideas have appeared in the literature—the use of LPG as a solvent flood, introduction of carbonated water while water flooding, use of many types of surfactants in water flooding, forcing research to recall the experimental use of soda ash in Pennsylvania floods some 30 years ago. These ideas and others are undergoing serious laboratory study and may be subjected to small field pilots before research organizations suggest that they join the rank of new recovery methods.

HISTORICAL SKETCH OF THE DEVELOPMENT OF RESEARCH ORGANIZATIONS BY COMPANIES

The growth and development of production-research organizations parallel in many respects the evolution and growth of the petroleum-engineering profession. Prior to 1900 there had been little production research, but after that time such research was started in a number of company laboratories. Oil-company engineers and production men were showing increased interest in such production problems as cementing casing uniformly and obtaining good water shutoffs, treating oil-field emulsions, and designing and operating natural-gasoline plants.

This early research was primarily for immediate utility and there was little organized fundamental research before about 1927. Often the laboratory-type research was conducted for producing departments by geological groups or refinery or natural-gasoline plant laboratories. The sporadic and unorganized early research aided significantly in solving pressing immediate production problems and contributed toward the accumulation of knowledge that hastened the emergence of more basic organized research.

In the light of this background, let us note the production-research activities of various oil companies prior to 1927.

Period Prior to 1927

In the Union Oil Co. of California, production research had its beginning in 1899 when the small geology department of that company assisted production people in improving oil-well cementing practices. In 1922 a research and development division was organized and given the status of a department, with headquarters in new research facilities at Wilmington, California. Most of the production-research work during the early 1920's was carried out at the request of other company departments. Included in this work were studies on oil-well cements, correlation of oil-field waters, preliminary studies of core analysis, and gas lift.

One of Standard Oil Co. of California's associated companies, the Kern River Trading and Oil Company, established a laboratory in the Kern River Field, California, as early as 1912 with William Purdew in charge. Two problems given emphasis were improving cement properties and utilizing water analyses for geologic purposes. Another associated company, the Pacific Oil Company, maintained a laboratory in San Francisco in 1922-23, which worked on some production problems. Production research was conducted also in Standard of California's own operations as early as 1912. A laboratory was started in Taft, California, about 1916 where problems concerning water, oil, and gas analyses were studied. Ralph Halloran and C. C. Scharpenberg were active in early oil-field research on such problems as developing gas traps, turbodrills, and drilling fluids. H. C. Miller worked on drilling-fluid problems in 1922.

In addition to the Taft laboratory, there were other producing-department laboratories at Whittier, California, starting about 1919, and at La Habra, California, starting in 1927. Also a development department was started at the Richmond refinery in 1919 which worked on problems concerned with producing operations, e.g., model studies of the effects of well spacing and production rate on oil recovery. In 1923 a research and development department was organized to handle the research facilities for the entire Standard of California operations.

From 1912, when Shell Oil Company entered the United States oil industry, its research was confined largely to the production and mechanical-engineering department where ways and means were sought to solve many problems connected with drilling, fishing for lost tools, coring and logging formations, cementing, and well completion.

The first production research in the Socony Mobil Oil Co. organization was done by General Petroleum Corporation. First production research in General Petroleum Corporation seems to have been done by geologists in 1912. From then until 1921 the geologists devoted increasing effort to problems of oil-field development. In 1923, an engineering test department started research on well-pumping equipment and producing-well performance. Soon thereafter this department studied fundamentals of gas-lift operation experimentally and measured PVT relations and solubility of gas in oil.

Production research in Cities Service Oil Company was conducted in various places under a variety of names. As early as 1914 a laboratory in

Bartlesville, Oklahoma, was engaged in research on improving drilling equipment. A production laboratory was started in 1918 at Oil Hill, Kansas, under the direction of John C. Walker. Among the problems worked on were oil-field emulsions, scaling of production equipment, corrosion, brine-water analyses and their correlation.

The Gulf Oil Corporation established a research department at Houston, Texas, in 1917 with F. M. Siebert in charge. Studies included oil-field emulsions, corrosion, and drilling muds. Initial studies were carried out on oil-well cores. In 1924 Stanley H. Gill was the incumbent of a Gulf-sponsored fellowship at Mellon Institute concerned with a study of corrosion problems in production and pipeline work.

Production research at The Carter Oil Company was carried out by its petroleum engineers for a number of years before a formal research organization was started. The engineering branch was organized in 1917 and functioned until 1936.

In 1919 one of Pan American Petroleum Corporation's predecessor companies, the Midwest Refining Company, established a laboratory in Midwest, Wyoming, to perform experiments relating to natural-gasoline plants. The man in charge, H. W. Young, had the title of research engineer. In the early 1920's this small laboratory also conducted occasional production research on such problems as paraffin deposition, corrosion, water treating, oil-field emulsions, and correlation of oil-field waters.

The first production research in the Humble Oil & Refining Company was carried out by the development department of the Baytown refinery, a group organized in the mid-20's under the supervision of Stewart P. Coleman to conduct research and development in refining operations. On occasion this group worked on specialized problems brought to their attention by the producing department. Its work included treating of oil-field emulsions and control of evaporation losses in pipeline operations.

Phillips Petroleum Company's production research had its beginning in 1923 with the equipping of a small laboratory in the corner of a warehouse at Bartlesville, Oklahoma. Initial efforts were centered on problems of analyzing oil-field waters and of breaking oil-water emulsions. Activities were shortly extended to include studies of methods for shutting off formation waters, appraisals of produced crudes, and methods of analysis.

What was destined to become The Texas Company's research division of its producing department began in 1925 as a geophysical laboratory housed in a warehouse building in Houston, Texas. It consisted mainly of a machine shop for developing and maintaining seismic equipment.

The Marland Oil Company began production research in early 1926 as a result of E. W. Marland's conversations with a pioneer in petroleum engineering, L. C. Uren. W. P. Haseman, who headed the research department, had earlier set up geophysical and geological research under E. A. Eckhardt, R. D. Wyckoff, and L. F. Athy. B. R. Stephenson and W. V. Vietti, among others, started in production research on the function of gas and water in the production of oil, determination of porosity and permeability of cores, control of paraffin, corrosion, and related problems. Marland's major contribution, resulting largely from Dr. Haseman's firm belief in engineering research, was the assembly of a petroleum-engineering staff and field organization under the leadership of E. O. Bennett. K. C. Sclater, E. V. Foran, Harold Vance, J. E. Warren, and B. B. Boatright made notable contributions to engineering research in the following period. The Marland Oil Company merged with Continental Oil Company in 1929.

Period from 1927 to 1957

As mentioned previously, many factors led producing companies to employ technical people and begin research investigations after 1926. This trend is reflected in the many formal research organizations started by various companies during this period and the greater specialization of research. It is apparent from this review that some of the pressing problems prior to 1927, such as brine-water analyses and their correlation and oil-field emulsions, had been brought under better control and research efforts were being shifted toward the more difficult drilling and producing problems encountered in deeper reservoirs and in developing a variety of basic information required in developing the science of reservoir engineering.

Continuing the review, the following organizational highlights appear in the research activities of the various oil companies.

Gulf Oil Corporation established the Gulf Research and Development Company in 1927 under Paul D. Foote, as a research department for the entire corporation. Included in the production-research problems were those relating to reservoir engineering, well completion, oil-well cementing, drilling muds, corrosion, and development of instruments for securing subsurface information such as bottom-hole pressure. Gulf expanded the Mellon Institute fellowship in 1927 to cover all drilling, production, and pipeline problems under Dr. Foote. In 1930 a small laboratory was built in Pittsburgh to house the expanded activities of this group, which was set up at this time as the research department of the Gulf Production Company. Included in the production-research problems were those relating to reservoir engineering, well completion, oil-well cementing, corrosion, and development of instruments for securing subsurface information such as bottom-hole pressures. In 1933 the Gulf Research and Development Company was formed to handle all research for the Gulf companies. In 1935 Gulf Research was moved to a 53-acre tract at Harmarville, Pennsylvania, which it still occupies.

Major research topics during the period of 1927 to 1940 included work by Wyckoff, Botset, and Muskat on flow of fluids through porous rock, and extensive mathematical work by Muskat relating to the development of the science of reservoir engineering. Since 1940 the Gulf Oil Corporation has continued an active production-research program which has included research on reservoir mechanics, well completion, drilling, drilling fluids, corrosion, and development of new instruments and equipment. During 1955 Gulf's production-research activities were reorganized and an expansion program started by which their effort in this field is to be more than doubled from the 1955 staff of 55 workers.

During the period 1927-1940, The Texas Company conducted production research on a variety of problems including drilling muds, cementing, salt-water disposal, and corrosion.

In 1941 the production and geophysical staff had grown to 33 employees. In that year the laboratory was moved to Bellaire, Texas. In 1947 this laboratory was reorganized to become the research division of the producing department and was divided into two sections dealing with geophysical research and production research. In 1953 the laboratory was enlarged. The staff as of 1956 consists of 115 researchers. Production research emphasizes reservoir engineering and improvement of production methods.

Emphasis was maintained by Phillips Petroleum Company on the development of improved methods for the analysis of hydrocarbon mixtures as research tools. In addition to routine appraisals of crude oils and gases, an organized program for analysis and correlation of formation-water compositions was initiated for the purpose of aiding in the identification of formations, prescribing proper well-completion practices, and water-disposal means. Studies of corrosion and means for combating corrosion were also initiated. Fundamental studies, particularly as regards hydrocarbon-mixture behavior, were started in 1932, the field measurements being paced by an extensive laboratory program involving solubility-shrinkage measurements of bottom-hole samples, the results of which were subsequently correlated with the compositions as determined from fractional analysis. In 1933 K. H. Hachmuth and D. L. Katz undertook the determination of the vaporization equilibrium constants for crude-oil —natural-gas systems and developed the now widely used K-value charts. Similar constants for natural-gas—distillate systems were subsequently determined by H. H. Kaveler and co-workers. Prior to 1934 reservoir-rock studies were largely limited to porosity tests on core samples. An expanded program of core analysis was started in 1935. The results of these studies were applied to reservoir-engineering studies on a number of fields during the period 1934 to 1940.

Since 1940 the production-research organization of Phillips Petroleum Company has continued its established program with some attention in the fields of secondary recovery, drilling muds, and well-completion practices. In 1940 the so-called back-pressure method for determining gas-well potentials was studied extensively. Somewhat later, work was done on developing a method of predicting the pressure traverses of flowing wells and gas-lift wells which permitted calculation of bottom-hole pressures of flowing wells from a knowledge of surface data.

Cities Service Oil Company established a laboratory at Tallant, Oklahoma, in 1927. Although primarily concerned with oxygenated chemicals, this laboratory did some production research beginning in 1927. The production research related principally to the development of emulsion breakers, and problems of corrosion, paraffin deposition, and gas hydration.

In 1947 the Cities Service Research and Development Company was formed to take over research activities formerly conducted by various Cities Service Company subsidiaries. In 1953 a production-research laboratory was established in Tulsa. Among the projects being worked on by this laboratory are those relating to reservoir mechanics, well stimulation, selective plugging agents, corrosion, and well logging.

Starting in 1927 petroleum production engineers of General Petroleum Corporation of the Socony Mobil organization took over studies of well and reservoir performance with special emphasis on means of increasing ultimate recovery of oil. In the early 1930's H. N. Marsh worked on problems relating to drilling muds, gas anchors, and well-pumping equipment. In 1937 a research physicist was employed to coordinate production-laboratory work with research information available from field operations and outside sources. Core-analysis and capillary studies were started, including effects of various waters on permeability. Also in 1937, the petroleum engineering department of Magnolia Petroleum Company organized a core laboratory at Kermit, Texas, with Jack Woodward in charge. He was joined by H. H. Mayfield in 1938 in laboratory work on cores, acidizing, and drilling muds. This laboratory worked on problems for the entire Magnolia Company and Socony Mobil affiliates. In 1939 a similar laboratory was set up by Magnolia's petroleum engineering department at Vanderbilt, Texas, and was soon expanded by adding facilities for phase-behavior determination under E. C. Patton.

Magnolia's field research laboratories were first organized in 1938 to study better means of utilizing natural gas. Soon thereafter research was directed to refinery processes, particularly those associated with aviation-gasoline manufacture. Later a limited amount of geophysical and geochemical research was started.

In 1942 the Kermit and Vanderbilt laboratories of Magnolia were consolidated in the present petroleum engineering laboratory at Dallas, Texas. This laboratory has continued to expand and has recently moved into a newly constructed building. In 1945 a production-research laboratory had been organized in General Petroleum's production department under the supervision of Norris Johnston. This laboratory was expanded into a technical service laboratory in 1946 when the parent company, Socony Mobil Oil Company, Inc., expanded both production and exploration research and centered these activities in Magnolia's field research laboratories in Dallas.

The initial staff in production research consisted of about 30 people, most of whom had technical training. From the outset this organization has been well-equipped with the most modern research instruments. Research originally centered on reservoir mechanics, rock properties, drilling fluids, corrosion, reservoir-fluid behavior, specialized production instruments, and field equipment. The scope of research activities and the research staff have continued to expand. Bacteriological and applied mathematics groups have been added, and a technical service unit organized to supplement the basic research activities and give specialized attention to specific field production problems. Approximately 120 people are presently engaged in production research. Scientific specialties of staff members include physics; physical, organic, and analytical chemistry; chemical, electrical, mechanical, and petroleum engineering; bacteriology; geology; and mathematics. In addition to concentrating its production research at Magnolia's field research laboratories, Socony Mobil has continued to expand its production-laboratory facilities in key locations.

Production personnel of Continental Oil Company (Marland Oil Company merged with Continental Oil Company through stock transfer in 1929) continued with studies to improve ultimate recoveries by gas repressuring. During the 1930's, R. Van A. Mills, J. G. Dyer, L. F. Athy, and H. R. Prescott worked on problems of oil-field emulsions, well stimulation, cementing, corrosion of underground pipe, well logging, and perforating.

In 1948 organized production research was resumed by Continental Oil Company under the direction of H. H. Hinson. A production research division and a reservoir engineering section were organized under the supervision of J. J. Reynolds and J. A. Murphy, respectively. In 1949, these two sections were incorporated into the newly organized development and research department. Construction of a $2\frac{1}{4}$ million dollar research building at Ponca City, Oklahoma, was completed in 1952 to house the production research division and other components of the research department. In 1955 further expansion of the research department necessitated the construction of a pilot-plant building which houses well-completion, stimulation, and logging laboratories. The building is unique in that it was constructed from an 80,000-bbl storage tank. Continental's production-research efforts are directed toward reservoir engineering and various drilling and production problems.

In 1928 the geological department of the Sun Oil Company was studying some production problems including well cores and crooked-hole problems. All production research during this period was conducted at service laboratories located in Beaumont and in Dallas. These laboratories had a succession of titles. A variety of miscellaneous problems were investigated including the development of bottom-hole pressure gages, a gyroscopic well-surveying instrument, and other instruments. At the Beaumont laboratory in 1939, a research investigation was started on drilling muds which has continued to this day.

The Dallas service laboratory of the Sun Oil Company began an active study of problems relating to corrosion in 1946. In 1945, Sun established a physical laboratory in Newton Square, Pennsylvania, which conducted considerable research for the production department. Included in the research program was development of high-speed reservoir analyzers for prediction of reservoir performance. In 1947 a new laboratory was constructed at Amelia, Texas, for seismograph research, development, and service. All research in this field is still conducted there. In 1955 a new production-research laboratory was completed at Richardson, Texas, near Dallas. All production research, with the exception of seismograph research, is now centralized at this newest facility.

By 1929 the Union Oil Co. of California was engaged in problems of measuring liquid level in oil wells, drilling muds, design of rotary drill pipe, studies of gas-oil ratios, core analysis, and flow of oil, gas, and water through producing formations. In 1937 a group under the supervision of P. H. Jones was established in the research department to work on production-research problems. From 1940, research efforts were emphasized toward secondary-recovery methods, well-stimulation methods, development of oil production from shale, tar sands, and western coals, and unconventional methods of oil recovery. In 1952 the research department was moved into new laboratories at Brea, California. Increased emphasis was directed toward fundamental studies.

Immediately after organization of the petroleum engineering division in June 1928, Humble Oil & Refining Company established its production research division in 1929 as one of the first units in industry devoted exclusively to fundamental and applied research in drilling and petroleum production. Initially a part of the development department under the supervision of H. D. Wilde, the production research division was placed under the production department in 1933.

This division pioneered in a number of research activities, particularly in reservoir behavior and drilling-mud control. Early work was directed toward increased oil recovery through gas repressuring and pressure-maintenance operations, studies of well spacing, development of improved drilling muds and oil-well cements, studies of natural-gasoline plant operation, crude stabilization, and development of subsurface instruments to measure pressures, temperatures, and to obtain subsurface oil and gas samples. Associated activities were laboratory investigations of reservoir-fluid properties, studies of rock characteristics, research on fluid flow through porous rocks, and advances in techniques to analyze reservoir and well behavior.

In the 1940's, the production research program was extended to include well-log interpretation, corrosion, and accelerated research on core analysis and fluid mechanics. Continued emphasis on fundamental studies of reservoir behavior, the mechanism of recovery, and the controls to effect greater oil recovery formed the foundation for widespread application of reservoir engineering to development and operation of oil and gas reserves. In 1950 the production research division was among the first in the oil industry to apply electronic digital computers to solution of production problems. Research in numerical methods extended the understanding of flow and recovery processes and permitted handling of complex engineering problems arising in production operations.

Currently, approximately 90 people are engaged in research in drilling and completing wells, formation identification, operation and control of wells, oil-recovery mechanisms, hydrocarbon behavior, reservoir performance, and numerical analysis. The production research organization has continued as a division of the production department throughout this period. Its research effort is closely coordinated with the petroleum engineering division to maintain operating contact and to facilitate application of research results.

In 1954 the production research division moved into its new laboratories in the Houston Research Center in Houston, Texas. This center, having more than 144,000 sq ft of floor space, houses 475 research and technical service employees and provides facilities for geophysical, geologic, and geochemical research and for reservoir engineering and service laboratories of the petroleum engineering division.

In 1931 Stanolind Oil and Gas Company was organized and absorbed associated companies (Dixie, Pan American Petroleum and Transport, Midwest Refining, etc.). At that time, George S. Bays and his staff of six engineers performed some production-research work. Later this group was designated as the "research engineering department" and worked on production research and special engineering problems. The first production laboratory work was performed by J. B. Clark in a small storage building in Tulsa. A small production laboratory was established in 1933 with T. H. Dunn as chief chemist. The work of this laboratory was closely integrated with desk petroleum-engineering research pursued by the engineering staff. Topics worked on included bottom-hole oil-sample collection and analysis, cementing, drilling muds, brine-water disposal, core analysis, oil recovery, recovery of distillate, drilling, and oil-field emulsions.

A research department was organized in 1943 and the producing department laboratory became the production research section (now division) of the research department. Well-completion and corrosion research have been emphasized since 1943 and reservoir-mechanics research has been a subject for major expansion since 1949. In 1953 a new research center in Tulsa was first occupied. This laboratory houses exploration and process research as well as production research. Facilities are designed to handle between 400 and 450 people and approximately one-third are in production research.

The research and development laboratories of The Pure Oil Company started in the early 1930's to assist the producing division in the solution of its field problems. Among the early projects were conditioning of water for flooding purposes, emulsion treating, paraffin solvents, corrosion, heaving shale, and sand acids. In 1950 new research and development facilities were established at Crystal Lake, Illinois. Since then there has been increasing emphasis on production research, the principal topics of investigation being reservoir mechanics, corrosion, acidizing, and water treating.

Sinclair Refining Company started production research in 1932 with a small core and water laboratory at Independence, Kansas, directed by the geological department, Sinclair Prairie Oil Company. This laboratory was moved to Tulsa in 1935. Principal problems were development of analytical methods for core analysis as applied to secondary-recovery methods for the production engineers. Attention was also given to oil-well cements and drilling muds.

In 1947 the research and development department of Sinclair Refining Company at Harvey, Illinois, started research on underground thermal oil-recovery methods. Consolidation of all production research was effected in 1952 when Sinclair Research Laboratories, Inc., established a branch in Tulsa. The staff has increased from 44 people in 1952 to 90 researchers in 1956. Emphasis is placed on reservoir mechanics, fluid flow, and thermal-recovery methods, as well as exploration research.

Standard Oil Co. of California in 1934 established a joint research laboratory at Kettleman Hills with the North Dome Association. This laboratory burned in 1936 and in that same year a production-technology laboratory was started in La Habra, California, under the direction of E. G. Gaylord and J. E. Gosline.

California Research Corporation was organized as a subsidiary of Standard of California in 1944. The nucleus of California Research Corporation was the research and development department that had been organized in 1923. It was not until 1927, however, that the oil-field research division of California Research Corporation was set up. This division was organized under the direction of E. G. Gaylord, who became a vice president of California Research Corporation. The elements of the division were the production-technology laboratory and the natural-gasoline group that had been developed under the research and development department's tutelage. The oil-field research division was charged with carrying out research and technical phases of the business. The laboratory is located at La Habra, California, where its present facilities occupy some 80,000 sq ft of research space.

Shell Oil Company's formal production research in the United States was started in 1936 at Shell Development Company, Emeryville, California, with a staff of about 10 people. Some of the early research problems included salt-water disposal, secondary recovery by water flooding, acid treatment, the shutoff of waters by chemical methods, cements, method of core analysis, and studies of rock properties.

Shell Oil Company in 1945 combined exploration and production research at a laboratory in Houston, Texas. At the end of 1954 the staff had increased to over 300 people with about half of the total effort devoted to production problems. The production-research program has been directed toward theoretical and experimental work on the physical and chemical properties of the rocks and fluids in the earth, and the development of equipment for making measurements in bore holes to determine the properties of the rocks and fluids in situ. An increased emphasis is being put upon fundamental research.

At The Carter Oil Company the production research previously handled as part of a production-engineering group was formally organized in 1937 under M. L. Haider, Chief Engineer. By 1938 the organization included two engineers, two chemists, and a physicist. From the beginning of organized research effort, reservoir-engineering studies were emphasized. Problems included well spacing, water-drive performance, and studies of the properties of formational cores and fluids.

The production-research group had grown to 12 researchers by 1945 and to 60 researchers by 1956. Emphasis has continued on reservoir-mechanics research. In 1945 research on drilling and other production equipment was also started. In 1952 a separate section was set up to study new or unconventional oil-recovery methods.

The year 1938 marked the beginning of production research by The Atlantic Refining Company. This first work was concerned with distillate recovery and was performed by the research and development department in Philadelphia to aid their production department.

In 1942 research was started on oil-production problems — a group of 8 researchers being set up in temporary quarters in Dallas. Research activities were expanded gradually in makeshift quarters until 1948, when adequate permanent quarters were obtained. Production research during the years 1942 to 1947 dealt in the main with fundamental flow of fluids through porous media, hydrocarbon phase relations, reservoir-engineering calculation methods, and natural-gasoline recovery. Since 1948, in addition to continuing active research on reservoir-mechanics problems, research efforts have been initiated and expanded on drilling and well-completion problems. Included in these problems are drilling muds, oil-well cementing, and theory and development of engineering methods for calculating the degree of improvement expected from fracturing a reservoir.

The Ohio Oil Company in 1954 established a research department as a separate department of the company. Initial research activities, with emphasis being placed on exploration and production research, were started in 1956 with the completion of a research laboratory at Denver, Colorado.

RESEARCH BY SERVICE LABORATORIES

Research by service laboratories has played an important role in the outstanding progress made by the oil-producing industry over the past several decades. Besides the many original research contributions of these laboratories, they have aided significantly in perfecting and speeding the field applications of discoveries originating from the oil companies and other sources. The research efforts of the service laboratories have aided in almost all phases of the producing industry — included being such subjects as oil-well cementing, oil-well acidizing, emulsion treating, formation fracturing and other well-completion methods, corrosion, drilling fluids, drilling and production equipment, special instruments and methods for obtaining subsurface samples, and other surface information.

REFERENCES

[1]Slichter, C. S: Theoretical Investigation of the Motion of Ground Waters, *U. S. Geol. Survey*, 295 (1899).

[2]Slichter, C. S: The Motions of Ground Water, *U. S. Geol. Survey*, 13 (1902).

[3]Slichter, C. S: Field Measurement of the Rate of Movement of Underground Water, *U. S. Geol. Survey*, 9 (1905).

[4]King, F. H: Conditions and Movements of Underground Waters, *U. S. Geol. Survey, 19th Annual Report* [2] (1899).

[5]Maldoon, R. F: Information Division Letter Search L51-21, Research Personnel in U. S., Standard Oil Company (Indiana) unpublished report, June 18, 1951.

[6]Gaylord, E. G: The Role of Research in the Production of Oil, *API Drilling and Production Practice*, 201 (1948).

[7]Holaday, W. M: Products Research, *Oil Gas J.*, 96, May (1950); Porter, Frank M: Record Year, *Oil Gas J.*, Dec. (1950).

[8]Egloff, G: *The Chemist*, 500, October (1952).

[9]Elkins, L. E: Importance of Organized Research in Drilling and Production, *API Drilling and Production Practice*, 365 (1952).

[10]Nolley, J. P; Cannon, G. E; and Ragland, Douglas: The Relation of Nozzle Fluid Velocity to Rate of Penetration with Drag-type Rotary Bits, *API Drilling and Production Practice*, 22 (1948).

[11]Bielstein, W. J. and Cannon, G. E: Factors Affecting the Rate of Penetration of Rock Bits, *API Drilling and Production Practice*, 61 (1950).

[12]Jackson, J. G. and Murdoch, J. B., Jr: Planning a Multiple Well Directional Drilling Program for Off-Shore Location, *Trans. Am. Inst. Mining Met. Engrs. (Petroleum Development and Technology)* **179,** 52 (1949).

[13]Garrison, A. D: Surface Chemistry of Clays and Shales, *Trans. Am. Inst. Mining Met. Engrs. (Petroleum Development and Technology)* **132,** 191 (1939) (reprint, p. 423).

[14]Beck, R. W; Nuss, W. F; and Dunn, T. H: The Flow Properties of Drilling Muds, *API Drilling and Production Practice,* 9 (1947).

[15]Stroud, B. K: Use of Barytes as a Mud-Laden Fluid, *Oil Weekly,* June 2 (1925).

[16]Lawton, Loomis, and Ambrose: U. S. Patent No. 1,999,766, 1935.

[17]Jones, P. H. and Babson, E. C: Evaluation of Rotary Drilling Muds, *API Drilling and Production Practice,* 22 (1935).

[18]Battle, Jack L: Lime-Base Muds, A Progress Report, *Oil Gas J.,* 81, March 16 (1950).

[19]Howard, G. C. and Scott, P. P: Analysis of the Control of Lost Circulation, *Trans. Am. Inst. Mining Met. Engrs. (Petroleum Development and Technology)* **192,** 171 (1951).

[20]Byck, H. T: Effect of Temperature on Plastering Properties and Viscosity of Rotary Drilling Muds, *Trans. Am. Inst. Mining Met. Engrs. (Petroleum Development and Technology)* **136,** 165 (1940) (reprint, p. 224).

[21]Teplitz, A. J: Investigations of Lost Circulation, *Oil Forum,* April (1950).

[22]Goins, W. C., Jr; Weichert, J. P; Burba, J. L., Jr; Dawson, D. D; and Teplitz, A. J: Down-the-Hole Pressure Surges and Their Effect on Lost Circulation, *API Drilling and Production Practice,* 125 (1951).

[23]Farris, R. F: Effects of Temperature and Pressure on Rheological Properties of Cement Slurries, *Trans. Am. Inst. Mining Met. Engrs. (Petroleum Development andl Technology)* **142,** 117 (1945) (reprint, p. 306).

[24]Farris, R. F: Method for Determining Minimum Waiting-on-Cement Time, *Trans. Am. Inst. Mining Met. Engrs. (Petroleum Development and Technology)* **165,** 175 (1946).

[25]Teplitz, A. J. and Hassebroek, W. E: An Investigation of Oil-well Cementing, *API Drilling and Production Practice,* 76 (1946).

[26]Howard, G. C. and Clark, J. B: Factors to be Considered in Obtaining Proper Cementing of Casing, *API Drilling and Production Practice,* 257 (1948).

[27]McLemore, R. H: Application of the Shaped-charge Process to Petroleum Production, *API Drilling and Production Practice,* 71 (1948).

[28]Teplitz, A. J: Review of Casing Cementing and Perforating Practices, *Oil Gas J.,* Sept. 9 (1948).

[29]Carll, John F: Report on Progress, *Second Geological Survey of Pennsylvania: 1875 to 1879,* **576-578,** 325-329.

[80]Lewis, P. F: Oil-Field Explosives — Their Characteristics and Use, *API Drilling and Production Practice,* 73 (1934).

[21]Putnam, S. W: Development of Acid Treatments of Oil Wells, *Oil Gas J.,* Feb. 23 (1933).

[32]Fitzgerald, Paul E: *AIME J. Petr. Tech.,* 1, Sept. (1953).

[33]Clark, J. B: Hydraulic Process for Increasing Productivity of Wells, *Trans. Am. Inst. Mining Met. Engrs. (Petroleum Development and Technology)* **186,** 1 (1949).

[34]Roberts, G., Jr: Hydraulic Fracturing After Four and One-Half Years, *Oil Gas J.,* **52** [43] 82, March 1 (1954).

[35]Clark, J. B; Fast, C. R; and Howard, G. C: A Multiple-fracturing Process for Increasing the Productivity of Wells, *API Drilling and Production Practice,* 104 (1952).

[36]Reynolds, J. J; Bocquet, P. E; Coffer, H. F; Lease Crude as Cheap Fracturing Fluid, *Oil Gas J.,* June 6 (1955).

[37]Clark, R. C., Jr. and Reynolds, J. J: Vertical Hydraulic Fracturing for Increasing Oil and Gas Production, API Paper No. 851-28-J, presented at Oklahoma City, March 17-19, 1954.

[38]Huber, T. A. and Tausch, G. H: Permanent-Type Well Completion, *Trans. Am. Inst. Mining Met. Engrs. (Petroleum Development and Technology)* **198,** 11 (1953).

[39]Mills, R. Van A: *Production of Oil and Gas Field Equipment Against Corrosion, U. S. Bur. Mines Bull. 238* (1925).

[40]Subcommittee on Production Corrosion: Corrosion of Production Equipment, *Proc. Am. Pet. Inst., (Prod. Bul. 206)* 153 (1930).

[41]Wescott, Blaine B. and Bowers, C. Norman: Corrosion Fatigue and Sucker Rod Failures, *Proc. Am. Pet. Inst., (Prod. Bul. 212)* 29 (1933).

[42]Bacon, T. S: Review of NGAA Research on Gas-Condensate Well Corrosion, *Oil Gas J.,* **46 [12]** 257, July 26 (1947).

[43]Report of Condensate Well Corrosion Committee of the NACE Covering the Field Testing of 32 Alloys in the Flow Stream of Seven Condensate Wells, April (1949).

[44]Dunn, T. H and Menaul, P. L: Formaldehyde as an Inhibitor of Corrosion Caused by Hydrogen Sulfide, *Trans. Am. Inst. Mining Met. Engrs. (Petroleum Development and Technology)* **165,** 26 (1946).

[45]Jewell, J. G: Chemical Treatment to Mitigate Corrosion, *Corrosion,* March (1952).

[46]Bacon, T. S: High-Pressure Production — Equipment Corrosion, *API Drilling and Production Practice,* 157 (1944).

[47]Eilerts, C. K., et al: Field and Laboratory Tests of Sodium Chromates and Alkalies for Controlling the Corrosion in Gas Condensate Wells, *World Oil,* July to December, incl. (1949).

[48]Ewing, S. P. and Bayhi, J. F: Cathodic Protection of Casing in Loudon Pool, *Corrosion,* **4 [6]** 264, June (1948).

[49]Howard, K. C: The Development and Operation of LPG Storage Cavities in Salt Strata, *AIME J. Petr. Tech.,* **III [3]** March (1951).

[50]Coberly, C. J: Hydraulic Power Applied to Oil-Well Pumping, *API Drilling and Production Practice,* 79 (1935).

[51]Vincent, R. P: A New Gas Lift System, *Am. Inst. Mining Met. Engrs. Paper No. 282-6* (1953).

[52]Lacey, W. N: Discussion of "The Big Lake Oil Field, Reagan County, Texas," by E. V. Foran, *Proc. Am. Pet. Inst., (Prod. Bul. 210)* 61 (1932).

[53]Sage, B. H; Lacey, W. N; and Schaafsma, J. G: Behavior of Hydrocarbon Mixtures Illustrated by a Simple Case, *Proc. Am. Pet. Inst., (Prod. Bul. 212)* 119 (1933).

[54]Melcher, A. F: Determination of Pore Space of Oil and Gas Sands, *Trans. Am. Inst. Mining Met. Engrs.,* **65,** 469 (1921).

[55]Carll, John F: *The Geology of the Oil Regions of Warren, Venango, Clarion, and Butler Counties, Pennsylvania,* Second Geological Survey of Pennsylvania, 1875-79, **III** (1880).

[56]Determination of Pore Space of Oil and Gas Sands, *Trans. Am. Inst. Mining Met. Engrs.,* **65,** 716 (1921).

[57]Fancher, G. H; Lewis, J. A; and Barnes, K. B: Some Physical Characteristics of Oil Sands, *Pennsylvania State College Bull. 12,* 65, May (1933).

[58]Wyckoff, R. D; Botset, H. G; Muskat, M; and Reed, D. W: The Measurement of the Permeability of Porous Media for Homogeneous Fluids, *Rev. Sci. Inst.,* **4,** 394, July (1933).

[59]Versluys, J. C: The Equation of Flow of Oil and Gas to a Well After Dynamic Equilibrium Has Been Established, *Proc. Royal Acad. Sci.*, **33**, 578 (Amsterdam 1930).

[60]Muskat, M. and Botset, H. G: Flow of Gases Through Porous Media, *Physics*, **1**, 1 (1931).

[61]Hassler, G. L; Rice, R. R; and Leeman, E. H: Investigations on the Recovery of Oil from Sandstones by Gas Drive, *Trans. Inst. Mining Met. Engrs. (Petroleum Development and Technology)* **118**, 116 (1936) (reprint, p. 114).

[62]Wyckoff, R. D and Botset, H. G: The Flow of Gas-Liquid Mixtures Through Unconsolidated Sands, *Physics*, 325, Sept. (1936).

[63]Muskat, M; Wyckoff, R. D; Botset, H. G; and Mores, M. W: Flow of Gas-Liquid Mixtures Through Sands, *Trans. Am. Inst. Mining Met. Engrs. (Petroleum Development and Technology*, **123**, 69 (1937) (reprint, p. 247).

Johnston, N. and van Wingen, N: Reservoir Fluid Flow Research, *Petr. Engineering*, **16**, 108, July (1945).

[64]Schlumberger, Conrad and Marcel: Electrical Logs and Correlations in Drilling Holes, *Mining and Metallurgy*, 515 (1929).

[65]Archie, G. E: The Electrical Resistivity Log as an Aid in Determining Some Reservoir Characteristics, *Am. Inst. Mining Met. Engrs. (Petroleum Development and Technology)* **146**, 54 (1942).

[66]Fettke, C. R: Core Studies of the Bradford Sand from Bradford Field, Pennsylvania, *Trans. Am. Inst. Mining Met. Engrs. (Petroleum Development and Technology)* 221 (1928-29).

[67]Schilthuis, R. J: Connate Water in Oil and Gas Sands, *Trans. Am. Inst. Mining Met. Engrs. (Petroleum Development and Technology)* **127**, 199 (1938) (reprint, p. 259).

[68]Smith, Foote, and Busang: *Phys. Rev.*, **36**, 524 (1930), and *Physics*, **1**, 18 (1930).

[69]Martin, M; Murray, G. H; and Gillingham, W. J: *Geophysics*, **III**, 258, (1938).

[70]Garrison, Allen D: Selective Wetting of Reservoir Rock and Its Relation to Oil Production, *API Drilling and Production Practice*, 130 (1935).

[71]Versluys, J: Can Absence of Edge Water in Certain Oil Fields be Ascribed to Capillarity? *Am. Assoc. Petroleum Geologists Bull.*, **15**, 197 (1931); Factors Involved in Segregation of Oil and Gas from Subterranean Water, *Am. Assoc. Petroleum Geologists Bull.*, **16**, 924 (1932).

[72]*U. S. Geol. Survey Bull. 394.*

[73]Arnold, Ralph, and Clapp, F. G: Wastes in the Production and Utilization of Natural Gas and Means for Their Prevention, *U. S. Bur. Mines TP 38* (1913).

[74]Gibson, H. S: Scientific Unit Control, *Sci. of Petroleum I*, 534.

[75]Beecher, C. E. and Parkhurst, I. P: Effect of Dissolved Gas upon the Viscosity and Surface Tension of Crude Oil, *Petroleum Development and Technology in 1926*, American Institute of Mining and Metallurgical Engineers, Inc., New York, 1927.

[76]Miller, H. C: *Function of Natural Gas in the Production of Oil*, American Petroleum Institute, New York, 1929.

[77]Coleman, Stewart; Wilde, H. D; and Moore, Thomas: Quantitative Effect of Gas-Oil Ratios on Decline of Average Rock Pressure, *Trans. Am. Inst. Mining Met Engrs. (Petroleum Development and Technology)* **86**, 174 (1930).

[78]Schilthuis, R. J: Active Oil and Reservoir Energy, *Trans. Am. Inst. Mining Met. Engrs. (Petroleum Development and Technology)* **118**, 33 (1936) (reprint, p. 31).

Katz, D. L: A Method of Estimating Oil and Gas Reserves, *Trans. Am. Inst. Mining Met. Engrs. (Petroleum Development and Technology)* **118**, 18 (1936) (reprint, p. 16).

[79]Hurst, W: Water Influx into a Reservoir and Its Application to the Equation of Volumetric Balance *Trans. Am. Inst. Mining Met. Engrs. (Petroleum Development and Technology)* **151,** 57 (1943) (reprint, p. 263).

[80]Van Everdingen, A. F. and Hurst, W: Application of the LaPlace Transformation to Flow Problems in Reservoirs, *Trans. Am. Inst. Mining Met. Engrs. (Petroleum Development and Technology)* **186,** 305 (1949).

[81]Elkins, L. E. and Pirson, S. J: Milestones in Two Decades of Reservoir Engineering, *AIME J. Petr. Tech.,* 59, Sept. (1952).

[82]Buckley, S. E. and Leverett, M. C: Mechanism of Fluid Displacement in Sands, *Trans. Am. Inst. Mining Met. Engrs. (Petroleum Development and Technology)* **146,** 107 (1941) (reprint, p. 149).

[83]Terwilliger, P. L; Wilsey, L. E; Hall, H. N; Bridges, P. M; and Morse, R. A: An Experimental and Theoretical Investigation of Gravity Drainage Performance, *Trans. Am. Inst. Mining Met. Engrs. (Petroleum Development and Technology)* **192,** 285 (1951).

[84]Holmgren, C. R. and Morse, R. A: Effect of Free Gas Saturation on Oil Recovery by Water Flooding, *Trans. Am. Inst. Mining Met. Engrs. (Petroleum Development and Technology)* **192,** 135 (1951).

[85]Geffen, T. M; Parrish, D. R; Haynes, G. W; and Morse, R. A: Efficiency of Gas Displacement from Porous Media by Liquid Flooding, *Trans. Am. Inst. Mining Met. Engrs. (Petroleum Development and Technology)* **195,** 29 (1952).

[86]Bruce, W. A: An Electrical Device for Analyzing Oil-Reservoir Behavior, *Trans. Am. Inst. Mining Met. Engrs. (Petroleum Development and Technology)* **151,** 112 (1943) (reprint, p. 318).

[87]Lee, B. D: Potentiometric Model of Fluid Flow in Petroleum Reservoirs, *Trans. Am. Inst. Mining Met. Engrs. (Petroleum Development and Technology)* **174,** 41 (1948).

[88]Leverett, M. C; Lewis, W. B; and True, M. E: Dimensional-model Studies of Oil-field Behavior, *Trans. Am. Inst. Mining Met. Engrs. (Petroleum Development and Technology)* **146,** 175 (1942) (reprint, p. 217).

[89]Whorton, L. P. and Kieschnick, W. F., Jr: A Preliminary Report on Oil Recovery by High-pressure Gas Injection, *API Drilling and Production Practice,* 247 (1950).

[90]Henderson, Gove, Ledbetter, and Griffith: *Trans. Am. Inst. Mining Met. Engrs. (Petroleum Development and Technology)* **198,** 33 (1953).

[91]Brownscombe, E. R. and Dyes, A. B: Water Imbibition Displacement—a Possibility for the Spraberry, *API Drilling and Production Practice,* 383 (1952).

[92]Kuhn, C. S. and Koch, R. L: In-Situ Combustion — Newest Method of Increasing Oil Recovery, *Oil Gas J.,* Aug. 10 (1953).

[93]Grant, B. F. and Szasz, S. E: Development of an Underground Heat Wave for Oil Recovery, *AIME J. Petr. Tech.,* 23, May (1954).

book four
notable cooperative efforts

Chapter 18

CONSERVATION

REX G. BAKER AND ROBERT E. HARDWICKE

REX G. BAKER, born in Big Valley, Mills County, Texas, in 1891, received B.A. and LL.B. degrees from the University of Texas. After a brief private practice he was employed, in 1920, in the law department of Humble Oil & Refining Co. He was advanced to a directorship of Humble Pipe Line Co. in 1929; to director and general counsel of the parent company in 1943; and to a vice presidency of that company in 1951. He retired from the company in 1956.

Mr. Baker's academic, professional and industrial honors and affiliations include Phi Beta Kappa, Chancellors, Friars; the Houston, State and National Bar Associations; directorship of the Houston Chamber of Commerce, and membership and chairmanship of committees of the United States Chamber of Commerce. He was commissioned second lieutenant in the United States Army in 1917; released from active duty as a captain in 1919, advancing later to lieutenant-colonel in the reserve.

Rex G. Baker

Robert E. Hardwicke

ROBERT E. HARDWICKE was born in Sherman, Texas in 1889 and educated at Virginia Military Institute and the University of Texas (LL.B., 1911). He engaged in private practice of law in Beaumont, Texas, mainly in oil and gas matters from 1911 to 1918 when he joined the legal staff of Gulf Oil Corporation. His service with the corporation extended for five years in Texas and six in Venezuela. Since 1929 he has been in private practice with the exception of World War II service as Associate General Counsel, then General Counsel, of the Petroleum Administration for War. He is currently senior partner in the Fort Worth firm of Hardwicke, Haddaway & Pope.

As an international specialist in oil and gas law and conservation law and practices, Mr. Hardwicke has assisted Texas Attorneys General in important litigation; served as petroleum consultant to the United States Department of State with respect to problems involving the continental shelf, and has served as Chairman of the Section on Mineral Law of the American Bar Association and of the State Bar of Texas. He is noted as a lecturer and author on regulation and conservation. *Antitrust Laws, et al. vs. Unit Operation of Oil or Gas Pools* and three other books authored by him have been widely circulated in legal and engineering circles.

1116

⮌ 18 ⮌

I. RESUMÉ OF CONDITIONS LEADING TO COMPREHENSIVE PROGRAMS FOR CONSERVATION OF OIL AND GAS

In most foreign countries, a grant of land by the sovereign did not and does not carry title to oil, gas, and other minerals. In most instances this is so, even though the grant does not contain an exception of the minerals. Ordinarily, in foreign countries, the right to develop minerals (usually called a concession) is obtained from the government and covers a large area, such as a district (county) or even the entire country. As a result, a concessionaire (lessee) usually is able to develop in the manner that he thinks is desirable, without the necessity of conducting operations to prevent drainage to wells on adjoining concessions of others. In other words, the concessionaire has a good chance to realize the dream of every oil man—discovery of an oil pool wholly on land with respect to which he has development rights, affording the opportunity to operate in compliance with recognized efficient methods, and to experiment in order to increase efficiency.

In the United States, the situation is quite different, for a grant of land by the sovereign, whether the United States or a state, carried with it—and still carries with it—the ownership of all of the minerals, unless there is an exception as to one or more minerals. The exception, of course, applies only to the minerals specified. The making of grants with such an exception is a recent and not a general practice. Consequently, in the United States, most of the land, including minerals, is privately owned in fee and in relatively small tracts.

The fee owner, or the owner of the minerals, may do the development; or he may make a lease or otherwise grant to another the right to develop the oil or gas, the lessee or developer succeeding to certain of the rights of the fee owner. Rarely does the owner develop. Instead, he executes an instrument, usually called "lease", that gives to the lessee the exclusive right to develop. Leases have not been standardized. In the early days of the industry, the leases were not nearly as comprehensive as they are now, although the lessee was given the exclusive right to develop, and was obligated to deliver to the lessor a share of the production, called "royalty". Some of the obligations of the lessee were expressed, some were implied.

Modern leases, although long indeed when compared with the leases used in the early days of the industry, vary in terms; but a typical lease, at least in an area not known to be productive, is based on a cash payment (bonus) made to the lessor; the lease is for a fairly short primary term; the lessee is given the right to delay drilling during the primary term for specified periods, such as annually, by paying in advance the "delay rental" specified for the period; the lessee agrees to deliver to the lessor, as royalty, a fraction of the production or its value; the lease terminates at the end of the primary term if there is no production in paying quantities or drilling operations are not continued as provided for; if production in paying quantities is obtained while the lease is in force, the lease remains in force as long as there is such production. Of course, many other subjects are dealt with in leases, but it is believed that those mentioned are the important ones for this discussion, together with the implied covenants that will be treated briefly.

The birth of the oil industry in the United States is generally given as August 1859, when the Seneca Oil Company, with Colonel Edwin L. Drake in charge of operations on a tract leased from the Pennsylvania Rock Oil Company, brought in an oil well—usually called the "Drake Well"—on Oil Creek near Titusville in western Pennsylvania. The first oil boom in the United States started. Leasing and drilling rapidly spread to neighboring tracts, then to other areas in Pennsylvania and on to Ohio and West Virginia, so that in a relatively short time many prolific fields were found. They were rapidly developed, as each operator drilled as many wells as he pleased on his tract. He located them close to the boundary lines or anywhere else on the tract as he thought desirable; and he produced the wells to capacity. The idea was to get the oil out fast; to drain oil from neighboring lands to his own wells, if he could; and at least to protect his land from being subjected to adverse drainage to wells on neighboring tracts.

Usually, the leased tract was small, or, if it were large, it was often split into small tracts for leasing and for the purpose of inducing competition and rapid development.

Lessors and lessees in those days may not have known much about the mechanics of production of oil; but they did realize the existence of a serious conflict of interests. They knew that wells were drilled close to boundary lines to drain oil from adjoining tracts, and that they had that effect unless offset. They knew that rapid development and capacity production were for the purpose of producing oil before others did—but that production, after reaching a peak, declined quickly, often because large amounts of water were produced with the oil. They knew that such practices caused feasts and famines in supply; and they doubtless wondered whether such operations were efficient.

The lessors and lessees discussed their rights, duties, and problems with their lawyers; but doubtless got opinions that were not positive for, unfortunately, there was no established common law of oil and gas at that time from which to determine rights with respect to ownership and development. Indeed, there was no established body of law that offered a convincing analogy for the solution of many of the questions that arose. However, as was logical, the courts, in the litigation that ensued, sought answers in similarities—as by analogy to the law applicable to the capture of wild animals—on the theory that oil and gas freely roamed about underground over great distances, here today and there tomorrow, or by analogy to the law of percolating or underground waters. Although much progress has been made, especially since about 1920, toward the establishment of an applicable body of law, it may fairly be said that oil and gas law is still in the process of development.

The courts in the early days were called upon to decide these difficult questions:

1. Does Jones own the oil produced from wells on his land?
2. If Jones operates wells so that oil migrates from the adjoining tract of Smith and is produced by the wells of Jones, can Smith enjoin the operations or recover damages?
3. If Smith is not entitled to injunction or damages, what is his remedy?
4. If Jones operates negligently, causing damage to wells of Smith or reduces the recovery of oil by Smith, what is Smith's remedy?
5. If Smith or Jones, being a lessee of Thomas, fails to develop the leased tract after the oil is found in paying quantities, or fails to drill and operate wells to prevent migration of oil to neighboring lands, what is the remedy of Thomas, the lessor?

A landmark case involved the complaint of a landowner who sought injunction or damages because the adjoining landowner (lessee) had drilled wells close to the boundary line and was draining oil to those wells from the lands of the plaintiff. The court denied relief, saying:

"An oil or gas well may draw its product from an indefinite distance and in time exhaust a large space. Exact knowledge on this subject is not at present attainable, but the vagrant character of the mineral and the porous sand rock in which it is found and through which it moves fully justify the general conclusion we have stated above [cannot enjoin drilling and operating well that drains adjoining land, but should offset] and have led to its general adoption by practical operators. 'The right of every land-owner to drill a well on his own land at whatever spot he may see fit' certainly must be conceded. If, then, the landowner drills on his land at such a spot as best subserves his purposes, what is the standing of the adjoining landowner whose oil or gas may be drained by this well? He certainly ought not to be allowed to stop his neighbor from developing his own farm. There is no certain way of ascertaining how much of the oil and gas that comes out of the well was when in situ under this farm and how much under that. What, then, has been held to be the law? It is this, as we understand it, every landowner or his lessee may locate his well wherever he pleases, regardless of the interests of others. He may distribute them over the whole farm or locate them only on one part of it. He may crowd the adjoining farms so as to enable him to draw the oil and gas from them. What, then, can the neighbor do? Nothing; only go and do likewise. He must protect his own oil and gas. He knows it is wild and will run away if it finds an opening and it is his business to keep it at home. This may not be the best rule; but neither the Legislature nor our highest court has given us any better. No doubt many thousands of dollars have been expended 'in protecting lines' in oil and gas territory that would not have been expended if some rule had existed by which it could have been avoided. Injunction certainly is not the remedy." *Barnard v. Monongahela Gas Company*, 216 Pa. 362, 65 Atl. 801 (1907).

In that case, the Pennsylvania court as late as 1907, being 46 years after the completion of the Drake Well, declared that meager information existed as to oil and gas pools, as to the reactions following production, and as to the extent and direction of migration of oil or gas. Consequently, under common law, the remedy of the plaintiff was *self help*—*"go and do likewise"* though the consequences be unfortunate.

The opinion in the *Barnard* case answered the first three questions stated previously as follows:

1. Jones owns the oil and gas produced from wells on his land,
2. Although some or all of the oil and gas that is produced by Jones migrates from Smith's land to the wells of Jones; and
3. Smith's remedy is not injunction or damages, but is self help, or protection against drainage by offsetting the wells on the land of Jones and matching production or producing to capacity.

The holding expressed in answers 1 and 2 is usually called the *Rule of Capture*, which may be called a rule to quiet title to oil and gas produced, for the producer was recognized as having title to oil and gas captured by his wells, although drained from neighboring lands; while the rule expressed in 3 is usually called the *Offset Rule*. Sometimes the *Rule of Capture* is defined as including the right to drill and produce as the landowner pleases on his own land. So defined, the Rule is modified or made ineffective by regulation that controls drilling and operations such as spacing and fixing production quotas. If the Rule be defined as merely a rule to quiet title in the owner of a tract (includes lessee) to oil and gas produced from a well or wells on the tract, the Rule is modified by agreement that otherwise provides or by an order under a conservation statute, such as an order pooling separately owned tracts within a drilling unit for the drilling and producing of a well, with allocation of the allowable to the unit among the tract owners in the unit, not solely to the owner of the tract on which the well is located.[1]

---

[1] Citations are at the end of the chapter.

The courts in other cases also answered questions 4 and 5 as stated, by holding in answer to question 4 that an operator, who by negligence causes injury to a neighbor's well or by negligence or improper operations otherwise reduces the recovery, is liable for the damage;[2] and by holding in answer to question 5 that, if a lessee fails to offset wells producing in paying quantities, he is liable to his lessor for damages and, in some instances, may suffer cancellation of his lease.[3]

Furthermore, it soon became well established that, unless a lease provided otherwise (and few lessors would agree to provide otherwise), two covenants or obligations of the lessee are implied:

1. The obligation to develop reasonably after oil or gas is discovered in paying quantities.

2. The obligation to drill and produce offset wells for the purpose of preventing drainage from the leased tract to a well or wells on adjoining tracts to the extent that a reasonably prudent operator would drill under the same or similar circumstances.[3]

In the ordinary situation in the United States where oil or gas was found, there were many landowners and many lessees with rights in the area beneath which a pool existed, and this increased the number of problems.

The oil industry, under common law, was therefore plagued with the results of the following:

1. Each owner of a tract of land had the right, on his tract, to drill as many wells as he pleased and to locate them where he pleased.

2. The owner of a well had the right to produce to capacity.

3. Production caused migration of oil in the pool to the wells, often for a considerable distance in a relatively short time, with no regard for property lines.

4. The owner of a tract had the right to locate the wells close to the boundary, and produce them to capacity in an effort to produce as much as possible from the pool and to drain as much oil as he could from neighboring tracts.

5. The owner of a well was recognized as the owner of the oil produced by the well, although it be proved that the oil migrated from neighboring lands. This was called the "law or rule of capture".

6. The courts refused to enjoin one tract owner from drilling wells close to boundary lines and producing them to capacity, even though drainage was proved, or to award damages. The

courts held that the remedy to prevent such drainage was "Go and do likewise!" which made the situation worse.

7. An operator who, by negligent operations, caused damage to another, was liable. However, producing to capacity was for many years not considered to be improper or negligent operation.

8. With few exceptions, the leases or other instruments executed by landowners to give to another the right to develop did not in terms specify the extent of development required. The courts held that two covenants were implied, briefly stated as follows:

   a. The developer is required to protect against drainage by drilling and operating offset wells, if it appears that they would be profitable.

   b. If a well producing in paying quantities is brought in, the developer must reasonably develop the tract.

It was inevitable that the discovery of each pool brought about rapid development by many operators with adverse and conflicting interests, causing in a short time capacity production and a rapid decline in producing capacity.

We now know that the rapid decline in capacity resulted largely from dissipation of reservoir energy, premature encroachment of water, or inefficient or improper flooding of oil sands by water, or by a combination of two or all of such causes. The result was great waste or reduction in possible ultimate recovery. Furthermore, the gas produced with the oil was for many years considered a nuisance, and was blown to the air for lack of a use or a market.

Because the supply of oil varied with fortuitous discovery of new pools and their sizes and with rapid decline in capacity — not with consumptive needs or with amounts that could be produced without waste—feasts and famines in the supply were natural consequences of *1*, the nature of an oil reservoir; *2*, oil and gas law; and *3*, the lack of regulation.

Prices were quite high when oil was scarce and quite low when the supply was great; and, although low prices tended to retard development so that supply would not exceed demand, the necessity to drill to hold or comply with leases, and to produce to prevent drainage, kept production at excessive levels for long periods far beyond the time at which most operators realized the situation and were willing to retard development, but could not unless others did so. In this respect, the industry differed and still differs from all other industries, for the owner of a mine or factory may slow down or stop production when stocks are excessive and prices fall, without risk that his neighbor will capture his minerals or manufactured products and become the *owner* thereof.

Moreover, low prices caused physical waste, as by the abandonment and plugging of small or marginal wells that became unprofitable at the low prices, resulting in the loss or waste of much oil (reserves). This was so because the cost of drilling new wells to produce the reserve was not justified.

It was virtually impossible to get all interested persons in a pool, much less all such persons in all pools in a state, to agree upon a program of operations; and even a large majority, such as 99 percent, of interested persons was powerless to enforce upon the minority a program to prevent the happenings outlined, no matter how fair and effective the program was proved to be. Consequently, the situation as outlined changed very little in most states until experience with governmental regulations under conservation statutes demonstrated clearly that the drill-and-produce-as-you-please practices were unnecessary and that pools could be developed to prevent waste and protect correlative rights.

The next section deals with the development of conservation practices and the beginning of pool-wide and state-wide regulations under state statutes.

II. BEGINNING OF DISCUSSION OF WASTE AND CONSERVATION — 1890-1930

First, what is the meaning of "conservation" when used in connection with oil and gas operations, especially with respect to regulation that has taken place under state conservation statutes?

"Conservation", by common usage and statutory definition, means the prevention of reasonably avoidable "waste" of oil or gas aboveground and underground, in drilling and production operations, including storage.

Waste does not include failure to recover oil or gas, or to prevent loss, by uneconomic operations. This is so because loss of some oil or gas is not reasonably avoidable. Under efficient operations, a considerable part of the oil in place is not recovered; although more of it might be recovered by operations, such as mining, that in most instances would cost much more than the value of the oil additionally recovered. The failure to carry on such uneconomic operations may result in the nonrecovery of oil and gas that physically could be recovered, and in a sense there would be a loss of oil or gas, but it should not be referred to as "waste".

Various forms of aboveground loss of oil and gas have always been evident. Examples are:

1. Escape or flaring of gas from a gas well.
2. Permitting oil to be produced when it could not be saved, such as opening up a gusher for amusement, or producing and letting the oil run down the creek rather than let it be produced by a neighbor who had storage facilities.
3. Blowouts or fires that could reasonably have been avoided.
4. In open or pit storage, losses due to evaporation of the more volatile hydrocarbons.
5. In steel storage, similar evaporation losses, but in reduced amounts.

As will be shown, the posting of higher prices for higher-gravity crude that began in 1918 stimulated conservation measures. Prior to 1918, so far as can be determined, refiners posted single prices for crude oil, i.e., they did not post differential prices within a given field on the basis of gravity. On August 19, 1918, The Texas Company posted prices for Caddo light crude ranging from $2.25 per barrel for 38-deg gravity to $2.10 for 32-deg gravity crude. Effective November 22, 1922, Prairie Oil & Gas Company posted prices for Mid-Continent crude on a gravity scale ranging from 90 cents per barrel for crude below 28-deg gravity to $1.80 for crude from 39-deg to 40.9-deg gravity.[4] Other companies soon followed suit, and the practice of posting prices on a gravity scale in some areas has persisted up to the present time. It can fairly be stated that the gravity scale was inserted because it gave recognition to the differential in the value of crude oils to refineries, depending upon gravity. Gasoline was the prime product of refiners, their profits being dependent upon producing the maximum amount of gasoline. Crude oils capable of producing high yields of straight-run gasoline were worth more than heavy crudes producing a lesser yield.

The fact that light crudes were more valuable to refiners than most heavy crude oils made it worthwhile for producers to conserve the light ends by providing storage and other facilities that would reduce to a minimum losses by evaporation.

Prior to the 1920's, oil men generally had only a vague understanding of underground damage or waste, except with respect to individual wells. Examples are:

1. Improper plugging, resulting in oil migrating to the surface or into water sands.
2. Improper use or cementing of casing or failure to use proper fluid (usually called mud) in drilling, resulting in similar migration or infiltration of water into oil sands.

A number of states had passed statutes before 1922 that were designed to prevent aboveground and underground waste or loss with respect to individual wells.[5] Statutes in California are typical of early legislation in most of the oil-producing states that was designed to prevent aboveground and underground waste or loss with respect to such wells. The first waste act in California was passed in 1903 (Stats. 1903, p. 399), providing for casing and plugging of wells to prevent damage by water intrusion. It was replaced 6 years later by a new act (Stats. 1909, p. 576) covering the same ground, but also requiring logs to be kept, and creating a commission in each county with a few enforcement duties. These acts dealt with damage to deposits of oil and gas while in the reservoir, or underground waste.

The next act in California was passed two years later. (Stats. 1911, p. 499. Sections 3500-3503 of the Public Resources Code are based on the 1911 act). It dealt with aboveground waste—Section 3500 prohibits wilfully permitting natural gas wastefully to escape into the atmosphere; and Section 3501 requires the capping of an abandoned well from which natural gas flows, "so as to prevent the unnecessary or wasteful escape of natural gas into the atmosphere".

The act of 1915 (Stats. 1915, p. 1404) was an elaborate one of 54 sections, many of which are the bases for several sections of the present California Public Resources Code, such as Section 3219, requiring measures to prevent blowouts, explosions, and fires; Section 3228, requiring the owner of a well, when abandoning it, to use methods to exclude water from all oil or gas strata encountered; and Section 3300, declaring to be unlawful the unreasonable waste of natural gas.

When those early acts in California and similar acts in other states were passed, information as to reservoirs was meager, especially as to such things as the function of water and gas in the production of oil, and the need, with few exceptions, to limit the production from pools to prevent waste and protect property rights.

It is true that a number of scientists, many of them in the United States Bureau of Mines, had over many years published papers and books on the subject of underground waste, especially with respect to the function of gas in producing oil, but this literature failed to bring about material changes in production practices throughout the industry. However, by 1920, more than a few members of the industry were interested in better production techniques, and they had sponsored technical research and investigation, in the field and in the laboratory, and sought men who by education or training would be qualified to incorporate the results of this work into field practices.

Several facts and events may be selected as having much to do with stimulating general interest in conservation or efficient production practices that occurred in the middle of the 1920's. They were:

1. Oil played a large part in the victory of the Allies in World War I, and made it clear that adequate supplies of oil were necessary for national security, and there was widespread feeling within and without the petroleum industry that more efficient methods of production should be adopted in the United States to increase the supply.

2. Orgiastic development of large pools—as in Arkansas, California, Louisiana, Oklahoma, and Texas between 1900 and 1924 (a few were El Dorado and Smackover in Arkansas; Santa Fe Springs and Long Beach in California; Caddo in Louisiana; Cushing, Glenn Pool, and Healdton in Oklahoma; Spindletop, Ranger, Burkburnett, and Mexia in Texas)—offered abundant proof of the many evils of drill-and-produce-as-you-please, and of the need for more efficient operations.

3. Numerous public discussions of waste and efficient practices took place in connection with the passage of fairly comprehensive conservation statutes in California and Oklahoma in 1915, in Louisiana in 1918 and 1920, and in Texas in 1919.[6]

4. Publication of the records of the hearings before, and the reports of, the Federal Oil Conservation Board (FOCB) offered material that was widely read and discussed.

5. The number of petroleum engineers (production or reservoir engineers) was increasing, and their accomplishments in demonstrating and explaining the mechanics of production and reservoir behavior were potent factors in disseminating information as to more efficient production practices.

The period 1925-1930 may be called the "organized-study period", during which various organizations — such as the Federal Oil Conservation Board (FOCB), the American Petroleum Institute (API), the American Institute of Mining and Metallurgical Engineers (AIME), the American Bar Association (ABA), and the Mid-Continent Oil and Gas Assocation — offered public forums for discussion that attracted leaders in the industry and brought about widespread dissemination of information among oil men as to the issues and the remedies. In this period, technologists perfected equipment with which to obtain more accurate information concerning petroleum reservoirs, and in determining the mechanics of production, and the methods to reduce waste.

III. FEDERAL OIL CONSERVATION BOARD — 1924-1930

The FOCB was created by President Coolidge by letter dated December 19, 1924. It was composed of Hubert Work, Secretary of the Interior; Dwight F. Davis, Secretary of War; Curtis D. Wilbur, Secretary of the Navy; and Herbert Hoover, Secretary of Commerce.

On its staff, with George Otis Smith, Director of the United States Geological Survey, as chairman, were able men who were technically trained, such as geologists, engineers, and economists. The Board and staff, with some variation in personnel but not in competence, functioned until 1933, when President Roosevelt succeeded President Hoover.[7]

The record of the FOCB is outstanding. The Board held numerous hearings; it stimulated research and studies as to efficient oil production; it published five excellent reports; and generally made oil men conscious of wasteful practices and the need for improvement. Its first report in 1926, at pp. 7, 11, 13, and 14, *deplored the practice of producing wells wide open without utilizing the gas, partly because of the loss of the gas, and partly because the gas should be used in making more effective the recovery of oil from the sands.* The report, beginning at p. 15, also pointed out that pool-wide development and control of production by voluntary agreement of practice offered a most effective method of preventing waste and protecting the "mutual rights" of operators.

Report III of the FOCB, dated February 25, 1929, repeated the need for waste prevention, especially by controlling the production from a pool, and not permitting wells to produce to capacity. To that report was attached a 1927 report of a technical subcommittee entitled *The Conservation of Gas*, in which the importance of gas in oil production was discussed, and also various methods of individual well control that would be of help. The last sentence in the subcommittee report pointed out the difficulties that were inherent if solution of the problems were based on individual action without a common plan as a guide. It reads as follows:

"Unless a field is operated as a unit, whether by cooperation or control, there is little chance of holding down the gas-oil ratio, utilizing the energy and solution values of the gas, making the gas do the maximum work in the production of oil, or producing the greatest total amount of oil at the smallest cost." Report III, Appendix II, p. 25.

Repeatedly the need was stressed by the FOCB for operating each oil pool as a unit, whether that be accomplished by an agreement under which one operator carries on development for all, ignoring property lines in conducting efficient development, or whether it be accomplished by the operators separately developing their own tracts, but following a common plan designed to prevent waste or increase ultimate recovery and to protect property rights and adjust reciprocal duties. The one-operator plan offered, at least in theory, better results and economies; yet the results could be approximated under the separate-tract plan, which had one advantage: each lessee would conduct the operations on his own lease, and would control the expense.

Repeatedly in the reports of the FOCB it is asserted that wide-open flow should not be tolerated; that waste cannot be prevented without limiting production; and that waste takes place if production materially exceeds the needs for current consumption.

It is doubtful whether anyone else has pointed out the fundamental problems and outlined the remedies as forcibly and attractively as did the Board in its Report IV, dated May 28, 1930. At that time, Ray Lyman Wilbur, of California, was the Secretary of the Interior and chairman of the Board. Parts of the report will be quoted to show the soundness and excellence of the entire report. At pp. 19, 20, 21, and 24, this language was used:

"The unit idea in producing oil is bound to win out, because the natural unit is the oil pool. Man may draw property lines on the surface, making a checkerboard for title searchers and lease lawyers to play on, but nature has fixed a boundary line around the underground deposit for geologists to discover and engineers to use in the development of the hidden resources. The unit-operation plan is a 'back-to-nature' movement. Codes of laws and judicial decisions relating to oil deposits have accorded to the surface checkerboard a sanctity quite beyond its deserts, while the facts of nature as now known have received little attention and have commanded less respect.

"Fences, walls, and other land lines serve effectively as property boundaries where the property is fixed in character and position, whether it is valuable as tillable soil or as a structural foundation. These same lines may be extended downward as vertical planes and serve no less acceptably to define property rights in the ores we mine. The essential part of the property-line idea is our faith in the continuing relation of the line to the fixed property. It serves best of all when by triangulation we tie our private land corners to the geodetic constants; then the hand of man can not erase beyond recovery the boundaries of our estate. Quite different, however, is the relation of any land lines to property rights in the winds that blow and the waters that flow across these man-marked boundaries. The mobile and fugitive nature of air and water makes our rights to their possession and use related to the rights of our neighbors, so that some coordination is required, lest the use by one interfere with that by others.

". . . The pool is the natural unit of property ownership in oil.

"Within this natural unit, once a beginning is made in bringing the oil to the surface and thus giving value to the underground resources, the oil beneath the surface becomes movable property and the only boundaries to be considered are the exterior limits of the pool. Thereupon the division of the oil property between surface owners is no longer fixed — hence the 'ferae naturae' figure of speech of the lawyers. But anyone who sees the oil pool as a natural unit with divided ownership might reasonably ask, Why not adopt a procedure that will preserve rather than destroy preexisting property rights? Why sanction practices and formulate rules that lead directly to a contest for possession among the owners, each trying to get more than his share of the whole property? By reason of its loss of fixed character, why should not the oil be regarded as taking on the nature of common property? At least this would be substituting equity for war, business in the open for underground robbery.

"   *   *   *

"Of more recent date than the general understanding of this underground movement of oil after drilling has started is the tardy realization of the function that gas plays in winning oil for the use of man. The natural gas associated with the oil in the pool largely determines its mobility and controls its movement to the well and to the surface. Deplete this gas supply and reduce the pressure, and the recovery of some part of the oil content of the pool becomes more difficult or even impossible, and to that extent the other owners are deprived of what is rightfully theirs. The Saratoga gas case seems to have established this principle for carbon dioxide and water, and might logically be extended to natural gas and oil . . . .

"   *   *   *

"Self-regulation in the handling of an oil pool means both efficiency in development and operation and the determination of equities among the owners, and this can best be accomplished by unit operation. By this plan only can each and every owner secure full economic benefits. By this plan only can the public be assured of the largest possible supply of oil and gas from a particular field, won from the ground at lowest cost, and over a period measured by market demand rather than fixed by individualistic greed.

"Justice to all owners and benefit to the public can both result from this observance of natural and economic law in recognizing the oil pool as the natural unit."

The Federal Oil Conservation Board recognized the difficulties in preventing waste and adjusting property rights by voluntary action of the operators, and recommended regulation under statutory authority as the surest and quickest method to effect a cure by requiring efficient practices and coordination of operations, "lest the use by one [of his rights] interfere with that by others." The Board consistently recommended regulation by the state governments, not by the Federal Government.

IV. EARLY REGULATION UNDER STATE STATUTES — 1930-1932

Conditions in the petroleum industry in 1930, when Report IV of the FOCB was made, were alarming. That report pointed out the mounting overproduction and tremendous waste that were inherent without adequate control of operations, saying that production far exceeded current consumptive demand. Indeed, all-time peaks were reached in 1929 in production and storage in the United States, and in production in the world. Conditions were especially bad in California, Oklahoma, and Texas.[8]

Beyond question, the activities of, and the hearings conducted by, the FOCB gave an unusual opportunity for the geologist, petroleum engineer, and others—who, by education or training, had more than a superficial knowledge of petroleum reservoirs and the mechanics of production—to explain publicly the causes of waste and proper methods to prevent or minimize it. Moreover, more and more public officials and oil men listened and became interested.

Though much was known about reservoir behavior and good conservation practices, it clearly appeared that neither the "law" of supply and demand nor voluntary actions by the operators would be effective to cure or even to minimize appreciably the unfortunate results of a drill-and-produce-as-you-please situation, especially the waste of oil and gas aboveground and underground, attributable to the continuing excessive production that was the inevitable result of the discovery of many new pools, and the wild race among operators to produce "the mostest firstest".

Leaders in the industry reluctantly accepted the fact that some type of governmental regulation was necessary. As between regulation by the Federal Government or by state governments, most lawyers expressed the opinion, supported by many decisions of the Supreme Court of the United States, that the Federal Government had no power to regulate oil or gas operations, a local activity, with possible exception of operations on the Federal public domain or other public lands. Even if the power existed, oil men preferred state regulation, partly because they were "states righters", but principally because many formidable administrative difficulties were thought to be inherent in regulating from Washington the production of oil in the states. Moreover, statutes were already on the books in several states where conditions were deplorable, as in Texas and Oklahoma, on which conservation regulations could be based. Furthermore, the Federal Oil Conservation Board had recommended state, not Federal, regulation. Finally, oil men as a whole were violently opposed to comprehensive unit operations under Federal statutes as advocated by Henry L. Doherty.

While the opinion was that the Federal Government lacked the power to regulate oil or gas production in the states on non-Federal lands, it seemed to be well-established that a state had the power to regulate *a*, to prevent waste, or *b*, to protect property rights, including adjustment of conflicting property rights (correlative rights), either under a constitutional provision — such as Article XVI, Section 59, of the Constitution of Texas — or under the inherent power of a state, called "police power" in legal parlance.

The use of the term "police power" causes some confusion among non-lawyers, as it has little to do with the power of the police. Police power has been defined as follows:

" 'Police power' is a power inherent in every sovereignty to govern men and things under which the Legislature may, within constitutional limitations, not only prohibit all things hurtful to the comfort, safety, and welfare of society, but prescribe regulations to promote the public health, morals, and safety and add to the general public convenience, prosperity, and welfare." (12 Corpus Juris, p. 904.)

This quotation is applicable:

"The police power is an attribute of sovereignty and exists without any reservation in the constitution, being founded on the duty of the state to protect its citizens and provide for the safety and good order of society. It corresponds to the right of self-preservation in the individual, and is an essential element in all orderly governments, because necessary to proper maintenance of the government and the general welfare of the community. On it depends the security of social order, the life and health of the citizen, the comfort of and existence in a thickly populated community, the enjoyment of private and social life, and the beneficial use of property. And it is said to be the very foundation on which our social system rests. It has for its object the improvements of social and economic conditions affecting the community at large and collectively with a view of bringing about 'the greatest good to the greatest number.' It is founded largely on the maxim, *Sic utere tuo ut alienum non laedas,** and also to some extent on that other maxim of public policy, *salus populi suprema lex.*†
The constitution presupposes the existence of police power and is to be construed with reference to that fact." (12 Corpus Juris, p. 907.)

With respect to this discussion, it is well-established that, unless a constitutional provision denies such a power, a state has the power to

---

*So use your own as not to injure another's property.
†The safety of the people is the supreme law.

regulate oil and gas production and operations in a reasonable manner for either or both of the following purposes:

1. To prevent waste of oil or gas.
2. To protect property rights.

Actually, the power of a state under its police power to control the production of oil and gas had been sustained as early as 1899 in the case of *Ohio Oil Company* v. *Indiana,* 177 U.S. 188, 44 L.Ed. 729.

Some advocates of Federal regulations as a substitute for state regulation said that state conservation statutes were not, and would not be, uniform; and that each state would be inclined to act in its own interest, or not to act effectively, or to act in a manner that harmed other states. The argument has been repeated with each effort to obtain Federal regulation. Advocates of state regulation said that freedom of action by the states is one advantage that exists under our system of division of powers between state governments and Federal Government, for it permits the states to follow different courses, to experiment in no regulation at all and in various degrees and types of regulation, and thus to educate and give proof of effective and desirable regulation by comparison of results under different systems. Thus, each state is permitted to solve problems within its jurisdiction as seems best for that state, even if it acts in a selfish manner; and, even so, it is believed that there is no justification for substituting Federal for state regulation, or for assuming that Federal laws and officials would be superior to state laws and officials, or that too often a state or states would act so unwisely that Federal regulation is necessary or desirable or would be any better. Indeed, there are many reasons for believing that, from many points of view, it would be worse.

By 1929, it was reasonably clear that regulation of individual wells was not effective to prevent waste and to protect property rights. State statutes were examined to determine whether more elaborate methods were authorized. Conservation agencies in several states concluded that such authority did exist, and they moved to exercise it. Fortunately, such was the situation in Texas and Oklahoma where the over-production and waste were great.

Fairly comprehensive regulation under state statutes began in several states in 1930, and with it the opportunity of the technically trained men to prove by results the efficacy of their recommendations, based on scientific principles, to prevent waste. This was so, because specific reservoirs, actual not assumed problems, and detailed regulation were involved. Scientific principles that supported remedies long advocated by technologists were put into practice and were tested in the field for all to see and understand. Moreover, each operator in those states, many of whom were aided by a technical staff or consultant, was keen to prevent any regulation or method that was unsound or that did not adequately give protection to his property and rights.

Oklahoma took the lead in comprehensive regulation in 1930, partly because of earlier experience, and partly because the conservation statute that had been enacted in 1915 was not limited to individual well problems, and seemed clearly to give adequate authority to the administrative agency to restrict production and to provide for other action that would prevent waste and protect property rights. The administrative agency, Corporation Commission, acted on a state-wide scale by its order of June 30, 1930. Production in the state was materially restricted, for that was proved to be the essential step in waste prevention and protection of property rights.[9]

In *Texas,* in 1930, the Railroad Commission concluded that it, too, was not limited to dealing with individual wells, but had rather broad powers to prevent waste of oil and gas, especially by the statutes with respect to conservation of oil and gas as codified in 1925 and amended in 1929. The Commission held a public hearing in the summer of 1930 that lasted for days, at which the facts were discussed at length, such as the nature of petroleum reservoirs, the causes of waste, and the methods for preventing it. At that time, there was no restriction on the amount of production of oil. The Commission's order of August 14, 1930 restricted the production of oil in many pools below capacity or previous levels; and it made other provisions for prevention of waste of both oil and gas and for protection of property rights.[10]

In Texas — as in Oklahoma — the administrative agency, having restricted production in a pool, thereby taking away the common-law right to produce to capacity and the right of self-help of operators to protect their leases by offsetting wells in compliance with lease obligations, was under the duty to fix allowables for wells or properties as a substitute for the right of self-help. It probably is true that in many, perhaps in most, instances the fairness of the method for distribution or proration of a pool allowable was debated with equal or greater vigor than the need for the pool allowable or for other restriction or regulation made to prevent waste. However, this is not to say that there was no dispute as to causes of waste or as to what were appropriate and reasonable methods to prevent it.

The situation in *Kansas* duplicated in many respects the situation in Oklahoma and Texas. In 1929 and 1930, the operators in a number of pools in Kansas had agreed upon restrictions and allowables for the purpose of preventing waste and protecting property rights, but such agreements were too few, and one or more operators, by refusing to agree to or to conform with the common program, nullified the good that was contemplated. During this period, much was said about the need for comprehensive governmental regulation in Kansas under a state statute. An act that was passed in 1931, and amended in 1933, followed the pattern of the Oklahoma act. Some regulation in Kansas took place prior to 1933, but it need not now be detailed.[11]

As already pointed out, the California statutes that were on the books in the 1930-1932 period dealt primarily with waste occurring from individual wells. It was generally agreed that the supervisor, as the administrative agent named in the statutes, had no comprehensive authority to regulate production, such as that set forth in the Oklahoma and Texas conservation statutes.

The facts as to over-production and waste existing in those two states were substantially the same in California, but it appeared that the necessary remedies could not be had in California by regulation under the existing statutes, and it was doubtful whether adequate legislation, if it could be had, would be passed promptly. Oil men in California were confronted with at least these alternatives: *1*, do nothing, or *2*, seek adequate legislation, and *3*, undertake, in the meantime, to persuade the operators to adopt operating practices that would prevent waste and minimize drainage across property lines, thereby adjusting correlative rights.

Alternatives 2 and 3 were adopted. A bill thought to be adequate was prepared and was introduced in the Legislature by Senator Sharkey. It passed, but was defeated by referendum vote on May 3, 1931.

Anticipating failure to get adequate legislation, a voluntary program was worked out. A brief statement of the program will suffice here. A great mass of information was obtained about each pool, about the storage of California oil and products and the trend up or down, about the market demand, and about other factors bearing on waste. The information obtained was similar to that obtained in other states in the administration of conservation statutes or to work out a voluntary program. A committee then announced its conclusion as to the market demand for current production from the California pools, and made recommendations as to the production for the next month from various pools and from the wells or properties.

Clearly, the program was similar to that adopted in other states under comprehensive conservation statutes, with one important difference. In California, the organization of operators had no authority to require compliance with the recommendations. Operators complied or refused to comply as they pleased, and refusals to comply were many. Even so, a fairly good job of waste prevention was done.

V. REGULATION IN 1930-1932 BASED ON SOUND ENGINEERING PRINCIPLES

In other parts of this book will be found detailed discussion of petroleum reservoirs, including methods of operation to prevent waste. The discussion here will be pointed to the state of knowledge in 1930-1932 as to physical waste of oil and gas and its prevention; the types of regulation that were adopted, especially in Oklahoma and Texas; and the reasons for and the effectiveness of the regulation and operations that took place to prevent waste and protect property rights.

1.

Regulation of individual wells continued, such as the regulation of the spacing of wells, the casing and equipment, the water-oil and gas-oil ratios, storage facilities, and the flaring of gas from gas wells — to name a few subjects.

2.

Prior to 1930, wells were usually produced wide open or to capacity. The technical men, by 1930, were largely in agreement that, as to most pools, *such operation caused underground waste, even if every barrel of the oil and every cubic foot of gas that was produced should be promptly used for current consumption.* Competent technical men, including scientists in the United States Bureau of Mines, had written articles between 1913 and 1930, saying that capacity production usually causes dissipation of reservoir energy, especially when the primary energy comes from gas; that it also reduces the viscosity of the oil in the reservoir so that more energy is required to force the oil to the well; and that wells usually become non-productive because of an insufficient amount of gas in the reservoir, not because all of the oil has been produced. Many competent technologists made similar statements in public hearings and in the trial of cases in the period 1930-1932.

These technical men agreed that, in most pools, the rate of production affected the volume of gas produced with a barrel of oil — or the gas-oil ratio — with the ratio increasing with higher rates, and that restriction of production was usually necessary to conserve the gas and to use its energy more effectively.

Stated differently and generally, it was fairly well-established that, ordinarily, capacity production from a pool dissipates gas energy, even if all of the gas produced is used for superior purposes; while limiting production from the pool reduces or minimizes the dissipation, depending upon the character of the reservoir and its fluids and the degree of restriction.

3.

Competent technologists proved that capacity production in many pools where the oil is in contact with the water tends to pull water prematurely to the well, and to pull gas from the gas cap—if there is one—prematurely to the well, although the well is originally completed in the oil-saturated portion of the sand. In both instances, the ultimate recovery is reduced. Restricted or a slower rate of production is one effective remedy to prevent the waste or increase ultimate recovery.

4.

It was established that in nearly all pools, where there is a gas cap above the oil-saturated portion of the reservoir or water beneath the oil portion (especially if it is a prime source of energy), the wells should be produced so that the gas cap will expand in a fairly even manner, or so that the pressure differentials will not be great throughout the reservoir, and so that the water will encroach or shove the oil in a relatively even manner, instead of moving raggedly or fingering. It was well known that the oil sands in a pool are almost always of different permeability — some areas are very permeable, as where the pores are relatively large and connected, while other areas are less permeable, having small pores and dead ends. In such a situation, it appeared that capacity production, or a high rate of production, increased the likelihood of great variations in pressures and the likelihood of fingering. Furthermore, when the production is at capacity or at a high rate, the water moves through the more permeable areas and around the tight areas before the oil in the tight areas can be produced. Limitation of production from the pool was a method used to reduce the occurring waste, by producing a greater amount from the tight areas. Production control to cause a relatively even expansion of the gas cap or a relatively even movement of water was often called "ratable production", a waste-prevention measure and a prime factor in protecting property rights. It seemed clear that ratable production usually tends to minimize drainage from one property to another, and was, therefore, an important, if not governing, factor in protecting property rights.

5.

The amount of crude oil required for current consumption from production was — and is usually — called "market demand" or "reasonable market demand". The demand for oil products was shown to be relatively inelastic, and could be forecast with remarkable accuracy, especially if the forecast were for the following month or even for the following three or six months. The proof was that the part of the demand for current production of oil to supply the product demand could also be forecast with great accuracy, as well as the areas or states that would almost surely supply the current production.

An acceptable method for forecasting market demand, for the nation and for each state or area, was worked out about 1926 by petroleum economists and others on the staff of the FOCB. The determination or forecast of the demand for a commodity was nothing new to econmists. It was commonplace in private business and in government. Agencies of the Federal Government had, long before 1926, made forecasts of market demand for wheat, cotton, corn, and other commodities for the following year. Forecasts of demand for crude production and for products of oil were made for a very short period by the FOCB — surely with better chance of accuracy than making a forecast in the summer or fall as to the demand for cotton or other commodity for the next year.

The method for forecasting the demand for crude oil for current consumption, usually for the next month, involved and still involves consideration of much information — such as the season, the number of motor vehicles and other internal-combustion engines in use, the quantity of oil and products in storage and the probable withdrawals, probable imports, and former records of demands and imports. Storage statistics were important because, if storage was unusually high, the demand for current production normally would decrease. If, for instance, the statistics showed that storage of crude produced in a state had been decreasing for months and was below a normal level, it was almost certain that the demand for production from that state would increase the next month. If, however, the storage of crude produced in a state had been going up and was above normal level, the indication of decreased demand for production in that state was clear.

6.

Proof was made that production of crude oil in any state substantially in excess of reasonable market demand for such oil inevitably causes reasonably avoidable physical waste aboveground and underground; and that physical waste is also economic waste, but all economic waste is not physical waste. It appeared that excess production also inevitably results in inequities among producers and royalty owners; and that when production is far beyond the needs for current consumptive use, the oil—unless it is "run down the creek"—must be stored for an indefinite time. It was known that losses from storage by the escape of the lighter hydrocarbons was considerable, even in good steel storage; and that storage resulted in substantial losses by fire — all physical waste aboveground. Evidence established that storage was costly, and buying oil for speculation had virtually ceased by 1930. Many, if not all, of the producers in numerous pools were unable to sell all of the current production.

In such a situation, as was often true in Texas before the market-demand statute was passed and production in the state was effectively limited to the current market demand, the amount of oil produced in many oil fields was considerably in excess of pipeline capacities. The result was that some producers were able in one way or another to produce and market all of their allowables, while their neighbors could not find a market for much of the oil their leases were permitted to produce. In these circumstances much oil was run to earthen storage, and enormous physical waste resulted. Some operators were able for a limited time to find steel storage for the oil they could not run to a pipeline. This, of course, was very expensive; physical waste from evaporation ensued and the danger of loss by fire was increased. More commonly, many producers were simply not able to produce ratably with their neighbors who had pipeline or other outlets or storage, with the result that non-ratable withdrawals from the reservoir were made, established drainage patterns were disturbed, there was unequal encroachment of the water drive in fields having a water drive, inefficient use of gas energy occurred, and in some cases there was coning and channeling of water as well as increase of gas-oil ratios in wells with excessive production. Combinations of these factors produced both surface and underground waste of oil and gas.

This is the inevitable consequence of non-ratable taking of oil in a reservoir over a considerable period of time. Furthermore, obviously, correlative rights of the several operators were not protected. Some operators produced more than their fair shares, and others had oil and gas drained from under their properties. These evil consequences of production substantially in excess of current market demand were avoided when the state regulatory agencies, with the aid of a market-demand statute, were able to limit production in oil pools both to the MER* and to current market demand, using the lower figure.

7.

Stripper or marginal pools are those, usually old ones, where the production from most wells has declined to a low level and where the income from such a small amount barely exceeds the expense of operation. The total production from such wells was considerable in 1930-1932. When there was substantial production in excess of the reasonable market demand, the price for crude usually dropped. The decrease made a substantial number of marginal wells and pools unprofitable; and, if

---

*Maximum efficient rate.

the loss continued for longer than a short period, the wells were abandoned and plugged, and the reserves were lost because the expense of drilling and completing new wells was not economically feasible. Stated differently, it was well known that substantial production in excess of the reasonable market demand usually resulted in waste in marginal pools. An effective remedy was to restrict production in the state so that it would not exceed the reasonable market demand, and favor the marginal pools in allocating the allowable, unless serious inequities would occur.

The function of limitation when there is substantial over-production is not to make the supply short for, if the limitation is realistic, the needs for current consumptive use of oil produced in the state will be supplied. The intention is to produce without waste *all* the crude that is necessary to supply the needs of the market, not to make the supply short or to try to force a higher price level. Keeping oil underground until needed for current consumption is using the best and the cheapest storage, and the oil is just as available when needed as if in aboveground storage.[13]

8.

It appeared that, almost without exception, effective prevention of waste underground required limitation of the production of a pool substantially below capacity production. The evidence was that the proper degree of limitation below capacity varied among pools, depending upon the conditions. The term "maximum efficient rate" (MER) was not in current use in 1930-1932, but is now in common use, and implies that substantial production in a pool above its MER will cause physical waste of oil or gas, or both. The time when the term MER was adopted is not clear. Joseph Pogue, in his paper for the TNEC hearing in 1939, spoke of the "optimum rate" for each pool.[14] Perhaps that was the beginning of the term MER. The concept, however, had long been understood, for it was generally agreed that production should be less than capacity, and not wide open. In hearings before the Railroad Commission of Texas, and in litigation involving the East Texas Field in 1930-1935, many engineers testified that waste in that field (water drive and no gas cap) would take place if production exceeded 400,000 bbl a day. Some engineers concluded that 400,000 bbl was too high. The term MER was not used, but it would have been applicable.

9.

Opinions may differ as to the MER for a pool at any specified time; but even in 1930-1932, technologists were able to establish a reasonably accurate figure that could be used until conditions in the reservoir materially changed. From an engineering viewpoint, the production from a pool should not be permitted to exceed substantially its MER, but it may be less without causing waste. It followed that, if the allowable for a pool on some formula — such as a share of the state allowable — was greater than its MER, production was nevertheless restricted to its MER to prevent waste. If the applicable allowable for a pool on some formula — such as a share of the state allowable — was less than its MER, then the production was restricted to the lower figure to prevent waste.

10.

The regulatory agencies in Oklahoma and Texas, because of overwhelming proof that wide-open production caused physical waste of oil, that production materially in excess of the needs of the market resulted in physical waste of oil, that physical waste of oil occurred if a pool was permitted to produce substantially in excess of its MER, and that waste resulted from other facts, conditions, and practices as outlined, issued orders of the type described to prevent the waste and, as an incident thereto, adjusted conflicting property rights of the operators or protected property rights. The Oklahoma statute since 1915, and the Texas statutes since 1932, in defining waste specifically declared that production of oil in excess of reasonable market demand was waste, and specifically authorized restriction so that production would not exceed the demand.

VI. THE PETROLEUM ADMINISTRATIVE BOARD AND STATE REGULATION — 1933-1935

The Federal Oil Conservation Board, the non-statutory agency created by President Coolidge and continued by President Hoover, became *functus officio* when President Roosevelt was inaugurated. However, an elaborate program for regulation of oil production, as well as other phases of the petroleum industry, was formulated under the National Industrial Recovery Act enacted in 1933, shortly after the inauguration of President Roosevelt. The program was set forth in the Code of Fair Competition for the Petroleum Industry that became effective August 19, 1933, with Harold L. Ickes, the Secretary of the Interior, as the Administrator. He organized the Petroleum Administrative Board to assist him in administering the Petroleum Code and Section 9C of the NIRA, which related to movements of oil in interstate and foreign commerce.

The Petroleum Code contained provisions for prevention of waste in production, including storage, that were similar to those in conservation laws. The Code made clear that wells in a pool should not be produced to capacity, and that production in excess of the reasonable needs for current consumption caused waste and should be avoided. The Administrator certified quotas to the states, based upon forecasts made by the staff, leaving to the states, such as Oklahoma, Texas, and Kansas — which had administrative agencies — the task of allocating the state quota among the pools, properties, and wells. The staff of PAB used the method that had been worked out by the staff of the FOCB, but with some improvements.

Since it appeared that in California there was no administrative agency with the authority to allocate the state quotas and compel compliance, the Administrator, through PAB, called upon the voluntary organization, Central Committee of California Oil Producers, to act as agent of the government in compiling information and recommending quotas, formulas for allocations, and other action. The Central Committee was selected because of its experience of several years in gathering information and making recommendations prior to the approval of the Petroleum Code. The Administrator, after considering the recommendations and applicable information furnished by the committee and the PAB and after making any changes that were believed to be advisable, promulgated schedules and other regulatory devices.

It is significant that the Petroleum Administrator (the Secretary of the Interior) and the PAB, another agency of the Federal Government with a different membership and staff from the FOCB — this time under a Democratic administration — reached the same conclusions as did the FOCB, the state agencies in Oklahoma, Texas, and Kansas, and the oil producers in California[15] as to the primary causes of waste in oil production, the adequate method that prevailed for protection of property rights, and reasonably effective methods, in the light of the existing information, that would prevent waste and protect property rights.

State regulation continued during the Code days along the lines adopted in 1930-1932. However, in Texas, the difficulties attending successful regulation of the East Texas Field seemed without solution until the statute was amended, specifically declaring that production in excess of market demand causes waste; and until the courts after much effort were at long last convinced that the facts as to the East Texas Field, solely from an engineering viewpoint, justified the restriction of production in that field far below capacity production, or to not more than 400,000 bbl a day. If the term MER had been in common use, doubtless the court that finally upheld an order for the field would have said that the MER was at least as low as 400,000 bbl daily, and restriction to that point was justified as a waste-prevention measure, even though the market-demand figure for the field was much higher. Indeed, for many years, the total net production of oil and water has been kept at considerably less than 400,000 bbl a day.[16]

Here it may be said that, although much more is now known about petroleum reservoirs, and although improvements have been made in waste-prevention methods and in methods to protect property rights, the principles or fundamentals upon which were based regulation and voluntary action in the earlier 1930's were sound. Furthermore, the efforts that were made to pass a Federal conservation act during PAB days were founded on those principles or fundamentals. One of the main arguments for Federal regulation was the doubtful claim that Federal officials would do a better job than some state officials were doing, or than was being done by voluntary action in California and elsewhere, and that compulsory regulation from Washington was advisable in all states.

Such a Federal statute was not passed, but the Congress did pass in 1935 the Connally or "Hot Oil" Act to cure the defective drafting of Section 9c of the NIRA.[17] In brief, the Connally Act prohibited the movement in interstate and foreign commerce of oil (including products by definition) produced or withdrawn from storage in violation of a state statute or regulation. The act was passed to aid enforcement of state conservation statutes and orders. Its provisions clearly show the belief of the Congress that excess production causes waste, and aid should be given to the states in preventing such excess by prohibiting interstate and foreign movement of "hot" oil and products.

The holding of the Supreme Court of the United States in 1935 that the NIRA was unconstitutional had the effect of nullifying the Petroleum Code and the activities of the Administrator and the PAB thereunder.[18]

VII. INTERSTATE OIL COMPACT

In the period 1930-1935, the need for governmental regulation of production of oil and gas to prevent waste and protect property rights was fairly well-established; but there was disagreement as to how it should be accomplished. There were those who favored regulation by the Federal Government, those who favored regulation by state governments, and those who favored regulation under an interstate compact.

As already pointed out, only weak support was given to Federal regulation. State regulation was generally preferred, but some officials and oil men argued that a compact of states was advisable. Representative of several states met several times to discuss such a compact. Some of the representatives, especially for Oklahoma, insisted that the compact should be drafted so that state quotas could be fixed, not only to assure that each state would be permitted to produce its "fair share" and no more, but so that a "fair price" would be had. Other representatives, especially for Texas, refused to accept any such provisions, for they were against regulation for the purpose of fixing prices; and they refused to make any agreement that would give to other states, or any board or commission created by the compact, the right to fix allowables for Texas or to regulate the production in Texas.

Finally, an agreement was reached in 1935, called the "Interstate Compact to Conserve Oil and Gas", with the Interstate Oil Compact Commission as the administrative agency. The compact was approved in 1935 by 6 states: New Mexico, Oklahoma, Kansas, Colorado, Texas, and Illinois; and was approved by the Congress by resolution of August 27, 1935.[19] The compact provides for no regulation, although it urges each state to pass adequate laws to prevent physical waste of oil and gas. It declares that it is not the purpose of the compact to stabilize or fix prices or create or perpetuate monopoly or promote regimentation, but it is the purpose to prevent the avoidable waste of oil and gas "within reasonable limitations".

The strength of the compact is partially the absence of any authority to compel any state to do anything. Its effectiveness comes from the dissemination of information as to conservation practices. This is done by providing a forum for discussion, by committee activities and reports, and by distribution of books, articles, reports, and similar items. Valuable technical contributions to conservation are made by the Engineering Committee, the Legal Committee, the Public Lands Committee, the Regulatory Practice Committee, the Research Committee, and the Secondary-recovery and Pressure-maintenance Committee. The committee meetings are open to the public.

As of January 1957, the member states numbered 26 and there were 4 associate states. In addition, the following had official observers: the Province of Alberta and the Province of Saskatchewan, Canada; Colombia; Venezuela; and agencies of the Federal Government — the Department of Defense, the Department of the Interior, and the Federal Power Commission.

VIII. REGULATION UNDER STATE CONSERVATION STATUTES — 1935-1957

During this period, especially during 1935-1942, many of the fundamental questions involving state conservation statutes and regulations were settled — a good number of them by litigation, more by education as to the causes of waste, the effectiveness of methods to prevent or minimize waste, the need for regulation, and the character of regulation required to protect property rights as an incident to waste prevention.[20]

Conservation statutes in Oklahoma, Texas, and Kansas were improved by amendments during this period. New Mexico passed in 1935 what may be called the first comprehensive, modern, conservation act. The pattern of that act was followed by the Arkansas Act of 1939, the Louisiana Act of 1940, to some degree by the Michigan Act of 1937, and by the form for an Oil and Gas Conservation Act prepared by the Legal Committee of the Interstate Oil Compact Commission (the first in 1943, the second in 1946, and the third in 1950). The New Mexico, Arkansas, and Louisiana Acts, and the Compact form greatly influenced the Alabama Act of 1945, the Arizona Act of 1951, the Florida Act of 1945, the Georgia Act of 1945, the Mississippi Act of 1948, the North Dakota Act of 1953, the Washington Act of 1951, the Utah Act of 1955, and the Alaska Act of 1955. Acts in several other states were passed, but they did not follow so closely the scope or provisions of what may be called the "pattern acts".

The oil and gas-conservation statutes as of January 1, 1933, were compiled by Northcutt Ely for the book, *The Oil and Gas Conservation Statutes* (annotated), published by the FOCB. Many of the very early statutes were still on the books at the beginning of 1933.

In two books published by the Section of Mineral Law, American Bar Association, will be found the history, legal and otherwise, of the conservation statutes and of the conservation movement. The books are: *Legal History of Conservation of Oil and Gas — A Symposium* (1939), and *Conservation of Oil and Gas, A Legal History — 1948* (1948).

The conservation statutes of all the states, as of 1956, may be found in Vol. 5 and 5A of Summers, *The Law of Oil and Gas* (Perm. ed.).

It is not unusual that these statutes vary in scope and language. Conditions vary, as do the necessities for waste prevention, and as do the views as to what is desirable and workable. In spite of some differences, most of the states that have substantial production have conservation statutes that fall within the classification of comprehensive, to-wit: Alabama, Arizona, Arkansas, Colorado, Kansas, Louisiana, Michigan, Mississippi, New Mexico, North Dakota, Oklahoma, Texas, Utah, and Wyoming. Florida, Georgia, North Carolina, Washington, and Alaska have comprehensive statutes in anticipation of substantial production.

Most of the state acts and administration thereunder were based on these fundamental concepts:

1. Waste cannot adequately be prevented or property rights protected by treating each well separately or in isolation, for in some degree each well affects every well producing from the same pool.

2. Production of a pool to its maximum capacity causes waste.

3. With rare exceptions, wells in pools or the pools themselves should not be permitted to produce to capacity or wide open.

4. Restriction of production from a pool is ordinarily effected by fixing the pool allowable which should not exceed its MER; or, stated differently, production in excess of the MER should be prohibited in order to prevent waste.

5. Spacing wells in a pool on a fairly uniform pattern, restricting the number of wells to those reasonably necessary in order efficiently to produce the recoverable oil in a pool, and the allocation of the allowable production in the pool among wells and tracts in a pool on such a basis as will avoid unratable withdrawals (i.e., will avoid non-compensated drainage across property lines in a pool) will aid in the prevention of waste.

6. The allocation of pool allowables among properties or wells in such manner as to afford to each only a reasonable opportunity to produce his fair share of the pool allowable are necessary in order to protect property rights (adjust correlative rights).

Of course, statutes have been amended — some of the amendments weakening authority, most of them strengthening it — as the states undertake to work out an effective program. No state statute has been repealed that has provided for comprehensive regulation along the lines indicated in the comprehensive statutes.

California has never had a comprehensive conservation statute of the type that is on the books in many states. The story as to regulation in that state under PAB will be given in the next section, and, as to voluntary practices, in Section X herein.

IX. THE PETROLEUM ADMINISTRATION FOR WAR — 1941-1946

Except for regulation applicable to interstate and foreign transportation under the Connally Hot Oil Act, there was no agency of the Federal Government, after the death of NIRA and the Petroleum Code in 1935, that undertook to regulate production until World War II. The "Office of Coordinator for National Defense" was created in 1941 to cooperate with industry to solve petroleum problems that were caused by World War II. Shortly after 1941, the agency became the Office of Petroleum Coordinator for War; and, on December 2, 1942, the agency was called "Petroleum Administration for War". It had considerable authority.[21]

One of the functions of PAW was to make regulations and coordinate activities of the petroleum industry to avoid scarcity of oil and products for war needs and for essential civilian activities. PAW also assisted other agencies in regulating the use of scarce materials that were allocated to the petroleum industry.

We are here concerned only with the control of production by PAW. At first, and fortunately for the nation, the total of the MER's in the various states at the beginning of World War II greatly exceeded the needs for crude oil. The reserve capacity, being the difference between actual production and the MER, was about one million barrels a day. This reserve existed because of conservation practices and regulation that began in 1930 and were considerably improved and expanded between 1935 and 1942. The reserve capacity would not have existed in the absence of regulation or if there had been wide-open production. PAW officials acknowledged that this was so. The chart at p. 175 of *A History of the Petroleum Administration for War*[21] shows the reserve capacity and its course during the war.

It clearly appeared, however, in 1942 that the large reserve capacity would likely be exhausted by increasingly heavy demands for oil, here and abroad. Consequently, the finding of new reserves and enforcing effective conservation measures were imperative. *Once more a Federal agency, this time acting in the interest of national defense and for effective prosecution of a war, not for any economic reasons or to protect property rights, adopted a conservation program that was based on the causes of waste and the effective remedies that were recognized in connection with regulation under state statutes, and had been recognized by the Federal Oil Conservation Board and by the Administrator of the Petroleum Code and the Petroleum Administrative Board.*

In brief, PAW affirmed that wide-open production almost always causes physical waste of oil; that such waste occurs if production substantially exceeds current needs; that restriction in production is usually necessary, *and that no pool should produce above its MER except in an emergency.* As part of the program, PAW determined the current consumptive needs for production for the country and established state allowables, using substantially the same method that had been used by PAB and by the United States Bureau of Mines after PAB was abolished. PAW also caused a careful survey to be made to establish MER's throughout the nation. The work was completed in 1943.

In those states that had adequate conservation laws, PAW relied upon the state agencies to allocate the state allowables and to take other action to prevent waste and protect property rights. The record of the agencies in cooperating with PAW was excellent, making unnecessary more direct regulation by PAW.

During the latter part of World War II, and in spite of efforts to increase materially the reserves and productive capacity, the production required was greater than the MER's. Consequently, each of a number of pools was selected to produce in excess of its MER, regardless of the ensuing waste. However, the pools were carefully selected, as some could stand the excess production better than others. The chart on p. 175 of the history of PAW shows that, in the fall of 1945, the production of oil in excess of MER's was about 500,000 bbl a day.

PAW, being a World War II agency, quickly ended all regulation after the war was over, and liquidation of the organization was begun. The formal order terminating PAW was signed May 3, 1946.

An account of the voluntary conservation practices in California between the cessation of regulation by PAB and the end of regulation by PAW is given in the next section.

X. CONSERVATION IN CALIFORNIA — 1935-1957

A sketch of what has taken place in California in the last 23 years with respect to conservation of oil and gas is believed to be justified.

The termination of regulation of oil production in California under the Petroleum Code, administered with the aid of the Petroleum Administrative Board, ended in 1935 when the NIRA was declared to be unconstitutional.

Between that date and the regulation by PAW during World War II, California operators were on their own except for the prohibitions in, and the few regulations under, the statutes as codified in the California Public Resources Code. Those statutes deal primarily with waste with respect to individual wells, not with pool-wide problems, although the prohibitions against the unnecessary waste of gas in connection with oil production did offer the opportunity to prevent some dissipation of reservoir energy and of gas, and steps were taken to prevent such waste in several instances. The courts upheld the sections as to unreasonable waste of gas.[22]

In 1955, several sections of the Public Resources Code (Sections 3307, 3308, 3314) were amended to make easier the prevention of unreasonable waste of gas. Also, Section 3450 was added, specifically declaring that the recommendations of the Conservation Committee of California Producers as to MER and intrapool distribution were in the interest of conservation of oil and gas; that it was lawful to make such recommendations; and lawful for producers to comply or to agree to comply.

The experience in 1933-1935 under the Petroleum Code regulation as to production control to prevent waste, and the knowledge of the results of regulation under conservation statutes in other states, proved the necessity in California for conservation practices that could not be compelled under the provisions of the Public Resources Code. With the end of NIRA and the Petroleum Code, the operators in California again sought to obtain better practices and protection of property rights by voluntary action through recommendations of the Conservation Committee. Compliance was voluntary but not wholly effective, although the record of waste prevention and adjustment of conflicting property rights was much better than it would have been if no recommendations had been made.

Again a conservation bill (Atkinson Act) passed the Legislature, and once more, in 1939, it was defeated by a referendum vote. The situation in California in 1935-1942, as to waste and protection of property rights, doubtless would have become deplorable in the absence of a voluntary program. Fortunately, the great demands for crude that came as a result of World War II, evidenced as early as 1941, could in part be satisfied by large storage stocks and by production from pools in California that had been restricted by voluntary action to prevent waste, and therefore had greater productive capacity than they would have had without the program.

The need for highly effective waste-prevention measures in California was quickly realized by PAW when it was created. The hazard of relying on voluntary action was too great to risk. Consequently, a comprehensive program was established by PAW to restrict the production in California so that it would not exceed the current needs, with allocation to pools and wells and properties. The PAW program was similar to the voluntary program, and to the programs in states under comprehensive statutes.

For the second time, the California organization formed for the voluntary program was called upon to assist an agency of the Federal Government. The PAW adopted a plan under which the amount of production from California for the next month was determined at an amount that would prevent production in excess of current needs. The Production Committee of PAW, assisted by a committee of the voluntary organization, made studies, gathered information, and made recommendations to PAW for allowables to pools, wells, and properties, with MER's as an important factor. Much information as to conditions was submitted to and obtained by PAW. The staff in the Production Division of PAW in Washington studied the information and recommendations, frequently changing the recommended schedules. The contemplated schedules, with the recommendations, including the comments and recommendations of the Production Division, were then submitted to the General Counsel of PAW. If he approved and the Petroleum Administrator also approved, the schedules became effective, but not otherwise. The schedules and regulations of PAW were orders or directives, not mere suggestions that the operators were free to ignore if they wished. In California, the PAW did substantially what state agencies under conservation statutes were doing. Its regulations did not conflict in principle with the recommendations that had been made by the voluntary organization in 1935-1942, although doubtless improvements were made.

With the progress of the war and the heavy demands for crude oil on the West Coast, the excess productive capacity of pools in California dwindled until finally there was none. The problems changed. No longer was it necessary to fix an allowable for a pool below its MER to prevent waste and other evils incident to over-production. Instead, the emergency justified production in California above the total of the MER's, but specific pools were selected to produce above the MER's in order to minimize the occurring waste.

The shortage of crude oil became so serious on the West Coast in 1944 that the Congress authorized the opening of the Elk Hills Naval Reserve in the San Joaquin Valley; and by VJ Day the costly tank-car shipments of crude oil from West Texas to the West Coast averaged 35,000 bbl a day.

With the end of World War II, PAW promptly rescinded all orders and regulations, and the agency was abolished.[23]

The PAW program and the history of programs in many states under conservation statutes — such as those in Arkansas, Kansas, Louisiana, New Mexico, Oklahoma, and Texas — offered overwhelming proof of the validity of these statements:

1. Excessive production of oil causes waste, and what constitutes excessive production can be determined.

2. With few exceptions, the wells in a pool which is not a marginal or stripper pool should not be produced to capacity.

3. Petroleum technologists can determine for a pool the maximum amount or rate of production that will not cause underground waste, usually called the maximum efficient rate or MER.

4. Technologists may express differences of opinion as to the MER for a pool, for judgment is required after weighing much information, but an MER can be determined with reasonable accuracy, and be suitable for prevention of waste and protection of property rights until conditions in the pool materially change.

5. Production from a pool should not exceed its MER.

6. When the production from a pool is restricted, such as to its MER, the total production from the wells in the pool must not exceed the figure representing the MER. Consequently, the total to be produced must be allocated to wells and properties.

1149

7. Conditions applicable to some wells, such as wells with excessive gas-oil ratios, may require special treatment.

8. The distribution of a pool allowable should be such as to prevent waste, and, subject to the necessities of waste prevention, the distribution should protect property rights.

9. Property rights are protected in part by prevention of waste, and in part by the allocation formula or the amount to be produced from the various wells and tracts.

At the end of World War II (1945), the operators in California again had to decide whether to dissolve the voluntary organization or to continue to make efforts to prevent waste and adjust property rights by gathering additional information and making recommendations to the operators, with the hope that the degree of voluntary compliance would justify the program.

The operators decided to make efforts to prevent waste and adjust conflicting property rights. To carry out the program, the Conservation Committee of California Oil Producers, the voluntary organization that had voluminous records as to pools and wells and had aided the PAW for some five years, was continued.[24] It gathered information and made recommendations. The organization was still functioning when this chapter was written.

In one respect, the conditions in California in the period 1946-1957 were quite different from those that existed in the early 1930's and in 1935-1942. Except for short periods in the last 10 years, the problem in California has been to supply current consumptive needs without causing waste or, stated differently, without exceeding the MER's.

Problems and waste incident to over-production in the state as a whole no longer exist in California. However, some pools have been over-produced or produced in excess of their MER's, and the need for conservation practices of the highest order are greater than in the days of excess capacity. The California voluntary program during the last 10 years conforms with the 9 numbered statements just set out, and great good has been done in spite of production practices of some operators that vary considerably from the methods recommended. However, in 1955, the California Legislature added Section 3450 to the Public Resources Code by which the Legislature declared that the recommendations of the Conservation Committee of California Producers as to MER's and intrapool distribution were in the interest of conservation of oil and gas; that it was lawful to make such recommendations; and lawful for producers to comply or to agree to comply.

For the third time in California, efforts were made to obtain state authority for comprehensive regulation, instead of relying on the voluntary program. In 1956, a proposed act was submitted to the people of California. It was vigorously supported by some and vigorously opposed by others. The proposed act was defeated. The chance seems remote of obtaining adequate regulation by an administrative agency in California. However, much good could be accomplished as a result of agreements provided for in the aforementioned Section 3450 of the Public Resources Code.

The Federal Government recently brought suit in California against seven large oil companies and the conservation committee, claiming in part that, under the guise of a conservation program and activities for the control of oil production, they had violated Federal antitrust laws.[25] The consequences of the final judgment in that case may be far reaching.

XI. PRESENT AND FUTURE TRENDS IN CONSERVATION LEGISLATION AND REGULATION

The following states have fairly comprehensive conservation statutes: Alabama, Alaska, Arizona, Arkansas, Colorado, Florida, Georgia, Kansas, Louisiana, Michigan, Mississippi, Montana, Nevada, New Mexico, North Dakota, North Carolina, Oklahoma, Texas, Washington, Utah, and Wyoming.[26] The statutes in those states vary, some being broader than others, but most of them are based on these fundamental concepts and provisions:

1. Physical waste of oil and gas aboveground or underground from production and storage practices is defined and prohibited.
2. An administrative agency is created with authority, usually after notice and a hearing, to make orders (including rules and regulations) to prevent waste, and, subject to necessities for waste prevention, to protect property rights.
3. A penalty is imposed for a violation, and usually an injunction is authorized to prevent further violation.
4. Court review of administrative action is provided.
   Some of the statutes specifically provide for compulsory pooling of tracts and interests to form a drilling unit or to effect compliance with well-spacing regulations, to prevent drilling of unnecessary wells, and to protect property rights; others do not. Some provide specifically for compulsory unit operation of a pool or large area of a pool; others do not. This is not the place to discuss the arguments for and against compulsory pooling and compulsory unit operations. Statutes and orders thereunder have been upheld by the courts.[27] Support for or opposition to a statute authorizing compulsion in any state is based upon many factors, including:
   a. The conditions existing without compulsion.

1151

   b. The ease with which voluntary agreements can be made for pooling or unit operations.

   c. The far-reaching effects of a compulsory order, especially for unit operations, by the allocation of expense and production.

   d. The reputation of the administrative agency.

   e. The scope of judicial review when the validity of an order is questioned by litigation.

5. To the foregoing should be added the six fundamental concepts stated previously (pp. 1144-45).

The comprehensive statutes, by specific language or by implication, authorize the agency to provide for such things as spacing of wells, gas-oil and water-oil ratios, casing and equipping of wells, rate of production, dissipation of reservoir energy, and loss or dissipation of gas that could be economically saved.

Since the language and scope of the statutes vary, each statute should be studied in the light of its interpretation by the courts in order to determine its meaning and scope. It follows that this discussion of the statutes is limited to generalizations.

Two states with substantial production, California and Illinois, do not have statutes that can be classified as "fairly comprehensive conservation statutes". Of the two, California statutes are broader, for they do deal rather comprehensively with waste involving individual wells and with unnecessary waste of gas.

Experience and the growth of knowledge as to petroleum reservoirs will surely bring about improvement in conservation regulation and practices, and also any necessary revision of the statutes so that a better conservation job may be done.

Clearly, the petroleum engineer and lawyer must work together, the engineer to determine what causes waste and how to prevent it, the lawyer to determine how that can legally be brought about and give protection to property rights.

Finally, it can be said that the administrative agencies on the whole have done a much better job of waste prevention than of protection of property rights.

XII. REGULATION BY ADMINISTRATIVE AGENCY

1. General Powers and Restrictions

Conditions in oil pools vary, as do the means for waste prevention. Moreover, constant supervision is required, and changes in the waste-prevention measures are often in order. It was recognized that a legislature could not write a statute that would be self-executing, being one that would prescribe, under all conditions for each operator, precise rules of conduct that would be effective to prevent waste and protect property rights. Stated differently, it seemed to be impossible by statute to do more than prescribe general standards expressing the will of the legislature, leaving precise regulation to an official or agency. The lawyers say that the device of an "administrative agency" is used. It is vested with authority to determine the facts and implement the statute by prescribing definite rules of conduct, such as well allowables, gas-oil ratios, casing requirements, and well spacing.

The regulatory acts of administrative agencies are sometimes called rules, sometimes regulations, sometimes orders. There is no need to discuss the distinction that is often made in administrative law with respect to differences in rules, regulations, and orders, for in regulation under conservation statutes virtually all regulatory acts are orders. For instance, field rules or regulations are made effective by an *order* declaring that the rules or regulations are adopted and control conduct.

Without undertaking to indicate statutory and constitutional limitations that are applicable to administration of conservation statutes, it may be said that the administrative agency usually has wide discretion under the common form of statute concerning what should be done to prevent waste.

As far as waste prevention is concerned, a regulation to be valid must not be contrary to constitutional or statutory direction or prohibition, and must meet the test of reasonableness even though the regulation is effective in preventing waste. To illustrate: Restricting a pool allowable to a very small amount, say 2,000 bbl a day, and wells therein to $\frac{1}{2}$ bbl to 2 bbl, may result in only a slightly greater ultimate recovery than would a higher pool allowable, say 40,000 bbl a day. The restriction to 2,000 bbl may be unreasonable or arbitrary. So would be a requirement to use gold casing, although as effective as steel, for unnecessary expense would be caused by the use of gold casing.

2. *Allocation of Pool Allowable*

It probably is true that fewer difficulties or problems attend waste prevention than protection of property rights (adjusting conflicting property rights). In the absence of regulation, owners of tracts within the limits of a pool have various rights and duties under general law ("common law" or non-statutory law). As already pointed out, each has the right to drill wells on his tract and produce as he pleases by non-negligent operations, even though oil or gas is drained from lands of his neighbors; and each has the right, by drilling and operating offset wells, to protect against drainage and to keep the oil and gas in his tract "at home", to use the language of the court in the *Barnard* case. Each is also under the duty not to operate negligently to the injury of another owner, such as improperly shooting a well, or operating in a manner that reduces the ultimate recovery from the pool to the injury of all, such as dissipating reservoir energy. It follows that the owners are reciprocally interested in the pool, or they have reciprocal or mutual relations. *They have correlative rights,* also duties.

When, therefore, it is said that an administrative agency is required to protect or adjust correlative rights, it is implied that the agency should regulate operations to prevent waste and otherwise protect the property rights of the owners of tracts within the pool, or adjust their reciprocal rights and duties. The controlling principle may be stated as follows:

> Subject to reasonable necessities in preventing waste, the regulation should give to each owner a reasonable opportunity to recover or receive an amount substantially equivalent to the recoverable oil and gas in his land, shortly called his fair share, without being required by the regulation to drill unnecessary wells or otherwise to suffer unnecessary burdens as a predicate to getting his fair share.

The statement uses the term "fair share". Similar terms are often used, such as "just" or "equitable" or "reasonable" share. Obviously, if used alone, those terms are broad and require interpretation. Fortunately, excellent discussion is found in Section VI of the book, *Standards of Allocation of Oil Production Within Pools and Among Pools,* published in 1942 by several committees of the American Petroleum Institute. Several paragraphs are quoted.

> "This immediately raises the question of what is meant by 'fair,' 'just,' 'equitable,' and 'reasonable.' Abstractly, these words are not easily defined. Their meaning becomes significant when applied to fixed facts and circumstances. It is impossible, in a legal sense, to say that this or that formula for allocation among separate owners within an oil pool is fair, just, equitable, and reasonable unless the result of the application of such formula to the facts and circumstances existing within the pool is known. Thus, the fairness and reasonableness of a proposed formula to a given set of circumstances depend upon the result obtained. Generally speaking, it is the view of the Legal Advisory Committee that, when a pool is regulated, if each operator is afforded a 'reasonable opportunity' to produce the 'recoverable oil' under his land, or an equivalent amount; or putting it in another way, if the regulation is such as to protect against reasonable avoidable drainage not offset by counter-drainage — the result is fair, just, equitable, and reasonable, and, therefore, the formula which accomplished such result is, in a legal sense, just, equitable, and reasonable.

> "This again raises the question as to the legal concepts of the terms 'reasonable opportunity' and 'recoverable oil,' and why recov-

erable oil is the measure or yardstick instead of oil in place. 'Recoverable oil' is used because it appears that non-recoverable oil should be ignored. For instance, two tracts may have exactly the same amount of oil in place; but, if nearly all of the oil in one tract can be recovered by ordinary methods during the life of the field, and if only a small part of the oil in the other can be recovered under similar conditions during the expected life of the field, then a formula giving the opportunity to produce an amount of oil equivalent to the amount of oil in place would almost surely bring about quite different results from one giving the opportunity to produce an amount which is equivalent to the recoverable oil in place under normal conditions. The term 'reasonable opportunity' is used because, if a reasonable opportunity be given to produce, and the operator refuses or fails to drill or produce, then he should not be heard to complain if he loses by such act.

"The correct date or time for determining recoverable oil must be stated, be it the recoverable oil in place when the field is first opened, or at the time of the application of the regulatory order, or at some other time. Moreover, the term 'recoverable oil' could refer to the recoverable oil in a large tract or to just a part of it. It seems, therefore, that the recoverable oil to be taken into account should be limited to the recoverable oil in the developed portion of the tract, so that, to use a common expression, there would be no credit for undrilled acreage. The amount should, it seems, be determined as of the date of the development, if the field is under police regulation at the time. On the other hand, if the tract has been developed prior to such regulation, then the recoverable oil should be determined as of the date the field is placed under statutory control.

"There is no intention to say that the original determination is not subject to change. Later development and operations may show material errors, or some operators may fail to exercise their rights, or other things may take place which require adjustments, so that the ultimate recovery may be more or less than the amount thought originally to be in the land or which actually was the amount originally in the land. These adjustments or variations do not militate seriously against the use of what may be called the recoverable-oil standard, or protection-against-unreasonable-drainage standard. Absolute accuracy is not required, and probably the best answer to the criticism that so many errors and complications enter into the use of such a standard that, from a practical standpoint, it could never be made to work is to point out that the standard has been used, and it does work.

"After all, the important thing is to deal with relative values. If one tract be twice as good as another, or has twice the recoverable oil, it makes little difference whether it is twice X or twice Y, for the relative rights or values would be the same. And, if unreasonable drainage be prevented, the amount of recoverable oil will take care of itself, no matter what estimates be made as to the amount at any given time. Some lawyers suggest that allowables should be based on relative producing or productivity values, or upon relativity of reservoir conditions. Regardless of the terms used, all seem to intend to convey substantially the same ideas or fundamental concepts. A clear and simple way of expressing briefly and broadly the fundamental idea is to say that protection should be given against reasonably avoidable adverse drainage.

"It should be remembered, of course, that the administrative agency is authorized by statute to regulate production to prevent waste. The necessities of waste prevention may require regulation which will cause one operator to get more than his fair share, while another gets less. The regulation to prevent waste, in such instances, is paramount, and will stand if it does not go beyond the reasonable necessities of the case.

"A comprehensive statement of legal principles applicable to allocation is set forth in Sub-section (d) of Section 8 of Act 157 of the Laws of Louisiana, 1940, as follows:

" 'Subject to the reasonable necessities for prevention of waste, and to reasonable adjustment because of structural position, a producer's just and equitable share of the oil and gas in the pool (also sometimes referred to as tract's just and equitable share) is that part of the authorized production for the pool . . . which is substantially in the proportion that the quantity of recoverable oil and gas in the developed area of his tract or tracts in the pool bears to the recoverable oil and gas in the total developed area of the pool, insofar as these amounts can be practically ascertained; and, to that end, the rules, regulations and orders of the commissioner shall be such as will prevent or minimize reasonably avoidable net drainage from each developed area (that is, drainage which is not equalized by counterdrainage), and will give to each producer the opportunity to use his just and equitable share of the reservoir energy.'

"It will be noticed that the Louisiana act introduces a factor which has not yet been discussed: that of structural position. The producing life of a property depends partly upon structural position and its effect on regional migration, especially where there is an active water drive or an expanding gas cap; and this life can be made relatively long or short, and the ultimate recovery can be made high or low, as compared to other properties in the field, by the method of allocation. Clearly, then, structural position must be taken into ac-

1156

count because of its effect upon ultimate recovery and drainage. What must be done in any particular field depends upon the conditions in that field. For instance, properties which, because of structural position and regional migration, would not have the opportunity to produce the amount of recoverable oil originally in place if the pool allowable should be based upon relative reserves, should be given higher allowables than the properties which, because of the restriction on the pool allowable, are benefited by regional migration. These last-mentioned properties, in the absence of restriction on the pool allowable, would not, as a rule, be favorably situated; therefore, in most instances, it may be said that, *if they have a favorable producing position,* it is *because of the restriction* in the allowable of the pool, *and the method of allocation, not because* of any inherent advantage existing in nature. The problem is to give high enough allowables to the properties subject to adverse regional drainage so that they will have a reasonable opportunity to recover their recoverable oil without waste, and at the same time not to restrict unduly the properties favored by regional drainage.

"If, under all the facts, the problem just stated is met in a reasonable way, it is likely that the courts will uphold the method of allocation, saying that the producers are given a reasonable opportunity to produce their fair shares consistent with waste prevention. On the other hand, if it appears that the administrative body has acted arbitrarily, and has not given reasonable opportunity to the producers to produce their fair shares consistent with waste prevention, then the courts, or at least the state courts, will likely declare the method of allocation to be invalid, even if the methods be stated in the statute itself.

"It seems that the Louisiana act not only gives a correct definition of 'fair share,' but, in so doing, it states the property rights of a property owner — whether his property be in Louisiana, Texas, or some other state. The conservation statutes of Arkansas, New Mexico, and Michigan contain provisions quite similar to the quotation just given from the Louisiana act.

"Obviously, a formula suitable for one field may be wholly unsuitable for another. A field of the piercement-dome type offers complications which do not exist in fields having relatively uniform blanket sands; and fields with uniform spacing do not present some of the problems which exist in fields with great variation in drilling density. Yet it may be said that property rights and principles are constant, whatever may be the difficulties in determining the fair share of each operator, or in formulating a method of allocation suitable to all conditions in the field."

1157

XIII. SPECIAL POOL PROBLEMS

1. Spacing of Wells and Unnecessary Wells

Control of the spacing of wells has been justified and upheld on two main grounds: *a,* to prevent waste, as by minimizing fire or blowout, or by requiring a well pattern to make easier reservoir control and efficient recovery; and *b,* to avoid substantial net drainage from tracts of others, or to afford the owner of each tract the opportunity to produce his share without being required to drill unnecessary wells.

A few conclusions of a legal nature may be stated with respect to spacing. A spacing regulation, whether by fixing a minimum distance between wells or by fixing the size of a spacing unit (sometimes called drilling unit), should not ordinarily result in an area attributable to a well that is substantially smaller than the effective drainage area of the well. Stated differently, if one well will effectively drain 40 acres, the unit should not be less than 40 acres, at least for fixing allowables. Furthermore, the regulation should not require the drilling of two or more wells to get an allowable applicable to 40 acres, for that would cause unnecessary expense. However, if danger of fire or blowout did not exist if two or more wells were drilled on a 40-acre unit, a regulation might properly permit an operator to drill two or more wells if he wished, provided he did not crowd the lines of competitive units, and if the unit allowable or total allowable for all the wells on the unit should be the same amount that it would be if only one well were drilled. If, in the assumed situation, the operator elected (which he doubtless would not) to drill more than one well on the 40-acre unit, he could not with reason claim that he was required to drill an unnecessary well to get an allowable applicable to 40 acres.

As far as the regulatory agency is concerned, there is no requirement to drill wells as close as the rules permit. Although authorization be granted to drill wells 660 ft apart, the operator may, if he wishes, space them wider. However, the allocation formula may be such as to induce an operator to forego wider spacing. For example, if 40-acre spacing and 40-acre units for allowables are established, an operator could space his wells on an 80-acre pattern if he wished; but the allowable usually would be only that applicable to 40 acres to each well. Sometimes, in such a situation, the allowable for one well on 80 acres is more than, but not double, the 40-acre allowable.

Many of the problems as to spacing, and also of allocation of production, or protection or adjustment of correlative rights, involve small tracts. For instance, a spacing unit of 40 acres is established, also a 40-acre unit for allocation, as the administrative agency finds that 1 well will adequately drain more than 40 acres; within the unit are 4 separately owned tracts, 1 acre, 2 acres, 7 acres, and 30 acres. Leaving aside any question of fire hazard or danger from blowouts or results of ragged spacing, if a well should be drilled on each tract, it is obvious that the drilling of 4 wells would result in 3 unnecessary wells, as far as effective recovery is concerned. If each owner is permitted to drill and if the allowable of each is that part of the 40-acre allowable that corresponds to the acreage in his tract (assuming that recoverable oil and gas under each acre is about the same), the recovery from one or several tracts may not justify the expense of drilling and operating. If a greater allowable is given, then each owner receiving the excess allowable gets more than his "fair share," taking the excess from others.

Such taking from one to give to another is not legally justified. However, it is a common occurrence. Many operators hesitate to bring suit to invalidate orders that, in their opinion, fail to give them their fair shares, because of the expense of litigation and because the courts have shown reluctance to invalidate orders; and, in some states, the courts apply the "substantial-evidence rule," saying that if there is substantial evidence as to facts necessary to support the order, it will be upheld, though the preponderance of the evidence would require contrary findings as to the facts. It follows that many operators who feel sure that their property rights have not been protected do not bring suit to invalidate orders, especially as to fairness of allocation, for they realize that technical controversies as to underground conditions can always be created, making relatively easy the introduction of evidence that the courts will consider to be "substantial evidence," requiring a holding that the order is not invalid as far as fact questions are concerned.

The difficulty in Texas arising from small tracts or irregularly shaped tracts that cannot be drilled in compliance with spacing regulations is largely created by what is known as "exceptions" to a spacing rule, called Rule 37. The Texas statutes do not include provisions for compulsory pooling. Consequently, the Railroad Commission grants exceptions "to prevent waste or to prevent the confiscation of property." In the example given previously, each owner of a separate tract within the 40-acre unit would be permitted by orders of the Commission to drill, unless the tract was cut off of the 40-acre tract or from a part of it, after the spacing rule became effective in the area. It is clear that the mere drilling of a well on a small tract does little harm. It is the excessive allowable that hurts, for almost always the small tract is permitted to produce more than its "fair share".

There are too many complications and ramifications as to the law bearing on well-spacing problems, especially in Texas, to be discussed here; but it is clear that, as long as wells may be drilled on small tracts or at locations not conforming with a relatively uniform pattern, and as long as exceptions are granted to a general rule *and excessive allowables are given,* the owners of tracts that cannot be drilled in compliance with the general rule or pattern will refuse to integrate or pool their tracts or parts of them. One remedy that is available in many states is compulsory pooling, so that only one well will be drilled for the benefit of all and in conformity with the general rule or pattern.

Many of the oil-producing states have passed statutes that authorize compulsory pooling. Texas has not, although compulsory pooling of drilling units in other states is generally considered to be a workable and adequate remedy. There are a number of articles giving detailed information about spacing problems, allowables, and pooling.[28]

Condensate pools, gas-cap pools, and pools in which regional migration occurs present unusually difficult problems. This is so as to condensate pools, because usually the failure to maintain pressure at a level approaching original reservoir pressure results in waste; and, ordinarily, maintenance of pressure—as by injection of gas after removal of heavier hydrocarbons (cycling)—must be on a pool-wide basis for efficiency and satisfactory adjustment of property rights. Under the ordinary conservation statute, it is believed that the administrative agency has the power to prohibit production in a condensate pool until the operators arrange for an efficient cycling program. In a considerable number of states, if the operators do not agree on an efficient cycling program, the statutes authorize compulsion by an order providing for cycling.

As to gas-cap pools, where substantial production from the gas cap will cause waste of oil, the problems are indeed difficult, depending in part upon many factors — such as the size, shape, and character of the reservoir, the pressure, extent of gas cap, location of gas cap, and the oil-saturated sands. Where waste-prevention of oil requires that there be very little or no production from the gas cap for a long period, the law requires that the property rights of those having gas-cap properties be protected, if a reasonable method exists. The situation is somewhat similar to that in a condensate pool. If the operators are unable to agree upon a plan, then it may be argued that the administrative agency would have the right to prohibit production until operations were commenced that prevented waste and adjusted property rights, or until a compulsory order — if the statute authorized it — was carried into effect.

The problems existing when regional migration occurs have already been discussed in Section XII of this chapter.

It is not always easy for operators in a condensate or gas-cap pool to agree upon operations and a plan for adjustment of property rights. Prohibiting production or materially limiting it for a long period necessarily results in far-reaching consequences, including perhaps bankruptcy or loss of leases.

What to do to prevent waste in condensate and gas-cap pools is less difficult to determine than what to do to protect property rights. Usually the serious disputes involve the fraction of participation for each tract, presenting questions primarily for the reservoir engineer and other technicians. The situation as to one pool of the Rangley Field in Colorado is a well-known example. The operators in that pool were in substantial agreement as to how to operate to obtain greatly increased ultimate recovery, but were unable for several years to agree as to the share of each. The administrative agency passed orders that required unit operations, but the Supreme Court of Colorado held that the administrative agency has no authority to compel such operations.[29] Consequently, the waste continued for years for failure of the operators to reach an agreement for unit operations, and for want of a statute under which the administrative agency could effectively prevent waste and protect property rights. Fortunately, the operators were able to reach an agreement in 1957 that resulted in unit operations, and provides for allocation of expense and production.

In some states, as in Oklahoma and Arkansas, the statutes authorize compulsion (compulsory unit operation of a pool). In others, as in Texas, California, and Colorado, there is no such statute although, in those states, statutes have been passed that authorize voluntary agreements to be approved by the administrative agency. Various reasons have been given for the failure to enact statutes that authorize compulsory unit operations. For instance, it is said that extensive authority over private property must be given to an administrative agency to compel unit operation of an entire pool, or a large part of it, with the risk of unfortunate errors or misuse of authority. Consequently, no such authority should be given, as usually the operators and others interested in the pool can agree if the need is clear.

When the geologists, reservoir engineers, and other technicians are able to come closer to an agreement in any pool upon the facts concerning the reservoir and the necessities for waste prevention, it will be easier to agree on unit operations or to establish that a compulsory order is or is not valid. The difficulty of invalidating by litigation a compulsory order for unit operations covering a pool or large part, when the testimony of the technicians is materially conflicting as to what is the "fair share" or correct "percent of participation" applicable to each tract, is doubtless another reason for the reluctance of some legislatures to enact statutes authorizing compulsion.

2. Allocation Among Pools and Fields

When an administrative agency fixes a state allowable, as is usually done when production is restricted so that it will not exceed the market demand, it becomes necessary to allocate the allowable production among the fields, and, if a field is composed of two or more pools, then among the pools in the field.

Section 4, B, of the Form for An Oil and Gas Conservation Statute as prepared in 1950 by the Legal Committee of the Interstate Oil Compact Commission provides for allocation as follows:

"Whenever the Commission limits the total amount of oil or gas which may be produced in the state, the Commission shall allocate or distribute the allowable production among the pools therein on a reasonable basis, giving, where reasonable under the circumstances to each pool with small wells of settled production an allowable production which prevents the general premature abandonment of the wells in the pool."

As yet, it is doubtful whether anyone has been able to write a better or more precise formula, especially as to oil. Too many variables exist, such as reserves, depth of wells and cost, quality of oil, pipeline capacity, fields serviced by each purchaser, amount to be purchased by each purchaser, etc. That is why the section quoted merely says to allocate "on a reasonable basis," which means "without discrimination," all facts considered.[30]

One limitation that is implied in most statutes, but not necessarily in the section that provides for allocation of the state allowable, is that the amount allocated should not exceed the MER for a pool. The East Texas Field has been restricted to less than 250,000 bbl of oil per day, although the amount might be greater under the rather vague formula that is used for allocating to most fields in the state.

In some states, as in Texas, the statute limits the authority to restrict below specified amounts the wells that are defined as marginal wells. The theory is that, if restricted to a lesser amount, such wells will be unprofitable, they will be plugged, and the reserves will be lost. The group of lawyers who prepared Section 4, B, of the Compact form must have thought that such a marginal-well statute usually created inequities. They probably remembered the situation that exists in the East Texas Field as a result of the marginal-well statute, and concluded that a better method could be found for preventing loss of reserves attributable to small or stripper wells, and at the same time property rights could be protected. The section provides that each pool with small wells of settled production should be given an allowable, if reasonable under all the circumstances, to prevent "the general premature abandonment of wells in the pool." In other words, the method is a pool allowable for a stripper pool, not minimum allowables for marginal wells in any pool.

Additional legal problems with respect to field allocation exist as to cycling, pressure maintenance, repressuring, and secondary-recovery operations. Inadequate income, as from the value of the production allowed, may not justify the expense of initiating a project; and reduction of income from the project, as by the allowable assigned for the pool under any general formula, may make the operations unprofitable and cause cessation of the operations and resulting waste. It should follow that the agency should consider all the facts, and, if reasonable under all the circumstances, should fix an allowable that will justify such projects or their continuance. Here again, it may be said that the duty is to allocate "without discrimination." Discrimination does not exist merely because of differences in treatment. The facts may justify the different treatment.

Conservation — the prevention of waste — of oil and gas is essential to our domestic economy and national defense, and to protection of property rights. Remarkable progress has been made in knowledge concerning oil and gas reservoirs and the use of reservoir energy, in the technology of developing and producing oil and gas reservoirs, and in the use of this technology in framing conservation laws and regulations designed to prevent waste of oil and gas and protect the correlative rights of producers and royalty holders. Within the confines of this chapter, an effort has been made briefly to trace the development and content of oil- and gas-conservation laws and regulations, and the influence of reservoir engineering. It has been possible only to hit the highlights. Those who wish to pursue the subject further may find ample material in the items cited in the footnotes and in other chapters of this History. The conservation statutes of the various states are readily available, and treatises, such as Summers' *The Law of Oil and Gas* (Perm. Ed.), can be found in most law libraries. It is hoped that the reader of this chapter may be able to gain some idea of the scope and importance of problems involved in the conservation of oil and gas, and of the progress that has been made in solving them.

CITATIONS

[1]Hardwicke, Robert E: *The Rule of Capture and Its Implications as Applied to Oil and Gas*, 13 Tex.L.Rev. 391 (June 1935); Moses, Leslie: *Some Legal and Economic Aspects of Unit Operations of Oil Fields*, 21 Tex.L.Rev. 748, 749 (June 1943); Summers: *The Law of Oil and Gas* (Perm. Ed.) Sec. 63; Sullivan, Robert: *Handbook of Oil and Gas Law*, Sec. 13; Hazlett, George W: *Conservation and Property Rights*, Proc. Am. Pet. Inst. (Prod. Bul. 234) 13 (1950); Garrett, Rufus S., Jr: *Effect of Drilling Regulations Upon the Law of Capture*, 4 S.W.L.J. 469 (Fall 1950); Kuntz, Eugene: *The Law of Capture*, 10 Okla.L.Rev. 406 (Nov. 1957). Cases and other articles are cited in the items listed.

[2]Typical cases: Comanche Duke Oil Co. v. Texas Pac. Coal and Oil Co., 298 S.W. 554 (Tex. Comm. App. 1927, involving the shooting of a well); Empire Oil and Ref.

Co. v. Hoyt, 112 F.2d 356 (6th Cir., 1940, involving the use of acid); Elliff v. Texon Drilling Co., 146 Tex. 575, 210 S.W.2d 558 (1948 involving injury from a blowout); comment on *Elliff* case by John E. Thomason, 27 Tex.L.Rev. 349 (January 1949).

[3]Summers: *op. cit.* Note 1, Chapter 15.

[4]Information about The Texas Company posting was furnished by that company; about the Prairie, *National Petroleum News,* **XIV [48],** 178, Nov. 29 (1922); also reproduction in *Petroleum Week,* issue of Sept. 14, 1956, p. 9, of Prairie's gravity-scale prices that appeared in a Tulsa newspaper, date line November 25, 1922.

[5]Ely: *Oil Conservation Statutes—Annotated* (1933).

[6]The statutes are identified and discussed in the chapters for California, Louisiana, and Texas in the book, *Legal History of Conservation of Oil and Gas, A Symposium* (1939), published by the Section of Mineral Law, American Bar Association. A short title, *Legal History,* will be used herein.

[7]An account of the activities of the FOCB is given by Hardwicke in *Antitrust Laws et al. v. Unit Operation of Oil or Gas Pools,* 11-13, 15-23, 35-36 (1948).

[8]*Legal History,* 28, 154-160, 221.

[9]German, W.P.Z., in *Legal History,* 163.

[10]Hardwicke, Robert E., in *Legal History,* 222.

[11]Harris, Innes D., in *Legal History,* 44-45.

[12]Marshall, J. Howard, in *Legal History,* 28-29.

[13]Hardwicke, Robert E: Market Demand as a Factor in the Conservation of Oil, in Institute on Oil and Gas Law (1st Annual 1949), 149-182; Fell, Harold B: Excess Oil Production Causes Waste, in *Oil for Today—And for Tomorrow,* 59-69 (1953); Baker, Hines H: *Achievements and Unsolved Problems in Oil and Gas Conservation* (booklet), 15 (1949); O'Connor, J. A., Jr: The Essential Role of Market Demand, *Oil and Gas Compact Bull.,* **17,** 40, June (1958).

[14]Petroleum Industry Hearings (a digest by a committee of the American Petroleum Institute, including statements before the TNEC by industry witnesses), 217. Pogue's statement appears at p. 7435-7457 of the official record. The API book shows references by several industry witnesses to "optimum rate of flow", or "optimum rate."

[15]Marshall, J. Howard, in *Legal History,* 30.

[16]Amazon Petroleum Corporation v. Railroad Commission, 5 F.Supp. 633 (U.S. District Court, Eastern District of Texas, 1934, no appeal). See discussion of the case in *Legal History,* 246-247. For an account of the effect of net withdrawals on pressures and wastes, see *Salt Water Disposal, East Texas Oil Field,* 1st ed. 1953, 2nd ed. 1958.

[17]Act of February 22, 1935, Chapter 18, 49 Stat. 35, 15 U.S.C. 715-715L.

[18]A. L. A. Schechter Poultry Company v. United States, 295 U.S. 495, L.ed. 1570 (1935).

[19]A good account of the events leading to the Compact, and its history, appears in the symposium, *Conservation of Oil and Gas, A Legal History—1948* (1948), beginning at p. 556, a supplemental volume to *Legal History,* published by the Section of Mineral Law, American Bar Association, in 1948. A short title, *Legal History* (1948 ed.), will be used herein. See also p. 30 et seq. of the report of the Attorney General to the President and the Congress as to the Interstate Compact to Conserve Oil and Gas, dated September 1, 1956; and *Legal History,* 250-253.

[20]Much information is given in *Legal History* and *Legal History* (1948 ed.), referred to in Notes 6 and 19. Reports of conservation activities in oil-producing states, and

also reports as to conservation activities by the Federal Government, are made annually. The reports have been compiled in one or two volumes and distributed by the Interstate Oil Compact Commission. They supplement the two books mentioned, and are the bases for a third volume, now being written to tell the legal history of conservation. This third volume will be published in late 1959 or early 1960.

[21]Frey, John W. and Ide, H. Chandler (editors): *A History of the Petroleum Administration for War, 1941-1945* (1946).

[22]*Legal History* (1948 ed.), 40.

[23]Frey and Ide (editors): *op. cit.* Note 21, at 38.

[24]See annual reports as to California that are mentioned in Note 20.

[25]United States v. Standard Oil Company of California et al., Civil Action No. 11584-C, in the United States District Court for the Southern District of California, Central Division. Progress in the disposition of the suit should appear in the 1958 and 1959 reports for California. See Note 20.

[26]The statutes are found in Volumes 5 and 5A of Summers, *The Law of Oil and Gas* (Perm. Ed.).

[27]Recent books on the subjects, giving many citations, are: Hoffman, Leo J: *Voluntary Pooling and Unitization—Oil and Gas*, Matthew Bender & Company, 1954; and Myers, Raymond M: *The Law of Pooling and Unitization, Voluntary-Compulsory*, Banks and Company, 1957.

[28]See Robert E. Hardwicke, *Oil-Well Spacing Regulations and Protection of Property Rights in Texas*, 31 Tex.L.Rev. 99 (December 1952), for discussion and references.

[29]Union Pacific Ry. Co. et al. v. Oil and Gas Conservation Commission of Colorado, 131 Colo. 528, 284 P.2d 242 (1955).

[30]On April 6, 1959, statewide *Rules and Regulations* were made effective in Arizona which contain, in Section 501, a formula for the allocation of state allowable oil production.

Chapter 19

UNITIZATION

HERMAN H. KAVELER

HERMAN HENRY KAVELER was born in St. Charles, Missouri in 1905. He obtained B.S. and M.S. degrees at Missouri School of Mines and Metallurgy in 1927 and 1928 and a Ph.D. degree in chemistry in 1931 from the University of Maryland. His earliest professional employment was as an instructor in chemistry at the University of Maryland and at George Washington University. In 1935 and 1936 he was with the Pittsburgh Experiment Station of the U. S. Bureau of Mines. In 1936 Mr. Kaveler joined the production research department of Phillips Petroleum Company and advanced to the position of assistant to the vice-president in charge of production. In 1952 he resigned this position to open the engineering and management consulting offices in Tulsa, Oklahoma which he still maintains.

Professional and industrial honors and affiliations include Tau Beta Pi, Sigma Xi, Phi Kappa Phi, American Chemical Society, American Association for the Advancement of Science, AIME, AAPG, and API, whose *Certificate of Appreciation* he has received. Mr. Kaveler has written extensively for professional publications, mainly upon reservoir engineering subjects, and is regarded particularly as an authority on secondary-recovery methods, conservation practices, and unit operations.

INTRODUCTION

The tendency to waste in the production of petroleum is created in large part by a conflict arising from two fundamental circumstances. Petroleum occurs in commercial quantity in the earth in permeable, porous rock and is contained in the earth in pools or reservoirs constituting common sources of supply to all wells drilled within the productive limits of a deposit. Petroleum in the earth is undivided. In the United States and Canada, among the important petroleum-producing nations of the world, the right to take oil or gas from the earth is a divided right because it is a private right vested in or arising from ownership of one or more of the separately owned tracts of land within an area embraced by a pool. The right to take petroleum from a pool in the United States or Canada may be exercised by as many as there are owners or groups of owners of separately owned lands on which productive wells may be drilled. The inescapable consequence of divided ownership of an undivided common supply is that the oil and gas recovered from any known pool must be divided and shared.

METHODS OF DIVISION

There are three methods for accomplishing the division of petroleum among the owners entitled to share in the production from a pool. The methods have been discussed in historical aspect in Chapter 18 of this history. They need be referred to in this chapter only briefly.

Pioneer producers who followed Drake in 1859 were mainly concerned with discovery of more and more pools to supply the ever-growing demand for oil as the frontier was extended and the Industrial Age brought new comforts to society. Division of petroleum reservoirs was accomplished by drill-and-produce-as-you-please practices, with little or no thought to the fact that the resource was limited or that the practices indulged in resulted in less ultimate recovery than might otherwise be had from a pool. An owner's share of a pool was the amount of oil or gas that the owner or owners of a separate tract of land could reduce to possession under the *Rule of Capture*. The result was a "feast-and-famine" economy in the industry and often great waste on the surface as well as in the subsurface. It was a primitive method of division by taking without regard to consequences.

Petroleum became too important during and following World War I to permit the continued division of pools through unrestricted conduct of owners of productive land. In time, the rule of capture was modified by enactment of state conservation laws that resulted in regulations designed to minimize waste in production operations. A "doctrine of correlative rights" became the guiding principle under conservation regulation.[1] Market-demand proration, well spacing, allocation of pool production, and gas-oil and water-oil ratio rules promulgated by conservation authorities served to bring about economic stability and more efficient operating practices. The old principle of establishing ownership of oil and gas by capture and reduction to possession on separately owned lands was not done away with, but owners in states having conservation laws were no longer free to drill and produce as they pleased in *complete* disregard of the consequences. The rules and regulations enforced by conservation authorities had a substantial effect in determining the amount of petroleum recovered on any separate tract within a pool. Thus, after adequate conservation laws were passed in a state, division of the recoverable oil in any pool was determined in large measure by "field rules" intended to give to each separate owner a "fair and equitable share" of the recoverable oil and gas in place.

Conservation laws providing for the determination of reasonable market demand and for the proration of market demand to fields, to pools, and to separate lands and wells removed the division of a common source of supply from the unfettered hands of the owners of the wells and placed it in the hands of a regulatory authority. The task of allocating "without discrimination" under a conservation system was not, and is not, an easy task. The restraints imposed did not eliminate all competitive effort to reduce petroleum to possession on separate lands. Nevertheless, "proration" of reasonable market demand under state law, allocation of market to wells, and related regulations have been a great success and are the cornerstone of a sound conservation program.[2, 3]

The third method of meeting the inescapable necessity for dividing a common source of supply is division by agreement among the owners before the petroleum is produced. That system eliminates the necessity of establishing ownership by capture with or without regulation under conservation statutes. The merit of division before production rests in the fact that each owner has an interest in every barrel of oil or cubic foot of gas to be produced. There is no incentive to waste any part of the common fund. There is no "conservation problem" under that system. In addition to removing incentive to waste, the system of division before production permits recovery operations to be conducted without regard to separate property lines. The result is that operations designed to cause the "maximum economic ultimate" recovery may be employed. This is a substantial step beyond what can be achieved by conservative competitive division of a pool. It is the ultimate goal of conservation policy. There is a way, a better way, and a best way, exemplified by the three methods of dividing a common source of supply of petroleum. Division by agreement before production is the method of unit operation. It is a method

---

[1]References are at the end of the chapter.

that substitutes an undivided share for the divided share of each owner. It creates a type of ownership consistent with the unitary nature of the mineral itself.

Unit operation of a common source of supply may be the result of voluntary agreement among the owners; or, when conservation of petroleum is important enough, it may be—in one form or another—by compulsory agreement under statutory conservation regulation.

THE FIRST VOICE

Petroleum engineering is the artful application of scientific principles of drilling and completion of wells (field development), flow through porous media (recovery), lifting to the surface (production), and surface handling (separation). Conservation of the petroleum resource involves economic efficiency in each of the steps comprising the development and operation of an oil and gas reservoir. Unit operation permits improvement in each, although its greatest contribution is in improved recovery. Thus, the history of unit operation is not separable from the history of reservoir engineering or petroleum conservation. Those histories have been presented in other chapters. It will be sufficient here to limit discussion to a history of the industry effort to devise a practical plan to accomplish, through unit operation, the improvement the new technology made possible.

The idea of unit operation is as old as the petroleum industry. There is a vast literature on the subject. Many have contributed to development of the idea, although a few individuals stand out in history as persons in possession of that extra bit of insight with courage enough to voice their convictions and point to new paths not readily accepted at the time.

The first voice was that of John F. Carll. His pioneering observations in respect to petroleum have been cited frequently in this book. About 20 years after completion of the Drake Well, Carll concluded:

"The flooding of an oil district [by water] is generally viewed as a great calamity, yet it may be questioned whether a larger amount of oil cannot be drawn from the rocks in that way than by any other, for it is certain all the oil cannot be drawn from the reservoir without the admission of something to take its place.

"If one company owned all the wells drawing upon a pool, and had accurate records of the depths and characteristics of the oil-producing stratum in each well, it is quite possible that some system might be devised by which water could be let down through certain shafts, and the oil forced toward certain other shafts where the pumps were kept in motion, and thus the rocks be completely voided of oil and left full of water. As it is however, no systematized plan of action can be adopted. The careless handling of one well, by which water is let down to the oil rock, may spoil several others belonging to different parties. A clashing of interests at once arises and is likely to result in disaster to the whole district."[4]

Carll made his observations without the benefit of the engineering technology that some 50 years later would broaden and give full meaning to his sound judgment. He also spoke without benefit of knowledge of the ultimately important place that oil and gas would occupy in the social order taking root in his time. He had to be content with only the conviction that there must be a better way to make full use of known pools of oil. He could only speak of the desirability of a "systematized plan of action" in the negative sense. It could not then be adopted.

The "clashing of interests" which Carll recognized as the overwhelming force governing the operation of an oil pool was ultimately to bring the producing industry in the decade of the 1920's to a grinding climax of debate over the necessity for "a systematized plan of action." Petroleum by that time had become a "vital" resource. The "clashing of interests" had to yield, insofar as production practices were concerned, to conservation policy. Sharing by capture was to be tempered by sharing under rule and regulation of state conservation authorities.

THE SECOND VOICE

The next voice was that of Henry L. Doherty, whose effort to bring about a "systematized plan" of operation of oil and gas pools is generally dated from December 1924 when, as president of H. L. Doherty and Company, fiscal agents for the Cities Service Companies, he laid his ideas before the Board of Directors of the American Petroleum Institute in Fort Worth, Texas.[5] Doherty made a public issue of the "clashing of interests" between owners of separate lands located in a pool. He was a vigorous and outspoken advocate whereas John Carll, in earlier time, was content to record his observations in the quiet pages of a technical report. Doherty took the public stage and, in a fearless challenge, charged the petroleum industry with great waste and disregard of the importance of the petroleum resource. He created the "great debate" of the 1920's which led to what the preceding chapter properly called the "organized study period, 1925-1930," when the public issue of waste led to the formulation of a petroleum conservation policy under state law.[6]

Robert E. Hardwicke has rendered a distinguished service in presenting a history of unit operation in particular reference to the work of Doherty and practical and legal problems that had to be dealt with in fitting the idea of unit operation into conservation law and practice.[7] Jones has presented a biographical sketch and an account of the business career of Doherty.[8]

As Hardwicke has stated, it is difficult to determine just what was said as Doherty laid his plan of unit operation before the directors of the

American Petroleum Institute.[9] Beaty[10] stated the Doherty Plan comprised the following principles:

"First—No one should be allowed to drill for oil without first receiving a state permit to do so.

"Second—Nobody would be given a permit to drill for oil until an exploration district had beeen established.

"Third—Exploration for oil should be restricted to that part of the exploration district one-half mile inward from the outer boundaries.

"Fourth—The strip of one-half mile within the outer boundaries of the district should not be drilled for a period of one year after oil or gas had been found in commercial quantities or sooner, but not or until the exploration district had been enlarged or another district had been established adjacent to it and that the contractors on the two districts, if separate districts are formed, should not attempt to drill either half mile strip until they had agreed on a plan on which it should be drilled, and failing to agree upon a plan, then the state engineer could specify the plan suggested by either contractor or a plan of his own.

"Fifth—Royalties should be paid to the trustees of the district and they would settle with the individual land holders according to the calculated amount of oil or gas underlying each man's land . . ."

The principles of the Doherty Plan were to be put into effect by compulsion under Federal law. It was this feature that drew the sharpest criticism and caused almost universal opposition to the plan. Many then thought—as many do today—that the industry could solve its problems without the exercise of compulsion by either state or Federal government. There were numerous suggestions, but at the time, no one offered a plan that appeared to meet objections raised by those who thought unit operation would violate antitrust laws—either state or Federal, or both.

Looking back, it is obvious now that the main defect of the Doherty Plan was that it was too inclusive. It contemplated a pooled or joint effort to find as well as produce petroleum in a "district". It was not established, however, that all competitive effort in finding and producing petroleum resulted in destructive competition. Waste, if it did occur, was found to be associated only with the destructive competition associated with the effort to capture and reduce petroleum to possession in the operation of wells. Competitive effort in exploring, drilling, finding, transporting, refining, and marketing could not be other than constructive. Thus, the great debate at least narrowed the issue of waste to production operating practices.

Doherty spoke out and voiced his opinions in a turbulent time. All industry came under close scrutiny following World War I as adjustments were being made to meet significant social and political changes occurring throughout the world. The petroleum industry was particularly burdened by a low rate of new pool discovery that marked the early years of the 1920's. There was widespread fear of critical shortage of a resource that by then had become essential to civilian as well as military needs.

The temper of the charge that initiated the "great debate" can be judged by Doherty's remarks before the American Bar Association on August 30, 1927, when he said in part:[11]

"Oil is our most important munition of war and its waste and dissipation have reached proportions which can hardly be described by the use of conservative language—in fact, our overproduction and waste are nothing short of scandalous. It would be a national calamity if we should exhaust our oil resources to the point where our national defense was imperiled. Even a slight shortage of petroleum might, in the case of war, bring about a frightful sacrifice of the blood and treasure of the nation and possible defeat."

At an earlier time, before the American Petroleum Institute in December 1923, Doherty said in part:[12]

"The oil man has talked oil famine for so long and has governed himself accordingly, and the history up to date is that he has fooled himself and noboby else, and his continual expectation of a famine has cost the oil industry billions of dollars . . .

"It is our duty to prevent the devastation of the oil resources of this country to the best of our ability, and when we have done this, then it is up to us to sell whatever oil must come on the market, be that amount much or little, to the customer who can pay the best price.

"We are cursed primarily by the fact that the rules for property ownership are different in the production end of the oil business than in any other business in the world and we are likened only to the rules relating to the ownership of wild animals and birds.

"This makes it impossible for us to have vast bodies of oil resources located and large bodies of it blocked out that can be drawn upon as the market demands it. The location of an oil pool means under present conditions that it must be immediately forced upon the market whether the market can take it or not. If there is no market for other mineral products they can be left on the ground. This is not true with oil. We are continually vibrating back and forth between an overproduction of oil and the threat of a shortage of oil with no adequate resources on which to draw to stabilize either our supplies or our prices. Our customers are alarmed at times for fear

they will not have a supply and are continually irritated and an-
noyed by wide fluctuations in price. The man on the street compares
our business with every other branch of business and concludes that
such fluctuations in price can only result from either mismanagement
or manipulation . . ."

Doherty was equal to the task he set for himself. His campaign for
conservation and for unit operation was based on more than dogged
determination, and involved more than blind dedication to a cause. He
had a record of successful pioneering effort in the development of gas
utilities. He had the foresight to appreciate the opportunities for extending
the use of natural gas for domestic, industrial, and commercial uses provided an adequate and stable supply could be established. As a self-taught
engineer with a wide range of interests, he also had the insight to conclude
that the production of natural gas associated with oil had a relationship
to oil recovery and that waste of associated gas resulted in waste of oil.
Studies had been undertaken in the laboratories of his company to establish fundamental facts about the properties of petroleum in the earth.[13]
The U. S. Bureau of Mines had begun to publish reports of investigations
on the relationship of oil and gas in reservoirs.[14] Reservoir engineering was
beginning to be recognized and petroleum producers were searching for
improved production practices.[15]

Doherty made a number of contributions to unit-operation theory,
even though there was vigorous opposition to the particular plan he
advocated. He did have a plan of "systematized operations," unpopular
though it was. He was the first to call the plan a "plan of unit operation."
He first suggested that the oil and gas in a pool (or district) should be
produced as a common fund and distributed to the persons entitled to
share in the production. He first proposed that the common fund be
distributed in proportion to the oil and gas in place on each person's land
within the pool (or district). These basic conceptions carried through
the period of stormy appraisal of the Doherty Plan to become essential
elements of plans of unit operation that were to finally emerge.

As early as 1924, Doherty was in a position to say before the AIME:[16]

"If the unit plan is adopted, we can recover at least double as
much oil as we do now and can conserve at least 66⅔ percent of our
gas . . ."

There were some at the time who appreciated the wisdom of that conclusion, but the great debate turned more on the means which Doherty
advocated to accomplish the "unit plan" than on the ultimate result he
claimed for it. After the great debate had subsided somewhat and the
industry was giving serious consideration to all Doherty had advocated,
he remarked before a discussion group:[17]

"The criticism that I have not explained as much about this as I should [unit operations] cannot be made by the men who have sat with me in the meetings behind closed doors. I did get to the point where I did not want to discuss detail because you can wreck a plan by discussing detail. When they passed the Federal Reserve Bank Law they did not name the 13 cities that were going to be the regional cities, because they would have wrecked the plan if they had. I finally went to work and tore up every plan I had so that I could say conscientiously that I had no detailed plan, because I realized that I could not discuss the details until we were ready to say whether we wanted unit operation of pools first."

At the same meeting, he further stated:[17]

"I want to put this one thought before the meeting for fear they might get the wrong idea of what unit operation is. When Mr. Hill speaks about these foreign pools being operated as units, I do not know whether there are any or not being operated as units, as I see the problem, because the unit operation of pools is something else than mere geography. From what little I know about the foreign field . . . there was nothing then in the real sense of unit operations of pools where advantage was taken of all the possibilities that are presented, by preventing waste of gas, and keeping the oil always [in the condition in which it is found while it is] being produced from the oil horizon."

Thus, by 1930 a shift in emphasis, argument, and objective was apparent. The great debate opened with a vigorous indictment of waste created by unrestricted competitive practices against a background of fear of scarcity. As time passed, it turned more to the technical aspects for utilizing natural gas both as a marketed product and as a reservoir pressure-maintenance agent for oil recovery. Discussion had shown that an all-embracing plan of including exploration, development, and marketing was not practical. It was evident by 1930 that unit operation, if it were justified, was to be a system for increasing ultimate recovery from known pools. In this sense, unit operation would be nothing more than another means for preventing waste.

But the question of "how" remained. What was the systematized plan, as a conservation measure, to be in principle and in form? That question was still before the industry in the year 1930.

THE ADVENT OF PRORATION

The public has little interest in unromantic history of business enterprise, and composers of great opera—even if one were equal to the task—would not be inclined to memorialize conservation of the petroleum resource in lyric and song. But certainly the attractive theme and its colorful background is there. The great debate of the 1920's had its heroes and villains in a struggle of good and evil. It was dramatic enough, but the climactic discovery of the Seminole and Oklahoma City Fields in Oklahoma and the great East Texas Field that brought the petroleum-producing industry to the brink of destruction in 1931 was the peak of dramatic circumstance in American industry. The discoveries that created a great over-supply at the end of the decade of scarcity removed all doubt about the need for some kind of governmental regulation. Leaders of the industry moved forward to support state regulations designed to conserve oil and gas.[18, 19] The flood of oil and the advent of state regulation had the effect of turning attention of the industry to the more immediate problems of over-production and economic stability. The world-wide depression and the business recession of the 1930's only emphasized the fact that, whereas "famine" in the early 1920's created interest in conservation, the need for a constructive policy was to be met in the "feast" of excess supply in the 1930's. Hardwicke has said, ". . . few people even now realize the extraordinary influence which the great East Texas Oil Field has had upon the oil industry, the jurisprudence of the country, and upon legislative bodies."[20]

Interest in unit operations waned after proration under conservation laws solved the immediate problem of over-supply and brought about effective waste-prevention measures, but the discussion of unit operation had left a deep impression on the industry. The American Petroleum Institute continued to give a great deal of attention to the question. A symposium, "The New Conception of Oil Production," occupied the main part of the general session of the Division of Production in 1931. At that session, Robert R. Penn, Chairman of the Division, said in part:[21]

"We have been seared and scorched, and bear terrible scars. Our industry will not again willingly undergo such tortures as we have in 1931. We have the intelligence, we have the leadership, to take the necessary steps to prevent a recurrence of a cataclysm such as we have had this year. The only question is whether we have the united will . . . More and more we are becoming conscious that unit, or pool, development is the only permanent cure for many of our present producing ills . . ."

When J. Edgar Pew addressed the symposium, he urged acceptance of two principles:[22]

"1. Complete and unqualified adoption of a unit plan of production.

"2. Corollary to the first, the acceptance as fundamental that each owner in a pool is entitled to his equitable share in its oil and gas, as opposed to the present anarchic rule of everybody getting all he can as fast as he can."

At the same meeting, John R. Suman discussed "Principles Governing Equitable and Efficient Oil Pool Development."[23] The legal problems involved in the "new conception" were discussed by W. P. Z. German, who brought attention to the fact that agreements forming unit operations to achieve conservation and to prevent waste would not be construed as agreements to restrain trade and prevent competition. But at this time, German and other lawyers recommended that legislation to remove any fear of prosecution under the antitrust laws would be desirable.[24, 25]

A committee appointed to recommend ways of putting the new conception into practical operation reported to the Board of Directors of the American Petroleum Institute in November 1932, in part as follows:[26]

"Unit operation is the best method for approaching and accomplishing the new conception in oil production, because it enables the operators in a single pool to determine the physical characteristics of the pool in a most orderly and scientific manner and to inaugurate and carry out a development and production program best adapted to the pool involved and to adjust by common agreement the rights and equities of all owners therein. In the event the laws of the state do not permit agreements for unit operations, its conservation agency should be empowered—with proper public safeguard—to authorize such agreements."

The AIME Petroleum Division sponsored a committee "to make a special study of the advantages of unit operation and means of promoting it" for the purpose of presenting "a record of existing results" and discussion at the meeting of the Division in 1930.[27] Earl Oliver was chairman of the special committee. As a result of the committee's work, a report and 11 papers were presented and extensively discussed at the meeting in 1930.[28] The papers and the heated discussion in the AIME sessions concerned the principles that should be embodied in any practical plan of unit operation. The special committee in its report said: "Popularly the term 'unitization' has been expanded to include all the partial steps that are being taken toward the ideal of unit operation, such as drilling and spacing agreements, cooperative repressuring and flooding..." F. H. Lahee defined unit operation as: "The development and operation of a single entire pool, or reservoir, of petroleum by one management, on a systematic and scientific plan which is best calculated ultimately to extract from the pay sand and bring to the surface of the ground the largest possible amount of oil with the greatest possible total profit."[29] That definition was a statement of what unit operation would ultimately come to mean, but few papers delivered at the meeting presented that clear conception of the idea. The reason was that in 1930 no pools were being operated as "units" except where the lessee interest alone may have been pooled or where the lessor interest was common to separate leases. Oliver was responsible for maintaining interest on the part of the AIME for many years, but the results of his good efforts were not to be realized for another decade. The Petroleum Division held a symposium related to unit operation in 1932 under the title "Stabilization", and again in 1933; but in spite of Oliver's efforts, the subject of unit operation passed out of the light of main interest. The reason was that "proration" under state conservation laws was working well and the days of crisis had passed.

The status of unit operation in the year 1940 can be judged by the following statement from the book, *Elements of the Petroleum Industry,* edited by E. DeGolyer with the assistance of a distinguished editorial advisory board and published under sponsorship of the AIME.[30]

"Operation of each pool as a physical unit, which is the essential thing required, can conceivably be accomplished in three different ways, as follows:

"1. Single ownership of all land or leases on all land on which the pool occurs. If the lands are leased, it would be essential that all royalty be held in common by the owners thereof.

"2. Pooling for management purposes of all lands or leases and of all royalty interests.

"3. Separate ownership and management where all parties in interest coordinate their interests and operations to secure the best exploitation of the pool as a whole. For instance, each operator might contract with all other operators and royalty interests to produce in proportion to the recoverable oil on his land relative to the total for the pool and to produce no free gas and no water, and each to inject his proportionate part of such gas or water necessary to maintain the original reservoir pressure if this proved desirable and economically possible. Another instance would be where the State or other governmental body imposed specifications of competent nature to ensure pool-wide exploitation as under one competent management.

"To a considerable extent the industry at present is producing under method 3, except that there are many imperfections in the specifications imposed. How far this form of operation may be developed toward handling the pool as a physical unit and application of the best principles and skill remains to be seen. It appears, however, that there may always be considerable temptation for operators to waste gas and water energy unless there is suitable compensation for not doing so. No suitable form of compensation has yet been developed, although penalties exist for excessive wastage of gas.

"It is greatly to be regretted that our country, in which the modern exploitation of oil began, and in which the greatest progress has been made, has so far failed to provide a workable procedure

whereby the most efficient and least expensive methods of pool operation can be realized. No major pool in the history of the American
industry has been developed and operated as a physical unit with a
viewpoint devoted to the application of all that experience, science,
and engineering have found necessary to obtain best extraction. Many
fields in other parts of the world are in the hands of a single operating
company and hence provide complete freedom of opportunity for
the application of all acquired experience."

Little progress had been made toward putting the principle into
practice, but the idea had been firmly planted. The "systematized plan"
that Carll envisioned, Doherty vigorously advocated, and the industry
endorsed but could not formulate because of legal and political barriers
had to be reached by steps. Acceptance of the idea—the biggest step—
had been taken. That was the result of the great debate of the 1920's and
the serious study that all professional groups had given to the waste-
prevention problem in the years 1924 through the 1930's. By 1940, petroleum engineering had developed to the point where there was sufficient
understanding of reservoirs, reserves, and recovery potentials to permit
reasonable quantitative measures of the results to be had from developing or operating a pool in one way as compared to another. The concept of
a petroleum reservoir passed from fiction to fact or, at least, from mainly
fiction to substantially fact. The law as it applied to the varied problems
arising out of oil and gas production operations could now be applied and
interpreted with a degree of understanding. Legislation could be based
upon rational conclusions provided by the new technology. Old laws and
new were turned toward the goal of achieving waste prevention through
state conservation regulation. In that atmosphere, practical plans of unit
operation were finally to emerge. The linkage of the law and engineering
that brought this all about has been aptly characterized by Hardwicke's
reference to the role of "lawgineers and enginawyers".[31]

PARTNERSHIP OPERATION

The plan of unit operation that was to appear would, in effect, be
a partnership operation of a type that had been taking form for a number
of years and by 1940 had become a common practice with a more or less
standard form of agreement between the operating partners.

"Partnership" operations arose from a number of circumstances. As
referred to in this connection, the term applies to co-ownership where
lessees were tenants-in-common. Lessee partnerships were created when
separate lessees acquired undivided partial interests in a tract of land.
Unless there was a proceeding to partition the common property, the
several parties were forced into a joint drilling and recovery operation.
Each had separate income and separate expense in proportion to his own-

ership. As a practical matter, one of the parties conducted the joint operation.

In a great many instances lessees of separate lands consolidated their leasehold interests and entered into partnership agreements in respect to further development of the lands. Consolidations of this type were, and are today, usually entered into prior to discovery and are primarily a device for promoting exploratory ventures. Such agreements result, when the royalty interests are not pooled, in what may be termed "working-interest units." The partner owners common to a block of leases remain subject to the obligations of each separate lease. Usually one party is the operator, but in some instances two or more operators may be in charge of segments of the jointly owned property. Agreements creating "working-interest units" were in existence from early time but became very popular in the 1920's after Doherty had raised the issue of unit operation. Practically all of the unit operations discussed at the AIME sessions in 1930-40 were that type of partial unit. In instances when the royalty ownership was common to all the leases, as in the South Burbank Field Unit in Osage County, Okla. in 1935 and in Federal land areas, the "unit" created did accomplish a pooling of all the existing separate interests. But, in the case of the South Burbank Unit, two important lessees refused to join the unit and that early unit operation, as with many others, covered only a part of the pool.

A great impetus was given to the formation of various forms of "working-interest units" by the Mid-Continent Oil and Gas Association *Handbook on Unitization.*[32] The book was a statement by the Association of the merit of unit operation with examples of what could be accomplished by them. The comments contained therein are of particular interest as reflecting thought of industry leaders in the year 1930. Concerning consolidation of lessors' interests in production, the statement was:

"... while it is true that the ideal situation would be one where the royalty as well as the working interest were unitized, it is generally conceded that unitization of the working interest alone is only a degree less desirable than the combination of the two. Consequently, unitization of leasehold interest is going ahead rapidly while royalty owners are studying the question and estimating the benefits that would result to them from the more orderly and scientific development, increased recovery and stabilization attendant upon complete unitization."

POOLING

Conservation laws in a number of states—beginning with Oklahoma in 1935 followed by New Mexico, Arkansas, and Louisiana—provided for well-spacing units of uniform size and shape specifying the location of the well on each unit.[33] Regulations requiring spacing units often required the consolidation of separately owned lands into well-drainage units of from 10 acres to 640 acres in area. The integration of separate lessee or lessor interests, or both, for the purpose of forming well-drainage units is generally referred to as "pooling" to distinguish integration of property interests for that purpose from integration of the ownership of entire pools for unit operation.

Pooling to form well-spacing units, whether by voluntary agreement or by compulsion, does not differ in basic principle from integration of an entire pool, except that the problem of determining the equitable share of each owner is a relatively simple problem in connection with spacing units.

Experience with compulsory pooling and related regulation of well spacing contributed a great deal to the further development of principles of law, property rights, partnership operating contracts, and accounting procedures that were directly related and applicable to field-wide unit plans. It is an interesting fact that, in those states where conservation was important enough to cause compulsory pooling for well spacing to be a part of conservation law, compulsory unit operation also ultimately became a part of statutory conservation. The conservation principle involved in both procedures is identical. Thus, though industry interest in unit operation lagged while conservation statutes were taking shape in the several states, the principles of unit operation were being established by way of pooling for well spacing.

THE THIRD VOICE

By the year 1940, three avenues were rapidly converging to create a broad highway of progress in the petroleum industry as the United States emerged from the business depression of the preceding decade. One avenue was conservation practice brought about by state law and regulation.[34] Another was the practice of "fluid injection" that had been applied in a number of reservoirs and was regarded generally as proved by practice.[35] The third, and not the least important, was the emergence of reservoir engineering which established an appreciation of the relationship of operating practice to economic ultimate recovery of oil in place.[36] The "new conception" in production practice had lost its novelty in 10 years. Conservation laws made it possible to appraise an oil pool from the standpoint of getting more recovery at less ultimate cost to consumers. Secondary recovery became as important as primary recovery. The new technology provided a basis of understanding petroleum in the earth and provided the technical basis for doing a better job in petroleum recovery from known pools.

Unit operation became more important than ever. It was particularly attractive to the producing industry in the State of Oklahoma as a means of increasing the reserve of known fields and as an opportunity to more economically recover reserves in place. There were many in both major and independent companies in Oklahoma in 1940 who had participated in the great debate over the Doherty Plan. The contributions of the U. S. Bureau of Mines were received with great interest.[37] Successful water-flooding operations in northeastern Oklahoma and southeastern Kansas were under way. The South Burbank Unit (1935) in Osage County had made an impressive showing as a primary-pressure-maintenance project in a partially unitized pool.[38] That 20-acre spaced pool showed substantially greater recovery under unitized pressure maintenance than the neighboring North Burbank Pool drilled on 10-acre spacing. The difference in the result in recovery efficiency was particularly impressive. The success of the Salt Creek Unit in Wyoming (1935) attracted a great deal of attention. Efforts to institute gas-injection pressure maintenance in the Shuler Jones Sand Pool in Arkansas were under way (1937-41). Gas-condensate production was becoming important in the Gulf Coast and north Louisiana. Cycling projects at Long Lake in Texas and Cotton Valley in Louisiana were forerunners of many important projects that were dependent upon unit operation. The advantage of a unit-operation statute, such as Louisiana adopted in 1940 to aid in forming units for cycling operations, came to general attention. The Haynesville pressure-maintenance project in Louisiana was one which drew a great deal of attention.

The American Petroleum Institute published *Secondary Recovery of Oil in the United States,* which had a very important influence in turning industry attention to that important practice.[39]

Everywhere the majority of owners in a field who wished to engage in the practice of fluid injection were confronted with the problem of getting voluntary unit agreements approved by all the lessee and lessor interests in a pool. The only relief from minority-owner objection was in Louisiana in instances where gas injection and cycling were involved.[40] The need for a practical means to effect unit operating agreements was widely recognized, but the first response was in Oklahoma where a representative group of the industry organized to promote compulsory unit operation under conservation statutes. In this way, the third voice was raised in support of unit operation. It was, in fact, the voice of industry.

The movement to make unit operation practically possible got under way when operators interested mainly in the Oklahoma City Wilcox Pool formed an association for the purpose of instituting unit operation in the Oklahoma City Wilcox reservoir. That pool was particularly attractive as a secondary project because of the great waste of gas that occurred from the beginning of production in 1931. The lessee and particularly the lessor ownership was so widely diversified that there was no reasonable opportunity to bring about unit operation by voluntary agreement. The association employed R. M. Williams[41] to draft a unit operation bill practically limited to the Oklahoma City Wilcox reservoir. It was submitted to the 1941 session of the Oklahoma Legislature. The bill was overwhelmingly defeated. That effort, however, won wide support from industry for a more general law. By the time of the next legislative session, industry committees were formed to conduct an educational campaign. The Mid-Continent Oil and Gas Association supported the move and had the assistance of T. Murray Robinson and W. P. Z. German in drafting a general unit plan statute that was introduced in the 1943 session. That effort failed. Finally, the 1945 session passed H. B. 339 providing for compulsory unit operation under certain specified conditions. Immediately the West Cement Medrano Unit was formed and became effective after appeal of the Oklahoma Corporation Commission order to both the Oklahoma and the United States Supreme Courts (December 1947). The West Edmond Hunton Lime Unit was formed under the Act (October 1947). The Southwest Antioch Unit was formed in April 1948. The Chitwood Unit, including the Cunningham sand gas-condensate pool, was formed in April 1949 and was the subject of important court decisions on appeal.

While these important unit operating programs were being put into effect, there was determined effort in Oklahoma to have the unit operation law repealed in sessions of the Legislature in 1947 and 1949. But the benefits of the Act were too evident. In the 1951 session, the Act was amended to remove some objectionable features that arose out of practical experience as well as from applicable legal principles. The amended statute stands today as a generally accepted conservation principle and is now no more than another ordinary part of the petroleum conservation regulation of the State of Oklahoma.

Robinson discussed the stormy battle to have the law passed.[42] Myers discussed the Oklahoma law, procedures under it, and the provisions of plans of unit operation that conform to it.[43] Robinson, perhaps reflecting the air of triumph that the debate over the Act entitled the advocates to express, wrote in 1948 in relation to conservation history in Oklahoma:[44]

> "The King is dead. Long live the King. A new ruler has come to the throne in the last ten years. Not by one blow, but by a series of thrusts and jabs, the legislature, the courts and the Oklahoma Corporation Commission have buried individual (I own) property rights, and raised to the throne the greatest good for the greatest number . . ."

R. M. Williams, whose task it was to guide the industry committees in support of the Oklahoma Act, as a valedictory to the effort of all who participated in the campaign to have the legislation adopted, said:[45]

> ". . . No longer can the engineers say to the lawyers that they have the know-how to bring about the greatest recovery and con-

servation of the nation's natural resources but that the limitations of the law stand as a barrier. The progressive thinking on the part of the courts has opened the way. The answer is not the result of any new or radical thinking but simply the application of old and established principles to a modern problem . . . "

Twenty-one plans of unit operation created under the Act were in effect by November 1952.

SUBSEQUENT ENACTMENTS

Other states followed the pattern set by the industry in Oklahoma. That they did is evidence of the wide industry support given the unit operation law in Oklahoma. A compulsory unit operation statute patterned after the Oklahoma law was enacted in Arkansas (1951), Washington (1951), Nevada (1953), Alaska (1955), Alabama (1957), Michigan (1959). The States of Florida and Georgia have compulsory unit operation applying to cycling operations patterned after the Louisiana Act of 1940. In the 1960 session of the Louisiana Legislature, the limited unit operation Act 157 of the 1940 session was amended to provide for compulsory unit operation for pressure-maintenance operations generally. This was the fourth session at which the general field-wide unitization provision had been before the Legislature of Louisiana since 1950. The Canadian provinces enacted compulsory unit operation laws in Saskatchewan (1952), Alberta (1957), Manitoba (1960). The Saskatchewan Conservation Act is of particular interest. It requires no consent on the part of any owners as do all other of the statutes that followed the principle of the Oklahoma law. In Saskatchewan, therefore, unit operation has the status of a conservation measure no different than any other rule or regulation that the Minister, after hearing, is empowered to promulgate.

The Legislature of California passed a Subsidence Act in 1958 that makes compulsory unit operation applicable when repressuring operations are necessary to combat subsidence.

Myers presents an analysis of various unit operation laws.[46] The reviews published by the American Bar Association analyze both practical and legal aspects of the unit operation history in the various states.[47]

THE INTERSTATE OIL COMPACT COMMISSION

The cause of conservation of oil and gas has been greatly advanced through the Interstate Oil Compact Commission.[48] The Commission has endorsed unit operation and has provided a forum for discussing the various legal, engineering, and practical problems connected with the creation and operation of units. The first report of the Engineering Committee of the Commission (1941) endorsed unit operation as the "best" way to operate a pool "from the viewpoint of conservation".[49]

Perhaps one of the most useful contributions of the Commission has been its "Form for an Oil and Gas Conservation Statute", the last revision of which was approved by its Legal Committee in 1958 and by the Commission in February 1959. The model statute has a provision for compulsory unit operation if the regulatory authority finds, after hearing on its own motion or upon application of any interested person that:[50]

    1. Such operation is reasonably necessary to increase substantially the ultimate recovery of oil or gas; and

    2. The value of the estimated additional recovery of oil or gas exceeds the estimated additional cost incident to conducting such operations.

The model statute also states the conditions and the terms under which the unit operation program shall be conducted.

Many states have adopted all or many parts of the form of the IOCC model statute, particularly those states that have a compulsory unit operation law.

The significance of the Interstate Oil Compact Commission's endorsement of compulsory unit operation is that it brings an end, in an official and convincing way, to the search for a "systematized plan" that Carll envisioned, Doherty advocated, and the Oklahoma industry first reduced to practical and lawful form. The stamp of approval that the Interstate Oil Compact Commission has given puts unit operation in its proper place — a means for accomplishing the conservation of known reservoirs of petroleum.

THE NUMBER OF UNIT OPERATIONS

Pooling, consolidation, integration, or unitization of separately owned lands has occurred for many years in the business of producing petroleum. Many such programs were labeled "unit operations" even though not all were consolidations for the specific purpose of increasing the economic ultimate recovery from a known pool defined by drilling and development. It has been only in recent years that the term "unit operation" has come to have the restricted definition of an integration of the separate property in all or a substantial portion of a known pool for the primary purpose of increasing recovery from a known reservoir. The available statistics on the number of unit operations in force from time to time are therefore not too reliable because of the lack of standard definitions of what was meant by the term.

Perhaps the most reliable census of unit operations in the United States was the report published by the Interstate Oil Compact Commission in January 1959.[51] The report lists 779 unit operations, including those where less than the entire common source of supply is a part of the operating unit. The report refers to a survey made in 1956 that showed 404 unit operations and a prior report that listed 92 projects as of January 1, 1951.

An appendix to the IOCC report lists 398 "units" formed under the jurisdiction of the United States Department of the Interior as of December 31, 1958. Unit operations have been an important part of the development and conservation program of the Federal Government. Since 1935, practically every lease issued by the Department of the Interior on public lands has contained a provision whereby the lessee agrees to subject his interest in the lease to such reasonable unit or cooperative plan as may be approved or prescribed by the Secretary of the Interior.[52] Although a majority of the Federal units are entered into for exploration purposes, many are for the purpose of increasing recovery from known pools. Little Buffalo Basin (Wyoming) and North Dome of Kettleman Hills (California) were the first two units organized under the original Federal law regarding unit operation of oil and gas pools under the Act of July 3, 1930, which expired January 31, 1931 to be followed by other legislation.[53]

CONCLUSION

Thus, 100 years after Drake, 80 years after Carll, 36 years after Doherty, and 15 years after the Oklahoma statute, unit operation has been lodged in conservation policy and doctrine as the practical means for accomplishing the ultimate in petroleum conservation. Wherever and whenever conservation is important enough, unit operation under compulsory statute is accepted. It has been reduced to practice to the extent that the American Petroleum Institute has published and continues to study a "Model Form of Unit Agreement" and "Model Form of Unit Operating Agreement".[54] Thus, the "new conception" of the 1930's comes to standardized practice in 1960. Myers discusses unit agreements and unit operating agreements in detail.[55]

Voluntary or compulsory? That question is still widely debated within the industry. If one had a choice, the almost universal vote would be in favor of "voluntary" unit agreements. They may result from resort to community form leases, or inclusion of pooling clauses in leases.[56] They may result from voluntary acceptance of supplementary agreements modifying existing leases. In this chapter the history of voluntary units has not been dealt with at length. That, however, does not diminish the significance nor the importance of that most desirable of all methods for accomplishing unit operation. States which do not have compulsory pooling or unit operation statutes do have statutes approving pooling and unit operation on a voluntary basis. Many important units have been formed in those states.

It is not the object here to attempt to present the pro and con viewpoints in the inevitable debate that arises when the issue of voluntary or compulsory unit operation is raised. The history of unit operation reveals, however, that compulsion is necessary if unit operation is to be practical of attainment and become an ordinary means available to the majority of owners in a pool if the majority elects to follow the best conservation practices. The debate over voluntary vs. compulsory unit operation usually comes to a final point. Is the protesting minority dealt with more fairly under an explicit statutory procedure, or under circumstances where the compulsive force may be indirect?

"Compulsory" is an objectionable word. But conservation is compulsory too, although when it was imposed it did not carry the offensive adjective into its name and title. Perhaps in the distant future unit operation will become, for business as well as conservation reasons, a matter of such common practice that no owner of an interest in a petroleum reservoir need be concerned with whether the oil and gas recovery operation will be maximized in value as a result of voluntary or compulsory joinder. The "clash of interests" that prevents voluntary agreements to form units is still present in many instances.[57] The more militant objections to compulsory unit operation have been stated by Hyder[58] and by Bryant.[59] The lessee viewpoint, based on terms of a lease, has been recently discussed by Burtchaell.[60] But history has taught that unit operation is not practical of attainment without an appropriate administrative procedure under conservation statutes, as Bergen has recently stated.[61]

REFERENCES

[1]Hazlett, George W: Conservation and Property Rights, *Proc. Am. Pet. Inst. (Prod. Bul. 236)* 13 (1950). Discussed common-law principles as applied to conservation statutes, with particular reference to unit operation.

[2]The problem of administering conservation laws is briefly discussed in Chap. 18 herein, and has been the subject of an extensive literature noted in that chapter.

[3]Sullivan, Robert E: *Handbook of Oil and Gas Law,* Chap. 15, Prentice-Hall, Inc., New York, 1956, discusses all aspects of the problem.

[4]Carll, John F: *The Geology of the Oil Regions of Warren, Venango, Clarion, and Butler Counties, Pennsylvania,* par. 476, Second Geological Survey of Pennsylvania, 1875-79, **III** (1880).

[5]Hardwicke, Robert E: *Antitrust Laws, et al. v. Unit Operation of Oil or Gas Pools,* 1, American Institute of Mining and Metallurgical Engineers, Inc., New York, 1948. At present, Mr. Hardwicke is undertaking a revision of this work.

[6]Baker, Rex G. and Hardwicke, Robert E: Conservation, Chap. 18, *History of Petroleum Engineering,* American Petroleum Institute, Dallas, Texas, 1961.

[7]*Loc. cit:* ref. 5.

[8]Jones, W. Alton: *The Cities Service Story,* The Newcomen Society of North America, New York, 1955.

[9]*Loc. cit:* ref. 5, 1.

[10]Beaty, Amos L: The Petroleum Triangle, *API Bulletin,* **V [75]** 13 (1924).

[11]*Loc. cit:* ref. 8; quoted by Jones, 18.

[12]Doherty, Henry L: The Utilization of Petroleum Products, *API Bulletin,* **IV [73]** 6 (1923).

[13]Beecher, C. E. and Parkhurst, I. P: Effect of Dissolved Gas upon the Viscosity and

Surface Tension of Crude Oil, *Petroleum Development and Technology in 1926,* 51, American Institute of Mining and Metallurgical Engineers, Inc., New York, 1927.

[14]Reistle, C. E., Jr: Reservoir Engineering, Chap. 12, 818, *History of Petroleum Engineering,* American Petroleum Institute, Dallas, Texas, 1961. A particularly interesting study from a historical point of view was the paper by Wm. F. McMurray and J. O. Lewis, "Underground Wastes in Oil and Gas Fields and Methods of Prevention", *U. S. Bur. Mines TP 130* (1916), when at that early date the authors declared that unit operation would produce the most beneficial results and doubtless could only be had by compulsion (ref. 6, 213, Citation 3).

[15]*Ibid:* 823.

[16]Suggestions for Conservation of Petroleum by Control of Production, *AIME Petr. Tech.,* 7 (1924).

[17]Discussion, *Trans. Am. Inst. Mining Met. Engrs. (Petroleum Development and Technology)* 83-84 (1930).

[18]*Loc. cit:* ref. 6.

[19]*Conservation of Oil and Gas, A Legal History—1948,* edited by Blakely M. Murphy and published by the Section of Mineral Law, American Bar Association (1948).

[20]*Loc. cit:* ref. 5, 87.

[21]Penn, Robert R: Report of the Chairman of the Division of Production, *Proc. Am. Pet. Inst. (Prod. Bul 208)* 4 (1931).

[22]Pew, J. Edgar: The New Conception of Oil Production, *Proc. Am. Pet. Inst. (Prod. Bul. 208)* 7, 10 (1931).

[23]Suman, John R: Principles Governing Equitable and Efficient Oil Pool Development, *Proc. Am. Pet. Inst. (Prod. Bul. 208)* 12 (1931).

[24]German, W. P. Z: Legal Aspects of Equitable Extraction and Distribution of Recoverable Oil, *Proc. Am. Pet. Inst. (Prod. Bul. 208)* 15 (1931).

[25]German, W. P. Z: Oil Conservation and the Champlin Decision, *57 A.B.A. Rep. 724,* 33 (1932).

[26]Roeser, Charles F: Report of the Committee on Production Practice to the Board of Directors of the American Petroleum Institute, *Proc. Am. Pet. Inst. (Prod. Bul. 210)* 108 (1932).

[27]*Trans. Am. Inst. Mining Met. Engrs. (Petroleum Development and Technology)* 11 (1930).

[28]*Ibid:* 11-128.

[29]*Ibid:* 34.

[30]*Elements of the Petroleum Industry,* 286, edited by E. DeGolyer, American Institute of Mining and Metallurgical Engineers, Inc., New York, 1940.

[31]*Loc. cit:* ref. 5, 64-66, where Hardwicke has defined a "lawgineer" but, in apparent courtesy, did not define an "enginawyer".

[32]*Handbook of Unitization,* 17, Mid-Continent Oil & Gas Association, 1930.

[33]The literature on the subject of well spacing is voluminous. The more important references to law and legal aspects are given in ref. 5, 161; ref. 3, 287. See also ref. 19, and Hoffman, Leo J: *Voluntary Pooling and Unitization,* Matthew Bender and Company, 1954. For a summary of well-spacing laws to 1958, see *Conservation of Oil and Gas, A Legal History—1958,* edited by Robert E. Sullivan, American Bar Association.

[34]*Loc. cit:* ref. 6.

[35]Lewis, James A: Fluid Injection, Chap. 13, 847, *History of Petroleum Engineering,* American Petroleum Institute, Dallas, Texas, 1961.

[36]*Loc. cit:* ref. 14.

[37]The work of the U. S. Bureau of Mines is noted in other chapters herein. The fact that the main branch of its Petroleum Experiment Station was located in Oklahoma was

particularly important in creating local attention to the results of the work being done.

[88] McWilliams, L. L: Unitization and Gas Injection in South Burbank, *API Drilling and Production Practice*, 175 (1946).

[89] *Secondary Recovery of Oil in the United States*, American Petroleum Institute, New York, 1st Edn., 1942; 2nd Edn., 1950.

[40] Act 157 of the 1940 Legislature, State of Louisiana.

[41] R. M. Williams was an attorney in private practice at the time, and later was attorney for Phillips Petroleum Company, Bartlesville, Okla.

[42] *Loc. cit:* ref. 19, 394-403.

[43] Myers, Raymond M: *The Law of Pooling and Unitization*, Banks and Company, 1957.

[44] *Loc. cit:* ref. 19, 369.

[45] Conservation and The Constitution, *Oklahoma Law Review*, **6**, 155 (1953).

[46] *Loc. cit:* ref. 43.

[47] *Loc. cit:* ref. 19 and 33.

[48] The history and work of the Interstate Oil Compact Commission is available in publications of the Commission. Other references are: Hardwicke, ref. 5, 96-102; Murphy, ref. 19, 545-596; Foster, ref. 33, *Conservation of Oil and Gas, A Legal History—1958*, 279-292.

[49] Fundamental Principles Applicable to the Production of Oil, Par. 25, IOCC Eng. Com. (E. DeGolyer, Chairman), April 14, 1941.

[50] *Form of Oil and Gas Conservation Statute*, Sec. 7, published and distributed by the Interstate Oil Compact Commission, Oklahoma City, Okla., 1959. Gen. E. O. Thompson was chairman of the Legal Committee, and T. Murray Robinson, Floyd Green, and R. M. Williams were chairmen of successive drafting subcommittees during the period 1954-58 when the 1959 version of the model statute was formulated. The IOCC had endorsed unit operation in various forms of statutes as early as 1942.

[51] Unitized Oil-field Conservation Projects in the United States, January 1, 1959, a report of the Secondary-recovery and Pressure-maintenance Committee, IOCC. W. L. Horner was chairman of the subcommittee preparing this report. The unit projects listed "were formed by the working-interest owners for the purpose of promoting conservation, preventing waste and increasing ultimate recovery by fluid injection . . ."

[52] Hines, LeRoy H: *Unitization of Federal Lands*, 22, F. H. Gower, Denver, 1953. See also Ely, Northcutt: The Government in the Capacity of Land Owner, ref. 19, Chap. 40, 599-629; and ref. 33, *Conservation of Oil and Gas, A Legal History—1958*, Chap. 41, 295-309.

[53] *Supra:* Hines, 20. The various Federal statutes are given by reference in ref. 52 *supra*.

[54] *Model Form of Unit Agreement*, 1st Edn., 1957; 2nd Edn., 1961; *Model Form of Unit Operating Agreement*, 1st Edn., 1957, 2nd Edn., 1961; American Petroleum Institute, Dallas, Texas.

[55] *Loc. cit:* ref. 43, Chap. 15 et seq.

[56] *Ibid:* Chap. 3; see also Hoffman, ref. 33.

[57] Williams, R. M: The Problems of Unitization, presented at the API Mid-Continent District Meeting, June 1946; abstracted, *API Drilling and Production Practice*, 411 (1946). Cited by Hardwicke, ref. 5, Note 158, 165.

[58] Hyder, Elton M., Jr: An Analysis of Compulsory Unitization; What Is the Price to the Industry?, *IOCC Quarterly Bulletin*, **XIV [2]** 51 (1955).

[59] Bryant, M. B: Compulsory Unitization on the Label but Socialism in the Bottle, *The Oil Forum*, 405, Nov. (1953).

[60] Burtchaell, E. P: A Landowner Looks at Unitization, presented at the API Pacific Coast District Meeting, May 1960; abstracted, *Petroleum Engr.*, B-114, Sept. (1960).

[61] Bergen, Richard C: Legal Aspects of Unitization, presented at the API Pacific Coast District Meeting, May 1960; abstracted, *Petroleum Engr.*, B-112, Sept. (1960).

Chapter 20

STANDARDIZATION OF OIL-FIELD EQUIPMENT

C. C. Scharpenberg

CHARLES C. SCHARPENBERG was born at Girard, Illinois in 1884 and received from Rose Polytechnic Institute the degrees of B.S. in C.E. (1907), M.S. (1909) and C.E. (1937). From 1907 unitl 1911 he served The Ohio Oil Co. as engineer in the pipeline department. He moved to California in 1911 to join Standard Oil Co. of California as a civil engineer, later progressing through the positions of superintendent, Kern River District (1913); assistant manager of operations, and chief engineer, producing department (1929), holding the latter position until company retirement in 1938. After retirement Mr. Scharpenberg became chairman of the San Joaquin Valley Protective Committee.

A pioneer in the American Petroleum Institute standardization program, Mr. Scharpenberg served in several national positions, including the chairmanship of the Committee on Standardization of Wire Rope and Manila Cordage from 1929 until 1938. He received the Institute's *Certificate of Appreciation* in 1948 for this work, and has received the American Legion Distinguished Citizen Award.

❧ 20 ❧

INTRODUCTION

The American Petroleum Institute program for standardization of oil-field equipment and materials is essentially an engineering achievement. Since their first issuance in 1924, API standards have been accorded wide acceptance in the domestic industry. By the latter part of the 1940's these standards had become an integral part of world-wide commerce in oil-field equipment. This steady progression to international pre-eminence is strong testimony to the engineering knowledge and perception through which these standards have been conceived and formulated.

The standardization program has given to the petroleum engineer no less than it required from him. The discussions and exchanges prerequisite to the preparation of standards have constituted a major technical forum from which all participants have gained knowledge and understanding not immediately available from intracompany sources. With the growing acceptance of standards, engineers have been freed from routine technicalities of design and purchase in order that they might better concentrate on the unknown and the unusual.

The API standardization program has been a concerted, continuous development by the petroleum industry and its suppliers of standard specifications which define minimum properties and dimensional limits for various items of equipment and material. This process has often required the establishment of grade, type, and size classifications to improve quality and to provide interchangeability. When adequate and generally accepted methods of testing to determine minimum properties or performance qualities have not been available, these too have been developed by the Institute's standardization committees — often through highly original applications of engineering knowledge. Another important function of the program has been the development of recommendations as to methods of handling, storing, installing, and maintaining equipment and material. Publications of this type were originally called "Codes of Care and Use" and more lately referred to as "Recommended Practices". The term "standard" is used herein to describe both specifications and recommended practices.

INCEPTION OF OIL-FIELD STANDARDS

Material shortages brought about by World War I gave impetus to standardization in several industries. Herbert Hoover, then United States Secretary of Commerce, and other prominent industrialists urgently advocated intra- and inter-industry action to reduce the useless multiplicity of sizes and types that was draining raw materials and thwarting industrial efficiency.

The oil industry was growing at a furious pace and the oil-field equipment situation was particularly chaotic. Few of the many manufacturers of pipe, for example, made their product in the same sizes, or with the same thread. Drilling operations were subject to expensive shutdowns in order to search for pipe and other items that could be used with those on hand. Costs mounted; purchasing became a frenzied pursuit of the unobtainable; and crude, dangerous, and expensive operational practices were resorted to. E. W. Clark, president of the Institute in 1927, described the situation up until 1925 as ". . . a wilderness of individual effort."

The need for standardization was recognized by many even prior to the organization of the Institute. At the first Institute meeting in 1919, a conference on standardization was held by R. L. Welch, API secretary; John Glover, Oil Well Supply Company; H. J. Lockhart, Parkersburg Rig and Reel Company; and C. A. Young, Lucey Manufacturing Corporation. This conference led to the presentation at a 1922 meeting of a session devoted to standardization and simplification of oil-field equipment.* Thomas A. O'Donnell, API president, and W. S. Farish, president of Humble Oil & Refining Company, presided over this session. Quoting the former: "The petroleum industry cannot expect the manufacturer to meet its requirements . . . unless there is a great demand from the industry itself to get some kind of standardization. Today there is the purchase of drill pipe . . . that never has been or never will be strong enough to stand the strains put on it. Sometimes it won't stand its own weight. We frequently get into trouble with the drill stand *(sic)* and the tool joints, not knowing ourselves what the different combinations of carbon and steel should be in order that the different joints make up together. We find that we have a lot of fishing jobs . . . The tool joint maker says, 'It is not my joint; it is the casing.' . . . The casing people say that it is not their casing; it is the tool joint. If any of you have ever been able to find a manufacturer who sold you the wrong kind of stuff you have done better than I have."

At the conclusion of this session a resolution was passed which called upon the Board of Directors to appoint such committees as were necessary to promote simplification and standardization. This resolution has further historical significance because of its mention of the organized standardization activities then in existence, viz.:

---

*At this session papers were presented by F. B. Tough and F. B. Foley, U. S. Bureau of Mines; Frank N. Speller, National Tube Co.; F. F. McIntosh, Carnegie Institute of Technology; Wm. A. Durgin, U. S. Dept. of Commerce; A. B. Steen, The Texas Co.; O. V. Borden, Purchasing Agents Association of Tulsa; J. Edgar Pew, Sun Oil Co.; S. A. Guiberson, Jr., Guiberson Corp.; and Grant Hubley, Oil Well Supply Co. These papers described in detail the penalties the industry was paying for lack of standardized equipment. They are printed in full in *API Bulletin*, **III** [62] December 30 (1922).

Committee on Casing and Rotary Drill Pipe of the Mid-Continent Oil and Gas Association (J. Edgar Pew, Chairman).

Committee Conference on Cable Tools, held in 1922 under API auspices (Louis C. Sands, Oil Well Supply Company, Chairman).

Voluntary Committee of Rig Iron Manufacturers (H. J. Lockhart, Chairman). This group was sponsored jointly by the API and the Purchasing Agents Association of Tulsa.*

Also acknowledged were the efforts of S. A. Guiberson, Jr. who had been cooperating with various agencies to bring about standardization of tool joints.

While standardization had the active and articulate support of numerous industry leaders from its first mention in Institute circles, and although proposals gained rapidly in clarity and momentum from 1924 to 1929, support was far from being universal. Some oil-company representatives were fearful that standardization would stifle initiative and innovation. Many manufacturers were concerned about the loss of competitive advantage and the expense of plant and process modifications which standardization would require. These fears continued to be expressed from this direction and that until the 1940's, but with diminishing force and mostly by organizations newly touched by the constantly increasing scope of the Institute program.

In December 1923, the API Board authorized the formation of a Division of Standardization. This authority was implemented almost immediately by the organization of several standardization committees. From 1924 onward the Institute was regarded as the authoritative source of oil-field equipment standards, although other associations — notably the Western Oil & Gas Association — maintained standardization committees with an advisory function for several years thereafter.

DYNAMIC LEADERSHIP

Among the thousands of industry representatives who have taken part, two individuals — J. Edgar Pew and John R. Suman — are the acknowledged paterfamilias. Pew, a vice-president of Sun Oil Company, was the leader in oil-field standardization from its inception until his retirement in 1946. His strong personality and ability to win the confidence and cooperation of able men was instrumental in the rapid success of the program. He served as the first chairman of the standardization committee on casing of the Mid-Continent Oil and Gas Association, and successively as chairman of the General Committee of the Division

---

*From records available, it appears that the first direct attempt to achieve standardization in petroleum equipment was made in 1919 by the Purchasing Agents Association of Tulsa through formation of a committee on rig irons headed by J. R. Stockton.

of Standardization (1923-1924), chairman of the Committee on Standardization of Oil-country Tubular Goods (1923-1929), and chairman of the Central Committee on Standardization of Oil-field Equipment (1924-1945). He was active in all of these assignments, even during the period of his presidency of the Institute. His contributions to standardization were acknowledged in the first presentation of the Anthony F. Lucas Medal by the American Institute of Mining and Metallurgical Engineers.

John R. Suman's first contribution to standardization was as a member of the Committee on Standardization of Belting (1925), representing the Rio Bravo Oil Company. In 1929 he became chairman of the important Committee on Standardization of Oil-country Tubular Goods, relinquishing this office in 1947 to become chairman of the Central Committee on Standardization of Oil-field Equipment. In the meantime he had become successively a vice-president of Humble Oil & Refining Company and of Standard Oil Company (New Jersey). Suman, also an AIME Lucas Medalist, provided an invaluable continuation of the inspiring leadership and keen perception of J. Edgar Pew.

On retirement in 1955, Suman was succeeded as Central Committee chairman by H. W. Ladd, Stanolind Oil and Gas Company. Ladd — who had 23 years of prior experience in standardization, including the chairmanship of the Committee on Standardization of Tubular Goods — was exceptionally qualified to guide this extensive and complex activity until completion of his tenure at Jan. 1, 1960, when he was succeeded by R. E. Foss, senior vice-president of Sunray Mid-Continent Oil Company.

COMMITTEE ORGANIZATION

Although it has had little effect on the fundamental organization and procedures of standardization, it should be noted that the Division of Standardization was merged in 1927 with the Division of Development and Production Engineering to form the Division of Production. This merger continued—without disturbance—the Central Committee on Standardization,* which had carried from the beginning the ultimate responsibility for the formulation of standards and the immediate responsibility for definition of standardization policies and procedures. Created by and reporting to the Central Committee there were other committees, each with an immediate responsibility for standards within a limited field—as, for example, the "Committee on Standardization of Rotary Drilling Equipment". These committees sponsored subcommittees and task groups according to need, with a typical committee containing a permanent User Subcommittee and a permanent Manufacturer

---

*Redesignated in 1959 as the Executive Committee on Standardization of Oil-field Equipment and Materials.

Subcommittee in addition to several subordinate groups of a temporary nature and with limited functions. User and Manufacturer Subcommittees considered the same proposals and problems — first separately, then jointly — in an effort to obtain a coincidence of views which could be ratified by letter ballot of the entire committee. Where reconciliation was impossible, the matter was continued until agreement was obtained or seemed to be impossible of attainment. This parallel flow of proposals through user and manufacturer groups, ending in reconciliation by joint discussion and final action by the committee as a whole, has been the fundamental method of operation from the beginning to the present.

SCOPE OF OIL-FIELD STANDARDIZATION

Standardization committees have been created as the need became apparent, and have been dissolved as changes in industry practice have indicated. Following are the major areas that have been subject to API standardization, in chronological order, and with mention of the climactic points in the development of standards.

Oil-field Tubular Goods

This committee was organized in 1923, with J. Edgar Pew as its first chairman. Within a year the committee achieved a standardization of sizes and threads on casing and tubing. The original specification (1924) established 2 classes of lap-welded and 3 grades of seamless casing and tubing, the strongest of which had a minimum yield strength of 45,000 psi. In addition, there were included wrought-iron and open-hearth-iron pipe. In 1929, a higher grade of seamless steel pipe having a specified minimum yield strength of 55,000 psi, designated D-grade and later redesignated J-55, was adopted as standard. In 1939, a still higher grade of seamless steel casing and tubing having a specified minimum yield strength of 80,000 psi (N-80) became standard. The N-80 grade did not long satisfy the industry's requirements and intensive studies of processes adaptable to the production of a higher grade were undertaken. In 1955, a 110,000-psi minimum yield casing (P-110) and 105,000-psi minimum yield tubing (P-105) were made standard. It was soon found that the "P" grades could be made more economically and satisfactorily by quench-and-temper thermal treatment, rather than by the customary normalization. This innovation opened the way for production of grades of even higher strength.

As seamless and resistance-welded casing and tubing became available in higher-strength grades than could be attained in lap-welded pipe, the committee undertook a study of the mechanism of collapse, with manufacturers taking the leading role. After a number of years, and on the basis of a large number of tests, this study resulted in the adoption in 1940 of formulas for the calculation of ultimate collapse strengths involving plastic and elastic types of failure. The minimum collapse values calculated by means of these formulas, for all API sizes, weights, and grades of casing, are the present basis of design for most tubing and casing strings.

In 1939, the committee took an important step in changing the form of thread for casing, tubing, and drill pipe from the truncated **V** (as for line pipe) to a form with greater truncation and rounded crests and roots. The ⅜ in. per foot of thread taper was also changed to ¾ in. per foot. Primary advantages achieved were greater accuracy of thread finish and greater resistance to leakage. Other advantages of the round thread were a lower concentration of stress at the thread roots and less injury to the threads in handling, transportation, and stabbing. This API thread form has since become generally accepted as standard in all countries.

For the N-80 grade of casing in some applications, and for the "P" grades, the API threaded-and-coupled connection proved less popular than certain patented designs. Much of the committee's activity in 1956-58 was devoted to the quest for a high-strength joint design that was amenable to standardization. Late in 1959 it appeared that this problem would be solved by transfer of patents on proved design to the public domain, thus permitting their adoption by the Institute.

With deeper drilling, higher pressures became commonplace. By 1948, several instances of casing and tubing failure caused by elevated pressures were documented, with these failures being caused both by thread leakage and body defects. The committee moved effectively in two directions by establishment of a research project on thread compounds at Mellon Institute and by adoption of a requirement that N-80 and higher grades of casing and tubing be mill-tested at hydrostatic pressures equivalent to 80 percent of specified minimum yield strength. The thread-compound project resulted in two formulations which soon after dedication to public use were produced commercially in a quantity in excess of one million pounds annually. The hydrostatic-test requirement went far toward satisfying the requirement for a reliable non-destructive method of test. By 1957 the committee had under consideration further non-destructive tests, with a view to eventual elimination of all field failures resulting from mill defects.

The first draft of an API specification for line pipe was developed in 1926 in cooperation with a committee of the American Gas Association. In 1947, in answer to the requirements of long-distance transmission lines—particularly natural-gas lines—the API committee developed *Std* 5LX, which specified pipe of high yield strength and eventually provided for hydrostatic mill tests of from 75 to 90 percent of the specified yield strength. This standard was also subjected to regular revision, the seventh edition being current in 1958. The maintenance of *Std 5LX* was a service of great magnitude to the pipeline industry during the 1947-1957 period of record expansion. Hal H. Anderson, vice-president of Shell Pipe Line Company, and his successor as vice-chairman of the Committee on Standardization of Oil-field Tubular Goods, R. G. Strong, Natural Gas Pipeline Company of America, made outstanding contributions to the development of API line-pipe standards.

Chairmen of the Committee on Standardization of Oil-field Tubular Goods following J. Edgar Pew were Charles Fitzgerald, Sinclair Pipe Line Company (1928-29); John R. Suman (1929-45); H. W. Ladd, (1945-55); C. A. Dunlop, Humble Oil & Refining Company (1955-59), and C. W. Dawson, Standard Oil Co. of California (1959-   ).

Rig Irons

This committee was organized in 1923 with H. J. Lockhart, of Parkersburg Rig and Reel Company, serving as its chairman from organization until 1935, when he was succeeded by Wm. Schwemlein of Parkersburg. The committee was dissolved in 1936 and rig-iron specifications were made the responsibility of the Committee on Standardization of Standard Rigs and Derricks. API efforts on rig irons benefited from and were given impetus by standardization initiated in 1919 by the Purchasing Agents Association of Tulsa.

Cable Tools

This committee was organized in 1924, with Louis C. Sands, Oil Well Supply Company, as its first chairman. The confused multiplicity of sizes and types was then as pronounced in the cable-tool drilling equipment as it was in tubular goods. One large manufacturer reported the need for 306 gages in order to supply the connections for the cable tools that were then being marketed. In the first edition of *Std 3* (1924), the committee reduced this profusion to 11 standard connections; and these, with 3 later added, have since met all of the industry's requirements. In 1928, the committee completed a recommended-practice publication on care and use of cable drilling and fishing tools that was so adequate it was reissued 14 years later without change. The cable-tool standard was published in 11 editions from 1924 through 1955. Because of reduced activity and lack of evolution in cable tools, the standard was declared obsolescent in 1957 and the committee was dissolved. Chairmen of the committee following Sands were Grant Hubley (1924), John T. Kirby (1924-25), and Thomas Fleming, Jr. (1925-29), all of Oil Well Supply Company; E. H. Williams, National Supply Company (1926-46); and F. J. Spang, Spang & Company (1946-57).

Boilers

This committee was organized in 1924, with A. B. Steen, of The Texas Company, as its first chairman. The early work of this committee was simplified by the existence of the ASME Boiler Code. Most boilers of the locomotive — or fire-box — type were manufactured in accordance with this code. However, there was no recognized standard on measurement of boiler horsepower, nor on the location or size of boiler openings and related fittings and connections. In the first edition of *Std 2*, 10 sq ft of heating surface per boiler horsepower was adopted as the basis for rating, and 4 sizes — 30, 50, 65, and 85 hp — were made standard for oil-field usage. Ten editions of the standard were issued, with the tenth being current from 1949 through 1958. In 1957, because of the marked decline in steam drilling, the standard was declared obsolescent and the committee was dissolved. Chairmen of the committee following Steen were S. J. Dickey, General Petroleum Corporation (1927-32); L. W. Voorhees, Union Oil Co. of California (1932-37); and Chase Sutton, The Pure Oil Company (1937-57).

Production Equipment

This committee, which for many years was called "Committee on Standardization of Pumping Equipment and Engines," was organized in 1924 under A. V. Hoenig, of The Carter Oil Company. Hoenig was succeeded in 1926 by W. L. McLaine, General Petroleum Corporation, who was in turn succeeded in 1927 by Theodore E. Swigart, Shell Oil Company, who served for 17 years.

Because of the number and variety of equipment items under the jurisdiction of this committee, its work involved a great amount of engineering detail. First efforts were toward recommending standard tubing joints to the tubular-goods committee. At the same time the committee, recognizing certain advantages of several manufacturers' sucker-rod joints, ended up by designing a new API standard joint *(Std 11B)*. Perhaps its greatest achievement — at least from the point of view of volume of detail — was in connection with oil-well pumps *(Std 11A)*. This standard presented standard diameters for working barrels and a series of thread standards covering pump parts from $1\frac{1}{2}$ to 4 in. in diameter, including thread tolerances and gage dimensions and tolerances. In 1928, standards were adopted for polished rods, pull rods, countershafts, pumping-unit reduction gears, and wellhead taps and fittings. The first standard for pumping units was issued in 1936. Chairman of the committee succeeding Swigart were H. N. Marsh, General Petroleum Corporation (1944-55); J. H. Field, Sohio Petroleum Company (1955-60); and T. S. Mitchel, Shell Oil Company (1960-   ).

Belting

This committee was organized in 1925 with A. H. Riney, Phillips Petroleum Company, as its first chairman. The first edition of *Std 1* (1926) covered leather, cotton-fabric, woven-hair, balata, and rubber flat belting. Tests for elongation, ultimate tensile strength, fatigue, and function made up the bulk of this standard. In 1937, the standard was extended to include **V** belts and **V**-belt sheaves. Committee chairmen subsequent to Riney were D. L. Trax, Gulf Oil Corporation (1951-53); J. E. Orrell, Shell Oil Company (1953-57); and Max Halderson, Phillips Petroleum Company (1957-   ).

Wire Rope

This committee was organized in 1925 with the author as its first chairman. The first edition of *Std 9* — issued in 1926 — established 6 grades of steel appropriate to wire rope intended for use as drilling line, sucker-rod and tubing line, sand line, pumping line, guy line, power pull line, torpedo line, and bailing line. Properties of wire and methods of test were prescribed. Standard sizes for each of the ordinary types of wire-rope construction were specified. New editions were issued at an average interval of 2 years, with the 14th edition being current in 1958. A recommended procedure for care and handling of wire rope was included in the second and several subsequent editions, and was later published separately. A signal contribution in this connection were the ton-mile formulas for wire-rope evaluation derived by H. H. Anderson. Chairmen of the committee succeeding the author were K. N. Saatjian, The Texas Company (1938-41); J. E. Toussaint (1941-49) and C. W. Dawson (1949-53), of Standard Oil Co. of California; H. S. Kelly, Phillips Petroleum Company (1953-57); and R. B. Anderson, Columbian Carbon Company (1958-   ).

Storage Tanks

This committee was organized in 1925 with G. M. Vandaveer, Midwest Refining Company, as its chairman. The first standard, covering storage tanks with riveted shells, was issued in 1927. Additional standards issued, with date of first edition, were: bolted tanks (1929); welded oil-storage tanks (1930); large welded production tanks (1935); wooden production tanks (1943); small welded production tanks (1954); and aluminum-alloy welded storage tanks (1957). API tank standards proved so effective that numerous state and local code authorities adopted them as the only approved basis for construction. API standard tanks soon became commonplace in numerous other industries, such as the chemical and food processing. The standards became exceptionally valuable during World War II as the basis for standardized military tanks.

1201

Chairmen of the committee following Vandaveer were Ralph J. Reed, Union Oil Co. of California (1927-31); R. W. Howe, Atlantic Pipe Line Company (1931-36); W. M. Giffen, Shell Oil Company (1936-37); C. C. Ashley, Shell Oil Company (1937-53); and C. V. Lynn, Sinclair Refining Company (1953-58). At least half of the tank standardization effort from 1927 to 1958 was put forth by representatives of the refining branch of the industry, with a sizeable assist from transportation personnel. In 1958, because of the narrowing community of interest between large tanks of the refinery type and the smaller lease vessels, the committee was dissolved and responsibility for standards on riveted and welded storage tanks, including the aluminum-alloy type, was transferred to the API Division of Refining. Maintenance of standards on bolted, welded, and wooden production tanks was assigned to a new Committee on Standardization of Lease Production Vessels, the first chairman of which was C. F. McLaren, Jr., Humble Oil & Refining Company, who served until 1961 and was succeeded by F. S. Goddard, Sunray Mid-Continent Oil Co.

Rotary Drilling Equipment

This committee was organized in 1926 with Capt. J. F. Lucey, founder of the Lucey Manufacturing Corporation, as its first chairman. The situation in rotary tool joints was much the same as in cable tools, i.e., complete confusion; and it was on tapered tool joints that early efforts were concentrated. API standardization soon reduced the number of joints from over 200 to 7. The full-hole type of connection was adopted in 1934, and the internal-flush in 1946. In 1958, the whole range of requirements was spanned by 17 standard connections applicable to swivels, kellys, tool joints, subs, drill collars, and drill bits. The rotary-drilling equipment series was then progressively expanded to cover sheaves and hoisting blocks, drilling hooks, rotary hose, brake blocks, slush pumps, rotary table, transmission components, and rating of internal-combustion engines. Committee chairmen succeeding Lucey were E. J. Nicklos, Nicklos Drilling Company (1928-49); G. B. Kitchel, Kerr-McGee Oil Industries, Inc. (1949-57), and John M. Payne, Shell Oil Company (1958-   ).

Derricks and Masts

This committee was organized in 1927, as the Committee on Standard Rigs and Derricks, with Walter W. Fondren, a vice-president of Humble Oil & Refining Company, as its first chairman. The first edition of *Std 4,* adopted in 1928, achieved a reduction in number of derrick heights and base sizes from 200 to 6, and introduced engineering and consistency into the dimensioning of important structural members. Subsequent editions of *Std 4* presented methods of calculation of safe loading and extended dimensional specifications to all important parts of the derrick and substructure. Effective with the 1952 (14th) edition, steel derrick and wooden derrick specifications were published as separate standards. From 1938 until 1957, when it was declared obsolescent, the committee maintained the rig-iron standard.

Increasing popularity of portable masts prompted the renaming of the Committee in 1951 to Committee on Standardization of Derricks and Masts and the issuance in 1952 of a covering standard. Since then the committee's main effort has been on guyed and free-standing masts. An original contribution of great value in mast standardization was made by Henry Schaefer, Stanolind Oil and Gas Company, in derivation of a method for calculating the design stresses in welded-end compression members.

Chairmen of the committee succeeding Fondren were W. H. Meier, The Atlantic Refining Company (1933-38); C. A. Dunlop, Humble Oil & Refining Company (1939-55); L. A. Ogden, The Pure Oil Company (1955-57), and Geo. B. Kitchel, Kerr-McGee Oil Industries, Inc. (1958-   ).

Valves and Fittings

This committee was organized in 1946, with W. S. Crake, Shell Oil Company, as its first chairman. Previously all API valve standardization work had been carried on, beginning in 1936, by the Committee on Standardization of Tubular Goods. The new committee issued revisions of the ring joint, thread, pipeline valve, and gate and plug valve (drilling and production service) standards. In 1949 and 1958, respectively, new standards were published covering wellhead equipment and ring-joint flanges for extreme pressures.

In 1956 C. H. Taylor, Shell Oil Company, succeeded Crake as chairman of the committee, and was succeeded in 1961 by T. V. Miller, Humble Oil & Refining Company.

Cements

This committee was organized in 1951, with C. W. Dawson, Standard Oil Co. of California, as its first chairman. The committee revised the standard procedures for cement testing (*API Code 32*, later designated *RP 10B*), to afford an adequate basis for the first API cement specification, which was issued in 1953. This specification, as later expanded, covered chemical and physical requirements, sampling, test methods, packaging, storing, and marking requirements for six classes of portland cement spanning the range of oil-field requirements.

Walter F. Rogers, Gulf Oil Corporation, succeeded Dawson as chairman of the committee in 1955, and was succeeded in 1961 by George Howard, Pan American Petroleum Corp.

Hoisting Equipment

The committee was organized in 1956, with John O. Hills, General Petroleum Corporation, as its first chairman. The committee assumed responsibility for the rating specifications on drilling and production hoisting equipment which had theretofore been a joint charge of the Committees on Standardization of Production Equipment and Rotary Drilling Equipment. C. H. Griffin, of the R. L. Manning Company, succeeded to the chairmanship in 1961.

Drilling-fluids Materials

This committee was organized in late 1959 with H. W. Perkins, Sun Oil Company, as its chairman. Its objective is the formulation of specifications for the more common components of drilling fluids and the maintenance of *API RP 29* on the testing of drilling fluids.

API GAGES AND GAGING PRACTICE

One of the earliest problems of great magnitude confronting the standardization effort was that of obtaining interchangeability between similar parts or items of different manufacturers. This problem was particularly acute with respect to threaded parts. In the 1920's few manufacturers had complete gaging equipment and those that did own gages did not pursue a consistent or uniform gaging practice nor entertain the same ideas as to reasonable tolerances. The mere writing of standard specifications in order to establish dimensional limits would obviously be insufficient to assure interchangeability unless all plants manufacturing the standard product used the same types of gages with the same frequency, and in the same manner. It was recognized that provision must also be made for periodic checks of plant working gages against reference master gages, and checks of reference master gages against regional or grand master gages.

Thus, among the earliest and most important requirements of API standards were those which concerned the manufacturer's possession, use, and periodic testing of gages. The number, sizes, and types of gages required varied widely as between standards. For those products such as pipe and tool joints that required numerous and relatively complex gages, the manufacturer was required to possess plant working gages (with which actual product inspection was performed) and reference master gages. Plant gages were required to be checked frequently against reference masters, and reference masters were required to be checked at intervals against regional master gages in the possession of independent testing agencies, or against grand master gages in possession of the National Bureau of Standards. It was further required that all reference gages be registered with the Institute, as the basis for a system of reporting which assured compliance by manufacturers with the gage-testing requirements of the standards.

Major credit for the conception of the API gage and gaging practice program belongs to the Committee on Gages and Gaging Practice, which was organized in 1926 under the chairmanship of A. B. Steen, of The Texas Company. This committee, working in direct collaboration with all standardization committees, specified the dimensional limits and accuracy of all API gages, and formulated the approved gaging procedures. Many of the specified gages have been adapted from those in common industrial use — the design of others has been entirely original with the committee. Invaluable assistance has been rendered since 1922 by the National Bureau of Standards, both in an advisory capacity and as a certificant on gage tests.

Chairmen of the committee following Steen were H. W. Fletcher, Hughes Tool Company (1928-42); J. J. Dunn, National Tube Company (1942-48); and W. O. Clinedinst, National Tube Division, U. S. Steel Corporation (1948-   ).

The unique API gage and gaging practice system has been so effective in achieving interchangeability of mating parts that drilling and production equipment components can be purchased from literally hundreds of different manufacturers and assembled without regard to origin and without difficulty.

COOPERATING ASSOCIATIONS

Since its inception the standardization program has been characterized by wide and intensive cooperation with other associations and societies in and out of the petroleum industry. In frequent instances API standardization has been expedited by the existence of adequate standards or methods of test developed by other bodies. In other cases research or investigation by other groups has given direction and impetus to API standards. To identify the contributions of each of these groups would require excessive space. It can only be mentioned that the associations, societies, and agencies listed in Appendix A have made continuous contributions to the standardization of oil-field equipment.

CONTRIBUTION OF THE MANUFACTURERS

Since the chairmanship of API standardization committees has almost invariably been reserved to oil-company or drilling-contractor representatives, i. e., the "users", the listing of these chairmen, past and present, might convey the erroneous impression that virtually all leadership and effort in the standardization program has been put forth by those directly employed by the industry. This is far from true. Manufacturer personnel, which throughout the history of the program has been as strong numerically as user representation, has played a vital part. Manufacturers generally were as eager for the inauguration of the program as were the oil companies. Without the manufacturer's zeal in surmounting early obstacles, his continuous counsel, and his willingness to occasionally subordinate immediate competitive advantage to the broader requirements of the industry, the standardization program would have been a confused and probably futile gesture on the part of the users. Manufacturers' representatives on each committee — usually concentrated in the Manufacturers Subcommittees thereof — have been with few exceptions either holders of engineering or scientific degrees or men who had achieved an engineering perspective, through long and intensive exposure to the science of materials and methods of fabrication. Many manufacturers' representatives have been mechanical engineers, many others have been metallurgists and there has at all times been a leavening of chemical, civil and electrical engineers, physicists, and mathematicians.

From its first presentation in 1948, through 1959, 43 API *Certificates of Appreciation* were awarded in recognition of outstanding service to the standardization program. The following 16 manufacturers' representatives were so honored. Unfortunately this listing gives no indication of the many manufacturers' representatives who served conspicuously over the years 1924-48, but were deceased or became inactive before a formal recognition of their services became possible.

C. R. Athy, Ideco, Inc.

F. E. Bernsen, Lucey Products Corp.

W. O. Clinedinst, National Tube Div., U. S. Steel Corp.

D. R. Dale, S. M. Jones Co.

J. J. Dunn, National Tube Co.

T. C. Ervin, Lucey Boiler & Mfg. Co.

H. O. Hill, Bethlehem Steel Co.

J. R. Mahan, The National Supply Co.

A. J. Morgan, John A. Roebling Sons Corp.

S. S. Parker, National Tank Co.

Gwynne Raymond, Union Tank & Supply Co.

J. C. Siegle, Youngstown Sheet & Tube Co.

J. C. Slonneger, Continental Supply Co.

F. J. Spang, Spang & Co.

Thos. G. Stitt, Pittsburgh Steel Corp.

C. R. Weiss, Link Belt Co.

THE ADMINISTRATION OF STANDARIZATION

Adherence by any manufacturer to the provisions of any API standard is a purely voluntary act on the part of that manufacturer. Just as voluntary is the act of a purchaser in specifying that the equipment he desires be made in accordance with an API standard. With this fundamental premise for the entire program, it would have been theoretically possible for the Institute to follow the practice of other standards-making bodies by paying no attention, unless forced to do so, to any events subsequent to the issuance of a standard. There were, however, certain compelling reasons for the adoption of a distinctive and permanent mark to be applied to equipment made to a standard. Because of the gage requirements, and to insure as far as possible the significance and integrity of this identifying mark, it was also deemed advisable to formally license manufacturers under each standard.

The identifying mark adopted was the API monogram — ⏣ — . Manufacturers, in order to obtain the right to apply this mark to their products — and as the only consideration in obtaining a license — were required to furnish evidence of competence and stability, and to certify that the monogram would be applied only to products conforming completely with the applicable standard. In order that the petroleum industry may have the economic advantage of numerous and widely scattered sources of standard equipment, the licensing policy has been a liberal one. From commencement of the program through 1959 over 1,350 manufacturers have been licensed. In 1959, nearly 900 active licensees were on the rolls, with over one-third of these being foreign concerns. There have been very few instances of wilful abuse of monogram privileges. These have been countered by cancellation of license.

The API monogram has fully served its purpose as an identifying symbol manifesting the manufacturer's warranty that the product conforms to specifications. Its significance is recognized in every oil field of the world. With the possible exception of the conventional derrick, it has become the symbol most identified with the American oil industry.

The administrative aspects of standardization, in distinction to the responsibility for formulating standards, have been responsibility of the Institute's Dallas office. In addition to licensing of manufacturers and monogram administration, these functions include the publication and distribution of standards and the processing of committee appointments, agenda, and reports. In December 1923, when authorizing the formation of the Division of Standardization, the API Board made provision for a full-time divisional secretary. This position was filled in 1924 by C. A. Young, who in succeeding titles and despite frequently broadened responsibilities continued to supervise staff services to the standardization program for the first 29 years of its existence. His faith in and devotion to the advantages of standardization, and particularly to the Institute's accomplishments in this field, was a strong force in the development of the program. Other key staff members with major responsibilities in the administrative phases of the program were standardization engineers J. E. Stillwell (1926-1948), Edwin Joyce (1946-1957), J. E. Ubben (1956-   ), and S. G. Creaghe (1957-   ). Wm. H. Strang succeeded Young as Director of the Division of Production upon Young's retirement in 1953.

INTERNATIONAL ASPECTS OF STANDARDIZATION

API standards received international attention soon after their first issuance. However, because of the relatively limited geographical spread of foreign operations, the standardization program was dominantly a domestic one until the end of World War II. The growth of exploration and development around the world then encouraged a rapid growth in foreign production of oil-field equipment and applications for monogram rights from foreign manufacturers almost doubled each year from 1948 through 1959, in many cases outnumbering the domestic applications. Foreign standards-making bodies, such as the British Standards Institution, have adopted API specifications as the basis for their national standards. Foreign translations — including German, French, Spanish, Italian, Portugese, and Yugoslavian — became freely available in the period 1950-59.

In 1956, the Central Committee on Standardization entered into a liaison arrangement with the United Kingdom's Oil Companies Materials Committee (later Association) the objective of which was to promote maximum coincidence between API and British standards.

ECONOMIC VALUE OF STANDARDIZATION

Various estimates of the savings resulting from API standardization have been presented by many well-informed analysts and executives. Invariably these estimates have been so large as to sound fantastic to individuals not conversant with the size of annual expenditures for oil-field materials and equipment.

In 1957, the total production of casing, tubing, and drill pipe from both domestic and foreign mills was 3,336,824 tons, all of which was purchased by the oil industry at an estimated cost of 600 million dollars. In the same year, the production of line pipe for oil-industry use — from domestic mills only — was 4,034,353 tons, representing another 600 million dollars. Other products covered by API standards represent further enormous expenditures, such as for storage tanks, production tanks, drilling lines, sucker rods, pipeline valves, oil-well cement, pumping units, tool joints, drill collars, slush pumps, hoisting tools, reduction gears, wellhead equipment, derricks, drilling and servicing masts, and bottom-hole pumps.

The production of these and other items in a volume sufficient to permit the annual drilling of 50,000 wells and the continual operation of 500,000 producing wells has provided a fertile field for standardization and the consequent economies of mass production. John R. Suman, in addressing the 1955 annual meeting of the Institute, said ". . . since the program was begun, many billions of dollars worth of oil-field equipment has been manufactured to these API standards. A figure of 10 percent of the dollar value of material produced is now generally taken as the savings that accrue to standardization, and this figure will, it is believed, put the savings at between 50 and 100 million dollars annually."

An additional and less measurable but highly significant economy achieved through standardization has been the improvement in quality and serviceability of equipment. This upgrading, which was stimulated by the continually increasing stringency of standard methods of test and rating, has promoted economy in all operations and opened the way to deeper drilling and safer manipulation of high pressures.

One measure of these advantages is given in an article by E. De-Golyer in *Science of Petroleum,* published by Oxford University Press in 1938. He said:

"The greatest and possibly the most important improvement in drilling technique from the standpoint of the prospector has been the constantly improving ability to achieve increasingly greater depths. We are finding important oil pools today at depths of 7,000 ft. to 10,000 ft. which would not have been reached by the drill under the best practices of ten years ago. Oklahoma City and Kettlemen Hills have already been cited as examples of pools, previously drilled, which remained undiscovered until we had achieved ability to drill to necessary depths. A consideration of well depth and some acquaintanceship with the technique of drilling suggests that increasing depth has come about as a result of better material equipment, and greater power rather than from any fundamental change in design. In the opinion of the writer, the standardization program of the American Petroleum Institute's Division of Production has been one of the greatest single factors in contributing to this condition."

Most observers would agree that the same statement if made today, with reference to attained depths of over 25,000 ft, would be no less appropriate.

The worldwide currency of the API monogram as the hallmark of thoroughly engineered oil-field equipment is a tribute to the faith of the petroleum engineer in standardization and to his proficiency in analysis and solution of the countless technical problems involved.

APPENDIX A

Associations, Societies, and Agencies Which Have by Direct Participation or the Free Exchange of Expert Knowledge Rendered Major Services to the Standardization of Oil-field Equipment

American Association of Oilwell Drilling Contractors
American Gas Association
American Gear Manufacturers Association

American Iron and Steel Institute
American Society for Testing Materials
American Society of Mechanical Engineers
American Standards Association
American Welding Society
Anti-Friction Bearing Manufacturers Association
Association of Well Head Equipment Manufacturers
Chain Belt Manufacturers Association
Division of Refining, American Petroleum Institute
Division of Transportation, American Petroleum Institute
Industrial Fasteners Institute
Manufacturers Standardization Society of the Valves and Fittings Industry
Multiple V-Belt Drive Association and Mechanical Power Transmission Association
National Association of Corrosion Engineers
National Bureau of Standards
National Electrical Manufacturers Association
National Fire Protection Association
National Lumber Manufacturers Association
Rubber Manufacturers Association
Society of the Plastics Industry, Inc.
Southern Gas Association
Western Oil and Gas Association

Chapter 21

IMPACT UPON SOCIETY

D. V. CARTER

DE VERE VAUGHT CARTER was born in Russell Township, Lawrence County, Illinois, in 1901. He attended the University of Denver and received an A.B. degree in geology from Indiana University in 1926. His earliest employers were the Dominion Oil Company and Gulf Oil Corporation, both of which he served as petroleum engineer and geologist. He was employed in 1931 by Magnolia Petroleum Company as its first petroleum engineer and organized the petroleum engineering department of that company. He was advanced in 1934 to chief petroleum engineer and continued in that position until 1960, when he became Houston division engineering manager for Mobil Oil Company. He was responsible for the selection and training of many engineers who now hold positions of responsibility, not only in Socony Mobil Oil Company, Incorporated, and its divisions, but throughout the industry. He is a director of the Great National Life Insurance Company.

Academic honors include Tau Beta Pi, Sigma Gamma Epsilon and Pi Epsilon Tau. Professional and industrial affiliations include API, whose *Certificate of Appreciation* he has twice received for extensive service to its Division of Production and Committee on Crude Oil Reserves; SPE of AIME, and AAPG. During World War II, he served on committees of the Petroleum Administration for War, subsequently on committees of the National Petroleum Council, and the Military Petroleum Advisory Board.

Mr. Carter has contributed extensively to technical literature, is the holder of patents on production equipment, and is credited with other improvements in this field. He has done especially significant work with respect to the organization of engineering and unitization committees; unitization, development planning, conservation, evaluation and comprehensive reserve surveys; and the initiation and application of improved recovery techniques.

To appraise the impact of petroleum engineering on society, consider first the place of the petroleum industry in modern society.

We have only to examine our growing use of oil-based energy and products to see how vital the petroleum industry has become. Constantly increasing numbers of trucks, cars, buses, and planes, the use of light fuel oil and gas for domestic heating and of heavy fuel oils for industrial purposes, the new petrochemical industry, the prospective increase in asphalt and road-oil products in the expanded highway program— all of these demonstrate the indispensability of petroleum and natural gas to the American economy and standard of living. The impact of hydrocarbon energy upon our economy is fundamental and widespread. Its use in many forms permeates our everyday activities and is vital to the national security as well as to the economy.

The petroleum industry has supplied the raw materials for a multitude of other industries, with the pharmaceutical and petrochemical industries being high on the list. Fuels and lubricants for water, air, and land transportation are provided at economic prices and at hundreds of thousands of distribution points. Our great highway system and the development of equally impressive airfield and terminal facilities throughout the nation are other important examples of transportation progress made possible by an adequate and economic supply of petroleum derivatives. Dieselization of our country's railroad system, starting in 1935, has virtually been completed. This, and greatly improved and new machinery for earth moving and agriculture, are additional major accomplishments which would have been impossible except for an ample supply of hydrocarbons.

Of these many changes fostered by a plentiful supply of petroleum, some might have developed, to some degree, solely through continued utilization of coal. Most notable among the changes which are totally and exclusively attributable to petroleum are our modern systems of automotive and aerial transport. Commerce and the individual have been freed from the restrictions of iron rails and navigable waterways. This freedom has wrought a change in American economic, social, and political systems so profound as to be almost immeasurable.

By almost any yardstick which may be applied, the automotive industry is the prime example of an industry whose growth has been almost totally dependent upon availability of petroleum. This industry is one of the largest single industrial consumers of steel. In addition to steel, vast quantities of natural and synthetic rubber, plastics, glass, aluminum, and other nonferrous metals, textiles, paints, and other products are used by the automotive industry. Obviously, the production resulting from these activities has contributed to our high standard of living.

Of most recent vintage among petroleum-dependent industries is the petrochemical industry. Some 300 of the more than 3,000 hydrocarbons so far identified are important as raw material for the production of an almost endless list of products whose petroleum origin is realized by relatively few. The quantity of aromatics, naphthenes, and aliphatic hydrocarbons produced from crude oil and natural gas rose from 1.6 million tons in 1945 to 10.5 million tons in 1958. This rate may double and redouble as additional useful hydrocarbon derivatives are discovered. The hydrocarbon chemists' test tube is literally a horn of plenty from which the expanding needs of tomorrow will be met.

The petroleum industry has provided a very important source of tax revenue. Without an ample supply of crude oil, gas, and natural-gas liquids—all of which are taxed from the point of recovery through many steps to final consumption—our tax structure and tax sources would be significantly different. Petroleum and its products have been heavily burdened with taxes compared with other commodities. In fact, the very efficiency and accomplishments of the industry have made it a target for undue tax loads. In spite of this handicap, many of its products sell for no more than they did several decades ago when taxes were lower. In addition, quality and variety of products have increased significantly.

Utilization of hydrocarbons is pulling the world more closely together through faster transportation. It is creating more leisure time, with tremendous recreational industries following this change. Our nation could not have achieved its present productive capacity and resulting high standard of living without an adequate, dependable, and reasonably priced supply of petroleum and natural gas. Evidence of gain in living standards is given by the 36-percent increase in United States per-capita energy consumption—from 180 million BTU in 1930 to 244 million BTU in 1957.*

The vast expansion in the usefulness of petroleum products reflects best in the increasing domestic production of oil and gas. This is shown in the following table, which also presents the substantial growth in reserves in the face of constantly increasing rates of production.

---

*U. S. Bur. Mines Bull. 585: Minerals Facts and Problems, Table VI, p. 13, 1960 Ed.

	PRODUCTION				PROVED RESERVES*	
	Liquid Hydrocarbons, Billions of Barrels		Natural Gas, Trillions of Cubic Feet		Liquid Hydrocarbons, Billions of Barrels	Natural Gas, Trillions of Cubic Feet
Year	During Year	Cumulative at End of Year	During Year	Cumulative at End of Year		
1936	1.14	19.27	2.64	35.40	13.06	†
1940	1.41	24.60	3.69	48.52	19.02	†
1950	2.15	42.93	8.48	109.88	29.54	185.59
1960	2.90	70.19	13.09‡	225.32‡	38.43	263.70

*As defined in and taken from *Proved Reserves of Crude Oil, Natural Gas Liquids, and Natural Gas,* an annual joint publication of American Petroleum Institute and American Gas Association. All other figures in the table, with the exception of cumulative gas production at the end of 1936, are taken from this and other API statistical publications.

†No authoritative estimate available.

‡Exclusive of gas produced with oil 1958, 1959, 1960.

Let us consider for a moment what *might have been* the condition of the producing and development phase of the oil and gas industry in the total or partial absence of petroleum engineering as we know it today. The industry until three decades ago was subject to the cyclic effects of new field discoveries and the attendant wasteful procedures of development and resulting low recoveries. It was also saddled with the tremendous financial responsibility of storing vast quantities of crude oil in times of over-supply. This, coupled with burdensome financial outlay during the periods of intensive development immediately following discovery, placed a compound load upon the industry. These recurring conditions were looked upon as inherent to the industry until the emergence of sound petroleum engineering principles, including unitization. This achievement made possible greater recovery with less drilling, thus stabilizing and insuring the availability of an ample hydrocarbon supply. This, in turn, permitted the enactment of effective conservation legislation which within a few years brought order out of chaos—removing overnight the well-nigh intolerable burden of unnecessary development and the problem of storing aboveground an extensive amount of crude oil. This is a direct accomplishment of petroleum engineering—the impact of which is of the greatest importance.

If one considers the astounding growth not only in consumption but also in the increase of the variety and number of petroleum products and natural gas since the mid-20's, it is obvious that the domestic industry without the benefits of petroleum engineering would not have been capable of supplying the hydrocarbon demands of our country, notwithstanding imports. We must also consider the fact that the petroleum industry of the United States has not only provided the peace-time economy with reasonably priced petroleum products but that it has been the bulwark of the Nation and its allies with respect to military petroleum needs during World War II and succeeding military conflicts.

Now how does the petroleum engineer perform within the broad framework of the petroleum industry?

In the beginning, before petroleum engineering was recognized as a profession, petroleum engineers held various academic degrees in the fields of science and engineering. Their talents were devoted to the determination and satisfactory solution of the many problems relating to the drilling and production phases of the oil industry, and to the improvement of and addition to the technology of the profession.

Petroleum engineers have helped establish the vital function of the petroleum industry by assisting in the development of an adequate, ever-increasing supply of crude hydrocarbons. They have helped make the supply of petroleum adequate to increasing demand by: 1, the development of drilling and production techniques which enable man to produce from reservoirs formerly inaccessible because of depth, locale, or other practical considerations; 2, the development, improvement, and application of recovery techniques which increase production from known hydrocarbon deposits. Petroleum engineers have helped to stabilize the supply of hydrocarbons by recognizing the need for and promotion of conservation practices, including proper and adequate legislation and regulation on the part of most active and prospective oil and gas-producing states.

The petroleum engineer's knowledge of reservoir performance and production practices has provided a reliable basis for reservoir evaluation. Improvements in oil and gas property evaluation, directly attributable to the petroleum engineer, have encouraged investment in the petroleum industry from such sources as banks, insurance companies and pension funds, and other conservative investors.

Petroleum engineers have developed more efficient operating practices which have helped to maintain the economic attractiveness of the oil industry. This has been done in the face of a sharp increase in drilling and production costs as new reserves become more difficult to find, and as additional recovery from known deposits becomes more difficult.

Petroleum engineers have had to "sell" their ideas on conservation, unitization, improved recovery, and the like. In the face of the natural instinct of self-interest, the petroleum engineer has been able to convince those directly concerned to yield to practices which seemingly achieved common benefits at individual expense. The engineer achieved this in many cases without coercive legislation. This is surely one prime example of the influence the petroleum engineer has had on society to its betterment.

The petroleum industry itself has, as a whole, been keenly aware of the contributions of petroleum engineering. In retrospect, industry management has been quite tolerant and has generally encouraged the furtherance of the profession. However, during the formative period of petroleum engineering, some managements were at times, and in certain quarters, somewhat reluctant to utilize petroleum engineering to the fullest extent possible. With time, however, competition has caused these few reluctant managements to adopt more modern practices. In other words, a small segment did not always "farm as well as we knew how".

Let us consider briefly some other aspects of society which have been influenced by petroleum engineering.

Petroleum engineering has emerged as a specialized branch of engineering within the last 40 years. A large number of colleges and universities now offer work in petroleum engineering. Educating petroleum engineers has caused an increase in faculty personnel, together with all necessary buildings and other facilities. The Society of Petroleum Engineers of the American Institute of Mining, Metallurgical and Petroleum Engineers has grown from a membership of 820 in 1924 to 13,000 in 1960. There are probably 25,000 petroleum engineers in the world today.

Petroleum engineers are a prolific source of manpower for transfer or promotion to operation and management within large and small companies of the industry. Many thousands of experienced engineers function as consultants or enter into the oil business on an ownership or entrepreneur basis.

Petroleum engineers have played an important role as proprietors and employees of equipment manufacturers and service companies. These companies engage in such important work as logging, sampling, testing, cementing, various forms of well stimulation, and many other services.

Further, the petroleum engineering profession has been a source of vital manpower to the government, both in war and in peace. Petroleum engineers have made material contributions to the security and well-being of our nation from a national-defense standpoint.

Petroleum engineering has drawn liberally from geology, physics, chemistry, mathematics, and other branches of science and engineering. Many important contributors to petroleum technology received their education in one of the more fundamental scientific or technical disciplines.

There are many unsolved problems in petroleum engineering and related research. However, we can look forward with the confident hope that satisfactory solutions will be found. The most important of these problems is that of increasing recovery of hydrocarbons. As someone has said, "We have not achieved the ultimate in oil recovery so long as one barrel of oil remains unrecoverable."

We have seen that petroleum engineering has affected society, *1*, by its direct contribution to the petroleum industry; *2*, by its existence as a profession with the attendant educational specialization; *3*, as a supply of manpower with specialized talents; and *4*, through its relationship with fundamental sciences and with other branches of engineering. Petroleum engineering as a profession has made its contributions to society. It has been rewarding to the individuals participating and contributing. It is a technology created by a group of people of which the industry, Americans, and the world can be justly proud.

Thus, petroleum engineering can be directly credited with having made possible the bringing of order and stabilization to an industry whose early history was replete with recurring chaos and crisis. Highest on the list of its accomplishments are improved recovery, unitization, and the ability to economically develop petroleum deposits at ever-increasing depths under both land and sea.

index